B.C.     B.C. A.D.     A.D. 100     A.D. 200

PLUTARCH

PLOTINUS

TACITUS

AUGUSTINE

EPICTETUS

NICOMACHUS

*Birth and death of Jesus Christ*

LUCRETIUS

PTOLEMY

VIRGIL

MARCUS AURELIUS

*Books replace scrolls*

GALEN

*Julius Caesar assassinated*

*Hadrian's wall constructed*

---

1600     1700     1800

DESCARTES

MONTESQUIEU

MILTON

VOLTAIRE

MOLIÈRE

HUME

*French Revolution*

PASCAL

ROUSSEAU

HUYGENS

DIDEROT

ADAM SMITH

*Church bans Galileo's teaching of Copernican doctrine*

KANT

GIBBON

LOCKE

BOSWELL

NTAIGNE

SPINOZA

JEFFERSON

ILBERT

RACINE

CERVANTES

LAVOISIER

NEWTON

BACON

JOHN JAY

SWIFT

GALILEO

GOETHE

BERKELEY

SHAKESPEARE

MADISON

KEPLER

HAMILTON

HARVEY

*Industrial Revolution begins*

HOBBES

# Great Books of the Western World

Mortimer J. Adler
*Editor in Chief*

## 10

### EUCLID
### ARCHIMEDES
### NICOMACHUS

Clifton Fadiman, Philip W. Goetz, *Associate Editors*
*Members of the Advisory Board:* Douglas Allanbrook, Jacques Barzun,
Norman Cousins, John Kenneth Galbraith, Heinz Pagels,
Anthony Quinton

# THE THIRTEEN BOOKS
# OF EUCLID'S ELEMENTS

---

# THE WORKS OF ARCHIMEDES
# INCLUDING THE METHOD

---

# INTRODUCTION TO ARITHMETIC
# BY NICOMACHUS

Peter B. Norton, *President and Chief Executive Officer*
Robert McHenry, *Editor in Chief*

## ENCYCLOPÆDIA BRITANNICA, INC.
### CHICAGO
AUCKLAND LONDON MADRID MANILA PARIS
ROME SEOUL SYDNEY TOKYO TORONTO

The Thirteen Books of Euclid's *Elements* and *The Works of Archimedes,* including *The Method,* translated by Sir Thomas L. Heath, are reprinted by arrangement with Cambridge University Press.

Nicomachus of Gerasa: *Introduction to Arithmetic,* translated by Martin Luther D'Ooge, with studies in Greek arithmetic by Frank Egleston Robbins, and Louis Charles Karpinski, is reprinted by arrangement with The University of Michigan Press. Copyright, 1926, by Francis W. Kelsey.

No part of this work may be reproduced or utilized in any form or by any means, electronic or mechanical, including photocopying, recording, or by any information storage and retrieval system, without permission in writing from the publisher.

First Edition © 1952
Second Edition © 1990
Fourth Printing, 1993
Fifth Printing, 1994

Encyclopædia Britannica, Inc.
All Rights Reserved

Library of Congress Catalog Card Number: 90-80213
International Standard Book Number: 0-85229-531-6

**Manufactured in the United States of America**

# GENERAL CONTENTS

---

### EUCLID'S ELEMENTS, Page 1
*Translated by Sir Thomas L. Heath*

### THE WORKS OF ARCHIMEDES INCLUDING THE METHOD, Page 403
*Translated by Sir Thomas L. Heath*

### THE INTRODUCTION TO ARITHMETIC OF NICOMACHUS, Page 599
*By Nicomachus of Gerasa*
*Translated by Martin L. D'Ooge*

---

# EUCLID'S ELEMENTS

# BIOGRAPHICAL NOTE
## Euclid, *fl. c.* 300 b.c.

Euclid is said to have been younger than the first pupils of Plato but older than Archimedes, which would place the time of his flourishing about 300 b.c. He probably received his early mathematical education in Athens from the pupils of Plato, since most of the geometers and mathematicians on whom he depended were of that school. Proclus, the Neo-Platonist of the fifth century, asserts that Euclid was of the school of Plato and "intimate with that philosophy." His opinion, however, may have been based only on his view that the treatment of the five regular ("Platonic") solids in Book XIII is the "end of the whole *Elements.*"

The only other fact concerning Euclid is that he taught and founded a school at Alexandria in the time of Ptolemy I, who reigned from 306 to 283 b.c. The evidence for the place comes from Pappus (fourth century a.d.), who notes that Apollonius "spent a very long time with the pupils of Euclid at Alexandria, and it was thus that he acquired such a scientific habit of thought." Proclus claims that it was Ptolemy I who asked Euclid if there was no shorter way to geometry than the *Elements* and received as answer: "There is no royal road to geometry." The other story about Euclid that has come down from antiquity concerns his answer to a pupil who at the end of his first lesson in geometry asked what he would get by learning such things, whereupon Euclid called his slave and said: "Give him a coin since he must needs make gain by what he learns."

Something of Euclid's character would seem to be disclosed in the remark of Pappus regarding Euclid's "scrupulous fairness and his exemplary kindness towards all who advance mathematical science to however small an extent." The context of the remark seems to indicate, however, that Pappus is not giving a traditional account of Euclid but offering an explanation of his own of Euclid's failure to go further than he did with his investigation of a certain problem in conics.

Euclid's great work, the thirteen books of the *Elements*, must have become a classic soon after publication. From the time of Archimedes they are constantly referred to and used as a basic text-book. It was recognized in antiquity that Euclid had drawn upon all his predecessors. According to Proclus, he "collected many of the theorems of Eudoxus, perfected many of those of Theatetus, and also brought to incontrovertible demonstration the things which were only loosely proved by his predecessors." The other extant works of Euclid include: the *Data*, for use in the solution of problems by geometrical analysis, *On Divisions* (of figures), the *Optics*, and the *Phenomena*, a treatise on the geometry of the sphere for use in astronomy. His lost *Elements of Music* may have provided the basis for the extant *Sectio Canonis* on the Pythagorean theory of music. Of lost geometrical works all except one belonged to higher geometry.

Since the later Greeks knew nothing about the life of Euclid, the mediaeval translators and editors were left to their own devices. He was usually called *Megarensis*, through confusion with the philosopher Eucleides of Megara, Plato's contemporary. The Arabs found that the name of Euclid, which they took to be compounded from *ucli* (key) and *dis* (measure) revealed the "key of geometry." They claimed that the Greek philosophers used to post upon the doors of their schools the well-known notice: "Let no one come to our school who has not learned the *Elements* of Euclid," thus transferring the inscription over Plato's Academy to all scholastic doors and substituting the *Elements* for geometry.

# CONTENTS

BIOGRAPHICAL NOTE, p. ix

| | | | |
|---|---|---|---|
| BOOK | I. | DEFINITIONS, POSTULATES, COMMON NOTIONS | 1 |
| | | PROPOSITIONS | 2 |
| BOOK | II. | DEFINITIONS | 30 |
| | | PROPOSITIONS | 30 |
| BOOK | III. | DEFINITIONS | 41 |
| | | PROPOSITIONS | 41 |
| BOOK | IV. | DEFINITIONS | 67 |
| | | PROPOSITIONS | 67 |
| BOOK | V. | DEFINITIONS | 81 |
| | | PROPOSITIONS | 82 |
| BOOK | VI. | DEFINITIONS | 99 |
| | | PROPOSITIONS | 99 |
| BOOK | VII. | DEFINITIONS | 127 |
| | | PROPOSITIONS | 128 |
| BOOK | VIII. | | 150 |
| BOOK | IX. | | 171 |
| BOOK | X. | DEFINITIONS I. | 191 |
| | | PROPOSITIONS 1—47 | 191–229 |
| | | DEFINITIONS II. | 229 |
| | | PROPOSITIONS 48—84 | 229–264 |
| | | DEFINITIONS III. | 264 |
| | | PROPOSITIONS 85—115 | 264–300 |
| BOOK | XI. | DEFINITIONS | 301 |
| | | PROPOSITIONS | 302 |
| BOOK | XII. | PROPOSITIONS | 338 |
| BOOK | XIII. | PROPOSITIONS | 369 |

# BOOK ONE

## DEFINITIONS

1. A *point* is that which has no part.
2. A *line* is breadthless length.
3. The extremities of a line are points.
4. A *straight line* is a line which lies evenly with the points on itself.
5. A *surface* is that which has length and breadth only.
6. The extremities of a surface are lines.
7. A *plane surface* is a surface which lies evenly with the straight lines on itself.
8. A *plane angle* is the inclination to one another of two lines in a plane which meet one another and do not lie in a straight line.
9. And when the lines containing the angle are straight, the angle is called *rectilineal*.
10. When a straight line set up on a straight line makes the adjacent angles equal to one another, each of the equal angles is *right* and the straight line standing on the other is called a *perpendicular* to that on which it stands.
11. An *obtuse angle* is an angle greater than a right angle.
12. An *acute angle* is an angle less than a right angle.
13. A *boundary* is that which is an extremity of anything.
14. A *figure* is that which is contained by any boundary or boundaries.
15. A *circle* is a plane figure contained by one line such that all the straight lines falling upon it from one point among those lying within the figure are equal to one another;
16. And the point is called the *centre* of the circle.
17. A *diameter* of the circle is any straight line drawn through the centre and terminated in both directions by the circumference of the circle, and such a straight line also bisects the circle.
18. A *semicircle* is the figure contained by the diameter and the circumference cut off by it. And the centre of the semicircle is the same as that of the circle.
19. *Rectilineal figures* are those which are contained by straight lines, *trilateral* figures being those contained by three, *quadrilateral* those contained by four, and *multilateral* those contained by more than four straight lines.
20. Of trilateral figures, an *equilateral triangle* is that which has its three sides equal, an *isosceles triangle* that which has two of its sides alone equal, and a *scalene triangle* that which has its three sides unequal.
21. Further, of trilateral figures, a *right-angled triangle* is that which has a right angle, an *obtuse-angled triangle* that which has an obtuse angle, and an *acute-angled triangle* that which has its three angles acute.

22. Of quadrilateral figures, a *square* is that which is both equilateral and right-angled; an *oblong* that which is right-angled but not equilateral; a *rhombus* that which is equilateral but not right-angled; and a *rhomboid* that which has its opposite sides and angles equal to one another but is neither equilateral nor right-angled. And let quadrilaterals other than these be called *trapezia*.

23. *Parallel* straight lines are straight lines which, being in the same plane and being produced indefinitely in both directions, do not meet one another in either direction.

## POSTULATES

Let the following be postulated:
1. To draw a straight line from any point to any point.
2. To produce a finite straight line continuously in a straight line.
3. To describe a circle with any centre and distance.
4. That all right angles are equal to one another.
5. That, if a straight line falling on two straight lines make the interior angles on the same side less than two right angles, the two straight lines, if produced indefinitely, meet on that side on which are the angles less than the two right angles.

## COMMON NOTIONS

1. Things which are equal to the same thing are also equal to one another.
2. If equals be added to equals, the wholes are equal.
3. If equals be subtracted from equals, the remainders are equal.
[7] 4. Things which coincide with one another are equal to one another.
[8] 5. The whole is greater than the part.

## BOOK I. PROPOSITIONS

### PROPOSITION 1

*On a given finite straight line to construct an equilateral triangle.*

Let $AB$ be the given finite straight line.

Thus it is required to construct an equilateral triangle on the straight line $AB$.

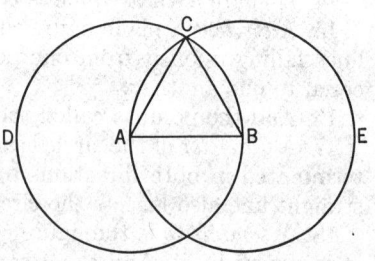

With centre $A$ and distance $AB$ let the circle $BCD$ be described; [Post. 3] again, with centre $B$ and distance $BA$ let the circle $ACE$ be described; [Post. 3] and from the point $C$, in which the circles cut one another, to the points $A$, $B$ let the straight lines $CA$, $CB$ be joined. [Post. 1]

Now, since the point $A$ is the centre of the circle $CDB$,

$AC$ is equal to $AB$.  [Def. 15]

Again, since the point $B$ is the centre of the circle $CAE$,

$BC$ is equal to $BA$.  [Def. 15]

But $CA$ was also proved equal to $AB$;

therefore each of the straight lines $CA$, $CB$ is equal to $AB$.

And things which are equal to the same thing are also equal to one another;

therefore $CA$ is also equal to $CB$.  [C. N. 1]

Therefore the three straight lines $CA$, $AB$, $BC$ are equal to one another.

Therefore the triangle $ABC$ is equilateral; and it has been constructed on the given finite straight line $AB$.

(Being) what it was required to do.

## Proposition 2

*To place at a given point (as an extremity) a straight line equal to a given straight line.*

Let $A$ be the given point, and $BC$ the given straight line.

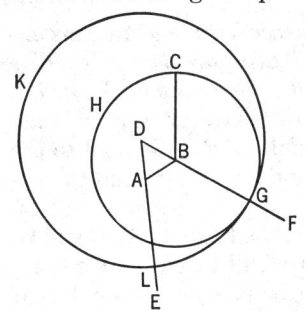

Thus it is required to place at the point $A$ (as an extremity) a straight line equal to the given straight line $BC$.

From the point $A$ to the point $B$ let the straight line $AB$ be joined; [Post. 1]
and on it let the equilateral triangle $DAB$ be constructed. [I. 1]

Let the straight lines $AE$, $BF$ be produced in a straight line with $DA$, $DB$; [Post. 2]
with centre $B$ and distance $BC$ let the circle $CGH$ be described; [Post. 3]
and again, with centre $D$ and distance $DG$ let the circle $GKL$ be described. [Post. 3]

Then, since the point $B$ is the centre of the circle $CGH$,
$BC$ is equal to $BG$.
Again, since the point $D$ is the centre of the circle $GKL$,
$DL$ is equal to $DG$.
And in these $DA$ is equal to $DB$;
therefore the remainder $AL$ is equal to the remainder $BG$. [C.N. 3]
But $BC$ was also proved equal to $BG$;
therefore each of the straight lines $AL$, $BC$ is equal to $BG$.
And things which are equal to the same thing are also equal to one another; [C.N. 1]
therefore $AL$ is also equal to $BC$.

Therefore at the given point $A$ the straight line $AL$ is placed equal to the given straight line $BC$.

(Being) what it was required to do.

## Proposition 3

*Given two unequal straight lines, to cut off from the greater a straight line equal to the less.*

Let $AB$, $C$ be the two given unequal straight lines, and let $AB$ be the greater of them.

Thus it is required to cut off from $AB$ the greater a straight line equal to $C$ the less.

At the point $A$ let $AD$ be placed equal to the straight line $C$; [I. 2]
and with centre $A$ and distance $AD$ let the circle $DEF$ be described. [Post. 3]
Now, since the point $A$ is the centre of the circle $DEF$,
$AE$ is equal to $AD$. [Def. 15]

But $C$ is also equal to $AD$.

Therefore each of the straight lines $AE$, $C$ is equal to $AD$;

so that $AE$ is also equal to $C$. [C.N. 1]

Therefore, given the two straight lines $AB$, $C$, from $AB$ the greater $AE$ has been cut off equal to $C$ the less.

(Being) what it was required to do.

## Proposition 4

*If two triangles have the two sides equal to two sides respectively, and have the angles contained by the equal straight lines equal, they will also have the base equal to the base, the triangle will be equal to the triangle, and the remaining angles will be equal to the remaining angles respectively, namely those which the equal sides subtend.*

Let $ABC$, $DEF$ be two triangles having the two sides $AB$, $AC$ equal to the two sides $DE$, $DF$ respectively, namely $AB$ to $DE$ and $AC$ to $DF$, and the angle $BAC$ equal to the angle $EDF$.

I say that the base $BC$ is also equal to the base $EF$, the triangle $ABC$ will be equal to the triangle $DEF$, and the remaining angles will be equal to the remaining angles respectively, namely those which the equal sides subtend, that is, the angle $ABC$ to the angle $DEF$, and the angle $ACB$ to the angle $DFE$.

For, if the triangle $ABC$ be applied to the triangle $DEF$,
and if the point $A$ be placed on the point $D$
and the straight line $AB$ on $DE$,
then the point $B$ will also coincide with $E$, because $AB$ is equal to $DE$.

Again, $AB$ coinciding with $DE$,
the straight line $AC$ will also coincide with $DF$, because the angle $BAC$ is equal to the angle $EDF$;
hence the point $C$ will also coincide with the point $F$, because $AC$ is again equal to $DF$.

But $B$ also coincided with $E$;

hence the base $BC$ will coincide with the base $EF$.

[For if, when $B$ coincides with $E$ and $C$ with $F$, the base $BC$ does not coincide with the base $EF$, two straight lines will enclose a space: which is impossible.

Therefore the base $BC$ will coincide with $EF$] and will be equal to it. [C.N. 4]
Thus the whole triangle $ABC$ will coincide with the whole triangle $DEF$, and will be equal to it.

And the remaining angles will also coincide with the remaining angles and will be equal to them,

the angle $ABC$ to the angle $DEF$,
and the angle $ACB$ to the angle $DFE$.

Therefore etc.

(Being) what it was required to prove.

## Proposition 5

*In isosceles triangles the angles at the base are equal to one another, and, if the equal straight lines be produced further, the angles under the base will be equal to one another.*

Let $ABC$ be an isosceles triangle having the side $AB$ equal to the side $AC$;

ELEMENTS I

and let the straight lines $BD$, $CE$ be produced further in a straight line with $AB$, $AC$. [Post. 2]

I say that the angle $ABC$ is equal to the angle $ACB$, and the angle $CBD$ to the angle $BCE$.

Let a point $F$ be taken at random on $BD$; from $AE$ the greater let $AG$ be cut off equal to $AF$ the less; [I. 3]

and let the straight lines $FC$, $GB$ be joined. [Post. 1]

Then, since $AF$ is equal to $AG$ and $AB$ to $AC$,
the two sides $FA$, $AC$ are equal to the two sides $GA$, $AB$, respectively;
and they contain a common angle, the angle $FAG$.

Therefore the base $FC$ is equal to the base $GB$,
and the triangle $AFC$ is equal to the triangle $AGB$,
and the remaining angles will be equal to the remaining angles respectively, namely those which the equal sides subtend,
that is, the angle $ACF$ to the angle $ABG$,
and the angle $AFC$ to the angle $AGB$. [I. 4]

And, since the whole $AF$ is equal to the whole $AG$,
and in these $AB$ is equal to $AC$,
the remainder $BF$ is equal to the remainder $CG$.

But $FC$ was also proved equal to $GB$;
therefore the two sides $BF$, $FC$ are equal to the two sides $CG$, $GB$ respectively;
and the angle $BFC$ is equal to the angle $CGB$,
while the base $BC$ is common to them;
therefore the triangle $BFC$ is also equal to the triangle $CGB$, and the remaining angles will be equal to the remaining angles respectively, namely those which the equal sides subtend;
therefore the angle $FBC$ is equal to the angle $GCB$,
and the angle $BCF$ to the angle $CBG$.

Accordingly, since the whole angle $ABG$ was proved equal to the angle $ACF$,
and in these the angle $CBG$ is equal to the angle $BCF$,
the remaining angle $ABC$ is equal to the remaining angle $ACB$;
and they are at the base of the triangle $ABC$.

But the angle $FBC$ was also proved equal to the angle $GCB$;
and they are under the base.

Therefore etc. Q. E. D.

PROPOSITION 6

*If in a triangle two angles be equal to one another, the sides which subtend the equal angles will also be equal to one another.*

Let $ABC$ be a triangle having the angle $ABC$ equal to the angle $ACB$;

I say that the side $AB$ is also equal to the side $AC$.

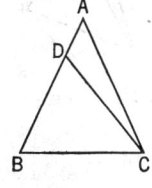

For, if $AB$ is unequal to $AC$, one of them is greater.

Let $AB$ be greater; and from $AB$ the greater let $DB$ be cut off equal to $AC$ the less;

let $DC$ be joined.

Then, since $DB$ is equal to $AC$,
and $BC$ is common,

the two sides $DB$, $BC$ are equal to the two sides $AC$, $CB$ respectively;
and the angle $DBC$ is equal to the angle $ACB$;
therefore the base $DC$ is equal to the base $AB$,
and the triangle $DBC$ will be equal to the triangle $ACB$,
the less to the greater:
which is absurd.

Therefore $AB$ is not unequal to $AC$;
it is therefore equal to it.

Therefore etc.

Q. E. D.

## Proposition 7

*Given two straight lines constructed on a straight line (from its extremities) and meeting in a point, there cannot be constructed on the same straight line (from its extremities), and on the same side of it, two other straight lines meeting in another point and equal to the former two respectively, namely each to that which has the same extremity with it.*

For, if possible, given two straight lines $AC$, $CB$ constructed on the straight line $AB$ and meeting at the point $C$, let two other straight lines $AD$, $DB$ be constructed on the same straight line $AB$, on the same side of it, meeting in another point $D$ and equal to the former two respectively, namely each to that which has the same extremity with it, so that $CA$ is equal to $DA$ which has the same extremity $A$ with it, and $CB$ to $DB$ which has the same extremity $B$ with it; and let $CD$ be joined.

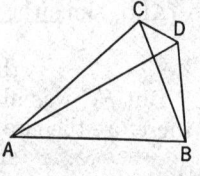

Then, since $AC$ is equal to $AD$,
the angle $ACD$ is also equal to the angle $ADC$; [I. 5]
therefore the angle $ADC$ is greater than the angle $DCB$;
therefore the angle $CDB$ is much greater than the angle $DCB$.

Again, since $CB$ is equal to $DB$,
the angle $CDB$ is also equal to the angle $DCB$.

But it was also proved much greater than it:
which is impossible.

Therefore etc.

Q. E. D.

## Proposition 8

*If two triangles have the two sides equal to two sides respectively, and have also the base equal to the base, they will also have the angles equal which are contained by the equal straight lines.*

Let $ABC$, $DEF$ be two triangles having the two sides $AB$, $AC$ equal to the two sides $DE$, $DF$ respectively, namely $AB$ to $DE$, and $AC$ to $DF$; and let them have the base $BC$ equal to the base $EF$;

I say that the angle $BAC$ is also equal to the angle $EDF$.

For, if the triangle $ABC$ be applied to the triangle $DEF$, and if the point $B$ be placed on the point $E$ and the straight line $BC$ on $EF$,
the point $C$ will also coincide with $F$,

because *BC* is equal to *EF*.

Then, *BC* coinciding with *EF*,

*BA, AC* will also coincide with *ED, DF*;

for, if the base *BC* coincides with the base *EF*, and the sides *BA, AC* do not coincide with *ED, DF* but fall beside them as *EG, GF*,

then, given two straight lines constructed on a straight line (from its extremities) and meeting in a point, there will have been constructed on the same straight line (from its extremities), and on the same side of it, two other straight lines meeting in another point and equal to the former two respectively, namely each to that which has the same extremity with it.

But they cannot be so constructed. [I. 7]

Therefore it is not possible that, if the base *BC* be applied to the base *EF*, the sides *BA, AC* should not coincide with *ED, DF*;

they will therefore coincide,

so that the angle *BAC* will also coincide with the angle *EDF*, and will be equal to it.

If therefore etc. Q. E. D.

## Proposition 9

*To bisect a given rectilineal angle.*

Let the angle *BAC* be the given rectilineal angle.

Thus it is required to bisect it.

Let a point *D* be taken at random on *AB*;

let *AE* be cut off from *AC* equal to *AD*; [I. 3]

let *DE* be joined, and on *DE* let the equilateral triangle *DEF* be constructed;

let *AF* be joined.

I say that the angle *BAC* has been bisected by the straight line *AF*.

For, since *AD* is equal to *AE*,

and *AF* is common,

the two sides *DA, AF* are equal to the two sides *EA, AF* respectively.

And the base *DF* is equal to the base *EF*;

therefore the angle *DAF* is equal to the angle *EAF*. [I. 8]

Therefore the given rectilineal angle *BAC* has been bisected by the straight line *AF*. Q. E. F.

## Proposition 10

*To bisect a given finite straight line.*

Let *AB* be the given finite straight line.

Thus it is required to bisect the finite straight line *AB*.

Let the equilateral triangle *ABC* be constructed on it, [I. 1]

and let the angle *ACB* be bisected by the straight line *CD*; [I. 9]

I say that the straight line *AB* has been bisected at the point *D*.

For, since *AC* is equal to *CB*,

and *CD* is common,

the two sides *AC, CD* are equal to the two sides *BC, CD* respectively;

and the angle *ACD* is equal to the angle *BCD*;

therefore the base $AD$ is equal to the base $BD$.    [I. 4]

Therefore the given finite straight line $AB$ has been bisected at $D$.  Q. E. F.

## PROPOSITION 11

*To draw a straight line at right angles to a given straight line from a given point on it.*

Let $AB$ be the given straight line, and $C$ the given point on it.

Thus it is required to draw from the point $C$ a straight line at right angles to the straight line $AB$.

Let a point $D$ be taken at random on $AC$;
let $CE$ be made equal to $CD$;    [I. 3]
on $DE$ let the equilateral triangle $FDE$ be constructed,    [I. 1]
and let $FC$ be joined;

I say that the straight line $FC$ has been drawn at right angles to the given straight line $AB$ from $C$ the given point on it.

For, since $DC$ is equal to $CE$,
and $CF$ is common,
the two sides $DC$, $CF$ are equal to the two sides $EC$, $CF$ respectively;
and the base $DF$ is equal to the base $FE$;
therefore the angle $DCF$ is equal to the angle $ECF$;    [I. 8]
and they are adjacent angles.

But, when a straight line set up on a straight line makes the adjacent angles equal to one another, each of the equal angles is right;    [Def. 10]
therefore each of the angles $DCF$, $FCE$ is right.

Therefore the straight line $CF$ has been drawn at right angles to the given straight line $AB$ from the given point $C$ on it.    Q. E. F.

## PROPOSITION 12

*To a given infinite straight line, from a given point which is not on it, to draw a perpendicular straight line.*

Let $AB$ be the given infinite straight line, and $C$ the given point which is not on it;

thus it is required to draw to the given infinite straight line $AB$, from the given point $C$ which is not on it, a perpendicular straight line.

For let a point $D$ be taken at random on the other side of the straight line $AB$, and with centre $C$ and distance $CD$ let the circle $EFG$ be described;    [Post. 3]
let the straight line $EG$ be bisected at $H$,    [I. 10]
and let the straight lines $CG$, $CH$, $CE$ be joined.    [Post. 1]

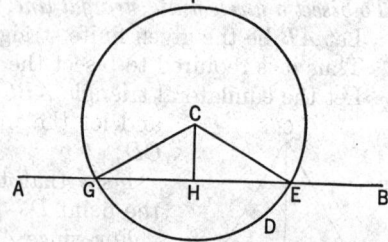

I say that $CH$ has been drawn perpendicular to the given infinite straight line $AB$ from the given point $C$ which is not on it.

For, since $GH$ is equal to $HE$,
and $HC$ is common,

the two sides $GH$, $HC$ are equal to the two sides $EH$, $HC$ respectively;
and the base $CG$ is equal to the base $CE$;
therefore the angle $CHG$ is equal to the angle $EHC$. [I. 8]
And they are adjacent angles.

But, when a straight line set up on a straight line makes the adjacent angles equal to one another, each of the equal angles is right, and the straight line standing on the other is called a perpendicular to that on which it stands.
[Def. 10]

Therefore $CH$ has been drawn perpendicular to the given infinite straight line $AB$ from the given point $C$ which is not on it. Q. E. F.

## Proposition 13

*If a straight line set up on a straight line make angles, it will make either two right angles or angles equal to two right angles.*

For let any straight line $AB$ set up on the straight line $CD$ make the angles $CBA$, $ABD$;

I say that the angles $CBA$, $ABD$ are either two rights angles or equal to two right angles.

Now, if the angle $CBA$ is equal to the angle $ABD$, they are two right angles. [Def. 10]

But, if not, let $BE$ be drawn from the point $B$ at right angles to $CD$; [I. 11]
therefore the angles $CBE$, $EBD$ are two right angles.

Then, since the angle $CBE$ is equal to the two angles $CBA$, $ABE$,
let the angle $EBD$ be added to each;
therefore the angles $CBE$, $EBD$ are equal to the three angles $CBA$, $ABE$, $EBD$. [C.N. 2]

Again, since the angle $DBA$ is equal to the two angles $DBE$, $EBA$,
let the angle $ABC$ be added to each;
therefore the angles $DBA$, $ABC$ are equal to the three angles $DBE$, $EBA$, $ABC$. [C.N. 2]

But the angles $CBE$, $EBD$ were also proved equal to the same three angles; and things which are equal to the same thing are also equal to one another;
[C.N. 1]

therefore the angles $CBE$, $EBD$ are also equal to the angles $DBA$, $ABC$.
But the angles $CBE$, $EBD$ are two right angles;
therefore the angles $DBA$, $ABC$ are also equal to two right angles.
Therefore etc. Q. E. D.

## Proposition 14

*If with any straight line, and at a point on it, two straight lines not lying on the same side make the adjacent angles equal to two right angles, the two straight lines will be in a straight line with one another.*

For with any straight line $AB$, and at the point $B$ on it, let the two straight lines $BC$, $BD$ not lying on the same side make the adjacent angles $ABC$, $ABD$ equal to two right angles;

I say that $BD$ is in a straight line with $CB$.

For, if $BD$ is not in a straight line with $BC$, let $BE$ be in a straight line with $CB$.

Then, since the straight line $AB$ stands on the straight line $CBE$,
the angles $ABC$, $ABE$ are equal to two right angles. [I. 13]
But the angles $ABC$, $ABD$ are also equal to two right angles;
therefore the angles $CBA$, $ABE$ are equal to the angles $CBA$, $ABD$. [Post. 4 and C.N. 1]
Let the angle $CBA$ be subtracted from each;
therefore the remaining angle $ABE$ is equal to the remaining angle $ABD$, [C.N. 3]
the less to the greater: which is impossible.
Therefore $BE$ is not in a straight line with $CB$.
Similarly we can prove that neither is any other straight line except $BD$.
Therefore $CB$ is in a straight line with $BD$.
Therefore etc.
Q. E. D.

## Proposition 15

*If two straight lines cut one another, they make the vertical angles equal to one another.*

For let the straight lines $AB$, $CD$ cut one another at the point $E$;
I say that the angle $AEC$ is equal to the angle $DEB$,
and the angle $CEB$ to the angle $AED$.
For, since the straight line $AE$ stands on the straight line $CD$, making the angles $CEA$, $AED$,
the angles $CEA$, $AED$ are equal to two right angles. [I. 13]
Again, since the straight line $DE$ stands on the straight line $AB$, making the angles $AED$, $DEB$,
the angles $AED$, $DEB$ are equal to two right angles. [I. 13]
But the angles $CEA$, $AED$ were also proved equal to two right angles;
therefore the angles $CEA$, $AED$ are equal to the angles $AED$, $DEB$. [Post. 4 and C.N. 1]
Let the angle $AED$ be subtracted from each;
therefore the remaining angle $CEA$ is equal to the remaining angle $BED$. [C.N. 3]
Similarly it can be proved that the angles $CEB$, $DEA$ are also equal.
Therefore etc.
Q. E. D.

[PORISM. From this it is manifest that, if two straight lines cut one another, they will make the angles at the point of section equal to four right angles.]

## Proposition 16

*In any triangle, if one of the sides be produced, the exterior angle is greater than either of the interior and opposite angles.*

Let $ABC$ be a triangle, and let one side of it $BC$ be produced to $D$;
I say that the exterior angle $ACD$ is greater than either of the interior and opposite angles $CBA$, $BAC$.
Let $AC$ be bisected at $E$ [I. 10], and let $BE$ be joined and produced in a straight line to $F$;
let $EF$ be made equal to $BE$, [I. 3]
let $FC$ be joined [Post. 1], and let $AC$ be drawn through to $G$. [Post. 2]

ELEMENTS I

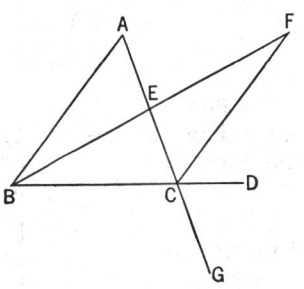

Then, since $AE$ is equal to $EC$, and $BE$ to $EF$,
the two sides $AE$, $EB$ are equal to the two sides $CE$, $EF$ respectively;
and the angle $AEB$ is equal to the angle $FEC$,
for they are vertical angles. [I. 15]
Therefore the base $AB$ is equal to the base $FC$,
and the triangle $ABE$ is equal to the triangle $CFE$,
and the remaining angles are equal to the remaining angles respectively, namely, those which the equal sides subtend; [I. 4]
therefore the angle $BAE$ is equal to the angle $ECF$.
But the angle $ECD$ is greater than the angle $ECF$; [C.N. 5]
therefore the angle $ACD$ is greater than the angle $BAE$.
Similarly also, if $BC$ be bisected, the angle $BCG$, that is, the angle $ACD$ [I. 15], can be proved greater than the angle $ABC$ as well.
Therefore etc. Q. E. D.

## Proposition 17

*In any triangle two angles taken together in any manner are less than two right angles.*

Let $ABC$ be a triangle;
I say that two angles of the triangle $ABC$ taken together in any manner are less than two right angles.

For let $BC$ be produced to $D$. [Post. 2]
Then, since the angle $ACD$ is an exterior angle of the triangle $ABC$,
it is greater than the interior and opposite angle $ABC$. [I. 16]
Let the angle $ACB$ be added to each;
therefore the angles $ACD$, $ACB$ are greater than the angles $ABC$, $BCA$.
But the angles $ACD$, $ACB$ are equal to two right angles. [I. 13]
Therefore the angles $ABC$, $BCA$ are less than two right angles.
Similarly we can prove that the angles $BAC$, $ACB$ are also less than two right angles, and so are the angles $CAB$, $ABC$ as well.
Therefore etc. Q. E. D.

## Proposition 18

*In any triangle the greater side subtends the greater angle.*

For let $ABC$ be a triangle having the side $AC$ greater than $AB$;
I say that the angle $ABC$ is also greater than the angle $BCA$.

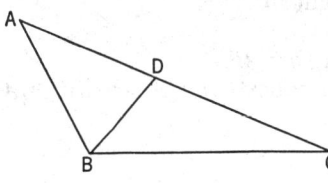

For, since $AC$ is greater than $AB$, let $AD$ be made equal to $AB$ [I. 3], and let $BD$ be joined.
Then, since the angle $ADB$ is an exterior angle of the triangle $BCD$,
it is greater than the interior and opposite angle $DCB$. [I. 16]
But the angle $ADB$ is equal to the angle $ABD$,
since the side $AB$ is equal to $AD$;

therefore the angle $ABD$ is also greater than the angle $ACB$;
therefore the angle $ABC$ is much greater than the angle $ACB$.
Therefore etc.

Q. E. D.

## Proposition 19

*In any triangle the greater angle is subtended by the greater side.*

Let $ABC$ be a triangle having the angle $ABC$ greater than the angle $BCA$;
I say that the side $AC$ is also greater than the side $AB$.

For, if not, $AC$ is either equal to $AB$ or less.

Now $AC$ is not equal to $AB$;
for then the angle $ABC$ would also have been equal to the angle $ACB$; [I. 5]
but it is not;
therefore $AC$ is not equal to $AB$.

Neither is $AC$ less than $AB$,
for then the angle $ABC$ would also have been less than the angle $ACB$; [I. 18]
but it is not;
therefore $AC$ is not less than $AB$.

And it was proved that it is not equal either.

Therefore $AC$ is greater than $AB$.

Therefore etc.

Q. E. D.

## Proposition 20

*In any triangle two sides taken together in any manner are greater than the remaining one.*

For let $ABC$ be a triangle;
I say that in the triangle $ABC$ two sides taken together in any manner are greater than the remaining one, namely

$BA, AC$ greater than $BC$,
$AB, BC$ greater than $AC$,
$BC, CA$ greater than $AB$.

For let $BA$ be drawn through to the point $D$, let $DA$ be made equal to $CA$, and let $DC$ be joined.

Then, since $DA$ is equal to $AC$,
the angle $ADC$ is also equal to the angle $ACD$; [I. 5]
therefore the angle $BCD$ is greater than the angle $ADC$.
[C.N. 5]

And, since $DCB$ is a triangle having the angle $BCD$ greater than the angle $BDC$,
and the greater angle is subtended by the greater side, [I. 19]
therefore $DB$ is greater than $BC$.

But $DA$ is equal to $AC$;
therefore $BA, AC$ are greater than $BC$.

Similarly we can prove that $AB, BC$ are also greater than $CA$, and $BC, CA$ than $AB$.

Therefore etc.

Q. E. D.

## Proposition 21

*If on one of the sides of a triangle, from its extremities, there be constructed two*

ELEMENTS I

*straight lines meeting within the triangle, the straight lines so constructed will be less than the remaining two sides of the triangle, but will contain a greater angle.*

On $BC$, one of the sides of the triangle $ABC$, from its extremities $B$, $C$, let the two straight lines $BD$, $DC$ be constructed meeting within the triangle;

I say that $BD$, $DC$ are less than the remaining two sides of the triangle $BA$, $AC$, but contain an angle $BDC$ greater than the angle $BAC$.

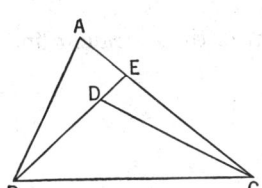

For let $BD$ be drawn through to $E$.

Then, since in any triangle two sides are greater than the remaining one, [I. 20]

therefore, in the triangle $ABE$, the two sides $AB$, $AE$ are greater than $BE$.

Let $EC$ be added to each;

therefore $BA$, $AC$ are greater than $BE$, $EC$.

Again, since, in the triangle $CED$,

the two sides $CE$, $ED$ are greater than $CD$,

let $DB$ be added to each;

therefore $CE$, $EB$ are greater than $CD$, $DB$.

But $BA$, $AC$ were proved greater than $BE$, $EC$;

therefore $BA$, $AC$ are much greater than $BD$, $DC$.

Again, since in any triangle the exterior angle is greater than the interior and opposite angle, [I. 16]

therefore, in the triangle $CDE$,

the exterior angle $BDC$ is greater than the angle $CED$.

For the same reason, moreover, in the triangle $ABE$ also,

the exterior angle $CEB$ is greater than the angle $BAC$.

But the angle $BDC$ was proved greater than the angle $CEB$;

therefore the angle $BDC$ is much greater than the angle $BAC$.

Therefore etc. Q. E. D.

## Proposition 22

*Out of three straight lines, which are equal to three given straight lines, to construct a triangle: thus it is necessary that two of the straight lines taken together in any manner should be greater than the remaining one.* [I. 20]

Let the three given straight lines be $A$, $B$, $C$, and of these let two taken together in any manner be greater than the remaining one,

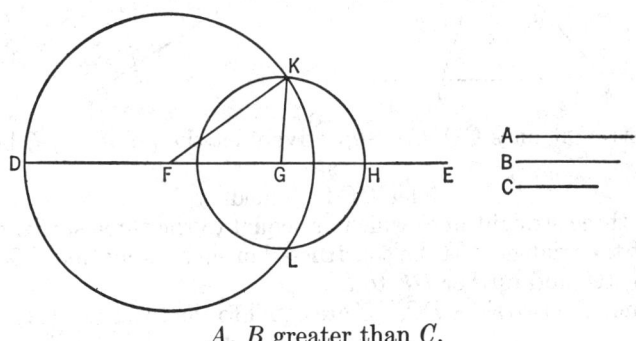

namely $\qquad$ $A$, $B$ greater than $C$,

$A$, $C$ greater than $B$,

and $\qquad$ $B$, $C$ greater than $A$;

thus it is required to construct a triangle out of straight lines equal to $A, B, C$.

Let there be set out a straight line $DE$, terminated at $D$ but of infinite length in the direction of $E$,

and let $DF$ be made equal to $A$, $FG$ equal to $B$, and $GH$ equal to C. [I. 3]

With centre $F$ and distance $FD$ let the circle $DKL$ be described;

again, with centre $G$ and distance $GH$ let the circle $KLH$ be described;

and let $KF$, $KG$ be joined;

I say that the triangle $KFG$ has been constructed out of three straight lines equal to $A, B, C$.

For, since the point $F$ is the centre of the circle $DKL$,

$FD$ is equal to $FK$.

But $FD$ is equal to $A$;

therefore $KF$ is also equal to $A$.

Again, since the point $G$ is the centre of the circle $LKH$,

$GH$ is equal to $GK$.

But $GH$ is equal to $C$;

therefore $KG$ is also equal to $C$.

And $FG$ is also equal to $B$;

therefore the three straight lines $KF$, $FG$, $GK$ are equal to the three straight lines $A, B, C$.

Therefore out of the three straight lines $KF$, $FG$, $GK$, which are equal to the three given straight lines $A, B, C$, the triangle $KFG$ has been constructed.

Q. E. F.

## Proposition 23

*On a given straight line and at a point on it to construct a rectilineal angle equal to a given rectilineal angle.*

Let $AB$ be the given straight line, $A$ the point on it, and the angle $DCE$ the given rectilineal angle;

thus it is required to construct on the given straight line $AB$, and at the point $A$ on it, a rectilineal angle equal to the given rectilineal angle $DCE$.

On the straight lines $CD$, $CE$ respectively let the points $D$, $E$ be taken at random;

let $DE$ be joined,

and out of three straight lines which are equal to the three straight lines $CD$, $DE$, $CE$ let the triangle $AFG$ be constructed in such a way that $CD$ is equal to $AF$, $CE$ to $AG$, and further $DE$ to $FG$. [I. 22]

Then, since the two sides $DC$, $CE$ are equal to the two sides $FA$, $AG$ respectively,

and the base $DE$ is equal to the base $FG$,

the angle $DCE$ is equal to the angle $FAG$. [I. 8]

# ELEMENTS I

Therefore on the given straight line $AB$, and at the point $A$ on it, the rectilineal angle $FAG$ has been constructed equal to the given rectilineal angle $DCE$.

Q. E. F.

## Proposition 24

*If two triangles have the two sides equal to two sides respectively, but have the one of the angles contained by the equal straight lines greater than the other, they will also have the base greater than the base.*

Let $ABC$, $DEF$ be two triangles having the two sides $AB$, $AC$ equal to the two sides $DE$, $DF$ respectively, namely $AB$ to $DE$, and $AC$ to $DF$, and let the angle at $A$ be greater than the angle at $D$;

I say that the base $BC$ is also greater than the base $EF$.

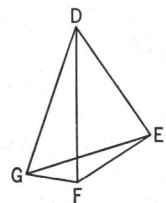

For, since the angle $BAC$ is greater than the angle $EDF$, let there be constructed, on the straight line $DE$, and at the point $D$ on it, the angle $EDG$ equal to the angle $BAC$; [I. 23] let $DG$ be made equal to either of the two straight lines $AC$, $DF$, and let $EG$, $FG$ be joined.

Then, since $AB$ is equal to $DE$, and $AC$ to $DG$,
    the two sides $BA$, $AC$ are equal to the two sides $ED$, $DG$, respectively;
        and the angle $BAC$ is equal to the angle $EDG$;
        therefore the base $BC$ is equal to the base $EG$. [I. 4]
Again, since $DF$ is equal to $DG$,
    the angle $DGF$ is also equal to the angle $DFG$; [I. 5]
    therefore the angle $DFG$ is greater than the angle $EGF$.
Therefore the angle $EFG$ is much greater than the angle $EGF$.
And, since $EFG$ is a triangle having the angle $EFG$ greater than the angle $EGF$,
    and the greater angle is subtended by the greater side, [I. 19]
        the side $EG$ is also greater than $EF$.
But $EG$ is equal to $BC$.
Therefore $BC$ is also greater than $EF$.
Therefore etc.

Q. E. D.

## Proposition 25

*If two triangles have the two sides equal to two sides respectively, but have the base greater than the base, they will also have the one of the angles contained by the equal straight lines greater than the other.*

Let $ABC$, $DEF$ be two triangles having the two sides $AB$, $AC$ equal to the two sides $DE$, $DF$ respectively, namely $AB$ to $DE$, and $AC$ to $DF$; and let the base $BC$ be greater than the base $EF$;

I say that the angle $BAC$ is also greater than the angle $EDF$.

For, if not, it is either equal to it or less.

Now the angle $BAC$ is not equal to the angle $EDF$; for then the base $BC$ would also have been equal to the base $EF$, [I. 4]
    but it is not;
    therefore the angle $BAC$ is not equal to the angle $EDF$.

Neither again is the angle *BAC* less than the angle *EDF*; for then the base *BC* would also have been less than the base *EF*, [I. 24]

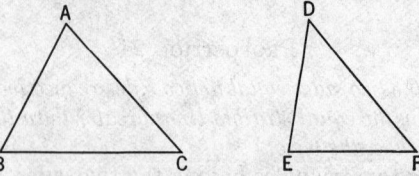

but it is not; therefore the angle *BAC* is not less than the angle *EDF*.
But it was proved that it is not equal either;
therefore the angle *BAC* is greater than the angle *EDF*.
Therefore etc.

Q. E. D.

## Proposition 26

*If two triangles have the two angles equal to two angles respectively, and one side equal to one side, namely, either the side adjoining the equal angles, or that subtending one of the equal angles, they will also have the remaining sides equal to the remaining sides and the remaining angle to the remaining angle.*

Let *ABC*, *DEF* be two triangles having the two angles *ABC*, *BCA* equal to the two angles *DEF*, *EFD* respectively, namely the angle *ABC* to the angle *DEF*, and the angle *BCA* to the angle *EFD*; and let them also have one side equal to one side, first that adjoining the equal angles, namely *BC* to *EF*;

I say that they will also have the remaining sides equal to the remaining sides respectively, namely *AB* to *DE* and *AC* to *DF*, and the remaining angle to the remaining angle, namely the angle *BAC* to the angle *EDF*.

For, if *AB* is unequal to *DE*, one of them is greater.
Let *AB* be greater, and let *BG* be made equal to *DE*; and let *GC* be joined.
Then, since *BG* is equal to *DE*, and *BC* to *EF*,
the two sides *GB*, *BC* are equal to the two sides *DE*, *EF* respectively;
and the angle *GBC* is equal to the angle *DEF*;
therefore the base *GC* is equal to the base *DF*,
and the triangle *GBC* is equal to the triangle *DEF*,
and the remaining angles will be equal to the remaining angles, namely those which the equal sides subtend; [I. 4]
therefore the angle *GCB* is equal to the angle *DFE*.
But the angle *DFE* is by hypothesis equal to the angle *BCA*;
therefore the angle *BCG* is equal to the angle *BCA*,
the less to the greater: which is impossible.
Therefore *AB* is not unequal to *DE*,
and is therefore equal to it.
But *BC* is also equal to *EF*;

therefore the two sides $AB$, $BC$ are equal to the two sides $DE$, $EF$ respectively,
and the angle $ABC$ is equal to the angle $DEF$;
therefore the base $AC$ is equal to the base $DF$,
and the remaining angle $BAC$ is equal to the remaining angle $EDF$. [I. 4]

Again, let sides subtending equal angles be equal, as $AB$ to $DE$;

I say again that the remaining sides will be equal to the remaining sides, namely $AC$ to $DF$ and $BC$ to $EF$, and further the remaining angle $BAC$ is equal to the remaining angle $EDF$.

For, if $BC$ is unequal to $EF$, one of them is greater.

Let $BC$ be greater, if possible, and let $BH$ be made equal to $EF$; let $AH$ be joined.

Then, since $BH$ is equal to $EF$, and $AB$ to $DE$,
the two sides $AB$, $BH$ are equal to the two sides $DE$, $EF$ respectively, and they contain equal angles;
therefore the base $AH$ is equal to the base $DF$,
and the triangle $ABH$ is equal to the triangle $DEF$,
and the remaining angles will be equal to the remaining angles, namely those which the equal sides subtend; [I. 4]
therefore the angle $BHA$ is equal to the angle $EFD$.

But the angle $EFD$ is equal to the angle $BCA$;
therefore, in the triangle $AHC$, the exterior angle $BHA$ is equal to the interior and opposite angle $BCA$:
which is impossible. [I. 16]

Therefore $BC$ is not unequal to $EF$,
and is therefore equal to it.

But $AB$ is also equal to $DE$;
therefore the two sides $AB$, $BC$ are equal to the two sides $DE$, $EF$ respectively, and they contain equal angles;
therefore the base $AC$ is equal to the base $DF$,
the triangle $ABC$ equal to the triangle $DEF$,
and the remaining angle $BAC$ equal to the remaining angle $EDF$. [I. 4]
Therefore etc. Q. E. D.

## Proposition 27

*If a straight line falling on two straight lines make the alternate angles equal to one another, the straight lines will be parallel to one another.*

For let the straight line $EF$ falling on the two straight lines $AB$, $CD$ make the alternate angles $AEF$, $EFD$ equal to one another;

I say that $AB$ is parallel to $CD$.

For, if not, $AB$, $CD$ when produced will meet either in the direction of $B$, $D$ or towards $A$, $C$.

Let them be produced and meet, in the direction of $B$, $D$, at $G$.

Then, in the triangle $GEF$,
the exterior angle $AEF$ is equal to the interior and opposite angle $EFG$:
which is impossible. [I. 16]

Therefore $AB$, $CD$ when produced will not meet in the direction of $B$, $D$.
Similarly it can be proved that neither will they meet towards $A$, $C$.

But straight lines which do not meet in either direction are parallel;
[Def. 23]

therefore *AB* is parallel to *CD*.

Therefore etc. Q. E. D.

## PROPOSITION 28

*If a straight line falling on two straight lines make the exterior angle equal to the interior and opposite angle on the same side, or the interior angles on the same side equal to two right angles, the straight lines will be parallel to one another.*

For let the straight line *EF* falling on the two straight lines *AB*, *CD* make the exterior angle *EGB* equal to the interior and opposite angle *GHD*, or the interior angles on the same side, namely *BGH*, *GHD*, equal to two right angles;

I say that *AB* is parallel to *CD*.

For, since the angle *EGB* is equal to the angle *GHD*,
while the angle *EGB* is equal to the angle *AGH*, [I. 15]
the angle *AGH* is also equal to the angle *GHD*;
and they are alternate;
therefore *AB* is parallel to *CD*. [I. 27]

Again, since the angles *BGH*, *GHD* are equal to two right angles, and the angles *AGH*, *BGH* are also equal to two right angles, [I. 13]
the angles *AGH*, *BGH* are equal to the angles *BGH*, *GHD*.

Let the angle *BGH* be subtracted from each;
therefore the remaining angle *AGH* is equal to the remaining angle *GHD*;
and they are alternate;
therefore *AB* is parallel to *CD*. [I. 27]

Therefore etc. Q. E. D.]

## PROPOSITION 29

*A straight line falling on parallel straight lines makes the alternate angles equal to one another, the exterior angle equal to the interior and opposite angle, and the interior angles on the same side equal to two right angles.*

For let the straight line *EF* fall on the parallel straight lines *AB*, *CD*;

I say that it makes the alternate angles *AGH*, *GHD* equal, the exterior angle *EGB* equal to the interior and opposite angle *GHD*, and the interior angles on the same side, namely *BGH*, *GHD*, equal to two right angles.

For, if the angle *AGH* is unequal to the angle *GHD*, one of them is greater.

Let the angle *AGH* be greater.

Let the angle *BGH* be added to each;
therefore the angles *AGH*, *BGH* are greater than the angles *BGH*, *GHD*.

But the angles *AGH*, *BGH* are equal to two right angles; [I. 13]
therefore the angles *BGH*, *GHD* are less than two right angles.

But straight lines produced indefinitely from angles less than two right angles meet; [Post. 5]
therefore *AB*, *CD*, if produced indefinitely, will meet;

ELEMENTS I

but they do not meet, because they are by hypothesis parallel.
Therefore the angle $AGH$ is not unequal to the angle $GHD$,
and is therefore equal to it.
Again, the angle $AGH$ is equal to the angle $EGB$; [I. 15]
therefore the angle $EGB$ is also equal to the angle $GHD$. [C.N. 1]
Let the angle $BGH$ be added to each;
therefore the angles $EGB$, $BGH$ are equal to the angles $BGH$, $GHD$. [C.N. 2]
But the angles $EGB$, $BGH$ are equal to two right angles; [I. 13]
therefore the angles $BGH$, $GHD$ are also equal to two right angles.
Therefore etc. Q. E. D.

## PROPOSITION 30

*Straight lines parallel to the same straight line are also parallel to one another.*

Let each of the straight lines $AB$, $CD$ be parallel to $EF$; I say that $AB$ is also parallel to $CD$.

For let the straight line $GK$ fall upon them.
Then, since the straight line $GK$ has fallen on the parallel straight lines $AB$, $EF$,
the angle $AGK$ is equal to the angle $GHF$. [I. 29]
Again, since the straight line $GK$ has fallen on the parallel straight lines $EF$, $CD$,
the angle $GHF$ is equal to the angle $GKD$. [I. 29]
But the angle $AGK$ was also proved equal to the angle $GHF$;
therefore the angle $AGK$ is also equal to the angle $GKD$; [C.N. 1]
and they are alternate.
Therefore $AB$ is parallel to $CD$. Q. E. D.

## PROPOSITION 31

*Through a given point to draw a straight line parallel to a given straight line.*

Let $A$ be the given point, and $BC$ the given straight line;
thus it is required to draw through the point $A$ a straight line parallel to the straight line $BC$.

Let a point $D$ be taken at random on $BC$, and let $AD$ be joined; on the straight line $DA$, and at the point $A$ on it, let the angle $DAE$ be constructed equal to the angle $ADC$ [I. 23]; and let the straight line $AF$ be produced in a straight line with $EA$.

Then, since the straight line $AD$ falling on the two straight lines $BC$, $EF$ has made the alternate angles $EAD$, $ADC$ equal to one another,
therefore $EAF$ is parallel to $BC$. [I. 27]
Therefore through the given point $A$ the straight line $EAF$ has been drawn parallel to the given straight line $BC$. Q. E. F.

## PROPOSITION 32

*In any triangle, if one of the sides be produced, the exterior angle is equal to the two interior and opposite angles, and the three interior angles of the triangle are equal to two right angles.*

Let $ABC$ be a triangle, and let one side of it $BC$ be produced to $D$;

I say that the exterior angle $ACD$ is equal to the two interior and opposite angles $CAB$, $ABC$, and the three interior angles of the triangle $ABC$, $BCA$, $CAB$ are equal to two right angles.

For let $CE$ be drawn through the point $C$ parallel to the straight line $AB$.
[I. 31]

Then, since $AB$ is parallel to $CE$,
    and $AC$ has fallen upon them,
the alternate angles $BAC$, $ACE$ are equal to one another. [I. 29]

Again, since $AB$ is parallel to $CE$,
 and the straight line $BD$ has fallen upon them,
the exterior angle $ECD$ is equal to the interior and opposite angle $ABC$. [I. 29]

But the angle $ACE$ was also proved equal to the angle $BAC$;
therefore the whole angle $ACD$ is equal to the two interior and opposite angles $BAC$, $ABC$.

Let the angle $ACB$ be added to each;
therefore the angles $ACD$, $ACB$ are equal to the three angles $ABC$, $BCA$, $CAB$.

But the angles $ACD$, $ACB$ are equal to two right angles; [I. 13]
therefore the angles $ABC$, $BCA$, $CAB$ are also equal to two right angles.

Therefore etc.      Q. E. D.

## Proposition 33

*The straight lines joining equal and parallel straight lines (at the extremities which are) in the same directions (respectively) are themselves also equal and parallel.*

Let $AB$, $CD$ be equal and parallel, and let the straight lines $AC$, $BD$ join them (at the extremities which are) in the same directions (respectively);

I say that $AC$, $BD$ are also equal and parallel.

Let $BC$ be joined.

Then, since $AB$ is parallel to $CD$, and $BC$ has fallen upon them,
the alternate angles $ABC$, $BCD$ are equal to one another. [I. 29]

And, since $AB$ is equal to $CD$,
    and $BC$ is common,
the two sides $AB$, $BC$ are equal to the two sides $DC$, $CB$;
and the angle $ABC$ is equal to the angle $BCD$;
    therefore the base $AC$ is equal to the base $BD$,
    and the triangle $ABC$ is equal to the triangle $DCB$,
and the remaining angles will be equal to the remaining angles respectively, namely those which the equal sides subtend; [I. 4]
    therefore the angle $ACB$ is equal to the angle $CBD$.

And, since the straight line $BC$ falling on the two straight lines $AC$, $BD$ has made the alternate angles equal to one another,
    $AC$ is parallel to $BD$. [I. 27]

And it was also proved equal to it.

Therefore etc.      Q. E. D.

ELEMENTS I 21

## Proposition 34

*In parallelogrammic areas the opposite sides and angles are equal to one another, and the diameter bisects the areas.*

Let $ACDB$ be a parallelogrammic area, and $BC$ its diameter;
I say that the opposite sides and angles of the parallelogram $ACDB$ are equal to one another, and the diameter $BC$ bisects it.

For, since $AB$ is parallel to $CD$,
and the straight line $BC$ has fallen upon them,
the alternate angles $ABC$, $BCD$ are equal to one another. [I. 29]

Again, since $AC$ is parallel to $BD$, and $BC$ has fallen upon them,
the alternate angles $ACB$, $CBD$ are equal to one another. [I. 29]

Therefore $ABC$, $DCB$ are two triangles having the two angles $ABC$, $BCA$ equal to the two angles $DCB$, $CBD$ respectively, and one side equal to one side, namely that adjoining the equal angles and common to both of them, $BC$; therefore they will also have the remaining sides equal to the remaining sides respectively, and the remaining angle to the remaining angle; [I. 26]

therefore the side $AB$ is equal to $CD$,
and $AC$ to $BD$,
and further the angle $BAC$ is equal to the angle $CDB$.

And, since the angle $ABC$ is equal to the angle $BCD$,
and the angle $CBD$ to the angle $ACB$,
the whole angle $ABD$ is equal to the whole angle $ACD$. [C.N. 2]

And the angle $BAC$ was also proved equal to the angle $CDB$.

Therefore in parallelogrammic areas the opposite sides and angles are equal to one another.

I say, next, that the diameter also bisects the areas.

For, since $AB$ is equal to $CD$,
and $BC$ is common,
the two sides $AB$, $BC$ are equal to the two sides $DC$, $CB$ respectively;
and the angle $ABC$ is equal to the angle $BCD$;
therefore the base $AC$ is also equal to $DB$,
and the triangle $ABC$ is equal to the triangle $DCB$. [I. 4]

Therefore the diameter $BC$ bisects the parallelogram $ACDB$. Q. E. D.

## Proposition 35

*Parallelograms which are on the same base and in the same parallels are equal to one another.*

Let $ABCD$, $EBCF$ be parallelograms on the same base $BC$ and in the same parallels $AF$, $BC$;
I say that $ABCD$ is equal to the parallelogram $EBCF$.

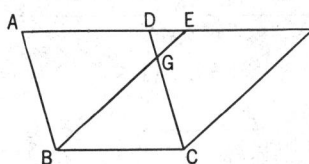

For, since $ABCD$ is a parallelogram,
$AD$ is equal to $BC$. [I. 34]
For the same reason also
$EF$ is equal to $BC$,
so that $AD$ is also equal to $EF$; [C.N. 1]
and $DE$ is common;

therefore the whole *AE* is equal to the whole *DF*. [C.N. 2]
But *AB* is also equal to *DC*; [I. 34]
therefore the two sides *EA*, *AB* are equal to the two sides *FD*, *DC* respectively,
and the angle *FDC* is equal to the angle *EAB*,
the exterior to the interior; [I. 29]
therefore the base *EB* is equal to the base *FC*,
and the triangle *EAB* will be equal to the triangle *FDC*. [I. 4]
Let *DGE* be subtracted from each;
therefore the trapezium *ABGD* which remains is equal to the trapezium *EGCF* which remains. [C.N. 3]
Let the triangle *GBC* be added to each;
therefore the whole parallelogram *ABCD* is equal to the whole parallelogram *EBCF*. [C.N. 2]
Therefore etc.   Q. E. D.

## Proposition 36

*Parallelograms which are on equal bases and in the same parallels are equal to one another.*

Let *ABCD*, *EFGH* be parallelograms which are on equal bases *BC*, *FG* and in the same parallels *AH*, *BG*;
I say that the parallelogram *ABCD* is equal to *EFGH*.
For let *BE*, *CH* be joined.
Then, since *BC* is equal to *FG*, while
    *FG* is equal to *EH*,
  *BC* is also equal to *EH*. [C.N. 1]
But they are also parallel.
And *EB*, *HC* join them;

but straight lines joining equal and parallel straight lines (at the extremities which are) in the same directions (respectively) are equal and parallel. [I. 33]
Therefore *EBCH* is a parallelogram. [I. 34]
And it is equal to *ABCD*;
for it has the same base *BC* with it, and is in the same parallels *BC*, *AH* with it. [I. 35]
For the same reason also *EFGH* is equal to the same *EBCH*; [I. 35]
so that the parallelogram *ABCD* is also equal to *EFGH*. [C.N. 1]
Therefore etc.   Q. E. D.

## Proposition 37

*Triangles which are on the same base and in the same parallels are equal to one another.*

Let *ABC*, *DBC* be triangles on the same base *BC* and in the same parallels *AD*, *BC*;
I say that the triangle *ABC* is equal to the triangle *DBC*.
Let *AD* be produced in both directions to *E*, *F*;
through *B* let *BE* be drawn parallel to *CA*, [I. 31]

and through $C$ let $CF$ be drawn parallel to $BD$. [I. 31]

Then each of the figures $EBCA$, $DBCF$ is a parallelogram; and they are equal,

for they are on the same base $BC$ and in the same parallels $BC$, $EF$. [I. 35]

Moreover the triangle $ABC$ is half of the parallelogram $EBCA$; for the diameter $AB$ bisects it. [I. 34]

And the triangle $DBC$ is half of the parallelogram $DBCF$; for the diameter $DC$ bisects it. [I. 34]

[But the halves of equal things are equal to one another.]

Therefore the triangle $ABC$ is equal to the triangle $DBC$.

Therefore etc.
Q. E. D.

## Proposition 38

*Triangles which are on equal bases and in the same parallels are equal to one another.*

Let $ABC$, $DEF$ be triangles on equal bases $BC$, $EF$ and in the same parallels $BC$, $AD$;

I say that the triangle $ABC$ is equal to the triangle $DEF$.

For let $AD$ be produced in both directions to $G$, $H$;

through $B$ let $BG$ be drawn parallel to $CA$, [I. 31]

and through $F$ let $FH$ be drawn parallel to $DE$.

Then each of the figures $GBCA$, $DEFH$ is a parallelogram;

and $GBCA$ is equal to $DEFH$;

for they are on equal bases $BC$, $EF$ and in the same parallels $BF$, $GH$. [I. 36]

Moreover the triangle $ABC$ is half of the parallelogram $GBCA$; for the diameter $AB$ bisects it. [I. 34]

And the triangle $FED$ is half of the parallelogram $DEFH$; for the diameter $DF$ bisects it. [I. 34]

[But the halves of equal things are equal to one another.]

Therefore the triangle $ABC$ is equal to the triangle $DEF$.

Therefore etc.
Q. E. D.

## Proposition 39

*Equal triangles which are on the same base and on the same side are also in the same parallels.*

Let $ABC$, $DBC$ be equal triangles which are on the same base $BC$ and on the same side of it;

[I say that they are also in the same parallels.]

And [For] let $AD$ be joined; I say that $AD$ is parallel to $BC$.

For, if not, let $AE$ be drawn through the point $A$ parallel to the straight line $BC$, [I. 31]

and let $EC$ be joined.

Therefore the triangle $ABC$ is equal to the triangle $EBC$;

for it is on the same base $BC$ with it and in the same parallels. [I. 37]

But $ABC$ is equal to $DBC$;

therefore $DBC$ is also equal to $EBC$, [C.N. 1]
the greater to the less: which is impossible.
Therefore $AE$ is not parallel to $BC$.
Similarly we can prove that neither is any other straight line except $AD$;
therefore $AD$ is parallel to $BC$.
Therefore etc.

Q. E. D.

## Proposition 40

*Equal triangles which are on equal bases and on the same side are also in the same parallels.*

Let $ABC$, $CDE$ be equal triangles on equal bases $BC$, $CE$ and on the same side.

I say that they are also in the same parallels.
For let $AD$ be joined;
I say that $AD$ is parallel to $BE$.
For, if not, let $AF$ be drawn through $A$ parallel to $BE$ [I. 31], and let $FE$ be joined.

Therefore the triangle $ABC$ is equal to the triangle $FCE$;
for they are on equal bases $BC$, $CE$ and in the same parallels $BE$, $AF$. [I. 38]
But the triangle $ABC$ is equal to the triangle $DCE$;
therefore the triangle $DCE$ is also equal to the triangle $FCE$,
[C.N. 1]
the greater to the less: which is impossible.
Therefore $AF$ is not parallel to $BE$.
Similarly we can prove that neither is any other straight line except $AD$;
therefore $AD$ is parallel to $BE$.
Therefore etc.

Q. E. D.

## Proposition 41

*If a parallelogram have the same base with a triangle and be in the same parallels, the parallelogram is double of the triangle.*

For let the parallelogram $ABCD$ have the same base $BC$ with the triangle $EBC$, and let it be in the same parallels $BC$, $AE$;
I say that the parallelogram $ABCD$ is double of the triangle $BEC$.
For let $AC$ be joined.
Then the triangle $ABC$ is equal to the triangle $EBC$;
for it is on the same base $BC$ with it and in the same parallels $BC$, $AE$. [I. 37]
But the parallelogram $ABCD$ is double of the triangle $ABC$;
for the diameter $AC$ bisects it; [I. 34]
so that the parallelogram $ABCD$ is also double of the triangle $EBC$.
Therefore etc.

Q. E. D.

## Proposition 42

*To construct, in a given rectilineal angle, a parallelogram equal to a given triangle.*

Let $ABC$ be the given triangle, and $D$ the given rectilineal angle;
thus it is required to construct in the rectilineal angle $D$ a parallelogram equal

ELEMENTS I

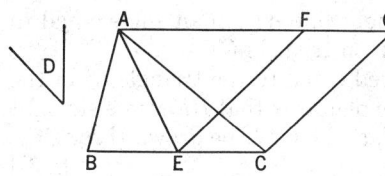

to the triangle $ABC$.

Let $BC$ be bisected at $E$, and let $AE$ be joined;
on the straight line $EC$, and at the point $E$ on it, let the angle $CEF$ be constructed equal to the angle $D$; [I. 23]
through $A$ let $AG$ be drawn parallel to $EC$, and [I. 31]
through $C$ let $CG$ be drawn parallel to $EF$.
Then $FECG$ is a parallelogram.
And, since $BE$ is equal to $EC$,
the triangle $ABE$ is also equal to the triangle $AEC$,
for they are on equal bases $BE$, $EC$ and in the same parallels $BC$, $AG$; [I. 38]
therefore the triangle $ABC$ is double of the triangle $AEC$.
But the parallelogram $FECG$ is also double of the triangle $AEC$, for it has the same base with it and is in the same parallels with it; [I. 41]
therefore the parallelogram $FECG$ is equal to the triangle $ABC$.
And it has the angle $CEF$ equal to the given angle $D$.
Therefore the parallelogram $FECG$ has been constructed equal to the given triangle $ABC$, in the angle $CEF$ which is equal to $D$.     Q. E. F.

## Proposition 43

*In any parallelogram the complements of the parallelograms about the diameter are equal to one another.*

Let $ABCD$ be a parallelogram, and $AC$ its diameter;
and about $AC$ let $EH$, $FG$ be parallelograms, and $BK$, $KD$ the so-called complements;
I say that the complement $BK$ is equal to the complement $KD$.
For, since $ABCD$ is a parallelogram, and $AC$ its diameter,
the triangle $ABC$ is equal to the triangle $ACD$. [I. 34]
Again, since $EH$ is a parallelogram, and $AK$ is its diameter,
the triangle $AEK$ is equal to the triangle $AHK$.
For the same reason
the triangle $KFC$ is also equal to $KGC$.
Now, since the triangle $AEK$ is equal to the triangle $AHK$,
and $KFC$ to $KGC$,
the triangle $AEK$ together with $KGC$ is equal to the triangle $AHK$ together with $KFC$. [C.N. 2]
And the whole triangle $ABC$ is also equal to the whole $ADC$;
therefore the complement $BK$ which remains is equal to the complement $KD$ which remains. [C.N. 3]
Therefore etc.     Q. E. D.

## Proposition 44

*To a given straight line to apply, in a given rectilineal angle, a parallelogram equal to a given triangle.*

Let $AB$ be the given straight line, $C$ the given triangle and $D$ the given rectilineal angle;

thus it is required to apply to the given straight line $AB$, in an angle equal to the angle $D$, a parallelogram equal to the given triangle $C$.

Let the parallelogram $BEFG$ be constructed equal to the triangle $C$, in the angle $EBG$ which is equal to $D$ [I. 42]; let it be placed so that $BE$ is in a straight line with $AB$; let $FG$ be drawn through to $H$, and let $AH$ be drawn through $A$ parallel to either $BG$ or $EF$. [I. 31]

Let $HB$ be joined.

Then, since the straight line $HF$ falls upon the parallels $AH$, $EF$, the angles $AHF$, $HFE$ are equal to two right angles. [I. 29]

Therefore the angles $BHG$, $GFE$ are less than two right angles; and straight lines produced indefinitely from angles less than two right angles meet; [Post. 5]

therefore $HB$, $FE$, when produced, will meet.

Let them be produced and meet at $K$; through the point $K$ let $KL$ be drawn parallel to either $EA$ or $FH$, [I. 31]

and let $HA$, $GB$ be produced to the points $L$, $M$.

Then $HLKF$ is a parallelogram, $HK$ is its diameter, and $AG$, $ME$ are parallelograms, and $LB$, $BF$ the so-called complements, about $HK$;

therefore $LB$ is equal to $BF$. [I. 43]

But $BF$ is equal to the triangle $C$;

therefore $LB$ is also equal to $C$. [C.N. 1]

And, since the angle $GBE$ is equal to the angle $ABM$, [I. 15]

while the angle $GBE$ is equal to $D$,

the angle $ABM$ is also equal to the angle $D$.

Therefore the parallelogram $LB$ equal to the given triangle $C$ has been applied to the given straight line $AB$, in the angle $ABM$ which is equal to $D$.

Q. E. F.

## Proposition 45

*To construct, in a given rectilineal angle, a parallelogram equal to a given rectilineal figure.*

Let $ABCD$ be the given rectilineal figure and $E$ the given rectilineal angle; thus it is required to construct, in the given angle $E$, a parallelogram equal to the rectilineal figure $ABCD$.

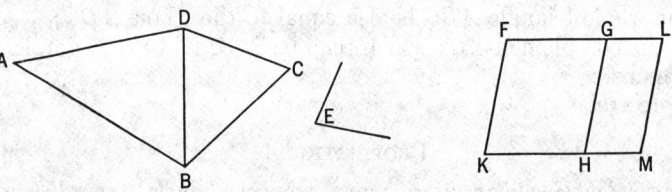

Let $DB$ be joined, and let the parallelogram $FH$ be constructed equal to the triangle $ABD$, in the angle $HKF$ which is equal to $E$; [I. 42]

let the parallelogram $GM$ equal to the triangle $DBC$ be applied to the straight

line $GH$, in the angle $GHM$ which is equal to $E$.  [I. 44]
    Then, since the angle $E$ is equal to each of the angles $HKF$, $GHM$,
            the angle $HKF$ is also equal to the angle $GHM$. [C.N. 1]
    Let the angle $KHG$ be added to each;
    therefore the angles $FKH$, $KHG$ are equal to the angles $KHG$, $GHM$.
    But the angles $FKH$, $KHG$ are equal to two right angles;  [I. 29]
    therefore the angles $KHG$, $GHM$ are also equal to two right angles.
    Thus, with a straight line $GH$, and at the point $H$ on it, two straight lines $KH$, $HM$ not lying on the same side make the adjacent angles equal to two right angles;
            therefore $KH$ is in a straight line with $HM$. [I. 14]
    And, since the straight line $HG$ falls upon the parallels $KM$, $FG$, the alternate angles $MHG$, $HGF$ are equal to one another.  [I. 29]
    Let the angle $HGL$ be added to each;
therefore the angles $MHG$, $HGL$ are equal to the angles $HGF$, $HGL$. [C.N. 2]
    But the angles $MHG$, $HGL$ are equal to two right angles;  [I. 29]
therefore the angles $HGF$, $HGL$ are also equal to two right angles. [C.N. 1]
    Therefore $FG$ is in a straight line with $GL$.  [I. 14]
    And, since $FK$ is equal and parallel to $HG$,  [I. 34]
            and $HG$ to $ML$ also,
    $KF$ is also equal and parallel to $ML$;  [C.N. 1; I. 30]
and the straight lines $KM$, $FL$ join them (at their extremities); therefore $KM$, $FL$ are also equal and parallel.  [I. 33]
    Therefore $KFLM$ is a parallelogram.
    And, since the triangle $ABD$ is equal to the parallelogram $FH$,
            and $DBC$ to $GM$,
the whole rectilineal figure $ABCD$ is equal to the whole parallelogram $KFLM$.
    Therefore the parallelogram $KFLM$ has been constructed equal to the given rectilineal figure $ABCD$, in the angle $FKM$ which is equal to the given angle $E$.
                                            Q. E. F.

## Proposition 46

*On a given straight line to describe a square.*

Let $AB$ be the given straight line; thus it is required to describe a square on the straight line $AB$.

Let $AC$ be drawn at right angles to the straight line $AB$ from the point $A$ on it [I. 11], and let $AD$ be made equal to $AB$;

through the point $D$ let $DE$ be drawn parallel to $AB$, and through the point $B$ let $BE$ be drawn parallel to $AD$. [I. 31]

Therefore $ADEB$ is a parallelogram;
    therefore $AB$ is equal to $DE$, and $AD$ to $BE$. [I. 34]
But $AB$ is equal to $AD$;
therefore the four straight lines $BA$, $AD$, $DE$, $EB$ are equal to one another;
    therefore the parallelogram $ADEB$ is equilateral.
I say next that it is also right-angled.
For, since the straight line $AD$ falls upon the parallels $AB$, $DE$,
    the angles $BAD$, $ADE$ are equal to two right angles. [I. 29]

But the angle $BAD$ is right;
therefore the angle $ADE$ is also right.
And in parallelogrammic areas the opposite sides and angles are equal to one another; [I. 34]
therefore each of the opposite angles $ABE$, $BED$ is also right.
Therefore $ADEB$ is right-angled.
And it was also proved equilateral.
Therefore it is a square; and it is described on the straight line $AB$. Q. E. F.

## Proposition 47

*In right-angled triangles the square on the side subtending the right angle is equal to the squares on the sides containing the right angle.*

Let $ABC$ be a right-angled triangle having the angle $BAC$ right;
I say that the square on $BC$ is equal to the squares on $BA$, $AC$.

For let there be described on $BC$ the square $BDEC$, and on $BA$, $AC$ the squares $GB$, $HC$; [I. 46]
through $A$ let $AL$ be drawn parallel to either $BD$ or $CE$, and let $AD$, $FC$ be joined.

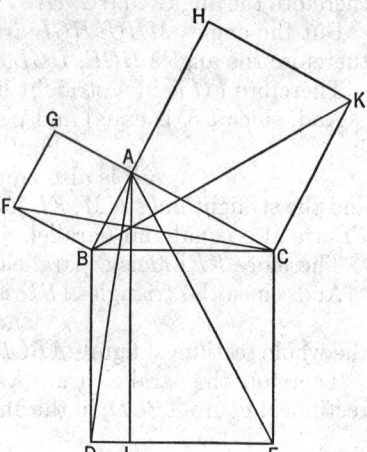

Then, since each of the angles $BAC$, $BAG$ is right, it follows that with a straight line $BA$, and at the point $A$ on it, the two straight lines $AC$, $AG$ not lying on the same side make the adjacent angles equal to two right angles;
therefore $CA$ is in a straight line with $AG$. [I. 14]

For the same reason
$BA$ is also in a straight line with $AH$.
And, since the angle $DBC$ is equal to the angle $FBA$: for each is right:
let the angle $ABC$ be added to each;
therefore the whole angle $DBA$ is equal to the whole angle $FBC$. [C.N. 2]
And, since $DB$ is equal to $BC$, and $FB$ to $BA$,
the two sides $AB$, $BD$ are equal to the two sides $FB$, $BC$ respectively;
and the angle $ABD$ is equal to the angle $FBC$;
therefore the base $AD$ is equal to the base $FC$,
and the triangle $ABD$ is equal to the triangle $FBC$. [I. 4]
Now the parallelogram $BL$ is double of the triangle $ABD$, for they have the same base $BD$ and are in the same parallels $BD$, $AL$. [I. 41]
And the square $GB$ is double of the triangle $FBC$,
for they again have the same base $FB$ and are in the same parallels $FB$, $GC$. [I. 41]
[But the doubles of equals are equal to one another.]
Therefore the parallelogram $BL$ is also equal to the square $GB$.
Similarly, if $AE$, $BK$ be joined,
the parallelogram $CL$ can also be proved equal to the square $HC$;
therefore the whole square $BDEC$ is equal to the two squares $GB$, $HC$. [C.N. 2]
And the square $BDEC$ is described on $BC$,

ELEMENTS I

and the squares *GB*, *HC* on *BA*, *AC*.
Therefore the square on the side *BC* is equal to the squares on the sides *BA*, *AC*.
Therefore etc.
Q. E. D.

## Proposition 48

*If in a triangle the square on one of the sides be equal to the squares on the remaining two sides of the triangle, the angle contained by the remaining two sides of the triangle is right.*

For in the triangle *ABC* let the square on one side *BC* be equal to the squares on the sides *BA*, *AC*;

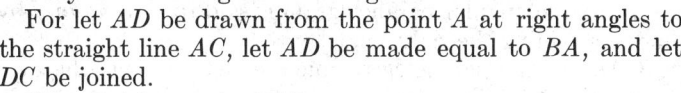

I say that the angle *BAC* is right.

For let *AD* be drawn from the point *A* at right angles to the straight line *AC*, let *AD* be made equal to *BA*, and let *DC* be joined.

Since *DA* is equal to *AB*,
the square on *DA* is also equal to the square on *AB*.
Let the square on *AC* be added to each;
therefore the squares on *DA*, *AC* are equal to the squares on *BA*, *AC*.

But the square on *DC* is equal to the squares on *DA*, *AC*, for the angle *DAC* is right; [I. 47]
and the square on *BC* is equal to the squares on *BA*, *AC*, for this is the hypothesis;
therefore the square on *DC* is equal to the square on *BC*,
so that the side *DC* is also equal to *BC*.
And, since *DA* is equal to *AB*,
and *AC* is common,
the two sides *DA*, *AC* are equal to the two sides *BA*, *AC*;
and the base *DC* is equal to the base *BC*;
therefore the angle *DAC* is equal to the angle *BAC*. [I. 8]
But the angle *DAC* is right;
therefore the angle *BAC* is also right.
Therefore etc.
Q. E. D.

# BOOK TWO

## DEFINITIONS

1. Any rectangular parallelogram is said to be *contained* by the two straight lines containing the right angle.

2. And in any parallelogrammic area let any one whatever of the parallelograms about its diameter with the two complements be called a *gnomon*.

## BOOK II. PROPOSITIONS.

### PROPOSITION 1

*If there be two straight lines, and one of them be cut into any number of segments whatever, the rectangle contained by the two straight lines is equal to the rectangles contained by the uncut straight line and each of the segments.*

Let $A$, $BC$ be two straight lines, and let $BC$ be cut at random at the points $D$, $E$;

I say that the rectangle contained by $A$, $BC$ is equal to the rectangle contained by $A$, $BD$, that contained by $A$, $DE$ and that contained by $A$, $EC$.

For let $BF$ be drawn from $B$ at right angles to $BC$; [I. 11]
    let $BG$ be made equal to $A$, [I. 3]
through $G$ let $GH$ be drawn parallel to $BC$, [I. 31]
and through $D$, $E$, $C$ let $DK$, $EL$, $CH$ be drawn parallel to $BG$.

Then $BH$ is equal to $BK$, $DL$, $EH$.

Now $BH$ is the rectangle $A$, $BC$, for it is contained by $GB$, $BC$, and $BG$ is equal to $A$;

$BK$ is the rectangle $A$, $BD$, for it is contained by $GB$, $BD$, and $BG$ is equal to $A$;
    and $DL$ is the rectangle $A$, $DE$, for $DK$, that is $BG$ is equal to $A$. [I. 34]

Similarly also $EH$ is the rectangle $A$, $EC$.

Therefore the rectangle $A$, $BC$ is equal to the rectangle $A$, $BD$, the rectangle $A$, $DE$ and the rectangle $A$, $EC$.

Therefore etc.

                                                          Q. E. D.

### PROPOSITION 2

*If a straight line be cut at random, the rectangle contained by the whole and both of the segments is equal to the square on the whole.*

For let the straight line $AB$ be cut at random at the point $C$;

I say that the rectangle contained by $AB$, $BC$ together with the rectangle contained by $BA$, $AC$ is equal to the square on $AB$.

For let the square $ADEB$ be described on $AB$ [I. 46], and let $CF$ be drawn through $C$ parallel to either $AD$ or $BE$. [I. 31]

Then $AE$ is equal to $AF$, $CE$.

Now $AE$ is the square on $AB$;

$AF$ is the rectangle contained by $BA$, $AC$, for it is contained by $DA$, $AC$, and $AD$ is equal to $AB$;

and $CE$ is the rectangle $AB$, $BC$, for $BE$ is equal to $AB$.

Therefore the rectangle $BA$, $AC$ together with the rectangle $AB$, $BC$ is equal to the square on $AB$.

Therefore etc.

Q. E. D.

## Proposition 3

*If a straight line be cut at random, the rectangle contained by the whole and one of the segments is equal to the rectangle contained by the segments and the square on the aforesaid segment.*

For let the straight line $AB$ be cut at random at $C$;

I say that the rectangle contained by $AB$, $BC$ is equal to the rectangle contained by $AC$, $CB$ together with the square on $BC$.

For let the square $CDEB$ be described on $CB$; [I. 46]

let $ED$ be drawn through to $F$,

and through $A$ let $AF$ be drawn parallel to either $CD$ or $BE$. [I. 31]

Then $AE$ is equal to $AD$, $CE$.

Now $AE$ is the rectangle contained by $AB$, $BC$, for it is contained by $AB$, $BE$, and $BE$ is equal to $BC$;

$AD$ is the rectangle $AC$, $CB$, for $DC$ is equal to $CB$;

and $DB$ is the square on $CB$.

Therefore the rectangle contained by $AB$, $BC$ is equal to the rectangle contained by $AC$, $CB$ together with the square on $BC$.

Therefore etc.

Q. E. D.

## Proposition 4

*If a straight line be cut at random, the square on the whole is equal to the squares on the segments and twice the rectangle contained by the segments.*

For let the straight line $AB$ be cut at random at $C$;

I say that the square on $AB$ is equal to the squares on $AC$, $CB$ and twice the rectangle contained by $AC$, $CB$.

For let the square $ADEB$ be described on $AB$, [I. 46]

let $BD$ be joined;

through $C$ let $CF$ be drawn parallel to either $AD$ or $EB$,

and through $G$ let $HK$ be drawn parallel to either $AB$ or $DE$. [I. 31]

Then, since $CF$ is parallel to $AD$, and $BD$ has fallen on them,

the exterior angle $CGB$ is equal to the interior and opposite angle $ADB$. [I. 29]

But the angle $ADB$ is equal to the angle $ABD$,

since the side $BA$ is also equal to $AD$; [I. 5]

therefore the angle $CGB$ is also equal to the angle $GBC$,
so that the side $BC$ is also equal to the side $CG$. [I. 6]
But $CB$ is equal to $GK$, and $CG$ to $KB$; [I. 34]
therefore $GK$ is also equal to $KB$;
therefore $CGKB$ is equilateral.

I say next that it is also right-angled.
For, since $CG$ is parallel to $BK$,
the angles $KBC$, $GCB$ are equal to two right angles. [I. 29]
But the angle $KBC$ is right;
therefore the angle $BCG$ is also right,
so that the opposite angles $CGK$, $GKB$ are also right. [I. 34]
Therefore $CGKB$ is right-angled;
and it was also proved equilateral;
therefore it is a square;
and it is described on $CB$.

For the same reason
$HF$ is also a square;
and it is described on $HG$, that is $AC$. [I. 34]
Therefore the squares $HF$, $KC$ are the squares on $AC$, $CB$.

Now, since $AG$ is equal to $GE$,
and $AG$ is the rectangle $AC$, $CB$, for $GC$ is equal to $CB$,
therefore $GE$ is also equal to the rectangle $AC$, $CB$.
Therefore $AG$, $GE$ are equal to twice the rectangle $AC$, $CB$.

But the squares $HF$, $CK$ are also the squares on $AC$, $CB$; therefore the four areas $HF$, $CK$, $AG$, $GE$ are equal to the squares on $AC$, $CB$ and twice the rectangle contained by $AC$, $CB$.

But $HF$, $CK$, $AG$, $GE$ are the whole $ADEB$,
which is the square on $AB$.

Therefore the square on $AB$ is equal to the squares on $AC$, $CB$ and twice the rectangle contained by $AC$, $CB$.

Therefore etc. Q. E. D.

## Proposition 5

*If a straight line be cut into equal and unequal segments, the rectangle contained by the unequal segments of the whole together with the square on the straight line between the points of section is equal to the square on the half.*

For let a straight line $AB$ be cut into equal segments at $C$ and into unequal segments at $D$;

I say that the rectangle contained by $AD$, $DB$ together with the square on $CD$ is equal to the square on $CB$.

For let the square $CEFB$ be described on $CB$, [I. 46]
and let $BE$ be joined;
through $D$ let $DG$ be drawn parallel to either $CE$ or $BF$,
through $H$ again let $KM$ be drawn parallel to either $AB$ or $EF$,
and again through $A$ let $AK$ be drawn parallel to either $CL$ or $BM$. [I. 31]
Then, since the complement $CH$ is equal to the complement $HF$, [I. 43]

let $DM$ be added to each;
therefore the whole $CM$ is equal to the whole $DF$.
But $CM$ is equal to $AL$,
since $AC$ is also equal to $CB$; [I. 36]
therefore $AL$ is also equal to $DF$.
Let $CH$ be added to each;
therefore the whole $AH$ is equal to the gnomon $NOP$.
But $AH$ is the rectangle $AD$, $DB$, for $DH$ is equal to $DB$,
therefore the gnomon $NOP$ is also equal to the rectangle $AD$, $DB$.
Let $LG$, which is equal to the square on $CD$, be added to each;
therefore the gnomon $NOP$ and $LG$ are equal to the rectangle contained by $AD$, $DB$ and the square on $CD$.
But the gnomon $NOP$ and $LG$ are the whole square $CEFB$, which is described on $CB$;
therefore the rectangle contained by $AD$, $DB$ together with the square on $CD$ is equal to the square on $CB$.
Therefore etc. Q. E.D.

## Proposition 6

*If a straight line be bisected and a straight line be added to it in a straight line, the rectangle contained by the whole with the added straight line and the added straight line together with the square on the half is equal to the square on the straight line made up of the half and the added straight line.*

For let a straight line $AB$ be bisected at the point $C$, and let a straight line $BD$ be added to it in a straight line;
I say that the rectangle contained by $AD$, $DB$ together with the square on $CB$ is equal to the square on $CD$.
For let the square $CEFD$ be described on $CD$, [I. 46]
and let $DE$ be joined;
through the point $B$ let $BG$ be drawn parallel to either $EC$ or $DF$,
through the point $H$ let $KM$ be drawn parallel to either $AB$ or $EF$,
and further through $A$ let $AK$ be drawn parallel to either $CL$ or $DM$. [I. 31]
Then, since $AC$ is equal to $CB$,
$AL$ is also equal to $CH$. [I. 36]
But $CH$ is equal to $HF$. [I. 43]
Therefore $AL$ is also equal to $HF$.
Let $CM$ be added to each;
therefore the whole $AM$ is equal to the gnomon $NOP$.
But $AM$ is the rectangle $AD$, $DB$,
for $DM$ is equal to $DB$;
therefore the gnomon $NOP$ is also equal to the rectangle $AD$, $DB$.
Let $LG$, which is equal to the square on $BC$, be added to each;
therefore the rectangle contained by $AD$, $DB$ together with the square on $CB$ is equal to the gnomon $NOP$ and $LG$.
But the gnomon $NOP$ and $LG$ are the whole square $CEFD$, which is described on $CD$;
therefore the rectangle contained by $AD$, $DB$ together with the square on $CB$ is equal to the square on $CD$.
Therefore etc. Q. E. D.

## Proposition 7

*If a straight line be cut at random, the square on the whole and that on one of the segments both together are equal to twice the rectangle contained by the whole and the said segment and the square on the remaining segment.*

For let a straight line $AB$ be cut at random at the point $C$;
I say that the squares on $AB$, $BC$ are equal to twice the rectangle contained by $AB$, $BC$ and the square on $CA$.

For let the square $ADEB$ be described on $AB$, [I. 46]
and let the figure be drawn.

Then, since $AG$ is equal to $GE$ [I. 43], let $CF$ be added to each;
therefore the whole $AF$ is equal to the whole $CE$.
Therefore $AF$, $CE$ are double of $AF$.
But $AF$, $CE$ are the gnomon $KLM$ and the square $CF$;
therefore the gnomon $KLM$ and the square $CF$ are double of $AF$.
But twice the rectangle $AB$, $BC$ is also double of $AF$;
for $BF$ is equal to $BC$;
therefore the gnomon $KLM$ and the square $CF$ are equal to twice the rectangle $AB$, $BC$.
Let $DG$, which is the square on $AC$, be added to each;
therefore the gnomon $KLM$ and the squares $BG$, $GD$ are equal to twice the rectangle contained by $AB$, $BC$ and the square on $AC$.
But the gnomon $KLM$ and the squares $BG$, $GD$ are the whole $ADEB$ and $CF$,
which are squares described on $AB$, $BC$;
therefore the squares on $AB$, $BC$ are equal to twice the rectangle contained by $AB$, $BC$ together with the square on $AC$.
Therefore etc.

Q. E. D.

## Proposition 8

*If a straight line be cut at random, four times the rectangle contained by the whole and one of the segments together with the square on the remaining segment is equal to the square described on the whole and the aforesaid segment as on one straight line.*

For let a straight line $AB$ be cut at random at the point $C$;
I say that four times the rectangle contained by $AB$, $BC$ together with the square on $AC$ is equal to the square described on $AB$, $BC$ as on one straight line.

For let [the straight line] $BD$ be produced in a straight line [with $AB$], and let $BD$ be made equal to $CB$;
let the square $AEFD$ be described on $AD$, and let the figure be drawn double.
Then, since $CB$ is equal to $BD$, while $CB$ is equal to $GK$, and $BD$ to $KN$,
therefore $GK$ is also equal to $KN$.
For the same reason
$QR$ is also equal to $RP$.
And, since $BC$ is equal to $BD$, and $GK$ to $KN$,
therefore $CK$ is also equal to $KD$, and $GR$ to $RN$. [I. 36]
But $CK$ is equal to $RN$, for they are complements of the parallelogram $CP$;
[I. 43]

ELEMENTS II

therefore *KD* is also equal to *GR*;
therefore the four areas *DK*, *CK*, *GR*, *RN* are equal to one another.
Therefore the four are quadruple of *CK*.

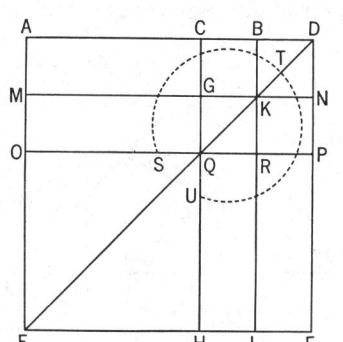

Again, since *CB* is equal to *BD*,
while *BD* is equal to *BK*, that is *CG*,
and *CB* is equal to *GK*, that is *GQ*,
therefore *CG* is also equal to *GQ*.

And, since *CG* is equal to *GQ*, and *QR* to *RP*,
*AG* is also equal to *MQ*, and *QL* to *RF*.  [I. 36]

But *MQ* is equal to *QL*, for they are complements of the parallelogram *ML*;  [I. 43]
therefore *AG* is also equal to *RF*;
therefore the four areas *AG*, *MQ*, *QL*, *RF* are equal to one another.

Therefore the four are quadruple of *AG*.

But the four areas *CK*, *KD*, *GR*, *RN* were proved to be quadruple of *CK*;
therefore the eight areas, which contain the gnomon *STU*, are quadruple of *AK*.

Now, since *AK* is the rectangle *AB*, *BD*, for *BK* is equal to *BD*,
therefore four times the rectangle *AB*, *BD* is quadruple of *AK*.
But the gnomon *STU* was also proved to be quadruple of *AK*;
therefore four times the rectangle *AB*, *BD* is equal to the gnomon *STU*.

Let *OH*, which is equal to the square on *AC*, be added to each;
therefore four times the rectangle *AB*, *BD* together with the square on *AC* is equal to the gnomon *STU* and *OH*.

But the gnomon *STU* and *OH* are the whole square *AEFD*,
which is described on *AD*;
therefore four times the rectangle *AB*, *BD* together with the square on *AC* is equal to the square on *AD*.

But *BD* is equal to *BC*;
therefore four times the rectangle contained by *AB*, *BC* together with the square on *AC* is equal to the square on *AD*, that is to the square described on *AB* and *BC* as on one straight line.

Therefore etc.                                    Q. E. D.

## Proposition 9

*If a straight line be cut into equal and unequal segments, the squares on the unequal segments of the whole are double of the square on the half and of the square on the straight line between the points of section.*

For let a straight line *AB* be cut into equal segments at *C*, and into unequal segments at *D*;
I say that the squares on *AD*, *DB* are double of the squares on *AC*, *CD*.

For let *CE* be drawn from *C* at right angles to *AB*, and let it be made equal to either *AC* or *CB*;
let *EA*, *EB* be joined,
let *DF* be drawn through *D* parallel to *EC*,
and *FG* through *F* parallel to *AB*,
and let *AF* be joined.

Then, since $AC$ is equal to $CE$,
the angle $EAC$ is also equal to the angle $AEC$.
And, since the angle at $C$ is right,
the remaining angles $EAC$, $AEC$ are equal to one right angle. [I. 32]
And they are equal;
therefore each of the angles $CEA$, $CAE$ is half a right angle.

For the same reason
each of the angles $CEB$, $EBC$ is also half a right angle;
therefore the whole angle $AEB$ is right.

And, since the angle $GEF$ is half a right angle,
and the angle $EGF$ is right, for it is equal to the interior and opposite angle $ECB$, [I. 29]
the remaining angle $EFG$ is half a right angle; [I. 32]
therefore the angle $GEF$ is equal to the angle $EFG$,
so that the side $EG$ is also equal to $GF$. [I. 6]

Again, since the angle at $B$ is half a right angle,
and the angle $FDB$ is right, for it is again equal to the interior and opposite angle $ECB$, [I. 29]
the remaining angle $BFD$ is half a right angle; [I. 32]
therefore the angle at $B$ is equal to the angle $DFB$,
so that the side $FD$ is also equal to the side $DB$. [I. 6]

Now, since $AC$ is equal to $CE$,
the square on $AC$ is also equal to the square on $CE$;
therefore the squares on $AC$, $CE$ are double of the square on $AC$.
But the square on $EA$ is equal to the squares on $AC$, $CE$, for the angle $ACE$ is right; [I. 47]
therefore the square on $EA$ is double of the square on $AC$.

Again, since $EG$ is equal to $GF$,
the square on $EG$ is also equal to the square on $GF$;
therefore the squares on $EG$, $GF$ are double of the square on $GF$.
But the square on $EF$ is equal to the squares on $EG$, $GF$;
therefore the square on $EF$ is double of the square on $GF$.
But $GF$ is equal to $CD$; [I. 34]
therefore the square on $EF$ is double of the square on $CD$.
But the square on $EA$ is also double of the square on $AC$;
therefore the squares on $AE$, $EF$ are double of the squares on $AC$, $CD$.

And the square on $AF$ is equal to the squares on $AE$, $EF$, for the angle $AEF$ is right; [I. 47]
therefore the square on $AF$ is double of the squares on $AC$, $CD$.

But the squares on $AD$, $DF$ are equal to the square on $AF$, for the angle at $D$ is right; [I. 47]
therefore the squares on $AD$, $DF$ are double of the squares on $AC$, $CD$.
And $DF$ is equal to $DB$;
therefore the squares on $AD$, $DB$ are double of the squares on $AC$, $CD$.
Therefore etc. Q. E. D.

## Proposition 10

*If a straight line be bisected, and a straight line be added to it in a straight line, the square on the whole with the added straight line and the square on the added straight line both together are double of the square on the half and of the square described on the straight line made up of the half and the added straight line as on one straight line.*

For let a straight line $AB$ be bisected at $C$, and let a straight line $BD$ be added to it in a straight line;

I say that the squares on $AD$, $DB$ are double of the squares on $AC$, $CD$.

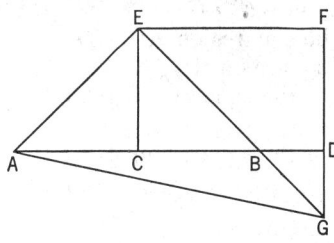

For let $CE$ be drawn from the point $C$ at right angles to $AB$ [I. 11], and let it be made equal to either $AC$ or $CB$ [I. 3];

let $EA$, $EB$ be joined;

through $E$ let $EF$ be drawn parallel to $AD$, and through $D$ let $FD$ be drawn parallel to $CE$. [I. 31]

Then, since a straight line $EF$ falls on the parallel straight lines $EC$, $FD$,

the angles $CEF$, $EFD$ are equal to two right angles; [I. 29]

therefore the angles $FEB$, $EFD$ are less than two right angles.

But straight lines produced from angles less then two right angles meet;

[I. Post. 5]

therefore $EB$, $FD$, if produced in the direction $B$, $D$, will meet.

Let them be produced and meet at $G$,

and let $AG$ be joined.

Then, since $AC$ is equal to $CE$,

the angle $EAC$ is also equal to the angle $AEC$; [I. 5]

and the angle at $C$ is right;

therefore each of the angles $EAC$, $AEC$ is half a right angle. [I. 32]

For the same reason

each of the angles $CEB$, $EBC$ is also half a right angle;

therefore the angle $AEB$ is right.

And, since the angle $EBC$ is half a right angle,

the angle $DBG$ is also half a right angle. [I. 15]

But the angle $BDG$ is also right,

for it is equal to the angle $DCE$, they being alternate; [I. 29]

therefore the remaining angle $DGB$ is half a right angle; [I. 32]

therefore the angle $DGB$ is equal to the angle $DBG$,

so that the side $BD$ is also equal to the side $GD$. [I. 6]

Again, since the angle $EGF$ is half a right angle,

and the angle at $F$ is right, for it is equal to the opposite angle, the angle at $C$,

[I. 34]

the remaining angle $FEG$ is half a right angle; [I. 32]

therefore the angle $EGF$ is equal to the angle $FEG$,

so that the side $GF$ is also equal to the side $EF$. [I. 6]

Now, since the square on $EC$ is equal to the square on $CA$,

the squares on $EC$, $CA$ are double of the square on $CA$.

But the square on $EA$ is equal to the squares on $EC$, $CA$; [I. 47]

therefore the square on $EA$ is double of the square on $AC$. [C.N. 1]
Again, since $FG$ is equal to $EF$,
the square on $FG$ is also equal to the square on $FE$;
therefore the squares on $GF$, $FE$ are double of the square on $EF$.
But the square on $EG$ is equal to the squares on $GF$, $FE$; [I. 47]
therefore the square on $EG$ is double of the square on $EF$.
And $EF$ is equal to $CD$; [I. 34]
therefore the square on $EG$ is double of the square on $CD$.
But the square on $EA$ was also proved double of the square on $AC$;
therefore the squares on $AE$, $EG$ are double of the squares on $AC$, $CD$.
And the square on $AG$ is equal to the squares on $AE$, $EG$; [I. 47]
therefore the square on $AG$ is double of the squares on $AC$, $CD$.
But the squares on $AD$, $DG$ are equal to the square on $AG$; [I. 47]
therefore the squares on $AD$, $DG$ are double of the squares on $AC$, $CD$.
And $DG$ is equal to $DB$;
therefore the squares on $AD$, $DB$ are double of the squares on $AC$, $CD$.
Therefore etc. Q. E. D.

## Proposition 11

*To cut a given straight line so that the rectangle contained by the whole and one of the segments is equal to the square on the remaining segment.*

Let $AB$ be the given straight line;
thus it is required to cut $AB$ so that the rectangle contained by the whole and one of the segments is equal to the square on the remaining segment.

For let the square $ABDC$ be described on $AB$; [I. 46]
let $AC$ be bisected at the point $E$, and let $BE$ be joined;
let $CA$ be drawn through to $F$, and let $EF$ be made equal to $BE$;
let the square $FH$ be described on $AF$, and let $GH$ be drawn through to $K$.

I say that $AB$ has been cut at $H$ so as to make the rectangle contained by $AB$, $BH$ equal to the square on $AH$.

For, since the straight line $AC$ has been bisected at $E$, and $FA$ is added to it,
the rectangle contained by $CF$, $FA$ together with the square on $AE$ is equal to the square on $EF$. [II. 6]
But $EF$ is equal to $EB$;
therefore the rectangle $CF$, $FA$ together with the square on $AE$ is equal to the square on $EB$.

But the squares on $BA$, $AE$ are equal to the square on $EB$, for the angle at $A$ is right: [I. 47]
therefore the rectangle $CF$, $FA$ together with the square on $AE$ is equal to the squares on $BA$, $AE$.

Let the square on $AE$ be subtracted from each;
therefore the rectangle $CF$, $FA$ which remains is equal to the square on $AB$.
Now the rectangle $CF$, $FA$ is $FK$, for $AF$ is equal to $FG$;
and the square on $AB$ is $AD$;
therefore $FK$ is equal to $AD$.
Let $AK$ be subtracted from each;

therefore $FH$ which remains is equal to $HD$.

And $HD$ is the rectangle $AB$, $BH$, for $AB$ is equal to $BD$; and $FH$ is the square on $AH$;

therefore the rectangle contained by $AB$, $BH$ is equal to the square on $HA$.

therefore the given straight line $AB$ has been cut at $H$ so as to make the rectangle contained by $AB$, $BH$ equal to the square on $HA$. Q. E. F.

PROPOSITION 12

*In obtuse-angled triangles the square on the side subtending the obtuse angle is greater than the squares on the sides containing the obtuse angle by twice the rectangle contained by one of the sides about the obtuse angle, namely that on which the perpendicular falls, and the straight line cut off outside by the perpendicular towards the obtuse angle.*

Let $ABC$ be an obtuse-angled triangle having the angle $BAC$ obtuse, and let $BD$ be drawn from the point $B$ perpendicular to $CA$ produced;

I say that the square on $BC$ is greater than the squares on $BA$, $AC$ by twice the rectangle contained by $CA$, $AD$.

For, since the straight line $CD$ has been cut at random at the point $A$,

the square on $DC$ is equal to the squares on $CA$, $AD$ and twice the rectangle contained by $CA$, $AD$. [II. 4]

Let the square on $DB$ be added to each;

therefore the squares on $CD$, $DB$ are equal to the squares on $CA$, $AD$, $DB$ and twice the rectangle $CA$, $AD$.

But the square on $CB$ is equal to the squares on $CD$, $DB$, for the angle at $D$ is right; [I. 47]

and the square on $AB$ is equal to the squares on $AD$, $DB$; [I. 47]

therefore the square on $CB$ is equal to the squares on $CA$, $AB$ and twice the rectangle contained by $CA$, $AD$;

so that the square on $CB$ is greater than the squares on $CA$, $AB$ by twice the rectangle contained by $CA$, $AD$.

Therefore etc. Q. E. D.

PROPOSITION 13

*In acute-angled triangles the square on the side subtending the acute angle is less than the squares on the sides containing the acute angle by twice the rectangle contained by one of the sides about the acute angle, namely that on which the perpendicular falls, and the straight line cut off within by the perpendicular towards the acute angle.*

Let $ABC$ be an acute-angled triangle having the angle at $B$ acute, and let $AD$ be drawn from the point $A$ perpendicular to $BC$;

I say that the square on $AC$ is less than the squares on $CB$, $BA$ by twice the rectangle contained by $CB$, $BD$.

For, since the straight line $CB$ has been cut at random at $D$,

the squares on $CB$, $BD$ are equal to twice the rectangle contained by $CB$, $BD$ and the square on $DC$.

[II. 7]

Let the square on $DA$ be added to each;

therefore the squares on $CB$, $BD$, $DA$ are equal to twice the rectangle contained by $CB$, $BD$ and the squares on $AD$, $DC$.

But the square on $AB$ is equal to the squares on $BD$, $DA$, for the angle at $D$ is right; [I. 47]

and the square on $AC$ is equal to the squares on $AD$, $DC$;

therefore the squares on $CB$, $BA$ are equal to the square on $AC$ and twice the rectangle $CB$, $BD$,

so that the square on $AC$ alone is less than the squares on $CB$, $BA$ by twice the rectangle contained by $CB$, $BD$.

Therefore etc.

Q. E. D.

## Proposition 14

*To construct a square equal to a given rectilineal figure.*

Let $A$ be the given rectilineal figure;

thus it is required to construct a square equal to the rectilineal figure $A$.

For let there be constructed the rectangular parallelogram $BD$ equal to the rectilineal figure $A$.

[I. 45]

Then, if $BE$ is equal to $ED$, that which was enjoined will have been done; for a square $BD$ has been constructed equal to the rectilineal figure $A$.

But, if not, one of the straight lines $BE$, $ED$ is greater.

Let $BE$ be greater, and let it be produced to $F$;

let $EF$ be made equal to $ED$, and let $BF$ be bisected at $G$.

With centre $G$ and distance one of the straight lines $GB$, $GF$ let the semicircle $BHF$ be described; let $DE$ be produced to $H$, and let $GH$ be joined.

Then, since the straight line $BF$ has been cut into equal segments at $G$, and into unequal segments at $E$,

the rectangle contained by $BE$, $EF$ together with the square on $EG$ is equal to the square on $GF$. [II. 5]

But $GF$ is equal to $GH$;

therefore the rectangle $BE$, $EF$ together with the square on $GE$ is equal to the square on $GH$.

But the squares on $HE$, $EG$ are equal to the square on $GH$; [I. 47]

therefore the rectangle $BE$, $EF$ together with the square on $GE$ is equal to the squares on $HE$, $EG$.

Let the square on $GE$ be subtracted from each;

therefore the rectangle contained by $BE$, $EF$ which remains is equal to the square on $EH$.

But the rectangle $BE$, $EF$ is $BD$, for $EF$ is equal to $ED$;

therefore the parallelogram $BD$ is equal to the square on $HE$.

And $BD$ is equal to the rectilineal figure $A$.

Therefore the rectilineal figure $A$ is also equal to the square which can be described on $EH$.

Therefore a square, namely that which can be described on $EH$, has been constructed equal to the given rectilineal figure $A$.

Q. E. F.

# BOOK THREE

## DEFINITIONS

1. *Equal circles* are those the diameters of which are equal, or the radii of which are equal.
2. A straight line is said to *touch a circle* which, meeting the circle and being produced, does not cut the circle.
3. *Circles* are said to *touch one another* which, meeting one another, do not cut one another.
4. In a circle straight lines are said *to be equally distant from the centre* when the perpendiculars drawn to them from the centre are equal.
5. And that straight line is said to be *at a greater distance* on which the greater perpendicular falls.
6. A *segment of a circle* is the figure contained by a straight line and a circumference of a circle.
7. An *angle of a segment* is that contained by a straight line and a circumference of a circle.
8. An *angle in a segment* is the angle which, when a point is taken on the circumference of the segment and straight lines are joined from it to the extremities of the straight line which is the *base of the segment*, is contained by the straight lines so joined.
9. And, when the straight lines containing the angle cut off a circumference, the angle is said to *stand upon* that circumference.
10. A *sector of a circle* is the figure which, when an angle is constructed at the centre of the circle, is contained by the straight lines containing the angle and the circumference cut off by them.
11. *Similar segments of circles* are those which admit equal angles, or in which the angles are equal to one another.

## BOOK III. PROPOSITIONS

### Proposition 1

*To find the centre of a given circle.*
    Let $ABC$ be the given circle;
        thus it is required to find the centre of the circle $ABC$.
    Let a straight line $AB$ be drawn through it at random, and let it be bisected at the point $D$;
from $D$ let $DC$ be drawn at right angles to $AB$ and let it be drawn through to $E$; let $CE$ be bisected at $F$;
    I say that $F$ is the centre of the circle $ABC$.
    For suppose it is not, but, if possible, let $G$ be the centre,

and let *GA*, *GD*, *GB* be joined.

Then, since *AD* is equal to *DB*, and *DG* is common,
the two sides *AD*, *DG* are equal to the two sides *BD*, *DG* respectively;
and the base *GA* is equal to the base *GB*, for they are radii;

therefore the angle *ADG* is equal to the angle *GDB*.
[I. 8]

But, when a straight line set up on a straight line makes the adjacent angles equal to one another, each of the equal angles is right; [I. Def. 10]

therefore the angle *GDB* is right.

But the angle *FDB* is also right;
therefore the angle *FDB* is equal to the angle *GDB*, the greater to the less: which is impossible.

Therefore *G* is not the centre of the circle *ABC*.

Similarly we can prove that neither is any other point except *F*.

Therefore the point *F* is the centre of the circle *ABC*.

PORISM. From this it is manifest that, if in a circle a straight line cut a straight line into two equal parts and at right angles, the centre of the circle is on the cutting straight line.    Q. E. F.

## PROPOSITION 2

*If on the circumference of a circle two points be taken at random, the straight line joining the points will fall within the circle.*

Let *ABC* be a circle, and let two points *A*, *B* be taken at random on its circumference;

I say that the straight line joined from *A* to *B* will fall within the circle.

For suppose it does not, but, if possible, let it fall outside, as *AEB*;
let the centre of the circle *ABC* be taken [III. 1], and let it be *D*; let *DA*, *DB* be joined, and let *DFE* be drawn through.

Then, since *DA* is equal to *DB*,
the angle *DAE* is also equal to the angle *DBE*. [I. 5]
And, since one side *AEB* of the triangle *DAE* is produced,
the angle *DEB* is greater than the angle *DAE*. [I. 16]

But the angle *DAE* is equal to the angle *DBE*;
therefore the angle *DEB* is greater than the angle *DBE*.

And the greater angle is subtended by the greater side; [I. 19]

therefore *DB* is greater than *DE*.

But *DB* is equal to *DF*;
therefore *DF* is greater than *DE*,
the less than the greater: which is impossible.

Therefore the straight line joined from *A* to *B* will not fall outside the circle.

Similarly we can prove that neither will it fall on the circumference itself;
therefore it will fall within.

Therefore etc.    Q. E. D.

ELEMENTS III

### PROPOSITION 3

*If in a circle a straight line through the centre bisect a straight line not through the centre, it also cuts it at right angles; and if it cut it at right angles, it also bisects it.*

Let $ABC$ be a circle, and in it let a straight line $CD$ through the centre bisect a straight line $AB$ not through the centre at the point $F$;

I say that it also cuts it at right angles.

For let the centre of the circle $ABC$ be taken, and let it be $E$; let $EA$, $EB$ be joined.

Then, since $AF$ is equal to $FB$, and $FE$ is common, two sides are equal to two sides; and the base $EA$ is equal to the base $EB$; therefore the angle $AFE$ is equal to the angle $BFE$.    [I. 8]

But, when a straight line set up on a straight line makes the adjacent angles equal to one another, each of the equal angles is right;    [I. Def. 10]

therefore each of the angles $AFE$, $BFE$ is right.

Therefore $CD$, which is through the centre, and bisects $AB$ which is not through the centre, also cuts it at right angles.

Again, let $CD$ cut $AB$ at right angles;

I say that it also bisects it, that is, that $AF$ is equal to $FB$.

For, with the same construction,
since $EA$ is equal to $EB$,
the angle $EAF$ is also equal to the angle $EBF$.    [I. 5]

But the right angle $AFE$ is equal to the right angle $BFE$, therefore $EAF$, $EBF$ are two triangles having two angles equal to two angles and one side equal to one side, namely $EF$, which is common to them, and subtends one of the equal angles;

therefore they will also have the remaining sides equal to the remaining sides;    [I. 26]

therefore $AF$ is equal to $FB$.

Therefore etc.    Q. E. D.

### PROPOSITION 4

*If in a circle two straight lines cut one another which are not through the centre, they do not bisect one another.*

Let $ABCD$ be a circle, and in it let the two straight lines $AC$, $BD$, which are not through the centre, cut one another at $E$;

I say that they do not bisect one another.

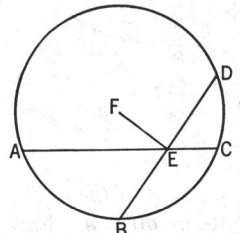

For, if possible, let them bisect one another, so that $AE$ is equal to $EC$, and $BE$ to $ED$;

let the centre of the circle $ABCD$ be taken [III. 1], and let it be $F$; let $FE$ be joined.

Then, since a straight line $FE$ through the centre bisects a straight line $AC$ not through the centre,
it also cuts it at right angles;    [III. 3]

therefore the angle $FEA$ is right.

Again, since a straight line *FE* bisects a straight line *BD*,
it also cuts it at right angles; [III. 3]
therefore the angle *FEB* is right.

But the angle *FEA* was also proved right;
therefore the angle *FEA* is equal to the angle *FEB*, the less to the greater: which is impossible.

Therefore *AC*, *BD* do not bisect one another.

Therefore etc. Q. E. D.

## Proposition 5

*If two circles cut one another, they will not have the same centre.*

For let the circles *ABC*, *CDG* cut one another at the points *B*, *C*;
I say that they will not have the same centre.

For, if possible, let it be *E*; let *EC* be joined, and let *EFG* be drawn through at random.

Then, since the point *E* is the centre of the circle *ABC*,
*EC* is equal to *EF*. [I. Def. 15]

Again, since the point *E* is the centre of the circle *CDG*,
*EC* is equal to *EG*.

But *EC* was proved equal to *EF* also;
therefore *EF* is also equal to *EG*, the less to the greater: which is impossible.

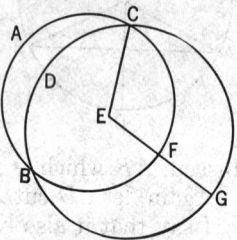

Therefore the point E is not the centre of the circles *ABC*, *CDG*.

Therefore etc. Q. E. D.

## Proposition 6

*If two circles touch one another, they will not have the same centre.*

For let the two circles *ABC*, *CDE* touch one another at the point *C*;
I say that they will not have the same centre.

For, if possible, let it be *F*; let *FC* be joined, and let *FEB* be drawn through at random.

Then, since the point *F* is the centre of the circle *ABC*,
*FC* is equal to *FB*.

Again, since the point *F* is the centre of the circle *CDE*,
*FC* is equal to *FE*.

But *FC* was proved equal to *FB*;
therefore *FE* is also equal to *FB*, the less to the greater: which is impossible.

Therefore *F* is not the centre of the circles *ABC*, *CDE*.

Therefore etc. Q. E. D.

## Proposition 7

*If on the diameter of a circle a point be taken which is not the centre of the circle, and from the point straight lines fall upon the circle, that will be greatest on which the centre is, the remainder of the same diameter will be least, and of the rest the*

ELEMENTS III

*nearer to the straight line through the centre is always greater than the more remote, and only two equal straight lines will fall from the point on the circle, one on each side of the least straight line.*

Let $ABCD$ be a circle, and let $AD$ be a diameter of it; on $AD$ let a point $F$ be taken which is not the centre of the circle, let $E$ be the centre of the circle,

and from $F$ let straight lines $FB$, $FC$, $FG$ fall upon the circle $ABCD$;

I say that $FA$ is greatest, $FD$ is least, and of the rest $FB$ is greater than $FC$, and $FC$ than $FG$.

For let $BE$, $CE$, $GE$ be joined.

Then, since in any triangle two sides are greater than the remaining one,
[I. 20]

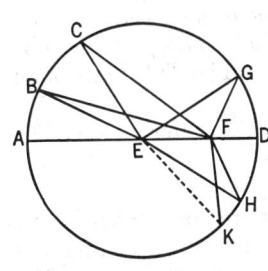

$EB$, $EF$ are greater than $BF$.

But $AE$ is equal to $BE$;

therefore $AF$ is greater than $BF$.

Again, since $BE$ is equal to $CE$, and $FE$ is common,

the two sides $BE$, $EF$ are equal to the two sides $CE$, $EF$.

But the angle $BEF$ is also greater than the angle $CEF$;

therefore the base $BF$ is greater than the base $CF$.
[I. 24]

For the same reason

$CF$ is also greater than $FG$.

Again, since $GF$, $FE$ are greater than $EG$,

and $EG$ is equal to $ED$,

$GF$, $FE$ are greater than $ED$.

Let $EF$ be subtracted from each;

therefore the remainder $GF$ is greater than the remainder $FD$.

Therefore $FA$ is greatest, $FD$ is least, and $FB$ is greater than $FC$, and $FC$ than $FG$.

I say also that from the point $F$ only two equal straight lines will fall on the circle $ABCD$, one on each side of the least $FD$.

For on the straight line $EF$, and at the point $E$ on it, let the angle $FEH$ be constructed equal to the angle $GEF$ [I. 23], and let $FH$ be joined.

Then, since $GE$ is equal to $EH$,

and $EF$ is common,

the two sides $GE$, $EF$ are equal to the two sides $HE$, $EF$;

and the angle $GEF$ is equal to the angle $HEF$;

therefore the base $FG$ is equal to the base $FH$. [I. 4]

I say again that another straight line equal to $FG$ will not fall on the circle from the point $F$.

For, if possible, let $FK$ so fall.

Then, since $FK$ is equal to $FG$, and $FH$ to $FG$,

$FK$ is also equal to $FH$,

the nearer to the straight line through the centre being thus equal to the more remote: which is impossible.

Therefore another straight line equal to $GF$ will not fall from the point $F$ upon the circle;

therefore only one straight line will so fall.
Therefore etc.

Q. E. D.

## Proposition 8

*If a point be taken outside a circle and from the point straight lines be drawn through to the circle, one of which is through the centre and the others are drawn at random, then, of the straight lines which fall on the concave circumference, that through the centre is greatest, while of the rest the nearer to that through the centre is always greater than the more remote, but, of the straight lines falling on the convex circumference, that between the point and the diameter is least, while of the rest the nearer to the least is always less than the more remote, and only two equal straight lines will fall on the circle from the point, one on each side of the least.*

Let $ABC$ be a circle, and let a point $D$ be taken outside $ABC$; let there be drawn through from it straight lines $DA$, $DE$, $DF$, $DC$, and let $DA$ be through the centre;

I say that, of the straight lines falling on the concave circumference $AEFC$, the straight line $DA$ through the centre is greatest,

while $DE$ is greater than $DF$ and $DF$ than $DC$;
but, of the straight lines falling on the convex circumference $HLKG$, the straight line $DG$ between the point and the diameter $AG$ is least; and the nearer to the least $DG$ is always less than the more remote, namely $DK$ than $DL$, and $DL$ than $DH$.

For let the centre of the circle $ABC$ be taken [III. 1], and let it be $M$; let $ME$, $MF$, $MC$, $MK$, $ML$, $MH$ be joined.

Then, since $AM$ is equal to $EM$, let $MD$ be added to each;

therefore $AD$ is equal to $EM$, $MD$.
But $EM$, $MD$ are greater than $ED$;
therefore $AD$ is also greater than $ED$.
Again, since $ME$ is equal to $MF$,
and $MD$ is common,
therefore $EM$, $MD$ are equal to $FM$, $MD$;
and the angle $EMD$ is greater than the angle $FMD$;
therefore the base $ED$ is greater than the base $FD$. [I. 24]

Similarly we can prove that $FD$ is greater than $CD$; therefore $DA$ is greatest, while $DE$ is greater than $DF$, and $DF$ than $DC$.

Next, since $MK$, $KD$ are greater than $MD$, [I. 20]
and $MG$ is equal to $MK$,
therefore the remainder $KD$ is greater than the remainder $GD$,
so that $GD$ is less than $KD$.

And, since on $MD$, one of the sides of the triangle $MLD$, two straight lines $MK$, $KD$ were constructed meeting within the triangle,
therefore $MK$, $KD$ are less than $ML$, $LD$; [I. 21]
and $MK$ is equal to $ML$;
therefore the remainder $DK$ is less than the remainder $DL$.
Similarly we can prove that $DL$ is also less than $DH$;
therefore $DG$ is least, while $DK$ is less than $DL$, and $DL$ than $DH$.

I say also that only two equal straight lines will fall from the point $D$ on the

ELEMENTS III

circle, one on each side of the least $DG$.

On the straight line $MD$, and at the point $M$ on it, let the angle $DMB$ be constructed equal to the angle $KMD$, and let $DB$ be joined.

Then, since $MK$ is equal to $MB$,
and $MD$ is common,
the two sides $KM$, $MD$ are equal to the two sides $BM$, $MD$ respectively;
and the angle $KMD$ is equal to the angle $BMD$;
therefore the base $DK$ is equal to the base $DB$. [I. 4]

I say that no other straight line equal to the straight line $DK$ will fall on the circle from the point $D$.

For, if possible, let a straight line so fall, and let it be $DN$.

Then, since $DK$ is equal to $DN$,
while $DK$ is equal to $DB$,
$DB$ is also equal to $DN$,
that is, the nearer to the least $DG$ equal to the more remote: which was proved impossible.

Therefore no more than two equal straight lines will fall on the circle $ABC$ from the point $D$, one on each side of $DG$ the least.

Therefore etc.
Q. E. D.

## Proposition 9

*If a point be taken within a circle, and more than two equal straight lines fall from the point on the circle, the point taken is the centre of the circle.*

Let $ABC$ be a circle and $D$ a point within it, and from $D$ let more than two equal straight lines, namely $DA$, $DB$, $DC$, fall on the circle $ABC$;

I say that the point $D$ is the centre of the circle $ABC$.

For let $AB$, $BC$ be joined and bisected at the points $E$, $F$, and let $ED$, $FD$ be joined and drawn through to the points $G$, $K$, $H$, $L$.

Then, since $AE$ is equal to $EB$, and $ED$ is common,
the two sides $AE$, $ED$ are equal to the two sides $BE$, $ED$;
and the base $DA$ is equal to the base $DB$;
therefore the angle $AED$ is equal to the angle $BED$. [I. 8]

Therefore each of the angles $AED$, $BED$ is right; [I. Def. 10]
therefore $GK$ cuts $AB$ into two equal parts and at right angles.

And since, if in a circle a straight line cut a straight line into two equal parts and at right angles, the centre of the circle is on the cutting straight line, [III. 1, Por.]
the centre of the circle is on $GK$.

For the same reason
the centre of the circle $ABC$ is also on $HL$.

And the straight lines $GK$, $HL$ have no other point common but the point $D$;
therefore the point $D$ is the centre of the circle $ABC$.

Therefore etc.
Q. E. D.

## Proposition 10

*A circle does not cut a circle at more points than two.*

For, if possible, let the circle $ABC$ cut the circle $DEF$ at more points than two, namely $B, C, F, H$;

let $BH, BG$ be joined and bisected at the points $K, L$,
and from $K, L$ let $KC, LM$ be drawn at right angles to $BH, BG$ and carried through to the points $A, E$.

Then, since in the circle $ABC$ a straight line $AC$ cuts a straight line $BH$ into two equal parts and at right angles,

the centre of the circle $ABC$ is on $AC$.
[III. 1, Por.]

Again, since in the same circle $ABC$ a straight line $NO$ cuts a straight line $BG$ into two equal parts and at right angles,

the centre of the circle $ABC$ is on $NO$.

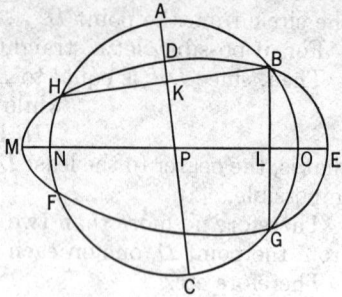

But it was also proved to be on $AC$, and the straight lines $AC, NO$ meet at no point except at $P$;

therefore the point $P$ is the centre of the circle $ABC$.

Similarly we can prove that $P$ is also the centre of the circle $DEF$;
therefore the two circles $ABC, DEF$ which cut one another have the same centre $P$: which is impossible. [III. 5]

Therefore etc.

Q. E. D.

## Proposition 11

*If two circles touch one another internally, and their centres be taken, the straight line joining their centres, if it be also produced, will fall on the point of contact of the circles.*

For let the two circles $ABC, ADE$ touch one another internally at the point $A$, and let the centre $F$ of the circle $ABC$, and the centre $G$ of $ADE$, be taken;

I say that the straight line joined from $G$ to $F$ and produced will fall on $A$.

For suppose it does not, but, if possible, let it fall as $FGH$, and let $AF, AG$ be joined.

Then, since $AG, GF$ are greater than $FA$, that is, than $FH$,

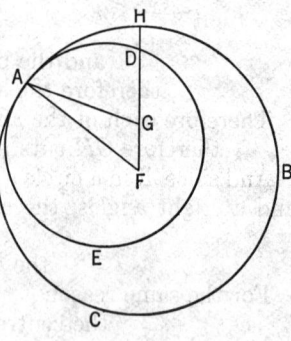

let $FG$ be subtracted from each;
therefore the remainder $AG$ is greater than the remainder $GH$.

But $AG$ is equal to $GD$;

therefore $GD$ is also greater than $GH$,
the less than the greater: which is impossible.

Therefore the straight line joined from $F$ to $G$ will not fall outside;

therefore it will fall at $A$ on the point of contact.

Therefore etc.

Q. E. D

ELEMENTS III

## Proposition 12

*If two circles touch one another externally, the straight line joining their centres will pass through the point of contact.*

For let the two circles $ABC$, $ADE$ touch one another externally at the point $A$, and let the centre $F$ of $ABC$, and the centre $G$ of $ADE$, be taken;

I say that the straight line joined from $F$ to $G$ will pass through the point of contact at $A$.

For suppose it does not, but, if possible, let it pass as $FCDG$, and let $AF$, $AG$ be joined.

Then, since the point $F$ is the centre of the circle $ABC$,

$FA$ is equal to $FC$.

Again, since the point $G$ is the centre of the circle $ADE$,

$GA$ is equal to $GD$.

But $FA$ was also proved equal to $FC$;

therefore $FA$, $AG$ are equal to $FC$, $GD$,

so that the whole $FG$ is greater than $FA$, $AG$;

but it is also less [I. 20]: which is impossible.

Therefore the straight line joined from $F$ to $G$ will not fail to pass through the point of contact at $A$;

therefore it will pass through it.

Therefore etc.

Q. E. D.

## Proposition 13

*A circle does not touch a circle at more points than one, whether it touch it internally or externally.*

For, if possible, let the circle $ABDC$ touch the circle $EBFD$, first internally, at more points than one, namely $D$, $B$.

Let the centre $G$ of the circle $ABDC$, and the centre $H$ of $EBFD$, be taken. Therefore the straight line joined from $G$ to $H$ will fall on $B$, $D$. [III. 11]

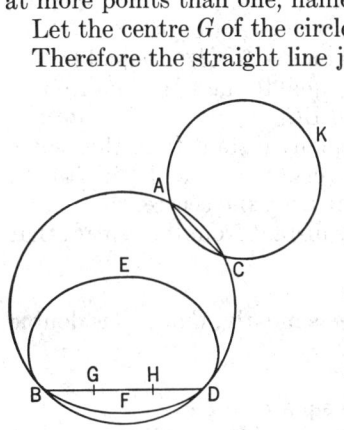

Let it so fall, as $BGHD$.

Then, since the point $G$ is the centre of the circle $ABCD$,

$BG$ is equal to $GD$;

therefore $BG$ is greater than $HD$;

therefore $BH$ is much greater than $HD$.

Again, since the point $H$ is the centre of the circle $EBFD$,

$BH$ is equal to $HD$;

but it was also proved much greater than it: which is impossible.

Therefore a circle does not touch a circle internally at more points than one.

I say further that neither does it so touch it externally.

For, if possible, let the circle $ACK$ touch the circle $ABDC$ at more points than one, namely $A$, $C$, and let $AC$ be joined.

Then, since on the circumference of each of the circles $ABDC$, $ACK$ two points $A$, $C$ have been taken at random, the straight line joining the points will fall within each circle; [III. 2]
but it fell within the circle $ABDC$ and outside $ACK$ [III. Def. 3]: which is absurd.

Therefore a circle does not touch a circle externally at more points than one. And it was proved that neither does it so touch it internally.
Therefore etc.

Q. E. D.

## PROPOSITION 14

*In a circle equal straight lines are equally distant from the centre, and those which are equally distant from the centre are equal to one another.*

Let $ABDC$ be a circle, and let $AB$, $CD$ be equal straight lines in it;
I say that $AB$, $CD$ are equally distant from the centre.

For let the centre of the circle $ABDC$ be taken [III. 1], and let it be $E$; from $E$ let $EF$, $EG$ be drawn perpendicular to $AB$, $CD$, and let $AE$, $EC$ be joined.

Then, since a straight line $EF$ through the centre cuts a straight line $AB$ not through the centre at right angles, it also bisects it. [III. 3]
Therefore $AF$ is equal to $FB$;
therefore $AB$ is double of $AF$.

For the same reason
$CD$ is also double of $CG$;
and $AB$ is equal to $CD$;
therefore $AF$ is also equal to $CG$.

And, since $AE$ is equal to $EC$,
the square on $AE$ is also equal to the square on $EC$.

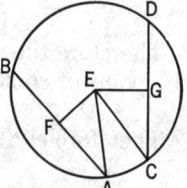

But the squares on $AF$, $EF$ are equal to the square on $AE$, for the angle at $F$ is right;
and the squares on $EG$, $GC$ are equal to the square on $EC$, for the angle at $G$ is right; [I. 47]
therefore the squares on $AF$, $FE$ are equal to the squares on $CG$, $GE$,
of which the square on $AF$ is equal to the square on $CG$, for $AF$ is equal to $CG$;
therefore the square on $FE$ which remains is equal to the square on $EG$,
therefore $EF$ is equal to $EG$.

But in a circle straight lines are said to be equally distant from the centre when the perpendiculars drawn to them from the centre are equal [III. Def. 4];
therefore $AB$, $CD$ are equally distant from the centre.

Next, let the straight lines $AB$, $CD$ be equally distant from the centre; that is, let $EF$ be equal to $EG$.

I say that $AB$ is also equal to $CD$.

For, with the same construction, we can prove, similarly, that $AB$ is double of $AF$, and $CD$ of $CG$.

And, since $AE$ is equal to $CE$,
the square on $AE$ is equal to the square on $CE$.

But the squares on $EF$, $FA$ are equal to the square on $AE$, and the squares on $EG$, $GC$ equal to the square on $CE$. [I. 47]

Therefore the squares on $EF$, $FA$ are equal to the squares on $EG$, $GC$,
of which the square on $EF$ is equal to the square on $EG$, for $EF$ is equal to $EG$;

ELEMENTS III

therefore the square on $AF$ which remains is equal to the square on $CG$;
therefore $AF$ is equal to $CG$.
And $AB$ is double of $AF$, and $CD$ double of $CG$;
therefore $AB$ is equal to $CD$.
Therefore etc.                                                              Q. E. D.

## Proposition 15

*Of straight lines in a circle the diameter is greatest, and of the rest the nearer to the centre is always greater than the more remote.*

Let $ABCD$ be a circle, let $AD$ be its diameter and $E$ the centre; and let $BC$ be nearer to the diameter $AD$, and $FG$ more remote;

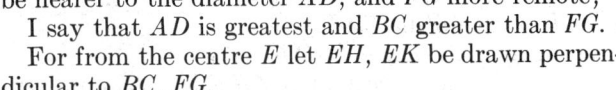

I say that $AD$ is greatest and $BC$ greater than $FG$.

For from the centre $E$ let $EH$, $EK$ be drawn perpendicular to $BC$, $FG$.

Then, since $BC$ is nearer to the centre and $FG$ more remote, $EK$ is greater than $EH$.          [III. Def. 5]

Let $EL$ be made equal to $EH$, through $L$ let $LM$ be drawn at right angles to $EK$ and carried through to $N$, and let $ME$, $EN$, $FE$, $EG$ be joined.

Then, since $EH$ is equal to $EL$,
$BC$ is also equal to $MN$.                                 [III. 14]
Again, since $AE$ is equal to $EM$, and $ED$ to $EN$,
$AD$ is equal to $ME$, $EN$.
But $ME$, $EN$ are greater than $MN$,                         [I. 20]
and $MN$ is equal to $BC$;
therefore $AD$ is greater than $BC$.
And, since the two sides $ME$, $EN$ are equal to the two sides $FE$, $EG$,
and the angle $MEN$ greater than the angle $FEG$,
therefore the base $MN$ is greater than the base $FG$.           [I. 24]
But $MN$ was proved equal to $BC$.
Therefore the diameter $AD$ is greatest and $BC$ greater than $FG$.
Therefore etc.                                                              Q. E. D.

## Proposition 16

*The straight line drawn at right angles to the diameter of a circle from its extremity will fall outside the circle, and into the space between the straight line and the circumference another straight line cannot be interposed; further the angle of the semicircle is greater, and the remaining angle less, than any acute rectilineal angle.*

Let $ABC$ be a circle about $D$ as centre and $AB$ as diameter;

I say that the straight line drawn from $A$ at right angles to $AB$ from its extremity will fall outside the circle.

For suppose it does not, but, if possible, let it fall within as $CA$, and let $DC$ be joined.

Since $DA$ is equal to $DC$,
the angle $DAC$ is also equal to the angle $ACD$.          [I. 5]
But the angle $DAC$ is right;
therefore the angle $ACD$ is also right:
thus, in the triangle $ACD$, the two angles $DAC$, $ACD$ are equal to two right angles: which is impossible.          [I. 17]

Therefore the straight line drawn from the point $A$ at right angles to $BA$ will not fall within the circle.

Similarly we can prove that neither will it fall on the circumference;

therefore it will fall outside.

Let it fall as $AE$;

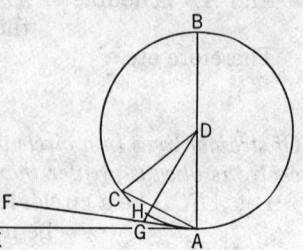

I say next that into the space between the straight line $AE$ and the circumference $CHA$ another straight line cannot be interposed.

For, if possible, let another straight line be so interposed, as $FA$, and let $DG$ be drawn from the point $D$ perpendicular to $FA$.

Then, since the angle $AGD$ is right,
and the angle $DAG$ is less than a right angle,
$AD$ is greater than $DG$.  [I. 19]

But $DA$ is equal to $DH$;

therefore $DH$ is greater than $DG$, the less than the greater: which is impossible.

Therefore another straight line cannot be interposed into the space between the straight line and the circumference.

I say further that the angle of the semicircle contained by the straight line $BA$ and the circumference $CHA$ is greater than any acute rectilineal angle, and the remaining angle contained by the circumference $CHA$ and the straight line $AE$ is less than any acute rectilineal angle.

For, if there is any rectilineal angle greater than the angle contained by the straight line $BA$ and the circumference $CHA$, and any rectilineal angle less than the angle contained by the circumference $CHA$ and the straight line $AE$, then into the space between the circumference and the straight line $AE$ a straight line will be interposed such as will make an angle contained by straight lines which is greater than the angle contained by the straight line $BA$ and the circumference $CHA$, and another angle contained by straight lines which is less than the angle contained by the circumference $CHA$ and the straight line $AE$.

But such a straight line cannot be interposed;

therefore there will not be any acute angle contained by straight lines which is greater than the angle contained by the straight line $BA$ and the circumference $CHA$, nor yet any acute angle contained by straight lines which is less than the angle contained by the circumference $CHA$ and the straight line $AE$.—

PORISM. From this it is manifest that the straight line drawn at right angles to the diameter of a circle from its extremity touches the circle.    Q. E. D.

## PROPOSITION 17

*From a given point to draw a straight line touching a given circle.*

Let $A$ be the given point, and $BCD$ the given circle;

thus it is required to draw from the point $A$ a straight line touching the circle $BCD$.

For let the centre $E$ of the circle be taken;    [III. 1]

let $AE$ be joined, and with centre $E$ and distance $EA$ let the circle $AFG$ be described;

from $D$ let $DF$ be drawn at right angles to $EA$,
and let $EF$, $AB$ be joined;

I say that $AB$ has been drawn from the point $A$ touching the circle $BCD$.
For, since $E$ is the centre of the circles $BCD$, $AFG$,
    $EA$ is equal to $EF$, and $ED$ to $EB$;
therefore the two sides $AE$, $EB$ are equal to the two sides $FE$, $ED$;

and they contain a common angle, the angle at $E$;
    therefore the base $DF$ is equal to the base $AB$,
    and the triangle $DEF$ is equal to the triangle $BEA$,
    and the remaining angles to the remaining angles;
                                            [I. 4]
therefore the angle $EDF$ is equal to the angle $EBA$.
But the angle $EDF$ is right;
    therefore the angle $EBA$ is also right.
Now $EB$ is a radius;
and the straight line drawn at right angles to the diameter of a circle, from its extremity, touches the circle;                    [III. 16, Por.]
    therefore $AB$ touches the circle $BCD$.
Therefore from the given point $A$ the straight line $AB$ has been drawn touching the circle $BCD$.
                                            Q. E. F.

## Proposition 18

*If a straight line touch a circle, and a straight line be joined from the centre to the point of contact, the straight line so joined will be perpendicular to the tangent.*

For let a straight line $DE$ touch the circle $ABC$ at the point $C$, let the centre $F$ of the circle $ABC$ be taken, and let $FC$ be joined from $F$ to $C$;

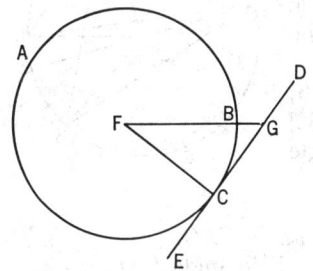

I say that $FC$ is perpendicular to $DE$.
For, if not, let $FG$ be drawn from $F$ perpendicular to $DE$.
Then, since the angle $FGC$ is right,
    the angle $FCG$ is acute;            [I. 17]
and the greater angle is subtended by the greater side;                                        [I. 19]
    therefore $FC$ is greater than $FG$.
But $FC$ is equal to $FB$;
    therefore $FB$ is also greater than $FG$,
the less than the greater: which is impossible.
Therefore $FG$ is not perpendicular to $DE$.
Similarly we can prove that neither is any other straight line except $FC$;
    therefore $FC$ is perpendicular to $DE$.
Therefore etc.                            Q. E. D.

## Proposition 19

*If a straight line touch a circle, and from the point of contact a straight line be drawn at right angles to the tangent, the centre of the circle will be on the straight line so drawn.*

For let a straight line $DE$ touch the circle $ABC$ at the point $C$, and from $C$ let $CA$ be drawn at right angles to $DE$;
I say that the centre of the circle is on $AC$.
For suppose it is not, but, if possible, let $F$ be the centre,

and let $CF$ be joined.

Since a straight line $DE$ touches the circle $ABC$,
and $FC$ has been joined from the centre to the point of contact,

$FC$ is perpendicular to $DE$;      [III. 18]

therefore the angle $FCE$ is right.

But the angle $ACE$ is also right;
therefore the angle $FCE$ is equal to the angle $ACE$,

the less to the greater: which is impossible.

Therefore $F$ is not the centre of the circle $ABC$.

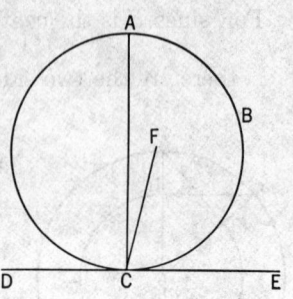

Similarly we can prove that neither is any other point except a point on $AC$.

Therefore etc.      Q. E. D.

## Proposition 20

*In a circle the angle at the centre is double of the angle at the circumference, when the angles have the same circumference as base.*

Let $ABC$ be a circle, let the angle $BEC$ be an angle at its centre, and the angle $BAC$ an angle at the circumference, and let them have the same circumference $BC$ as base;

I say that the angle $BEC$ is double of the angle $BAC$.

For let $AE$ be joined and drawn through to $F$.

Then, since $EA$ is equal to $EB$,
the angle $EAB$ is also equal to the angle $EBA$; [I. 5]
therefore the angles $EAB$, $EBA$ are double of the angle $EAB$.

But the angle $BEF$ is equal to the angles $EAB$, $EBA$;      [I. 32]
therefore the angle $BEF$ is also double of the angle $EAB$.

For the same reason
the angle $FEC$ is also double of the angle $EAC$.

Therefore the whole angle $BEC$ is double of the whole angle $BAC$.

Again let another straight line be inflected, and let there be another angle $BDC$; let $DE$ be joined and produced to $G$.

Similarly then we can prove that the angle $GEC$ is double of the angle $EDC$,
of which the angle $GEB$ is double of the angle $EDB$;
therefore the angle $BEC$ which remains is double of the angle $BDC$.

Therefore etc.      Q. E. D.

## Proposition 21

*In a circle the angles in the same segment are equal to one another.*

Let $ABCD$ be a circle, and let the angles $BAD$, $BED$ be angles in the same segment $BAED$;

I say that the angles $BAD$, $BED$ are equal to one another.

For let the centre of the circle $ABCD$ be taken, and let it be $F$; let $BF$, $FD$ be joined.

ELEMENTS III

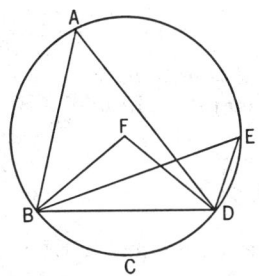

Now, since the angle BFD is at the centre,
and the angle BAD at the circumference,
and they have the same circumference BCD as base,
therefore the angle BFD is double of the angle
BAD. [III. 20]

For the same reason
the angle BFD is also double of the angle BED;
therefore the angle BAD is equal to the angle BED.
Therefore etc.                         Q. E. D.

## Proposition 22

*The opposite angles of quadrilaterals in circles are equal to two right angles.*

Let ABCD be a circle, and let ABCD be a quadrilateral in it;
I say that the opposite angles are equal to two right angles.

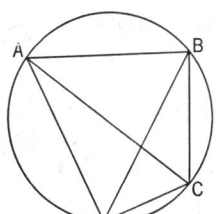

Let AC, BD be joined.
Then, since in any triangle the three angles are equal
to two right angles, [I. 32]
the three angles CAB, ABC, BCA of the triangle ABC
are equal to two right angles.
But the angle CAB is equal to the angle BDC, for they
are in the same segment BADC; [III. 21]
and the angle ACB is equal to the angle ADB, for they
are in the same segment ADCB;
therefore the whole angle ADC is equal to the angles BAC, ACB.
Let the angle ABC be added to each;
therefore the angles ABC, BAC, ACB are equal to the angles ABC, ADC.
But the angles ABC, BAC, ACB are equal to two right angles;
therefore the angles ABC, ADC are also equal to two right angles.
Similarly we can prove that the angles BAD, DCB are also equal to two
right angles.
Therefore etc.                         Q. E. D.

## Proposition 23

*On the same straight line there cannot be constructed two similar and unequal segments of circles on the same side.*

For, if possible, on the same straight line AB let two similar and unequal
segments of circles ACB, ADB be constructed on the
same side;

let ACD be drawn through, and let CB, DB be joined.
Then, since the segment ACB is similar to the segment ADB,
and similar segments of circles are those which admit equal angles [III. Def. 11],
the angle ACB is equal to the angle ADB, the exterior to the interior: which is
impossible. [I. 16]
Therefore etc.                         Q. E. D.

56                               EUCLID

## Proposition 24

*Similar segments of circles on equal straight lines are equal to one another.*

For let $AEB$, $CFD$ be similar segments of circles on equal straight lines $AB$, $CD$;

I say that the segment $AEB$ is equal to the segment $CFD$.

For, if the segment $AEB$ be applied to $CFD$, and if the point $A$ be placed on $C$ and the straight line $AB$ on $CD$,

the point $B$ will also coincide with the point $D$, because $AB$ is equal to $CD$;

and, $AB$ coinciding with $CD$,
the segment $AEB$ will also coincide with $CFD$.

For, if the straight line $AB$ coincide with $CD$ but the segment $AEB$ do not coincide with $CFD$,

it will either fall within it, or outside it;

or it will fall awry, as $CGD$, and a circle cuts a circle at more points than two: which is impossible.                                                        [III. 10]

Therefore, if the straight line $AB$ be applied to $CD$, the segment $AEB$ will not fail to coincide with $CFD$ also;

therefore it will coincide with it and will be equal to it.

Therefore etc.                                                                  Q. E. D.

## Proposition 25

*Given a segment of a circle, to describe the complete circle of which it is a segment.*

Let $ABC$ be the given segment of a circle;

thus it is required to describe the complete circle belonging to the segment $ABC$, that is, of which it is a segment.

For let $AC$ be bisected at $D$, let $DB$ be drawn from the point $D$ at right angles to $AC$, and let $AB$ be joined;

the angle $ABD$ is then greater than, equal to, or less than the angle $BAD$.

First let it be greater;

and on the straight line $BA$, and at the point $A$ on it, let the angle $BAE$ be constructed equal to the angle $ABD$; let $DB$ be drawn through to $E$, and let $EC$ be joined.

Then, since the angle $ABE$ is equal to the angle $BAE$,

the straight line $EB$ is also equal to $EA$.     [I. 6]

And, since $AD$ is equal to $DC$, and $DE$ is common,

the two sides $AD$, $DE$ are equal to the two sides $CD$, $DE$ respectively;

and the angle $ADE$ is equal to the angle $CDE$, for each is right;

therefore the base $AE$ is equal to the base $CE$.

But $AE$ was proved equal to $BE$;

therefore $BE$ is also equal to $CE$;

therefore the three straight lines $AE$, $EB$, $EC$ are equal to one another.

Therefore the circle drawn with centre $E$ and distance one of the straight lines $AE$, $EB$, $EC$ will also pass through the remaining points and will have been completed. [III. 9]

Therefore, given a segment of a circle, the complete circle has been described.

And it is manifest that the segment $ABC$ is less than a semicircle, because the centre $E$ happens to be outside it.

Similarly, even if the angle $ABD$ be equal to the angle $BAD$,

$AD$ being equal to each of the two $BD$, $DC$,

the three straight lines $DA$, $DB$, $DC$ will be equal to one another,

$D$ will be the centre of the completed circle,

and $ABC$ will clearly be a semicircle.

But, if the angle $ABD$ be less than the angle $BAD$, and if we construct, on the straight line $BA$ and at the point $A$ on it, an angle equal to the angle $ABD$, the centre will fall on $DB$ within the segment $ABC$, and the segment $ABC$ will clearly be greater than a semicircle.

Therefore, given a segment of a circle, the complete circle has been described. Q. E. F.

PROPOSITION 26

*In equal circles equal angles stand on equal circumferences, whether they stand at the centres or at the circumferences.*

Let $ABC$, $DEF$ be equal circles, and in them let there be equal angles, namely at the centres the angles $BGC$, $EHF$, and at the circumferences the angles $BAC$, $EDF$;

I say that the circumference $BKC$ is equal to the circumference $ELF$.

For let $BC$, $EF$ be joined.

Now, since the circles $ABC$, $DEF$ are equal,

the radii are equal.

Thus the two straight lines $BG$, $GC$ are equal to the two straight lines $EH$, $HF$;

and the angle at $G$ is equal to the angle at $H$;

therefore the base $BC$ is equal to the base $EF$. [I. 4]

And, since the angle at $A$ is equal to the angle at $D$,

the segment $BAC$ is similar to the segment $EDF$; [III. Def. 11]

and they are upon equal straight lines.

But similar segments of circles on equal straight lines are equal to one another; [III. 24]

therefore the segment $BAC$ is equal to $EDF$.

But the whole circle $ABC$ is also equal to the whole circle $DEF$;

therefore the circumference $BKC$ which remains is equal to the circumference $ELF$.

Therefore etc. Q. E. D.

## Proposition 27

*In equal circles angles standing on equal circumferences are equal to one another, whether they stand at the centres or at the circumferences.*

For in equal circles $ABC$, $DEF$, on equal circumferences $BC$, $EF$, let the angles $BGC$, $EHF$ stand at the centres $G$, $H$, and the angles $BAC$, $EDF$ at the circumferences;

I say that the angle $BGC$ is equal to the angle $EHF$,
and the angle $BAC$ is equal to the angle $EDF$.

For, if the angle $BGC$ is unequal to the angle $EHF$,
one of them is greater.
Let the angle $BGC$ be greater: and on the straight line $BG$, and at the point $G$ on it, let the angle $BGK$ be constructed equal to the angle $EHF$ [I. 23].

Now equal angles stand on equal circumferences, when they are at the centres; [III. 26]
therefore the circumference $BK$ is equal to the circumference $EF$.
But $EF$ is equal to $BC$;
therefore $BK$ is also equal to $BC$, the less to the greater: which is impossible.
Therefore the angle $BGC$ is not unequal to the angle $EHF$;
therefore it is equal to it.
And the angle at $A$ is half of the angle $BGC$,
and the angle at $D$ half of the angle $EHF$; [III. 20]
therefore the angle at $A$ is also equal to the angle at $D$.
Therefore etc.
Q. E. D.

## Proposition 28

*In equal circles equal straight lines cut off equal circumferences, the greater equal to the greater and the less to the less.*

Let $ABC$, $DEF$ be equal circles, and in the circles let $AB$, $DE$ be equal straight lines cutting off $ACB$, $DFE$ as greater circumferences and $AGB$, $DHE$ as lesser;

I say that the greater circumference $ACB$ is equal to the greater circumference $DFE$, and the less circumference $AGB$ to $DHE$.

For let the centres $K$, $L$ of the circles be taken, and let $AK$, $KB$, $DL$, $LE$ be joined.

Now, since the circles are equal,
the radii are also equal;
therefore the two sides $AK$, $KB$ are equal to the two sides $DL$, $LE$;
and the base $AB$ is equal to the base $DE$;
therefore the angle $AKB$ is equal to the angle $DLE$. [I. 8]
But equal angles stand on equal circumferences, when they are at the centres; [III. 26]
therefore the circumference $AGB$ is equal to $DHE$.
And the whole circle $ABC$ is also equal to the whole circle $DEF$;

therefore the circumference $ACB$ which remains is also equal to the circumference $DFE$ which remains.

Therefore etc.
Q. E. D.

### Proposition 29

*In equal circles equal circumferences are subtended by equal straight lines.*

Let $ABC$, $DEF$ be equal circles, and in them let equal circumferences $BGC$, $EHF$ be cut off; and let the straight lines $BC$, $EF$ be joined;

I say that $BC$ is equal to $EF$.

 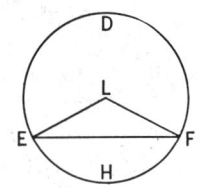

For let the centres of the circles be taken, and let them be $K$, $L$; let $BK$, $KC$, $EL$, $LF$ be joined.

Now, since the circumference $BGC$ is equal to the circumference $EHF$,

the angle $BKC$ is also equal to the angle $ELF$. [III. 27]

And, since the circles $ABC$, $DEF$ are equal,
the radii are also equal;

therefore the two sides $BK$, $KC$ are equal to the two sides $EL$, $LF$; and they contain equal angles;

therefore the base $BC$ is equal to the base $EF$. [I. 4]

Therefore etc.
Q. E. D.

### Proposition 30

*To bisect a given circumference.*

Let $ADB$ be the given circumference;

thus it is required to bisect the circumference $ADB$.

Let $AB$ be joined and bisected at $C$; from the point $C$ let $CD$ be drawn at right angles to the straight line $AB$, and let $AD$, $DB$ be joined.

Then, since $AC$ is equal to $CB$, and $CD$ is common,

the two sides $AC$, $CD$ are equal to the two sides $BC$, $CD$;

and the angle $ACD$ is equal to the angle $BCD$, for each is right;

therefore the base $AD$ is equal to the base $DB$. [I. 4]

But equal straight lines cut off equal circumferences, the greater equal to the greater, and the less to the less; [III. 28]

and each of the circumferences $AD$, $DB$ is less than a semicircle;

therefore the circumference $AD$ is equal to the circumference $DB$.

Therefore the given circumference has been bisected at the point $D$.
Q. E. F.

### Proposition 31

*In a circle the angle in the semicircle is right, that in a greater segment less than a right angle, and that in a less segment greater than a right angle; and further the angle of the greater segment is greater than a right angle, and the angle of the less segment less than a right angle.*

Let $ABCD$ be a circle, let $BC$ be its diameter, and $E$ its centre, and let $BA$, $AC$, $AD$, $DC$ be joined;

I say that the angle BAC in the semicircle BAC is right,
the angle ABC in the segment ABC greater than the semicircle is less than a right angle,
and the angle ADC in the segment ADC less than the semicircle is greater than a right angle.

Let AE be joined, and let BA be carried through to F.

Then, since BE is equal to EA,
the angle ABE is also equal to the angle BAE.
[I. 5]

Again, since CE is equal to EA,
the angle ACE is also equal to the angle CAE.
[I. 5]

Therefore the whole angle BAC is equal to the two angles ABC, ACB.

But the angle FAC exterior to the triangle ABC is also equal to the two angles ABC, ACB; [I. 32]

therefore the angle BAC is also equal to the angle FAC;
therefore each is right; [I. Def. 10]
therefore the angle BAC in the semicircle BAC is right.

Next, since in the triangle ABC the two angles ABC, BAC are less than two right angles, [I. 17]
and the angle BAC is a right angle,
the angle ABC is less than a right angle;
and it is the angle in the segment ABC greater than the semicircle.

Next, since ABCD is a quadrilateral in a circle,
and the opposite angles of quadrilaterals in circles are equal to two right angles, [III. 22]
while the angle ABC is less than a right angle,
therefore the angle ADC which remains is greater than a right angle;
and it is the angle in the segment ADC less than the semicircle.

I say further that the angle of the greater segment, namely that contained by the circumference ABC and the straight line AC, is greater than a right angle;
and the angle of the less segment, namely that contained by the circumference ADC and the straight line AC, is less than a right angle.

This is at once manifest.

For, since the angle contained by the straight lines BA, AC is right,
the angle contained by the circumference ABC and the straight line AC is greater than a right angle.

Again, since the angle contained by the straight lines AC, AF is right,
the angle contained by the straight line CA and the circumference ADC is less than a right angle.

Therefore etc. Q. E. D.

## Proposition 32

*If a straight line touch a circle, and from the point of contact there be drawn across, in the circle, a straight line cutting the circle, the angles which it makes with the tangent will be equal to the angles in the alternate segments of the circle.*

For let a straight line EF touch the circle ABCD at the point B, and from the point $B$ let there be drawn across, in the circle $ABCD$, a straight line $BD$ cutting it;

I say that the angles which $BD$ makes with the tangent $EF$ will be equal to the angles in the alternate segments of the circle, that is, that the angle $FBD$ is equal to the angle constructed in the segment $BAD$, and the angle $EBD$ is equal to the angle constructed in the segment $DCB$.

For let $BA$ be drawn from $B$ at right angles to $EF$,

let a point $C$ be taken at random on the circumference $BD$,

and let $AD$, $DC$, $CB$ be joined.

Then, since a straight line $EF$ touches the circle $ABCD$ at $B$,

and $BA$ has been drawn from the point of contact at right angles to the tangent, the centre of the circle $ABCD$ is on $BA$. [III. 19]

Therefore $BA$ is a diameter of the circle $ABCD$;

therefore the angle $ADB$, being an angle in a semicircle, is right. [III. 31]

Therefore the remaining angles $BAD$, $ABD$ are equal to one right angle. [I. 32]

But the angle $ABF$ is also right;

therefore the angle $ABF$ is equal to the angles $BAD$, $ABD$.

Let the angle $ABD$ be subtracted from each;

therefore the angle $DBF$ which remains is equal to the angle $BAD$ in the alternate segment of the circle.

Next, since $ABCD$ is a quadrilateral in a circle,

its opposite angles are equal to two right angles. [III. 22]

But the angles $DBF$, $DBE$ are also equal to two right angles;

therefore the angles $DBF$, $DBE$ are equal to the angles $BAD$, $BCD$,

of which the angle $BAD$ was proved equal to the angle $DBF$;

therefore the angle $DBE$ which remains is equal to the angle $DCB$ in the alternate segment $DCB$ of the circle.

Therefore etc. Q. E. D.

## Proposition 33

*On a given straight line to describe a segment of a circle admitting an angle equal to a given rectilineal angle.*

Let $AB$ be the given straight line, and the angle at $C$ the given rectilineal angle;

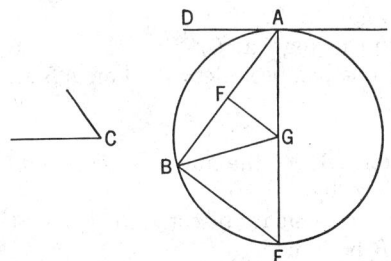

thus it is required to describe on the given straight line $AB$ a segment of a circle admitting an angle equal to the angle at $C$.

The angle at $C$ is then acute, or right, or obtuse.

First, let it be acute, and, as in the first figure, on the straight line $AB$, and at the point $A$, let the angle $BAD$ be constructed equal to the angle at $C$;

therefore the angle $BAD$ is also acute.

Let $AE$ be drawn at right angles to $DA$, let $AB$ be bisected at $F$, let $FG$ be drawn from the point $F$ at right angles to $AB$, and let $GB$ be joined.

Then, since $AF$ is equal to $FB$,
and $FG$ is common,
the two sides $AF$, $FG$ are equal to the two sides $BF$, $FG$;
and the angle $AFG$ is equal to the angle $BFG$;
therefore the base $AG$ is equal to the base $BG$. [I. 4]

Therefore the circle described with centre $G$ and distance $GA$ will pass through $B$ also.

Let it be drawn, and let it be $ABE$;
let $EB$ be joined.

Now, since $AD$ is drawn from $A$, the extremity of the diameter $AE$, at right angles to $AE$,
therefore $AD$ touches the circle $ABE$. [III. 16, Por.]

Since then a straight line $AD$ touches the circle $ABE$, and from the point of contact at $A$ a straight line $AB$ is drawn across in the circle $ABE$,
the angle $DAB$ is equal to the angle $AEB$ in the alternate segment of the circle. [III. 32]

But the angle $DAB$ is equal to the angle at $C$;
therefore the angle at $C$ is also equal to the angle $AEB$.

Therefore on the given straight line $AB$ the segment $AEB$ of a circle has been described admitting the angle $AEB$ equal to the given angle, the angle at $C$.

Next let the angle at $C$ be right;
and let it be again required to describe on $AB$ a segment of a circle admitting an angle equal to the right angle at $C$.

Let the angle $BAD$ be constructed equal to the right angle at $C$, as is the case in the second figure;
let $AB$ be bisected at $F$, and with centre $F$ and distance either $FA$ or $FB$ let the circle $AEB$ be described.

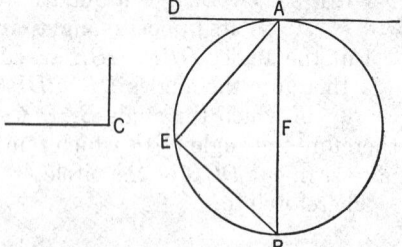

Therefore the straight line $AD$ touches the circle $ABE$, because the angle at $A$ is right. [III. 16, Por.]

And the angle $BAD$ is equal to the angle in the segment $AEB$, for the latter too is itself a right angle, being an angle in a semicircle. [III. 31]

But the angle $BAD$ is also equal to the angle at $C$.

Therefore the angle $AEB$ is also equal to the angle at $C$.

Therefore again the segment $AEB$ of a circle has been described on $AB$ admitting an angle equal to the angle at $C$.

Next, let the angle at $C$ be obtuse;
and on the straight line $AB$, and at the point $A$, let the angle $BAD$ be constructed equal to it, as is the case in the third figure;
let $AE$ be drawn at right angles to $AD$, let $AB$ be again bisected at $F$, let $FG$ be drawn at right angles to $AB$, and let $GB$ be joined.

Then, since $AF$ is again equal to $FB$,
and $FG$ is common,

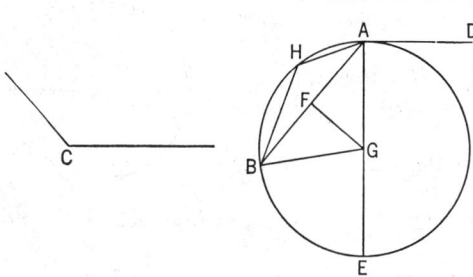

the two sides $AF$, $FG$ are equal to the two sides $BF$, $FG$;
and the angle $AFG$ is equal to the angle $BFG$;
therefore the base $AG$ is equal to the base $BG$. [I. 4]

Therefore the circle described with centre $G$ and distance $GA$ will pass through $B$ also; let it so pass, as $AEB$.

Now, since $AD$ is drawn at right angles to the diameter $AE$ from its extremity,

$AD$ touches the circle $AEB$. [III. 16, Por.]

And $AB$ has been drawn across from the point of contact at $A$;
therefore the angle $BAD$ is equal to the angle constructed in the alternate segment $AHB$ of the circle. [III. 32]

But the angle $BAD$ is equal to the angle at $C$.

Therefore the angle in the segment $AHB$ is also equal to the angle at $C$.

Therefore on the given straight line $AB$ the segment $AHB$ of a circle has been described admitting an angle equal to the angle at $C$. Q. E. F.

## PROPOSITION 34

*From a given circle to cut off a segment admitting an angle equal to a given rectilineal angle.*

Let $ABC$ be the given circle, and the angle at $D$ the given rectilineal angle; thus it is required to cut off from the circle $ABC$ a segment admitting an angle equal to the given rectilineal angle, the angle at $D$.

Let $EF$ be drawn touching $ABC$ at the point $B$, and on the straight line $FB$, and at the point $B$ on it, let the angle $FBC$ be constructed equal to the angle at $D$. [I. 23]

Then, since a straight line $EF$ touches the circle $ABC$,
and $BC$ has been drawn across from the point of contact at $B$,
the angle $FBC$ is equal to the angle constructed in the alternate segment $BAC$. [III. 32]

But the angle $FBC$ is equal to the angle at $D$;
therefore the angle in the segment $BAC$ is equal to the angle at $D$.

Therefore from the given circle $ABC$ the segment $BAC$ has been cut off admitting an angle equal to the given rectilineal angle, the angle at $D$. Q. E. F.

## PROPOSITION 35

*If in a circle two straight lines cut one another, the rectangle contained by the segments of the one is equal to the rectangle contained by the segments of the other.*

For in the circle $ABCD$ let the two straight lines $AC$, $BD$ cut one another at the point $E$;

I say that the rectangle contained by $AE$, $EC$ is equal to the rectangle contained by $DE$, $EB$.

If now $AC$, $BD$ are through the centre, so that $E$ is the centre of the circle $ABCD$,

it is manifest that, $AE$, $EC$, $DE$, $EB$ being equal, the rectangle contained by $AE$, $EC$ is also equal to the rectangle contained by $DE$, $EB$.

Next let $AC$, $DB$ not be through the centre; let the centre of $ABCD$ be taken, and let it be $F$;
from $F$ let $FG$, $FH$ be drawn perpendicular to the straight lines $AC$, $DB$, and let $FB$, $FC$, $FE$ be joined.

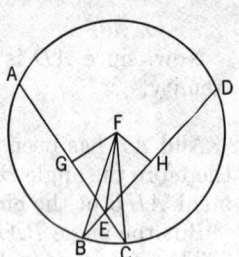

Then, since a straight line $GF$ through the centre cuts a straight line $AC$ not through the centre at right angles,

      it also bisects it;     [III. 3]
    therefore $AG$ is equal to $GC$.

Since, then, the straight line $AC$ has been cut into equal parts at $G$ and into unequal parts at $E$,
the rectangle contained by $AE$, $EC$ together with the square on $EG$ is equal to the square on $GC$;  [II. 5]

Let the square on $GF$ be added;
therefore the rectangle $AE$, $EC$ together with the squares on $GE$, $GF$ is equal to the squares on $CG$, $GF$.

But the square on $FE$ is equal to the squares on $EG$, $GF$, and the square on $FC$ is equal to the squares on $CG$, $GF$;             [I. 47]
therefore the rectangle $AE$, $EC$ together with the square on $FE$ is equal to the square on $FC$.

And $FC$ is equal to $FB$;
therefore the rectangle $AE$, $EC$ together with the square on $EF$ is equal to the square on $FB$.

For the same reason, also,
the rectangle $DE$, $EB$ together with the square on $FE$ is equal to the square on $FB$.

But the rectangle $AE$, $EC$ together with the square on $FE$ was also proved equal to the square on $FB$;
therefore the rectangle $AE$, $EC$ together with the square on $FE$ is equal to the rectangle $DE$, $EB$ together with the square on $FE$.

Let the square on $FE$ be subtracted from each;
therefore the rectangle contained by $AE$, $EC$ which remains is equal to the rectangle contained by $DE$, $EB$.

Therefore etc.                         Q. E. D.

## Proposition 36

*If a point be taken outside a circle and from it there fall on the circle two straight lines, and if one of them cut the circle and the other touch it, the rectangle contained by the whole of the straight line which cuts the circle and the straight line intercepted on it outside between the point and the convex circumference will be equal to the square on the tangent.*

For let a point $D$ be taken outside the circle $ABC$, and from $D$ let the two straight lines $DCA$, $DB$ fall on the circle $ABC$; let $DCA$ cut the circle $ABC$ and let $BD$ touch it;

I say that the rectangle contained by $AD$, $DC$ is equal to the square on $DB$.

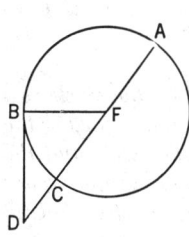

Then $DCA$ is either through the centre or not through the centre.

First let it be through the centre, and let $F$ be the centre of the circle $ABC$; let $FB$ be joined;

therefore the angle $FBD$ is right. [III. 18]

And, since $AC$ has been bisected at $F$, and $CD$ is added to it,

the rectangle $AD$, $DC$ together with the square on $FC$ is equal to the square on $FD$. [II. 6]

But $FC$ is equal to $FB$;

therefore the rectangle $AD$, $DC$ together with the square on $FB$ is equal to the square on $FD$.

And the squares on $FB$, $BD$ are equal to the square on $FD$; [I. 47]

therefore the rectangle $AD$, $DC$ together with the square on $FB$ is equal to the squares on $FB$, $BD$.

Let the square on $FB$ be subtracted from each;

therefore the rectangle $AD$, $DC$ which remains is equal to the square on the tangent $DB$.

Again, let $DCA$ not be through the centre of the circle $ABC$;

let the centre $E$ be taken, and from $E$, let $EF$ be drawn perpendicular to $AC$;

let $EB$, $EC$, $ED$ be joined.

Then the angle $EBD$ is right. [III. 18]

And, since a straight line $EF$ through the centre cuts a straight line $AC$ not through the centre at right angles,

it also bisects it; [III. 3]

therefore $AF$ is equal to $FC$.

Now, since the straight line $AC$ has been bisected at the point $F$, and $CD$ is added to it,

the rectangle contained by $AD$, $DC$ together with the square on $FC$ is equal to the square on $FD$. [II. 6]

Let the square on $FE$ be added to each;

therefore the rectangle $AD$, $DC$ together with the squares on $CF$, $FE$ is equal to the squares on $FD$, $FE$.

But the square on $EC$ is equal to the squares on $CF$, $FE$, for the angle $EFC$ is right; [I. 47]

and the square on $ED$ is equal to the squares on $DF$, $FE$;

therefore the rectangle $AD$, $DC$ together with the square on $EC$ is equal to the square on $ED$.

And $EC$ is equal to $EB$;

therefore the rectangle $AD$, $DC$ together with the square on $EB$ is equal to the square on $ED$.

But the squares on $EB$, $BD$ are equal to the square on $ED$, for the angle $EBD$ is right; [I. 47] therefore the rectangle $AD, DC$ together with the square on $EB$ is equal to the squares on $EB, BD$.

Let the square on $EB$ be subtracted from each;

therefore the rectangle $AD, DC$ which remains is equal to the square on $DB$.

Therefore etc. Q. E. D.

## Proposition 37

*If a point be taken outside a circle and from the point there fall on the circle two straight lines, if one of them cut the circle, and the other fall on it, and if further the rectangle contained by the whole of the straight line which cuts the circle and the straight line intercepted on it outside between the point and the convex circumference be equal to the square on the straight line which falls on the circle, the straight line which falls on it will touch the circle.*

For let a point $D$ be taken outside the circle $ABC$; from $D$ let the two straight lines $DCA, DB$ fall on the circle $ABC$; let $DCA$ cut the circle and $DB$ fall on it; and let the rectangle $AD, DC$ be equal to the square on $DB$.

I say that $DB$ touches the circle $ABC$.

For let $DE$ be drawn touching $ABC$; let the centre of the circle $ABC$ be taken, and let it be $F$; let $FE, FB, FD$ be joined.

Thus the angle $FED$ is right. [III. 18]

Now, since $DE$ touches the circle $ABC$, and $DCA$ cuts it, the rectangle $AD, DC$ is equal to the square on $DE$. [III. 36]

But the rectangle $AD, DC$ was also equal to the square on $DB$;

therefore the square on $DE$ is equal to the square on $DB$;

therefore $DE$ is equal to $DB$.

And $FE$ is equal to $FB$;

therefore the two sides $DE, EF$ are equal to the two sides $DB, BF$;

and $FD$ is the common base of the triangles;

therefore the angle $DEF$ is equal to the angle $DBF$. [I. 8]

But the angle $DEF$ is right;

therefore the angle $DBF$ is also right.

And $FB$ produced is a diameter;

and the straight line drawn at right angles to the diameter of a circle, from its extremity, touches the circle; [III. 16, Por.]

therefore $DB$ touches the circle.

Similarly this can be proved to be the case even if the centre be on $AC$.

Therefore etc. Q. E. D.

# BOOK FOUR

## DEFINITIONS

1. A rectilineal figure is said to be *inscribed in a rectilineal figure* when the respective angles of the inscribed figure lie on the respective sides of that in which it is inscribed.
2. Similarly a figure is said to be *circumscribed about a figure* when the respective sides of the circumscribed figure pass through the respective angles of that about which it is circumscribed.
3. A rectilineal figure is said to be *inscribed in a circle* when each angle of the inscribed figure lies on the circumference of the circle.
4. A rectilineal figure is said to be *circumscribed about a circle*, when each side of the circumscribed figure touches the circumference of the circle.
5. Similarly a circle is said to be *inscribed in a figure* when the circumference of the circle touches each side of the figure in which it is inscribed.
6. A circle is said to be *circumscribed about a figure* when the circumference of the circle passes through each angle of the figure about which it is circumscribed.
7. A straight line is said to be *fitted into a circle* when its extremities are on the circumference of the circle.

## BOOK IV. PROPOSITIONS

### Proposition 1

*Into a given circle to fit a straight line equal to a given straight line which is not greater than the diameter of the circle.*

Let $ABC$ be the given circle, and $D$ the given straight line not greater than the diameter of the circle;
thus it is required to fit into the circle $ABC$ a straight line equal to the straight line $D$.

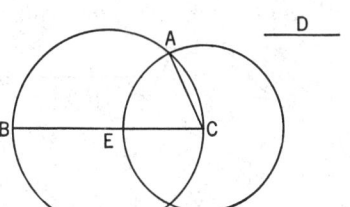

Let a diameter $BC$ of the circle $ABC$ be drawn.

Then, if $BC$ is equal to $D$, that which was enjoined will have been done; for $BC$ has been fitted into the circle $ABC$ equal to the straight line $D$.

But, if $BC$ is greater than $D$, let $CE$ be made equal to $D$, and with centre $C$ and distance $CE$ let the circle $EAF$ be described;
let $CA$ be joined.

Then, since the point $C$ is the centre of the circle $EAF$,

68                                  EUCLID
                        *CA* is equal to *CE*.
But *CE* is equal to *D*;
                    therefore *D* is also equal to *CA*.
   Therefore into the given circle *ABC* there has been fitted *CA* equal to the given straight line *D*.                                Q. E. F.

### PROPOSITION 2

*In a given circle to inscribe a triangle equiangular with a given triangle.*

Let *ABC* be the given circle, and *DEF* the given triangle; thus it is required to inscribe in the circle *ABC* a triangle equiangular with the triangle *DEF*.

Let *GH* be drawn touching the circle *ABC* at *A* [III. 16, Por.]; on the straight line *AH*, and at the point *A* on it, let the angle *HAC* be constructed equal to the angle *DEF*,

and on the straight line *AG*, and at the point *A* on it, let the angle *GAB* be constructed equal to the angle *DFE*;   [I. 23]
            let *BC* be joined.

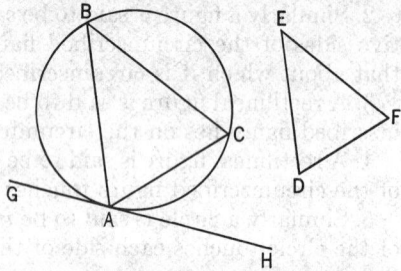

Then, since a straight line *AH* touches the circle *ABC*, and from the point of contact at *A* the straight line *AC* is drawn across in the circle,
therefore the angle *HAC* is equal to the angle *ABC* in the alternate segment of the circle.   [III. 32]

But the angle *HAC* is equal to the angle *DEF*;
   therefore the angle *ABC* is also equal to the angle *DEF*.
For the same reason
        the angle *ACB* is also equal to the angle *DFE*;
therefore the remaining angle *BAC* is also equal to the remaining angle *EDF*.
                                                          [I. 32]
   Therefore in the given circle there has been inscribed a triangle equiangular with the given triangle.                                Q. E. F.

### PROPOSITION 3

*About a given circle to circumscribe a triangle equiangular with a given triangle.*

Let *ABC* be the given circle, and *DEF* the given triangle; thus it is required to circumscribe about the circle *ABC* a triangle equiangular with the triangle *DEF*.

Let *EF* be produced in both directions to the points *G*, *H*, let the centre *K* of the circle *ABC* be taken [III. 1], and let the straight line *KB* be drawn across at random;
on the straight line *KB*, and at the point *K* on it, let the angle *BKA* be constructed equal to the angle *DEG*, and the angle *BKC* equal to the angle *DFH*;   [I. 23]

ELEMENTS IV

and through the points $A$, $B$, $C$ let $LAM$, $MBN$, $NCL$ be drawn touching the circle $ABC$.  [III. 16, Por.]

Now, since $LM$, $MN$, $NL$ touch the circle $ABC$ at the points $A$, $B$, $C$, and $KA$, $KB$, $KC$ have been joined from the centre $K$ to the points $A$, $B$, $C$,
therefore the angles at the points $A$, $B$, $C$ are right.  [III. 18]

And, since the four angles of the quadrilateral $AMBK$ are equal to four right angles, inasmuch as $AMBK$ is in fact divisible into two triangles,
and the angles $KAM$, $KBM$ are right,
therefore the remaining angles $AKB$, $AMB$ are equal to two right angles.
But the angles $DEG$, $DEF$ are also equal to two right angles;  [I. 13]
therefore the angles $AKB$, $AMB$ are equal to the angles $DEG$, $DEF$,
of which the angle $AKB$ is equal to the angle $DEG$;
therefore the angle $AMB$ which remains is equal to the angle $DEF$ which remains.

Similarly it can be proved that the angle $LNB$ is also equal to the angle $DFE$;
therefore the remaining angle $MLN$ is equal to the angle $EDF$. [I. 32]

Therefore the triangle $LMN$ is equiangular with the triangle $DEF$; and it has been circumscribed about the circle $ABC$.

Therefore about a given circle there has been circumscribed a triangle equiangular with the given triangle.  Q. E. F.

## Proposition 4

*In a given triangle to inscribe a circle.*

Let $ABC$ be the given triangle;
thus it is required to inscribe a circle in the triangle $ABC$.

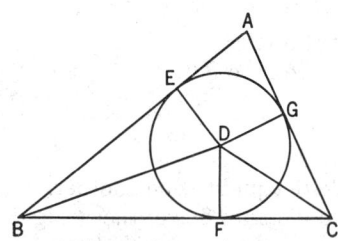

Let the angles $ABC$, $ACB$ be bisected by the straight lines $BD$, $CD$ [I. 9], and let these meet one another at the point $D$;
from $D$ let $DE$, $DF$, $DG$ be drawn perpendicular to the straight lines $AB$, $BC$, $CA$.

Now, since the angle $ABD$ is equal to the angle $CBD$,
and the right angle $BED$ is also equal to the right angle $BFD$,
$EBD$, $FBD$ are two triangles having two angles equal to two angles and one side equal to one side, namely that subtending one of the equal angles, which is $BD$ common to the triangles;
therefore they will also have the remaining sides equal to the remaining sides;
[I. 26]
therefore $DE$ is equal to $DF$.

For the same reason
$DG$ is also equal to $DF$.

Therefore the three straight lines $DE$, $DF$, $DG$ are equal to one another;
therefore the circle described with centre $D$ and distance one of the straight lines $DE$, $DF$, $DG$ will pass also through the remaining points, and will touch the straight lines $AB$, $BC$, $CA$, because the angles at the points $E$, $F$, $G$ are right.

For, if it cuts them, the straight line drawn at right angles to the diameter of

the circle from its extremity will be found to fall within the circle: which was proved absurd; [III. 16]
therefore the circle described with centre $D$ and distance one of the straight lines $DE$, $DF$, $DG$ will not cut the straight lines $AB$, $BC$, $CA$;
therefore it will touch them, and will be the circle inscribed in the triangle $ABC$. [IV. Def. 5]

Let it be inscribed, as $FGE$.

Therefore in the given triangle $ABC$ the circle $EFG$ has been inscribed.

Q. E. F.

## Proposition 5

*About a given triangle to circumscribe a circle.*

Let $ABC$ be the given triangle;
thus it is required to circumscribe a circle about the given triangle $ABC$.

  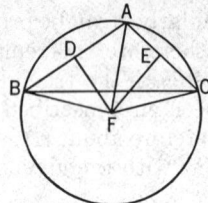

Let the straight lines $AB$, $AC$ be bisected at the points $D$, $E$ [I. 10], and from the points $D$, $E$ let $DF$, $EF$ be drawn at right angles to $AB$, $AC$;
they will then meet within the triangle $ABC$, or on the straight line $BC$, or outside $BC$.

First let them meet within at $F$, and let $FB$, $FC$, $FA$ be joined.

Then, since $AD$ is equal to $DB$,
and $DF$ is common and at right angles,
therefore the base $AF$ is equal to the base $FB$. [I. 4]
Similarly we can prove that
$CF$ is also equal to $AF$;
so that $FB$ is also equal to $FC$;
therefore the three straight lines $FA$, $FB$, $FC$ are equal to one another.

Therefore the circle described with centre $F$ and distance one of the straight lines $FA$, $FB$, $FC$ will pass also through the remaining points, and the circle will have been circumscribed about the triangle $ABC$.

Let it be circumscribed, as $ABC$.

Next, let $DF$, $EF$ meet on the straight line $BC$ at $F$, as is the case in the second figure; and let $AF$ be joined.

Then, similarly, we shall prove that the point $F$ is the centre of the circle circumscribed about the triangle $ABC$.

Again, let $DF$, $EF$ meet outside the triangle $ABC$ at $F$, as is the case in the third figure, and let $AF$, $BF$, $CF$ be joined.

Then again, since $AD$ is equal to $DB$,
and $DF$ is common and at right angles,
therefore the base $AF$ is equal to the base $BF$. [I. 4]
Similarly we can prove that
$CF$ is also equal to $AF$;
so that $BF$ is also equal to $FC$;

# ELEMENTS IV

therefore the circle described with centre $F$ and distance one of the straight lines $FA$, $FB$, $FC$ will pass also through the remaining points, and will have been circumscribed about the triangle $ABC$.

Therefore about the given triangle a circle has been circumscribed.

Q. E. F.

And it is manifest that, when the centre of the circle falls within the triangle, the angle $BAC$, being in a segment greater than the semicircle, is less than a right angle;

when the centre falls on the straight line $BC$, the angle $BAC$, being in a semicircle, is right;

and when the centre of the circle falls outside the triangle, the angle $BAC$, being in a segment less than the semicircle, is greater than a right angle. [III. 31]

## Proposition 6

*In a given circle to inscribe a square.*

Let $ABCD$ be the given circle;

thus it is required to inscribe a square in the circle $ABCD$.

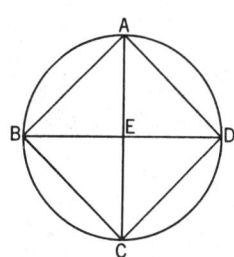

Let two diameters $AC$, $BD$ of the circle $ABCD$ be drawn at right angles to one another, and let $AB$, $BC$, $CD$, $DA$ be joined.

Then, since $BE$ is equal to $ED$, for $E$ is the centre, and $EA$ is common and at right angles,

therefore the base $AB$ is equal to the base $AD$. [I. 4]

For the same reason

each of the straight lines $BC$, $CD$ is also equal to each of the straight lines $AB$, $AD$;

therefore the quadrilateral $ABCD$ is equilateral.

I say next that it is also right-angled.

For, since the straight line $BD$ is a diameter of the circle $ABCD$,

therefore $BAD$ is a semicircle;

therefore the angle $BAD$ is right. [III. 31]

For the same reason

each of the angles $ABC$, $BCD$, $CDA$ is also right;

therefore the quadrilateral $ABCD$ is right-angled.

But it was also proved equilateral;

therefore it is a square; [I. Def. 22]

and it has been inscribed in the circle $ABCD$.

Therefore in the given circle the square $ABCD$ has been inscribed. Q. E. F.

## Proposition 7

*About a given circle to circumscribe a square.*

Let $ABCD$ be the given circle;

thus it is required to circumscribe a square about the circle $ABCD$.

Let two diameters $AC$, $BD$ of the circle $ABCD$ be drawn at right angles to one another, and through the points $A$, $B$, $C$, $D$ let $FG$, $GH$, $HK$, $KF$ be drawn touching the circle $ABCD$. [III. 16, Por.]

Then, since $FG$ touches the circle $ABCD$,

and $EA$ has been joined from the centre $E$ to the point of contact at $A$,

therefore the angles at $A$ are right. [III. 18]

72  EUCLID

For the same reason
the angles at the points B, C, D are also right.
Now, since the angle AEB is right,
and the angle EBG is also right,
therefore GH is parallel to AC.     [I. 28]
For the same reason
AC is also parallel to FK,
so that GH is also parallel to FK.    [I. 30]
Similarly we can prove that
each of the straight lines GF, HK is parallel to BED.
Therefore GK, GC, AK, FB, BK are parallelograms;
therefore GF is equal to HK, and GH to FK.   [I. 34]
And, since AC is equal to BD,
and AC is also equal to each of the straight lines GH, FK,
while BD is equal to each of the straight lines GF, HK,   [I. 34]
therefore the quadrilateral FGHK is equilateral.
I say next that it is also right-angled.
For, since GBEA is a parallelogram,
and the angle AEB is right,
therefore the angle AGB is also right.    [I. 34]
Similarly we can prove that
the angles at H, K, F are also right.
Therefore FGHK is right-angled.
But it was also proved equilateral;
therefore it is a square;
and it has been circumscribed about the circle ABCD.
Therefore about the given circle a square has been circumscribed. Q. E. F.

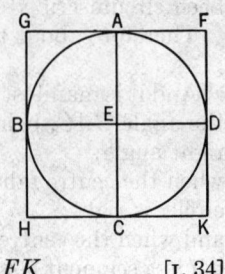

## Proposition 8

*In a given square to inscribe a circle.*

Let ABCD be the given square;
thus it is required to inscribe a circle in the given square ABCD.

Let the straight lines AD, AB be bisected at the
points E, F respectively,     [I. 10]
through E let EH be drawn parallel to either AB or
CD, and through F let FK be drawn parallel to either
AD or BC;     [I. 31]
therefore each of the figures AK, KB, AH, HD, AG,
GC, BG, GD is a parallelogram, and their opposite
sides are evidently equal.     [I. 34]
Now, since AD is equal to AB,
and AE is half of AD, and AF half of AB,
therefore AE is equal to AF,
so that the opposite sides are also equal;
therefore FG is equal to GE.
Similarly we can prove that each of the straight lines GH, GK is equal to
each of the straight lines FG, GE;
therefore the four straight lines GE, GF, GH, GK are equal to one another.

## ELEMENTS IV

Therefore the circle described with centre $G$ and distance one of the straight lines $GE$, $GF$, $GH$, $GK$ will pass also through the remaining points.

And it will touch the straight lines $AB$, $BC$, $CD$, $DA$, because the angles at $E$, $F$, $H$, $K$ are right.

For, if the circle cuts $AB$, $BC$, $CD$, $DA$, the straight line drawn at right angles to the diameter of the circle from its extremity will fall within the circle: which was proved absurd; [III. 16]
therefore the circle described with centre $G$ and distance one of the straight lines $GE$, $GF$, $GH$, $GK$ will not cut the straight lines $AB$, $BC$, $CD$, $DA$.

Therefore it will touch them, and will have been inscribed in the square $ABCD$.

Therefore in the given square a circle has been inscribed. Q. E. F.

### PROPOSITION 9

*About a given square to circumscribe a circle.*

Let $ABCD$ be the given square;
thus it is required to circumscribe a circle about the square $ABCD$.

For let $AC$, $BD$ be joined, and let them cut one another at $E$.

Then, since $DA$ is equal to $AB$, and $AC$ is common,
therefore the two sides $DA$, $AC$ are equal to the two sides $BA$, $AC$;
and the base $DC$ is equal to the base $BC$;
therefore the angle $DAC$ is equal to the angle $BAC$. [I. 8]

Therefore the angle $DAB$ is bisected by $AC$.

Similarly we can prove that each of the angles $ABC$, $BCD$, $CDA$ is bisected by the straight lines $AC$, $DB$.

Now, since the angle $DAB$ is equal to the angle $ABC$,
and the angle $EAB$ is half the angle $DAB$,
and the angle $EBA$ half the angle $ABC$,
therefore the angle $EAB$ is also equal to the angle $EBA$;
so that the side $EA$ is also equal to $EB$. [I. 6]

Similarly we can prove that each of the straight lines $EA$, $EB$ is equal to each of the straight lines $EC$, $ED$.

Therefore the four straight lines $EA$, $EB$, $EC$, $ED$ are equal to one another.

Therefore the circle described with centre $E$ and distance one of the straight lines $EA$, $EB$, $EC$, $ED$ will pass also through the remaining points;
and it will have been circumscribed about the square $ABCD$.

Let it be circumscribed, as $ABCD$.

Therefore about the given square a circle has been circumscribed. Q. E. F.

### PROPOSITION 10

*To construct an isosceles triangle having each of the angles at the base double of the remaining one.*

Let any straight line $AB$ be set out, and let it be cut at the point $C$ so that the rectangle contained by $AB$, $BC$ is equal to the square on $CA$; [II. 11]
with centre $A$ and distance $AB$ let the circle $BDE$ be described,
and let there be fitted in the circle $BDE$ the straight line $BD$ equal to the straight line $AC$ which is not greater than the diameter of the circle $BDE$. [IV. 1]

Let $AD$, $DC$ be joined, and let the circle $ACD$ be circumscribed about the triangle $ACD$. [IV. 5]

Then, since the rectangle $AB$, $BC$ is equal to the square on $AC$,
and $AC$ is equal to $BD$,
therefore the rectangle $AB$, $BC$ is equal to the square on $BD$.

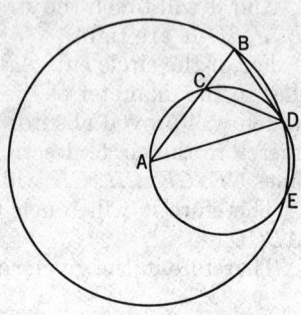

And, since a point $B$ has been taken outside the circle $ACD$,
and from $B$ the two straight lines $BA$, $BD$ have fallen on the circle $ACD$, and one of them cuts it, while the other falls on it,
and the rectangle $AB$, $BC$ is equal to the square on $BD$,

therefore $BD$ touches the circle $ACD$. [III. 37]

Since, then, $BD$ touches it, and $DC$ is drawn across from the point of contact at $D$,
therefore the angle $BDC$ is equal to the angle $DAC$ in the alternate segment of the circle. [III. 32]

Since, then, the angle $BDC$ is equal to the angle $DAC$,
let the angle $CDA$ be added to each;
therefore the whole angle $BDA$ is equal to the two angles $CDA$, $DAC$.

But the exterior angle $BCD$ is equal to the angles $CDA$, $DAC$; [I. 32]
therefore the angle $BDA$ is also equal to the angle $BCD$.

But the angle $BDA$ is equal to the angle $CBD$, since the side $AD$ is also equal to $AB$; [I. 5]
so that the angle $DBA$ is also equal to the angle $BCD$.

Therefore the three angles $BDA$, $DBA$, $BCD$ are equal to one another.

And, since the angle $DBC$ is equal to the angle $BCD$,
the side $BD$ is also equal to the side $DC$. [I. 6]

But $BD$ is by hypothesis equal to $CA$;
therefore $CA$ is also equal to $CD$,
so that the angle $CDA$ is also equal to the angle $DAC$; [I. 5]
therefore the angles $CDA$, $DAC$ are double of the angle $DAC$.

But the angle $BCD$ is equal to the angles $CDA$, $DAC$;
therefore the angle $BCD$ is also double of the angle $CAD$.

But the angle $BCD$ is equal to each of the angles $BDA$, $DBA$;
therefore each of the angles $BDA$, $DBA$ is also double of the angle $DAB$.

Therefore the isosceles triangle $ABD$ has been constructed having each of the angles at the base $DB$ double of the remaining one. Q. E. F.

## PROPOSITION 11

*In a given circle to inscribe an equilateral and equiangular pentagon.*

Let $ABCDE$ be the given circle;
thus it is required to inscribe in the circle $ABCDE$ an equilateral and equiangular pentagon.

Let the isosceles triangle $FGH$ be set out having each of the angles at $G$, $H$ double of the angle at $F$; [IV. 10]
let there be inscribed in the circle $ABCDE$ the triangle $ACD$ equiangular with

the triangle $FGH$, so that the angle $CAD$ is equal to the angle at $F$ and the angles at $G$, $H$ respectively equal to the angles $ACD$, $CDA$; [IV. 2]

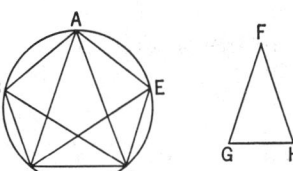

therefore each of the angles $ACD$, $CDA$ is also double of the angle $CAD$.

Now let the angles $ACD$, $CDA$ be bisected respectively by the straight lines $CE$, $DB$ [I. 9], and let $AB$, $BC$, $DE$, $EA$ be joined.

Then, since each of the angles $ACD$, $CDA$ is double of the angle $CAD$,

and they have been bisected by the straight lines $CE$, $DB$,

therefore the five angles $DAC$, $ACE$, $ECD$, $CDB$, $BDA$ are equal to one another.

But equal angles stand on equal circumferences; [III. 26]
therefore the five circumferences $AB$, $BC$, $CD$, $DE$, $EA$ are equal to one another.

But equal circumferences are subtended by equal straight lines; [III. 29]
therefore the five straight lines $AB$, $BC$, $CD$, $DE$, $EA$ are equal to one another;
therefore the pentagon $ABCDE$ is equilateral.

I say next that it is also equiangular.

For, since the circumference $AB$ is equal to the circumference $DE$, let $BCD$ be added to each;

therefore the whole circumference $ABCD$ is equal to the whole circumference $EDCB$.

And the angle $AED$ stands on the circumference $ABCD$, and the angle $BAE$ on the circumference $EDCB$;

therefore the angle $BAE$ is also equal to the angle $AED$. [III. 27]

For the same reason
each of the angles $ABC$, $BCD$, $CDE$ is also equal to each of the angles $BAE$, $AED$;

therefore the pentagon $ABCDE$ is equiangular.

But it was also proved equilateral;
therefore in the given circle an equilateral and equiangular pentagon has been inscribed. Q. E. F.

## Proposition 12

*About a given circle to circumscribe an equilateral and equiangular pentagon.*

Let $ABCDE$ be the given circle;
thus it is required to circumscribe an equilateral and equiangular pentagon about the circle $ABCDE$.

Let $A$, $B$, $C$, $D$, $E$ be conceived to be the angular points of the inscribed pentagon, so that the circumferences $AB$, $BC$, $CD$, $DE$, $EA$ are equal; [IV. 11]
through $A$, $B$, $C$, $D$, $E$ let $GH$, $HK$, $KL$, $LM$, $MG$ be drawn touching the circle;
[III. 16, Por.]
let the centre $F$ of the circle $ABCDE$ be taken [III. 1], and let $FB$, $FK$, $FC$, $FL$, $FD$ be joined.

Then, since the straight line $KL$ touches the circle $ABCDE$ at $C$,
and $FC$ has been joined from the centre $F$ to the point of contact at $C$,
therefore $FC$ is perpendicular to $KL$; [III. 18]

therefore each of the angles at $C$ is right.

For the same reason

the angles at the points $B$, $D$ are also right.

And, since the angle $FCK$ is right,

therefore the square on $FK$ is equal to the squares on $FC$, $CK$.

For the same reason [I. 47]

the square on $FK$ is also equal to the squares on $FB$, $BK$;

so that the squares on $FC$, $CK$ are equal to the squares on $FB$, $BK$,

of which the square on $FC$ is equal to the square on $FB$;

therefore the square on $CK$ which remains is equal to the square on $BK$.

Therefore $BK$ is equal to $CK$.

And, since $FB$ is equal to $FC$,

and $FK$ common,

the two sides $BF$, $FK$ are equal to the two sides $CF$, $FK$; and the base $BK$ equal to the base $CK$;

therefore the angle $BFK$ is equal to the angle $KFC$, [I. 8]

and the angle $BKF$ to the angle $FKC$.

Therefore the angle $BFC$ is double of the angle $KFC$,

and the angle $BKC$ of the angle $FKC$.

For the same reason

the angle $CFD$ is also double of the angle $CFL$,

and the angle $DLC$ of the angle $FLC$.

Now, since the circumference $BC$ is equal to $CD$,

the angle $BFC$ is also equal to the angle $CFD$. [III. 27]

And the angle $BFC$ is double of the angle $KFC$, and the angle $DFC$ of the angle $LFC$;

therefore the angle $KFC$ is also equal to the angle $LFC$.

But the angle $FCK$ is also equal to the angle $FCL$;

therefore $FKC$, $FLC$ are two triangles having two angles equal to two angles and one side equal to one side, namely $FC$ which is common to them;

therefore they will also have the remaining sides equal to the remaining sides, and the remaining angle to the remaining angle; [I. 26]

therefore the straight line $KC$ is equal to $CL$,

and the angle $FKC$ to the angle $FLC$,

And, since $KC$ is equal to $CL$,

therefore $KL$ is double of $KC$.

For the same reason it can be proved that

$HK$ is also double of $BK$.

And $BK$ is equal to $KC$;

therefore $HK$ is also equal to $KL$.

Similarly each of the straight lines $HG$, $GM$, $ML$ can also be proved equal to each of the straight lines $HK$, $KL$;

therefore the pentagon $GHKLM$ is equilateral.

I say next that it is also equiangular.

For, since the angle $FKC$ is equal to the angle $FLC$,

ELEMENTS IV

and the angle $HKL$ was proved double of the angle $FKC$,
and the angle $KLM$ double of the angle $FLC$,
therefore the angle $HKL$ is also equal to the angle $KLM$.

Similarly each of the angles $KHG$, $HGM$, $GML$ can also be proved equal to each of the angles $HKL$, $KLM$;
therefore the five angles $GHK$, $HKL$, $KLM$, $LMG$, $MGH$ are equal to one another.

Therefore the pentagon $GHKLM$ is equiangular.

And it was also proved equilateral; and it has been circumscribed about the circle $ABCDE$.  Q. E. F.

PROPOSITION 13

*In a given pentagon, which is equilateral and equiangular, to inscribe a circle.*
Let $ABCDE$ be the given equilateral and equiangular pentagon;
thus it is required to inscribe a circle in the pentagon $ABCDE$.

For let the angles $BCD$, $CDE$ be bisected by the straight lines $CF$, $DF$ respectively; and from the point $F$, at which the straight lines $CF$, $DF$ meet one another, let the straight lines $FB$, $FA$, $FE$ be joined.

Then, since $BC$ is equal to $CD$, and $CF$ common,

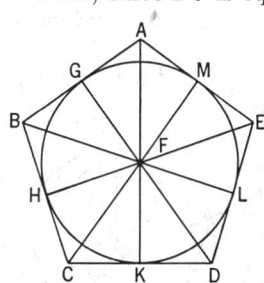

the two sides $BC$, $CF$ are equal to the two sides $DC$, $CF$;
and the angle $BCF$ is equal to the angle $DCF$;
therefore the base $BF$ is equal to the base $DF$,
and the triangle $BCF$ is equal to the triangle $DCF$,
and the remaining angles will be equal to the remaining angles, namely those which the equal sides subtend. [I. 4]

Therefore the angle $CBF$ is equal to the angle $CDF$.

And, since the angle $CDE$ is double of the angle $CDF$,
and the angle $CDE$ is equal to the angle $ABC$,
while the angle $CDF$ is equal to the angle $CBF$;
therefore the angle $CBA$ is also double of the angle $CBF$;
therefore the angle $ABF$ is equal to the angle $FBC$;
therefore the angle $ABC$ has been bisected by the straight line $BF$.

Similarly it can be proved that
the angles $BAE$, $AED$ have also been bisected by the straight lines $FA$, $FE$ respectively.

Now let $FG$, $FH$, $FK$, $FL$, $FM$ be drawn from the point $F$ perpendicular to the straight lines $AB$, $BC$, $CD$, $DE$, $EA$.

Then, since the angle $HCF$ is equal to the angle $KCF$,
and the right angle $FHC$ is also equal to the angle $FKC$,
$FHC$, $FKC$ are two triangles having two angles equal to two angles and one side equal to one side, namely $FC$ which is common to them and subtends one of the equal angles;
therefore they will also have the remaining sides equal to the remaining sides;
[I. 26]
therefore the perpendicular $FH$ is equal to the perpendicular $FK$.
Similarly it can be proved that

each of the straight lines $FL, FM, FG$ is also equal to each of the straight lines $FH, FK$;

therefore the five straight lines $FG, FH, FK, FL, FM$ are equal to one another.

Therefore the circle described with centre $F$ and distance one of the straight lines $FG, FH, FK, FL, FM$ will pass also through the remaining points; and it will touch the straight lines $AB, BC, CD, DE, EA$, because the angles at the points $G, H, K, L, M$ are right.

For, if it does not touch them, but cuts them,

it will result that the straight line drawn at right angles to the diameter of the circle from its extremity falls within the circle: which was proved absurd.

[III. 16]

Therefore the circle described with centre $F$ and distance one of the straight lines $FG, FH, FK, FL, FM$ will not cut the straight lines $AB, BC, CD, DE, EA$;

therefore it will touch them.

Let it be described, as $GHKLM$.

Therefore in the given pentagon, which is equilateral and equiangular, a circle has been inscribed.                                    Q. E. F.

## PROPOSITION 14

*About a given pentagon, which is equilateral and equiangular, to circumscribe a circle.*

Let $ABCDE$ be the given pentagon, which is equilateral and equiangular; thus it is required to circumscribe a circle about the pentagon $ABCDE$.

Let the angles $BCD, CDE$ be bisected by the straight lines $CF, DF$ respectively, and from the point $F$, at which the straight lines meet, let the straight lines $FB, FA, FE$ be joined to the points $B, A, E$.

Then in manner similar to the preceding it can be proved that the angles $CBA, BAE, AED$ have also been bisected by the straight lines $FB, FA, FE$ respectively.

Now, since the angle $BCD$ is equal to the angle $CDE$,
and the angle $FCD$ is half of the angle $BCD$,
and the angle $CDF$ half of the angle $CDE$,
therefore the angle $FCD$ is also equal to the angle $CDF$,
so that the side $FC$ is also equal to the side $FD$.        [I. 6]

Similarly it can be proved that

each of the straight lines $FB, FA, FE$ is also equal to each of the straight lines $FC, FD$;

therefore the five straight lines $FA, FB, FC, FD, FE$ are equal to one another.

Therefore the circle described with centre $F$ and distance one of the straight lines $FA, FB, FC, FD, FE$ will pass also through the remaining points, and will have been circumscribed.

Let it be circumscribed, and let it be $ABCDE$.

Therefore about the given pentagon, which is equilateral and equiangular, a circle has been circumscribed.                                    Q. E. F.

## Proposition 15

*In a given circle to inscribe an equilateral and equiangular hexagon.*

Let $ABCDEF$ be the given circle;
thus it is required to inscribe an equilateral and equiangular hexagon in the circle $ABCDEF$.

Let the diameter $AD$ of the circle $ABCDEF$ be drawn;

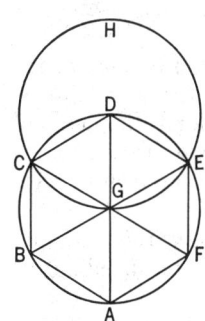

let the centre $G$ of the circle be taken, and with centre $D$ and distance $DG$ let the circle $EGCH$ be described;
let $EG$, $CG$ be joined and carried through to the points $B$, $F$,
and let $AB$, $BC$, $CD$, $DE$, $EF$, $FA$ be joined.

I say that the hexagon $ABCDEF$ is equilateral and equiangular.

For, since the point $G$ is the centre of the circle $ABCDEF$,
$GE$ is equal to $GD$.

Again, since the point $D$ is the centre of the circle $GCH$,
$DE$ is equal to $DG$.

But $GE$ was proved equal to $GD$;
therefore $GE$ is also equal to $ED$;
therefore the triangle $EGD$ is equilateral;
and therefore its three angles $EGD$, $GDE$, $DEG$ are equal to one another, inasmuch as, in isosceles triangles, the angles at the base are equal to one another.
[I. 5]

And the three angles of the triangle are equal to two right angles; [I. 32]
therefore the angle $EGD$ is one-third of two right angles.

Similarly, the angle $DGC$ can also be proved to be one-third of two right angles.

And, since the straight line $CG$ standing on $EB$ makes the adjacent angles $EGC$, $CGB$ equal to two right angles,
therefore the remaining angle $CGB$ is also one-third of two right angles.

Therefore the angles $EGD$, $DGC$, $CGB$ are equal to one another;
so that the angles vertical to them, the angles $BGA$, $AGF$, $FGE$ are equal.
[I. 15]

Therefore the six angles $EGD$, $DGC$, $CGB$, $BGA$, $AGF$, $FGE$ are equal to one another.

But equal angles stand on equal circumferences; [III. 26]
therefore the six circumferences $AB$, $BC$, $CD$, $DE$, $EF$, $FA$ are equal to one another.

And equal circumferences are subtended by equal straight lines; [III. 29]
therefore the six straight lines are equal to one another;
therefore the hexagon $ABCDEF$ is equilateral.

I say next that it is also equiangular.

For, since the circumference $FA$ is equal to the circumference $ED$,
let the circumference $ABCD$ be added to each;
therefore the whole $FABCD$ is equal to the whole $EDCBA$;
and the angle $FED$ stands on the circumference $FABCD$,

and the angle $AFE$ on the circumference $EDCBA$;
therefore the angle $AFE$ is equal to the angle $DEF$.   [III. 27]

Similarly it can be proved that the remaining angles of the hexagon $ABCDEF$ are also severally equal to each of the angles $AFE$, $FED$;
therefore the hexagon $ABCDEF$ is equiangular.

But it was also proved equilateral;
and it has been inscribed in the circle $ABCDEF$.

Therefore in the given circle an equilateral and equiangular hexagon has been inscribed.   Q. E. F.

PORISM. From this it is manifest that the side of the hexagon is equal to the radius of the circle.

And, in like manner as in the case of the pentagon, if through the points of division on the circle we draw tangents to the circle, there will be circumscribed about the circle an equilateral and equiangular hexagon in conformity with what was explained in the case of the pentagon.

And further by means similar to those explained in the case of the pentagon we can both inscribe a circle in a given hexagon and circumscribe one about it.

Q. E. F.

## PROPOSITION 16

*In a given circle to inscribe a fifteen-angled figure which shall be both equilateral and equiangular.*

Let $ABCD$ be the given circle;
thus it is required to inscribe in the circle $ABCD$ a fifteen-angled figure which shall be both equilateral and equiangular.

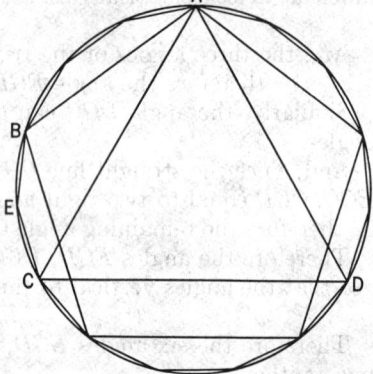

In the circle $ABCD$ let there be inscribed a side $AC$ of the equilateral triangle inscribed in it, and a side $AB$ of an equilateral pentagon;
therefore, of the equal segments of which there are fifteen in the circle $ABCD$, there will be five in the circumference $ABC$ which is one-third of the circle, and there will be three in the circumference $AB$ which is one-fifth of the circle;
therefore in the remainder $BC$ there will be two of the equal segments.

Let $BC$ be bisected at $E$;   [III. 30]
therefore each of the circumferences $BE$, $EC$ is a fifteenth of the circle $ABCD$.

If therefore we join $BE$, $EC$ and fit into the circle $ABCD$ straight lines equal to them and in contiguity, a fifteen-angled figure which is both equilateral and equiangular will have been inscribed in it.   Q. E. F.

And, in like manner as in the case of the pentagon, if through the points of division on the circle we draw tangents to the circle, there will be circumscribed about the circle a fifteen-angled figure which is equilateral and equiangular.

And further, by proofs similar to those in the case of the pentagon, we can both inscribe a circle in the given fifteen-angled figure and circumscribe one about it.   Q. E. F.

# BOOK FIVE

## DEFINITIONS

1. A magnitude is a *part* of a magnitude, the less of the greater, when it measures the greater.

2. The greater is a *multiple* of the less when it is measured by the less.

3. A *ratio* is a sort of relation in respect of size between two magnitudes of the same kind.

4. Magnitudes are said to *have a ratio* to one another which are capable, when multiplied, of exceeding one another.

5. Magnitudes are said to *be in the same ratio*, the first to the second and the third to the fourth, when, if any equimultiples whatever be taken of the first and third, and any equimultiples whatever of the second and fourth, the former equimultiples alike exceed, are alike equal to, or alike fall short of, the latter equimultiples respectively taken in corresponding order.

6. Let magnitudes which have the same ratio be called *proportional*.

7. When, of the equimultiples, the multiple of the first magnitude exceeds the multiple of the second, but the multiple of the third does not exceed the multiple of the fourth, then the first is said to *have a greater ratio* to the second than the third has to the fourth.

8. A proportion in three terms is the least possible.

9. When three magnitudes are proportional, the first is said to have to the third the *duplicate ratio* of that which it has to the second.

10. When four magnitudes are <continuously> proportional, the first is said to have to the fourth the *triplicate ratio* of that which it has to the second, and so on continually, whatever be the proportion.

11. The term *corresponding magnitudes* is used of antecedents in relation to antecedents, and of consequents in relation to consequents.

12. *Alternate ratio* means taking the antecedent in relation to the antecedent and the consequent in relation to the consequent.

13. *Inverse ratio* means taking the consequent as antecedent in relation to the antecedent as consequent.

14. *Composition of a ratio* means taking the antecedent together with the consequent as one in relation to the consequent by itself.

15. *Separation of a ratio* means taking the excess by which the antecedent exceeds the consequent in relation to the consequent by itself.

16. *Conversion of a ratio* means taking the antecedent in relation to the excess by which the antecedent exceeds the consequent.

17. A ratio *ex aequali* arises when, there being several magnitudes and another set equal to them in multitude which taken two and two are in the same proportion, as the first is to the last among the first magnitudes, so is the first to the last among the second magnitudes;

Or, in other words, it means taking the extreme terms by virtue of the removal of the intermediate terms.

18. A *perturbed proportion* arises when, there being three magnitudes and another set equal to them in multitude, as antecedent is to consequent among the first magnitudes, so is antecedent to consequent among the second magnitudes, while, as the consequent is to a third among the first magnitudes, so is a third to the antecedent among the second magnitudes.

## BOOK V. PROPOSITIONS

### Proposition 1

*If there be any number of magnitudes whatever which are, respectively, equimultiples of any magnitudes equal in multitude, then, whatever multiple one of the magnitudes is of one, that multiple also will all be of all.*

Let any number of magnitudes whatever $AB$, $CD$ be respectively equimultiples of any magnitudes $E$, $F$ equal in multitude;

I say that, whatever multiple $AB$ is of $E$, that multiple will $AB$, $CD$ also be of $E$, $F$.

For, since $AB$ is the same multiple of $E$ that $CD$ is of $F$, as many magnitudes as there are in $AB$ equal to $E$, so many also are there in $CD$ equal to $F$.

Let $AB$ be divided into the magnitudes $AG$, $GB$ equal to $E$,
and $CD$ into $CH$, $HD$ equal to $F$;
then the multitude of the magnitudes $AG$, $GB$ will be equal to the multitude of the magnitudes $CH$, $HD$.

Now, since $AG$ is equal to $E$, and $CH$ to $F$,
therefore $AG$ is equal to $E$, and $AG$, $CH$ to $E$, $F$.

For the same reason
$GB$ is equal to $E$, and $GB$, $HD$ to $E$, $F$;
therefore, as many magnitudes as there are in $AB$ equal to $E$, so many also are there in $AB$, $CD$ equal to $E$, $F$;
therefore, whatever multiple $AB$ is of $E$, that multiple will $AB$, $CD$ also be of $E$, $F$.

Therefore etc.

Q. E. D.

### Proposition 2

*If a first magnitude be the same multiple of a second that a third is of a fourth, and a fifth also be the same multiple of the second that a sixth is of the fourth, the sum of the first and fifth will also be the same multiple of the second that the sum of the third and sixth is of the fourth.*

Let a first magnitude, $AB$, be the same multiple of a second, $C$, that a third, $DE$, is of a fourth, $F$, and let a fifth, $BG$, also be the same multiple of the second, $C$, that a sixth, $EH$, is of the fourth $F$;

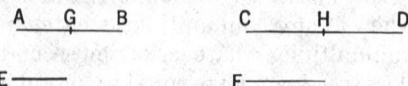

I say that the sum of the first and fifth, $AG$, will be the same multiple of the

# ELEMENTS

second, $C$, that the sum of the third and sixth, $DH$, is of the fourth, $F$.

For, since $AB$ is the same multiple of $C$ that $DE$ is of $F$, therefore, as many magnitudes as there are in $AB$ equal to $C$, so many also are there in $DE$ equal to $F$.

For the same reason also,
as many as there are in $BG$ equal to $C$, so many are there also in $EH$ equal to $F$; therefore, as many as there are in the whole $AG$ equal to $C$, so many also are there in the whole $DH$ equal to $F$.

Therefore, whatever multiple $AG$ is of $C$, that multiple also is $DH$ of $F$.

Therefore the sum of the first and fifth, $AG$, is the same multiple of the second, $C$, that the sum of the third and sixth, $DH$, is of the fourth, $F$.

Therefore etc.
Q. E. D.

## Proposition 3

*If a first magnitude be the same multiple of a second that a third is of a fourth, and if equimultiples be taken of the first and third, then also ex aequali the magnitudes taken will be equimultiples respectively, the one of the second, and the other of the fourth.*

Let a first magnitude $A$ be the same multiple of a second $B$ that a third $C$ is of a fourth $D$, and let equimultiples $EF$, $GH$ be taken of $A$, $C$;

I say that $EF$ is the same multiple of $B$ that $GH$ is of $D$.

For, since $EF$ is the same multiple of $A$ that $GH$ is of $C$, therefore, as many magnitudes as there are in $EF$ equal to $A$, so many also are there in $GH$ equal to $C$.

Let $EF$ be divided into the magnitudes $EK$, $KF$ equal to $A$, and $GH$ into the magnitudes $GL$, $LH$ equal to $C$; then the multitude of the magnitudes $EK$, $KF$ will be equal to the multitude of the magnitudes $GL$, $LH$.

And, since $A$ is the same multiple of $B$ that $C$ is of $D$, while $EK$ is equal to $A$, and $GL$ to $C$, therefore $EK$ is the same multiple of $B$ that $GL$ is of $D$.

For the same reason $KF$ is the same multiple of $B$ that $LH$ is of $D$.

Since, then, a first magnitude $EK$ is the same multiple of a second $B$ that a third $GL$ is of a fourth $D$,
and a fifth $KF$ is also the same multiple of the second $B$ that a sixth $LH$ is of the fourth $D$,
therefore the sum of the first and fifth, $EF$, is also the same multiple of the second $B$ that the sum of the third and sixth, $GH$, is of the fourth $D$. [v. 2]

Therefore etc.
Q. E. D.

## Proposition 4

*If a first magnitude have to a second the same ratio as a third to a fourth, any equimultiples whatever of the first and third will also have the same ratio to any equimultiples whatever of the second and fourth respectively, taken in corresponding order.*

For let a first magnitude $A$ have to a second $B$ the same ratio as a third $C$ to a fourth $D$; and let equimultiples $E$, $F$ be taken of $A$, $C$, and $G$, $H$ other, chance, equimultiples of $B$, $D$;

I say that, as $E$ is to $G$, so is $F$ to $H$.

For let equimultiples $K$, $L$ be taken of $E$, $F$, and other, chance, equimultiples $M$, $N$ of $G$, $H$.

Since $E$ is the same multiple of $A$ that $F$ is of $C$, and equimultiples $K$, $L$ of $E$, $F$ have been taken, therefore $K$ is the same multiple of $A$ that $L$ is of $C$.  [v. 3]

For the same reason $M$ is the same multiple of $B$ that $N$ is of $D$.

And, since, as $A$ is to $B$, so is $C$ to $D$,

and of $A$, $C$ equimultiples $K$, $L$ have been taken,
and of $B$, $D$ other, chance, equimultiples $M$, $N$,
therefore, if $K$ is in excess of $M$, $L$ also is in excess of $N$,
if it is equal, equal, and if less, less.  [v. Def. 5]
And $K$, $L$ are equimultiples of $E$, $F$,
and $M$, $N$ other, chance, equimultiples of $G$, $H$;
therefore, as $E$ is to $G$, so is $F$ to $H$.  [v. Def. 5]

Therefore etc.

Q. E. D.

## Proposition 5

*If a magnitude be the same multiple of a magnitude that a part subtracted is of a part subtracted, the remainder will also be the same multiple of the remainder that the whole is of the whole.*

For let the magnitude $AB$ be the same multiple of the magnitude $CD$ that the part $AE$ subtracted is of the part $CF$ subtracted;

I say that the remainder $EB$ is also the same multiple of the remainder $FD$ that the whole $AB$ is of the whole $CD$.

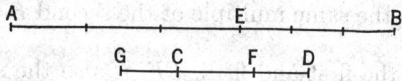

For, whatever multiple $AE$ is of $CF$, let $EB$ be made that multiple of $CG$.

Then, since $AE$ is the same multiple of $CF$ that $EB$ is of $GC$,
therefore $AE$ is the same multiple of $CF$ that $AB$ is of $GF$.  [v. 1]
But, by the assumption, $AE$ is the same multiple of $CF$ that $AB$ is of $CD$.
Therefore $AB$ is the same multiple of each of the magnitudes $GF$, $CD$;
therefore $GF$ is equal to $CD$.

Let $CF$ be subtracted from each;

therefore the remainder $GC$ is equal to the remainder $FD$.
And, since $AE$ is the same multiple of $CF$ that $EB$ is of $GC$,
and $GC$ is equal to $DF$,
therefore $AE$ is the same multiple of $CF$ that $EB$ is of $FD$.
But, by hypothesis,
$AE$ is the same multiple of $CF$ that $AB$ is of $CD$;
therefore $EB$ is the same multiple of $FD$ that $AB$ is of $CD$.
That is, the remainder $EB$ will be the same multiple of the remainder $FD$ that the whole $AB$ is of the whole $CD$.
Therefore etc. Q. E. D.

## Proposition 6

*If two magnitudes be equimultiples of two magnitudes, and any magnitudes subtracted from them be equimultiples of the same, the remainders also are either equal to the same or equimultiples of them.*

For let two magnitudes $AB$, $CD$ be equimultiples of two magnitudes $E$, $F$, and let $AG$, $CH$ subtracted from them be equimultiples of the same two $E$, $F$;
I say that the remainders also, $GB$, $HD$, are either equal to $E$, $F$ or equimultiples of them.
For, first, let $GB$ be equal to $E$;
I say that $HD$ is also equal to $F$.
For let $CK$ be made equal to $F$.
Since $AG$ is the same multiple of $E$ that $CH$ is of $F$,
while $GB$ is equal to $E$ and $KC$ to $F$,
therefore $AB$ is the same multiple of $E$ that $KH$ is of $F$. [v. 2]
But, by hypothesis, $AB$ is the same multiple of $E$ that $CD$ is of $F$;
therefore $KH$ is the same multiple of $F$ that $CD$ is of $F$.
Since then each of the magnitudes $KH$, $CD$ is the same multiple of $F$,
therefore $KH$ is equal to $CD$.
Let $CH$ be subtracted from each;
therefore the remainder $KC$ is equal to the remainder $HD$.
But $F$ is equal to $KC$;
therefore $HD$ is also equal to $F$.
Hence, if $GB$ is equal to $E$, $HD$ is also equal to $F$.
Similarly we can prove that, even if $GB$ be a multiple of $E$, $HD$ is also the same multiple of $F$.
Therefore etc. Q. E. D.

## Proposition 7

*Equal magnitudes have to the same the same ratio, as also has the same to equal magnitudes.*

Let $A$, $B$ be equal magnitudes and $C$ any other, chance, magnitude;
I say that each of the magnitudes $A$, $B$ has the same ratio to $C$, and $C$ has the same ratio to each of the magnitudes $A$, $B$.

For let equimultiples $D$, $E$ of $A$, $B$ be taken, and of $C$ another, chance, multiple $F$.
Then, since $D$ is the same multiple of $A$ that $E$ is of $B$, while $A$ is equal to $B$,
therefore $D$ is equal to $E$.

But $F$ is another, chance, magnitude.

If therefore $D$ is in excess of $F$, $E$ is also in excess of $F$, if equal to it, equal; and, if less, less.

And $D$, $E$ are equimultiples of $A$, $B$, while $F$ is another, chance, multiple of $C$; therefore, as $A$ is to $C$, so is $B$ to $C$.

[v. Def. 5]

I say next that $C$ also has the same ratio to each of the magnitudes $A$, $B$.

For, with the same construction, we can prove similarly that $D$ is equal to $E$; and $F$ is some other magnitude.

If therefore $F$ is in excess of $D$, it is also in excess of $E$, if equal, equal; and, if less, less.

And $F$ is a multiple of $C$, while $D$, $E$ are other, chance, equimultiples of $A$, $B$; therefore, as $C$ is to $A$, so is $C$ to $B$. [v. Def. 5]

Therefore etc.

PORISM. From this it is manifest that, if any magnitudes are proportional, they will also be proportional inversely.

Q. E. D.

## Proposition 8

*Of unequal magnitudes, the greater has to the same a greater ratio than the less has; and the same has to the less a greater ratio than it has to the greater.*

Let $AB$, $C$ be unequal magnitudes, and let $AB$ be greater; let $D$ be another, chance, magnitude;

I say that $AB$ has to $D$ a greater ratio than $C$ has to $D$, and $D$ has to $C$ a greater ratio than it has to $AB$.

For, since $AB$ is greater than $C$, let $BE$ be made equal to $C$;

then the less of the magnitudes $AE$, $EB$, if multiplied, will sometime be greater than $D$. [v. Def. 4]

First, let $AE$ be less than $EB$; let $AE$ be multiplied, and let $FG$ be a multiple of it which is greater than $D$;

then, whatever multiple $FG$ is of $AE$, let $GH$ be made the same multiple of $EB$ and $K$ of $C$;

and let $L$ be taken double of $D$, $M$ triple of it, and successive multiples increasing by one, until what is taken is a multiple of $D$ and the first that is greater than $K$. Let it be taken, and let it be $N$ which is quadruple of $D$ and the first multiple of it that is greater than $K$.

Then, since $K$ is less than $N$ first,
therefore $K$ is not less than $M$.

And, since $FG$ is the same multiple of $AE$ that $GH$ is of $EB$,
therefore $FG$ is the same multiple of $AE$ that $FH$ is of $AB$. [v. 1]

But $FG$ is the same multiple of $AE$ that $K$ is of $C$;
therefore $FH$ is the same multiple of $AB$ that $K$ is of $C$;
therefore $FH$, $K$ are equimultiples of $AB$, $C$.

Again, since $GH$ is the same multiple of $EB$ that $K$ is of $C$,
and $EB$ is equal to $C$,

therefore *GH* is equal to *K*.

But *K* is not less than *M*;

therefore neither is *GH* less than *M*.

And *FG* is greater than *D*;

therefore the whole *FH* is greater than *D*, *M* together.

But *D*, *M* together are equal to *N*, inasmuch as *M* is triple of *D*, and *M*, *D* together are quadruple of *D*, while *N* is also quadruple of *D*; whence *M*, *D* together are equal to *N*.

But *FH* is greater than *M*, *D*;

therefore *FH* is in excess of *N*,

while *K* is not in excess of *N*.

And *FH*, *K* are equimultiples of *AB*, *C*, while *N* is another, chance, multiple of *D*;

therefore *AB* has to *D* a greater ratio than *C* has to *D*. [v. Def. 7]

I say next, that *D* also has to *C* a greater ratio than *D* has to *AB*.

For, with the same construction, we can prove similarly that *N* is in excess of *K*, while *N* is not in excess of *FH*.

And *N* is a multiple of *D*,

while *FH*, *K* are other, chance, equimultiples of *AB*, *C*;

therefore *D* has to *C* a greater ratio than *D* has to *AB*. [v. Def. 7]

Again, let *AE* be greater than *EB*.

Then the less, *EB*, if multiplied, will sometime be greater than *D*. [v. Def. 4]

Let it be multiplied, and let *GH* be a multiple of *EB* and greater than *D*; and, whatever multiple *GH* is of *EB*, let *FG* be made the same multiple of *AE*, and *K* of *C*.

Then we can prove similarly that *FH*, *K* are equimultiples of *AB*, *C*;

and, similarly, let *N* be taken a multiple of *D* but the first that is greater than *FG*, so that *FG* is again not less than *M*.

But *GH* is greater than *D*;

therefore the whole *FH* is in excess of *D*, *M*, that is, of *N*.

Now *K* is not in excess of *N*, inasmuch as *FG* also, which is greater than *GH*, that is, than *K*, is not in excess of *N*.

And in the same manner, by following the above argument, we complete the demonstration.

Therefore etc.

Q. E. D.

## PROPOSITION 9

*Magnitudes which have the same ratio to the same are equal to one another; and magnitudes to which the same has the same ratio are equal.*

For let each of the magnitudes *A*, *B* have the same ratio to *C*;

I say that *A* is equal to *B*.

For, otherwise, each of the magnitudes *A*, *B* would not have had the same ratio to *C*;

but it has; [v. 8]

therefore *A* is equal to *B*.

Again, let $C$ have the same ratio to each of the magnitudes $A$, $B$;
I say that $A$ is equal to $B$.

For, otherwise, $C$ would not have had the same ratio to each of the magnitudes $A$, $B$; [v. 8]
but it has;
therefore $A$ is equal to $B$.

Therefore etc.

Q. E. D.

## Proposition 10

*Of magnitudes which have a ratio to the same, that which has a greater ratio is greater; and that to which the same has a greater ratio is less.*

For let $A$ have to $C$ a greater ratio than $B$ has to $C$;
I say that $A$ is greater than $B$.

For, if not, $A$ is either equal to $B$ or less.

Now $A$ is not equal to $B$;
for in that case each of the magnitudes $A$, $B$ would have had the same ratio to $C$; [v. 7]
but they have not;
therefore $A$ is not equal to $B$.

Nor again is $A$ less than $B$;
for in that case $A$ would have had to $C$ a less ratio than $B$ has to $C$; [v. 8]
but it has not;
therefore $A$ is not less than $B$.

But it was proved not to be equal either;
therefore $A$ is greater than $B$.

Again, let $C$ have to $B$ a greater ratio than $C$ has to $A$;
I say that $B$ is less than $A$.

For, if not, it is either equal or greater.

Now $B$ is not equal to $A$;
for in that case $C$ would have had the same ratio to each of the magnitudes $A$, $B$; [v. 7]
but it has not;
therefore $A$ is not equal to $B$.

Nor again is $B$ greater than $A$;
for in that case $C$ would have had to $B$ a less ratio than it has to $A$; [v. 8]
but it has not;
therefore $B$ is not greater than $A$.

But it was proved that it is not equal either;
therefore $B$ is less than $A$.

Therefore etc.

Q. E. D.

## Proposition 11

*Ratios which are the same with the same ratio are also the same with one another.*

For, as $A$ is to $B$, so let $C$ be to $D$,
and, as $C$ is to $D$, so let $E$ be to $F$;

I say that, as $A$ is to $B$, so is $E$ to $F$.

For of $A$, $C$, $E$ let equimultiples $G$, $H$, $K$ be taken, and of $B$, $D$, $F$ other,

```
A——        C——        E——
B——        D——        F—
G————      H————      K————
L————      M————      N————
```

chance, equimultiples $L$, $M$, $N$.

Then since, as $A$ is to $B$, so is $C$ to $D$,
    and of $A$, $C$ equimultiples $G$, $H$ have been taken,
    and of $B$, $D$ other, chance, equimultiples $L$, $M$,
therefore, if $G$ is in excess of $L$, $H$ is also in excess of $M$,
    if equal, equal,
    and if less, less.

Again, since, as $C$ is to $D$, so is $E$ to $F$,
    and of $C$, $E$ equimultiples $H$, $K$ have been taken,
    and of $D$, $F$ other, chance, equimultiples $M$, $N$,
therefore, if $H$ is in excess of $M$, $K$ is also in excess of $N$,
    if equal, equal,
    and if less, less.

But we saw that, if $H$ was in excess of $M$, $G$ was also in excess of $L$; if equal, equal; and if less, less;
so that, in addition, if $G$ is in excess of $L$, $K$ is also in excess of $N$,
    if equal, equal,
    and if less, less.

And $G$, $K$ are equimultiples of $A$, $E$,
    while $L$, $N$ are other, chance, equimultiples of $B$, $F$;
    therefore, as $A$ is to $B$, so is $E$ to $F$.

Therefore etc.

Q. E. D.

## Proposition 12

*If any number of magnitudes be proportional, as one of the antecedents is to one of the consequents, so will all the antecedents be to all the consequents.*

Let any number of magnitudes $A$, $B$, $C$, $D$, $E$, $F$ be proportional, so that, as $A$ is to $B$, so is $C$ to $D$ and $E$ to $F$;

I say that, as $A$ is to $B$, so are $A$, $C$, $E$ to $B$, $D$, $F$.

```
A——    B——    C——
D——    E——    F—
G————  L————
H————  M————
K——    N————
```

For of $A$, $C$, $E$ let equimultiples $G$, $H$, $K$ be taken,
and of $B$, $D$, $F$ other, chance, equimultiples $L$, $M$, $N$.

Then since, as $A$ is to $B$, so is $C$ to $D$, and $E$ to $F$,
and of $A$, $C$, $E$ equimultiples $G$, $H$, $K$ have been taken,
and of $B$, $D$, $F$ other, chance, equimultiples $L$, $M$, $N$,
therefore, if $G$ is in excess of $L$, $H$ is also in excess of $M$, and $K$ of $N$,
    if equal, equal,

and if less, less;
so that, in addition,
if $G$ is in excess of $L$, then $G, H, K$ are in excess of $L, M, N$,
if equal, equal,
and if less, less.

Now $G$ and $G, H, K$ are equimultiples of $A$ and $A, C, E$, since, if any number of magnitudes whatever are respectively equimultiples of any magnitudes equal in multitude, whatever multiple one of the magnitudes is of one, that multiple also will all be of all. [v. 1]

For the same reason
$L$ and $L, M, N$ are also equimultiples of $B$ and $B, D, F$;
therefore, as $A$ is to $B$, so are $A, C, E$ to $B, D, F$. [v. Def. 5]
Therefore etc.
Q. E. D.

## PROPOSITION 13

*If a first magnitude have to a second the same ratio as a third to a fourth, and the third have to the fourth a greater ratio than a fifth has to a sixth, the first will also have to the second a greater ratio than the fifth to the sixth.*

For let a first magnitude $A$ have to a second $B$ the same ratio as a third $C$ has to a fourth $D$,
and let the third $C$ have to the fourth $D$ a greater ratio than a fifth $E$ has to a sixth $F$;
I say that the first $A$ will also have to the second $B$ a greater ratio than the fifth $E$ to the sixth $F$.

A————
B——
C——————
D———
M————————
N—————
G————————————
K————

E—————
F————
H————————————
L——————————————

For, since there are some equimultiples of $C, E$,
and of $D, F$ other, chance, equimultiples, such that the multiple of $C$ is in excess of the multiple of $D$,
while the multiple of $E$ is not in excess of the multiple of $F$, [v. Def. 7]
let them be taken,
and let $G, H$ be equimultiples of $C, E$,
and $K, L$ other, chance, equimultiples of $D, F$,
so that $G$ is in excess of $K$, but $H$ is not in excess of $L$;
and, whatever multiple $G$ is of $C$, let $M$ be also that multiple of $A$,
and, whatever multiple $K$ is of $D$, let $N$ be also that multiple of $B$.
Now, since, as $A$ is to $B$, so is $C$ to $D$,
and of $A, C$ equimultiples $M, G$ have been taken,
and of $B, D$ other, chance, equimultiples $N, K$,
therefore, if $M$ is in excess of $N$, $G$ is also in excess of $K$,
if equal, equal,

and if less, less. [v. Def. 5]
But $G$ is in excess of $K$;
therefore $M$ is also in excess of $N$.
But $H$ is not in excess of $L$;
and $M$, $H$ are equimultiples of $A$, $E$,
and $N$, $L$ other, chance, equimultiples of $B$, $F$;
therefore $A$ has to $B$ a greater ratio than $E$ has to $F$. [v. Def. 7]
Therefore etc. Q. E. D.

## Proposition 14

*If a first magnitude have to a second the same ratio as a third has to a fourth, and the first be greater than the third, the second will also be greater than the fourth; if equal, equal; and if less, less.*

For let a first magnitude $A$ have the same ratio to a second $B$ as a third $C$ has to a fourth $D$; and let $A$ be greater than $C$;

I say that $B$ is also greater than $D$.

For, since $A$ is greater than $C$, and $B$ is another, chance, magnitude, therefore $A$ has to $B$ a greater ratio than $C$ has to $B$. [v. 8]

But, as $A$ is to $B$, so is $C$ to $D$;
therefore $C$ has also to $D$ a greater ratio than $C$ has to $B$. [v. 13]
But that to which the same has a greater ratio is less; [v. 10]
therefore $D$ is less than $B$;
so that $B$ is greater than $D$.

Similarly we can prove that, if $A$ be equal to $C$, $B$ will also be equal to $D$; and, if $A$ be less than $C$, $B$ will also be less than $D$.

Therefore etc. Q. E. D.

## Proposition 15

*Parts have the same ratio as the same multiples of them taken in corresponding order.*

For let $AB$ be the same multiple of $C$ that $DE$ is of $F$;

I say that, as $C$ is to $F$, so is $AB$ to $DE$.

For, since $AB$ is the same multiple of $C$ that $DE$ is of $F$, as many magnitudes as there are in $AB$ equal to $C$, so many are there also in $DE$ equal to $F$.

Let $AB$ be divided into the magnitudes $AG$, $GH$, $HB$ equal to $C$,
and $DE$ into the magnitudes $DK$, $KL$, $LE$ equal to $F$;
then the multitude of the magnitudes $AG$, $GH$, $HB$ will be equal to the multitude of the magnitudes $DK$, $KL$, $LE$.

And, since $AG$, $GH$, $HB$ are equal to one another,
and $DK$, $KL$, $LE$ are also equal to one another,
therefore, as $AG$ is to $DK$, so is $GH$ to $KL$, and $HB$ to $LE$. [v. 7]

Therefore, as one of the antecedents is to one of the consequents, so will all the antecedents be to all the consequents; [v. 12]
therefore, as $AG$ is to $DK$, so is $AB$ to $DE$.

## EUCLID

But $AG$ is equal to $C$ and $DK$ to $F$;
therefore, as $C$ is to $F$, so is $AB$ to $DE$.
Therefore etc.

Q. E. D.

### Proposition 16

*If four magnitudes be proportional, they will also be proportional alternately.*

Let $A, B, C, D$ be four proportional magnitudes,
so that, as $A$ is to $B$, so is $C$ to $D$;
I say that they will also be so alternately, that is, as $A$ is to $C$, so is $B$ to $D$.

For of $A, B$ let equimultiples $E, F$ be taken,
and of $C, D$ other, chance, equimultiples $G, H$.
Then, since $E$ is the same multiple of $A$ that $F$ is of $B$,
and parts have the same ratio as the same multiples of them,   [v. 15]
therefore, as $A$ is to $B$, so is $E$ to $F$.
But as $A$ is to $B$, so is $C$ to $D$;
therefore also, as $C$ is to $D$, so is $E$ to $F$.   [v. 11]
Again, since $G, H$ are equimultiples of $C, D$,
therefore, as $C$ is to $D$, so is $G$ to $H$.   [v. 15]
But, as $C$ is to $D$, so is $E$ to $F$;
therefore also, as $E$ is to $F$, so is $G$ to $H$.   [v. 11]
But, if four magnitudes be proportional, and the first be greater than the third,
the second will also be greater than the fourth;
if equal, equal;
and if less, less.   [v. 14]
Therefore, if $E$ is in excess of $G$, $F$ is also in excess of $H$,
if equal, equal,
and if less, less.
Now $E, F$ are equimultiples of $A, B$,
and $G, H$ other, chance, equimultiples of $C, D$;
therefore, as $A$ is to $C$, so is $B$ to $D$.   [v. Def. 5]
Therefore etc.

Q. E. D.

### Proposition 17

*If magnitudes be proportional componendo, they will also be proportional separando.*

Let $AB, BE, CD, DF$ be magnitudes proportional *componendo*, so that, as $AB$ is to $BE$, so is $CD$ to $DF$;
I say that they will also be proportional *separando*, that is, as $AE$ is to $EB$, so is $CF$ to $DF$.

For of $AE, EB, CF, FD$ let equimultiples $GH, HK, LM, MN$ be taken,
and of $EB, FD$ other, chance, equimultiples $KO, NP$.

Then, since $GH$ is the same multiple of $AE$ that $HK$ is of $EB$,
therefore $GH$ is the same multiple of $AE$ that $GK$ is of $AB$.  [v. 1]
But $GH$ is the same multiple of $AE$ that $LM$ is of $CF$;
therefore $GK$ is the same multiple of $AB$ that $LM$ is of $CF$.

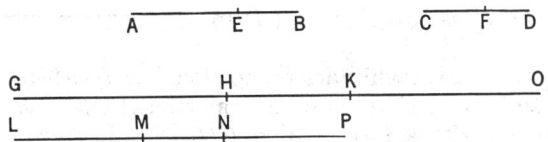

Again, since $LM$ is the same multiple of $CF$ that $MN$ is of $FD$,
therefore $LM$ is the same multiple of $CF$ that $LN$ is of $CD$.  [v. 1]
But $LM$ was the same multiple of $CF$ that $GK$ is of $AB$;
therefore $GK$ is the same multiple of $AB$ that $LN$ is of $CD$.
Therefore $GK$, $LN$ are equimultiples of $AB$, $CD$.
Again, since $HK$ is the same multiple of $EB$ that $MN$ is of $FD$,
and $KO$ is also the same multiple of $EB$ that $NP$ is of $FD$,
therefore the sum $HO$ is also the same multiple of $EB$ that $MP$ is of $FD$.
[v. 2]
And, since, as $AB$ is to $BE$, so is $CD$ to $DF$,
and of $AB$, $CD$ equimultiples $GK$, $LN$ have been taken,
and of $EB$, $FD$ equimultiples $HO$, $MP$,
therefore, if $GK$ is in excess of $HO$, $LN$ is also in excess of $MP$,
if equal, equal,
and if less, less.
Let $GH$ be in excess of $KO$;
then, if $HK$ be added to each,
$GK$ is also in excess of $HO$.
But we saw that, if $GK$ was in excess of $HO$, $LN$ was also in excess of $MP$;
therefore $LN$ is also in excess of $MP$,
and, if $MN$ be subtracted from each,
$LM$ is also in excess of $NP$;
so that, if $GH$ is in excess of $KO$, $LM$ is also in excess of $NP$.
Similarly we can prove that,
if $GH$ be equal to $KO$, $LM$ will also be equal to $NP$,
and if less, less.
And $GH$, $LM$ are equimultiples of $AE$, $CF$,
while $KO$, $NP$ are other, chance, equimultiples of $EB$, $FD$;
therefore, as $AE$ is to $EB$, so is $CF$ to $FD$.
Therefore etc. Q. E. D.

## Proposition 18

*If magnitudes be proportional* separando, *they will also be proportional* componendo.

Let $AE$, $EB$, $CF$, $FD$ be magnitudes proportional *separando*, so that, as $AE$ is to $EB$, so is $CF$ to $FD$;
I say that they will also be proportional *componendo*, that is, as $AB$ is to $BE$, so is $CD$ to $FD$.

For, if CD be not to DF as AB to BE,
then, as AB is to BE, so will CD be either to some magnitude less than DF or to a greater.

First, let it be in that ratio to a less magnitude DG.

Then, since, as AB is to BE, so is CD to DG,
    they are magnitudes proportional *componendo*;
      so that they will also be proportional *separando*.  [v. 17]
Therefore, as AE is to EB, so is CG to GD.
But also, by hypothesis,
      as AE is to EB, so is CF to FD.
Therefore also, as CG is to GD, so is CF to FD.  [v. 11]
But the first CG is greater than the third CF;
  therefore the second GD is also greater than the fourth FD.  [v. 14]
But it is also less: which is impossible.

Therefore, as AB is to BE, so is not CD to a less magnitude than FD.
Similarly we can prove that neither is it in that ratio to a greater;
    it is therefore in that ratio to FD itself.
Therefore etc.                 Q. E. D.

## Proposition 19

*If, as a whole is to a whole, so is a part subtracted to a part subtracted, the remainder will also be to the remainder as whole to whole.*

For, as the whole AB is to the whole CD, so let the part AE subtracted be to the part CF subtracted;

I say that the remainder EB will also be to the remainder FD as the whole AB to the whole CD.

For since, as AB is to CD, so is AE to CF,
    alternately also, as BA is to AE, so is DC to CF.  [v. 16]
And, since the magnitudes are proportional *componendo*, they will also be proportional *separando*,  [v. 17]
    that is, as BE is to EA, so is DF to CF,
    and, alternately,
    as BE is to DF, so is EA to FC.  [v. 16]
But, as AE is to CF, so by hypothesis is the whole AB to the whole CD.
Therefore also the remainder EB will be to the remainder FD as the whole AB is to the whole CD.  [v. 11]
Therefore etc.

[PORISM. From this it is manifest that, if magnitudes be proportional *componendo*, they will also be proportional *convertendo*.]   Q. E. D.

## Proposition 20

*If there be three magnitudes, and others equal to them in multitude, which taken two and two are in the same ratio, and if ex aequali the first be greater than the third, the fourth will also be greater than the sixth; if equal, equal; and, if less, less.*

Let there be three magnitudes A, B, C, and others D, E, F equal to them in multitude, which taken two and two are in the same ratio, so that,
    as A is to B, so is D to E,

and,
> as $B$ is to $C$, so is $E$ to $F$;
> and let $A$ be greater than $C$ ex aequali;

I say that $D$ will also be greater than $F$; if $A$ is equal to $C$, equal; and, if less, less.

For, since $A$ is greater than $C$, and $B$ is some other magnitude, and the greater has to the same a greater ratio than the less has, [v. 8] therefore $A$ has to $B$ a greater ratio than $C$ has to $B$.

But, as $A$ is to $B$, so is $D$ to $E$,
> and, as $C$ is to $B$, inversely, so is $F$ to $E$;

therefore $D$ has also to $E$ a greater ratio than $F$ has to $E$. [v. 13]

But, of magnitudes which have a ratio to the same, that which has a greater ratio is greater; [v. 10]
> therefore $D$ is greater than $F$.

Similarly we can prove that, if $A$ be equal to $C$, $D$ will also be equal to $F$; and if less, less.

Therefore etc.
Q. E. D.

## Proposition 21

*If there be three magnitudes, and others equal to them in multitude, which taken two and two together are in the same ratio, and the proportion of them be perturbed, then, if ex aequali the first magnitude is greater than the third, the fourth will also be greater than the sixth; if equal, equal; and if less, less.*

Let there be three magnitudes $A$, $B$, $C$, and others $D$, $E$, $F$ equal to them in multitude, which taken two and two are in the same ratio, and let the proportion of them be perturbed, so that,
> as $A$ is to $B$, so is $E$ to $F$,

and,
> as $B$ is to $C$, so is $D$ to $E$,
> and let $A$ be greater than $C$ ex aequali;

I say that $D$ will also be greater than $F$; if $A$ is equal to $C$, equal; and if less, less.

For, since $A$ is greater than $C$, and $B$ is some other magnitude, therefore $A$ has to $B$ a greater ratio than $C$ has to $B$. [v. 8]

But, as $A$ is to $B$, so is $E$ to $F$,
> and, as $C$ is to $B$, inversely, so is $E$ to $D$.

Therefore also $E$ has to $F$ a greater ratio than $E$ has to $D$. [v. 13]
But that to which the same has a greater ratio is less; [v. 10]
> therefore $F$ is less than $D$;
> therefore $D$ is greater than $F$.

Similarly we can prove that, if $A$ be equal to $C$, $D$ will also be equal to $F$; and if less, less.

Therefore etc.
Q. E. D.

## Proposition 22

*If there be any number of magnitudes whatever, and others equal to them in multitude, which taken two and two together are in the same ratio, they will also be in the same ratio* ex aequali.

Let there be any number of magnitudes $A$, $B$, $C$, and others $D$, $E$, $F$ equal to them in multitude, which taken two and two together are in the same ratio, so that,

as $A$ is to $B$, so is $D$ to $E$,
and, as $B$ is to $C$, so is $E$ to $F$;
I say that they will also be in the same ratio *ex aequali*,
<that is, as $A$ is to $C$, so is $D$ to $F$>.

For of $A$, $D$ let equimultiples $G$, $H$ be taken,
and of $B$, $E$ other, chance, equimultiples $K$, $L$;
and, further, of $C$, $F$ other, chance, equimultiples $M$, $N$.

Then, since, as $A$ is to $B$, so is $D$ to $E$,
and of $A$, $D$ equimultiples $G$, $H$ have been taken,
and of $B$, $E$ other, chance, equimultiples $K$, $L$,
therefore, as $G$ is to $K$, so is $H$ to $L$. [v. 4]
For the same reason also,
as $K$ is to $M$, so is $L$ to $N$.
Since, then, there are three magnitudes $G$, $K$, $M$, and others $H$, $L$, $N$ equal to them in multitude, which taken two and two together are in the same ratio,
therefore, *ex aequali*, if $G$ is in excess of $M$, $H$ is also in excess of $N$;
if equal, equal; and if less, less. [v. 20]
And $G$, $H$ are equimultiples of $A$, $D$,
and $M$, $N$ other, chance, equimultiples of $C$, $F$.
Therefore, as $A$ is to $C$, so is $D$ to $F$. [v. Def. 5]
Therefore etc.

Q. E. D.

## Proposition 23

*If there be three magnitudes, and others equal to them in multitude, which taken two and two together are in the same ratio, and the proportion of them be perturbed, they will also be in the same ratio* ex aequali.

Let there be three magnitudes $A$, $B$, $C$, and others equal to them in multitude, which, taken two and two together, are in the same proportion, namely $D$, $E$, $F$; and let the proportion of them be perturbed, so that,

as $A$ is to $B$, so is $E$ to $F$,
and, as $B$ is to $C$, so is $D$ to $E$;
I say that, as $A$ is to $C$, so is $D$ to $F$.
Of $A$, $B$, $D$ let equimultiples $G$, $H$, $K$ be taken,
and of $C$, $E$, $F$ other, chance, equimultiples $L$, $M$, $N$.
Then, since $G$, $H$ are equimultiples of $A$, $B$,

ELEMENTS V

and parts have the same ratio as the same multiples of them, [v. 15]
therefore, as $A$ is to $B$, so is $G$ to $H$.
For the same reason also,

as $E$ is to $F$, so is $M$ to $N$.
And, as $A$ is to $B$, so is $E$ to $F$;
therefore also, as $G$ is to $H$, so is $M$ to $N$. [v. 11]
Next, since, as $B$ is to $C$, so is $D$ to $E$,
alternately, also, as $B$ is to $D$, so is $C$ to $E$. [v. 16]
And, since $H$, $K$ are equimultiples of $B$, $D$,
and parts have the same ratio as their equimultiples,
therefore, as $B$ is to $D$, so is $H$ to $K$. [v. 15]
But, as $B$ is to $D$, so is $C$ to $E$;
therefore also, as $H$ is to $K$, so is $C$ to $E$. [v. 11]
Again, since $L$, $M$ are equimultiples of $C$, $E$,
therefore, as $C$ is to $E$, so is $L$ to $M$. [v. 15]
But, as $C$ is to $E$, so is $H$ to $K$;
therefore also, as $H$ is to $K$, so is $L$ to $M$, [v. 11]
and, alternately, as $H$ is to $L$, so is $K$ to $M$. [v. 16]
But it was also proved that,
as $G$ is to $H$, so is $M$ to $N$.
Since, then, there are three magnitudes $G$, $H$, $L$, and others equal to them in multitude $K$, $M$, $N$, which taken two and two together are in the same ratio,
and the proportion of them is perturbed,
therefore, *ex aequali*, if $G$ is in excess of $L$, $K$ is also in excess of $N$;
if equal, equal; and if less, less. [v. 21]
And $G$, $K$ are equimultiples of $A$, $D$,
and $L$ $N$ of $C$, $F$.
Therefore, as $A$ is to $C$, so is $D$ to $F$.
Therefore etc. Q. E. D.

## Proposition 24

*If a first magnitude have to a second the same ratio as a third has to a fourth, and also a fifth have to the second the same ratio as a sixth to the fourth, the first and fifth added together will have to the second the same ratio as the third and sixth have to the fourth.*

Let a first magnitude $AB$ have to a second $C$ the same ratio as a third $DE$ has to a fourth $F$; and let also a fifth $BG$ have to the second $C$ the same ratio as a sixth $EH$ has to the fourth $F$;
I say that the first and fifth added together, $AG$, will have to the second $C$ the same ratio as the third and sixth, $DH$, has to the fourth $F$.
For since, as $BG$ is to $C$, so is $EH$ to $F$,

inversely, as $C$ is to $BG$, so is $F$ to $EH$.

Since, then, as $AB$ is to $C$, so is $DE$ to $F$,
and, as $C$ is to $BG$, so is $F$ to $EH$,

therefore, *ex aequali*, as $AB$ is to $BG$, so is $DE$ to $EH$. [v. 22]

And, since the magnitudes are proportional *separando*, they will also be proportional *componendo*; [v. 18]

therefore, as $AG$ is to $GB$, so is $DH$ to $HE$.

But also, as $BG$ is to $C$, so is $EH$ to $F$;

therefore, *ex aequali*, as $AG$ is to $C$, so is $DH$ to $F$. [v. 22]

Therefore etc.

Q. E. D.

## Proposition 25

*If four magnitudes be proportional, the greatest and the least are greater than the remaining two.*

Let the four magnitudes $AB$, $CD$, $E$, $F$ be proportional so that, as $AB$ is to $CD$, so is $E$ to $F$, and let $AB$ be the greatest of them and $F$ the least;

I say that $AB$, $F$ are greater than $CD$, $E$.

For let $AG$ be made equal to $E$, and $CH$ equal to $F$.

Since, as $AB$ is to $CD$, so is $E$ to $F$,
and $E$ is equal to $AG$, and $F$ to $CH$,

therefore, as $AB$ is to $CD$, so is $AG$ to $CH$.

And since, as the whole $AB$ is to the whole $CD$, so is the part $AG$ subtracted to the part $CH$ subtracted,

the remainder $GB$ will also be to the remainder $HD$ as the whole $AB$ is to the whole $CD$. [v. 19]

But $AB$ is greater than $CD$;

therefore $GB$ is also greater than $HD$.

And, since $AG$ is equal to $E$, and $CH$ to $F$,

therefore $AG$, $F$ are equal to $CH$, $E$.

And if, $GB$, $HD$ being unequal, and $GB$ greater, $AG$, $F$ be added to $GB$ and $CH$, $E$ be added to $HD$,

it follows that $AB$, $F$ are greater than $CD$, $E$.

Therefore etc.

Q. E. D.

# BOOK SIX

## DEFINITIONS

1. *Similar rectilineal figures* are such as have their angles severally equal and the sides about the equal angles proportional.
2. A straight line is said to have been *cut in extreme and mean ratio* when, as the whole line is to the greater segment, so is the greater to the less.
3. The *height* of any figure is the perpendicular drawn from the vertex to the base.

## BOOK VI. PROPOSITIONS

### Proposition 1

*Triangles and parallelograms which are under the same height are to one another as their bases.*

Let $ABC$, $ACD$ be triangles and $EC$, $CF$ parallelograms under the same height;

I say that, as the base $BC$ is to the base $CD$, so is the triangle $ABC$ to the triangle $ACD$, and the parallelogram $EC$ to the parallelogram $CF$.

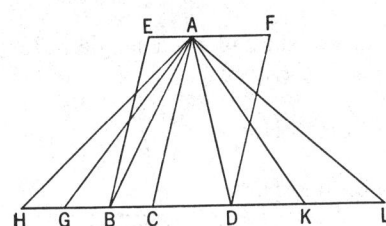

For let $BD$ be produced in both directions to the points $H$, $L$ and let [any number of straight lines] $BG$, $GH$ be made equal to the base $BC$, and any number of straight lines $DK$, $KL$ equal to the base $CD$;

let $AG$, $AH$, $AK$, $AL$ be joined.

Then, since $CB$, $BG$, $GH$ are equal to one another,

the triangles $ABC$, $AGB$, $AHG$ are also equal to one another. [i. 38]

Therefore, whatever multiple the base $HC$ is of the base $BC$, that multiple also is the triangle $AHC$ of the triangle $ABC$.

For the same reason,

whatever multiple the base $LC$ is of the base $CD$, that multiple also is the triangle $ALC$ of the triangle $ACD$;

and, if the base $HC$ is equal to the base $CL$, the triangle $AHC$ is also equal to the triangle $ACL$, [i. 38]

if the base $HC$ is in excess of the base $CL$, the triangle $AHC$ is also in excess of the triangle $ACL$,

and, if less, less.

Thus, there being four magnitudes, two bases $BC$, $CD$ and two triangles $ABC$, $ACD$,

equimultiples have been taken of the base $BC$ and the triangle $ABC$, namely the base $HC$ and the triangle $AHC$,
and of the base $CD$ and the triangle $ADC$ other, chance, equimultiples, namely the base $LC$ and the triangle $ALC$;

and it has been proved that,
if the base $HC$ is in excess of the base $CL$, the triangle $AHC$ is also in excess of the triangle $ALC$;

if equal, equal; and, if less, less.

Therefore, as the base $BC$ is to the base $CD$, so is the triangle $ABC$ to the triangle $ACD$. [v. Def. 5]

Next, since the parallelogram $EC$ is double of the triangle $ABC$, [I. 41]
and the parallelogram $FC$ is double of the triangle $ACD$,
while parts have the same ratio as the same multiples of them, [v. 15]
therefore, as the triangle $ABC$ is to the triangle $ACD$, so is the parallelogram $EC$ to the parallelogram $FC$.

Since, then, it was proved that, as the base $BC$ is to $CD$, so is the triangle $ABC$ to the triangle $ACD$,
and, as the triangle $ABC$ is to the triangle $ACD$, so is the parallelogram $EC$ to the parallelogram $CF$,
therefore also, as the base $BC$ is to the base $CD$, so is the parallelogram $EC$ to the parallelogram $FC$. [v. 11]

Therefore etc.

Q. E. D.

## Proposition 2

*If a straight line be drawn parallel to one of the sides of a triangle, it will cut the sides of the triangle proportionally; and, if the sides of the triangle be cut proportionally, the line joining the points of section will be parallel to the remaining side of the triangle.*

For let $DE$ be drawn parallel to $BC$, one of the sides of the triangle $ABC$;

I say that, as $BD$ is to $DA$, so is $CE$ to $EA$.

For let $BE$, $CD$ be joined.

Therefore the triangle $BDE$ is equal to the triangle $CDE$;
for they are on the same base $DE$ and in the same parallels $DE$, $BC$. [I. 38]

And the triangle $ADE$ is another area.

But equals have the same ratio to the same; [v. 7]
therefore, as the triangle $BDE$ is to the triangle $ADE$, so is the triangle $CDE$ to the triangle $ADE$.

But, as the triangle $BDE$ is to $ADE$, so is $BD$ to $DA$;
for, being under the same height, the perpendicular drawn from $E$ to $AB$, they are to one another as their bases. [VI. 1]

For the same reason also,

as the triangle $CDE$ is to $ADE$, so is $CE$ to $EA$.

Therefore also, as $BD$ is to $DA$, so is $CE$ to $EA$. [v. 11]

Again, let the sides $AB$, $AC$ of the triangle $ABC$ be cut proportionally, so that, as $BD$ is to $DA$, so is $CE$ to $EA$; and let $DE$ be joined.

I say that $DE$ is parallel to $BC$.

For, with the same construction,
since, as $BD$ is to $DA$, so is $CE$ to $EA$,
but, as $BD$ is to $DA$, so is the triangle $BDE$ to the triangle $ADE$,
and, as $CE$ is to $EA$, so is the triangle $CDE$ to the triangle $ADE$, [VI. 1]
therefore also,
as the triangle $BDE$ is to the triangle $ADE$, so is the triangle $CDE$ to the triangle $ADE$. [V. 11]
Therefore each of the triangles $BDE$, $CDE$ has the same ratio to $ADE$.
Therefore the triangle $BDE$ is equal to the triangle $CDE$; [V. 9]
and they are on the same base $DE$.
But equal triangles which are on the same base are also in the same parallels.
[I. 39]
Therefore $DE$ is parallel to $BC$.
Therefore etc.
Q. E. D.

## Proposition 3

*If an angle of a triangle be bisected and the straight line cutting the angle cut the base also, the segments of the base will have the same ratio as the remaining sides of the triangle; and, if the segments of the base have the same ratio as the remaining sides of the triangle, the straight line joined from the vertex to the point of section will bisect the angle of the triangle.*

Let $ABC$ be a triangle, and let the angle $BAC$ be bisected by the straight line $AD$;

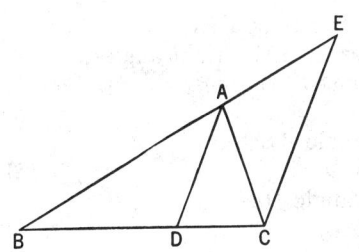

I say that, as $BD$ is to $CD$, so is $BA$ to $AC$.
For let $CE$ be drawn through $C$ parallel to $DA$, and let $BA$ be carried through and meet it at $E$.
Then, since the straight line $AC$ falls upon the parallels $AD$, $EC$,
the angle $ACE$ is equal to the angle $CAD$.
[I. 29]
But the angle $CAD$ is by hypothesis equal to the angle $BAD$;
therefore the angle $BAD$ is also equal to the angle $ACE$.
Again, since the straight line $BAE$ falls upon the parallels $AD$, $EC$,
the exterior angle $BAD$ is equal to the interior angle $AEC$. [I. 29]
But the angle $ACE$ was also proved equal to the angle $BAD$;
therefore the angle $ACE$ is also equal to the angle $AEC$,
so that the side $AE$ is also equal to the side $AC$. [I. 6]
And, since $AD$ has been drawn parallel to $EC$, one of the sides of the triangle $BCE$,
therefore, proportionally, as $BD$ is to $DC$, so is $BA$ to $AE$.
But $AE$ is equal to $AC$; [VI. 2]
therefore, as $BD$ is to $DC$, so is $BA$ to $AC$.
Again, let $BA$ be to $AC$ as $BD$ to $DC$, and let $AD$ be joined;
I say that the angle $BAC$ has been bisected by the straight line $AD$.
For, with the same construction,
since, as $BD$ is to $DC$, so is $BA$ to $AC$,
and also, as $BD$ is to $DC$, so is $BA$ to $AE$: for $AD$ has been drawn parallel to

$EC$, one of the sides of the triangle $BCE$: [VI. 2]
therefore also, as $BA$ is to $AC$, so is $BA$ to $AE$. [V. 11]
Therefore $AC$ is equal to $AE$, [V. 9]
so that the angle $AEC$ is also equal to the angle $ACE$. [I. 5]
But the angle $AEC$ is equal to the exterior angle $BAD$, [I. 29]
and the angle $ACE$ is equal to the alternate angle $CAD$; [*id.*]
therefore the angle $BAD$ is also equal to the angle $CAD$.
Therefore the angle $BAC$ has been bisected by the straight line $AD$.
Therefore etc.

Q. E. D.

## Proposition 4

*In equiangular triangles the sides about the equal angles are proportional, and those are corresponding sides which subtend the equal angles.*

Let $ABC$, $DCE$ be equiangular triangles having the angle $ABC$ equal to the angle $DCE$, the angle $BAC$ to the angle $CDE$, and further the angle $ACB$ to the angle $CED$;

I say that in the triangles $ABC$, $DCE$ the sides about the equal angles are proportional, and those are corresponding sides which subtend the equal angles.

For let $BC$ be placed in a straight line with $CE$.

Then, since the angles $ABC$, $ACB$ are less than two right angles, [I. 17]
and the angle $ACB$ is equal to the angle $DEC$,
therefore the angles $ABC$, $DEC$ are less than two right angles;
therefore $BA$, $ED$, when produced, will meet. [I. Post. 5]
Let them be produced and meet at $F$.

Now, since the angle $DCE$ is equal to the angle $ABC$,
$BF$ is parallel to $CD$. [I. 28]
Again, since the angle $ACB$ is equal to the angle $DEC$,
$AC$ is parallel to $FE$. [I. 28]
Therefore $FACD$ is a parallelogram;
therefore $FA$ is equal to $DC$, and $AC$ to $FD$. [I. 34]
And, since $AC$ has been drawn parallel to $FE$, one side of the triangle $FBE$,
therefore, as $BA$ is to $AF$, so is $BC$ to $CE$. [VI. 2]
But $AF$ is equal to $CD$;
therefore, as $BA$ is to $CD$, so is $BC$ to $CE$,
and alternately, as $AB$ is to $BC$, so is $DC$ to $CE$. [V. 16]
Again, since $CD$ is parallel to $BF$,
therefore, as $BC$ is to $CE$, so is $FD$ to $DE$. [VI. 2]
But $FD$ is equal to $AC$;
therefore, as $BC$ is to $CE$, so is $AC$ to $DE$,
and alternately, as $BC$ is to $CA$, so is $CE$ to $ED$. [V. 16]
Since, then, it was proved that,
as $AB$ is to $BC$, so is $DC$ to $CE$,
and, as $BC$ is to $CA$, so is $CE$ to $ED$;
therefore, *ex aequali*, as $BA$ is to $AC$, so is $CD$ to $DE$. [V. 22]
Therefore etc.

Q. E. D.

## Proposition 5

*If two triangles have their sides proportional, the triangles will be equiangular and will have those angles equal which the corresponding sides subtend.*

Let $ABC$, $DEF$ be two triangles having their sides proportional, so that,
as $AB$ is to $BC$, so is $DE$ to $EF$,
as $BC$ is to $CA$, so is $EF$ to $FD$,
and further, as $BA$ is to $AC$, so is $ED$ to $DF$;
I say that the triangle $ABC$ is equiangular with the triangle $DEF$, and they will have those angles equal which the corresponding sides subtend, namely the angle $ABC$ to the angle $DEF$, the angle $BCA$ to the angle $EFD$, and further the angle $BAC$ to the angle $EDF$.

For on the straight line $EF$, and at the points $E$, $F$ on it, let there be constructed the angle $FEG$ equal to the angle $ABC$, and the angle $EFG$ equal to the angle $ACB$; [I. 23]
therefore the remaining angle at $A$ is equal to the remaining angle at $G$. [I. 32]
Therefore the triangle $ABC$ is equiangular with the triangle $GEF$.

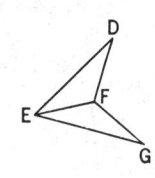

Therefore in the triangles $ABC$, $GEF$ the sides about the equal angles are proportional, and those are corresponding sides which subtend the equal angles; [VI. 4]
therefore, as $AB$ is to $BC$, so is $GE$ to $EF$.
But, as $AB$ is to $BC$, so by hypothesis is $DE$ to $EF$;
therefore, as $DE$ is to $EF$, so is $GE$ to $EF$. [V. 11]
Therefore each of the straight lines $DE$, $GE$ has the same ratio to $EF$;
therefore $DE$ is equal to $GE$. [V. 9]
For the same reason
$DF$ is also equal to $GF$.
Since then $DE$ is equal to $EG$,
and $EF$ is common,
the two sides $DE$, $EF$ are equal to the two sides $GE$, $EF$;
and the base $DF$ is equal to the base $FG$;
therefore the angle $DEF$ is equal to the angle $GEF$, [I. 8]
and the triangle $DEF$ is equal to the triangle $GEF$,
and the remaining angles are equal to the remaining angles, namely those which the equal sides subtend. [I. 4]
Therefore the angle $DFE$ is also equal to the angle $GFE$,
and the angle $EDF$ to the angle $EGF$.
And, since the angle $FED$ is equal to the angle $GEF$,
while the angle $GEF$ is equal to the angle $ABC$,
therefore the angle $ABC$ is also equal to the angle $DEF$.
For the same reason
the angle $ACB$ is also equal to the angle $DFE$,
and further, the angle at $A$ to the angle at $D$;
therefore the triangle $ABC$ is equiangular with the triangle $DEF$.
Therefore etc. Q. E. D.

## Proposition 6

*If two triangles have one angle equal to one angle and the sides about the equal angles proportional, the triangles will be equiangular and will have those angles equal which the corresponding sides subtend.*

Let $ABC$, $DEF$ be two triangles having one angle $BAC$ equal to one angle $EDF$ and the sides about the equal angles proportional, so that,

as $BA$ is to $AC$, so is $ED$ to $DF$;

I say that the triangle $ABC$ is equiangular with the triangle $DEF$, and will have the angle $ABC$ equal to the angle $DEF$, and the angle $ACB$ to the angle $DFE$.

For on the straight line $DF$, and at the points $D$, $F$ on it, let there be constructed the angle $FDG$ equal to either of the angles $BAC$, $EDF$, and the angle $DFG$ equal to the angle $ACB$;  [I. 23]
therefore the remaining angle at $B$ is equal to the remaining angle at $G$. [I. 32]

Therefore the triangle $ABC$ is equiangular with the triangle $DGF$.

Therefore, proportionally, as $BA$ is to $AC$, so is $GD$ to $DF$.  [VI. 4]

But, by hypothesis, as $BA$ is to $AC$, so also is $ED$ to $DF$;
therefore also, as $ED$ is to $DF$, so is $GD$ to $DF$.  [V. 11]

Therefore $ED$ is equal to $DG$;  [V. 9]
and $DF$ is common;
therefore the two sides $ED$, $DF$ are equal to the two sides $GD$, $DF$; and the angle $EDF$ is equal to the angle $GDF$;

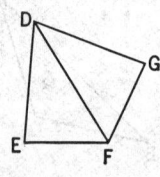

therefore the base $EF$ is equal to the base $GF$,
and the triangle $DEF$ is equal to the triangle $DGF$,
and the remaining angles will be equal to the remaining angles, namely those which the equal sides subtend.  [I. 4]

Therefore the angle $DFG$ is equal to the angle $DFE$,
and the angle $DGF$ to the angle $DEF$.

But the angle $DFG$ is equal to the angle $ACB$;
therefore the angle $ACB$ is also equal to the angle $DFE$.

And, by hypothesis, the angle $BAC$ is also equal to the angle $EDF$;
therefore the remaining angle at $B$ is also equal to the remaining angle at $E$;  [I. 32]

therefore the triangle $ABC$ is equiangular with the triangle $DEF$.

Therefore etc.

Q. E. D.

## Proposition 7

*If two triangles have one angle equal to one angle, the sides about other angles proportional, and the remaining angles either both less or both not less than a right angle, the triangles will be equiangular and will have those angles equal, the sides about which are proportional.*

Let $ABC$, $DEF$ be two triangles having one angle equal to one angle, the angle $BAC$ to the angle $EDF$, the sides about other angles $ABC$, $DEF$ proportional, so that, as $AB$ is to $BC$, so is $DE$ to $EF$, and, first, each of the remaining angles at $C$, $F$ less than a right angle;

I say that the triangle $ABC$ is equiangular with the triangle $DEF$, the angle $ABC$ will be equal to the angle $DEF$, and the remaining angle, namely the angle at $C$, equal to the remaining angle, the angle at $F$.

For, if the angle $ABC$ is unequal to the angle $DEF$, one of them is greater.

Let the angle $ABC$ be greater; and on the straight line $AB$, and at the point $B$ on it, let the angle $ABG$ be constructed equal to the angle $DEF$. [I. 23]

Then, since the angle $A$ is equal to $D$, and the angle $ABG$ to the angle $DEF$, therefore the remaining angle $AGB$ is equal to the remaining angle $DFE$. [I. 32]

Therefore the triangle $ABG$ is equiangular with the triangle $DEF$.

Therefore, as $AB$ is to $BG$, so is $DE$ to $EF$. [VI. 4]

But, as $DE$ is to $EF$, so by hypothesis is $AB$ to $BC$; therefore $AB$ has the same ratio to each of the straight lines $BC$, $BG$; [V. 11]

therefore $BC$ is equal to $BG$, [V. 9]

so that the angle at $C$ is also equal to the angle $BGC$. [I. 5]

But, by hypothesis, the angle at $C$ is less than a right angle; therefore the angle $BGC$ is also less than a right angle; so that the angle $AGB$ adjacent to it is greater than a right angle. [I. 13]

And it was proved equal to the angle at $F$; therefore the angle at $F$ is also greater than a right angle.

But it is by hypothesis less than a right angle: which is absurd.

Therefore the angle $ABC$ is not unequal to the angle $DEF$; therefore it is equal to it.

But the angle at $A$ is also equal to the angle at $D$; therefore the remaining angle at $C$ is equal to the remaining angle at $F$. [I. 32]

Therefore the triangle $ABC$ is equiangular with the triangle $DEF$.

But, again, let each of the angles at $C$, $F$ be supposed not less than a right angle;

I say again that, in this case too, the triangle $ABC$ is equiangular with the triangle $DEF$.

For, with the same construction, we can prove similarly that

$BC$ is equal to $BG$;

so that the angle at $C$ is also equal to the angle $BGC$. [I. 5]

But the angle at $C$ is not less than a right angle; therefore neither is the angle $BGC$ less than a right angle.

Thus in the triangle $BGC$ the two angles are not less than two right angles: which is impossible. [I. 17]

Therefore, once more, the angle $ABC$ is not unequal to the angle $DEF$; therefore it is equal to it.

But the angle at $A$ is also equal to the angle at $D$; therefore the remaining angle at $C$ is equal to the remaining angle at $F$. [I. 32]

Therefore the triangle $ABC$ is equiangular with the triangle $DEF$.

Therefore etc. Q. E. D.

## Proposition 8

*If in a right-angled triangle a perpendicular be drawn from the right angle to the base, the triangles adjoining the perpendicular are similar both to the whole and to one another.*

Let $ABC$ be a right-angled triangle having the angle $BAC$ right, and let $AD$ be drawn from $A$ perpendicular to $BC$;

I say that each of the triangles $ABD$, $ADC$ is similar to the whole $ABC$ and, further, they are similar to one another.

For, since the angle $BAC$ is equal to the angle $ADB$, for each is right, and the angle at $B$ is common to the two triangles $ABC$ and $ABD$,
therefore the remaining angle $ACB$ is equal to the remaining angle $BAD$; [I. 32]
therefore the triangle $ABC$ is equiangular with the triangle $ABD$.

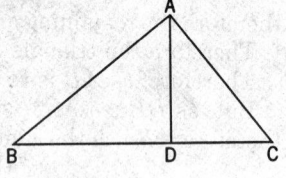

Therefore, as $BC$ which subtends the right angle in the triangle $ABC$ is to $BA$ which subtends the right angle in the triangle $ABD$, so is $AB$ itself which subtends the angle at $C$ in the triangle $ABC$ to $BD$ which subtends the equal angle $BAD$ in the triangle $ABD$, and so also is $AC$ to $AD$ which subtends the angle at $B$ common to the two triangles. [VI. 4]

Therefore the triangle $ABC$ is both equiangular to the triangle $ABD$ and has the sides about the equal angles proportional.

Therefore the triangle $ABC$ is similar to the triangle $ABD$. [VI. Def. 1]
Similarly we can prove that
the triangle $ABC$ is also similar to the triangle $ADC$;
therefore each of the triangles $ABD$, $ADC$ is similar to the whole $ABC$.

I say next that the triangles $ABD$, $ADC$ are also similar to one another.
For, since the right angle $BDA$ is equal to the right angle $ADC$,
and moreover the angle $BAD$ was also proved equal to the angle at $C$,
therefore the remaining angle at $B$ is also equal to the remaining angle $DAC$;
[I. 32]
therefore the triangle $ABD$ is equiangular with the triangle $ADC$.

Therefore, as $BD$ which subtends the angle $BAD$ in the triangle $ABD$ is to $DA$ which subtends the angle at $C$ in the triangle $ADC$ equal to the angle $BAD$, so is $AD$ itself which subtends the angle at $B$ in the triangle $ABD$ to $DC$ which subtends the angle $DAC$ in the triangle $ADC$ equal to the angle at $B$, and so also is $BA$ to $AC$, these sides subtending the right angles; [VI. 4]
therefore the triangle $ABD$ is similar to the triangle $ADC$. [VI. Def. 1]
Therefore etc.

PORISM. From this it is clear that, if in a right-angled triangle a perpendicular be drawn from the right angle to the base, the straight line so drawn is a mean proportional between the segments of the base. Q. E. D.

## Proposition 9

*From a given straight line to cut off a prescribed part.*

Let $AB$ be the given straight line;
thus it is required to cut off from $AB$ a prescribed part.

# ELEMENTS VI

Let the third part be that prescribed.
Let a straight line $AC$ be drawn through from $A$ containing with $AB$ any angle;

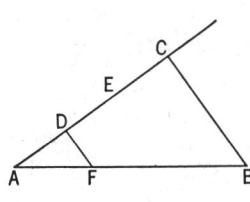

let a point $D$ be taken at random on $AC$, and let $DE$, $EC$ be made equal to $AD$. [I. 3]

Let $BC$ be joined, and through $D$ let $DF$ be drawn parallel to it. [I. 31]

Then, since $FD$ has been drawn parallel to $BC$, one of the sides of the triangle $ABC$,

therefore, proportionally, as $CD$ is to $DA$, so is $BF$ to $FA$. [VI. 2]

But $CD$ is double of $DA$;
therefore $BF$ is also double of $FA$;
therefore $BA$ is triple of $AF$.

Therefore from the given straight line $AB$ the prescribed third part $AF$ has been cut off. Q. E. F.

## Proposition 10

*To cut a given uncut straight line similarly to a given cut straight line.*

Let $AB$ be the given uncut straight line, and $AC$ the straight line cut at the points $D$, $E$; and let them be so placed as to contain any angle;

let $CB$ be joined, and through $D$, $E$ let $DF$, $EG$ be drawn parallel to $BC$, and through $D$ let $DHK$ be drawn parallel to $AB$. [I. 31]

Therefore each of the figures $FH$, $HB$ is a parallelogram;
therefore $DH$ is equal to $FG$ and $HK$ to $GB$. [I. 34]

Now, since the straight line $HE$ has been drawn parallel to $KC$, one of the sides of the triangle $DKC$,

therefore, proportionally, as $CE$ is to $ED$, so is $KH$ to $HD$. [VI. 2]

But $KH$ is equal to $BG$, and $HD$ to $GF$;
therefore, as $CE$ is to $ED$, so is $BG$ to $GF$.

Again, since $FD$ has been drawn parallel to $GE$, one of the sides of the triangle $AGE$,

therefore, proportionally, as $ED$ is to $DA$, so is $GF$ to $FA$. [VI. 2]

But it was also proved that,
as $CE$ is to $ED$, so is $BG$ to $GF$;
therefore, as $CE$ is to $ED$, so is $BG$ to $GF$,
and, as $ED$ is to $DA$, so is $GF$ to $FA$.

Therefore the given uncut straight line $AB$ has been cut similarly to the given cut straight line $AC$. Q. E. F.

## Proposition 11

*To two given straight lines to find a third proportional.*

Let $BA$, $AC$ be the two given straight lines, and let them be placed so as to contain any angle;

thus it is required to find a third proportional to $BA$, $AC$.

For let them be produced to the points *D*, *E*, and let *BD* be made equal to *AC*; [I. 3]
let *BC* be joined, and through *D* let *DE* be drawn parallel to it. [I. 31]

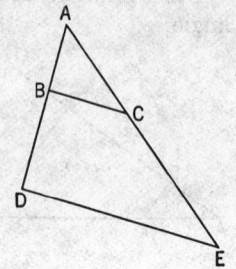

Since, then, *BC* has been drawn parallel to *DE*, one of the sides of the triangle *ADE*, proportionally, as *AB* is to *BD*, so is *AC* to *CE*. [VI. 2]

But *BD* is equal to *AC*;
 therefore, as *AB* is to *AC*, so is *AC* to *CE*.

Therefore to two given straight lines *AB*, *AC* a third proportional to them, *CE*, has been found.  Q. E. F.

PROPOSITION 12

*To three given straight lines to find a fourth proportional.*
 Let *A*, *B*, *C* be the three given straight lines;
  thus it is required to find a fourth proportional to *A*, *B*, *C*.

Let two straight lines *DE*, *DF* be set out containing any angle *EDF*;
let *DG* be made equal to *A*, *GE* equal to *B*, and further *DH* equal to *C*;
 let *GH* be joined, and let *EF* be drawn through *E* parallel to it. [I. 31]
Since, then, *GH* has been drawn parallel to *EF*, one of the sides of the triangle *DEF*,
  therefore, as *DG* is to *GE*, so is *DH* to *HF*. [VI. 2]
But *DG* is equal to *A*, *GE* to *B*, and *DH* to *C*;
  therefore, as *A* is to *B*, so is *C* to *HF*.
Therefore to the three given straight lines *A*, *B*, *C* a fourth proportional *HF* has been found.  Q. E. F.

PROPOSITION 13

*To two given straight lines to find a mean proportional.*
 Let *AB*, *BC* be the two given straight lines;
thus it is required to find a mean proportional to *AB*, *BC*.

Let them be placed in a straight line, and let the semicircle *ADC* be described on *AC*;
let *BD* be drawn from the point *B* at right angles to the straight line *AC*, and let *AD*, *DC* be joined.
 Since the angle *ADC* is an angle in a semicircle, it is right. [III. 31]
 And, since, in the right-angled triangle *ADC*, *DB* has been drawn from the right angle perpendicular to the base,

# ELEMENTS VI

therefore $DB$ is a mean proportional between the segments of the base, $AB$, $BC$. [VI. 8, Por.]

Therefore to the two given straight lines $AB$, $BC$ a mean proportional $DB$ has been found.   Q. E. F.

## PROPOSITION 14

*In equal and equiangular parallelograms the sides about the equal angles are reciprocally proportional; and equiangular parallelograms in which the sides about the equal angles are reciprocally proportional are equal.*

Let $AB$, $BC$ be equal and equiangular parallelograms having the angles at $B$ equal, and let $DB$, $BE$ be placed in a straight line;

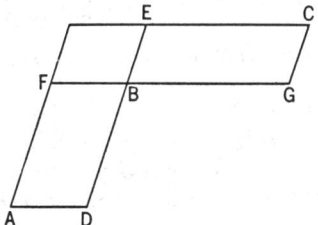

therefore $FB$, $BG$ are also in a straight line. [I. 14]

I say that, in $AB$, $BC$, the sides about the equal angles are reciprocally proportional, that is to say, that, as $DB$ is to $BE$, so is $GB$ to $BF$.

For let the parallelogram $FE$ be completed.

Since, then, the parallelogram $AB$ is equal to the parallelogram $BC$, and $FE$ is another area,

therefore, as $AB$ is to $FE$, so is $BC$ to $FE$. [v. 7]
But, as $AB$ is to $FE$, so is $DB$ to $BE$, [VI. 1]
and, as $BC$ is to $FE$, so is $GB$ to $BF$. [*id.*]
therefore also, as $DB$ is to $BE$, so is $GB$ to $BF$. [v. 11]

Therefore in the parallelograms $AB$, $BC$ the sides about the equal angles are reciprocally proportional.

Next, let $GB$ be to $BF$ as $DB$ to $BE$;

I say that the parallelogram $AB$ is equal to the parallelogram $BC$.

For since, as $DB$ is to $BE$, so is $GB$ to $BF$,

while, as $DB$ is to $BE$, so is the parallelogram $AB$ to the parallelogram $FE$, [VI. 1]

and, as $GB$ is to $BF$, so is the parallelogram $BC$ to the parallelogram $FE$, [VI. 1]

therefore also, as $AB$ is to $FE$, so is $BC$ to $FE$; [v. 11]

therefore the parallelogram $AB$ is equal to the parallelogram $BC$. [v. 9]

Therefore etc.   Q. E. D.

## PROPOSITION 15

*In equal triangles which have one angle equal to one angle the sides about the equal angles are reciprocally proportional; and those triangles which have one angle equal to one angle, and in which the sides about the equal angles are reciprocally proportional, are equal.*

Let $ABC$, $ADE$ be equal triangles having one angle equal to one angle, namely the angle $BAC$ to the angle $DAE$;

I say that in the triangles $ABC$, $ADE$ the sides about the equal angles are reciprocally proportional, that is to say, that,

as $CA$ is to $AD$, so is $EA$ to $AB$.

For let them be placed so that $CA$ is in a straight line with $AD$;

therefore $EA$ is also in a straight line with $AB$. [I. 14]

Let *BD* be joined.

Since, then, the triangle *ABC* is equal to the triangle *ADE*, and *BAD* is another area,

therefore, as the triangle *CAB* is to the triangle *BAD*, so is the triangle *EAD* to the triangle *BAD*. [v. 7]

But, as *CAB* is to *BAD*, so is *CA* to *AD*, [vi. 1]

and, as *EAD* is to *BAD*, so is *EA* to *AB*. [*id.*]

Therefore also, as *CA* is to *AD*, so is *EA* to *AB*. [v. 11]

Therefore in the triangles *ABC*, *ADE* the sides about the equal angles are reciprocally proportional.

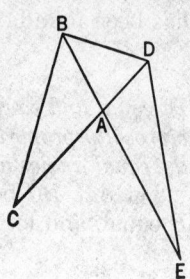

Next, let the sides of the triangles *ABC*, *ADE* be reciprocally proportional, that is to say, let *EA* be to *AB* as *CA* to *AD*;

I say that the triangle *ABC* is equal to the triangle *ADE*.

For, if *BD* be again joined,

since, as *CA* is to *AD*, so is *EA* to *AB*,

while, as *CA* is to *AD*, so is the triangle *ABC* to the triangle *BAD*,

and, as *EA* is to *AB*, so is the triangle *EAD* to the triangle *BAD*, [vi. 1]

therefore, as the triangle *ABC* is to the triangle *BAD*, so is the triangle *EAD* to the triangle *BAD*. [v. 11]

Therefore each of the triangles *ABC*, *EAD* has the same ratio to *BAD*.

Therefore the triangle *ABC* is equal to the triangle *EAD*. [v. 9]

Therefore etc.

Q. E. D.

## Proposition 16

*If four straight lines be proportional, the rectangle contained by the extremes is equal to the rectangle contained by the means; and, if the rectangle contained by the extremes be equal to the rectangle contained by the means, the four straight lines will be proportional.*

Let the four straight lines *AB*, *CD*, *E*, *F* be proportional, so that, as *AB* is to *CD*, so is *E* to *F*;

I say that the rectangle contained by *AB*, *F* is equal to the rectangle contained by *CD*, *E*.

Let *AG*, *CH* be drawn from the points *A*, *C* at right angles to the straight lines *AB*, *CD*, and let *AG* be made equal to *F*, and *CH* equal to *E*.

Let the parallelograms *BG*, *DH* be completed.

Then since, as *AB* is to *CD*, so is *E* to *F*,

while *E* is equal to *CH*, and *F* to *AG*,

therefore, as *AB* is to *CD*, so is *CH* to *AG*.

Therefore in the parallelograms *BG*, *DH* the sides about the equal angles are reciprocally proportional.

But those equiangular parallelograms in which the sides about the equal angles are reciprocally proportional are equal; [vi. 14] therefore the parallelogram $BG$ is equal to the parallelogram $DH$.

And $BG$ is the rectangle $AB$, $F$, for $AG$ is equal to $F$;
and $DH$ is the rectangle $CD$, $E$, for $E$ is equal to $CH$;
therefore the rectangle contained by $AB$, $F$ is equal to the rectangle contained by $CD$, $E$.

Next, let the rectangle contained by $AB$, $F$ be equal to the rectangle contained by $CD$, $E$;
I say that the four straight lines will be proportional, so that, as $AB$ is to $CD$, so is $E$ to $F$.

For, with the same construction,
since the rectangle $AB$, $F$ is equal to the rectangle $CD$, $E$,
and the rectangle $AB$, $F$ is $BG$, for $AG$ is equal to $F$,
and the rectangle $CD$, $E$ is $DH$, for $CH$ is equal to $E$,
therefore $BG$ is equal to $DH$.

And they are equiangular.

But in equal and equiangular parallelograms the sides about the equal angles are reciprocally proportional. [VI. 14]

Therefore, as $AB$ is to $CD$, so is $CH$ to $AG$.

But $CH$ is equal to $E$, and $AG$ to $F$;
therefore, as $AB$ is to $CD$, so is $E$ to $F$.

Therefore etc. Q. E. D.

## Proposition 17

*If three straight lines be proportional, the rectangle contained by the extremes is equal to the square on the mean; and, if the rectangle contained by the extremes be equal to the square on the mean, the three straight lines will be proportional.*

Let the three straight lines $A$, $B$, $C$ be proportional, so that, as $A$ is to $B$, so is $B$ to $C$;
I say that the rectangle contained by $A$, $C$ is equal to the square on $B$.

Let $D$ be made equal to $B$.

Then, since, as $A$ is to $B$, so is $B$ to $C$,
and $B$ is equal to $D$,
therefore, as $A$ is to $B$, so is $D$ to $C$.

But, if four straight lines be proportional, the rectangle contained by the extremes is equal to the rectangle contained by the means. [VI. 16]

Therefore the rectangle $A$, $C$ is equal to the rectangle $B$, $D$.

But the rectangle $B$, $D$ is the square on $B$, for $B$ is equal to $D$;
therefore the rectangle contained by $A$, $C$ is equal to the square on $B$.

Next, let the rectangle $A$, $C$ be equal to the square on $B$; I say that, as $A$ is to $B$, so is $B$ to $C$.

For, with the same construction,
since the rectangle $A$, $C$ is equal to the square on $B$,
while the square on $B$ is the rectangle $B$, $D$, for $B$ is equal to $D$,
therefore the rectangle $A$, $C$ is equal to the rectangle $B$, $D$.

But, if the rectangle contained by the extremes be equal to that contained by the means, the four straight lines are proportional. [VI. 16]

Therefore, as $A$ is to $B$, so is $D$ to $C$.

But $B$ is equal to $D$;
therefore, as $A$ is to $B$, so is $B$ to $C$.
Therefore etc.

Q. E. D.

## Proposition 18

*On a given straight line to describe a rectilineal figure similar and similarly situated to a given rectilineal figure.*

Let $AB$ be the given straight line and $CE$ the given rectilineal figure; thus it is required to describe on the straight line $AB$ a rectilineal figure similar and similarly situated to the rectilineal figure $CE$.

Let $DF$ be joined, and on the straight line $AB$, and at the points $A$, $B$ on it, let the angle $GAB$ be constructed equal to the angle at $C$, and the angle $ABG$ equal to the angle $CDF$. [I. 23]

 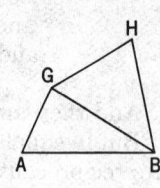

Therefore the remaining angle $CFD$ is equal to the angle $AGB$; [I. 32]
therefore the triangle $FCD$ is equiangular with the triangle $GAB$.

Therefore, proportionally, as $FD$ is to $GB$, so is $FC$ to $GA$, and $CD$ to $AB$.

Again, on the straight line $BG$, and at the points $B$, $G$ on it, let the angle $BGH$ be constructed equal to the angle $DFE$, and the angle $GBH$ equal to the angle $FDE$. [I. 23]

Therefore the remaining angle at $E$ is equal to the remaining angle at $H$; [I. 32]
therefore the triangle $FDE$ is equiangular with the triangle $GBH$;
therefore, proportionally, as $FD$ is to $GB$, so is $FE$ to $GH$, and $ED$ to $HB$. [VI. 4]

But it was also proved that, as $FD$ is to $GB$, so is $FC$ to $GA$, and $CD$ to $AB$; therefore also, as $FC$ is to $AG$, so is $CD$ to $AB$, and $FE$ to $GH$, and further $ED$ to $HB$.

And, since the angle $CFD$ is equal to the angle $AGB$,
and the angle $DFE$ to the angle $BGH$,
therefore the whole angle $CFE$ is equal to the whole angle $AGH$.
For the same reason
the angle $CDE$ is also equal to the angle $ABH$.
And the angle at $C$ is also equal to the angle at $A$,
and the angle at $E$ to the angle at $H$.
Therefore $AH$ is equiangular with $CE$;
and they have the sides about their equal angles proportional;
therefore the rectilineal figure $AH$ is similar to the rectilineal figure $CE$.
[VI. Def. 1]

Therefore on the given straight line $AB$ the rectilineal figure $AH$ has been described similar and similarly situated to the given rectilineal figure $CE$.

Q. E. F.

## Proposition 19

*Similar triangles are to one another in the duplicate ratio of the corresponding sides.*

Let $ABC$, $DEF$ be similar triangles having the angle at $B$ equal to the angle

ELEMENTS VI         113

at $E$, and such that, as $AB$ is to $BC$, so is $DE$ to $EF$, so that $BC$ corresponds to $EF$; [v. Def. 11]

I say that the triangle $ABC$ has to the triangle $DEF$ a ratio duplicate of that which $BC$ has to $EF$.

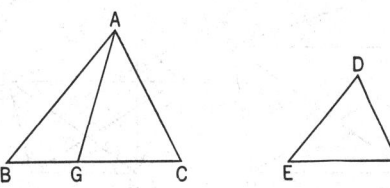

For let a third proportional $BG$ be taken to $BC$, $EF$, so that, as $BC$ is to $EF$, so is $EF$ to $BG$; [VI. 11]
and let $AG$ be joined.

Since then, as $AB$ is to $BC$, so is $DE$ to $EF$,
therefore, alternately, as $AB$ is to $DE$, so is $BC$ to $EF$. [v. 16]

But, as $BC$ is to $EF$, so is $EF$ to $BG$;
therefore also, as $AB$ is to $DE$, so is $EF$ to $BG$. [v. 11]

Therefore in the triangles $ABG$, $DEF$ the sides about the equal angles are reciprocally proportional.

But those triangles which have one angle equal to one angle, and in which the sides about the equal angles are reciprocally proportional, are equal; [VI. 15]

therefore the triangle $ABG$ is equal to the triangle $DEF$.

Now since, as $BC$ is to $EF$, so is $EF$ to $BG$,
and, if three straight lines be proportional, the first has to the third a ratio duplicate of that which it has to the second, [v. Def. 9]
therefore $BC$ has to $BG$ a ratio duplicate of that which $CB$ has to $EF$.

But, as $CB$ is to $BG$, so is the triangle $ABC$ to the triangle $ABG$; [VI. 1]
therefore the triangle $ABC$ also has to the triangle $ABG$ a ratio duplicate of that which $BC$ has to $EF$.

But the triangle $ABG$ is equal to the triangle $DEF$;
therefore the triangle $ABC$ also has to the triangle $DEF$ a ratio duplicate of that which $BC$ has to $EF$.

Therefore etc.

PORISM. From this it is manifest that, if three straight lines be proportional, then, as the first is to the third, so is the figure described on the first to that which is similar and similarly described on the second.    Q. E. D.

PROPOSITION 20

*Similar polygons are divided into similar triangles, and into triangles equal in multitude and in the same ratio as the wholes, and the polygon has to the polygon a ratio duplicate of that which the corresponding side has to the corresponding side.*

Let $ABCDE$, $FGHKL$ be similar polygons, and let $AB$ correspond to $FG$;

I say that the polygons $ABCDE$, $FGHKL$ are divided into similar triangles, and into triangles equal in multitude and in the same ratio as the wholes, and the polygon $ABCDE$ has to the polygon $FGHKL$ a ratio duplicate of that which $AB$ has to $FG$.

Let $BE$, $EC$, $GL$, $LH$ be joined.

Now, since the polygon $ABCDE$ is similar to the polygon $FGHKL$,
the angle $BAE$ is equal to the angle $GFL$;
and, as $BA$ is to $AE$, so is $GF$ to $FL$. [VI. Def. 1]

Since then $ABE$, $FGL$ are two triangles having one angle equal to one angle

114                                   EUCLID

and the sides about the equal angles proportional,
therefore the triangle *ABE* is equiangular with the triangle *FGL*; [VI. 6]
so that it is also similar; [VI. 4 and Def. 1]
therefore the angle *ABE* is equal to the angle *FGL*.

But the whole angle *ABC* is also equal to the whole angle *FGH* because of the similarity of the polygons;
therefore the remaining angle *EBC* is equal to the angle *LGH*.

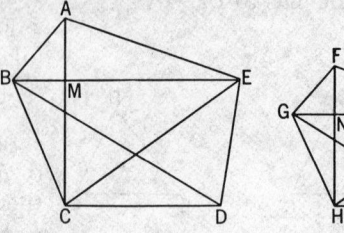

And, since, because of the similarity of the triangles *ABE*, *FGL*,
as *EB* is to *BA*, so is *LG* to *GF*,
and moreover also, because of the similarity of the polygons,
as *AB* is to *BC*, so is *FG* to *GH*,
therefore, *ex aequali*, as *EB* is to *BC*, so is *LG* to *GH*; [V. 22]
that is, the sides about the equal angles *EBC*, *LGH* are proportional;
therefore the triangle *EBC* is equiangular with the triangle *LGH*, [VI. 6]
so that the triangle *EBC* is also similar to the triangle *LGH*. [VI. 4 and Def. 1]
For the same reason
the triangle *ECD* is also similar to the triangle *LHK*.

Therefore the similar polygons *ABCDE*, *FGHKL* have been divided into similar triangles, and into triangles equal in multitude.

I say that they are also in the same ratio as the wholes, that is, in such manner that the triangles are proportional, and *ABE*, *EBC*, *ECD* are antecedents, while *FGL*, *LGH*, *LHK* are their consequents, and that the polygon *ABCDE* has to the polygon *FGHKL* a ratio duplicate of that which the corresponding side has to the corresponding side, that is *AB* to *FG*.

For let *AC*, *FH* be joined.

Then since, because of the similarity of the polygons,
the angle *ABC* is equal to the angle *FGH*,
and, as *AB* is to *BC*, so is *FG* to *GH*,
the triangle *ABC* is equiangular with the triangle *FGH*; [VI. 6]
therefore the angle *BAC* is equal to the angle *GFH*,
and the angle *BCA* to the angle *GHF*.
And, since the angle *BAM* is equal to the angle *GFN*,
and the angle *ABM* is also equal to the angle *FGN*,
therefore the remaining angle *AMB* is also equal to the remaining angle *FNG*;
[I. 32]
therefore the triangle *ABM* is equiangular with the triangle *FGN*.
Similarly we can prove that
the triangle *BMC* is also equiangular with the triangle *GNH*.
Therefore, proportionally, as *AM* is to *MB*, so is *FN* to *NG*,
and, as *BM* is to *MC*, so is *GN* to *NH*;
so that, in addition, *ex aequali*,
as *AM* is to *MC*, so is *FN* to *NH*.
But, as *AM* is to *MC*, so is the triangle *ABM* to *MBC*, and *AME* to *EMC*;
for they are to one another as their bases. [VI. 1]

# ELEMENTS VI

Therefore also, as one of the antecedents is to one of the consequents, so are all the antecedents to all the consequents; [v. 12]
therefore, as the triangle $AMB$ is to $BMC$, so is $ABE$ to $CBE$.
But, as $AMB$ is to $BMC$, so is $AM$ to $MC$;
therefore also, as $AM$ is to $MC$, so is the triangle $ABE$ to the triangle $EBC$.
For the same reason also,
as $FN$ is to $NH$, so is the triangle $FGL$ to the triangle $GLH$.
And, as $AM$ is to $MC$, so is $FN$ to $NH$;
therefore also, as the triangle $ABE$ is to the triangle $BEC$, so is the triangle $FGL$ to the triangle $GLH$;
and, alternately, as the triangle $ABE$ is to the triangle $FGL$, so is the triangle $BEC$ to the triangle $GLH$.

Similarly we can prove, if $BD$, $GK$ be joined, that, as the triangle $BEC$ is to the triangle $LGH$, so also is the triangle $ECD$ to the triangle $LHK$.

And since, as the triangle $ABE$ is to the triangle $FGL$, so is $EBC$ to $LGH$, and further $ECD$ to $LHK$,
therefore also, as one of the antecedents is to one of the consequents, so are all the antecedents to all the consequents; [v. 12]
therefore, as the triangle $ABE$ is to the triangle $FGL$,
so is the polygon $ABCDE$ to the polygon $FGHKL$.

But the triangle $ABE$ has to the triangle $FGL$ a ratio duplicate of that which the corresponding side $AB$ has to the corresponding side $FG$; for similar triangles are in the duplicate ratio of the corresponding sides. [VI. 19]

Therefore the polygon $ABCDE$ also has to the polygon $FGHKL$ a ratio duplicate of that which the corresponding side $AB$ has to the corresponding side $FG$.

Therefore etc.

PORISM. Similarly also it can be proved in the case of quadrilaterals that they are in the duplicate ratio of the corresponding sides. And it was also proved in the case of triangles; therefore also, generally, similar rectilineal figures are to one another in the duplicate ratio of the corresponding sides.
Q. E. D.

## PROPOSITION 21

*Figures which are similar to the same rectilineal figure are also similar to one another.*

For let each of the rectilineal figures $A$, $B$ be similar to $C$; I say that $A$ is also similar to $B$.

For, since $A$ is similar to $C$,

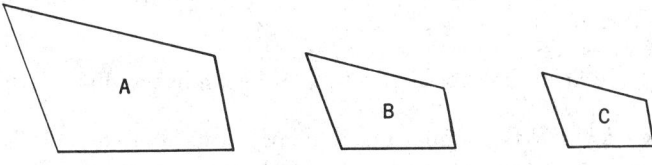

it is equiangular with it and has the sides about the equal angles proportional. [VI. Def. 1]

Again, since $B$ is similar to $C$,

# EUCLID

it is equiangular with it and has the sides about the equal angles proportional.

Therefore each of the figures $A$, $B$ is equiangular with $C$ and with $C$ has the sides about the equal angles proportional;

therefore $A$ is similar to $B$.

Q. E. D.

## Proposition 22

*If four straight lines be proportional, the rectilineal figures similar and similarly described upon them will also be proportional; and if the rectilineal figures similar and similarly described upon them be proportional, the straight lines will themselves also be proportional.*

Let the four straight lines $AB$, $CD$, $EF$, $GH$ be proportional,
so that, as $AB$ is to $CD$, so is $EF$ to $GH$,
and let there be described on $AB$, $CD$ the similar and similarly situated rectilineal figures $KAB$, $LCD$,
and on $EF$, $GH$ the similar and similarly situated rectilineal figures $MF$, $NH$;
I say that, as $KAB$ is to $LCD$, so is $MF$ to $NH$.

For let there be taken a third proportional $O$ to $AB$, $CD$, and a third proportional $P$ to $EF$, $GH$. [VI. 11]

Then since, as $AB$ is to $CD$, so is $EF$ to $GH$,
and, as $CD$ is to $O$, so is $GH$ to $P$,
therefore, *ex aequali*, as $AB$ is to $O$, so is $EF$ to $P$. [V. 22]
But, as $AB$ is to $O$, so is $KAB$ to $LCD$, [VI. 19, Por.]
and, as $EF$ is to $P$, so is $MF$ to $NH$;
therefore also, as $KAB$ is to $LCD$, so is $MF$ to $NH$. [V. 11]

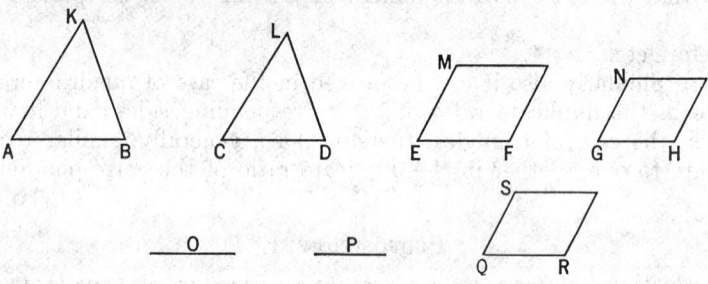

Next, let $MF$ be to $NH$ as $KAB$ is to $LCD$;
I say also that, as $AB$ is to $CD$, so is $EF$ to $GH$.

For, if $EF$ is not to $GH$ as $AB$ to $CD$,
let $EF$ be to $QR$ as $AB$ to $CD$, [VI. 12]
and on $QR$ let the rectilineal figure $SR$ be described similar and similarly situated to either of the two $MF$, $NH$. [VI. 18]

Since then, as $AB$ is to $CD$, so is $EF$ to $QR$,
and there have been described on $AB$, $CD$ the similar and similarly situated figures $KAB$, $LCD$,
and on $EF$, $QR$ the similar and similarly situated figures $MF$, $SR$,
therefore, as $KAB$ is to $LCD$, so is $MF$ to $SR$.
But also, by hypothesis,
as $KAB$ is to $LCD$, so is $MF$ to $NH$;
therefore also, as $MF$ is to $SR$, so is $MF$ to $NH$. [V. 11]

Therefore $MF$ has the same ratio to each of the figures $NH$, $SR$;
therefore $NH$ is equal to $SR$. [v. 9]
But it is also similar and similarly situated to it;
therefore $GH$ is equal to $QR$.
And, since, as $AB$ is to $CD$, so is $EF$ to $QR$,
while $QR$ is equal to $GH$,
therefore, as $AB$ is to $CD$, so is $EF$ to $GH$.
Therefore etc. Q. E. D.

## Proposition 23

*Equiangular parallelograms have to one another the ratio compounded of the ratios of their sides.*

Let $AC$, $CF$ be equiangular parallelograms having the angle $BCD$ equal to the angle $ECG$;

I say that the parallelogram $AC$ has to the parallelogram $CF$ the ratio compounded of the ratios of the sides.

For let them be placed so that $BC$ is in a straight line with $CG$;
therefore $DC$ is also in a straight line with $CE$.
Let the parallelogram $DG$ be completed;
let a straight line $K$ be set out, and let it be contrived that,
as $BC$ is to $CG$, so is $K$ to $L$,
and, as $DC$ is to $CE$, so is $L$ to $M$. [vi. 12]
Then the ratios of $K$ to $L$ and of $L$ to $M$ are the same as the ratios of the sides, namely of $BC$ to $CG$ and of $DC$ to $CE$.
But the ratio of $K$ to $M$ is compounded of the ratio of $K$ to $L$ and of that of $L$ to $M$;
so that $K$ has also to $M$ the ratio compounded of the ratios of the sides.
Now since, as $BC$ is to $CG$, so is the parallelogram $AC$ to the parallelogram $CH$, [vi. 1]
while, as $BC$ is to $CG$, so is $K$ to $L$,
therefore also, as $K$ is to $L$, so is $AC$ to $CH$. [v. 11]
Again, since, as $DC$ is to $CE$, so is the parallelogram $CH$ to $CF$, [vi. 1]
while, as $DC$ is to $CE$, so is $L$ to $M$,
therefore also, as $L$ is to $M$, so is the parallelogram $CH$ to the parallelogram $CF$. [v. 11]
Since, then, it was proved that, as $K$ is to $L$, so is the parallelogram $AC$ to the parallelogram $CH$,
and, as $L$ is to $M$, so is the parallelogram $CH$ to the parallelogram $CF$,
therefore, *ex aequali*, as $K$ is to $M$, so is $AC$ to the parallelogram $CF$.
But $K$ has to $M$ the ratio compounded of the ratios of the sides;
therefore $AC$ also has to $CF$ the ratio compounded of the ratios of the sides.
Therefore etc. Q. E. D.

## Proposition 24

*In any parallelogram the parallelograms about the diameter are similar both to the whole and to one another.*

Let $ABCD$ be a parallelogram, and $AC$ its diameter, and let $EG$, $HK$ be parallelograms about $AC$;

I say that each of the parallelograms $EG$, $HK$ is similar both to the whole $ABCD$ and to the other.

For, since $EF$ has been drawn parallel to $BC$, one of the sides of the triangle $ABC$,

proportionally, as $BE$ is to $EA$, so is $CF$ to $FA$.
[vi. 2]

Again, since $FG$ has been drawn parallel to $CD$, one of the sides of the triangle $ACD$,

proportionally, as $CF$ is to $FA$, so is $DG$ to $GA$. [vi. 2]

But it was proved that,

as $CF$ is to $FA$, so also is $BE$ to $EA$;

therefore also, as $BE$ is to $EA$, so is $DG$ to $GA$,

and therefore, *componendo*,

as $BA$ is to $AE$, so is $DA$ to $AG$, [v. 18]

and, alternately,

as $BA$ is to $AD$, so is $EA$ to $AG$. [v. 16]

Therefore in the parallelograms $ABCD$, $EG$, the sides about the common angle $BAD$ are proportional.

And, since $GF$ is parallel to $DC$,

the angle $AFG$ is equal to the angle $DCA$;

and the angle $DAC$ is common to the two triangles $ADC$, $AGF$;

therefore the triangle $ADC$ is equiangular with the triangle $AGF$.

For the same reason

the triangle $ACB$ is also equiangular with the triangle $AFE$,

and the whole parallelogram $ABCD$ is equiangular with the parallelogram $EG$.

Therefore, proportionally,

as $AD$ is to $DC$, so is $AG$ to $GF$,
as $DC$ is to $CA$, so is $GF$ to $FA$,
as $AC$ is to $CB$, so is $AF$ to $FE$,
and further, as $CB$ is to $BA$, so is $FE$ to $EA$.

And, since it was proved that,

as $DC$ is to $CA$, so is $GF$ to $FA$,

and, as $AC$ is to $CB$, so is $AF$ to $FE$,

therefore, *ex aequali*, as $DC$ is to $CB$, so is $GF$ to $FE$. [v. 22]

Therefore in the parallelograms $ABCD$, $EG$ the sides about the equal angles are proportional;

therefore the parallelogram $ABCD$ is similar to the parallelogram $EG$.
[vi. Def. 1]

For the same reason

the parallelogram $ABCD$ is also similar to the parallelogram $KH$;

therefore each of the parallelograms $EG$, $HK$ is similar to $ABCD$.

But figures similar to the same rectilineal figure are also similar to one another;
[vi. 21]

therefore the parallelogram *EG* is also similar to the parallelogram *HK*.
Therefore etc.
Q. E. D.

## Proposition 25

*To construct one and the same figure similar to a given rectilineal figure and equal to another given rectilineal figure.*

Let *ABC* be the given rectilineal figure to which the figure to be constructed must be similar, and *D* that to which it must be equal;
thus it is required to construct one and the same figure similar to *ABC* and equal to *D*.

Let there be applied to *BC* the parallelogram *BE* equal to the triangle *ABC* [I. 44], and to *CE* the parallelogram *CM* equal to *D* in the angle *FCE* which is equal to the angle *CBL*. [I. 45]

Therefore *BC* is in a straight line with *CF*, and *LE* with *EM*.

Now let *GH* be taken a mean proportional to *BC*, *CF* [VI. 13], and on *GH* let *KGH* be described similar and similarly situated to *ABC*. [VI. 18]

Then, since, as *BC* is to *GH*, so is *GH* to *CF*,
and, if three straight lines be proportional, as the first is to the third, so is the figure on the first to the similar and similarly situated figure described on the second, [VI. 19, Por.]
therefore, as *BC* is to *CF*, so is the triangle *ABC* to the triangle *KGH*.

But, as *BC* is to *CF*, so also is the parallelogram *BE* to the parallelogram *EF*. [VI. 1]

Therefore also, as the triangle *ABC* is to the triangle *KGH*, so is the parallelogram *BE* to the parallelogram *EF*;
therefore, alternately, as the triangle *ABC* is to the parallelogram *BE*, so is the triangle *KGH* to the parallelogram *EF*. [V. 16]

But the triangle *ABC* is equal to the parallelogram *BE*;
therefore the triangle *KGH* is also equal to the parallelogram *EF*.
But the parallelogram *EF* is equal to *D*;
therefore *KGH* is also equal to *D*.
And *KGH* is also similar to *ABC*.

Therefore one and the same figure *KGH* has been constructed similar to the given rectilineal figure *ABC* and equal to the other given figure *D*.  Q. E. D.

## Proposition 26

*If from a parallelogram there be taken away a parallelogram similar and similarly situated to the whole and having a common angle with it, it is about the same diameter with the whole.*

For from the parallelogram *ABCD* let there be taken away the parallelogram $AF$ similar and similarly situated to $ABCD$, and having the angle $DAB$ common with it;

I say that $ABCD$ is about the same diameter with $AF$.

For suppose it is not, but, if possible, let $AHC$ be the diameter < of $ABCD$ >, let $GF$ be produced and carried through to $H$, and let $HK$ be drawn through $H$ parallel to either of the straight lines $AD$, $BC$. [I. 31]

Since, then, $ABCD$ is about the same diameter with $KG$, therefore, as $DA$ is to $AB$, so is $GA$ to $AK$. [VI. 24]

But also, because of the similarity of $ABCD$, $EG$,
as $DA$ is to $AB$, so is $GA$ to $AE$;
therefore also, as $GA$ is to $AK$, so is $GA$ to $AE$. [V. 11]

Therefore $GA$ has the same ratio to each of the straight lines $AK$, $AE$.

Therefore $AE$ is equal to $AK$ [V. 9], the less to the greater: which is impossible.

Therefore $ABCD$ cannot but be about the same diameter with $AF$; therefore the parallelogram $ABCD$ is about the same diameter with the parallelogram $AF$.

Therefore etc.

Q. E. D.

PROPOSITION 27

*Of all the parallelograms applied to the same straight line and deficient by parallelogrammic figures similar and similarly situated to that described on the half of the straight line, that parallelogram is greatest which is applied to the half of the straight line and is similar to the defect.*

Let $AB$ be a straight line and let it be bisected at $C$; let there be applied to the straight line $AB$ the parallelogram $AD$ deficient by the parallelogrammic figure $DB$ described on the half of $AB$, that is, $CB$;

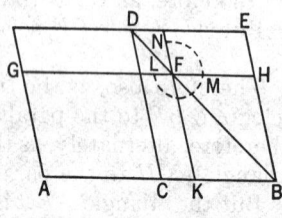

I say that, of the parallelograms applied to $AB$ and deficient by parallelogrammic figures similar and similarly situated to $DB$, $AD$ is greatest.

For let there be applied to the straight line $AB$ the parallelogram $AF$ deficient by the parallelogrammic figure $FB$ similar and similarly situated to $DB$;

I say that $AD$ is greater than $AF$.

For, since the parallelogram $DB$ is similar to the parallelogram $FB$, they are about the same diameter. [VI. 26]

Let their diameter $DB$ be drawn, and let the figure be described.

Then, since $CF$ is equal to $FE$, [I. 43]
and $FB$ is common,
therefore the whole $CH$ is equal to the whole $KE$.

But $CH$ is equal to $CG$, since $AC$ is also equal to $CB$. [I. 36]

Therefore $GC$ is also equal to $EK$.

Let $CF$ be added to each;
therefore the whole $AF$ is equal to the gnomon $LMN$;

ELEMENTS VI

so that the parallelogram $DB$, that is, $AD$, is greater than the parallelogram $AF$.

Therefore etc.                                                                   Q. E. D.

## Proposition 28

*To a given straight line to apply a parallelogram equal to a given rectilineal figure and deficient by a parallelogrammic figure similar to a given one: thus the given rectilineal figure must not be greater than the parallelogram described on the half of the straight line and similar to the defect.*

Let $AB$ be the given straight line, $C$ the given rectilineal figure to which the figure to be applied to $AB$ is required to be equal, not being greater than the parallelogram described on the half of $AB$ and similar to the defect, and $D$ the parallelogram to which the defect is required to be similar;

thus it is required to apply to the given straight line $AB$ a parallelogram equal to the given rectilineal figure $C$ and deficient by a parallelogrammic figure which is similar to $D$.

Let $AB$ be bisected at the point $E$, and on $EB$ let $EBFG$ be described similar and similarly situated to $D$;                                                              [VI. 18]

let the parallelogram $AG$ be completed.

If then $AG$ is equal to $C$, that which was enjoined will have been done;
for there has been applied to the given straight line $AB$ the parallelogram $AG$ equal to the given rectilineal figure $C$ and deficient by a parallelogrammic figure $GB$ which is similar to $D$.

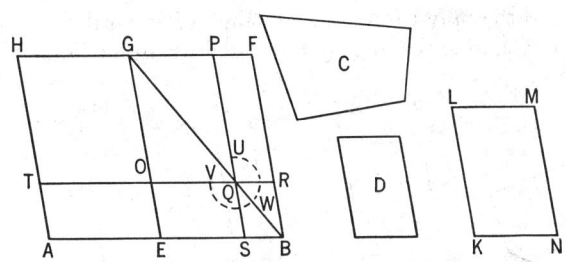

But, if not, let $HE$ be greater than $C$.
Now $HE$ is equal to $GB$;

therefore $GB$ is also greater than $C$.

Let $KLMN$ be constructed at once equal to the excess by which $GB$ is greater than $C$ and similar and similarly situated to $D$.                                    [VI. 25]

But $D$ is similar to $GB$;

therefore $KM$ is also similar to $GB$.                                          [VI. 21]

Let, then, $KL$ correspond to $GE$, and $LM$ to $GF$.
Now, since $GB$ is equal to $C$, $KM$,

therefore $GB$ is greater than $KM$;

therefore also $GE$ is greater than $KL$, and $GF$ than $LM$.

Let $GO$ be made equal to $KL$, and $GP$ equal to $LM$; and let the parallelogram $OGPQ$ be completed;

therefore it is equal and similar to $KM$.

Therefore $GQ$ is also similar to $GB$;                                          [VI. 21] therefore $GQ$ is about the same diameter with $GB$. [vi. 26]

Let $GQB$ be their diameter, and let the figure be described.

Then, since $BG$ is equal to $C$, $KM$,

and in them $GQ$ is equal to $KM$,

therefore the remainder, the gnomon $UWV$, is equal to the remainder $C$.

And, since $PR$ is equal to $OS$,

let $QB$ be added to each;

therefore the whole $PB$ is equal to the whole $OB$.

But $OB$ is equal to $TE$, since the side $AE$ is also equal to the side $EB$; [i. 36]

therefore $TE$ is also equal to $PB$.

Let $OS$ be added to each;

therefore the whole $TS$ is equal to the whole, the gnomon $VWU$.

But the gnomon $VWU$ was proved equal to $C$;

therefore $TS$ is also equal to $C$.

Therefore to the given straight line $AB$ there has been applied the parallelogram $ST$ equal to the given rectilineal figure $C$ and deficient by a parallelogrammic figure $QB$ which is similar to $D$.

Q. E. F.

## Proposition 29

*To a given straight line to apply a parallelogram equal to a given rectilineal figure and exceeding by a parallelogrammic figure similar to a given one.*

Let $AB$ be the given straight line, $C$ the given rectilineal figure to which the figure to be applied to $AB$ is required to be equal, and $D$ that to which the excess is required to be similar;

thus it is required to apply to the straight line $AB$ a parallelogram equal to the rectilineal figure $C$ and exceeding by a parallelogrammic figure similar to $D$.

Let $AB$ be bisected at $E$;

let there be described on $EB$ the parallelogram $BF$ similar and similarly situated to $D$;

and let $GH$ be constructed at once equal to the sum of $BF$, $C$ and similar and similarly situated to $D$. [vi. 25]

Let $KH$ correspond to $FL$ and $KG$ to $FE$.

Now, since $GH$ is greater than $FB$,

therefore $KH$ is also greater than $FL$, and $KG$ than $FE$.

Let $FL$, $FE$ be produced,

let $FLM$ be equal to $KH$, and $FEN$ to $KG$,

and let $MN$ be completed;

therefore $MN$ is both equal and similar to $GH$.

But $GH$ is similar to $EL$;
> therefore $MN$ is also similar to $EL$; [VI. 21]
> therefore $EL$ is about the same diameter with $MN$. [VI. 26]

Let their diameter $FO$ be drawn, and let the figure be described.
Since $GH$ is equal to $EL$, $C$,
> while $GH$ is equal to $MN$,
> therefore $MN$ is also equal to $EL$, $C$.

Let $EL$ be subtracted from each;
> therefore the remainder, the gnomon $XWV$, is equal to $C$.

Now, since $AE$ is equal to $EB$,
> $AN$ is also equal to $NB$ [I. 36], that is, to $LP$ [I. 43]

Let $EO$ be added to each;
> therefore the whole $AO$ is equal to the gnomon $VWX$.

But the gnomon $VWX$ is equal to $C$;
> therefore $AO$ is also equal to $C$.

Therefore to the given straight line $AB$ there has been applied the parallelogram $AO$ equal to the given rectilineal figure $C$ and exceeding by a parallelogrammic figure $QP$ which is similar to $D$, since $PQ$ is also similar to $EL$ [VI. 24].

Q. E. F.

## Proposition 30

*To cut a given finite straight line in extreme and mean ratio.*

Let $AB$ be the given finite straight line;
> thus it is required to cut $AB$ in extreme and mean ratio.
> On $AB$ let the square $BC$ be described; and let there be applied to $AC$ the parallelogram $CD$ equal to $BC$ and exceeding by the figure $AD$ similar to $BC$. [VI. 29]
> Now $BC$ is a square;
>> therefore $AD$ is also a square.
>
> And, since $BC$ is equal to $CD$,
> let $CE$ be subtracted from each;
> therefore the remainder $BF$ is equal to the remainder $AD$.
> But it is also equiangular with it;
> therefore in $BF$, $AD$ the sides about the equal angles are reciprocally proportional; [VI. 14]
> therefore, as $FE$ is to $ED$, so is $AE$ to $EB$.

But $FE$ is equal to $AB$, and $ED$ to $AE$.
Therefore, as $BA$ is to $AE$, so is $AE$ to $EB$.
And $AB$ is greater than $AE$;
> therefore $AE$ is also greater than $EB$.

Therefore the straight line $AB$ has been cut in extreme and mean ratio at $E$, and the greater segment of it is $AE$.

Q. E. F.

## Proposition 31

*In right-angled triangles the figure on the side subtending the right angle is equal to the similar and similarly described figures on the sides containing the right angle.*

Let $ABC$ be a right-angled triangle having the angle $BAC$ right;
I say that the figure on $BC$ is equal to the similar and similarly described figures on $BA$, $AC$.

Let $AD$ be drawn perpendicular.

Then since, in the right-angled triangle $ABC$, $AD$ has been drawn from the right angle at $A$ perpendicular to the base $BC$, the triangles $ABD$, $ADC$ adjoining the perpendicular are similar both to the whole $ABC$ and to one another. [VI. 8]

And, since $ABC$ is similar to $ABD$, therefore, as $CB$ is to $BA$, so is $AB$ to $BD$.
[VI. Def. 1]

And, since three straight lines are proportional, as the first is to the third, so is the figure on the first to the similar and similarly described figure on the second. [VI. 19, Por.]

Therefore, as $CB$ is to $BD$, so is the figure on $CB$ to the similar and similarly described figure on $BA$.

For the same reason also,
    as $BC$ is to $CD$, so is the figure on $BC$ to that on $CA$;
    so that, in addition,
as $BC$ is to $BD$, $DC$, so is the figure on $BC$ to the similar and similarly described figures on $BA$, $AC$.

But $BC$ is equal to $BD$, $DC$;

therefore the figure on $BC$ is also equal to the similar and similarly described figures on $BA$, $AC$.

Therefore etc.

Q. E. D.

## PROPOSITION 32

*If two triangles having two sides proportional to two sides be placed together at one angle so that their corresponding sides are also parallel, the remaining sides of the triangles will be in a straight line.*

Let $ABC$, $DCE$ be two triangles having the two sides $BA$, $AC$ proportional to the two sides $DC$, $DE$, so that, as $AB$ is to $AC$, so is $DC$ to $DE$, and $AB$ parallel to $DC$, and $AC$ to $DE$;
    I say that $BC$ is in a straight line with $CE$.

For, since $AB$ is parallel to $DC$, and the straight line $AC$ has fallen upon them, the alternate angles $BAC$, $ACD$ are equal to one another. [I. 29]

For the same reason the angle $CDE$ is also equal to the angle $ACD$;

so that the angle $BAC$ is equal to the angle $CDE$.

And, since $ABC$, $DCE$ are two triangles having one angle, the angle at $A$, equal to one angle, the angle at $D$,
    and the sides about the equal angles proportional,
        so that, as $BA$ is to $AC$, so is $CD$ to $DE$,
    therefore the triangle $ABC$ is equiangular with the triangle $DCE$; [VI. 6]

# ELEMENTS VI

therefore the angle $ABC$ is equal to the angle $DCE$.
But the angle $ACD$ was also proved equal to the angle $BAC$;
therefore the whole angle $ACE$ is equal to the two angles $ABC$, $BAC$.
Let the angle $ACB$ be added to each;
therefore the angles $ACE$, $ACB$ are equal to the angles $BAC$, $ACB$, $CBA$.
But the angles $BAC$, $ABC$, $ACB$ are equal to two right angles; [I. 32]
therefore the angles $ACE$, $ACB$ are also equal to two right angles.

Therefore with a straight line $AC$, and at the point $C$ on it, the two straight lines $BC$, $CE$ not lying on the same side make the adjacent angles $ACE$, $ACB$ equal to two right angles;

therefore $BC$ is in a straight line with $CE$. [I. 14]

Therefore etc.

Q. E. D.

## Proposition 33

*In equal circles angles have the same ratio as the circumferences on which they stand, whether they stand at the centres or at the circumferences.*

Let $ABC$, $DEF$ be equal circles, and let the angles $BGC$, $EHF$ be angles at their centres $G$, $H$, and the angles $BAC$, $EDF$ angles at the circumferences;

I say that, as the circumference $BC$ is to the circumference $EF$, so is the angle $BGC$ to the angle $EHF$, and the angle $BAC$ to the angle $EDF$.

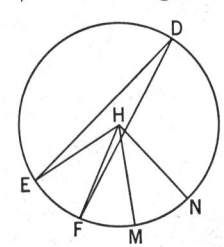

For let any number of consecutive circumferences $CK$, $KL$ be made equal to the circumference $BC$,
and any number of consecutive circumferences $FM$, $MN$ equal to the circumference $EF$;
and let $GK$, $GL$, $HM$, $HN$ be joined.

Then, since the circumferences $BC$, $CK$, $KL$ are equal to one another,
the angles $BGC$, $CGK$, $KGL$ are also equal to one another; [III. 27]
therefore, whatever multiple the circumference $BL$ is of $BC$, that multiple also is the angle $BGL$ of the angle $BGC$.

For the same reason also,
whatever multiple the circumference $NE$ is of $EF$, that multiple also is the angle $NHE$ of the angle $EHF$.

If then the circumference $BL$ is equal to the circumference $EN$, the angle $BGL$ is also equal to the angle $EHN$; [III. 27]
if the circumference $BL$ is greater than the circumference $EN$, the angle $BGL$ is also greater than the angle $EHN$;
and, if less, less.

There being then four magnitudes, two circumferences $BC$, $EF$, and two angles $BGC$, $EHF$,
there have been taken, of the circumference $BC$ and the angle $BGC$ equimultiples, namely the circumference $BL$ and the angle $BGL$,
and of the circumference $EF$ and the angle $EHF$ equimultiples, namely the circumference $EN$ and the angle $EHN$.

And it has been proved that,
if the circumference $BL$ is in excess of the circumference $EN$,

the angle $BGL$ is also in excess of the angle $EHN$;
if equal, equal;
and if less, less.

Therefore, as the circumference $BC$ is to $EF$, so is the angle $BGC$ to the angle $EHF$. [v. Def. 5]

But, as the angle $BGC$ is to the angle $EHF$, so is the angle $BAC$ to the angle $EDF$; for they are doubles respectively.

Therefore also, as the circumference $BC$ is to the circumference $EF$, so is the angle $BGC$ to the angle $EHF$, and the angle $BAC$ to the angle $EDF$.

Therefore etc.

Q. E. D.

# BOOK SEVEN

## DEFINITIONS

1. An *unit* is that by virtue of which each of the things that exist is called one.
2. A *number* is a multitude composed of units.
3. A number is *a part* of a number, the less of the greater, when it measures the greater;
4. but *parts* when it does not measure it.
5. The greater number is a *multiple* of the less when it is measured by the less.
6. An *even number* is that which is divisible into two equal parts.
7. An *odd number* is that which is not divisible into two equal parts, or that which differs by an unit from an even number.
8. An *even-times even number* is that which is measured by an even number according to an even number.
9. An *even-times odd number* is that which is measured by an even number according to an odd number.
10. An *odd-times odd number* is that which is measured by an odd number according to an odd number.
11. A *prime number* is that which is measured by an unit alone.
12. Numbers *prime to one another* are those which are measured by an unit alone as a common measure.
13. A *composite number* is that which is measured by some number.
14. Numbers *composite to one another* are those which are measured by some number as a common measure.
15. A number is said to *multiply* a number when that which is multiplied is added to itself as many times as there are units in the other, and thus some number is produced.
16. And, when two numbers having multiplied one another make some number, the number so produced is called *plane*, and its *sides* are the numbers which have multiplied one another.
17. And, when three numbers having multiplied one another make some number, the number so produced is *solid*, and its *sides* are the numbers which have multiplied one another.
18. A *square number* is equal multiplied by equal, or a number which is contained by two equal numbers.
19. And a *cube* is equal multiplied by equal and again by equal, or a number which is contained by three equal numbers.
20. Numbers are *proportional* when the first is the same multiple, or the same part, or the same parts, of the second that the third is of the fourth.

21. *Similar plane* and *solid* numbers are those which have their sides proportional.

22. A *perfect number* is that which is equal to its own parts.

## BOOK VII. PROPOSITIONS

### Proposition 1

*Two unequal numbers being set out, and the less being continually subtracted in turn from the greater, if the number which is left never measures the one before it until an unit is left, the original numbers will be prime to one another.*

For, the less of two unequal numbers $AB$, $CD$ being continually subtracted from the greater, let the number which is left never measure the one before it until an unit is left;

I say that $AB$, $CD$ are prime to one another, that is, that an unit alone measures $AB$, $CD$.

For, if $AB$, $CD$ are not prime to one another, some number will measure them.

Let a number measure them, and let it be $E$; let $CD$, measuring $BF$, leave $FA$ less than itself,

    let $AF$, measuring $DG$, leave $GC$ less than itself,

    and let $GC$, measuring $FH$, leave an unit $HA$.

Since, then, $E$ measures $CD$, and $CD$ measures $BF$,

    therefore $E$ also measures $BF$.

But it also measures the whole $BA$;

    therefore it will also measure the remainder $AF$.

But $AF$ measures $DG$;

    therefore $E$ also measures $DG$.

But it also measures the whole $DC$;

    therefore it will also measure the remainder $CG$.

But $CG$ measures $FH$;

    therefore $E$ also measures $FH$.

But it also measures the whole $FA$;

therefore it will also measure the remainder, the unit $AH$, though it is a number: which is impossible.

Therefore no number will measure the numbers $AB$, $CD$; therefore $AB$, $CD$ are prime to one another.     [VII. Def. 12]

Q. E. D.

### Proposition 2

*Given two numbers not prime to one another, to find their greatest common measure.*

Let $AB$, $CD$ be the two given numbers not prime to one another.

Thus it is required to find the greatest common measure of $AB$, $CD$.

If now $CD$ measures $AB$—and it also measures itself—$CD$ is a common measure of $CD$, $AB$.

And it is manifest that it is also the greatest; for no greater number than $CD$ will measure $CD$.

But, if $CD$ does not measure $AB$, then, the less of the numbers $AB$, $CD$ being continually subtracted from the greater, some number will be left which will measure the one before it.

For an unit will not be left; otherwise $AB$, $CD$ will be prime to one another [VII. 1], which is contrary to the hypothesis.

Therefore some number will be left which will measure the one before it.

Now let $CD$, measuring $BE$, leave $EA$ less than itself, let $EA$, measuring $DF$, leave $FC$ less than itself, and let $CF$ measure $AE$.

Since then, $CF$ measures $AE$, and $AE$ measures $DF$, therefore $CF$ will also measure $DF$.

But it also measures itself;

therefore it will also measure the whole $CD$.

But $CD$ measures $BE$;

therefore $CF$ also measures $BE$.

But it also measures $EA$;

therefore it will also measure the whole $BA$.

But it also measures $CD$;

therefore $CF$ measures $AB$, $CD$.

Therefore $CF$ is a common measure of $AB$, $CD$.

I say next that it is also the greatest.

For, if $CF$ is not the greatest common measure of $AB$, $CD$, some number which is greater than $CF$ will measure the numbers $AB$, $CD$.

Let such a number measure them, and let it be $G$.

Now, since $G$ measures $CD$, while $CD$ measures $BE$, $G$ also measures $BE$.

But it also measures the whole $BA$;

therefore it will also measure the remainder $AE$.

But $AE$ measures $DF$;

therefore $G$ will also measure $DF$.

But it also measures the whole $DC$;

therefore it will also measure the remainder $CF$, that is, the greater will measure the less: which is impossible.

Therefore no number which is greater than $CF$ will measure the numbers $AB$, $CD$;

therefore $CF$ is the greatest common measure of $AB$, $CD$.

PORISM. From this it is manifest that, if a number measure two numbers, it will also measure their greatest common measure.   Q. E. D.

## PROPOSITION 3

*Given three numbers not prime to one another, to find their greatest common measure.*

Let $A$, $B$, $C$ be the three given numbers not prime to one another; thus it is required to find the greatest common measure of $A$, $B$, $C$.

For let the greatest common measure, $D$, of the two numbers $A$, $B$ be taken; [VII. 2]

then $D$ either measures, or does not measure, $C$.

First, let it measure it.

But it measures $A$, $B$ also;

therefore $D$ measures $A$, $B$, $C$;

therefore $D$ is a common measure of $A$, $B$, $C$.

I say that it is also the greatest.

For, if $D$ is not the greatest common measure of $A$, $B$, $C$, some number which is greater than $D$ will measure the numbers $A$, $B$, $C$.

Let such a number measure them, and let it be $E$.

Since then $E$ measures $A$, $B$, $C$,
> it will also measure $A$, $B$;

therefore it will also measure the greatest common measure of $A$, $B$.
[VII. 2, Por.]

But the greatest common measure of $A$, $B$ is $D$;
> therefore $E$ measures $D$, the greater the less: which is impossible.

Therefore no number which is greater than $D$ will measure the numbers $A$, $B$, $C$;
> therefore $D$ is the greatest common measure of $A$, $B$, $C$.

Next, let $D$ not measure $C$;
> I say first that $C$, $D$ are not prime to one another.

For, since $A$, $B$, $C$ are not prime to one another, some number will measure them.

Now that which measures $A$, $B$, $C$ will also measure $A$, $B$, and will measure $D$, the greatest common measure of $A$, $B$. [VII. 2, Por.]

But it measures $C$ also;
> therefore some number will measure the numbers $D$, $C$;
>> therefore $D$, $C$ are not prime to one another.

Let then their greatest common measure $E$ be taken. [VII. 2]

Then, since $E$ measures $D$,
> and $D$ measures $A$, $B$,
>> therefore $E$ also measures $A$, $B$.

But it measures $C$ also;
> therefore $E$ measures $A$, $B$, $C$;
>> therefore $E$ is a common measure of $A$, $B$, $C$.

I say next that it is also the greatest.

For, if $E$ is not the greatest common measure of $A$, $B$, $C$, some number which is greater than $E$ will measure the numbers $A$, $B$, $C$.

Let such a number measure them, and let it be $F$.

Now, since $F$ measures $A$, $B$, $C$,
> it also measures $A$, $B$;

therefore it will also measure the greatest common measure of $A$, $B$.
[VII. 2, Por.]

But the greatest common measure of $A$, $B$ is $D$;
> therefore $F$ measures $D$.

And it measures $C$ also;
> therefore $F$ measures $D$, $C$;

therefore it will also measure the greatest common measure of $D$, $C$.
[VII. 2, Por.]

But the greatest common measure of $D$, $C$ is $E$;
> therefore $F$ measures $E$, the greater the less: which is impossible

Therefore no number which is greater than $E$ will measure the numbers $A$, $B$, $C$;
> therefore $E$ is the greatest common measure of $A$, $B$, $C$.

Q. E. D.

## Proposition 4

*Any number is either a part or parts of any number, the less of the greater.*

Let $A$, $BC$ be two numbers, and let $BC$ be the less;
I say that $BC$ is either a part, or parts, of $A$.

For $A$, $BC$ are either prime to one another or not.

First, let $A$, $BC$ be prime to one another.

Then, if $BC$ be divided into the units in it, each unit of those in $BC$ will be some part of $A$; so that $BC$ is parts of $A$.

Next let $A$, $BC$ not be prime to one another; then $BC$ either measures, or does not measure, $A$.

If now $BC$ measures $A$, $BC$ is a part of $A$.

But, if not, let the greatest common measure $D$ of $A$, $BC$ be taken; [VII. 2] and let $BC$ be divided into the numbers equal to $D$, namely $BE$, $EF$, $FC$.

Now, since $D$ measures $A$, $D$ is a part of $A$.

But $D$ is equal to each of the numbers $BE$, $EF$, $FC$;
therefore each of the numbers $BE$, $EF$, $FC$ is also a part of $A$; so that $BC$ is parts of $A$.

Therefore etc.
Q. E. D.

## Proposition 5

*If a number be a part of a number, and another be the same part of another, the sum will also be the same part of the sum that the one is of the one.*

For let the number $A$ be a part of $BC$,
and another, $D$, the same part of another $EF$ that $A$ is of $BC$;
I say that the sum of $A$, $D$ is also the same part of the sum of $BC$, $EF$ that $A$ is of $BC$.

For since, whatever part $A$ is of $BC$, $D$ is also the same part of $EF$,
therefore, as many numbers as there are in $BC$ equal to $A$, so many numbers are there also in $EF$ equal to $D$.

Let $BC$ be divided into the numbers equal to $A$, namely $BG$, $GC$,
and $EF$ into the numbers equal to $D$, namely $EH$, $HF$;
then the multitude of $BG$, $GC$ will be equal to the multitude of $EH$, $HF$.

And, since $BG$ is equal to $A$, and $EH$ to $D$,
therefore $BG$, $EH$ are also equal to $A$, $D$.

For the same reason
$GC$, $HF$ are also equal to $A$, $D$.

Therefore, as many numbers as there are in $BC$ equal to $A$, so many are there also in $BC$, $EF$ equal to $A$, $D$.

Therefore, whatever multiple $BC$ is of $A$, the same multiple also is the sum of $BC$, $EF$ of the sum of $A$, $D$.

Therefore, whatever part $A$ is to $BC$, the same part also is the sum of $A$, $D$ of the sum of $BC$, $EF$.
Q. E. D.

## Proposition 6

*If a number be parts of a number, and another be the same parts of another, the sum will also be the same parts of the sum that the one is of the one.*

For let the number $AB$ be parts of the number $C$, and another, $DE$, the same parts of another, $F$, that $AB$ is of $C$;

I say that the sum of $AB$, $DE$ is also the same parts of the sum of $C$, $F$ that $AB$ is of $C$.

For since, whatever parts $AB$ is of $C$, $DE$ is also the same parts of $F$,
therefore, as many parts of $C$ as there are in $AB$, so many parts of $F$ are there also in $DE$.

Let $AB$ be divided into the parts of $C$, namely $AG$, $GB$, and $DE$ into the parts of $F$, namely $DH$, $HE$;

thus the multitude of $AG$, $GB$ will be equal to the multitude of $DH$, $HE$.

And since, whatever part $AG$ is of $C$, the same part is $DH$ of $F$ also,
therefore, whatever part $AG$ is of $C$, the same part also is the sum of $AG$, $DH$ of the sum of $C$, $F$. [VII. 5]

For the same reason,
whatever part $GB$ is of $C$, the same part also is the sum of $GB$, $HE$ of the sum of $C$, $F$.

Therefore, whatever parts $AB$ is of $C$, the same parts also is the sum of $AB$, $DE$ of the sum of $C$, $F$.   Q. E. D.

## Proposition 7

*If a number be that part of a number, which a number subtracted is of a number subtracted, the remainder will also be the same part of the remainder that the whole is of the whole.*

For let the number $AB$ be that part of the number $CD$ which $AE$ subtracted is of $CF$ subtracted;

I say that the remainder $EB$ is also the same part of the remainder $FD$ that the whole $AB$ is of the whole $CD$.

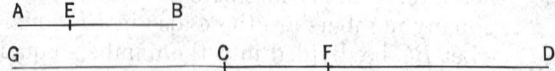

For, whatever part $AE$ is of $CF$, the same part also let $EB$ be of $CG$.

Now since, whatever part $AE$ is of $CF$, the same part also is $EB$ of $CG$,
therefore, whatever part $AE$ is of $CF$, the same part also is $AB$ of $GF$. [VII. 5]

But, whatever part $AE$ is of $CF$, the same part also, by hypothesis, is $AB$ of $CD$;
  therefore, whatever part $AB$ is of $GF$, the same part is it of $CD$ also;
    therefore $GF$ is equal to $CD$.

Let $CF$ be subtracted from each;
  therefore the remainder $GC$ is equal to the remainder $FD$.

Now since, whatever part $AE$ is of $CF$, the same part also is $EB$ of $GC$,
  while $GC$ is equal to $FD$,
therefore, whatever part $AE$ is of $CF$, the same part also is $EB$ of $FD$.

But, whatever part $AE$ is of $CF$, the same part also is $AB$ of $CD$;
therefore also the remainder $EB$ is the same part of the remainder $FD$ that the whole $AB$ is of the whole $CD$.   Q. E. D.

## Proposition 8

*If a number be the same parts of a number that a number subtracted is of a number subtracted, the remainder will also be the same parts of the remainder that the whole is of the whole.*

For let the number $AB$ be the same parts of the number $CD$ that $AE$ subtracted is of $CF$ subtracted;

I say that the remainder $EB$ is also the same parts of the remainder $FD$ that the whole $AB$ is of the whole $CD$.

For let $GH$ be made equal to $AB$.

Therefore, whatever parts $GH$ is of $CD$, the same parts also is $AE$ of $CF$.

Let $GH$ be divided into the parts of $CD$, namely $GK$, $KH$, and $AE$ into the parts of $CF$, namely $AL$, $LE$;

thus the multitude of $GK$, $KH$ will be equal to the multitude of $AL$, $LE$.

Now since, whatever part $GK$ is of $CD$, the same part also is $AL$ of $CF$,
        while $CD$ is greater than $CF$,
    therefore $GK$ is also greater than $AL$.

Let $GM$ be made equal to $AL$.

Therefore, whatever part $GK$ is of $CD$, the same part also is $GM$ of $CF$;
therefore also the remainder $MK$ is the same part of the remainder $FD$ that the whole $GK$ is of the whole $CD$.     [VII. 7]

Again, since, whatever part $KH$ is of $CD$, the same part also is $EL$ of $CF$,
        while $CD$ is greater than $CF$,
    therefore $HK$ is also greater than $EL$.

Let $KN$ be made equal to $EL$.

Therefore, whatever part $KH$ is of $CD$, the same part also is $KN$ of $CF$;
therefore also the remainder $NH$ is the same part of the remainder $FD$ that the whole $KH$ is of the whole $CD$.     [VII. 7]

But the remainder $MK$ was also proved to be the same part of the remainder $FD$ that the whole $GK$ is of the whole $CD$;
therefore also the sum of $MK$, $NH$ is the same parts of $DF$ that the whole $HG$ is of the whole $CD$.

But the sum of $MK$, $NH$ is equal to $EB$,
        and $HG$ is equal to $BA$;
therefore the remainder $EB$ is the same parts of the remainder $FD$ that the whole $AB$ is of the whole $CD$.     Q. E. D.

## Proposition 9

*If a number be a part of a number, and another be the same part of another, alternately also, whatever part or parts the first is of the third, the same part, or the same parts, will the second also be of the fourth.*

For let the number $A$ be a part of the number $BC$, and another, $D$, the same part of another, $EF$, that $A$ is of $BC$;

I say that, alternately also, whatever part or parts $A$ is of $D$, the same part or parts is $BC$ of $EF$ also.

For since, whatever part $A$ is of $BC$, the same part also is $D$ of $EF$, therefore, as many numbers as there are in $BC$ equal to $A$, so many also are there in $EF$ equal to $D$.

Let $BC$ be divided into the numbers equal to $A$, namely $BG$, $GC$, and $EF$ into those equal to $D$, namely $EH$, $HF$;

thus the multitude of $BG$, $GC$ will be equal to the multitude of $EH$, $HF$.

Now, since the numbers $BG$, $GC$ are equal to one another, and the numbers $EH$, $HF$ are also equal to one another,

while the multitude of $BG$, $GC$ is equal to the multitude of $EH$, $HF$,

therefore, whatever part or parts $BG$ is of $EH$, the same part or the same parts is $GC$ of $HF$ also;

so that, in addition, whatever part or parts $BG$ is of $EH$, the same part also, or the same parts, is the sum $BC$ of the sum $EF$. [VII. 5, 6]

But $BG$ is equal to $A$, and $EH$ to $D$;

therefore, whatever part or parts $A$ is of $D$, the same part or the same parts is $BC$ of $EF$ also. Q. E. D.

## Proposition 10

*If a number be parts of a number, and another be the same parts of another, alternately also, whatever parts or part the first is of the third, the same parts or the same part will the second also be of the fourth.*

For let the number $AB$ be parts of the number $C$, and another, $DE$, the same parts of another, $F$;

I say that, alternately also, whatever parts or part $AB$ is of $DE$, the same parts or the same part is $C$ of $F$ also.

For since, whatever parts $AB$ is of $C$, the same parts also is $DE$ of $F$,

therefore, as many parts of $C$ as there are in $AB$, so many parts also of $F$ are there in $DE$.

Let $AB$ be divided into the parts of $C$, namely $AG$, $GB$, and $DE$ into the parts of $F$, namely $DH$, $HE$;

thus the multitude of $AG$, $GB$ will be equal to the multitude of $DH$, $HE$.

Now since, whatever part $AG$ is of $C$, the same part also is $DH$ of $F$,

alternately also, whatever part or parts $AG$ is of $DH$,

the same part or the same parts is $C$ of $F$ also. [VII. 9]

For the same reason also,

whatever part or parts $GB$ is of $HE$, the same part or the same parts is $C$ of $F$ also;

so that, in addition, whatever part or parts $AB$ is of $DE$, the same parts also, or the same part, is $C$ of $F$. [VII. 5, 6]

Q. E. D.

## Proposition 11

*If, as whole is to whole, so is a number subtracted to a number subtracted, the remainder will also be to the remainder as whole to whole.*

As the whole $AB$ is to the whole $CD$, so let $AE$ subtracted be to $CF$ subtracted;

I say that the remainder $EB$ is also to the remainder $FD$ as the whole $AB$ to the whole $CD$.

Since, as $AB$ is to $CD$, so is $AE$ to $CF$,

whatever part or parts $AB$ is of $CD$, the same part or the same parts is $AE$ of $CF$ also; [VII. Def. 20]
Therefore also the remainder $EB$ is the same part or parts of $FD$ that $AB$ is of $CD$. [VII. 7, 8]
Therefore, as $EB$ is to $FD$, so is $AB$ to $CD$. [VII. Def. 20]

Q. E. D.

## Proposition 12

*If there be as many numbers as we please in proportion, then, as one of the antecedents is to one of the consequents, so are all the antecedents to all the consequents.*

Let $A, B, C, D$ be as many numbers as we please in proportion, so that,
$$\text{as } A \text{ is to } B, \text{ so is } C \text{ to } D;$$
I say that, as $A$ is to $B$, so are $A, C$ to $B, D$.
For since, as $A$ is to $B$, so is $C$ to $D$,
whatever part or parts $A$ is of $B$, the same part or parts is $C$ of $D$ also. [VII. Def. 20]
Therefore also the sum of $A, C$ is the same part or the same parts of the sum of $B, D$ that $A$ is of $B$. [VII. 5, 6]
Therefore, as $A$ is to $B$, so are $A, C$ to $B, D$. [VII. Def. 20]

Q. E. D.

## Proposition 13

*If four numbers be proportional, they will also be proportional alternately.*

Let the four numbers $A, B, C, D$ be proportional, so that,
$$\text{as } A \text{ is to } B, \text{ so is } C \text{ to } D;$$
I say that they will also be proportional alternately, so that,
$$\text{as } A \text{ is to } C, \text{ so will } B \text{ be to } D.$$
For since, as $A$ is to $B$, so is $C$ to $D$,
therefore, whatever part or parts $A$ is of $B$, the same part or the same parts is $C$ of $D$ also. [VII. Def. 20]
Therefore, alternately, whatever part or parts $A$ is of $C$, the same part or the same parts is $B$ of $D$ also. [VII. 10]
Therefore, as $A$ is to $C$, so is $B$ to $D$. [VII. Def. 20]

Q. E. D.

## Proposition 14

*If there be as many numbers as we please, and others equal to them in multitude, which taken two and two are in the same ratio, they will also be in the same ratio ex aequali.*

Let there be as many numbers as we please $A, B, C$, and others equal to them in multitude $D, E, F$, which taken two and two are in the same ratio, so that,
$$\text{as } A \text{ is to } B, \text{ so is } D \text{ to } E,$$
$$\text{and, as } B \text{ is to } C, \text{ so is } E \text{ to } F;$$
I say that, *ex aequali*,
as $A$ is to $C$, so also is $D$ to $F$.
For, since, as $A$ is to $B$, so is $D$ to $E$,
therefore, alternately,
as $A$ is to $D$, so is $B$ to $E$. [VII. 13]
Again, since, as $B$ is to $C$, so is $E$ to $F$,

therefore, alternately,
as $B$ is to $E$, so is $C$ to $F$. [VII. 13]

But, as $B$ is to $E$, so is $A$ to $D$;
therefore also, as $A$ is to $D$, so is $C$ to $F$.

Therefore, alternately,
as $A$ is to $C$, so is $D$ to $F$. [*id.*]

## Proposition 15

*If an unit measure any number, and another number measure any other number the same number of times, alternately also, the unit will measure the third number the same number of times that the second measures the fourth.*

For let the unit $A$ measure any number $BC$, and let another number $D$ measure any other number $EF$ the same number of times;

I say that, alternately also, the unit $A$ measures the number $D$ the same number of times that $BC$ measures $EF$.

For, since the unit $A$ measures the number $BC$ the same number of times that $D$ measures $EF$,
therefore, as many units as there are in $BC$, so many numbers equal to $D$ are there in $EF$ also.

Let $BC$ be divided into the units in it, $BG$, $GH$, $HC$,
and $EF$ into the numbers $EK$, $KL$, $LF$ equal to $D$.

Thus the multitude of $BG$, $GH$, $HC$ will be equal to the multitude of $EK$, $KL$, $LF$.

And, since the units $BG$, $GH$, $HC$ are equal to one another,
and the numbers $EK$, $KL$, $LF$ are also equal to one another,
while the multitude of the units $BG$, $GH$, $HC$ is equal to the multitude of the numbers $EK$, $KL$, $LF$,
therefore, as the unit $BG$ is to the number $EK$, so will the unit $GH$ be to the number $KL$, and the unit $HC$ to the number $LF$.

Therefore also, as one of the antecedents is to one of the consequents, so will all the antecedents be to all the consequents; [VII. 12]
therefore, as the unit $BG$ is to the number $EK$, so is $BC$ to $EF$.

But the unit $BG$ is equal to the unit $A$,
and the number $EK$ to the number $D$.

Therefore, as the unit $A$ is to the number $D$, so is $BC$ to $EF$.

Therefore the unit $A$ measures the number $D$ the same number of times that $BC$ measures $EF$. Q. E. D.

## Proposition 16

*If two numbers by multiplying one another make certain numbers, the numbers so produced will be equal to one another.*

Let $A$, $B$ be two numbers, and let $A$ by multiplying $B$ make $C$, and $B$ by multiplying $A$ make $D$;

I say that $C$ is equal to $D$.

For, since $A$ by multiplying $B$ has made $C$,
therefore $B$ measures $C$ according to the units in $A$.

But the unit $E$ also measures the number $A$ according to the units in it;
therefore the unit $E$ measures $A$ the same number of times that $B$ measures $C$.

Therefore, alternately, the unit $E$ measures the number $B$ the same number of times that $A$ measures $C$ [VII. 15].

Again, since $B$ by multiplying $A$ has made $D$,
therefore $A$ measures $D$ according to the units in $B$.

But the unit $E$ also measures $B$ according to the units in it;
therefore the unit $E$ measures the number $B$ the same number of times that $A$ measures $D$.

But the unit $E$ measured the number $B$ the same number of times that $A$ measures $C$;
therefore $A$ measures each of the numbers $C$, $D$ the same number of times.

Therefore $C$ is equal to $D$. Q. E. D.

### Proposition 17

*If a number by multiplying two numbers make certain numbers, the numbers so produced will have the same ratio as the numbers multiplied.*

For let the number $A$ be multiplying the two numbers $B$, $C$ make $D$, $E$;
I say that, as $B$ is to $C$, so is $D$ to $E$.

For, since $A$ by multiplying $B$ has made $D$,
therefore $B$ measures $D$ according to the units in $A$.

But the unit $F$ also measures the number $A$ according to the units in it;
therefore the unit $F$ measures the number $A$ the same number of times that $B$ measures $D$.

Therefore, as the unit $F$ is to the number $A$, so is $B$ to $D$. [VII. Def. 20]

For the same reason,
as the unit $F$ is to the number $A$, so also is $C$ to $E$;
therefore also, as $B$ is to $D$, so is $C$ to $E$.

Therefore, alternately, as $B$ is to $C$, so is $D$ to $E$. [VII. 13]

Q. E. D.

### Proposition 18

*If two numbers by multiplying any number make certain numbers, the numbers so produced will have the same ratio as the multipliers.*

For let two numbers $A$, $B$ by multiplying any number $C$ make $D$, $E$;
I say that, as $A$ is to $B$, so is $D$ to $E$.

For, since $A$ by multiplying $C$ has made $D$,
therefore also $C$ by multiplying $A$ has made $D$. [VII. 16]

For the same reason also
$C$ by multiplying $B$ has made $E$.

Therefore the number $C$ by multiplying the two numbers $A$, $B$ has made $D$, $E$.
Therefore, as $A$ is to $B$, so is $D$ to $E$. [VII. 17]

Q. E. D.

## Proposition 19

*If four numbers be proportional, the number produced from the first and fourth will be equal to the number produced from the second and third; and, if the number produced from the first and fourth be equal to that produced from the second and third, the four numbers will be proportional.*

Let $A, B, C, D$ be four numbers in proportion, so that,
$$\text{as } A \text{ is to } B, \text{ so is } C \text{ to } D;$$
and let $A$ by multiplying $D$ make $E$, and let $B$ by multiplying $C$ make $F$;
$$\text{I say that } E \text{ is equal to } F.$$
For let $A$ by multiplying $C$ make $G$.

Since, then, $A$ by multiplying $C$ has made $G$, and by multiplying $D$ has made $E$,
the number $A$ by multiplying the two numbers $C, D$ has made $G, E$.

Therefore, as $C$ is to $D$, so is $G$ to $E$. [vii. 17]
But, as $C$ is to $D$, so is $A$ to $B$;
therefore also, as $A$ is to $B$, so is $G$ to $E$.

Again, since $A$ by multiplying $C$ has made $G$,
but, further, $B$ has also by multiplying $C$ made $F$,
the two numbers $A, B$ by multiplying a certain number $C$ have made $G, F$.

Therefore, as $A$ is to $B$, so is $G$ to $F$. [vii. 18]
But further, as $A$ is to $B$, so is $G$ to $E$ also;
therefore also, as $G$ is to $E$, so is $G$ to $F$.

Therefore $G$ has to each of the numbers $E, F$ the same ratio;
therefore $E$ is equal to $F$. [cf. v. 9]

Again, let $E$ be equal to $F$;
I say that, as $A$ is to $B$, so is $C$ to $D$.

For, with the same construction,
since $E$ is equal to $F$,
therefore, as $G$ is to $E$, so is $G$ to $F$. [cf. v. 7]
But, as $G$ is to $E$, so is $C$ to $D$, [vii. 17]
and, as $G$ is to $F$, so is $A$ to $B$. [vii. 18]
Therefore also, as $A$ is to $B$, so is $C$ to $D$. Q. E. D.

## Proposition 20

*The least numbers of those which have the same ratio with them measure those which have the same ratio the same number of times, the greater the greater and the less the less.*

For let $CD, EF$ be the least numbers of those which have the same ratio with $A, B$;
I say that $CD$ measures $A$ the same number of times that $EF$ measures $B$.

Now $CD$ is not parts of $A$.

For, if possible, let it be so;
therefore $EF$ is also the same parts of $B$ that $CD$ is of $A$.
[vii. 13 and Def. 20]

Therefore, as many parts of $A$ as there are in $CD$, so many parts of $B$ are there also in $EF$.

Let $CD$ be divided into the parts of $A$, namely $CG$, $GD$, and $EF$ into the parts of $B$, namely $EH$, $HF$;
thus the multitude of $CG$, $GD$ will be equal to the multitude of $EH$, $HF$.

Now, since the numbers $CG$, $GD$ are equal to one another, and the numbers $EH$, $HF$ are also equal to one another, while the multitude of $CG$, $GD$ is equal to the multitude of $EH$, $HF$,

therefore, as $CG$ is to $EH$, so is $GD$ to $HF$.

Therefore also, as one of the antecedents is to one of the consequents, so will all the antecedents be to all the consequents. [VII. 12]

Therefore, as $CG$ is to $EH$, so is $CD$ to $EF$.

Therefore $CG$, $EH$ are in the same ratio with $CD$, $EF$, being less than they: which is impossible, for by hypothesis $CD$, $EF$ are the least numbers of those which have the same ratio with them.

Therefore $CD$ is not parts of $A$;
therefore it is a part of it. [VII. 4]
And $EF$ is the same part of $B$ that $CD$ is of $A$; [VII. 13 and Def. 20]
therefore $CD$ measures $A$ the same number of times that $EF$ measures $B$.

Q. E. D.

PROPOSITION 21

*Numbers prime to one another are the least of those which have the same ratio with them.*

Let $A$, $B$ be numbers prime to one another;
I say that $A$, $B$ are the least of those which have the same ratio with them.

For, if not, there will be some numbers less than $A$, $B$ which are in the same ratio with $A$, $B$.

Let them be $C$, $D$.

Since, then, the least numbers of those which have the same ratio measure those which have the same ratio the same number of times, the greater the greater and the less the less, that is, the antecedent the antecedent and the consequent the consequent, [VII. 20]

therefore $C$ measures $A$ the same number of times that $D$ measures $B$.

Now, as many times as $C$ measures $A$, so many units let there be in $E$.

Therefore $D$ also measures $B$ according to the units in $E$.

And, since $C$ measures $A$ according to the units in $E$,
therefore $E$ also measures $A$ according to the units in $C$. [VII. 16]

For the same reason
$E$ also measures $B$ according to the units in $D$. [VII. 16]

Therefore $E$ measures $A$, $B$ which are prime to one another: which is impossible. [VII. Def. 12]

Therefore there will be no numbers less than $A$, $B$ which are in the same ratio with $A$, $B$.

Therefore $A$, $B$ are the least of those which have the same ratio with them.

Q. E. D.

## Proposition 22

*The least numbers of those which have the same ratio with them are prime to one another.*

Let $A$, $B$ be the least numbers of those which have the same ratio with them;
I say that $A$, $B$ are prime to one another.

For, if they are not prime to one another, some number will measure them.

Let some number measure them, and let it be $C$.

And, as many times as $C$ measures $A$, so many units let there be in $D$,

and, as many times as $C$ measures $B$, so many units let there be in $E$.

Since $C$ measures $A$ according to the units in $D$,
therefore $C$ by multiplying $D$ has made $A$.     [VII. Def. 15]
For the same reason also
$C$ by multiplying $E$ has made $B$.

Thus the number $C$ by multiplying the two numbers $D$, $E$ has made $A$, $B$;
therefore, as $D$ is to $E$, so is $A$ to $B$;     [VII. 17]
therefore $D$, $E$ are in the same ratio with $A$, $B$, being less than they: which is impossible.

Therefore no number will measure the numbers $A$, $B$.

Therefore $A$, $B$ are prime to one another.     Q. E. D.

## Proposition 23

*If two numbers be prime to one another, the number which measures the one of them will be prime to the remaining number.*

Let $A$, $B$ be two numbers prime to one another, and let any number $C$ measure $A$;
I say that $C$, $B$ are also prime to one another.

For, if $C$, $B$ are not prime to one another,
some number will measure $C$, $B$.

Let a number measure them, and let it be $D$.

Since $D$ measures $C$, and $C$ measures $A$, therefore $D$ also measures $A$.

But it also measures $B$;
therefore $D$ measures $A$, $B$ which are prime to one another: which is impossible.     [VII. Def. 12]

Therefore no number will measure the numbers $C$, $B$.

Therefore $C$, $B$ are prime to one another.     Q. E. D.

## Proposition 24

*If two numbers be prime to any number, their product also will be prime to the same.*

For let the two numbers $A$, $B$ be prime to any number $C$, and let $A$ by multiplying $B$ make $D$;
I say that $C$, $D$ are prime to one another.

For, if $C$, $D$ are not prime to one another, some number will measure $C$, $D$.

Let a number measure them, and let it be $E$.

Now, since $C$, $A$ are prime to one another,

and a certain number $E$ measures $C$,
therefore $A$, $E$ are prime to one another. [VII. 23]
As many times, then, as $E$ measures $D$, so many units let there be in $F$;
therefore $F$ also measures
$D$ according to the units in $E$. [VII. 16]
Therefore $E$ by multiplying $F$ has made $D$. [VII. Def. 15]
But, further, $A$ by multiplying $B$ has also made $D$;
therefore the product of $E$, $F$ is equal to the product of $A$, $B$.

But, if the product of the extremes be equal to that of the means, the four numbers are proportional; [VII. 19]
therefore, as $E$ is to $A$, so is $B$ to $F$.

But $A$, $E$ are prime to one another,
numbers which are prime to one another are also the least of those which have the same ratio, [VII. 21]
and the least numbers of those which have the same ratio with them measure those which have the same ratio the same number of times, the greater the greater and the less the less, that is, the antecedent the antecedent and the consequent the consequent; [VII. 20]
therefore $E$ measures $B$.

But it also measures $C$;
therefore $E$ measures $B$, $C$ which are prime to one another: which is impossible. [VII. Def. 12]

Therefore no number will measure the numbers $C$, $D$.
Therefore $C$, $D$ are prime to one another. Q. E. D.

## Proposition 25

*If two numbers be prime to one another, the product of one of them into itself will be prime to the remaining one.*

Let $A$, $B$ be two numbers prime to one another,
and let $A$ by multiplying itself make $C$;
I say that $B$, $C$ are prime to one another.
For let $D$ be made equal to $A$.
Since $A$, $B$ are prime to one another, and $A$ is equal to $D$,
therefore $D$, $B$ are also prime to one another.
Therefore each of the two numbers $D$, $A$ is prime to $B$;
therefore the product of $D$, $A$ will also be prime to $B$. [VII. 24]
But the number which is the product of $D$, $A$ is $C$.
Therefore $C$, $B$ are prime to one another. Q. E. D.

## Proposition 26

*If two numbers be prime to two numbers, both to each, their products also will be prime to one another.*

For let the two numbers $A$, $B$ be prime to the two numbers $C$, $D$; both to each, and let $A$ by multiplying $B$ make $E$, and let $C$ by multiplying $D$ make $F$;
I say that $E$, $F$ are prime to one another.

For, since each of the numbers $A$, $B$ is prime to $C$,
therefore the product of $A$, $B$ will also be prime to $C$.  [VII. 24]
But the product of $A$, $B$ is $E$;
therefore $E$, $C$ are prime to one another.
For the same reason
$E$, $D$ are also prime to one another.
Therefore each of the numbers $C$, $D$ is prime to $E$.
Therefore the product of $C$, $D$ will also be prime to $E$.  [VII. 24]
But the product of $C$, $D$ is $F$.
Therefore $E$, $F$ are prime to one another.                   Q. E. D.

## Proposition 27

*If two numbers be prime to one another, and each by multiplying itself make a certain number, the products will be prime to one another; and, if the original numbers by multiplying the products make certain numbers, the latter will also be prime to one another [and this is always the case with the extremes].*

Let $A$, $B$ be two numbers prime to one another, let $A$ by multiplying itself make $C$, and by multiplying $C$ make $D$, and let $B$ by multiplying itself make $E$, and by multiplying $E$ make $F$;

I say that both $C$, $E$ and $D$, $F$ are prime to one another.

For, since $A$, $B$ are prime to one another, and $A$ by multiplying itself has made $C$,
therefore $C$, $B$ are prime to one another.  [VII. 25]
Since, then, $C$, $B$ are prime to one another,
and $B$ by multiplying itself has made $E$,
therefore $C$, $E$ are prime to one another.  [*id.*]
Again, since $A$, $B$ are prime to one another,
and $B$ by multiplying itself has made $E$,
therefore $A$, $E$ are prime to one another.  [*id.*]
Since, then, the two numbers $A$, $C$ are prime to the two numbers $B$, $E$, both to each,
therefore also the product of $A$, $C$ is prime to the product of $B$, $E$.  [VII. 26]
And the product of $A$, $C$ is $D$, and the product of $B$, $E$ is $F$.
Therefore $D$, $F$ are prime to one another.                   Q. E. D.

## Proposition 28

*If two numbers be prime to one another, the sum will also be prime to each of them; and, if the sum of two numbers be prime to any one of them, the original numbers will also be prime to one another.*

For let two numbers $AB$, $BC$ prime to one another be added;

I say that the sum $AC$ is also prime to each of the numbers $AB$, $BC$.

For, if $CA$, $AB$ are not prime to one another,
some number will measure $CA$, $AB$.
Let a number measure them, and let it be $D$.
Since then $D$ measures $CA$, $AB$,
therefore it will also measure the remainder $BC$.

But it also measures $BA$;
therefore $D$ measures $AB$, $BC$ which are prime to one another: which is impossible. [VII. Def. 12]

Therefore no number will measure the numbers $CA$, $AB$; therefore $CA$, $AB$ are prime to one another.

For the same reason

$AC$, $CB$ are also prime to one another.

Therefore $CA$ is prime to each of the numbers $AB$, $BC$.

Again, let $CA$, $AB$ be prime to one another;

I say that $AB$, $BC$ are also prime to one another.

For, if $AB$, $BC$ are not prime to one another,

some number will measure $AB$, $BC$.

Let a number measure them, and let it be $D$.

Now, since $D$ measures each of the numbers $AB$, $BC$, it will also measure the whole $CA$.

But it also measures $AB$;

therefore $D$ measures $CA$, $AB$ which are prime to one another: which is impossible. [VII. Def. 12]

Therefore no number will measure the numbers $AB$, $BC$.

Therefore $AB$, $BC$ are prime to one another. Q. E. D.

## Proposition 29

*Any prime number is prime to any number which it does not measure.*

Let $A$ be a prime number, and let it not measure $B$;

I say that $B$, $A$ are prime to one another.

For, if $B$, $A$ are not prime to one another,

some number will measure them.

Let $C$ measure them.

Since $C$ measures $B$,

and $A$ does not measure $B$,

therefore $C$ is not the same with $A$.

Now, since $C$ measures $B$, $A$,

therefore it also measures $A$ which is prime, though it is not the same with it: which is impossible.

Therefore no number will measure $B$, $A$.

Therefore $A$, $B$ are prime to one another. Q. E. D.

## Proposition 30

*If two numbers by multiplying one another make some number, and any prime number measure the product, it will also measure one of the original numbers.*

For let the two numbers $A$, $B$ by multiplying one another make $C$, and let any prime number $D$ measure $C$;

I say that $D$ measures one of the numbers $A$, $B$.

For let it not measure $A$.

Now $D$ is prime;

therefore $A$, $D$ are prime to one another. [VII. 29]

And, as many times as $D$ measures $C$, so many units let there be in $E$.

Since then $D$ measures $C$ according to the units in $E$,

therefore $D$ by multiplying $E$ has made $C$. [VII. Def. 15]
Further, $A$ by multiplying $B$ has also made $C$;
therefore the product of $D$, $E$ is equal to the product of $A$, $B$.
Therefore, as $D$ is to $A$, so is $B$ to $E$. [VII. 19]
But $D$, $A$ are prime to one another,
primes are also least, [VII. 21]
and the least measure the numbers which have the same ratio the same number of times, the greater the greater and the less the less, that is, the antecedent the antecedent and the consequent the consequent; [VII. 20]
therefore $D$ measures $B$.
Similarly we can also show that, if $D$ does not measure $B$, it will measure $A$.
Therefore $D$ measures one of the numbers $A$, $B$. Q. E. D.

## Proposition 31

*Any composite number is measured by some prime number.*

Let $A$ be a composite number;
I say that $A$ is measured by some prime number.
For, since $A$ is composite,
some number will measure it.
Let a number measure it, and let it be $B$.
Now, if $B$ is prime, what was enjoined will have been done.
But if it is composite, some number will measure it.
Let a number measure it, and let it be $C$.
Then, since $C$ measures $B$,
and $B$ measures $A$,
therefore $C$ also measures $A$.
And, if $C$ is prime, what was enjoined will have been done.
But if it is composite, some number will measure it.
Thus, if the investigation be continued in this way, some prime number will be found which will measure the number before it, which will also measure $A$.
For, if it is not found, an infinite series of numbers will measure the number $A$, each of which is less than the other:
which is impossible in numbers.
Therefore some prime number will be found which will measure the one before it, which will also measure $A$.
Therefore any composite number is measured by some prime number.
Q. E. D.

## Proposition 32

*Any number either is prime or is measured by some prime number.*

Let $A$ be a number;
I say that $A$ either is prime or is measured by some prime number.
If now $A$ is prime, that which was enjoined will have been done.
But if it is composite, some prime number will measure it. [VII. 31]
Therefore any number either is prime or is measured by some prime number.
Q. E. D.

## Proposition 33

*Given as many numbers as we please, to find the least of those which have the same ratio with them.*

Let $A, B, C$ be the given numbers, as many as we please;

thus it is required to find the least of those which have the same ratio with $A, B, C$.

$A, B, C$ are either prime to one another or not.

Now, if $A, B, C$ are prime to one another, they are the least of those which have the same ratio with them. [VII. 21]

But, if not, let $D$ the greatest common measure of $A, B, C$ be taken, [VII. 3]

and, as many times as $D$ measures the numbers $A, B, C$ respectively, so many units let there be in the numbers $E, F, G$ respectively.

Therefore the numbers $E, F, G$ measure the numbers $A, B, C$ respectively according to the units in $D$. [VII. 16]

Therefore $E, F, G$ measure $A, B, C$ the same number of times;

therefore $E, F, G$ are in the same ratio with $A, B, C$. [VII. Def. 20]

I say next that they are the least that are in that ratio.

For, if $E, F, G$ are not the least of those which have the same ratio with $A, B, C$,

there will be numbers less than $E, F, G$ which are in the same ratio with $A, B, C$.

Let them be $H, K, L$;

therefore $H$ measures $A$ the same number of times that the numbers $K, L$ measure the numbers $B, C$ respectively.

Now, as many times as $H$ measures $A$, so many units let there be in $M$;

therefore the numbers $K, L$ also measure the numbers $B, C$ respectively according to the units in $M$.

And, since $H$ measures $A$ according to the units in $M$,

therefore $M$ also measures $A$ according to the units in $H$. [VII. 16]

For the same reason

$M$ also measures the numbers $B, C$ according to the units in the numbers $K, L$ respectively;

Therefore $M$ measures $A, B, C$.

Now, since $H$ measures $A$ according to the units in $M$,

therefore $H$ by multiplying $M$ has made $A$. [VII. Def. 15]

For the same reason also

$E$ by multiplying $D$ has made $A$.

Therefore the product of $E, D$ is equal to the product of $H, M$.

Therefore, as $E$ is to $H$, so is $M$ to $D$. [VII. 19]

But $E$ is greater than $H$;

therefore $M$ is also greater than $D$.

And it measures $A, B, C$:

which is impossible, for by hypothesis, $D$ is the greatest common measure of $A, B, C$.

Therefore there cannot be any numbers less than $E, F, G$ which are in the same ratio with $A, B, C$.

Therefore $E, F, G$ are the least of those which have the same ratio with $A, B, C$.
                                                                Q. E. D.

### Proposition 34

*Given two numbers, to find the least number which they measure.*

Let $A, B$ be the two given numbers;
thus it is required to find the least number which they measure.

Now $A, B$ are either prime to one another or not.

First, let $A, B$ be prime to one another, and let $A$ by multiplying $B$ make $C$;
therefore also $B$ by multiplying $A$ has made $C$.

Therefore $A, B$ measure $C$.

I say next that it is also the least number they measure.

For, if not, $A, B$ will measure some number which is less than $C$.

Let them measure $D$.

Then, as many times as $A$ measures $D$, so many units let there be in $E$, and, as many times as $B$ measures $D$, so many units let there be in $F$;
therefore $A$ by multiplying $E$ has made $D$,
and $B$ by multiplying $F$ has made $D$;     [VII. Def. 15]
therefore the product of $A, E$ is equal to the product of $B, F$.

Therefore, as $A$ is to $B$, so is $F$ to $E$.     [VII. 19]

But $A, B$ are prime,
primes are also least,     [VII. 21]
and the least measure the numbers which have the same ratio the same number of times, the greater the greater and the less the less;     [VII. 20]
therefore $B$ measures $E$, as consequent consequent.

And, since $A$ by multiplying $B, E$ has made $C, D$,
therefore, as $B$ is to $E$, so is $C$ to $D$.     [VII. 17]

But $B$ measures $E$;
therefore $C$ also measures $D$, the greater the less:
which is impossible.

Therefore $A, B$ do not measure any number less than $C$;
therefore $C$ is the least that is measured by $A, B$.

Next, let $A, B$ not be prime to one another,
and let $F, E$, the least numbers of those which have the same ratio with $A, B$, be taken;     [VII. 33]
therefore the product of $A, E$ is equal to the product of $B, F$.     [VII. 19]

And let $A$ by multiplying $E$ make $C$;
therefore also $B$ by multiplying $F$ has made $C$;

therefore $A, B$ measure $C$.

I say next that it is also the least number that they measure.

For, if not, $A, B$ will measure some number which is less than $C$.

Let them measure $D$.

And, as many times as $A$ measures $D$, so many units let there be in $G$, and, as many times as $B$ measures $D$, so many units let there be in $H$.

Therefore $A$ by multiplying $G$ has made $D$,
and $B$ by multiplying $H$ has made $D$.

Therefore the product of $A$, $G$ is equal to the product of $B$, $H$;
therefore, as $A$ is to $B$, so is $H$ to $G$. [VII. 19]

But, as $A$ is to $B$, so is $F$ to $E$.

Therefore also, as $F$ is to $E$, so is $H$ to $G$.

But $F$, $E$ are least,
and the least measure the numbers which have the same ratio the same number of times, the greater the greater and the less the less; [VII. 20]
therefore $E$ measures $G$.

And, since $A$ by multiplying $E$, $G$ has made $C$, $D$,
therefore, as $E$ is to $G$, so is $C$ to $D$. [VII. 17]

But $E$ measures $G$;
therefore $C$ also measures $D$, the greater the less:
which is impossible.

Therefore $A$, $B$ will not measure any number which is less than $C$.

Therefore $C$ is the least that is measured by $A$, $B$. Q. E. D.

## Proposition 35

*If two numbers measure any number, the least number measured by them will also measure the same.*

For let the two numbers $A$, $B$ measure any number $CD$,
and let $E$ be the least that they measure;
I say that $E$ also measures $CD$.

For, if $E$ does not measure $CD$, let $E$, measuring $DF$, leave $CF$ less than itself.

Now, since $A$, $B$ measure $E$,
and $E$ measures $DF$,
therefore $A$, $B$ will also measure $DF$.

But they also measure the whole $CD$;
therefore they will also measure the remainder $CF$ which is less than $E$:
which is impossible.

Therefore $E$ cannot fail to measure $CD$;
therefore it measures it. Q. E. D.

## Proposition 36

*Given three numbers, to find the least number which they measure.*

Let $A$, $B$, $C$ be the three given numbers;
thus it is required to find the least number which they measure.

Let $D$, the least number measured by the two numbers $A$, $B$, be taken. [VII. 34]

Then $C$ either measures, or does not measure, $D$.

First, let it measure it.

But $A$, $B$ also measure $D$;
therefore $A$, $B$, $C$ measure $D$.

I say next that it is also the least that they measure.

For, if not, $A$, $B$, $C$ will measure some number which is less than $D$.
Let them measure $E$.
Since $A$, $B$, $C$ measure $E$,
    therefore also $A$, $B$ measure $E$.
Therefore the least number measured by $A$, $B$ will also measure $E$.  [VII. 35]
But $D$ is the least number measured by $A$, $B$;
   therefore $D$ will measure $E$, the greater the less:
    which is impossible.
Therefore $A$, $B$, $C$ will not measure any number which is less than $D$;
   therefore $D$ is the least that $A$, $B$, $C$ measure.
 Again, let $C$ not measure $D$,
and let $E$, the least number measured by $C$, $D$, be taken.  [VII. 34]
 Since $A$, $B$ measure $D$,
  and $D$ measures $E$,
  therefore also $A$, $B$ measure $E$.
But $C$ also measures $E$;
  therefore also $A$, $B$, $C$ measure $E$.
I say next that it is also the least that they measure.
For, if not, $A$, $B$, $C$ will measure some number which is less than $E$.
Let them measure $F$.
Since $A$, $B$, $C$ measure $F$,
   therefore also $A$, $B$ measure $F$;
therefore the least number measured by $A$, $B$ will also measure $F$.  [VII. 35]
But $D$ is the least number measured by $A$, $B$;
   therefore $D$ measures $F$.
But $C$ also measures $F$;
   therefore $D$, $C$ measure $F$,
so that the least number measured by $D$, $C$ will also measure $F$.
But $E$ is the least number measured by $C$, $D$;
   therefore $E$ measures $F$, the greater the less:
    which is impossible.
Therefore $A$, $B$, $C$ will not measure any number which is less than $E$.
Therefore $E$ is the least that is measured by $A$, $B$, $C$.  Q. E. D.

## Proposition 37

*If a number be measured by any number, the number which is measured will have a part called by the same name as the measuring number.*

For let the number $A$ be measured by any number $B$;
I say that $A$ has a part called by the same name as $B$.
For, as many times as $B$ measures $A$, so many units let there be in $C$.
Since $B$ measures $A$ according to the units in $C$,
and the unit $D$ also measures the number $C$ according to the units in it,
therefore the unit $D$ measures the number $C$ the same number of times as $B$ measures $A$.
Therefore, alternately, the unit $D$ measures the number $B$ the same number of times as $C$ measures $A$;  [VII. 15]

therefore, whatever part the unit $D$ is of the number $B$, the same part is $C$ of $A$ also.

But the unit $D$ is a part of the number $B$ called by the same name as it;
 therefore $C$ is also a part of $A$ called by the same name as $B$,
so that $A$ has a part $C$ which is called by the same name as $B$.   Q. E. D.

### Proposition 38

*If a number have any part whatever, it will be measured by a number called by the same name as the part.*

 For let the number $A$ have any part whatever, $B$,
  and let $C$ be a number called by the same name as the part $B$;
   I say that $C$ measures $A$.

   For, since $B$ is a part of $A$ called by the same name as $C$,
   and the unit $D$ is also a part of $C$ called by the same name as it,
  therefore, whatever part the unit $D$ is of the number $C$,
   the same part is $B$ of $A$ also;
therefore the unit $D$ measures the number $C$ the same number of times that $B$ measures $A$.

Therefore, alternately, the unit $D$ measures the number $B$ the same number of times that $C$ measures $A$.  [VII. 15]

Therefore $C$ measures $A$.  Q. E. D.

### Proposition 39

*To find the number which is the least that will have given parts.*

 Let $A$, $B$, $C$ be the given parts;
thus it is required to find the number which is the least that will have the parts $A$, $B$, $C$.

 Let $D$, $E$, $F$ be numbers called by the same name as the parts $A$, $B$, $C$,
  and let $G$, the least number measured by $D$, $E$, $F$, be taken.  [VII. 36]
  Therefore $G$ has parts called by the same name as $D$, $E$, $F$.  [VII. 37]
  But $A$, $B$, $C$ are parts called by the same name as $D$, $E$, $F$;
  therefore $G$ has the parts $A$, $B$, $C$.

I say next that it is also the least number that has.

For, if not, there will be some number less than $G$ which will have the parts $A$, $B$, $C$.

Let it be $H$.

Since $H$ has the parts $A$, $B$, $C$,
therefore $H$ will be measured by numbers called by the same name as the parts $A$, $B$, $C$.  [VII. 38]

But $D$, $E$, $F$ are numbers called by the same name as the parts $A$, $B$, $C$;
  therefore $H$ is measured by $D$, $E$, $F$.

And it is less than $G$: which is impossible.

Therefore there will be no number less than $G$ that will have the parts $A$, $B$, $C$.  Q. E. D.

# BOOK EIGHT

## PROPOSITION 1

*If there be as many numbers as we please in continued proportion, and the extremes of them be prime to one another, the numbers are the least of those which have the same ratio with them.*

Let there be as many numbers as we please, $A, B, C, D$, in continued proportion,
and let the extremes of them $A, D$ be prime to one another;
I say that $A, B, C, D$ are the least of those which have the same ratio with them.

For, if not, let $E, F, G, H$ be less than $A, B, C, D$, and in the same ratio with them.

Now, since $A, B, C, D$ are in the same ratio with $E, F, G, H$,
and the multitude of the numbers $A, B, C, D$ is equal to the multitude of the numbers $E, F, G, H$,

therefore, *ex aequali*,
as $A$ is to $D$, so is $E$ to $H$. [VII. 14]

But $A, D$ are prime,

primes are also least, [VII. 21]
and the least numbers measure those which have the same ratio the same number of times, the greater the greater and the less the less, that is, the antecedent the antecedent and the consequent the consequent. [VII. 20]

Therefore $A$ measures $E$, the greater the less:
which is impossible.

Therefore $E, F, G, H$ which are less than $A, B, C, D$ are not in the same ratio with them.

Therefore $A, B, C, D$ are the least of those which have the same ratio with them.

Q. E. D.

## PROPOSITION 2

*To find numbers in continued proportion, as many as may be prescribed, and the least that are in a given ratio.*

Let the ratio of $A$ to $B$ be the given ratio in least numbers;
thus it is required to find numbers in continued proportion, as many as may be prescribed, and the least that are in the ratio of $A$ to $B$.

Let four be prescribed;
let $A$ by multiplying itself make $C$, and by multiplying $B$ let it make $D$;
let $B$ by multiplying itself make $E$;
further, let $A$ by multiplying $C, D, E$ make $F, G, H$.

and let $B$ by multiplying $E$ make $K$.

Now, since $A$ by multiplying itself has made $C$, and by multiplying $B$ has made $D$, therefore, as $A$ is to $B$, so is $C$ to $D$. [VII. 17]

Again, since $A$ by multiplying $B$ has made $D$, and $B$ by multiplying itself has made $E$, therefore the numbers $A$, $B$ by multiplying $B$ have made the numbers $D$, $E$ respectively.

Therefore, as $A$ is to $B$, so is $D$ to $E$, [VII. 18]

But, as $A$ is to $B$, so is $C$ to $D$; therefore also, as $C$ is to $D$, so is $D$ to $E$.

And, since $A$ by multiplying $C$, $D$ has made $F$, $G$, therefore, as $C$ is to $D$, so is $F$ to $G$. [VII. 17]

But, as $C$ is to $D$, so was $A$ to $B$; therefore also, as $A$ is to $B$, so is $F$ to $G$.

Again, since $A$ by multiplying $D$, $E$ has made $G$, $H$, therefore, as $D$ is to $E$, so is $G$ to $H$. [VII. 17]

But, as $D$ is to $E$, so is $A$ to $B$.

Therefore also, as $A$ is to $B$, so is $G$ to $H$.

And, since $A$, $B$ by multiplying $E$ have made $H$, $K$, therefore, as $A$ is to $B$, so is $H$ to $K$. [VII. 18]

But, as $A$ is to $B$, so is $F$ to $G$, and $G$ to $H$.

Therefore also, as $F$ is to $G$, so is $G$ to $H$, and $H$ to $K$; therefore $C$, $D$, $E$, and $F$, $G$, $H$, $K$ are proportional in the ratio of $A$ to $B$.

I say next that they are the least numbers that are so.

For, since $A$, $B$ are the least of those which have the same ratio with them, and the least of those which have the same ratio are prime to one another, [VII. 22]

therefore $A$, $B$ are prime to one another.

And the numbers $A$, $B$ by multiplying themselves respectively have made the numbers $C$, $E$, and by multiplying the numbers $C$, $E$ respectively have made the numbers $F$, $K$; therefore $C$, $E$ and $F$, $K$ are prime to one another respectively. [VII. 27]

But, if there be as many numbers as we please in continued proportion, and the extremes of them be prime to one another, they are the least of those which have the same ratio with them. [VIII. 1]

Therefore $C$, $D$, $E$ and $F$, $G$, $H$, $K$ are the least of those which have the same ratio with $A$, $B$.

Q. E. D.

PORISM. From this it is manifest that, if three numbers in continued proportion be the least of those which have the same ratio with them, the extremes of them are squares, and, if four numbers, cubes.

## PROPOSITION 3

*If as many numbers as we please in continued proportion be the least of those which have the same ratio with them, the extremes of them are prime to one another.*

Let as many numbers as we please, $A, B, C, D$, in continued proportion be the least of those which have the same ratio with them;

I say that the extremes of them $A, D$ are prime to one another.

For let two numbers $E, F$, the least that are in the ratio of $A, B, C, D$, be taken, [VII. 33]
   then three others $G, H, K$ with the same property;
     and others, more by one continually, [VIII. 2]
until the multitude taken becomes equal to the multitude of the numbers $A, B, C, D$.

Let them be taken, and let them be $L, M, N, O$.

Now, since $E, F$ are the least of those which have the same ratio with them, they are prime to one another. [VII. 22]

And, since the numbers $E, F$ by multiplying themselves respectively have made the numbers $G, K$, and by multiplying the numbers $G, K$ respectively have made the numbers $L, O$, [VIII. 2, Por.]
   therefore both $G, K$ and $L, O$ are prime to one another. [VII. 27]

And, since $A, B, C, D$ are the least of those which have the same ratio with them,
while $L, M, N, O$ are the least that are in the same ratio with $A, B, C, D$,
and the multitude of the numbers $A, B, C, D$ is equal to the multitude of the numbers $L, M, N, O$,
therefore the numbers $A, B, C, D$ are equal to the numbers $L, M, N, O$ respectively;
   therefore $A$ is equal to $L$, and $D$ to $O$.

And $L, O$ are prime to one another.

Therefore $A, D$ are also prime to one another. Q. E. D.

## Proposition 4

*Given as many ratios as we please in least numbers, to find numbers in continued proportion which are the least in the given ratios.*

Let the given ratios in least numbers be that of $A$ to $B$, that of $C$ to $D$, and that of $E$ to $F$;
thus it is required to find numbers in continued proportion which are the least that are in the ratio of $A$ to $B$, in the ratio of $C$ to $D$, and in the ratio of $E$ to $F$.

Let $G$, the least number measured by $B, C$, be taken. [VII. 34]

And, as many times as $B$ measures $G$, so many times also let $A$ measure $H$, and, as many times as $C$ measures $G$, so many times also let $D$ measure $K$.

Now $E$ either measures or does not measure $K$.

First, let it measure it.

ELEMENTS VIII

And, as many times as $E$ measures $K$, so many times let $F$ measure $L$ also.
Now, since $A$ measures $H$ the same number of times that $B$ measures $G$, therefore, as $A$ is to $B$, so is $H$ to $G$. [VII. Def. 20, VII. 13]

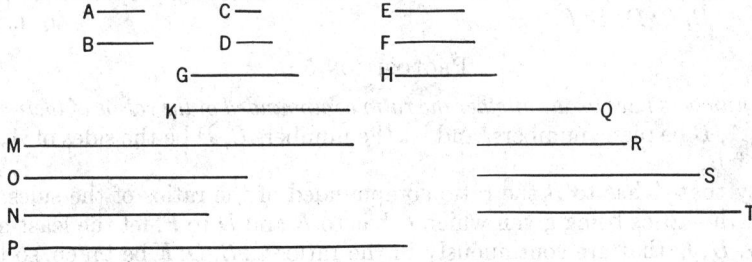

For the same reason also,
    as $C$ is to $D$, so is $G$ to $K$,
    and further, as $E$ is to $F$, so is $K$ to $L$;
therefore $H$, $G$, $K$, $L$ are continuously proportional in the ratio of $A$ to $B$, in the ratio of $C$ to $D$, and in the ratio of $E$ to $F$.

I say next that they are also the least that have this property.

For, if $H$, $G$, $K$, $L$ are not the least numbers continuously proportional in the ratios of $A$ to $B$, of $C$ to $D$, and of $E$ to $F$, let them be $N$, $O$, $M$, $P$.

Then since, as $A$ is to $B$, so is $N$ to $O$,
    while $A$, $B$ are least,
and the least numbers measure those which have the same ratio the same number of times, the greater the greater and the less the less, that is, the antecedent the antecedent and the consequent the consequent;
    therefore $B$ measures $O$. [VII. 20]

For the same reason
    $C$ also measures $O$;
    therefore $B$, $C$ measure $O$;
therefore the least number measured by $B$, $C$ will also measure $O$. [VII. 35]

But $G$ is the least number measured by $B$, $C$;
    therefore $G$ measures $O$, the greater the less:
    which is impossible.

Therefore there will be no numbers less than $H$, $G$, $K$, $L$ which are continuously in the ratio of $A$ to $B$, of $C$ to $D$, and of $E$ to $F$.

Next, let $E$ not measure $K$.

Let $M$, the least number measured by $E$, $K$, be taken.
And, as many times as $K$ measures $M$, so many times let $H$, $G$ measure $N$, $O$ respectively,

and, as many times as $E$ measures $M$, so many times let $F$ measure $P$ also.

Since $H$ measures $N$ the same number of times that $G$ measures $O$,

therefore, as $H$ is to $G$, so is $N$ to $O$. [VII. 13 and Def. 20]

But, as $H$ is to $G$, so is $A$ to $B$;

therefore also, as $A$ is to $B$, so is $N$ to $O$.

For the same reason also,

as $C$ is to $D$, so is $O$ to $M$.

Again, since $E$ measures $M$ the same number of times that $F$ measures $P$,

therefore, as $E$ is to $F$, so is $M$ to $P$; [VII. 13 and Def. 20]

therefore $N$, $O$, $M$, $P$ are continuously proportional in the ratios of $A$ to $B$, of $C$ to $D$, and of $E$ to $F$.

I say next that they are also the least that are in the ratios $A:B$, $C:D$, $E:F$.

For, if not, there will be some numbers less than $N$, $O$, $M$, $P$ continuously proportional in the ratios $A:B$, $C:D$, $E:F$.

Let them be $Q$, $R$, $S$, $T$.

Now since, as $Q$ is to $R$, so is $A$ to $B$.

while $A$, $B$ are least,

and the least numbers measure those which have the same ratio with them the same number of times, the antecedent the antecedent and the consequent the consequent, [VII. 20]

therefore $B$ measures $R$.

For the same reason $C$ also measures $R$;

therefore $B$, $C$ measure $R$.

Therefore the least number measured by $B$, $C$ will also measure $R$. [VII. 35]

But $G$ is the least number measured by $B$, $C$;

therefore $G$ measures $R$.

And, as $G$ is to $R$, so is $K$ to $S$: [VII. 13]

therefore $K$ also measures $S$.

But $E$ also measures $S$;

therefore $E$, $K$ measure $S$.

Therefore the least number measured by $E$, $K$ will also measure $S$. [VII. 35]

But $M$ is the least number measured by $E$, $K$;

therefore $M$ measures $S$, the greater the less:

which is impossible.

Therefore there will not be any numbers less than $N$, $O$, $M$, $P$ continuously proportional in the ratios of $A$ to $B$, of $C$ to $D$, and of $E$ to $F$;

therefore $N$, $O$, $M$, $P$ are the least numbers continuously proportional in the ratios $A:B$, $C:D$, $E:F$.
Q. E. D.

## Proposition 5

*Plane numbers have to one another the ratio compounded of the ratios of their sides.*

Let $A$, $B$ be plane numbers, and let the numbers $C$, $D$ be the sides of $A$, and $E$, $F$ of $B$;

I say that $A$ has to $B$ the ratio compounded of the ratios of the sides.

For, the ratios being given which $C$ has to $E$ and $D$ to $F$, let the least numbers $G$, $H$, $K$ that are continuously in the ratios $C:E$, $D:F$ be taken, so that,

as $C$ is to $E$, so is $G$ to $H$,

and, as $D$ is to $F$, so is $H$ to $K$. [VIII. 4]

And let $D$ by multiplying $E$ make $L$.

ELEMENTS VIII

Now, since $D$ by multiplying $C$ has made $A$, and by multiplying $E$ has made $L$,
> therefore, as $C$ is to $E$, so is $A$ to $L$. [VII. 17]

But, as $C$ is to $E$, so is $G$ to $H$;
> therefore also, as $G$ is to $H$, so is $A$ to $L$.

Again, since $E$ by multiplying $D$ has made $L$, and further by multiplying $F$ has made $B$,
> therefore, as $D$ is to $F$, so is $L$ to $B$. [VII. 17]

But, as $D$ is to $F$, so is $H$ to $K$;
> therefore also, as $H$ is to $K$, so is $L$ to $B$.

But it was also proved that,
> as $G$ is to $H$, so is $A$ to $L$;
> therefore, *ex aequali*,
> as $G$ is to $K$, so is $A$ to $B$. [VII. 14]

But $G$ has to $K$ the ratio compounded of the ratios of the sides;
therefore $A$ also has to $B$ the ratio compounded of the ratios of the sides.

Q. E. D.

## Proposition 6

*If there be as many numbers as we please in continued proportion, and the first do not measure the second, neither will any other measure any other.*

Let there be as many numbers as we please, $A, B, C, D, E$, in continued proportion, and let $A$ not measure $B$;

I say that neither will any other measure any other.

Now it is manifest that $A, B, C, D, E$ do not measure one another in order; for $A$ does not even measure $B$.

I say, then, that neither will any other measure any other.

For, if possible, let $A$ measure $C$.

And, however many $A, B, C$ are, let as many numbers $F, G, H$, the least of those which have the same ratio with $A, B, C$, be taken. [VII. 33]

Now, since $F, G, H$ are in the same ratio with $A, B, C$, and the multitude of the numbers $A, B, C$ is equal to the multitude of the numbers $F, G, H$,
> therefore, *ex aequali*, as $A$ is to $C$, so is $F$ to $H$. [VII. 14]

And since, as $A$ is to $B$, so is $F$ to $G$,
> while $A$ does not measure $B$,
> therefore neither does $F$ measure $G$; [VII. Def. 20]
therefore $F$ is not an unit, for the unit measures any number.
Now $F, H$ are prime to one another. [VIII. 3]
And, as $F$ is to $H$, so is $A$ to $C$;
> therefore neither does $A$ measure $C$.

Similarly we can prove that neither will any other measure any other.

Q. E. D.

## Proposition 7

*If there be as many numbers as we please in continued proportion, and the first measure the last, it will measure the second also.*

Let there be as many numbers as we please, $A, B, C, D$, in continued proportion; and let $A$ measure $D$;

I say that $A$ also measures $B$.

For, if $A$ does not measure $B$, neither will any other of the numbers measure any other. [VIII. 6]

But $A$ measures $D$.

Therefore $A$ also measures $B$.

Q. E. D.

## Proposition 8

*If between two numbers there fall numbers in continued proportion with them, then, however many numbers fall between them in continued proportion, so many will also fall in continued proportion between the numbers which have the same ratio with the original numbers.*

Let the numbers $C, D$ fall between the two numbers $A, B$ in continued proportion with them, and let $E$ be made in the same ratio to $F$ as $A$ is to $B$;

I say that, as many numbers as have fallen between $A, B$ in continued proportion, so many will also fall between $E, F$ in continued proportion.

For, as many as $A, B, C, D$ are in multitude, let so many numbers $G, H, K, L$, the least of those which have the same ratio with $A, C, D, B$, be taken; [VII. 33] therefore the extremes of them $G, L$ are prime to one another. [VIII. 3]

Now, since $A, C, D, B$ are in the same ratio with $G, H, K, L$, and the multitude of the numbers $A, C, D, B$ is equal to the multitude of the numbers $G, H, K, L$,

therefore, *ex aequali*, as $A$ is to $B$, so is $G$ to $L$. [VII. 14]

But, as $A$ is to $B$, so is $E$ to $F$;

therefore also, as $G$ is to $L$, so is $E$ to $F$.

But $G, L$ are prime,

primes are also least, [VII. 21]

and the least numbers measure those which have the same ratio the same number of times, the greater the greater and the less the less, that is, the antecedent the antecedent and the consequent the consequent. [VII. 20]

Therefore $G$ measures $E$ the same number of times as $L$ measures $F$.

Next, as many times as $G$ measures $E$, so many times let $H, K$ also measure $M, N$ respectively;

therefore $G, H, K, L$ measure $E, M, N, F$ the same number of times.

Therefore $G, H, K, L$ are in the same ratio with $E, M, N, F$. [VII. Def. 20]

But $G, H, K, L$ are in the same ratio with $A, C, D, B$;

therefore $A, C, D, B$ are also in the same ratio with $E, M, N, F$.

But $A$, $C$, $D$, $B$ are in continued proportion;
therefore $E$, $M$, $N$, $F$ are also in continued proportion.

Therefore, as many numbers as have fallen between $A$, $B$ in continued proportion with them, so many numbers have also fallen between $E$, $F$ in continued proportion.
Q. E. D.

## Proposition 9

*If two numbers be prime to one another, and numbers fall between them in continued proportion, then, however many numbers fall between them in continued proportion, so many will also fall between each of them and an unit in continued proportion.*

Let $A$, $B$ be two numbers prime to one another, and let $C$, $D$ fall between them in continued proportion,
and let the unit $E$ be set out;

I say that, as many numbers as fall between $A$, $B$ in continued proportion, so many will also fall between either of the numbers $A$, $B$ and the unit in continued proportion.

For let two numbers $F$, $G$, the least that are in the ratio of $A$, $C$, $D$, $B$, be taken,
three numbers $H$, $K$, $L$ with the same property,
and others more by one continually, until their multitude is equal to the multitude of $A$, $C$, $D$, $B$. [VIII. 2]

```
A———————
C————————————
D——————————————
B——————————————————
          E—              M———————
          F—              N————————
          G—              O——————————
                          P————————————
```

Let them be taken, and let them be $M$, $N$, $O$, $P$.

It is now manifest that $F$ by multiplying itself has made $H$ and by multiplying $H$ has made $M$, while $G$ by multiplying itself has made $L$ and by multiplying $L$ has made $P$. [VIII. 2, Por.]

And, since $M$, $N$, $O$, $P$ are the least of those which have the same ratio with $F$, $G$,
and $A$, $C$, $D$, $B$ are also the least of those which have the same ratio with $F$, $G$, [VIII. 1]
while the multitude of the numbers $M$, $N$, $O$, $P$ is equal to the multitude of the numbers $A$, $C$, $D$, $B$,
therefore $M$, $N$, $O$, $P$ are equal to $A$, $C$, $D$, $B$ respectively;
therefore $M$ is equal to $A$, and $P$ to $B$.

Now, since $F$ by multiplying itself has made $H$,
therefore $F$ measures $H$ according to the units in $F$.

But the unit $E$ also measures $F$ according to the units in it;
therefore the unit $E$ measures the number $F$ the same number of times as $F$ measures $H$.

Therefore, as the unit $E$ is to the number $F$, so is $F$ to $H$. [VII. Def. 20]

Again, since $F$ by multiplying $H$ has made $M$,

therefore $H$ measures $M$ according to the units in $F$.

But the unit $E$ also measures the number $F$ according to the units in it; therefore the unit $E$ measures the number $F$ the same number of times as $H$ measures $M$.

Therefore, as the unit $E$ is to the number $F$, so is $H$ to $M$.

But it was also proved that, as the unit $E$ is to the number $F$, so is $F$ to $H$; therefore also, as the unit $E$ is to the number $F$, so is $F$ to $H$, and $H$ to $M$.

But $M$ is equal to $A$;

therefore, as the unit $E$ is to the number $F$, so is $F$ to $H$, and $H$ to $A$.

For the same reason also,

as the unit $E$ is to the number $G$, so is $G$ to $L$ and $L$ to $B$.

Therefore, as many numbers as have fallen between $A$, $B$ in continued proportion, so many numbers also have fallen between each of the numbers $A$, $B$ and the unit $E$ in continued proportion. Q. E. D.

## PROPOSITION 10

*If numbers fall between each of two numbers and an unit in continued proportion however many numbers fall between each of them and an unit in continued proportion, so many also will fall between the numbers themselves in continued proportion.*

For let the numbers $D$, $E$ and $F$, $G$ respectively fall between the two numbers $A$, $B$ and the unit $C$ in continued proportion;

I say that, as many numbers as have fallen between each of the numbers $A$, $B$ and the unit $C$ in continued proportion, so many numbers will also fall between $A$, $B$ in continued proportion.

For let $D$ by multiplying $F$ make $H$, and let the numbers $D$, $F$ by multiplying $H$ make $K$, $L$ respectively.

Now, since, as the unit $C$ is to the number $D$, so is $D$ to $E$,

therefore the unit $C$ measures the number $D$ the same number of times as $D$ measures $E$. [VII. Def. 20]

But the unit $C$ measures the number $D$ according to the units in $D$;

therefore the number $D$ also measures $E$ according to the units in $D$;

therefore $D$ by multiplying itself has made $E$.

Again, since, as $C$ is to the number $D$, so is $E$ to $A$,

therefore the unit $C$ measures the number $D$ the same number of times as $E$ measures $A$.

But the unit $C$ measures the number $D$ according to the units in $D$;

therefore $E$ also measures $A$ according to the units in $D$;

therefore $D$ by multiplying $E$ has made $A$.

For the same reason also

$F$ by multiplying itself has made $G$, and by multiplying $G$ has made $B$.

ELEMENTS VIII

And, since $D$ by multiplying itself has made $E$ and by multiplying $F$ has made $H$,
>therefore, as $D$ is to $F$, so is $E$ to $H$. [VII. 17]

For the same reason also,
>as $D$ is to $F$, so is $H$ to $G$. [VII. 18]

Therefore also, as $E$ is to $H$, so is $H$ to $G$.

Again, since $D$ by multiplying the numbers $E$, $H$ has made $A$, $K$ respectively,
>therefore, as $E$ is to $H$, so is $A$ to $K$. [VII. 17]

But, as $E$ is to $H$, so is $D$ to $F$;
>therefore also, as $D$ is to $F$, so is $A$ to $K$.

Again, since the numbers $D$, $F$ by multiplying $H$ have made $K$, $L$ respectively,
>therefore, as $D$ is to $F$, so is $K$ to $L$. [VII. 18]

But, as $D$ is to $F$, so is $A$ to $K$;
>therefore also, as $A$ is to $K$, so is $K$ to $L$.

Further, since $F$ by multiplying the numbers $H$, $G$ has made $L$, $B$ respectively,
>therefore, as $H$ is to $G$, so is $L$ to $B$. [VII. 17]

But, as $H$ is to $G$, so is $D$ to $F$;
>therefore also, as $D$ is to $F$, so is $L$ to $B$.

But it was also proved that,
>as $D$ is to $F$, so is $A$ to $K$ and $K$ to $L$;

therefore also, as $A$ is to $K$, so is $K$ to $L$ and $L$ to $B$.

Therefore $A$, $K$, $L$, $B$ are in continued proportion.

Therefore, as many numbers as fall between each of the numbers $A$, $B$ and the unit $C$ in continued proportion, so many also will fall between $A$, $B$ in continued proportion.  Q. E. D.

## PROPOSITION 11

*Between two square numbers there is one mean proportional number, and the square has to the square the ratio duplicate of that which the side has to the side.*

Let $A$, $B$ be square numbers,
>and let $C$ be the side of $A$, and $D$ of $B$;

I say that between $A$, $B$ there is one mean proportional number, and $A$ has
>to $B$ the ratio duplicate of that which $C$ has to $D$.
>For let $C$ by multiplying $D$ make $E$.

Now, since $A$ is a square and $C$ is its side,
>therefore $C$ by multiplying itself has made $A$.

For the same reason also,
>$D$ by multiplying itself has made $B$.

Since, then, $C$ by multiplying the numbers $C$, $D$ has made $A$, $E$ respectively,
>therefore, as $C$ is to $D$, so is $A$ to $E$. [VII. 17]

For the same reason also,
>as $C$ is to $D$, so is $E$ to $B$. [VII. 18]

Therefore also, as $A$ is to $E$, so is $E$ to $B$.

Therefore between $A$, $B$ there is one mean proportional number.

I say next that $A$ also has to $B$ the ratio duplicate of that which $C$ has to $D$.

For, since $A$, $E$, $B$ are three numbers in proportion,

therefore $A$ has to $B$ the ratio duplicate of that which $A$ has to $E$. [v. Def. 9]
But, as $A$ is to $E$, so is $C$ to $D$.
Therefore $A$ has to $B$ the ratio duplicate of that which the side $C$ has to $D$.

Q. E. D.

## Proposition 12

*Between two cube numbers there are two mean proportional numbers, and the cube has to the cube the ratio triplicate of that which the side has to the side.*

Let $A, B$ be cube numbers,
and let $C$ be the side of $A$, and $D$ of $B$;
I say that between $A, B$ there are two mean proportional numbers, and $A$ has to $B$ the ratio triplicate of that which $C$ has to $D$.

For let $C$ by multiplying itself make $E$, and by multiplying $D$ let it make $F$;
let $D$ by multiplying itself make $G$,
and let the numbers $C, D$ by multiplying $F$ make $H, K$ respectively.

Now, since $A$ is a cube, and $C$ its side,
and $C$ by multiplying itself has made $E$,
therefore $C$ by multiplying itself has made $E$ and by multiplying $E$ has made $A$.
For the same reason also
$D$ by multiplying itself has made $G$ and by multiplying $G$ has made $B$.
And, since $C$ by multiplying the numbers $C, D$ has made $E, F$ respectively,
therefore, as $C$ is to $D$, so is $E$ to $F$. [vii. 17]
For the same reason also,
as $C$ is to $D$, so is $F$ to $G$. [vii. 18]
Again, since $C$ by multiplying the numbers $E, F$ has made $A, H$ respectively,
therefore, as $E$ is to $F$, so is $A$ to $H$. [vii. 17]
But, as $E$ is to $F$, so is $C$ to $D$.
Therefore also, as $C$ is to $D$, so is $A$ to $H$.
Again, since the numbers $C, D$ by multiplying $F$ have made $H, K$ respectively,
therefore, as $C$ is to $D$, so is $H$ to $K$. [vii. 18]
Again, since $D$ by multiplying each of the numbers $F, G$ has made $K, B$ respectively,
therefore, as $F$ is to $G$, so is $K$ to $B$. [vii. 17]
But, as $F$ is to $G$, so is $C$ to $D$;
therefore also, as $C$ is to $D$, so is $A$ to $H$, $H$ to $K$, and $K$ to $B$.
Therefore $H, K$ are two mean proportionals between $A, B$.
I say next that $A$ also has to $B$ the ratio triplicate of that which $C$ has to $D$.
For, since $A, H, K, B$ are four numbers in proportion,
therefore $A$ has to $B$ the ratio triplicate of that which $A$ has to $H$. [v. Def. 10]
But, as $A$ is to $H$, so is $C$ to $D$;
therefore $A$ also has to $B$ the ratio triplicate of that which $C$ has to $D$.

Q. E. D.

## Proposition 13

*If there be as many numbers as we please in continued proportion, and each by multiplying itself make some number, the products will be proportional; and, if the original numbers by multiplying the products make certain numbers, the latter will also be proportional.*

Let there be as many numbers as we please, $A, B, C$, in continued proportion, so that, as $A$ is to $B$, so is $B$ to $C$;
let $A, B, C$ by multiplying themselves make $D, E, F$, and by multiplying $D, E, F$ let them make $G, H, K$;
 I say that $D, E, F$ and $G, H, K$ are in continued proportion.

```
A——               G——————
B——               H————————
C——               K——————————
D———
E————             M—————————
F—————            N——————————
L————             P———————————
O—————            Q————————————
```

For let $A$ by multiplying $B$ make $L$,
 and let the numbers $A, B$ by multiplying $L$ make $M, N$ respectively.
And again let $B$ by multiplying $C$ make $O$,
 and let the numbers $B, C$ by multiplying $O$ make $P, Q$ respectively.
 Then, in manner similar to the foregoing, we can prove that
$D, L, E$ and $G, M, N, H$ are continuously proportional in the ratio of $A$ to $B$, and further $E, O, F$ and $H, P, Q, K$ are continuously proportional in the ratio of $B$ to $C$.
Now, as $A$ is to $B$, so is $B$ to $C$;
 therefore $D, L, E$ are also in the same ratio with $E, O, F$,
 and further $G, M, N, H$ in the same ratio with $H, P, Q, K$.
And the multitude of $D, L, E$ is equal to the multitude of $E, O, F$ and that of $G, M, N, H$ to that of $H, P, Q, K$;
 therefore, *ex aequali*,
  as $D$ is to $E$, so is $E$ to $F$,
and, as $G$ is to $H$, so is $H$ to $K$. [VII. 14]

Q. E. D.

## Proposition 14

*If a square measure a square, the side will also measure the side; and, if the side measure the side, the square will also measure the square.*

Let $A, B$ be square numbers, let $C, D$ be their sides, and let $A$ measure $B$;
 I say that $C$ also measures $D$.

```
A——
B——————————
—C     ——D
E————
```

For let $C$ by multiplying $D$ make $E$;
therefore $A, E, B$ are continuously proportional in the ratio of $C$ to $D$. [VIII. 11]
And, since $A, E, B$ are continuously proportional, and $A$ measures $B$,
therefore $A$ also measures $E$. [VIII. 7]

And, as $A$ is to $E$, so is $C$ to $D$;
therefore also $C$ measures $D$. [VII. Def. 20]
Again, let $C$ measure $D$;
I say that $A$ also measures $B$.

For, with the same construction, we can in a similar manner prove that $A$, $E$, $B$ are continuously proportional in the ratio of $C$ to $D$.

And since, as $C$ is to $D$, so is $A$ to $E$,
and $C$ measures $D$,
therefore $A$ also measures $E$. [VII. Def. 20]
And $A$, $E$, $B$ are continuously proportional;
therefore $A$ also measures $B$.

Therefore etc. Q. E. D.

## Proposition 15

*If a cube number measure a cube number, the side will also measure the side; and, if the side measure the side, the cube will also measure the cube.*

For let the cube number $A$ measure the cube $B$,
and let $C$ be the side of $A$ and $D$ of $B$;
I say that $C$ measures $D$.

For let $C$ by multiplying itself make $E$,
and let $D$ by multiplying itself make $G$;
further, let $C$ by multiplying $D$ make $F$,
and let $C$, $D$ by multiplying $F$ make $H$, $K$ respectively.

Now it is manifest that $E$, $F$, $G$ and $A$, $H$, $K$, $B$ are continuously proportional in the ratio of $C$ to $D$. [VIII. 11, 12]

And, since $A$, $H$, $K$, $B$ are continuously proportional,
and $A$ measures $B$,
therefore it also measures $H$.
[VIII. 7]

And, as $A$ is to $H$, so is $C$ to $D$;
therefore $C$ also measures $D$. [VII. Def. 20]
Next, let $C$ measure $D$;
I say that $A$ will also measure $B$.

For, with the same construction, we can prove in a similar manner that $A$, $H$, $K$, $B$ are continuously proportional in the ratio of $C$ to $D$.

And, since $C$ measures $D$,
and, as $C$ is to $D$, so is $A$ to $H$,
therefore $A$ also measures $H$, [VII. Def. 20]
so that $A$ measures $B$ also. Q. E. D.

## Proposition 16

*If a square number do not measure a square number, neither will the side measure the side; and, if the side do not measure the side, neither will the square measure the square.*

Let $A$, $B$ be square numbers, and let $C$, $D$ be their sides; and let $A$ not measure $B$;

ELEMENTS VIII

```
A————
B————————————
C——
D——
```

　　　　　　　　I say that neither does $C$ measure $D$.
　　　　　　　　For, if $C$ measures $D$, $A$ will also measure $B$.　　[VIII. 14]
　　　　　　　　But $A$ does not measure $B$;
　　　　　　　　　　therefore neither will $C$ measure $D$.
　　　　　　　　Again, let $C$ not measure $D$;
　　　　　　　　　　I say that neither will $A$ measure $B$.
For, if $A$ measures $B$, $C$ will also measure $D$.　　　　　[VIII. 14]
But $C$ does not measure $D$;
　　　　therefore neither will $A$ measure $B$.　　　　Q. E. D.

## Proposition 17

*If a cube number do not measure a cube number, neither will the side measure the side; and, if the side do not measure the side, neither will the cube measure the cube.*

　　For let the cube number $A$ not measure the cube number $B$,
　　　　　and let $C$ be the side of $A$, and $D$ of $B$;
　　　　　　　　I say that $C$ will not measure $D$.

```
A————
B————————————————
C—
D—
```

　　　　　　　　For if $C$ measures $D$, $A$ will also measure $B$.
　　　　　　　　　　　　　　　　　　　　　　　　　　　[VIII. 15]
　　　　　　　　But $A$ does not measure $B$;
　　　　　　　　　　therefore neither does $C$ measure $D$.
Again, let $C$ not measure $D$;
　　　　I say that neither will $A$ measure $B$.
For, if $A$ measures $B$, $C$ will also measure $D$.　　　　[VIII. 15]
But $C$ does not measure $D$;
　　　　therefore neither will $A$ measure $B$.　　　　Q. E. D.

## Proposition 18

*Between two similar plane numbers there is one mean proportional number; and the plane number has to the plane number the ratio duplicate of that which the corresponding side has to the corresponding side.*

Let $A$, $B$ be two similar plane numbers, and let the numbers $C$, $D$ be the sides of $A$, and $E$, $F$ of $B$.

```
A————————                        C——
B——————————————————              D——
                                 E———
G——————————————                  F—
```

Now, since similar plane numbers are those which have their sides proportional,　　　　　　　　　　　　　　　　　　　　　　　　　　　[VII. Def. 21]
　　　　　therefore, as $C$ is to $D$, so is $E$ to $F$.
I say then that between $A$, $B$ there is one mean proportional number, and $A$ has to $B$ the ratio duplicate of that which $C$ has to $E$, or $D$ to $F$, that is, of that which the corresponding side has to the corresponding side.
　Now since, as $C$ is to $D$, so is $E$ to $F$,
　　　　therefore, alternately, as $C$ is to $E$, so is $D$ to $F$.　　[VII. 13]
　And, since $A$ is plane, and $C$, $D$ are its sides,
　　　　therefore $D$ by multiplying $C$ has made $A$.
　For the same reason also

$E$ by multiplying $F$ has made $B$.

Now let $D$ by multiplying $E$ make $G$.

Then, since $D$ by multiplying $C$ has made $A$, and by multiplying $E$ has made $G$,

therefore, as $C$ is to $E$, so is $A$ to $G$. [VII. 17]

But, as $C$ is to $E$, so is $D$ to $F$;

therefore also, as $D$ is to $F$, so is $A$ to $G$.

Again, since $E$ by multiplying $D$ has made $G$, and by multiplying $F$ has made $B$,

therefore, as $D$ is to $F$, so is $G$ to $B$. [VII. 17]

But it was also proved that,

as $D$ is to $F$, so is $A$ to $G$;

therefore also, as $A$ is to $G$, so is $G$ to $B$.

Therefore $A$, $G$, $B$ are in continued proportion.

Therefore between $A$, $B$ there is one mean proportional number.

I say next that $A$ also has to $B$ the ratio duplicate of that which the corresponding side has to the corresponding side, that is, of that which $C$ has to $E$ or $D$ to $F$.

For, since $A$, $G$, $B$ are in continued proportion,

$A$ has to $B$ the ratio duplicate of that which it has to $G$. [v. Def. 9]

And, as $A$ is to $G$, so is $C$ to $E$, and so is $D$ to $F$.

Therefore $A$ also has to $B$ the ratio duplicate of that which $C$ has to $E$ or $D$ to $F$.

Q. E. D.

## Proposition 19

*Between two similar solid numbers there fall two mean proportional numbers; and the solid number has to the similar solid number the ratio triplicate of that which the corresponding side has to the corresponding side.*

Let $A$, $B$ be two similar solid numbers, and let $C$, $D$, $E$ be the sides of $A$, and $F$, $G$, $H$ of $B$.

Now, since similar solid numbers are those which have their sides proportional, [VII. Def. 21]

therefore, as $C$ is to $D$, so is $F$ to $G$,

and, as $D$ is to $E$, so is $G$ to $H$.

I say that between $A$, $B$ there fall two mean proportional numbers, and $A$ has to $B$ the ratio triplicate of that which $C$ has to $F$, $D$ to $G$, and also $E$ to $H$.

For let $C$ by multiplying $D$ make $K$, and let $F$ by multiplying $G$ make $L$.

Now, since $C$, $D$ are in the same ratio with $F$, $G$,

and $K$ is the product of $C$, $D$, and $L$ the product of $F$, $G$, $K$, $L$ are similar plane numbers; [VII. Def. 21]

# ELEMENTS VIII

therefore between $K, L$ there is one mean proportional number.  [VIII. 18]

Let it be $M$.

Therefore $M$ is the product of $D, F$, as was proved in the theorem preceding this.  [VIII. 18]

Now, since $D$ by multiplying $C$ has made $K$, and by multiplying $F$ has made $M$,

therefore, as $C$ is to $F$, so is $K$ to $M$.  [VII. 17]

But, as $K$ is to $M$, so is $M$ to $L$.

Therefore $K, M, L$ are continuously proportional in the ratio of $C$ to $F$.

And since, as $C$ is to $D$, so is $F$ to $G$,

alternately therefore, as $C$ is to $F$, so is $D$ to $G$.  [VII. 13]

For the same reason also,

as $D$ is to $G$, so is $E$ to $H$.

Therefore $K, M, L$ are continuously proportional in the ratio of $C$ to $F$, in the ratio of $D$ to $G$, and also in the ratio of $E$ to $H$.

Next, let $E, H$ by multiplying $M$ make $N, O$ respectively.

Now, since $A$ is a solid number, and $C, D, E$ are its sides,

therefore $E$ by multiplying the product of $C, D$ has made $A$.

But the product of $C, D$ is $K$;

therefore $E$ by multiplying $K$ has made $A$.

For the same reason also

$H$ by multiplying $L$ has made $B$.

Now, since $E$ by multiplying $K$ has made $A$, and further also by multiplying $M$ has made $N$,

therefore, as $K$ is to $M$, so is $A$ to $N$.  [VII. 17]

But, as $K$ is to $M$, so is $C$ to $F$, $D$ to $G$, and also $E$ to $H$;

therefore also, as $C$ is to $F$, $D$ to $G$, and $E$ to $H$, so is $A$ to $N$.

Again, since $E, H$ by multiplying $M$ have made $N, O$ respectively,

therefore, as $E$ is to $H$, so is $N$ to $O$.  [VII. 18]

But, as $E$ is to $H$, so is $C$ to $F$ and $D$ to $G$;

therefore also, as $C$ is to $F$, $D$ to $G$, and $E$ to $H$, so is $A$ to $N$ and $N$ to $O$.

Again, since $H$ by multiplying $M$ has made $O$, and further also by multiplying $L$ has made $B$,

therefore, as $M$ is to $L$, so is $O$ to $B$.  [VII. 17]

But, as $M$ is to $L$, so is $C$ to $F$, $D$ to $G$, and $E$ to $H$.

Therefore also, as $C$ is to $F$, $D$ to $G$, and $E$ to $H$, so not only is $O$ to $B$, but also $A$ to $N$ and $N$ to $O$.

Therefore $A, N, O, B$ are continuously proportional in the aforesaid ratios of the sides.

I say that $A$ also has to $B$ the ratio triplicate of that which the corresponding side has to the corresponding side, that is, of the ratio which the number $C$ has to $F$, or $D$ to $G$, and also $E$ to $H$.

For, since $A, N, O, B$ are four numbers in continued proportion,

therefore $A$ has to $B$ the ratio triplicate of that which $A$ has to $N$.  [v. Def. 10]

But, as $A$ is to $N$, so it was proved that $C$ is to $F$, $D$ to $G$, and also $E$ to $H$.

Therefore $A$ also has to $B$ the ratio triplicate of that which the corresponding side has to the corresponding side, that is, of the ratio which the number $C$ has to $F$, $D$ to $G$, and also $E$ to $H$.  Q. E. D.

## Proposition 20

*If one mean proportional number fall between two numbers, the numbers will be similar plane numbers.*

For let one mean proportional number $C$ fall between the two numbers $A$, $B$;

I say that $A$, $B$ are similar plane numbers.

Let $D$, $E$, the least numbers of those which have the same ratio with $A$, $C$, be taken; [vii. 33]

therefore $D$ measures $A$ the same number of times that $E$ measures $C$. [vii. 20]

Now, as many times as $D$ measures $A$, so many units let there be in $F$;

therefore $F$ by multiplying $D$ has made $A$,

so that $A$ is plane, and $D$, $F$ are its sides.

Again, since $D$, $E$ are the least of the numbers which have the same ratio with $C$, $B$,

therefore $D$ measures $C$ the same number of times that $E$ measures $B$. [vii. 20]

As many times, then, as $E$ measures $B$, so many units let there be in $G$;

therefore $E$ measures $B$ according to the units in $G$;

therefore $G$ by multiplying $E$ has made $B$.

Therefore $B$ is plane, and $E$, $G$ are its sides.

Therefore $A$, $B$ are plane numbers.

I say next that they are also similar.

For, since $F$ by multiplying $D$ has made $A$, and by multiplying $E$ has made $C$,

therefore, as $D$ is to $E$, so is $A$ to $C$, that is, $C$ to $B$. [vii. 17]

Again, since $E$ by multiplying $F$, $G$ has made $C$, $B$ respectively,

therefore, as $F$ is to $G$, so is $C$ to $B$. [vii. 17]

But, as $C$ is to $B$, so is $D$ to $E$;

therefore also, as $D$ is to $E$, so is $F$ to $G$.

And alternately, as $D$ is to $F$, so is $E$ to $G$. [vii. 13]

Therefore $A$, $B$ are similar plane numbers; for their sides are proportional.

Q. E. D.

## Proposition 21

*If two mean proportional numbers fall between two numbers, the numbers are similar solid numbers.*

For let two mean proportional numbers $C$, $D$ fall between the two numbers $A$, $B$;

I say that $A$, $B$ are similar solid numbers.

For let three numbers $E$, $F$, $G$, the least of those which have the same ratio with $A$, $C$, $D$, be taken; [vii. 33 or viii. 2]

ELEMENTS VIII             167

therefore the extremes of them $E$, $G$ are prime to one another.   [VIII. 3]
  Now, since one mean proportional number $F$ has fallen between $E$, $G$,
            therefore $E$, $G$ are similar plane numbers.   [VIII. 20]
  Let, then, $H$, $K$ be the sides of $E$, and $L$, $M$ of $G$.
  Therefore it is manifest from the theorem before this that $E$, $F$, $G$ are continuously proportional in the ratio of $H$ to $L$ and that of $K$ to $M$.

```
A——                              E—
B————————————————                F—
C———                             G——
D————                            H-
        N—                       K—
        O——                      L—
                                 M——
```

  Now, since $E$, $F$, $G$ are the least of the numbers which have the same ratio with $A$, $C$, $D$,
and the multitude of the numbers $E$, $F$, $G$ is equal to the multitude of the numbers $A$, $C$, $D$,
            therefore, *ex aequali*, as $E$ is to $G$, so is $A$ to $D$.   [VII. 14]
  But $E$, $G$ are prime,
                    primes are also least,                   [VII. 21]
and the least measure those which have the same ratio with them the same number of times, the greater the greater and the less the less, that is, the antecedent the antecedent and the consequent the consequent;   [VII. 20]
therefore $E$ measures $A$ the same number of times that $G$ measures $D$.
  Now, as many times as $E$ measures $A$, so many units let there be in $N$.
  Therefore $N$ by multiplying $E$ has made $A$.
  But $E$ is the product of $H$, $K$;
       therefore $N$ by multiplying the product of $H$, $K$ has made $A$.
  Therefore $A$ is solid, and $H$, $K$, $N$ are its sides.
  Again, since $E$, $F$, $G$ are the least of the numbers which have the same ratio as $C$, $D$, $B$,
       therefore $E$ measures $C$ the same number of times that $G$ measures $B$.
  Now, as many times as $E$ measures $C$, so many units let there be in $O$.
  Therefore $G$ measures $B$ according to the units in $O$;
              therefore $O$ by multiplying $G$ has made $B$.
  But $G$ is the product of $L$, $M$;
         therefore $O$ by multiplying the product of $L$, $M$ has made $B$.
  Therefore $B$ is solid, and $L$, $M$, $O$ are its sides;
                    therefore $A$, $B$ are solid.
  I say that they are also similar.
  For, since $N$, $O$ by multiplying $E$ have made $A$, $C$,
       therefore, as $N$ is to $O$, so is $A$ to $C$, that is, $E$ to $F$.   [VII. 18]
  But, as $E$ is to $F$, so is $H$ to $L$ and $K$ to $M$;
         therefore also, as $H$ is to $L$, so is $K$ to $M$ and $N$ to $O$.
  And $H$, $K$, $N$ are the sides of $A$, and $O$, $L$, $M$ the sides of $B$.
  Therefore $A$, $B$ are similar solid numbers.     Q. E. D.

## Proposition 22

*If three numbers be in continued proportion, and the first be square, the third will also be square.*

Let $A, B, C$ be three numbers in continued proportion, and let $A$ the first be square;
> I say that $C$ the third is also square.

For, since between $A, C$ there is one mean proportional number, $B$,
> therefore $A, C$ are similar plane numbers. [VIII. 20]

But $A$ is square;
> therefore $C$ is also square.

Q. E. D.

## Proposition 23

*If four numbers be in continued proportion, and the first be cube, the fourth will also be cube.*

Let $A, B, C, D$ be four numbers in continued proportion, and let $A$ be cube;
> I say that $D$ is also cube.

For, since between $A, D$ there are two mean proportional numbers $B, C$,
therefore $A, D$ are similar solid numbers. [VIII. 21]

But $A$ is cube;
> therefore $D$ is also cube.

Q. E. D.

## Proposition 24

*If two numbers have to one another the ratio which a square number has to a square number, and the first be square, the second will also be square.*

For let the two numbers $A, B$ have to one another the ratio which the square number $C$ has to the square number $D$, and let $A$ be square;
> I say that $B$ is also square.

For, since $C, D$ are square,
> $C, D$ are similar plane numbers.

Therefore one mean proportional number falls between $C, D$. [VIII. 18]
And, as $C$ is to $D$, so is $A$ to $B$;
therefore one mean proportional number falls between $A, B$ also. [VIII. 8]
And $A$ is square;
> therefore $B$ is also square. [VIII. 22]

Q. E. D.

## Proposition 25

*If two numbers have to one another the ratio which a cube number has to a cube number, and the first be cube, the second will also be cube.*

For let the two numbers $A, B$ have to one another the ratio which the cube number $C$ has to the cube number $D$, and let $A$ be cube;
> I say that $B$ is also cube.

For, since $C, D$ are cube,
> $C, D$ are similar solid numbers.

ELEMENTS VIII

Therefore two mean proportional numbers fall between $C, D$. [VIII. 19]
And, as many numbers as fall between $C, D$ in continued proportion, so many will also fall between those which have the same ratio with them; [VIII. 8] so that two mean proportional numbers fall between $A, B$ also.

Let $E, F$ so fall.
Since, then, the four numbers $A, E, F, B$ are in continued proportion,
and $A$ is cube,
therefore $B$ is also cube. [VIII. 23]

Q. E. D.

PROPOSITION 26

*Similar plane numbers have to one another the ratio which a square number has to a square number.*

Let $A, B$ be similar plane numbers;
I say that $A$ has to $B$ the ratio which a square number has to a square number.

For, since $A, B$ are similar plane numbers,
therefore one mean proportional number falls between $A, B$. [VIII. 18]
Let it so fall, and let it be $C$;
and let $D, E, F$, the least numbers of those which have the same ratio with $A, C, B$, be taken; [VII. 33 or VIII. 2]
therefore the extremes of them $D, F$ are square. [VIII. 2, Por.]
And since, as $D$ is to $F$, so is $A$ to $B$,
and $D, F$ are square,
therefore $A$ has to $B$ the ratio which a square number has to a square number.

Q. E. D.

PROPOSITION 27

*Similar solid numbers have to one another the ratio which a cube number has to a cube number.*

Let $A, B$ be similar solid numbers;
I say that $A$ has to $B$ the ratio which a cube number has to a cube number.

For, since $A, B$ are similar solid numbers,
therefore two mean proportional numbers fall between $A, B$. [VIII. 19]

Let $C$, $D$ so fall,
and let $E$, $F$, $G$, $H$, the least numbers of those which have the same ratio with $A$, $C$, $D$, $B$, and equal with them in multitude, be taken; [VII. 33 or VIII. 2]
therefore the extremes of them $E$, $H$ are cube. [VIII. 2, Por.]
And, as $E$ is to $H$, so is $A$ to $B$;
therefore $A$ also has to $B$ the ratio which a cube number has to a cube number.

Q. E. D.

# BOOK NINE

### Proposition 1

*If two similar plane numbers by multiplying one another make some number, the product will be square.*

Let $A$, $B$ be two similar plane numbers, and let $A$ by multiplying $B$ make $C$;
I say that $C$ is square.
For let $A$ by multiplying itself make $D$.
Therefore $D$ is square.
Since then $A$ by multiplying itself has made $D$, and by multiplying $B$ has made $C$,
therefore, as $A$ is to $B$, so is $D$ to $C$.  [VII. 17]

And, since $A$, $B$ are similar plane numbers,
therefore one mean proportional number falls between $A$, $B$.  [VIII. 18]

But, if numbers fall between two numbers in continued proportion, as many as fall between them, so many also fall between those which have the same ratio;  [VIII. 8]
so that one mean proportional number falls between $D$, $C$ also.
And $D$ is square;
therefore $C$ is also square.  [VIII. 22]

Q. E. D.

### Proposition 2

*If two numbers by multiplying one another make a square number, they are similar plane numbers.*

Let $A$, $B$ be two numbers, and let $A$ by multiplying $B$ make the square number $C$;
I say that $A$, $B$ are similar plane numbers.
For let $A$ by multiplying itself make $D$;
therefore $D$ is square.
Now, since $A$ by multiplying itself has made $D$, and by multiplying $B$ has made $C$,
therefore, as $A$ is to $B$, so is $D$ to $C$.  [VII. 17]

And, since $D$ is square, and $C$ is so also,
therefore $D$, $C$ are similar plane numbers.
Therefore one mean proportional number falls between $D$, $C$.  [VIII. 18]
And, as $D$ is to $C$, so is $A$ to $B$;
therefore one mean proportional number falls between $A$, $B$ also.  [VIII. 8]

But, if one mean proportional number fall between two numbers, they are similar plane numbers;  [VIII. 20]
therefore $A$, $B$ are similar plane numbers.

Q. E. D.

## Proposition 3

*If a cube number by multiplying itself make some number, the product will be cube.*

For let the cube number $A$ by multiplying itself make $B$;
I say that $B$ is cube.

For let $C$, the side of $A$, be taken, and let $C$ by multiplying itself make $D$.
It is then manifest that $C$ by multiplying $D$ has made $A$.

Now, since $C$ by multiplying itself has made $D$, therefore $C$ measures $D$ according to the units in itself.

But further the unit also measures $C$ according to the units in it;

therefore, as the unit is to $C$, so is $C$ to $D$.  [VII. Def. 20]

Again, since $C$ by multiplying $D$ has made $A$,
therefore $D$ measures $A$ according to the units in $C$.

But the unit also measures $C$ according to the units in it;
therefore, as the unit is to $C$, so is $D$ to $A$.

But, as the unit is to $C$, so is $C$ to $D$;
therefore also, as the unit is to $C$, so is $C$ to $D$, and $D$ to $A$.

Therefore between the unit and the number $A$ two mean proportional numbers $C$, $D$ have fallen in continued proportion.

Again, since $A$ by multiplying itself has made $B$,
therefore $A$ measures $B$ according to the units in itself.

But the unit also measures $A$ according to the units in it;
therefore, as the unit is to $A$, so is $A$ to $B$.  [VII. Def. 20]

But between the unit and $A$ two mean proportional numbers have fallen;
therefore two mean proportional numbers will also fall between $A$, $B$.  [VIII. 8]

But, if two mean proportional numbers fall between two numbers, and the first be cube, the second will also be cube.  [VIII. 23]

And $A$ is cube;

therefore $B$ is also cube.  Q. E. D.

## Proposition 4

*If a cube number by multiplying a cube number make some number, the product will be cube.*

For let the cube number $A$ by multiplying the cube number $B$ make $C$;
I say that $C$ is cube.

For let $A$ by multiplying itself make $D$;
therefore $D$ is cube.  [IX. 3]

And, since $A$ by multiplying itself has made $D$, and by multiplying $B$ has made $C$

therefore, as $A$ is to $B$, so is $D$ to $C$.  [VII. 17]

And, since $A$, $B$ are cube numbers,
$A$, $B$ are similar solid numbers.

Therefore two mean proportional numbers fall between $A$, $B$;  [VIII. 19]
so that two mean proportional numbers will fall between $D$, $C$ also.  [VIII. 8]

And $D$ is cube;

therefore $C$ is also cube  [VIII. 23]

Q. E. D.

# ELEMENTS IX

## Proposition 5

*If a cube number by multiplying any number make a cube number, the multiplied number will also be cube.*

For let the cube number $A$ by multiplying any number $B$ make the cube number $C$;

A————————
B————————
C————————————
D————————

I say that $B$ is cube.

For let $A$ by multiplying itself make $D$;
therefore $D$ is cube.   [IX. 3]
Now, since $A$ by multiplying itself has made $D$, and by multiplying $B$ has made $C$,
therefore, as $A$ is to $B$, so is $D$ to $C$.   [VII. 17]
And since $D$, $C$ are cube,
they are similar solid numbers.
Therefore two mean proportional numbers fall between $D$, $C$.   [VIII. 19]
And, as $D$ is to $C$, so is $A$ to $B$;
therefore two mean proportional numbers fall between $A$, $B$ also.   [VIII. 8]
And $A$ is cube;
therefore $B$ is also cube.   [VIII. 23]

## Proposition 6

*If a number by multiplying itself make a cube number, it will itself also be cube.*

For let the number $A$ by multiplying itself make the cube number $B$;
I say that $A$ is also cube.

A————————
B————————
C————————————

For let $A$ by multiplying $B$ make $C$.
Since, then, $A$ by multiplying itself has made $B$, and by multiplying $B$ has made $C$,
therefore $C$ is cube.
And, since $A$ by multiplying itself has made $B$,
therefore $A$ measures $B$ according to the units in itself.
But the unit also measures $A$ according to the units in it.
Therefore, as the unit is to $A$, so is $A$ to $B$.   [VII. Def. 20]
And, since $A$ by multiplying $B$ has made $C$,
therefore $B$ measures $C$ according to the units in $A$.
But the unit also measures $A$ according to the units in it.
Therefore, as the unit is to $A$, so is $B$ to $C$.   [VII. Def. 20]
But, as the unit is to $A$, so is $A$ to $B$;
therefore also, as $A$ is to $B$, so is $B$ to $C$.
And, since $B$, $C$ are cube,
they are similar solid numbers.
Therefore there are two mean proportional numbers between $B$, $C$.   [VIII. 19]
And, as $B$ is to $C$, so is $A$ to $B$.
Therefore there are two mean proportional numbers between $A$, $B$ also.
   [VIII. 8]
And $B$ is cube;
therefore $A$ is also cube.   [cf. VIII. 23]

Q. E. D.

## Proposition 7

*If a composite number by multiplying any number make some number, the product will be solid.*

For, let the composite number $A$ by multiplying any number $B$ make $C$;
I say that $C$ is solid.

For, since $A$ is composite, it will be measured by some number. [VII. Def. 13]

Let it be measured by $D$;
and, as many times as $D$ measures $A$, so many units let there be in $E$.

Since, then, $D$ measures $A$ according to the units in $E$,
therefore $E$ by multiplying $D$ has made $A$. [VII. Def. 15]

And, since $A$ by multiplying $B$ has made $C$,
and $A$ is the product of $D$, $E$,
therefore the product of $D$, $E$ by multiplying $B$ has made $C$.

Therefore $C$ is solid, and $D$, $E$, $B$ are its sides. Q. E. D.

## Proposition 8

*If as many numbers as we please beginning from an unit be in continued proportion, the third from the unit will be square, as will also those which successively leave out one; the fourth will be cube, as will also all those which leave out two; and the seventh will be at once cube and square, as will also those which leave out five.*

Let there be as many numbers as we please, $A$, $B$, $C$, $D$, $E$, $F$, beginning from an unit and in continued proportion;

I say that $B$, the third from the unit, is square, as are also all those which leave out one; $C$, the fourth, is cube, as are also all those which leave out two; and $F$, the seventh, is at once cube and square, as are also all those which leave out five.

For since, as the unit is to $A$, so is $A$ to $B$,
therefore the unit measures the number $A$ the same number of times that $A$ measures $B$. [VII. Def. 20]

But the unit measures the number $A$ according to the units in it;
therefore $A$ also measures $B$ according to the units in $A$.

Therefore $A$ by multiplying itself has made $B$;
therefore $B$ is square.

And, since $B$, $C$, $D$ are in continued proportion, and $B$ is square,
therefore $D$ is also square. [VIII. 22]

For the same reason
$F$ is also square.

Similarly we can prove that all those which leave out one are square.

I say next that $C$, the fourth from the unit, is cube, as are also all those which leave out two.

For since, as the unit is to $A$, so is $B$ to $C$,
therefore the unit measures the number $A$ the same number of times that $B$ measures $C$.

But the unit measures the number $A$ according to the units in $A$;

ELEMENTS IX

   therefore $B$ also measures $C$ according to the units in $A$.
Therefore $A$ by multiplying $B$ has made $C$.
Since then $A$ by multiplying itself has made $B$, and by multiplying $B$ has made $C$,
   therefore $C$ is cube.
And, since $C, D, E, F$ are in continued proportion, and $C$ is cube,
   therefore $F$ is also cube. [VIII. 23]
But it was also proved square;
   therefore the seventh from the unit is both cube and square.
Similarly we can prove that all the numbers which leave out five are also both cube and square. Q. E. D.

## Proposition 9

*If as many numbers as we please beginning from an unit be in continued proportion, and the number after the unit be square, all the rest will also be square. And, if the number after the unit be cube, all the rest will also be cube.*

Let there be as many numbers as we please, $A, B, C, D, E, F$, beginning from an unit and in continued proportion, and let $A$, the number after the unit, be square;
   I say that all the rest will also be square.
   Now it has been proved that $B$, the third from the unit, is square, as are also all those which leave out one; [IX. 8]
   I say that all the rest are also square.
For, since $A, B, C$ are in continued proportion,
   and $A$ is square,
      therefore $C$ is also square. [VIII. 22]
Again, since $B, C, D$ are in continued proportion,
   and $B$ is square,
      $D$ is also square. [VIII. 22]
Similarly we can prove that all the rest are also square.
Next, let $A$ be cube;
   I say that all the rest are also cube.
   Now it has been proved that $C$, the fourth from the unit, is cube, as also are all those which leave out two; [IX. 8]
   I say that all the rest are also cube.
For, since, as the unit is to $A$, so is $A$ to $B$,
therefore the unit measures $A$ the same number of times as $A$ measures $B$.
But the unit measures $A$ according to the units in it;
   therefore $A$ also measures $B$ according to the units in itself;
      therefore $A$ by multiplying itself has made $B$.
And $A$ is cube.
But, if a cube number by multiplying itself make some number, the product is cube. [IX. 3]
Therefore $B$ is also cube.
And, since the four numbers $A, B, C, D$ are in continued proportion,
   and $A$ is cube,
      $D$ also is cube. [VIII. 23]

For the same reason

$E$ is also cube, and similarly all the rest are cube.     Q. E. D.

## PROPOSITION 10

*If as many numbers as we please beginning from an unit be in continued proportion, and the number after the unit be not square, neither will any other be square except the third from the unit and all those which leave out one. And, if the number after the unit be not cube, neither will any other be cube except the fourth from the unit and all those which leave out two.*

Let there be as many numbers as we please, $A, B, C, D, E, F$, beginning from an unit and in continued proportion,

and let $A$, the number after the unit, not be square;

I say that neither will any other be square except the third from the unit <and those which leave out one>.

For, if possible, let $C$ be square.

But $B$ is also square;     [IX. 8]

[therefore $B, C$ have to one another the ratio which a square number has to a square number].

And, as $B$ is to $C$, so is $A$ to $B$;

therefore $A, B$ have to one another the ratio which a square number has to a square number;

[so that $A, B$ are similar plane numbers].     [VIII. 26, converse]

And $B$ is square;

therefore $A$ is also square:

which is contrary to the hypothesis.

Therefore $C$ is not square.

Similarly we can prove that neither is any other of the numbers square except the third from the unit and those which leave out one.

Next, let $A$ not be cube.

I say that neither will any other be cube except the fourth from the unit and those which leave out two.

For, if possible, let $D$ be cube.

Now $C$ is also cube; for it is fourth from the unit.     [IX. 8]

And, as $C$ is to $D$, so is $B$ to $C$;

therefore $B$ also has to $C$ the ratio which a cube has to a cube.

And $C$ is cube;

therefore $B$ is also cube.     [VIII. 25]

And since, as the unit is to $A$, so is $A$ to $B$,

and the unit measures $A$ according to the units in it,

therefore $A$ also measures $B$ according to the units in itself;

therefore $A$ by multiplying itself has made the cube number $B$.

But, if a number by multiplying itself make a cube number, it is also itself cube.     [IX. 6]

Therefore $A$ is also cube:

which is contrary to the hypothesis.

Therefore $D$ is not cube.

Similarly we can prove that neither is any other of the numbers cube except the fourth from the unit and those which leave out two.     Q. E. D.

# ELEMENTS IX

## Proposition 11

*If as many numbers as we please beginning from an unit be in continued proportion, the less measures the greater according to some one of the numbers which have place among the proportional numbers.*

Let there be as many numbers as we please, $B, C, D, E$, beginning from the unit $A$ and in continued proportion;

A————
B————
C—————
D——————
E———————————

I say that $B$, the least of the numbers $B, C, D, E$, measures $E$ according to some one of the numbers $C, D$.

For since, as the unit $A$ is to $B$, so is $D$ to $E$, therefore the unit $A$ measures the number $B$ the same number of times as $D$ measures $E$; therefore, alternately, the unit $A$ measures $D$ the same number of times as $B$ measures $E$. [VII. 15]

But the unit $A$ measures $D$ according to the units in it;

therefore $B$ also measures $E$ according to the units in $D$; so that $B$ the less measures $E$ the greater according to some number of those which have place among the proportional numbers.—

PORISM. And it is manifest that, whatever place the measuring number has, reckoned from the unit, the same place also has the number according to which it measures, reckoned from the number measured, in the direction of the number before it.— Q. E. D.

## Proposition 12

*If as many numbers as we please beginning from an unit be in continued proportion, by however many prime numbers the last is measured, the next to the unit will also be measured by the same.*

Let there be as many numbers as we please, $A, B, C, D$, beginning from an unit, and in continued proportion;

I say that, by however many prime numbers $D$ is measured, $A$ will also be measured by the same.

For let $D$ be measured by any prime number $E$;

A————  F————————
B————  G—————
C—————  H————
D——————
E——

I say that $E$ measures $A$.

For suppose it does not;

now $E$ is prime, and any prime number is prime to any which it does not measure; [VII. 29]

therefore $E, A$ are prime to one another.

And, since $E$ measures $D$, let it measure it according to $F$, therefore $E$ by multiplying $F$ has made $D$.

Again, since $A$ measures $D$ according to the units in $C$, [IX. 11 and Por.] therefore $A$ by multiplying $C$ has made $D$.

But, further, $E$ has also by multiplying $F$ made $D$;

therefore the product of $A, C$ is equal to the product of $E, F$.

Therefore, as $A$ is to $E$, so is $F$ to $C$. [VII. 19]

But $A, E$ are prime,

primes are also least, [VII. 21]

and the least measure those which have the same ratio the same number of times, the antecedent the antecedent and the consequent the consequent;

[VII. 20]

therefore $E$ measures $C$.

Let it measure it according to $G$;

therefore $E$ by multiplying $G$ has made $C$.

But, further, by the theorem before this,

$A$ has also by multiplying $B$ made $C$. [IX. 11 and Por]

Therefore the product of $A$, $B$ is equal to the product of $E$, $G$.

Therefore, as $A$ is to $E$, so is $G$ to $B$. [VII. 19]

But $A$, $E$ are prime,

primes are also least, [VII. 21]

and the least numbers measure those which have the same ratio with them the same number of times, the antecedent the antecedent and the consequent the consequent: [VII. 20]

therefore $E$ measures $B$.

Let it measure it according to $H$;

therefore $E$ by multiplying $H$ has made $B$.

But, further, $A$ has also by multiplying itself made $B$; [IX. 8]

therefore the product of $E$, $H$ is equal to the square on $A$.

Therefore, as $E$ is to $A$, so is $A$ to $H$. [VII. 19]

But $A$, $E$ are prime,

primes are also least, [VII. 21]

and the least measure those which have the same ratio the same number of times, the antecedent the antecedent and the consequent the consequent; [VII. 20]

therefore $E$ measures $A$, as antecedent antecedent.

But, again, it also does not measure it:

which is impossible.

Therefore $E$, $A$ are not prime to one another.

Therefore they are composite to one another.

But numbers composite to one another are measured by some number. [VII. Def. 14]

And, since $E$ is by hypothesis prime,

and the prime is not measured by any number other than itself,

therefore $E$ measures $A$, $E$,

so that $E$ measures $A$.

[But it also measures $D$;

therefore $E$ measures $A$, $D$.]

Similarly we can prove that, by however many prime numbers $D$ is measured, $A$ will also be measured by the same. Q. E. D.

## Proposition 13

*If as many numbers as we please beginning from an unit be in continued proportion, and the number after the unit be prime, the greatest will not be measured by any except those which have a place among the proportional numbers.*

Let there be as many numbers as we please, $A$, $B$, $C$, $D$, beginning from an unit and in continued proportion, and let $A$, the number after the unit, be prime;

I say that $D$, the greatest of them, will not be measured by any other number except $A$, $B$, $C$.

For, if possible, let it be measured by $E$, and let $E$ not be the same with any of the numbers $A$, $B$, $C$.

ELEMENTS IX

It is then manifest that $E$ is not prime.

For, if $E$ is prime and measures $D$,
it will also measure $A$ [IX. 12], which is prime, though it is not the same with it:
which is impossible.

A ———
B ———
C ————
D —————

E —
F ———
G ——
H ——

Therefore $E$ is not prime.
Therefore it is composite.
But any composite number is measured by some prime number;  [VII. 31]

therefore $E$ is measured by some prime number.

I say next that it will not be measured by any other prime except $A$.

For, if $E$ is measured by another,
and $E$ measures $D$,
that other will also measure $D$;
so that it will also measure $A$ [IX. 12], which is prime, though it is not the same with it:
which is impossible.

Therefore $A$ measures $E$.

And, since $E$ measures $D$, let it measure it according to $F$.

I say that $F$ is not the same with any of the numbers $A, B, C$.

For, if $F$ is the same with one of the numbers $A, B, C$,
and measures $D$ according to $E$,
therefore one of the numbers $A, B, C$ also measures $D$ according to $E$.

But one of the numbers $A, B, C$ measures $D$ according to some one of the numbers $A, B, C$; [IX. 11]
therefore $E$ is also the same with one of the numbers $A, B, C$:
which is contrary to the hypothesis.

Therefore $F$ is not the same as any one of the numbers $A, B, C$.

Similarly we can prove that $F$ is measured by $A$, by proving again that $F$ is not prime.

For, if it is, and measures $D$,
it will also measure $A$ [IX. 12], which is prime, though it is not the same with it:
which is impossible;
therefore $F$ is not prime.

Therefore it is composite.

But any composite number is measured by some prime number; [VII. 31]
therefore $F$ is measured by some prime number.

I say next that it will not be measured by any other prime except $A$.

For, if any other prime number measures $F$,
and $F$ measures $D$,
that other will also measure $D$;
so that it will also measure $A$ [IX. 12], which is prime, though it is not the same with it:
which is impossible.

Therefore $A$ measures $F$.

And, since $E$ measures $D$ according to $F$,
therefore $E$ by multiplying $F$ has made $D$.
But, further, $A$ has also by multiplying $C$ made $D$; [IX. 11]
therefore the product of $A, C$ is equal to the product of $E, F$.

Therefore, proportionally, as $A$ is to $E$, so is $F$ to $C$. [VII. 19]
But $A$ measures $E$;
therefore $F$ also measures $C$.
Let it measure it according to $G$.
Similarly, then, we can prove that $G$ is not the same with any of the numbers $A$, $B$, and that it is measured by $A$.
And, since $F$ measures $C$ according to $G$
therefore $F$ by multiplying $G$ has made $C$.
But, further, $A$ has also by multiplying $B$ made $C$; [IX. 11]
therefore the product of $A$, $B$ is equal to the product of $F$, $G$.
Therefore, proportionally, as $A$ is to $F$, so is $G$ to $B$. [VII. 19]
But $A$ measures $F$;
therefore $G$ also measures $B$.
Let it measure it according to $H$.
Similarly then we can prove that $H$ is not the same with $A$.
And, since $G$ measures $B$ according to $H$,
therefore $G$ by multiplying $H$ has made $B$.
But, further, $A$ has also by multiplying itself made $B$; [IX. 8]
therefore the product of $H$, $G$ is equal to the square on $A$.
Therefore, as $H$ is to $A$, so is $A$ to $G$. [VII. 19]
But $A$ measures $G$;
therefore $H$ also measures $A$, which is prime, though it is not the same with it:
which is absurd.
Therefore $D$ the greatest will not be measured by any other number except $A$, $B$, $C$.
Q. E. D.

## PROPOSITION 14

*If a number be the least that is measured by prime numbers, it will not be measured by any other prime number except those originally measuring it.*

For let the number $A$ be the least that is measured by the prime numbers $B$, $C$, $D$;
I say that $A$ will not be measured by any other prime number except $B$, $C$, $D$.
For, if possible, let it be measured by the prime number $E$, and let $F$ not be the same with any one of the numbers $B$, $C$, $D$.
Now, since $E$ measures $A$, let it measure it according to $F$;
therefore $E$ by multiplying $F$ has made $A$.
And $A$ is measured by the prime numbers $B$, $C$, $D$.
But, if two numbers by multiplying one another make some number, and any prime number measure the product, it will also measure one of the original numbers; [VII. 30]
therefore $B$, $C$, $D$ will measure one of the numbers $E$, $F$.
Now they will not measure $E$;
for $E$ is prime and not the same with any one of the numbers $B$, $C$, $D$.
Therefore they will measure $F$, which is less than $A$:
which is impossible, for $A$ is by hypothesis the least number measured by $B$, $C$, $D$.
Therefore no prime number will measure $A$ except $B$, $C$, $D$. Q. E. D.

ELEMENTS IX     181

PROPOSITION 15

*If three numbers in continued proportion be the least of those which have the same ratio with them, any two whatever added together will be prime to the remaining number.*

Let $A$, $B$, $C$, three numbers in continued proportion, be the least of those which have the same ratio with them;
I say that any two of the numbers $A, B, C$ whatever added together are prime to the remaining number, namely $A, B$ to $C$; $B, C$ to $A$; and further, $A, C$ to $B$.

For let two numbers $DE$, $EF$, the least of those which have the same ratio with $A, B, C$, be taken. [VII. 2]

It is then manifest that $DE$ by multiplying itself has made $A$, and by multiplying $EF$ has made $B$, and, further, $EF$ by multiplying itself has made $C$.
                                                                                                     [VIII. 2]

Now, since $DE$, $EF$ are least,
                     they are prime to one another. [VII. 22]
But, if two numbers be prime to one another,
                     their sum is also prime to each; [VII. 28]
therefore $DF$ is also prime to each of the numbers $DE$, $EF$.
But, further, $DE$ is also prime to $EF$;
                     therefore $DF$, $DE$ are prime to $EF$.
But, if two numbers be prime to any number,
                     their product is also prime to the other; [VII. 24]
so that the product of $FD$, $DE$ is prime to $EF$;
hence the product of $FD$, $DE$ is also prime to the square on $EF$. [VII. 25]

But the product of $FD$, $DE$ is the square on $DE$ together with the product of $DE$, $EF$; [II. 3]
therefore the square on $DE$ together with the product of $DE$, $EF$ is prime to the square on $EF$.

And the square on $DE$ is $A$,
                     the product of $DE$, $EF$ is $B$,
                     and the square on $EF$ is $C$;
therefore $A$, $B$ added together are prime to $C$.

Similarly we can prove that $B$, $C$ added together are prime to $A$.

I say next that $A$, $C$ added together are also prime to $B$.

For, since $DF$ is prime to each of the numbers $DE$, $EF$,
the square on $DF$ is also prime to the product of $DE$, $EF$. [VII. 24, 25]

But the squares on $DE$, $EF$ together with twice the product of $DE$, $EF$ are equal to the square on $DF$; [II. 4]
therefore the squares on $DE$, $EF$ together with twice the product of $DE$, $EF$ are prime to the product of $DE$, $EF$.

*Separando*, the squares on $DE$, $EF$ together with once the product of $DE$, $EF$ are prime to the product of $DE$, $EF$.

Therefore, *separando* again, the squares on $DE$, $EF$ are prime to the product of $DE$, $EF$.

And the square on $DE$ is $A$,
                     the product of $DE$, $EF$ is $B$,
                     and the square on $EF$ is $C$.

Therefore $A$, $C$ added together are prime to $B$.      Q. E. D.

## PROPOSITION 16

*If two numbers be prime to one another, the second will not be to any other number as the first is to the second.*

For let the two numbers $A$, $B$ be prime to one another;
I say that $B$ is not to any other number as $A$ is to $B$.
For, if possible, as $A$ is to $B$, so let $B$ be to $C$.
Now $A$, $B$ are prime,
    primes are also least,      [VII. 21]
and the least numbers measure those which have the same ratio the same number of times, the antecedent the antecedent and the consequent the consequent;      [VII. 20]
    therefore $A$ measures $B$ as antecedent antecedent.
But it also measures itself;
    therefore $A$ measures $A$, $B$ which are prime to one another:
    which is absurd.
Therefore $B$ will not be to $C$, as $A$ is to $B$.      Q. E. D.

## PROPOSITION 17

*If there be as many numbers as we please in continued proportion, and the extremes of them be prime to one another, the last will not be to any other number as the first to the second.*

For let there be as many numbers as we please, $A$, $B$, $C$, $D$, in continued proportion,
and let the extremes of them, $A$, $D$, be prime to one another;
I say that $D$ is not to any other number as $A$ is to $B$.
For, if possible, as $A$ is to $B$, so let $D$ be to $E$;
    therefore, alternately, as $A$ is to $D$, so is $B$ to $E$.      [VII. 13]
But $A$, $D$ are prime,
    primes are also least,      [VII. 21]
and the least numbers measure those which have the same ratio the same number of times, the antecedent the antecedent and the consequent the consequent.      [VII. 20]
Therefore $A$ measures $B$.
And, as $A$ is to $B$, so is $B$ to $C$.
Therefore $B$ also measures $C$;
    so that $A$ also measures $C$.
And since, as $B$ is to $C$, so is $C$ to $D$,
    and $B$ measures $C$,
    therefore $C$ also measures $D$.
But $A$ measured $C$;
    so that $A$ also measures $D$.
But it also measures itself;
    therefore $A$ measures $A$, $D$ which are prime to one another:
    which is impossible.
Therefore $D$ will not be to any other number as $A$ is to $B$.      Q. E. D.

ELEMENTS IX

## Proposition 18

*Given two numbers, to investigate whether it is possible to find a third proportional to them.*

Let $A$, $B$ be the given two numbers, and let it be required to investigate whether it is possible to find a third proportional to them.

Now $A$, $B$ are either prime to one another or not.

And, if they are prime to one another, it has been proved that it is impossible to find a third proportional to them.  [IX. 16]

Next, let $A$, $B$ not be prime to one another,
and let $B$ by multiplying itself make $C$.

Then $A$ either measures $C$ or does not measure it.

First, let it measure it according to $D$;
therefore $A$ by multiplying $D$ has made $C$.

But, further, $B$ has also by multiplying itself made $C$;
therefore the product of $A$, $D$ is equal to the square on $B$.

Therefore, as $A$ is to $B$, so is $B$ to $D$;  [VII. 19]
therefore a third proportional number $D$ has been found to $A$, $B$.

Next, let $A$ not measure $C$;

I say that it is impossible to find a third proportional number to $A$, $B$.

For, if possible, let $D$, such third proportional, have been found.

Therefore the product of $A$, $D$ is equal to the square on $B$.

But the square on $B$ is $C$;
therefore the product of $A$, $D$ is equal to $C$.

Hence $A$ by multiplying $D$ has made $C$;
therefore $A$ measures $C$ according to $D$.

But, by hypothesis, it also does not measure it:
which is absurd.

Therefore it is not possible to find a third proportional number to $A$, $B$ when $A$ does not measure $C$.  Q. E. D.

## Proposition 19

*Given three numbers, to investigate when it is possible to find a fourth proportional to them.*

Let $A$, $B$, $C$ be the given three numbers, and let it be required to investigate when it is possible to find a fourth proportional to them.

[The Greek text of this proposition is corrupt. However, analagously to Proposition 18 the condition that a fourth proportional to A, B, C exists is that A measure the product of B and C.]

## Proposition 20

*Prime numbers are more than any assigned multitude of prime numbers.*

Let $A$, $B$, $C$ be the assigned prime numbers;

I say that there are more prime numbers than $A$, $B$, $C$.

For let the least number measured by $A$, $B$, $C$ be taken,
and let it be $DE$;
let the unit $DF$ be added to $DE$.

Then $EF$ is either prime or not.
First, let it be prime;
then the prime numbers $A$, $B$, $C$, $EF$ have been found which are more than $A$, $B$, $C$.
Next, let $EF$ not be prime;
therefore it is measured by some prime number. [VII. 31]
Let it be measured by the prime number $G$.
I say that $G$ is not the same with any of the numbers $A$, $B$, $C$.
For, if possible, let it be so.
Now $A$, $B$, $C$ measure $DE$;
therefore $G$ also will measure $DE$.
But it also measures $EF$.
Therefore $G$, being a number, will measure the remainder, the unit $DF$:
which is absurd.
Therefore $G$ is not the same with any one of the numbers $A$, $B$, $C$.
And by hypothesis it is prime.
Therefore the prime numbers $A$, $B$, $C$, $G$ have been found which are more than the assigned multitude of $A$, $B$, $C$.   Q. E. D.

## Proposition 21

*If as many even numbers as we please be added together, the whole is even.*

For let as many even numbers as we please, $AB$, $BC$, $CD$, $DE$, be added together;

I say that the whole $AE$ is even.

For, since each of the numbers $AB$, $BC$, $CD$, $DE$ is even, it has a half part; [VII. Def. 6]
so that the whole $AE$ also has a half part.
But an even number is that which is divisible into two equal parts; [*id.*]
therefore $AE$ is even.   Q. E. D.

## Proposition 22

*If as many odd numbers as we please be added together, and their multitude be even, the whole will be even.*

For let as many odd numbers as we please, $AB$, $BC$, $CD$, $DE$, even in multitude, be added together;

I say that the whole $AE$ is even.

For, since each of the numbers $AB$, $BC$, $CD$, $DE$ is odd, if an unit be subtracted from each, each of the remainders will be even; [VII. Def. 7]
so that the sum of them will be even. [IX. 21]
But the multitude of the units is also even.
Therefore the whole $AE$ is also even. [IX. 21]
Q. E. D.

## Proposition 23

*If as many odd numbers as we please be added together, and their multitude be odd, the whole will also be odd.*

For let as many odd numbers as we please, $AB$, $BC$, $CD$, the multitude of which is odd, be added together;

I say that the whole $AD$ is also odd.

Let the unit $DE$ be subtracted from $CD$;
therefore the remainder $CE$ is even. [VII. Def. 7]
But $CA$ is also even; [IX. 22]
therefore the whole $AE$ is also even. [IX. 21]
And $DE$ is an unit.
Therefore $AD$ is odd. [VII. Def. 7]

Q. E. D.

## Proposition 24

*If from an even number an even number be subtracted, the remainder will be even.*

For from the even number $AB$ let the even number $BC$ be subtracted:

I say that the remainder $CA$ is even.

For, since $AB$ is even, it has a half part. [VII. Def. 6]
For the same reason $BC$ also has a half part;
so that the remainder [$CA$ also has a half part, and] $AC$ is therefore even.

Q. E. D.

## Proposition 25

*If from an even number an odd number be subtracted, the remainder will be odd.*

For from the even number $AB$ let the odd number $BC$ be subtracted;

I say that the remainder $CA$ is odd.

For let the unit $CD$ be subtracted from $BC$;
therefore $DB$ is even. [VII. Def. 7]
But $AB$ is also even;
therefore the remainder $AD$ is also even. [IX. 24]
And $CD$ is an unit;
therefore $CA$ is odd. [VII. Def. 7]

Q. E. D.

## Proposition 26

*If from an odd number an odd number be subtracted, the remainder will be even.*

For from the odd number $AB$ let the odd number $BC$ be subtracted;

I say that the remainder $CA$ is even.

For, since $AB$ is odd, let the unit $BD$ be subtracted;
therefore the remainder $AD$ is even. [VII. Def. 7]
For the same reason $CD$ is also even; [VII. Def. 7]
so that the remainder $CA$ is also even. [IX. 24]

Q. E. D.

## Proposition 27

*If from an odd number an even number be subtracted, the remainder will be odd.*

For from the odd number $AB$ let the even number $BC$ be subtracted;

I say that the remainder $CA$ is odd.

Let the unit $AD$ be subtracted;

therefore $DB$ is even. [VII. Def. 7]

But $BC$ is also even;

therefore the remainder $CD$ is even. [IX. 24]

Therefore $CA$ is odd. [VII. Def. 7]

Q. E. D.

## Proposition 28

*If an odd number by multiplying an even number make some number, the product will be even.*

For let the odd number $A$ by multiplying the even number $B$ make $C$;

I say that $C$ is even.

For, since $A$ by multiplying $B$ has made $C$, therefore $C$ is made up of as many numbers equal to $B$ as there are units in $A$. [VII. Def. 15]

And $B$ is even;

therefore $C$ is made up of even numbers.

But, if as many even numbers as we please be added together, the whole is even. [IX. 21]

Therefore $C$ is even.

Q. E. D.

## Proposition 29

*If an odd number by multiplying an odd number make some number, the product will be odd.*

For let the odd number $A$ by multiplying the odd number $B$ make $C$;

I say that $C$ is odd.

For, since $A$ by multiplying $B$ has made $C$, therefore $C$ is made up of as many numbers equal to $B$ as there are units in $A$. [VII. Def. 15]

And each of the numbers $A$, $B$ is odd;

therefore $C$ is made up of odd numbers the multitude of which is odd.

Thus $C$ is odd. [IX. 23]

Q. E. D.

## Proposition 30

*If an odd number measure an even number, it will also measure the half of it.*

For let the odd number $A$ measure the even number $B$;

I say that it will also measure the half of it.

For, since $A$ measures $B$,

let it measure it according to $C$;

I say that $C$ is not odd.

For, if possible, let it be so.

Then, since $A$ measures $B$ according to $C$,

therefore $A$ by multiplying $C$ has made $B$.

Therefore $B$ is made up of odd numbers the multitude of which is odd.

Therefore $B$ is odd: [IX. 23]

which is absurd, for by hypothesis it is even.

Therefore $C$ is not odd;

therefore $C$ is even.
Thus $A$ measures $B$ an even number of times.
For this reason then it also measures the half of it.       Q. E. D.

## Proposition 31

*If an odd number be prime to any number, it will also be prime to the double of it.*

For let the odd number $A$ be prime to any number $B$,
and let $C$ be double of $B$;
I say that $A$ is prime to $C$.

For, if they are not prime to one another, some number will measure them.
Let a number measure them, and let it be $D$.
Now $A$ is odd;
therefore $D$ is also odd.
And since $D$ which is odd measures $C$,
and $C$ is even,
therefore [$D$] will measure the half of $C$ also.    [IX. 30]
But $B$ is half of $C$;
therefore $D$ measures $B$.
But it also measures $A$;
therefore $D$ measures $A$, $B$ which are prime to one another:
which is impossible.
Therefore $A$ cannot but be prime to $C$.
Therefore $A$, $C$ are prime to one another.       Q. E. D.

## Proposition 32

*Each of the numbers which are continually doubled beginning from a dyad is even-times even only.*

For let as many numbers as we please, $B$, $C$, $D$, have been continually doubled beginning from the dyad $A$;

I say that $B$, $C$, $D$ are even-times even only.
Now that each of the numbers $B$, $C$, $D$ is even-times even is manifest; for it is doubled from a dyad.
I say that it is also even-times even only.
For let an unit be set out.
Since then as many numbers as we please beginning from an unit are in continued proportion,
and the number $A$ after the unit is prime,
therefore $D$, the greatest of the numbers $A$, $B$, $C$, $D$, will not be measured by any other number except $A$, $B$, $C$.       [IX. 13]
And each of the numbers $A$, $B$, $C$ is even;
therefore $D$ is even-times even only.       [VII. Def. 8]
Similarly we can prove that each of the numbers $B$, $C$ is even-times even only.       Q. E. D.

## Proposition 33

*If a number have its half odd, it is even-times odd only.*

For let the number $A$ have its half odd;

I say that $A$ is even-times odd only.

Now that it is even-times odd is manifest; for the half of it, being odd, measures it an even number of times. [VII. Def. 9]

I say next that it is also even-times odd only.

For, if $A$ is even-times even also,

it will be measured by an even number according to an even number; [VII. Def. 8]

so that the half of it will also be measured by an even number though it is odd: which is absurd.

Therefore $A$ is even-times odd only.   Q. E. D.

## PROPOSITION 34

*If a number neither be one of those which are continually doubled from a dyad, nor have its half odd, it is both even-times even and even-times odd.*

For let the number $A$ neither be one of those doubled from a dyad, nor have its half odd;

I say that $A$ is both even-times even and even-times odd.

Now that $A$ is even-times even is manifest;

for it has not its half odd. [VII. Def. 8]

I say next that it is also even-times odd.

For, if we bisect $A$, then bisect its half, and do this continually, we shall come upon some odd number which will measure $A$ according to an even number.

For, if not, we shall come upon a dyad,

and $A$ will be among those which are doubled from a dyad:

which is contrary to the hypothesis.

Thus $A$ is even-times odd.

But it was also proved even-times even.

Therefore $A$ is both even-times even and even-times odd.   Q. E. D.

## PROPOSITION 35

*If as many numbers as we please be in continued proportion, and there be subtracted from the second and the last numbers equal to the first, then, as the excess of the second is to the first, so will the excess of the last be to all those before it.*

Let there be as many numbers as we please in continued proportion, $A$, $BC$, $D$, $EF$, beginning from $A$ as least,

and let there be subtracted from $BC$ and $EF$ the numbers $BG$, $FH$, each equal to $A$;

I say that, as $GC$ is to $A$, so is $EH$ to $A$, $BC$, $D$.

For let $FK$ be made equal to $BC$, and $FL$ equal to $D$.

Then, since $FK$ is equal to $BC$,

and of these the part $FH$ is equal to the part $BG$,

therefore the remainder $HK$ is equal to the remainder $GC$.

And since, as $EF$ is to $D$, so is $D$ to $BC$, and $BC$ to $A$,

while $D$ is equal to $FL$, $BC$ to $FK$, and $A$ to $FH$,

therefore, as $EF$ is to $FL$, so is $LF$ to $FK$, and $FK$ to $FH$.

*Separando*, as $EL$ is to $LF$, so is $LK$ to $FK$, and $KH$ to $FH$.   [VII. 11, 13]

# ELEMENTS IX

Therefore also, as one of the antecedents is to one of the consequents, so are all the antecedents to all the consequents; [VII. 12]

therefore, as $KH$ is to $FH$, so are $EL, LK, KH$ to $LF, FK, HF$.

But $KH$ is equal to $CG$, $FH$ to $A$, and $LF, FK, HF$ to $D, BC, A$;

therefore, as $CG$ is to $A$, so is $EH$ to $D, BC, A$.

Therefore, as the excess of the second is to the first, so is the excess of the last to all those before it. Q. E. D.

## Proposition 36

*If as many numbers as we please beginning from an unit be set out continuously in double proportion, until the sum of all becomes prime, and if the sum multiplied into the last make some number, the product will be perfect.*

For let as many numbers as we please, $A, B, C, D$, beginning from an unit be set out in double proportion, until the sum of all becomes prime,

let $E$ be equal to the sum, and let $E$ by multiplying $D$ make $FG$;

I say that $FG$ is perfect.

For, however many $A, B, C, D$ are in multitude, let so many $E, HK, L, M$ be taken in double proportion beginning from $E$;

therefore, ex aequali, as $A$ is to $D$, so is $E$ to $M$. [VII. 14]

Therefore the product of $E, D$ is equal to the product of $A, M$. [VII. 19]

And the product of $E, D$ is $FG$;

therefore the product of $A, M$ is also $FG$.

Therefore $A$ by multiplying $M$ has made $FG$;

therefore $M$ measures $FG$ according to the units in $A$.

And $A$ is a dyad;

therefore $FG$ is double of $M$.

But $M, L, HK, E$ are continuously double of each other;

therefore $E, HK, L, M, FG$ are continuously proportional in double proportion.

Now let there be subtracted from the second $HK$ and the last $FG$ the numbers $HN, FO$, each equal to the first $E$;

therefore, as the excess of the second is to the first, so is the excess of the last to all those before it. [IX. 35]

Therefore, as $NK$ is to $E$, so is $OG$ to $M, L, KH, E$.

And $NK$ is equal to $E$;

therefore $OG$ is also equal to $M, L, HK, E$.

But $FO$ is also equal to $E$,

and $E$ is equal to $A, B, C, D$ and the unit.

Therefore the whole $FG$ is equal to $E, HK, L, M$ and $A, B, C, D$ and the unit;

and it is measured by them.

I say also that $FG$ will not be measured by any other number except $A$, $B$, $C$, $D$, $E$, $HK$, $L$, $M$ and the unit.

For, if possible, let some number $P$ measure $FG$, and let $P$ not be the same with any of the numbers $A$, $B$, $C$, $D$, $E$, $HK$, $L$, $M$.

And, as many times as $P$ measures $FG$, so many units let there be in $Q$;

therefore $Q$ by multiplying $P$ has made $FG$.

But, further, $E$ has also by multiplying $D$ made $FG$;

therefore, as $E$ is to $Q$, so is $P$ to $D$. [VII. 19]

And, since $A$, $B$, $C$, $D$ are continuously proportional beginning from an unit, therefore $D$ will not be measured by any other number except $A$, $B$, $C$. [IX. 13]

And, by hypothesis, $P$ is not the same with any of the numbers $A$, $B$, $C$;

therefore $P$ will not measure $D$.

But, as $P$ is to $D$, so is $E$ to $Q$;

therefore neither does $E$ measure $Q$. [VII. Def. 20]

And $E$ is prime;

and any prime number is prime to any number which it does not measure. [VII. 29]

Therefore $E$, $Q$ are prime to one another.

But primes are also least, [VII. 21]

and the least numbers measure those which have the same ratio the same number of times, the antecedent the antecedent and the consequent the consequent; [VII. 20]

and, as $E$ is to $Q$, so is $P$ to $D$;

therefore $E$ measures $P$ the same number of times that $Q$ measures $D$.

But $D$ is not measured by any other number except $A$, $B$, $C$;

therefore $Q$ is the same with one of the numbers $A$, $B$, $C$.

Let it be the same with $B$.

And, however many $B$, $C$, $D$ are in multitude, let so many $E$, $HK$, $L$ be taken beginning from $E$.

Now $E$, $HK$, $L$ are in the same ratio with $B$, $C$, $D$;

therefore, *ex aequali*, as $B$ is to $D$, so is $E$ to $L$. [VII. 14]

Therefore the product of $B$, $L$ is equal to the product of $D$, $E$. [VII. 19]

But the product of $D$, $E$ is equal to the product of $Q$, $P$;

therefore the product of $Q$, $P$ is also equal to the product of $B$, $L$.

Therefore, as $Q$ is to $B$, so is $L$ to $P$. [VII. 19]

And $Q$ is the same with $B$;

therefore $L$ is also the same with $P$:

which is impossible, for by hypothesis $P$ is not the same with any of the numbers set out.

Therefore no number will measure $FG$ except $A$, $B$, $C$, $D$, $E$, $HK$, $L$, $M$ and the unit.

And $FG$ was proved equal to $A$, $B$, $C$, $D$, $E$, $HK$, $L$, $M$ and the unit;

and a perfect number is that which is equal to its own parts; [VII. Def. 22]

therefore $FG$ is perfect. Q. E. D.

# BOOK TEN

### DEFINITIONS I

1. Those magnitudes are said to be *commensurable* which are measured by the same measure, and those *incommensurable* which cannot have any common measure.

2. Straight lines are *commensurable in square* when the squares on them are measured by the same area, and *incommensurable in square* when the squares on them cannot possibly have any area as a common measure.

3. With these hypotheses, it is proved that there exist straight lines infinite in multitude which are commensurable and incommensurable respectively, some in length only, and others in square also, with an assigned straight line. Let then the assigned straight line be called *rational*, and those straight lines which are commensurable with it, whether in length and in square or in square only, *rational*, but those which are incommensurable with it *irrational*.

4. And let the square on the assigned straight line be called *rational* and those areas which are commensurable with it *rational*, but those which are incommensurable with it *irrational*, and the straight lines which produce them *irrational*, that is, in case the areas are squares, the sides themselves, but in case they are any other rectilineal figures, the straight lines on which are described squares equal to them.

## BOOK X. PROPOSITIONS

### Proposition 1

*Two unequal magnitudes being set out, if from the greater there be subtracted a magnitude greater than its half, and from that which is left a magnitude greater than its half, and if this process be repeated continually, there will be left some magnitude which will be less than the lesser magnitude set out.*

Let $AB$, $C$ be two unequal magnitudes of which $AB$ is the greater:

I say that, if from $AB$ there be subtracted a magnitude greater than its half, and from that which is left a magnitude greater than its half, and if this process be repeated continually, there will be left some magnitude which will be less than the magnitude $C$.

For $C$ if multiplied will sometime be greater than $AB$.　　　[cf. v. Def. 4]

Let it be multiplied, and let $DE$ be a multiple of $C$, and greater than $AB$;
let $DE$ be divided into the parts $DF$, $FG$, $GE$ equal to $C$,
from $AB$ let there be subtracted $BH$ greater than its half,
and, from $AH$, $HK$ greater than its half,

and let this process be repeated continually until the divisions in $AB$ are equal in multitude with the divisions in $DE$.

Let, then, $AK$, $KH$, $HB$ be divisions which are equal in multitude with $DF$, $FG$, $GE$.

Now, since $DE$ is greater than $AB$,
>and from $DE$ there has been subtracted $EG$ less than its half,
>and, from $AB$, $BH$ greater than its half,

therefore the remainder $GD$ is greater than the remainder $HA$.

And, since $GD$ is greater than $HA$,
>and there has been subtracted, from $GD$, the half $GF$,
>and, from $HA$, $HK$ greater than its half,

therefore the remainder $DF$ is greater than the remainder $AK$.

But $DF$ is equal to $C$;
>therefore $C$ is also greater than $AK$.

Therefore $AK$ is less than $C$.

Therefore there is left of the magnitude $AB$ the magnitude $AK$ which is less than the lesser magnitude set out, namely $C$.   Q. E. D.

And the theorem can be similarly proved even if the parts subtracted be halves.

## Proposition 2

*If, when the less of two unequal magnitudes is continually subtracted in turn from the greater, that which is left never measures the one before it, the magnitudes will be incommensurable.*

For, there being two unequal magnitudes $AB$, $CD$, and $AB$ being the less, when the less is continually subtracted in turn from the greater, let that which is left over never measure the one before it;

I say that the magnitudes $AB$, $CD$ are incommensurable.

For, if they are commensurable, some magnitude will measure them.

Let a magnitude measure them, if possible, and let it be $E$;
>let $AB$, measuring $FD$, leave $CF$ less than itself,
>let $CF$ measuring $BG$, leave $AG$ less than itself,

and let this process be repeated continually, until there is left some magnitude which is less than $E$.

Suppose this done, and let there be left $AG$ less than $E$.

Then, since $E$ measures $AB$,
>while $AB$ measures $DF$,
>therefore $E$ will also measure $FD$.

But it measures the whole $CD$ also;
>therefore it will also measure the remainder $CF$.

But $CF$ measures $BG$;
>therefore $E$ also measures $BG$.

But it measures the whole $AB$ also;
therefore it will also measure the remainder $AG$, the greater the less:
>which is impossible.

ELEMENTS X

Therefore no magnitude will measure the magnitudes $AB$, $CD$;
therefore the magnitudes $AB$, $CD$ are incommensurable. [x. Def. 1]
Therefore etc.                                            Q. E. D.

PROPOSITION 3

*Given two commensurable magnitudes, to find their greatest common measure.*

Let the two given commensurable magnitudes be $AB$, $CD$ of which $AB$ is the less;
thus it is required to find the greatest common measure of $AB$, $CD$.

Now the magnitude $AB$ either measures $CD$ or it does not.

If then it measures it—and it measures itself also—$AB$ is a common measure of $AB$, $CD$.

And it is manifest that it is also the greatest;
for a greater magnitude than the magnitude $AB$ will not measure $AB$.

Next, let $AB$ not measure $CD$.

Then, if the less be continually subtracted in turn from the greater, that which is left over will sometime measure the one before it, because $AB$, $CD$ are not incommensurable;

[cf. x. 2]

let $AB$, measuring $ED$, leave $EC$ less than itself,
let $EC$, measuring $FB$, leave $AF$ less than itself,
and let $AF$ measure $CE$.

Since, then, $AF$ measures $CE$,
while $CE$ measures $FB$,
therefore $AF$ will also measure $FB$.

But it measures itself also;
therefore $AF$ will also measure the whole $AB$.

But $AB$ measures $DE$;
therefore $AF$ will also measure $ED$.

But it measures $CE$ also;
therefore it also measures the whole $CD$.

Therefore $AF$ is a common measure of $AB$, $CD$.

I say next that it is also the greatest.

For, if not, there will be some magnitude greater than $AF$ which will measure $AB$, $CD$.

Let it be $G$.

Since then $G$ measures $AB$,
while $AB$ measures $ED$,
therefore $G$ will also measure $ED$.

But it measures the whole $CD$ also;
therefore $G$ will also measure the remainder $CE$.

But $CE$ measures $FB$;
therefore $G$ will also measure $FB$.

But it measures the whole $AB$ also,
and it will therefore measure the remainder $AF$, the greater the less:
which is impossible.

Therefore no magnitude greater than $AF$ will measure $AB, CD$;

therefore $AF$ is the greatest common measure of $AB, CD$.

Therefore the greatest common measure of the two given commensurable magnitudes $AB, CD$ has been found.
Q. E. D.

PORISM. From this it is manifest that, if a magnitude measure two magnitudes, it will also measure their greatest common measure.

## PROPOSITION 4

*Given three commensurable magnitudes, to find their greatest common measure.*

Let $A, B, C$ be the three given commensurable magnitudes;
thus it is required to find the greatest common measure of $A, B, C$.

Let the greatest common measure of the two magnitudes $A, B$ be taken, and let it be $D$; [x. 3]
then $D$ either measures $C$, or does not measure it.

First, let it measure it.

Since then $D$ measures $C$,

while it also measures $A, B$,

therefore $D$ is a common measure of $A, B, C$.

And it is manifest that it is also the greatest;
for a greater magnitude than the magnitude $D$ does not measure $A, B$.

Next, let $D$ not measure $C$.

I say first that $C, D$ are commensurable.

For, since $A, B, C$ are commensurable,

some magnitude will measure them,

and this will of course measure $A, B$ also;

so that it will also measure the greatest common measure of $A, B$, namely $D$.
[x. 3, Por.]

But it also measures $C$;

so that the said magnitude will measure $C, D$;

therefore $C, D$ are commensurable.

Now let their greatest common measure be taken, and let it be $E$. [x. 3]

Since then $E$ measures $D$,

while $D$ measures $A, B$,

therefore $E$ will also measure $A, B$.

But it measures $C$ also;

therefore $E$ measures $A, B, C$;

therefore $E$ is a common measure of $A, B, C$.

I say next that it is also the greatest.

For, if possible, let there be some magnitude $F$ greater than $E$, and let it measure $A, B, C$.

Now, since $F$ measures $A, B, C$,

it will also measure $A, B$,

and will measure the greatest common measure of $A, B$. [x. 3, Por.]

But the greatest common measure of $A, B$ is $D$;

therefore $F$ measures $D$.

But it measures $C$ also;

therefore $F$ measures $C, D$;

therefore $F$ will also measure the greatest common measure of $C, D$.
[x. 3, Por.]

But that is $E$;
> therefore $F$ will measure $E$, the greater the less:
>> which is impossible.

Therefore no magnitude greater than the magnitude $E$ will measure $A, B, C$; therefore $E$ is the greatest common measure of $A, B, C$ if $D$ do not measure $C$,
> and, if it measure it, $D$ is itself the greatest common measure.

Therefore the greatest common measure of the three given commensurable magnitudes has been found.

PORISM. From this it is manifest that, if a magnitude measure three magnitudes, it will also measure their greatest common measure.

Similarly too, with more magnitudes, the greatest common measure can be found, and the porism can be extended. Q. E. D.

## PROPOSITION 5

*Commensurable magnitudes have to one another the ratio which a number has to a number.*

Let $A, B$ be commensurable magnitudes;
I say that $A$ has to $B$ the ratio which a number has to a number.
For, since $A, B$ are commensurable, some magnitude will measure them.
Let it measure them, and let it be $C$.

And, as many times as $C$ measures $A$, so many units let there be in $D$;
and, as many times as $C$ measures $B$, so many units let there be in $E$.

Since then $C$ measures $A$ according to the units in $D$,
> while the unit also measures $D$ according to the units in it,

therefore the unit measures the number $D$ the same number of times as the magnitude $C$ measures $A$;
> therefore as $C$, is to $A$, so is the unit to $D$; [VII. Def. 20]

therefore, inversely, as $A$ is to $C$, so is $D$ to the unit. [cf. V. 7, Por.]

Again, since $C$ measures $B$ according to the units in $E$,
> while the unit also measures $E$ according to the units in it,

therefore the unit measures $E$ the same number of times as $C$ measures $B$;
> therefore, as $C$ is to $B$, so is the unit to $E$.

But it was also proved that,
> as $A$ is to $C$, so is $D$ to the unit;
> therefore, *ex aequali*,
> as $A$ is to $B$, so is the number $D$ to $E$. [V. 22]

Therefore the commensurable magnitudes $A, B$ have to one another the ratio which the number $D$ has to the number $E$. Q. E. D.

## PROPOSITION 6

*If two magnitudes have to one another the ratio which a number has to a number, the magnitudes will be commensurable.*

For let the two magnitudes $A, B$ have to one another the ratio which the number $D$ has to the number $E$;
> I say that the magnitudes $A, B$ are commensurable.

For let $A$ be divided into as many equal parts as there are units in $D$, and let $C$ be equal to one of them;
and let $F$ be made up of as many magnitudes equal to $C$ as there are units in $E$.

Since then there are in $A$ as many magnitudes equal to $C$ as there are units in $D$,

whatever part the unit is of $D$, the same part is $C$ of $A$ also;
therefore, as $C$ is to $A$, so is the unit to $D$.  [VII. Def. 20]
But the unit measures the number $D$;
therefore $C$ also measures $A$.

And since, as $C$ is to $A$, so is the unit to $D$,
therefore, inversely, as $A$ is to $C$, so is the number $D$ to the unit.
[cf. v. 7, Por.]

Again, since there are in $F$ as many magnitudes equal to $C$ as there are units in $E$,
therefore, as $C$ is to $F$, so is the unit to $E$.  [VII. Def. 20]
But it was also proved that,
as $A$ is to $C$, so is $D$ to the unit;
therefore, *ex aequali*, as $A$ is to $F$, so is $D$ to $E$.  [v. 22]
But, as $D$ is to $E$, so is $A$ to $B$;
therefore also, as $A$ is to $B$, so is it to $F$ also.  [v. 11]
Therefore $A$ has the same ratio to each of the magnitudes $B$, $F$;
therefore $B$ is equal to $F$.  [v. 9]
But $C$ measures $F$;
therefore it measures $B$ also.
Further it measures $A$ also;
therefore $C$ measures $A$, $B$.
Therefore $A$ is commensurable with $B$.
Therefore etc.

PORISM. From this it is manifest that, if there be two numbers, as $D$, $E$, and a straight line, as $A$, it is possible to make a straight line $[F]$ such that the given straight line is to it as the number $D$ is to the number $E$.

And, if a mean proportional be also taken between $A$, $F$, as $B$, as $A$ is to $F$, so will the square on $A$ be to the square on $B$, that is, as the first is to the third, so is the figure on the first to that which is similar and similarly described on the second.  [VI. 19, Por.]

But, as $A$ is to $F$, so is the number $D$ to the number $E$;
therefore it has been contrived that, as the number $D$ is to the number $E$, so also is the figure on the straight line $A$ to the figure on the straight line $B$.

Q. E. D.

## PROPOSITION 7

*Incommensurable magnitudes have not to one another the ratio which a number has to a number.*

Let $A$, $B$ be incommensurable magnitudes;
I say that $A$ has not to $B$ the ratio which a number has to a number.
For, if $A$ has to $B$ the ratio which a number has to a number, $A$ will be com-

ELEMENTS X

mensurable with $B$. [x. 6]
But it is not;
therefore $A$ has not to $B$ the ratio which a number has to a number.

$\underline{\quad A \quad}$
$\underline{\quad B \quad}$

Therefore etc. Q. E. D.

## Proposition 8

*If two magnitudes have not to one another the ratio which a number has to a number, the magnitudes will be incommensurable.*

For let the two magnitudes $A$, $B$ not have to one another the ratio which a number has to a number;
I say that the magnitudes $A$, $B$ are incommensurable.
For, if they are commensurable, $A$ will have to $B$ the ratio which a number has to a number. [x. 5]
But it has not;
therefore the magnitudes $A$, $B$ are incommensurable.
Therefore etc. Q. E. D.

## Proposition 9

*The squares on straight lines commensurable in length have to one another the ratio which a square number has to a square number; and squares which have to one another the ratio which a square number has to a square number will also have their sides commensurable in length. But the squares on straight lines incommensurable in length have not to one another the ratio which a square number has to a square number; and squares which have not to one another the ratio which a square number has to a square number will not have their sides commensurable in length either.*

For let $A$, $B$ be commensurable in length;
I say that the square on $A$ has to the square on $B$ the ratio which a square number has to a square number.
For, since $A$ is commensurable in length with $B$,
therefore $A$ has to $B$ the ratio which a number has to a number. [x. 5]
Let it have to it the ratio which $C$ has to $D$.
Since then, as $A$ is to $B$, so is $C$ to $D$,
while the ratio of the square on $A$ to the square on $B$ is duplicate of the ratio of $A$ to $B$,
for similar figures are in the duplicate ratio of their corresponding sides;
[vi. 20, Por.]
and the ratio of the square on $C$ to the square on $D$ is duplicate of the ratio of $C$ to $D$,
for between two square numbers there is one mean proportional number, and the square number has to the square number the ratio duplicate of that which the side has to the side; [viii. 11]
therefore also, as the square on $A$ is to the square on $B$, so is the square on $C$ to the square on $D$.

Next, as the square on $A$ is to the square on $B$, so let the square on $C$ be to the square on $D$;

I say that $A$ is commensurable in length with $B$.

For since, as the square on $A$ is to the square on $B$, so is the square on $C$ to the square on $D$,
while the ratio of the square on $A$ to the square on $B$ is duplicate of the ratio of $A$ to $B$,
and the ratio of the square on $C$ to the square on $D$ is duplicate of the ratio of $C$ to $D$,

therefore also, as $A$ is to $B$, so is $C$ to $D$.

Therefore $A$ has to $B$ the ratio which the number $C$ has to the number $D$;
therefore $A$ is commensurable in length with $B$. [x. 6]

Next, let $A$ be incommensurable in length with $B$;

I say that the square on $A$ has not to the square on $B$ the ratio which a square number has to a square number.

For, if the square on $A$ has to the square on $B$ the ratio which a square number has to a square number, $A$ will be commensurable with $B$.

But it is not;
therefore the square on $A$ has not to the square on $B$ the ratio which a square number has to a square number.

Again, let the square on $A$ not have to the square on $B$ the ratio which a square number has to a square number;

I say that $A$ is incommensurable in length with $B$.

For, if $A$ is commensurable with $B$, the square on $A$ will have to the square on $B$ the ratio which a square number has to a square number.

But it has not;

therefore $A$ is not commensurable in length with $B$.

Therefore etc.

PORISM. And it is manifest from what has been proved that straight lines commensurable in length are always commensurable in square also, but those commensurable in square are not always commensurable in length also.

[LEMMA. It has been proved in the arithmetical books that similar plane numbers have to one another the ratio which a square number has to a square number, [VIII. 26]
and that, if two numbers have to one another the ratio which a square number has to a square number, they are similar plane numbers. [Converse of VIII. 26]

And it is manifest from these propositions that numbers which are not similar plane numbers, that is, those which have not their sides proportional, have not to one another the ratio which a square number has to a square number.

For, if they have, they will be similar plane numbers: which is contrary to the hypothesis.

Therefore numbers which are not similar plane numbers have not to one another the ratio which a square number has to a square number.]

## PROPOSITION 10

*To find two straight lines incommensurable, the one in length only, and the other in square also, with an assigned straight line.*

Let $A$ be the assigned straight line;
thus it is required to find two straight lines incommensurable, the one in length only, and the other in square also, with $A$.

Let two numbers $B$, $C$ be set out which have not to one another the ratio

ELEMENTS X

which a square number has to a square number, that is, which are not similar plane numbers;

A————————
D————————
E————————
B——————
C——————

and let it be contrived that,
as $B$ is to $C$, so is the square on $A$ to the square on $D$
—for we have learnt how to do this— [x. 6, Por.]
therefore the square on $A$ is commensurable with the square on $D$. [x. 6]

And, since $B$ has not to $C$ the ratio which a square number has to a square number,
therefore neither has the square on $A$ to the square on $D$ the ratio which a square number has to a square number;
therefore $A$ is incommensurable in length with $D$. [x. 9]

Let $E$ be taken a mean proportional between $A$, $D$;
therefore, as $A$ is to $D$, so is the square on $A$ to the square on $E$. [v. Def. 9]
But $A$ is incommensurable in length with $D$;
therefore the square on $A$ is also incommensurable with the square on $E$; [x. 11]

therefore $A$ is incommensurable in square with $E$.

Therefore two straight lines $D$, $E$ have been found incommensurable, $D$ in length only, and $E$ in square and of course in length also, with the assigned straight line $A$. Q. E. D.

## Proposition 11

*If four magnitudes be proportional, and the first be commensurable with the second, the third will also be commensurable with the fourth; and, if the first be incommensurable with the second, the third will also be incommensurable with the fourth.*

Let $A$, $B$, $C$, $D$ be four magnitudes in proportion, so that, as $A$ is to $B$, so is $C$ to $D$,

A———————————  B————————
C————————————  D———————

and let $A$ be commensurable with $B$;
I say that $C$ will also be commensurable with $D$.

For, since $A$ is commensurable with $B$,
therefore $A$ has to $B$ the ratio which a number has to a number. [x. 5]
And, as $A$ is to $B$, so is $C$ to $D$;
therefore $C$ also has to $D$ the ratio which a number has to a number;
therefore $C$ is commensurable with $D$. [x. 6]

Next, let $A$ be incommensurable with $B$;
I say that $C$ will also be incommensurable with $D$.
For, since $A$ is incommensurable with $B$,
therefore $A$ has not to $B$ the ratio which a number has to a number. [x. 7]
And, as $A$ is to $B$, so is $C$ to $D$;
therefore neither has $C$ to $D$ the ratio which a number has to a number;
therefore $C$ is incommensurable with $D$. [x. 8]
Therefore etc. Q. E. D.

## Proposition 12

*Magnitudes commensurable with the same magnitude are commensurable with one another also.*

For let each of the magnitudes $A$, $B$ be commensurable with $C$;

I say that $A$ is also commensurable with $B$.

For, since $A$ is commensurable with $C$, therefore $A$ has to $C$ the ratio which a number has to a number. [x. 5]

Let it have the ratio which $D$ has to $E$.

Again, since $C$ is commensurable with $B$,
therefore $C$ has to $B$ the ratio which a number has to a number. [x. 5]

Let it have the ratio which $F$ has to $G$.

And, given any number of ratios we please, namely the ratio which $D$ has to $E$ and that which $F$ has to $G$,
let the numbers $H$, $K$, $L$ be taken continuously in the given ratios; [cf. vIII. 4]
so that, as $D$ is to $E$, so is $H$ to $K$,
and, as $F$ is to $G$, so is $K$ to $L$.

Since, then, as $A$ is to $C$, so is $D$ to $E$,
while, as $D$ is to $E$, so is $H$ to $K$,
therefore also, as $A$ is to $C$, so is $H$ to $K$. [v. 11]

Again, since, as $C$ is to $B$, so is $F$ to $G$,
while, as $F$ is to $G$, so is $K$ to $L$,
therefore also, as $C$ is to $B$, so is $K$ to $L$. [v. 11]

But also, as $A$ is to $C$, so is $H$ to $K$;
therefore, *ex aequali*, as $A$ is to $B$, so is $H$ to $L$. [v. 22]

Therefore $A$ has to $B$ the ratio which a number has to a number;
therefore $A$ is commensurable with $B$. [x. 6]

Therefore etc.

Q. E. D.

## Proposition 13

*If two magnitudes be commensurable, and the one of them be incommensurable with any magnitude, the remaining one will also be incommensurable with the same.*

Let $A$, $B$ be two commensurable magnitudes, and let one of them, $A$, be incommensurable with any other magnitude $C$;

I say that the remaining one, $B$, will also be incommensurable with $C$.

For, if $B$ is commensurable with $C$,
while $A$ is also commensurable with $B$,
$A$ is also commensurable with $C$. [x. 12]

But it is also incommensurable with it:
which is impossible.

Therefore $B$ is not commensurable with $C$;
therefore it is incommensurable with it.

Therefore etc.

Q. E. D.

### Lemma

*Given two unequal straight lines, to find by what square the square on the greater is greater than the square on the less.*

Let $AB$, $C$ be the given two unequal straight lines, and let $AB$ be the greater of them;

thus it is required to find by what square the square on $AB$ is greater than the square on $C$.

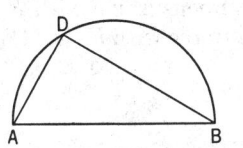

Let the semicircle $ADB$ be described on $AB$, and let $AD$ be fitted into it equal to $C$;   [IV. 1] let $DB$ be joined.

It is then manifest that the angle $ADB$ is right,   [III. 31] and that the square on $AB$ is greater than the square on $AD$, that is, $C$, by the square on $DB$.   [I. 47]

Similarly also, if two straight lines be given, the straight line the square on which is equal to the sum of the squares on them is found in this manner:

Let $AD$, $DB$ be the given two straight lines, and let it be required to find the straight line the square on which is equal to the sum of the squares on them.

Let them be placed so as to contain a right angle, that formed by $AD$, $DB$; and let $AB$ be joined.

It is again manifest that the straight line the square on which is equal to the sum of the squares on $AD$, $DB$ is $AB$.   [I. 47]

Q. E. D.

## Proposition 14

*If four straight lines be proportional, and the square on the first be greater than the square on the second by the square on a straight line commensurable with the first, the square on the third will also be greater than the square on the fourth by the square on a straight line commensurable with the third.*

*And, if the square on the first be greater than the square on the second by the square on a straight line incommensurable with the first, the square on the third will also be greater than the square on the fourth by the square on a straight line incommensurable with the third.*

Let $A$, $B$, $C$, $D$ be four straight lines in proportion, so that, as $A$ is to $B$, so is $C$ to $D$;

and let the square on $A$ be greater than the square on $B$ by the square on $E$,
and let the square on $C$ be greater than the square on $D$ by the square on $F$;
I say that, if $A$ is commensurable with $E$, $C$ is also commensurable with $F$,
and, if $A$ is incommensurable with $E$, $C$ is also incommensurable with $F$.

For since, as $A$ is to $B$, so is $C$ to $D$, therefore also, as the square on $A$ is to the square on $B$, so is the square on $C$ to the square on $D$.   [VI. 22]

But the squares on $E$, $B$ are equal to the square on $A$, and the squares on $D$, $F$ are equal to the square on $C$.

Therefore, as the squares on $E$, $B$ are to the square on $B$, so are the squares on $D$, $F$ to the square on $D$;

therefore, *separando*, as the square on $E$ is to the square on $B$, so is the square on $F$ to the square on $D$;   [V. 17]

therefore also, as $E$ is to $B$, so is $F$ to $D$;   [VI. 22]

therefore, inversely, as $B$ is to $E$, so is $D$ to $F$.

But, as $A$ is to $B$, so also is $C$ to $D$;
therefore, *ex aequali*, as $A$ is to $E$, so is $C$ to $F$. [v. 22]

Therefore, if $A$ is commensurable with $E$, $C$ is also commensurable with $F$, and, if $A$ is incommensurable with $E$, $C$ is also incommensurable with $F$. [x. 11]

Therefore etc.

Q. E. D.

## Proposition 15

*If two commensurable magnitudes be added together, the whole will also be commensurable with each of them; and, if the whole be commensurable with one of them, the original magnitudes will also be commensurable.*

For let the two commensurable magnitudes $AB$, $BC$ be added together;

I say that the whole $AC$ is also commensurable with each of the magnitudes $AB$, $BC$.

For, since $AB$, $BC$ are commensurable, some magnitude will measure them.

Let it measure them, and let it be $D$.

Since then $D$ measures $AB$, $BC$, it will also measure the whole $AC$.

But it measures $AB$, $BC$ also;
therefore $D$ measures $AB$, $BC$, $AC$;
therefore $AC$ is commensurable with each of the magnitudes $AB$, $BC$.

[x. Def. 1]

Next, let $AC$ be commensurable with $AB$;
I say that $AB$, $BC$ are also commensurable.

For, since $AC$, $AB$ are commensurable, some magnitude will measure them. Let it measure them, and let it be $D$.

Since then $D$ measures $CA$, $AB$, it will also measure the remainder $BC$.

But it measures $AB$ also;
therefore $D$ will measure $AB$, $BC$;
therefore $AB$, $BC$ are commensurable. [x. Def. 1]

Therefore etc.

Q. E. D.

## Proposition 16

*If two incommensurable magnitudes be added together, the whole will also be incommensurable with each of them; and, if the whole be incommensurable with one of them, the original magnitudes will also be incommensurable.*

For let the two incommensurable magnitudes $AB$, $BC$ be added together; I say that the whole $AC$ is also incommensurable with each of the magnitudes $AB$, $BC$.

For, if $CA$, $AB$ are not incommensurable, some magnitude will measure them.

Let it measure them, if possible, and let it be $D$.

Since then $D$ measures $CA$, $AB$,
therefore it will also measure the remainder $BC$.

But it measures $AB$ also;
therefore $D$ measures $AB$, $BC$.

Therefore $AB$, $BC$ are commensurable;
but they were also, by hypothesis, incommensurable:
which is impossible.

Therefore no magnitude will measure $CA$, $AB$;
therefore $CA$, $AB$ are incommensurable. [x. Def. 1]
Similarly we can prove that $AC$, $CB$ are also incommensurable.
Therefore $AC$ is incommensurable with each of the magnitudes $AB$, $BC$.
Next, let $AC$ be incommensurable with one of the magnitudes $AB$, $BC$.
First, let it be incommensurable with $AB$;
I say that $AB$, $BC$ are also incommensurable.
For, if they are commensurable, some magnitude will measure them.
Let it measure them, and let it be $D$.
Since, then, $D$ measures $AB$, $BC$,
therefore it will also measure the whole $AC$.
But it measures $AB$ also;
therefore $D$ measures $CA$, $AB$.
Therefore $CA$, $AB$ are commensurable;
but they were also, by hypothesis, incommensurable:
which is impossible.
Therefore no magnitude will measure $AB$, $BC$;
therefore $AB$, $BC$ are incommensurable. [x. Def. 1]
Therefore etc. Q. E. D.

## Lemma

*If to any straight line there be applied a parallelogram deficient by a square figure, the applied parallelogram is equal to the rectangle contained by the segments of the straight line resulting from the application.*

For let there be applied to the straight line $AB$ the parallelogram $AD$ deficient by the square figure $DB$;

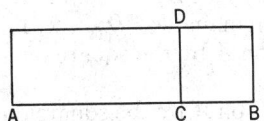

I say that $AD$ is equal to the rectangle contained by $AC$, $CB$.

This is indeed at once manifest;
for, since $DB$ is a square,
$DC$ is equal to $CB$;
and $AD$ is the rectangle $AC$, $CD$, that is, the rectangle $AC$, $CB$.
Therefore etc. Q. E. D.

## Proposition 17

*If there be two unequal straight lines, and to the greater there be applied a parallelogram equal to the fourth part of the square on the less and deficient by a square figure, and if it divide it into parts which are commensurable in length, then the square on the greater will be greater than the square on the less by the square on a straight line commensurable with the greater.*

*And, if the square on the greater be greater than the square on the less by the square on a straight line commensurable with the greater, and if there be applied to the greater a parallelogram equal to the fourth part of the square on the less and deficient by a square figure, it will divide it into parts which are commensurable in length.*

Let $A$, $BC$ be two unequal straight lines, of which $BC$ is the greater,
and let there be applied to $BC$ a parallelogram equal to the fourth part of the square on the less, $A$, that is, equal to the square on the half of $A$, and deficient by a square figure. Let this be the rectangle $BD$, $DC$, [cf. Lemma]

and let *BD* be commensurable in length with *DC*;

I say that the square on *BC* is greater than the square on *A* by the square on a straight line commensurable with *BC*.

For let *BC* be bisected at the point *E*,
and let *EF* be made equal to *DE*.

Therefore the remainder *DC* is equal to *BF*.

And, since the straight line *BC* has been cut into equal parts at *E*, and into unequal parts at *D*, therefore the rectangle contained by *BD*, *DC*, together with the square on *ED*, is equal to the square on *EC*; [II. 5]

And the same is true of their quadruples;

therefore four times the rectangle *BD*, *DC*, together with four times the square on *DE*, is equal to four times the square on *EC*.

But the square on *A* is equal to four times the rectangle *BD*, *DC*;
and the square on *DF* is equal to four times the square on *DE*, for *DF* is double of *DE*.

And the square on *BC* is equal to four times the square on *EC*, for again *BC* is double of *CE*.

Therefore the squares on *A*, *DF* are equal to the square on *BC*,
so that the square on *BC* is greater than the square on *A* by the square on *DF*.

It is to be proved that *BC* is also commensurable with *DF*.

Since *BD* is commensurable in length with *DC*,
therefore *BC* is also commensurable in length with *CD*. [x. 15]

But *CD* is commensurable in length with *CD*, *BF*, for *CD* is equal to *BF*. [x. 6]

Therefore *BC* is also commensurable in length with *BF*, *CD*, [x. 12]
so that *BC* is also commensurable in length with the remainder *FD*; [x. 15]
therefore the square on *BC* is greater than the square on *A* by the square on a straight line commensurable with *BC*.

Next, let the square on *BC* be greater than the square on *A* by the square on a straight line commensurable with *BC*,
let a parallelogram be applied to *BC* equal to the fourth part of the square on *A* and deficient by a square figure, and let it be the rectangle *BD*, *DC*.

It is to be proved that *BD* is commensurable in length with *DC*.

With the same construction, we can prove similarly that the square on *BC* is greater than the square on *A* by the square on *FD*.

But the square on *BC* is greater than the square on *A* by the square on a straight line commensurable with *BC*.

Therefore *BC* is commensurable in length with *FD*,
so that *BC* is also commensurable in length with the remainder, the sum of *BF*, *DC*. [x. 15]

But the sum of *BF*, *DC* is commensurable with *DC*, [x. 6]
so that *BC* is also commensurable in length with *CD*; [x. 12]
and therefore, *separando*, *BD* is commensurable in length with *DC*. [x. 15]

Therefore etc.
Q. E. D.

## Proposition 18

*If there be two unequal straight lines, and to the greater there be applied a parallelogram equal to the fourth part of the square on the less and deficient by a square* figure, and if it divide it into parts which are incommensurable, the square on the greater will be greater than the square on the less by the square on a straight line incommensurable with the greater.

And, if the square on the greater be greater than the square on the less by the square on a straight line incommensurable with the greater, and if there be applied to the greater a parallelogram equal to the fourth part of the square on the less and deficient by a square figure, it divides it into parts which are incommensurable.

Let $A$, $BC$ be two unequal straight lines, of which $BC$ is the greater, and to $BC$ let there be applied a parallelogram equal to the fourth part of the square on the less, $A$, and deficient by a square figure. Let this be the rectangle $BD$, $DC$, [cf. Lemma before x. 17] and let $BD$ be incommensurable in length with $DC$;

I say that the square on $BC$ is greater than the square on $A$ by the square on a straight line incommensurable with $BC$.

For, with the same construction as before, we can prove similarly that the square on $BC$ is greater than the square on $A$ by the square on $FD$.

It is to be proved that $BC$ is incommensurable in length with $DF$.

Since $BD$ is incommensurable in length with $DC$,
therefore $BC$ is also incommensurable in length with $CD$. [x. 16]
But $DC$ is commensurable with the sum of $BF$, $DC$; [x. 6]
therefore $BC$ is also incommensurable with the sum of $BF$, $DC$; [x. 13]
so that $BC$ is also incommensurable in length with the remainder $FD$. [x. 16]

And the square on $BC$ is greater than the square on $A$ by the square on $FD$; therefore the square on $BC$ is greater than the square on $A$ by the square on a straight line incommensurable with $BC$.

Again, let the square on $BC$ be greater than the square on $A$ by the square on a straight line incommensurable with $BC$, and let there be applied to $BC$ a parallelogram equal to the fourth part of the square on $A$ and deficient by a square figure. Let this be the rectangle $BD$, $DC$.

It is to be proved that $BD$ is incommensurable in length with $DC$.

For, with the same construction, we can prove similarly that the square on $BC$ is greater than the square on $A$ by the square on $FD$.

But the square on $BC$ is greater than the square on $A$ by the square on a straight line incommensurable with $BC$;
therefore $BC$ is incommensurable in length with $FD$,
so that $BC$ is also incommensurable with the remainder, the sum of $BF$, $DC$. [x. 16]
But the sum of $BF$, $DC$ is commensurable in length with $DC$; [x. 6]
therefore $BC$ is also incommensurable in length with $DC$, [x. 13]
so that, *separando*, $BD$ is also incommensurable in length with $DC$. [x. 16]
Therefore etc. Q. E. D.

## Lemma

Since it has been proved that straight lines commensurable in length are always commensurable in square also, while those commensurable in square are not always commensurable in length also, but can of course be either commensurable or incommensurable in length, it is manifest that, if any straight line be commensurable in length with a given rational straight line, it is called rational and commensurable with the other not only in length but in square also, since straight lines commensurable in length are always commensurable in square also.

But, if any straight line be commensurable in square with a given rational straight line, then, if it is also commensurable in length with it, it is called in this case also rational and commensurable with it both in length and in square; but, if again any straight line, being commensurable in square with a given rational straight line, be incommensurable in length with it, it is called in this case also rational but commensurable in square only.

## Proposition 19

*The rectangle contained by rational straight lines commensurable in length is rational.*

For let the rectangle $AC$ be contained by the rational straight lines $AB$, $BC$ commensurable in length;
I say that $AC$ is rational.
For on $AB$ let the square $AD$ be described;
therefore $AD$ is rational. [x. Def. 4]
And, since $AB$ is commensurable in length with $BC$,
while $AB$ is equal to $BD$,
therefore $BD$ is commensurable in length with $BC$.
And, as $BD$ is to $BC$, so is $DA$ to $AC$. [vi. 1]
Therefore $DA$ is commensurable with $AC$. [x. 11]
But $DA$ is rational;
therefore $AC$ is also rational. [x. Def. 4]
Therefore etc.
Q. E. D.

## Proposition 20

*If a rational area be applied to a rational straight line, it produces as breadth a straight line rational and commensurable in length with the straight line to which it is applied.*

For let the rational area $AC$ be applied to $AB$, a straight line once more rational in any of the aforesaid ways, producing $BC$ as breadth;
I say that $BC$ is rational and commensurable in length with $BA$.
For on $AB$ let the square $AD$ be described;
therefore $AD$ is rational. [x. Def. 4]
But $AC$ is also rational;
therefore $DA$ is commensurable with $AC$.
And, as $DA$ is to $AC$, so is $DB$ to $BC$. [vi. 1]
Therefore $DB$ is also commensurable with $BC$; [x. 11]
and $DB$ is equal to $BA$;
therefore $AB$ is also commensurable with $BC$.
But $AB$ is rational;
therefore $BC$ is also rational and commensurable in length with $AB$.
Therefore etc.
Q. E. D.

## Proposition 21

*The rectangle contained by rational straight lines commensurable in square only is irrational, and the side of the square equal to it is irrational. Let the latter be called* medial.

ELEMENTS X

For let the rectangle $AC$ be contained by the rational straight lines $AB$, $BC$ commensurable in square only;
I say that $AC$ is irrational, and the side of the square equal to it is irrational; and let the latter be called *medial*.

For on $AB$ let the square $AD$ be described;
therefore $AD$ is rational. [x. Def. 4]
And, since $AB$ is incommensurable in length with $BC$,
for by hypothesis they are commensurable in square only,
while $AB$ is equal to $BD$,
therefore $DB$ is also incommensurable in length with $BC$.
And, as $DB$ is to $BC$, so is $AD$ to $AC$; [vi. 1]
therefore $DA$ is incommensurable with $AC$. [x. 11]
But $DA$ is rational;
therefore $AC$ is irrational,
so that the side of the square equal to $AC$ is also irrational. [x. Def. 4]
And let the latter be called *medial*.    Q. E. D.

LEMMA

If there be two straight lines, then, as the first is to the second, so is the square on the first to the rectangle contained by the two straight lines.

Let $FE$, $EG$ be two straight lines.
I say that, as $FE$ is to $EG$, so is the square on $FE$ to the rectangle $FE$, $EG$.
For on $FE$ let the square $DF$ be described,
and let $GD$ be completed.
Since then, as $FE$ is to $EG$, so is $FD$ to $DG$, [vi. 1]
and $FD$ is the square on $FE$,
and $DG$ the rectangle $DE$, $EG$, that is, the rectangle $FE$, $EG$,
therefore, as $FE$ is to $EG$, so is the square on $FE$ to the rectangle $FE$, $EG$.
Similarly also, as the rectangle $GE$, $EF$ is to the square on $EF$, that is, as $GD$ is to $FD$, so is $GE$ to $EF$.    Q. E. D.

PROPOSITION 22

*The square on a medial straight line, if applied to a rational straight line, produces as breadth a straight line rational and incommensurable in length with that to which it is applied.*

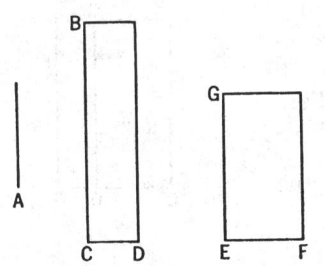

Let $A$ be medial and $CB$ rational,
and let a rectangular area $BD$ equal to the square on $A$ be applied to $BC$, producing $CD$ as breadth;
I say that $CD$ is rational and incommensurable in length with $CB$.
For, since $A$ is medial, the square on it is equal to a rectangular area contained by rational straight lines commensurable in square only. [x. 21]
Let the square on it be equal to $GF$.
But the square on it is also equal to $BD$;
therefore $BD$ is equal to $GF$.

But it is also equiangular with it;
and in equal and equiangular parallelograms the sides about the equal angles are reciprocally proportional; [VI. 14]
therefore, proportionally, as $BC$ is to $EG$, so is $EF$ to $CD$.
Therefore also, as the square on $BC$ is to the square on $EG$, so is the square on $EF$ to the square on $CD$. [VI. 22]
But the square on $CB$ is commensurable with the square on $EG$, for each of these straight lines is rational;
therefore the square on $EF$ is also commensurable with the square on $CD$.
[X. 11]
But the square on $EF$ is rational;
therefore the square on $CD$ is also rational; [X. Def. 4]
therefore $CD$ is rational.
And since $EF$ is incommensurable in length with $EG$,
for they are commensurable in square only,
and, as $EF$ is to $EG$, so is the square on $EF$ to the rectangle $FE$, $EG$, [Lemma]
therefore the square on $EF$ is incommensurable with the rectangle $FE$, $EG$.
[X. 11]
But the square on $CD$ is commensurable with the square on $EF$, for the straight lines are rational in square;
and the rectangle $DC$, $CB$ is commensurable with the rectangle $FE$, $EG$, for they are equal to the square on $A$;
therefore the square on $CD$ is also incommensurable with the rectangle $DC$, $CB$. [X. 13]
But, as the square on $CD$ is to the rectangle $DC$, $CB$, so is $DC$ to $CB$;
[Lemma]
therefore $DC$ is incommensurable in length with $CB$. [X. 11]
Therefore $CD$ is rational and incommensurable in length with $CB$.

Q. E. D.

## Proposition 23

*A straight line commensurable with a medial straight line is medial.*

Let $A$ be medial, and let $B$ be commensurable with $A$;
I say that $B$ is also medial.

For let a rational straight line $CD$ be set out,
and to $CD$ let the rectangular area $CE$ equal to the square on $A$ be applied, producing $ED$ as breadth; therefore $ED$ is rational and incommensurable in length with $CD$. [X. 22]

And let the rectangular area $CF$ equal to the square on $B$ be applied to $CD$, producing $DF$ as breadth.

Since, then, $A$ is commensurable with $B$,
the square on $A$ is also commensurable with the square on $B$.

But $EC$ is equal to the square on $A$,
and $CF$ is equal to the square on $B$;
therefore $EC$ is commensurable with $CF$.
And, as $EC$ is to $CF$, so is $ED$ to $DF$; [VI. 1]
therefore $ED$ is commensurable in length with $DF$. [X. 11]

# ELEMENTS X

But *ED* is rational and incommensurable in length with *DC*;
therefore *DF* is also rational [x. Def. 3] and incommensurable in length with *DC*. [x. 13]

Therefore *CD*, *DF* are rational and commensurable in square only.

But the straight line the square on which is equal to the rectangle contained by rational straight lines commensurable in square only is medial; [x. 21]
therefore the side of the square equal to the rectangle *CD*, *DF* is medial.

And *B* is the side of the square equal to the rectangle *CD*, *DF*;
therefore *B* is medial. Q. E. D.

PORISM. From this it is manifest that an area commensurable with a medial area is medial.

[And in the same way as was explained in the case of rationals [Lemma following x. 18] it follows, as regards medials, that a straight line commensurable in length with a medial straight line is called *medial* and commensurable with it not only in length but in square also, since, in general, straight lines commensurable in length are always commensurable in square also.

But, if any straight line be commensurable in square with a medial straight line, then, if it is also commensurable in length with it, the straight lines are called, in this case too, medial and commensurable in length and in square, but, if in square only, they are called medial straight lines commensurable in square only.]

## PROPOSITION 24

*The rectangle contained by medial straight lines commensurable in length is medial.*

For let the rectangle *AC* be contained by the medial straight lines *AB*, *BC* which are commensurable in length;

I say that *AC* is medial.

For on *AB* let the square *AD* be described;
therefore *AD* is medial.
And, since *AB* is commensurable in length with *BC*,
while *AB* is equal to *BD*,
therefore *DB* is also commensurable in length with *BC*;
so that *DA* is also commensurable with *AC*. [VI. 1, X. 11]
But *DA* is medial;
therefore *AC* is also medial. [x. 23, Por.]
Q. E. D.

## PROPOSITION 25

*The rectangle contained by medial straight lines commensurable in square only is either rational or medial.*

For let the rectangle *AC* be contained by the medial straight lines *AB*, *BC* which are commensurable in square only;

I say that *AC* is either rational or medial.

For on *AB*, *BC* let the squares *AD*, *BE* be described;
therefore each of the squares *AD*, *BE* is medial.

Let a rational straight line *FG* be set out,
to *FG* let there be applied the rectangular parallelogram *GH* equal to *AD*, producing *FH* as breadth,
to *HM* let there be applied the rectangular parallelogram *MK* equal to *AC*, producing *HK* as breadth,

and further to $KN$ let there be similarly applied $NL$ equal to $BE$, producing $KL$ as breadth;

therefore $FH, HK, KL$ are in a straight line.

Since then each of the squares $AD, BE$ is medial,

and $AD$ is equal to $GH$, and $BE$ to $NL$, therefore each of the rectangles $GH, NL$ is also medial.

And they are applied to the rational straight line $FG$;

therefore each of the straight lines $FH, KL$ is rational and incommensurable in length with $FG$. [x. 22]

And, since $AD$ is commensurable with $BE$,

therefore $GH$ is also commensurable with $NL$.

And, as $GH$ is to $NL$, so is $FH$ to $KL$; [vi. 1]

therefore $FH$ is commensurable in length with $KL$. [x. 11]

Therefore $FH, KL$ are rational straight lines commensurable in length;

therefore the rectangle $FH, KL$ is rational. [x. 19]

And, since $DB$ is equal to $BA$, and $OB$ to $BC$,

therefore, as $DB$ is to $BC$, so is $AB$ to $BO$.

But, as $DB$ is to $BC$, so is $DA$ to $AC$, [vi. 1]

and, as $AB$ is to $BO$, so is $AC$ to $CO$; [id.]

therefore, as $DA$ is to $AC$, so is $AC$ to $CO$.

But $AD$ is equal to $GH$, $AC$ to $MK$ and $CO$ to $NL$;

therefore, as $GH$ is to $MK$, so is $MK$ to $NL$;

therefore also, as $FH$ is to $HK$, so is $HK$ to $KL$; [vi. 1, v. 11]

therefore the rectangle $FH, KL$ is equal to the square on $HK$. [vi. 17]

But the rectangle $FH, KL$ is rational;

therefore the square on $HK$ is also rational.

Therefore $HK$ is rational.

And, if it is commensurable in length with $FG$,

$HN$ is rational; [x. 19]

but, if it is incommensurable in length with $FG$, $KH, HM$ are rational straight lines commensurable in square only, and therefore $HN$ is medial. [x. 21]

Therefore $HN$ is either rational or medial.

But $HN$ is equal to $AC$;

therefore $AC$ is either rational or medial.

Therefore etc.

Q. E. D.

## Proposition 26

*A medial area does not exceed a medial area by a rational area.*

For, if possible, let the medial area $AB$ exceed the medial area $AC$ by the rational area $DB$,

and let a rational straight line $EF$ be set out; to $EF$ let there be applied the rectangular parallelogram $FH$ equal to $AB$, producing $EH$ as breadth,

and let the rectangle $FG$ equal to $AC$ be subtracted;

therefore the remainder *BD* is equal to the remainder *KH*.
But *DB* is rational;
therefore *KH* is also rational.

Since, then, each of the rectangles *AB*, *AC* is medial,
and *AB* is equal to *FH*, and *AC* to *FG*,
therefore each of the rectangles *FH*, *FG* is also medial.

And they are applied to the rational straight line *EF*;
therefore each of the straight lines *HE*, *EG* is rational and incommensurable in length with *EF*. [x. 22]

And, since [*DB* is rational and is equal to *KH*,
therefore] *KH* is [also] rational;
and it is applied to the rational straight line *EF*;
therefore *GH* is rational and commensurable in length with *EF*. [x. 20]

But *EG* is also rational, and is incommensurable in length with *EF*;
therefore *EG* is incommensurable in length with *GH*. [x. 13]

And, as *EG* is to *GH*, so is the square on *EG* to the rectangle *EG*, *GH*;
therefore the square on *EG* is incommensurable with the rectangle *EG*, *GH*. [x. 11]

But the squares on *EG*, *GH* are commensurable with the square on *EG*, for both are rational;
and twice the rectangle *EG*, *GH* is commensurable with the rectangle *EG*, *GH*, for it is double of it; [x. 6]
therefore the squares on *EG*, *GH* are incommensurable with twice the rectangle *EG*, *GH*; [x. 13]
therefore also the sum of the squares on *EG*, *GH* and twice the rectangle *EG*, *GH*, that is, the square on *EH* [II. 4] is incommensurable with the squares on *EG*, *GH*. [x. 16]

But the squares on *EG*, *GH* are rational;
therefore the square on *EH* is irrational. [x. Def. 4]
Therefore *EH* is irrational.
But it is also rational:
which is impossible.

Therefore etc. Q. E. D.

## Proposition 27

*To find medial straight lines commensurable in square only which contain a rational rectangle.*

Let two rational straight lines *A*, *B* commensurable in square only be set out;
let *C* be taken a mean proportional between *A*, *B*, [VI. 13]
and let it be contrived that,
as *A* is to *B*, so is *C* to *D*. [VI. 12]

Then, since *A*, *B* are rational and commensurable in square only,
the rectangle *A*, *B*, that is, the square on *C* [VI. 17], is medial. [x. 21]

Therefore $C$ is medial. [x. 21]

And since, as $A$ is to $B$, so is $C$ to $D$,
and $A, B$ are commensurable in square only,
therefore $C, D$ are also commensurable in square only. [x. 11]
And $C$ is medial;
therefore $D$ is also medial. [x. 23, addition]
Therefore $C, D$ are medial and commensurable in square only.
I say that they also contain a rational rectangle.
For since, as $A$ is to $B$, so is $C$ to $D$,
therefore, alternately, as $A$ is to $C$, so is $B$ to $D$. [v. 16]
But, as $A$ is to $C$, so is $C$ to $B$;
therefore also, as $C$ is to $B$, so is $B$ to $D$;
therefore the rectangle $C, D$ is equal to the square on $B$.
But the square on $B$ is rational;
therefore the rectangle $C, D$ is also rational.

Therefore medial straight lines commensurable in square only have been found which contain a rational rectangle. Q. E. D.

## Proposition 28

*To find medial straight lines commensurable in square only, which contain a medial rectangle.*

Let the rational straight lines $A, B, C$ commensurable in square only be set out;
let $D$ be taken a mean proportional between $A, B$, [vi. 13]
and let it be contrived that,
as $B$ is to $C$, so is $D$ to $E$. [vi. 12]
Since $A, B$ are rational straight lines commensurable in square only, therefore the rectangle $A, B$, that is, the square on $D$ [vi. 17], is medial. [x. 21]

Therefore $D$ is medial. [x. 21]

And since $B, C$ are commensurable in square only,
and, as $B$ is to $C$, so is $D$ to $E$,
therefore $D, E$ are also commensurable in square only. [x. 11]
But $D$ is medial;
therefore $E$ is also medial. [x. 23, addition]
Therefore $D, E$ are medial straight lines commensurable in square only.
I say next that they also contain a medial rectangle.
For since, as $B$ is to $C$, so is $D$ to $E$,
therefore, alternately, as $B$ is to $D$, so is $C$ to $E$. [v. 16]
But, as $B$ is to $D$, so is $D$ to $A$;
therefore also, as $D$ is to $A$, so is $C$ to $E$;
therefore the rectangle $A, C$ is equal to the rectangle $D, E$. [vi. 16]
But the rectangle $A, C$ is medial; [x. 21]
therefore the rectangle $D, E$ is also medial.

Therefore medial straight lines commensurable in square only have been found which contain a medial rectangle. Q. E. D.

ELEMENTS X                     213

## Lemma 1

*To find two square numbers such that their sum is also square.*

Let two numbers $AB$, $BC$ be set out, and let them be either both even or both odd.

```
+--------+----+----+
A        D    C    B
```

Then since, whether an even number is subtracted from an even number, or an odd number from an odd number, the remainder is even, [IX. 24, 26] therefore the remainder $AC$ is even.

Let $AC$ be bisected at $D$.

Let $AB$, $BC$ also be either similar plane numbers, or square numbers, which are themselves also similar plane numbers.

Now the product of $AB$, $BC$ together with the square on $CD$ is equal to the square on $BD$.                                                    [II. 6]

And the product of $AB$, $BC$ is square, inasmuch as it was proved that, if two similar plane numbers by multiplying one another make some number, the product is square.                                                [IX. 1]

Therefore two square numbers, the product of $AB$, $BC$, and the square on $CD$, have been found which, when added together, make the square on $BD$.

And it is manifest that two square numbers, the square on $BD$ and the square on $CD$, have again been found such that their difference, the product of $AB$, $BC$, is a square, whenever $AB$, $BC$ are similar plane numbers.

But when they are not similar plane numbers, two square numbers, the square on $BD$ and the square on $DC$, have been found such that their difference, the product of $AB$, $BC$, is not square.         Q. E. D.

## Lemma 2

*To find two square numbers such that their sum is not square.*

For let the product of $AB$, $BC$, as we said, be square,
and $CA$ even,
and let $CA$ be bisected by $D$.

It is then manifest that the square product of $AB$, $BC$ together with the square on $CD$ is equal to the square on $BD$.
[See Lemma 1]

Let the unit $DE$ be subtracted;
therefore the product of $AB$, $BC$ together with the square on $CE$ is less than the square on $BD$.

I say then that the square product of $AB$, $BC$ together with the square on $CE$ will not be square.

For, if it is square, it is either equal to the square on $BE$, or less than the square on $BE$, but cannot any more be greater, lest the unit be divided.

First, if possible, let the product of $AB$, $BC$ together with the square on $CE$ be equal to the square on $BE$,
and let $GA$ be double of the unit $DE$.
Since then the whole $AC$ is double of the whole $CD$,
and in them $AG$ is double of $DE$,
therefore the remainder $GC$ is also double of the remainder $EC$;
therefore $GC$ is bisected by $E$.

214                                    EUCLID

Therefore the product of *GB*, *BC* together with the square on *CE* is equal to the square on *BE*.                                                                        [II. 6]

But the product of *AB*, *BC* together with the square on *CE* is also, by hypothesis, equal to the square on *BE*;

therefore the product of *GB*, *BC* together with the square on *CE* is equal to the product of *AB*, *BC* together with the square on *CE*.

And, if the common square on *CE* be subtracted,

it follows that *AB* is equal to *GB*:

which is absurd.

Therefore the product of *AB*, *BC* together with the square on *CE* is not equal to the square on *BE*.

I say next that neither is it less than the square on *BE*.

For, if possible, let it be equal to the square on *BF*,

and let *HA* be double of *DF*.

Now it will again follow that *HC* is double of *CF*;

so that *CH* has also been bisected at *F*,

and for this reason the product of *HB*, *BC* together with the square on *FC* is equal to the square on *BF*.                                                               [II. 6]

But, by hypothesis, the product of *AB*, *BC* together with the square on *CE* is also equal to the square on *BF*.

Thus the product of *HB*, *BC* together with the square on *CF* will also be equal to the product of *AB*, *BC* together with the square on *CE*:

which is absurd.

Therefore the product of *AB*, *BC* together with the square on *CE* is not less than the square on *BE*.

And it was proved that neither is it equal to the square on *BE*.

Therefore the product of *AB*, *BC* together with the square on *CE* is not square.

Q. E. D.

## Proposition 29

*To find two rational straight lines commensurable in square only and such that the square on the greater is greater than the square on the less by the square on a straight line commensurable in length with the greater.*

For let there be set out any rational straight line *AB*, and two square numbers *CD*, *DE* such that their difference *CE* is not square;                   [Lemma 1]

let there be described on *AB* the semicircle *AFB*,

and let it be contrived that,

as *DC* is to *CE*, so is the square on *BA* to the square on *AF*.                  [x. 6, Por.]

Let *FB* be joined.

Since, as the square on *BA* is to the square on *AF*, so is *DC* to *CE*,

therefore the square on *BA* has to the square on *AF* the ratio which the number *DC* has to the number *CE*;

therefore the square on *BA* is commensurable with the square on *AF*.                                                                          [x. 6]

But the square on *AB* is rational;           [x. Def. 4]

therefore the square on *AF* is also rational;                                                                  [*id.*]

therefore *AF* is also rational.

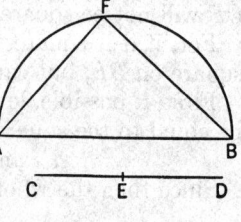

ELEMENTS X

And, since $DC$ has not to $CE$ the ratio which a square number has to a square number,
neither has the square on $BA$ to the square on $AF$ the ratio which a square number has to a square number;
therefore $AB$ is incommensurable in length with $AF$.   [x. 9]
Therefore $BA$, $AF$ are rational straight lines commensurable in square only.

And since, as $DC$ is to $CE$, so is the square on $BA$ to the square on $AF$, therefore, *convertendo*, as $CD$ is to $DE$, so is the square on $AB$ to the square on $BF$.   [v. 19, Por., III. 31, I. 47]

But $CD$ has to $DE$ the ratio which a square number has to a square number:
therefore also the square on $AB$ has to the square on $BF$ the ratio which a square number has to a square number;
therefore $AB$ is commensurable in length with $BF$.   [x. 9]

And the square on $AB$ is equal to the squares on $AF$, $FB$;
therefore the square on $AB$ is greater than the square on $AF$ by the square on $BF$ commensurable with $AB$.

Therefore there have been found two rational straight lines $BA$, $AF$ commensurable in square only and such that the square on the greater $AB$ is greater than the square on the less $AF$ by the square on $BF$ commensurable in length with $AB$.   Q. E. D.

PROPOSITION 30

*To find two rational straight lines commensurable in square only and such that the square on the greater is greater than the square on the less by the square on a straight line incommensurable in length with the greater.*

Let there be set out a rational straight line $AB$,

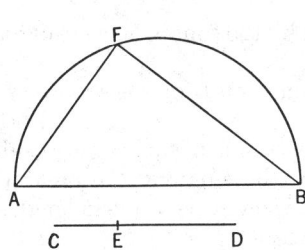

and two square numbers $CE$, $ED$ such that their sum $CD$ is not square;   [Lemma 2]
let there be described on $AB$ the semicircle $AFB$,
let it be contrived that,
as $DC$ is to $CE$, so is the square on $BA$ to the square on $AF$.   [x. 6, Por.]
and let $FB$ be joined.

Then, in a similar manner to the preceding, we can prove that $BA$, $AF$ are rational straight lines commensurable in square only.

And since, as $DC$ is to $CE$, so is the square on $BA$ to the square on $AF$, therefore, *convertendo*, as $CD$ is to $DE$, so is the square on $AB$ to the square on $BF$.   [v. 19, Por., III. 31, I. 47]

But $CD$ has not to $DE$ the ratio which a square number has to a square number;
therefore neither has the square on $AB$ to the square on $BF$ the ratio which a square number has to a square number;
therefore $AB$ is incommensurable in length with $BF$.   [x. 9]

And the square on $AB$ is greater than the square on $AF$ by the square on $FB$ incommensurable with $AB$.

Therefore $AB$, $AF$ are rational straight lines commensurable in square only, and the square on $AB$ is greater than the square on $AF$ by the square on $FB$ incommensurable in length with $AB$.   Q. E. D.

## Proposition 31

*To find two medial straight lines commensurable in square only, containing a rational rectangle, and such that the square on the greater is greater than the square on the less by the square on a straight line commensurable in length with the greater.*

Let there be set out two rational straight lines $A$, $B$ commensurable in square only and such that the square on $A$, being the greater, is greater than the square on $B$ the less by the square on a straight line commensurable in length with $A$. [x. 29]

And let the square on $C$ be equal to the rectangle $A$, $B$.
Now the rectangle $A$, $B$ is medial; [x. 21]
  therefore the square on $C$ is also medial;
   therefore $C$ is also medial. [x. 21]
Let the rectangle $C$, $D$ be equal to the square on $B$.
Now the square on $B$ is rational;
   therefore the rectangle $C$, $D$ is also rational.
And since, as $A$ is to $B$, so is the rectangle $A$, $B$ to the square on $B$,
  while the square on $C$ is equal to the rectangle $A$, $B$,
  and the rectangle $C$, $D$ is equal to the square on $B$,
 therefore, as $A$ is to $B$, so is the square on $C$ to the rectangle $C$, $D$.
But, as the square on $C$ is to the rectangle $C$, $D$, so is $C$ to $D$;
  therefore also, as $A$ is to $B$, so is $C$ to $D$.
But $A$ is commensurable with $B$ in square only;
 therefore $C$ is also commensurable with $D$ in square only. [x. 11]
And $C$ is medial;
   therefore $D$ is also medial. [x. 23, addition]
And since, as $A$ is to $B$, so is $C$ to $D$,
and the square on $A$ is greater than the square on $B$ by the square on a straight line commensurable with $A$,
therefore also the square on $C$ is greater than the square on $D$ by the square on a straight line commensurable with $C$. [x. 14]

Therefore two medial straight lines $C$, $D$, commensurable in square only and containing a rational rectangle, have been found, and the square on $C$ is greater than the square on $D$ by the square on a straight line commensurable in length with $C$.

Similarly also it can be proved that the square on $C$ exceeds the square on $D$ by the square on a straight line incommensurable with $C$, when the square on $A$ is greater than the square on $B$ by the square on a straight line incommensurable with $A$. [x. 30]

## Proposition 32

*To find two medial straight lines commensurable in square only, containing a medial rectangle, and such that the square on the greater is greater than the square on the less by the square on a straight line commensurable with the greater.*

Let there be set out three rational straight lines $A$, $B$, $C$ commensurable in square only, and such that the square on $A$ is greater than the square on $C$ by the square on a straight line commensurable with $A$, [x. 29]
  and let the square on $D$ be equal to the rectangle $A$, $B$.
Therefore the square on $D$ is medial;

ELEMENTS X

therefore $D$ is also medial. [x. 21]

Let the rectangle $D$, $E$ be equal to the rectangle $B$, $C$.

A————————

B————————

C————

D————————

E————————

Then since, as the rectangle $A$, $B$ is to the rectangle $B$, $C$, so is $A$ to $C$;
while the square on $D$ is equal to the rectangle $A$, $B$,
and the rectangle $D$, $E$ is equal to the rectangle $B$, $C$,
therefore, as $A$ is to $C$, so is the square on $D$ to the rectangle $D$, $E$.
But, as the square on $D$ is to the rectangle $D$, $E$, so is $D$ to $E$;
therefore also, as $A$ is to $C$, so is $D$ to $E$.
But $A$ is commensurable with $C$ in square only;
therefore $D$ is also commensurable with $E$ in square only. [x. 11]
But $D$ is medial;
therefore $E$ is also medial. [x. 23, addition]
And, since, as $A$ is to $C$, so is $D$ to $E$,
while the square on $A$ is greater than the square on $C$ by the square on a straight line commensurable with $A$,
therefore also the square on $D$ will be greater than the square on $E$ by the square on a straight line commensurable with $D$. [x. 14]
I say next that the rectangle $D$, $E$ is also medial.
For, since the rectangle $B$, $C$ is equal to the rectangle $D$, $E$, while the rectangle $B$, $C$ is medial, [x. 21]
therefore the rectangle $D$, $E$ is also medial.
Therefore two medial straight lines $D$, $E$, commensurable in square only, and containing a medial rectangle, have been found such that the square on the greater is greater than the square on the less by the square on a straight line commensurable with the greater.
Similarly again it can be proved that the square on $D$ is greater than the square on $E$ by the square on a straight line incommensurable with $D$, when the square on $A$ is greater than the square on $C$ by the square on a straight line incommensurable with $A$. [x. 30]

LEMMA

Let $ABC$ be a right-angled triangle having the angle $A$ right, and let the perpendicular $AD$ be drawn;

I say that the rectangle $CB$, $BD$ is equal to the square on $BA$,
the rectangle $BC$, $CD$ equal to the square on $CA$,
the rectangle $BD$, $DC$ equal to the square on $AD$,
and, further, the rectangle $BC$, $AD$ equal to the rectangle $BA$, $AC$.

And first that the rectangle $CB$, $BD$ is equal to the square on $BA$.
For, since in a right-angled triangle $AD$ has been drawn from the right angle perpendicular to the base,
therefore the triangles $ABD$, $ADC$ are similar both to the whole $ABC$ and to one another. [VI. 8]
And since the triangle $ABC$ is similar to the triangle $ABD$, therefore, as $CB$ is to $BA$, so is $BA$ to $BD$; [VI. 4]

218                                EUCLID

therefore the rectangle $CB$, $BD$ is equal to the square on $AB$. [vi. 17]

For the same reason the rectangle $BC$, $CD$ is also equal to the square on $AC$.

And since, if in a right-angled triangle a perpendicular be drawn from the right angle to the base, the perpendicular so drawn is a mean proportional between the segments of the base, [vi. 8, Por.]

therefore, as $BD$ is to $DA$, so is $AD$ to $DC$;

therefore the rectangle $BD$, $DC$ is equal to the square on $AD$. [vi. 17]

I say that the rectangle $BC$, $AD$ is also equal to the rectangle $BA$, $AC$.

For since, as we said, $ABC$ is similar to $ABD$,

therefore, as $BC$ is to $CA$, so is $BA$ to $AD$. [vi. 4]

Therefore the rectangle $BC$, $AD$ is equal to the rectangle $BA$, $AC$. [vi. 16]

Q. E. D.

## Proposition 33

*To find two straight lines incommensurable in square which make the sum of the squares on them rational but the rectangle contained by them medial.*

Let there be set out two rational straight lines $AB$, $BC$ commensurable in square only and such that the square on the greater $AB$ is greater than the square on the less $BC$ by the square on a straight line incommensurable with $AB$, [x. 30]

let $BC$ be bisected at $D$,

let there be applied to $AB$ a parallelogram equal to the square on either of the

straight lines $BD$, $DC$ and deficient by a square figure, and let it be the rectangle $AE$, $EB$; [vi. 28]

let the semicircle $AFB$ be described on $AB$,

let $EF$ be drawn at right angles to $AB$,

and let $AF$, $FB$ be joined.

Then, since $AB$, $BC$ are unequal straight lines,

and the square on $AB$ is greater than the square on $BC$ by the square on a straight line incommensurable with $AB$,

while there has been applied to $AB$ a parallelogram equal to the fourth part of the square on $BC$, that is, to the square on half of it, and deficient by a square figure, making the rectangle $AE$, $EB$,

therefore $AE$ is incommensurable with $EB$. [x. 18]

And, as $AE$ is to $EB$, so is the rectangle $BA$, $AE$ to the rectangle $AB$, $BE$,

while the rectangle $BA$, $AE$ is equal to the square on $AF$,

and the rectangle $AB$, $BE$ to the square on $BF$;

therefore the square on $AF$ is incommensurable with the square on $FB$;

therefore $AF$, $FB$ are incommensurable in square.

And, since $AB$ is rational,

therefore the square on $AB$ is also rational;

so that the sum of the squares on $AF$, $FB$ is also rational. [i. 47]

And since, again, the rectangle $AE$, $EB$ is equal to the square on $EF$,

and, by hypothesis, the rectangle $AE$, $EB$ is also equal to the square on $BD$,

therefore $FE$ is equal to $BD$;

therefore $BC$ is double of $FE$,

so that the rectangle $AB$, $BC$ is also commensurable with the rectangle $AB$, $EF$.

But the rectangle $AB$, $BC$ is medial; [x. 21]
therefore the rectangle $AB$, $EF$ is also medial. [x. 23, Por.]
But the rectangle $AB$, $EF$ is equal to the rectangle $AF$, $FB$; [Lemma]
therefore the rectangle $AF$, $FB$ is also medial.

But it was also proved that the sum of the squares on these straight lines is rational.

Therefore two straight lines $AF$, $FB$ incommensurable in square have been found which make the sum of the squares on them rational, but the rectangle contained by them medial.
Q. E. D.

## Proposition 34

*To find two straight lines incommensurable in square which make the sum of the squares on them medial but the rectangle contained by them rational.*

Let there be set out two medial straight lines $AB$, $BC$, commensurable in square only, such that the rectangle which they contain is rational, and the square on $AB$ is greater than the square on $BC$ by the square on a straight line incommensurable with $AB$; [x. 31, *ad fin.*]
let the semicircle $ADB$ be described on $AB$,
let $BC$ be bisected at $E$,
let there be applied to $AB$ a parallelogram equal to the square on $BE$ and deficient by a square figure, namely the rectangle $AF$, $FB$; [vi. 28]
therefore $AF$ is incommensurable in length with $FB$. [x. 18]
Let $FD$ be drawn from $F$ at right angles to $AB$,
and let $AD$, $DB$ be joined.

Since $AF$ is incommensurable in length with $FB$,
therefore the rectangle $BA$, $AF$ is also incommensurable with the rectangle $AB$, $BF$. [x. 11]
But the rectangle $BA$, $AF$ is equal to the square on $AD$, and the rectangle $AB$, $BF$ to the square on $DB$;
therefore the square on $AD$ is also incommensurable with the square on $DB$.

And, since the square on $AB$ is medial,
therefore the sum of the squares on $AD$, $DB$ is also medial. [iii. 31, i. 47]
And, since $BC$ is double of $DF$,
therefore the rectangle $AB$, $BC$ is also double of the rectangle $AB$, $FD$.
But the rectangle $AB$, $BC$ is rational;
therefore the rectangle $AB$, $FD$ is also rational. [x. 6]
But the rectangle $AB$, $FD$ is equal to the rectangle $AD$, $DB$; [Lemma]
so that the rectangle $AD$, $DB$ is also rational.

Therefore two straight lines $AD$, $DB$ incommensurable in square have been found which make the sum of the squares on them medial, but the rectangle contained by them rational.
Q. E. D.

## Proposition 35

*To find two straight lines incommensurable in square which make the sum of the squares on them medial and the rectangle contained by them medial and moreover incommensurable with the sum of the squares on them.*

Let there be set out two medial straight lines $AB$, $BC$ commensurable in square only, containing a medial rectangle, and such that the square on $AB$ is greater than the square on $BC$ by the square on a straight line incommensurable with $AB$; [x. 32, *ad fin.*]
let the semicircle $ADB$ be described on $AB$,
and let the rest of the construction be as above.

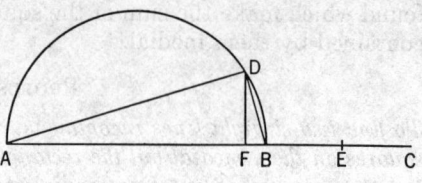

Then, since $AF$ is incommensurable in length with $FB$, [x. 18]
$AD$ is also incommensurable in square with $DB$. [x. 11]

And, since the square on $AB$ is medial,
therefore the sum of the squares on $AD$, $DB$ is also medial. [III. 31, I. 47]

And, since the rectangle $AF$, $FB$ is equal to the square on each of the straight lines $BE$, $DF$,
therefore $BE$ is equal to $DF$;
therefore $BC$ is double of $FD$,
so that the rectangle $AB$, $BC$ is also double of the rectangle $AB$, $FD$.

But the rectangle $AB$, $BC$ is medial;
therefore the rectangle $AB$, $FD$ is also medial. [x. 32, Por.]
And it is equal to the rectangle $AD$, $DB$; [Lemma after x. 32]
therefore the rectangle $AD$, $DB$ is also medial.

And, since $AB$ is incommensurable in length with $BC$,
while $CB$ is commensurable with $BE$,
therefore $AB$ is also incommensurable in length with $BE$, [x. 13]
so that the square on $AB$ is also incommensurable with the rectangle $AB$, $BE$. [x. 11]

But the squares on $AD$, $DB$ are equal to the square on $AB$, [I. 47]
and the rectangle $AB$, $FD$, that is, the rectangle $AD$, $DB$, is equal to the rectangle $AB$, $BE$;
therefore the sum of the squares on $AD$, $DB$ is incommensurable with the rectangle $AD$, $DB$.

Therefore two straight lines $AD$, $DB$ incommensurable in square have been found which make the sum of the squares on them medial and the rectangle contained by them medial and moreover incommensurable with the sum of the squares on them.
Q. E. D.

## PROPOSITION 36

*If two rational straight lines commensurable in square only be added together, the whole is irrational; and let it be called* binomial.

For let two rational straight lines $AB$, $BC$ commensurable in square only be added together;
I say that the whole $AC$ is irrational.

For, since $AB$ is incommensurable in length with $BC$—for they are commensurable in square only—
and, as $AB$ is to $BC$, so is the rectangle $AB$, $BC$ to the square on $BC$,
therefore the rectangle $AB$, $BC$ is incommensurable with the square on $BC$. [x. 11]

ELEMENTS X

But twice the rectangle $AB$, $BC$ is commensurable with the rectangle $AB$, $BC$ [x. 6], and the squares on $AB$, $BC$ are commensurable with the square on $BC$—for $AB$, $BC$ are rational straight lines commensurable in square only— [x. 15]
therefore twice the rectangle $AB$, $BC$ is incommensurable with the squares on $AB$, $BC$. [x. 13]

And, *componendo*, twice the rectangle $AB$, $BC$ together with the squares on $AB$, $BC$, that is, the square on $AC$ [ii. 4], is incommensurable with the sum of the squares on $AB$, $BC$. [x. 16]

But the sum of the squares on $AB$, $BC$ is rational;
therefore the square on $AC$ is irrational,
so that $AC$ is also irrational. [x. Def. 4]
And let it be called *binomial*. Q. E. D.

## Proposition 37

*If two medial straight lines commensurable in square only and containing a rational rectangle be added together, the whole is irrational; and let it be called a* first bimedial *straight line.*

For let two medial straight lines $AB$, $BC$ commensurable in square only and containing a rational rectangle be added together;
I say that the whole $AC$ is irrational.

For, since $AB$ is incommensurable in length with $BC$,
therefore the squares on $AB$, $BC$ are also incommensurable with twice the rectangle $AB$, $BC$; [cf. x. 36, ll. 9–20]
and, *componendo*, the squares on $AB$, $BC$ together with twice the rectangle $AB$, $BC$, that is, the square on $AC$ [ii. 4], is incommensurable with the rectangle $AB$, $BC$. [x. 16]

But the rectangle $AB$, $BC$ is rational, for, by hypothesis, $AB$, $BC$ are straight lines containing a rational rectangle;
therefore the square on $AC$ is irrational;
therefore $AC$ is irrational. [x. Def. 4]
And let it be called a *first bimedial* straight line. Q. E. D.

## Proposition 38

*If two medial straight lines commensurable in square only and containing a medial rectangle be added together, the whole is irrational; and let it be called a* second bimedial *straight line.*

For let two medial straight lines $AB$, $BC$ commensurable in square only and containing a medial rectangle be added together;
I say that $AC$ is irrational.

For let a rational straight line $DE$ be set out, and let the parallelogram $DF$ equal to the square on $AC$ be applied to $DE$, producing $DG$ as breadth. [i. 44]

Then, since the square on $AC$ is equal to the squares on $AB$, $BC$ and twice the rectangle $AB$, $BC$, [ii. 4]
let $EH$, equal to the squares on $AB$, $BC$, be applied to $DE$;

therefore the remainder $HF$ is equal to twice the rectangle $AB$, $BC$.

And, since each of the straight lines $AB$, $BC$ is medial,
therefore the squares on $AB$, $BC$ are also medial.
But, by hypothesis, twice the rectangle $AB$, $BC$ is also medial.
And $EH$ is equal to the squares on $AB$, $BC$,
while $FH$ is equal to twice the rectangle $AB$, $BC$;
therefore each of the rectangles $EH$, $HF$ is medial.

And they are applied to the rational straight line $DE$;
therefore each of the straight lines $DH$, $HG$ is rational and incommensurable in length with $DE$. [x. 22]

Since then $AB$ is incommensurable in length with $BC$,
and, as $AB$ is to $BC$, so is the square on $AB$ to the rectangle $AB$, $BC$,
therefore the square on $AB$ is incommensurable with the rectangle $AB$, $BC$. [x. 11]

But the sum of the squares on $AB$, $BC$ is commensurable with the square on $AB$, [x. 15]
and twice the rectangle $AB$, $BC$ is commensurable with the rectangle $AB$, $BC$. [x. 6]

Therefore the sum of the squares on $AB$, $BC$ is incommensurable with twice the rectangle $AB$, $BC$. [x. 13]

But $EH$ is equal to the squares on $AB$, $BC$,
and $HF$ is equal to twice the rectangle $AB$, $BC$.
Therefore $EH$ is incommensurable with $HF$,
so that $DH$ is also incommensurable in length with $HG$. [vi. 1, x. 11]
Therefore $DH$, $HG$ are rational straight lines commensurable in square only;
so that $DG$ is irrational. [x. 36]

But $DE$ is rational;
and the rectangle contained by an irrational and a rational straight line is irrational; [cf. x. 20]
therefore the area $DF$ is irrational,
and the side of the square equal to it is irrational. [x. Def. 4]

But $AC$ is the side of the square equal to $DF$;
therefore $AC$ is irrational.

And let it be called a *second bimedial* straight line. Q. E. D.

## Proposition 39

*If two straight lines incommensurable in square which make the sum of the squares on them rational, but the rectangle contained by them medial, be added together, the whole straight line is irrational: and let it be called* major.

For let two straight lines $AB$, $BC$ incommensurable in square, and fulfilling the given conditions [x. 33], be added together;
I say that $AC$ is irrational.

For, since the rectangle $AB$, $BC$ is medial,
twice the rectangle $AB$, $BC$ is also medial. [x. 6 and 23, Por.]
But the sum of the squares on $AB$, $BC$ is rational;
therefore twice the rectangle $AB$, $BC$ is incommensurable with the sum of the squares on $AB$, $BC$,
so that the squares on $AB$, $BC$ together with twice the rectangle $AB$, $BC$, that

is, the square on $AC$, is also incommensurable with the sum of the squares on $AB$, $BC$; [x. 16]

therefore the square on $AC$ is irrational,

so that $AC$ is also irrational. [x. Def. 4]

And let it be called *major*.
Q. E. D.

## Proposition 40

*If two straight lines incommensurable in square which make the sum of the squares on them medial, but the rectangle contained by them rational, be added together, the whole straight line is irrational; and let it be called the* side of a rational plus a medial area.

For let two straight lines $AB$, $BC$ incommensurable in square, and fulfilling the given conditions [x. 34], be added together;

I say that $AC$ is irrational.

For, since the sum of the squares on $AB$, $BC$ is medial, while twice the rectangle $AB$, $BC$ is rational,

therefore the sum of the squares on $AB$, $BC$ is incommensurable with twice the rectangle $AB$, $BC$;

so that the square on $AC$ is also incommensurable with twice the rectangle $AB$, $BC$. [x. 16]

But twice the rectangle $AB$, $BC$ is rational;

therefore the square on $AC$ is irrational.

Therefore $AC$ is irrational. [x. Def. 4]

And let it be called the *side of a rational plus a medial area*. Q. E. D.

## Proposition 41

*If two straight lines incommensurable in square which make the sum of the squares on them medial, and the rectangle contained by them medial and also incommensurable with the sum of the squares on them, be added together, the whole straight line is irrational; and let it be called the* side of the sum of two medial areas.

For let two straight lines $AB$, $BC$ incommensurable in square and satisfying the given conditions [x. 35] be added together;

I say that $AC$ is irrational.

Let a rational straight line $DE$ be set out, and let there be applied to $DE$ the rectangle $DF$ equal to the squares on $AB$, $BC$, and the rectangle $GH$ equal to twice the rectangle $AB$, $BC$;

therefore the whole $DH$ is equal to the square on $AC$. [II. 4]

Now, since the sum of the squares on $AB$, $BC$ is medial,

and is equal to $DF$,

therefore $DF$ is also medial.

And it is applied to the rational straight line $DE$;

therefore $DG$ is rational and incommensurable in length with $DE$. [x. 22]

For the same reason $GK$ is also rational and incommensurable in length with $GF$, that is, $DE$.

And, since the squares on $AB$, $BC$ are incommensurable with twice the rectangle $AB$, $BC$,

$DF$ is incommensurable with $GH$;

so that *DG* is also incommensurable with *GK*. [vi. 1, x. 11]

And they are rational;

therefore *DG*, *GK* are rational straight lines commensurable in square only;

therefore *DK* is irrational and what is called binomial. [x. 36]

But *DE* is rational;

therefore *DH* is irrational, and the side of the square which is equal to it is irrational. [x. Def. 4]

But *AC* is the side of the square equal to *HD*;

therefore *AC* is irrational.

And let it be called the *side of the sum of two medial areas*. Q. E. D.

### Lemma

And that the aforesaid irrational straight lines are divided only in one way into the straight lines of which they are the sum and which produce the types in question, we will now prove after premising the following lemma.

Let the straight line *AB* be set out, let the whole be cut into unequal parts at each of the points *C*, *D*,

and let *AC* be supposed greater than *DB*;

I say that the squares on *AC*, *CB* are greater than the squares on *AD*, *DB*.

For let *AB* be bisected at *E*.

Then, since *AC* is greater than *DB*,

let *DC* be subtracted from each;

therefore the remainder *AD* is greater than the remainder *CB*.

But *AE* is equal to *EB*;

therefore *DE* is less than *EC*;

therefore the points *C*, *D* are not equidistant from the point of bisection.

And, since the rectangle *AC*, *CB* together with the square on *EC* is equal to the square on *EB*, [ii. 5]

and, further, the rectangle *AD*, *DB* together with the square on *DE* is equal to the square on *EB*, [*id.*]

therefore the rectangle *AC*, *CB* together with the square on *EC* is equal to the rectangle *AD*, *DB* together with the square on *DE*.

And of these the square on *DE* is less than the square on *EC*;

therefore the remainder, the rectangle *AC*, *CB*, is also less than the rectangle *AD*, *DB*,

so that twice the rectangle *AC*, *CB* is also less than twice the rectangle *AD*, *DB*.

Therefore also the remainder, the sum of the squares on *AC*, *CB*, is greater than the sum of the squares on *AD*, *DB*. Q. E. D.

### Proposition 42

*A binomial straight line is divided into its terms at one point only.*

Let *AB* be a binomial straight line divided into its terms at *C*;

therefore *AC*, *CB* are rational straight lines commensurable in square only.

I say that *AB* is not divided at another point into two rational straight lines commensurable in square only.

ELEMENTS X

For, if possible, let it be divided at $D$ also, so that $AD$, $DB$ are also rational straight lines commensurable in square only.

It is then manifest that $AC$ is not the same with $DB$.

For, if possible, let it be so.

Then $AD$ will also be the same as $CB$,

and, as $AC$ is to $CB$, so will $BD$ be to $DA$;

thus $AB$ will be divided at $D$ also in the same way as by the division at $C$:

which is contrary to the hypothesis.

Therefore $AC$ is not the same with $DB$.

For this reason also the points $C$, $D$ are not equidistant from the point of bisection.

Therefore that by which the squares on $AC$, $CB$ differ from the squares on $AD$, $DB$ is also that by which twice the rectangle $AD$, $DB$ differs from twice the rectangle $AC$, $CB$,

because both the squares on $AC$, $CB$ together with twice the rectangle $AC$, $CB$, and the squares on $AD$, $DB$ together with twice the rectangle $AD$, $DB$, are equal to the square on $AB$. [II. 4]

But the squares on $AC$, $CB$ differ from the squares on $AD$, $DB$ by a rational area,

for both are rational;

therefore twice the rectangle $AD$, $DB$ also differs from twice the rectangle $AC$, $CB$ by a rational area, though they are medial [x. 21]:

which is absurd, for a medial area does not exceed a medial by a rational area.

[x. 26]

Therefore a binomial straight line is not divided at different points;

therefore it is divided at one point only.   Q. E. D.

## Proposition 43

*A first bimedial straight line is divided at one point only.*

Let $AB$ be a first bimedial straight line divided at $C$, so that $AC$, $CB$ are medial straight lines commensurable in square only and containing a rational rectangle; [x. 37]

I say that $AB$ is not so divided at another point.

For, if possible, let it be divided at $D$ also, so that $AD$, $DB$ are also medial straight lines commensurable in square only and containing a rational rectangle.

Since, then, that by which twice the rectangle $AD$, $DB$ differs from twice the rectangle $AC$, $CB$ is that by which the squares on $AC$, $CB$ differ from the squares on $AD$, $DB$,

while twice the rectangle $AD$, $DB$ differs from twice the rectangle $AC$, $CB$ by a rational area—for both are rational—

therefore the squares on $AC$, $CB$ also differ from the squares on $AD$, $DB$ by a rational area, though they are medial:

which is absurd. [x. 26]

Therefore a first bimedial straight line is not divided into its terms at different points;

therefore it is so divided at one point only.   Q. E. D.

## Proposition 44

*A second bimedial straight line is divided at one point only.*

Let $AB$ be a second bimedial straight line divided at $C$, so that $AC$, $CB$ are medial straight lines commensurable in square only and containing a medial rectangle; [x. 38]
it is then manifest that $C$ is not at the point of bisection, because the segments are not commensurable in length.

I say that $AB$ is not so divided at another point.

For, if possible, let it be divided at $D$ also, so that $AC$ is not the same with $DB$, but $AC$ is supposed greater;
it is then clear that the squares on $AD$, $DB$ are also, as we proved above [Lemma], less than the squares on $AC$, $CB$;
and suppose that $AD$, $DB$ are medial straight lines commensurable in square only and containing a medial rectangle.

Now let a rational straight line $EF$ be set out,
let there be applied to $EF$ the rectangular parallelogram $EK$ equal to the square on $AB$,

and let $EG$, equal to the squares on $AC$, $CB$, be subtracted;
therefore the remainder $HK$ is equal to twice the rectangle $AC$, $CB$. [II. 4]

Again, let there be subtracted $EL$, equal to the squares on $AD$, $DB$, which were proved less than the squares on $AC$, $CB$ [Lemma];
therefore the remainder $MK$ is also equal to twice the rectangle $AD$, $DB$.

Now, since the squares on $AC$, $CB$ are medial,
therefore $EG$ is medial.
And it is applied to the rational straight line $EF$;
therefore $EH$ is rational and incommensurable in length with $EF$. [x. 22]
For the same reason
$HN$ is also rational and incommensurable in length with $EF$.

And, since $AC$, $CB$ are medial straight lines commensurable in square only,
therefore $AC$ is incommensurable in length with $CB$.

But, as $AC$ is to $CB$, so is the square on $AC$ to the rectangle $AC$, $CB$;
therefore the square on $AC$ is incommensurable with the rectangle $AC$, $CB$.

[x. 11]

But the squares on $AC$, $CB$ are commensurable with the square on $AC$; for $AC$, $CB$ are commensurable in square. [x. 15]

And twice the rectangle $AC$, $CB$ is commensurable with the rectangle $AC$, $CB$. [x. 6]

Therefore the squares on $AC$, $CB$ are also incommensurable with twice the rectangle $AC$, $CB$. [x. 13]

But $EG$ is equal to the squares on $AC, CB$,
and $HK$ is equal to twice the rectangle $AC, CB$;
therefore $EG$ is incommensurable with $HK$,
so that $EH$ is also incommensurable in length with $HN$. [VI. 1, X. 11]
And they are rational;
therefore $EH, HN$ are rational straight lines commensurable in square only.

But, if two rational straight lines commensurable in square only be added together, the whole is the irrational which is called binomial. [X. 36]

Therefore $EN$ is a binomial straight line divided at $H$.

In the same way $EM, MN$ will also be proved to be rational straight lines commensurable in square only;
and $EN$ will be a binomial straight line divided at different points, $H$ and $M$.

And $EH$ is not the same with $MN$.

For the squares on $AC, CB$ are greater than the squares on $AD, DB$.

But the squares on $AD, DB$ are greater than twice the rectangle $AD, DB$;
therefore also the squares on $AC, CB$, that is, $EG$, are much greater than twice the rectangle $AD, DB$, that is, $MK$,
so that $EH$ is also greater than $MN$.

Therefore $EH$ is not the same with $MN$. Q. E. D.

## Proposition 45

*A major straight line is divided at one and the same point only.*

Let $AB$ be a major straight line divided at $C$, so that $AC, CB$ are incommensurable in square and make the sum of the squares on $AC, CB$ rational, but the rectangle $AC, CB$ medial;

I say that $AB$ is not so divided at another point.

For, if possible, let it be divided at $D$ also, so that $AD, DB$ are also incommensurable in square and make the sum of the squares on $AD, DB$ rational, but the rectangle contained by them medial.

Then, since that by which the squares on $AC, CB$ differ from the squares on $AD, DB$ is also that by which twice the rectangle $AD, DB$ differs from twice the rectangle $AC, CB$,
while the squares on $AC, CB$ exceed the squares on $AD, DB$ by a rational area
—for both are rational—
therefore twice the rectangle $AD, DB$ also exceeds twice the rectangle $AC, CB$ by a rational area, though they are medial:
which is impossible. [X. 26]

Therefore a major straight line is not divided at different points;
therefore it is only divided at one and the same point. Q. E. D.

## Proposition 46

*The side of a rational plus a medial area is divided at one point only.*

Let $AB$ be the side of a rational plus a medial area divided at $C$, so that $AC, CB$ are incommensurable in square and make the sum of the squares on $AC, CB$ medial, but twice the rectangle $AC, CB$ rational; [X. 40]

I say that $AB$ is not so divided at another point.

For, if possible, let it be divided at $D$ also, so that $AD, DB$ are also incommensurable in square and make the sum of the squares on $AD$, $DB$ medial, but twice the rectangle $AD$, $DB$ rational.

Since, then, that by which twice the rectangle $AC$, $CB$ differs from twice the rectangle $AD$, $DB$ is also that by which the squares on $AD$, $DB$ differ from the squares on $AC$, $CB$,
while twice the rectangle $AC$, $CB$ exceeds twice the rectangle $AD$, $DB$ by a rational area,
therefore the squares on $AD$, $DB$ also exceed the squares on $AC$, $CB$ by a rational area, though they are medial:

which is impossible. [x. 26]

Therefore the side of a rational plus a medial area is not divided at different points;
therefore it is divided at one point only. Q. E. D.

## Proposition 47

*The side of the sum of two medial areas is divided at one point only.*

Let $AB$ be divided at $C$, so that $AC$, $CB$ are incommensurable in square and make the sum of the squares on $AC$, $CB$ medial, and the rectangle $AC$, $CB$ medial and also incommensurable with the sum of the squares on them;

I say that $AB$ is not divided at another point so as to fulfil the given conditions.

For, if possible, let it be divided at $D$, so that again $AC$ is of course not the same as $BD$, but $AC$ is supposed greater;
let a rational straight line $EF$ be set out,
and let there be applied to $EF$ the rectangle $EG$ equal to the squares on $AC$, $CB$,
and the rectangle $HK$ equal to twice the rectangle $AC$, $CB$;
therefore the whole $EK$ is equal to the square on $AB$. [II. 4]

Again, let $EL$, equal to the squares on $AD$, $DB$, be applied to $EF$;
therefore the remainder, twice the rectangle $AD$, $DB$, is equal to the remainder $MK$.

And since, by hypothesis, the sum of the squares on $AC$, $CB$ is medial,
therefore $EG$ is also medial.

And it is applied to the rational straight line $EF$;
therefore $HE$ is rational and incommensurable in length with $EF$. [x. 22]
For the same reason
$HN$ is also rational and incommensurable in length with $EF$.

And, since the sum of the squares on $AC$, $CB$ is incommensurable with twice the rectangle $AC$, $CB$,
therefore $EG$ is also incommensurable with $GN$,
so that $EH$ is also incommensurable with $HN$. [VI. 1, X. 11]
And they are rational;
therefore $EH$, $HN$ are rational straight lines commensurable in square only;
therefore $EN$ is a binomial straight line divided at $H$. [x. 36]

Similarly we can prove that it is also divided at $M$.

And $EH$ is not the same with $MN$;

therefore a binomial has been divided at different points:

which is absurd. [x. 42]

Therefore a side of the sum of two medial areas is not divided at different points;

therefore it is divided at one point only.  Q. E. D.

## DEFINITIONS II

1. Given a rational straight line and a binomial, divided into its terms, such that the square on the greater term is greater than the square on the lesser by the square on a straight line commensurable in length with the greater, then, if the greater term be commensurable in length with the rational straight line set out, let the whole be called a *first binomial* straight line;

2. but if the lesser term be commensurable in length with the rational straight line set out, let the whole be called a *second binomial*;

3. and if neither of the terms be commensurable in length with the rational straight line set out, let the whole be called a *third binomial*.

4. Again, if the square on the greater term be greater than the square on the lesser by the square on a straight line incommensurable in length with the greater, then, if the greater term be commensurable in length with the rational straight line set out, let the whole be called a *fourth binomial*;

5. if the lesser, a *fifth binomial*;

6. and if neither, a *sixth binomial*.

## Proposition 48

*To find the first binomial straight line.*

Let two numbers $AC$, $CB$ be set out such that the sum of them $AB$ has to $BC$ the ratio which a square number has to a square number, but has not to $CA$ the ratio which a square number has to a square number; [Lemma 1 after x. 28] let any rational straight line $D$ be set out, and let $EF$ be commensurable in length with $D$.

Therefore $EF$ is also rational.

Let it be contrived that,

as the number $BA$ is to $AC$, so is the square on $EF$ to the square on $FG$.

[x. 6, Por.]

But $AB$ has to $AC$ the ratio which a number has to a number;

therefore the square on $EF$ also has to the square on $FG$ the ratio which a number has to a number,

so that the square on $EF$ is commensurable with the square on $FG$. [x. 6]

And $EF$ is rational;

therefore $FG$ is also rational.

And, since $BA$ has not to $AC$ the ratio which a square number has to a square number,

neither, therefore, has the square on $EF$ to the square on $FG$ the ratio which a square number has to a square number;

therefore $EF$ is incommensurable in length with $FG$. [x. 9]

230                                    EUCLID

Therefore $EF$, $FG$ are rational straight lines commensurable in square only;
therefore $EG$ is binomial. [x. 36]

I say that it is also a first binomial straight line.

For since, as the number $BA$ is to $AC$, so is the square on $EF$ to the square on $FG$,

while $BA$ is greater than $AC$,

therefore the square on $EF$ is also greater than the square on $FG$.

Let then the squares on $FG$, $H$ be equal to the square on $EF$.

Now since, as $BA$ is to $AC$, so is the square on $EF$ to the square on $FG$,
therefore, *convertendo*,
as $AB$ is to $BC$, so is the square on $EF$ to the square on $H$. [v. 19, Por.]

But $AB$ has to $BC$ the ratio which a square number has to a square number; therefore the square on $EF$ also has to the square on $H$ the ratio which a square number has to a square number.

Therefore $EF$ is commensurable in length with $H$; [x. 9]
therefore the square on $EF$ is greater than the square on $FG$ by the square on a straight line commensurable with $EF$.

And $EF$, $FG$ are rational, and $EF$ is commensurable in length with $D$.

Therefore $EF$ is a first binomial straight line.                Q. E. D.

## Proposition 49

*To find the second binomial straight line.*

Let two numbers $AC$, $CB$ be set out such that the sum of them $AB$ has to $BC$ the ratio which a square number has to a square number, but has not to $AC$ the ratio which a square number has to a square number;
let a rational straight line $D$ be set out, and let $EF$ be commensurable in length with $D$;
therefore $EF$ is rational.

Let it be contrived then that,
as the number $CA$ is to $AB$, so also is the square on $EF$ to the square on $FG$; [x. 6, Por.]
therefore the square on $EF$ is commensurable with the square on $FG$. [x. 6]

Therefore $FG$ is also rational.

Now, since the number $CA$ has not to $AB$ the ratio which a square number has to a square number, neither has the square on $EF$ to the square on $FG$ the ratio which a square number has to a square number.

Therefore $EF$ is incommensurable in length with $FG$; [x. 9]
therefore $EF$, $FG$ are rational straight lines commensurable in square only;
therefore $EG$ is binomial. [x. 36]

It is next to be proved that it is also a second binomial straight line.

For since, inversely, as the number $BA$ is to $AC$, so is the square on $GF$ to the square on $FE$,

while $BA$ is greater than $AC$,

therefore the square on $GF$ is greater than the square on $FE$.

Let the squares on $EF$, $H$ be equal to the square on $GF$;
therefore, *convertendo*, as $AB$ is to $BC$, so is the square on $FG$ to the square on $H$. [v. 19, Por.]

But $AB$ has to $BC$ the ratio which a square number has to a square number;

ELEMENTS X

therefore the square on $FG$ also has to the square on $H$ the ratio which a square number has to a square number.

Therefore $FG$ is commensurable in length with $H$; [x. 9]
so that the square on $FG$ is greater than the square on $FE$ by the square on a straight line commensurable with $FG$.

And $FG$, $FE$ are rational straight lines commensurable in square only, and $EF$, the lesser term, is commensurable in length with the rational straight line $D$ set out.

Therefore $EG$ is a second binomial straight line. Q. E. D.

PROPOSITION 50

*To find the third binomial straight line.*

Let two numbers $AC$, $CB$ be set out such that the sum of them $AB$ has to $BC$ the ratio which a square number has to a square number, but has not to $AC$ the ratio which a square number has to a square number.

Let any other number $D$, not square, be set out also, and let it not have to either of the numbers $BA$, $AC$ the ratio which a square number has to a square number.

Let any rational straight line $E$ be set out,
and let it be contrived that, as $D$ is to $AB$, so is the square on $E$ to the square on $FG$; [x. 6, Por.]
therefore the square on $E$ is commensurable with the square on $FG$. [x. 6]
And $E$ is rational;
therefore $FG$ is also rational.

And, since $D$ has not to $AB$ the ratio which a square number has to a square number,
neither has the square on $E$ to the square on $FG$ the ratio which a square number has to a square number;
therefore $E$ is incommensurable in length with $FG$. [x. 9]

Next let it be contrived that, as the number $BA$ is to $AC$, so is the square on $FG$ to the square on $GH$; [x. 6, Por.]
therefore the square on $FG$ is commensurable with the square on $GH$. [x. 6]
But $FG$ is rational;
therefore $GH$ is also rational.

And, since $BA$ has not to $AC$ the ratio which a square number has to a square number,
neither has the square on $FG$ to the square on $HG$ the ratio which a square number has to a square number;
therefore $FG$ is incommensurable in length with $GH$. [x. 9]

Therefore $FG$, $GH$ are rational straight lines commensurable in square only;
therefore $FH$ is binomial. [x. 36]

I say next that it is also a third binomial straight line.

For since, as $D$ is to $AB$, so is the square on $E$ to the square on $FG$,
and, as $BA$ is to $AC$, so is the square on $FG$ to the square on $GH$,
therefore, *ex aequali*, as $D$ is to $AC$, so is the square on $E$ to the square on $GH$.
[v. 22]

But $D$ has not to $AC$ the ratio which a square number has to a square number;

therefore neither has the square on $E$ to the square on $GH$ the ratio which a square number has to a square number;

therefore $E$ is incommensurable in length with $GH$.  [x. 9]

And since, as $BA$ is to $AC$, so is the square on $FG$ to the square on $GH$,

therefore the square on $FG$ is greater than the square on $GH$.

Let then the squares on $GH$, $K$ be equal to the square on $FG$;

therefore, *convertendo*, as $AB$ is to $BC$, so is the square on $FG$ to the square on $K$.  [v. 19, Por.]

But $AB$ has to $BC$ the ratio which a square number has to a square number;

therefore the square on $FG$ also has to the square on $K$ the ratio which a square number has to a square number;

therefore $FG$ is commensurable in length with $K$.  [x. 9]

Therefore the square on $FG$ is greater than the square on $GH$ by the square on a straight line commensurable with $FG$.

And $FG$, $GH$ are rational straight lines commensurable in square only, and neither of them is commensurable in length with $E$.

Therefore $FH$ is a third binomial straight line.  Q. E. D.

## Proposition 51

*To find the fourth binomial straight line.*

Let two numbers $AC$, $CB$ be set out such that $AB$ neither has to $BC$, nor yet to $AC$, the ratio which a square number has to a square number.

Let a rational straight line $D$ be set out,

and let $EF$ be commensurable in length with $D$;

therefore $EF$ is also rational.

Let it be contrived that, as the number $BA$ is to $AC$, so is the square on $EF$ to the square on $FG$;  [x. 6, Por.]

therefore the square on $EF$ is commensurable with the square on $FG$;  [x. 6]

therefore $FG$ is also rational.

Now, since $BA$ has not to $AC$ the ratio which a square number has to a square number,

neither has the square on $EF$ to the square on $FG$ the ratio which a square number has to a square number;

therefore $EF$ is incommensurable in length with $FG$.  [x. 9]

Therefore $EF$, $FG$ are rational straight lines commensurable in square only;

so that $EG$ is binomial.

I say next that it is also a fourth binomial straight line.

For since, as $BA$ is to $AC$, so is the square on $EF$ to the square on $FG$,

therefore the square on $EF$ is greater than the square on $FG$.

Let then the squares on $FG$, $H$ be equal to the square on $EF$;

therefore, *convertendo*, as the number $AB$ is to $BC$, so is the square on $EF$ to the square on $H$.  [v. 19, Por.]

But $AB$ has not to $BC$ the ratio which a square number has to a square number;

therefore neither has the square on $EF$ to the square on $H$ the ratio which a square number has to a square number.

Therefore $EF$ is incommensurable in length with $H$; [x. 9]
therefore the square on $EF$ is greater than the square on $GF$ by the square on a straight line incommensurable with $EF$.

And $EF$, $FG$ are rational straight lines commensurable in square only, and $EF$ is commensurable in length with $D$.

Therefore $EG$ is a fourth binomial straight line. Q. E. D.

## Proposition 52

*To find the fifth binomial straight line.*

Let two numbers $AC$, $CB$ be set out such that $AB$ has not to either of them the ratio which a square number has to a square number;
let any rational straight line $D$ be set out,
and let $EF$ be commensurable with $D$;
therefore $EF$ is rational.

Let it be contrived that, as $CA$ is to $AB$, so is the square on $EF$ to the square on $FG$. [x. 6, Por.]

But $CA$ has not to $AB$ the ratio which a square number has to a square number;
therefore neither has the square on $EF$ to the square on $FG$ the ratio which a square number has to a square number.

Therefore $EF$, $FG$ are rational straight lines commensurable in square only; [x. 9]

therefore $EG$ is binomial. [x. 36]

I say next that it is also a fifth binomial straight line.

For since, as $CA$ is to $AB$, so is the square on $EF$ to the square on $FG$, inversely, as $BA$ is to $AC$, so is the square on $FG$ to the square on $FE$;
therefore the square on $GF$ is greater than the square on $FE$.

Let then the squares on $EF$, $H$ be equal to the square on $GF$;
therefore, *convertendo*, as the number $AB$ is to $BC$, so is the square on $GF$ to the square on $H$. [v. 19, Por.]

But $AB$ has not to $BC$ the ratio which a square number has to a square number;
therefore neither has the square on $FG$ to the square on $H$ the ratio which a square number has to a square number.

Therefore $FG$ is incommensurable in length with $H$; [x. 9]
so that the square on $FG$ is greater than the square on $FE$ by the square on a straight line incommensurable with $FG$.

And $GF$, $FE$ are rational straight lines commensurable in square only, and the lesser term $EF$ is commensurable in length with the rational straight line $D$ set out.

Therefore $EG$ is a fifth binomial straight line. Q. E. D.

## Proposition 53

*To find the sixth binomial straight line.*

Let two numbers $AC$, $CB$ be set out such that $AB$ has not to either of them the ratio which a square number has to a square number;
and let there also be another number $D$ which is not square and which has not to either of the numbers $BA$, $AC$ the ratio which a square number has to a square number.

Let any rational straight line $E$ be set out,
and let it be contrived that, as $D$ is to $AB$, so is the square on $E$ to the square on $FG$; [x. 6, Por.]
therefore the square on $E$ is commensurable with the square on $FG$. [x. 6]

And $E$ is rational;
therefore $FG$ is also rational.

Now, since $D$ has not to $AB$ the ratio which a square number has to a square number,
neither has the square on $E$ to the square on $FG$ the ratio which a square number has to a square number;
therefore $E$ is incommensurable in length with $FG$. [x. 9]

Again, let it be contrived that, as $BA$ is to $AC$, so is the square on $FG$ to the square on $GH$. [x. 6, Por.]

Therefore the square on $FG$ is commensurable with the square on $HG$. [x. 6]
Therefore the square on $HG$ is rational;
therefore $HG$ is rational.

And, since $BA$ has not to $AC$ the ratio which a square number has to a square number,
neither has the square on $FG$ to the square on $GH$ the ratio which a square number has to a square number;
therefore $FG$ is incommensurable in length with $GH$. [x. 9]

Therefore $FG$, $GH$ are rational straight lines commensurable in square only;
therefore $FH$ is binomial. [x. 36]

It is next to be proved that it is also a sixth binomial straight line.

For since, as $D$ is to $AB$, so is the square on $E$ to the square on $FG$,
and also, as $BA$ is to $AC$, so is the square on $FG$ to the square on $GH$,
therefore, *ex aequali*, as $D$ is to $AC$, so is the square on $E$ to the square on $GH$. [v. 22]

But $D$ has not to $AC$ the ratio which a square number has to a square number;
therefore neither has the square on $E$ to the square on $GH$ the ratio which a square number has to a square number;
therefore $E$ is incommensurable in length with $GH$. [x. 9]

But it was also proved incommensurable with $FG$;
therefore each of the straight lines $FG$, $GH$ is incommensurable in length with $E$.

And, since, as $BA$ is to $AC$, so is the square on $FG$ to the square on $GH$,
therefore the square on $FG$ is greater than the square on $GH$.

Let then the squares on $GH$, $K$ be equal to the square on $FG$;
therefore, *convertendo*, as $AB$ is to $BC$, so is the square on $FG$ to the square on $K$. [v. 19, Por.]

But $AB$ has not to $BC$ the ratio which a square number has to a square number;
so that neither has the square on $FG$ to the square on $K$ the ratio which a square number has to a square number.

Therefore $FG$ is incommensurable in length with $K$; [x. 9]
therefore the square on $FG$ is greater than the square on $GH$ by the square on a straight line incommensurable with $FG$.

ELEMENTS X

And *FG, GH* are rational straight lines commensurable in square only, and neither of them is commensurable in length with the rational straight line *E* set out.

Therefore *FH* is a sixth binomial straight line.  Q. E. D.

## Lemma

Let there be two squares *AB, BC*, and let them be placed so that *DB* is in a straight line with *BE*;

therefore *FB* is also in a straight line with *BG*.

Let the parallelogram *AC* be completed;

I say that *AC* is a square, that *DG* is a mean proportional between *AB, BC*, and further that *DC* is a mean proportional between *AC, CB*.

For, since *DB* is equal to *BF*, and *BE* to *BG*,

therefore the whole *DE* is equal to the whole *FG*.

But *DE* is equal to each of the straight lines *AH, KC*, and *FG* is equal to each of the straight lines *AK, HC* [I. 34];

therefore each of the straight lines *AH, KC* is also equal to each of the straight lines *AK, HC*.

Therefore the parallelogram *AC* is equilateral.

And it is also rectangular;

therefore *AC* is a square.

And since, as *FB* is to *BG*, so is *DB* to *BE*,
while, as *FB* is to *BG*, so is *AB* to *DG*,
and, as *DB* is to *BE*, so is *DG* to *BC*, [VI. 1]
therefore also, as *AB* is to *DG*, so is *DG* to *BC*. [V. 11]

Therefore *DG* is a mean proportional between *AB, BC*.

I say next that *DC* is also a mean proportional between *AC, CB*.

For since, as *AD* is to *DK*, so is *KG* to *GC*—
for they are equal respectively—
and, *componendo*, as *AK* is to *KD*, so is *KC* to *CG*, [V. 18]
while, as *AK* is to *KD*, so is *AC* to *CD*,
and, as *KC* is to *CG*, so is *DC* to *CB*, [VI. 1]
therefore also, as *AC* is to *DC*, so is *DC* to *BC*. [V. 11]

Therefore *DC* is a mean proportional between *AC, CB*.

Being what it was proposed to prove.

## Proposition 54

*If an area be contained by a rational straight line and the first binomial, the "side" of the area is the irrational straight line which is called binomial.*

For let the area *AC* be contained by the rational straight line *AB* and the first binomial *AD*;

I say that the "side" of the area *AC* is the irrational straight line which is called binomial.

For, since *AD* is a first binomial straight line, let it be divided into its terms at *E*,

and let *AE* be the greater term.

It is then manifest that *AE, ED* are rational straight lines commensurable in square only,

the square on $AE$ is greater than the square on $ED$ by the square on a straight line commensurable with $AE$,
and $AE$ is commensurable in length with the rational straight line $AB$ set out.
[x. Deff. II. 1]

Let $ED$ be bisected at the point $F$.

 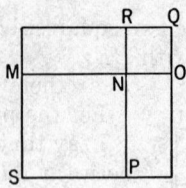

Then, since the square on $AE$ is greater than the square on $ED$ by the square on a straight line commensurable with $AE$,
therefore, if there be applied to the greater $AE$ a parallelogram equal to the fourth part of the square on the less, that is, to the square on $EF$, and deficient by a square figure, it divides it into commensurable parts. [x. 17]

Let then the rectangle $AG$, $GE$ equal to the square on $EF$ be applied to $AE$;
therefore $AG$ is commensurable in length with $EG$.

Let $GH$, $EK$, $FL$ be drawn from $G$, $E$, $F$ parallel to either of the straight lines $AB$, $CD$;
let the square $SN$ be constructed equal to the parallelogram $AH$, and the square $NQ$ equal to $GK$, [II. 14]
and let them be placed so that $MN$ is in a straight line with $NO$;
therefore $RN$ is also in a straight line with $NP$.

And let the parallelogram $SQ$ be completed;
therefore $SQ$ is a square. [Lemma]

Now, since the rectangle $AG$, $GE$ is equal to the square on $EF$,
therefore, as $AG$ is to $EF$, so is $FE$ to $EG$; [VI. 17]
therefore also, as $AH$ is to $EL$, so is $EL$ to $KG$; [VI. 1]
therefore $EL$ is a mean proportional between $AH$, $GK$.

But $AH$ is equal to $SN$, and $GK$ to $NQ$;
therefore $EL$ is a mean proportional between $SN$, $NQ$.

But $MR$ is also a mean proportional between the same $SN$, $NQ$; [Lemma]
therefore $EL$ is equal to $MR$,
so that it is also equal to $PO$.

But $AH$, $GK$ are also equal to $SN$, $NQ$;
therefore the whole $AC$ is equal to the whole $SQ$, that is, to the square on $MO$;
therefore $MO$ is the "side" of $AC$.

I say next that $MO$ is binomial.

For, since $AG$ is commensurable with $GE$,
therefore $AE$ is also commensurable with each of the straight lines $AG$, $GE$.
[x. 15]

But $AE$ is also, by hypothesis, commensurable with $AB$;
therefore $AG$, $GE$ are also commensurable with $AB$. [x. 12]
And $AB$ is rational;
therefore each of the straight lines $AG$, $GE$ is also rational;
therefore each of the rectangles $AH$, $GK$ is rational, [x. 19]

and *AH* is commensurable with *GK*.

But *AH* is equal to *SN*, and *GK* to *NQ*;
therefore *SN*, *NQ*, that is, the squares on *MN*, *NO*, are rational and commensurable.

And, since *AE* is incommensurable in length with *ED*,
while *AE* is commensurable with *AG*, and *DE* is commensurable with *EF*,
    therefore *AG* is also incommensurable with *EF*,   [x. 13]
    so that *AH* is also incommensurable with *EL*.   [vi. 1, x. 11]
But *AH* is equal to *SN*, and *EL* to *MR*;
    therefore *SN* is also incommensurable with *MR*.
But, as *SN* is to *MR*, so is *PN* to *NR*;   [vi. 1]
    therefore *PN* is incommensurable with *NR*.   [x. 11]
But *PN* is equal to *MN*, and *NR* to *NO*;
    therefore *MN* is incommensurable with *NO*.
And the square on *MN* is commensurable with the square on *NO*,
    and each is rational;
therefore *MN*, *NO* are rational straight lines commensurable in square only.
Therefore *MO* is binomial [x. 36] and the "side" of *AC*.   Q. E. D.

## Proposition 55

*If an area be contained by a rational straight line and the second binomial, the "side" of the area is the irrational straight line which is called a first bimedial.*

For let the area *ABCD* be contained by the rational straight line *AB* and the second binomial *AD*;
I say that the "side" of the area *AC* is a first bimedial straight line.

For, since *AD* is a second binomial straight line, let it be divided into its terms at *E*, so that *AE* is the greater term;
therefore *AE*, *ED* are rational straight lines commensurable in square only, the square on *AE* is greater than the square on *ED* by the square on a straight line commensurable with *AE*,
and the lesser term *ED* is commensurable in length with *AB*.   [x. Deff. ii. 2]

Let *ED* be bisected at *F*,
and let there be applied to *AE* the rectangle *AG*, *GE* equal to the square on *EF* and deficient by a square figure;
    therefore *AG* is commensurable in length with *GE*.   [x. 17]
Through *G*, *E*, *F* let *GH*, *EK*, *FL* be drawn parallel to *AB*, *CD*,
let the square *SN* be constructed equal to the parallelogram *AH*, and the square *NQ* equal to *GK*,

and let them be placed so that *MN* is in a straight line with *NO*;
    therefore *RN* is also in a straight line with *NP*.
Let the square *SQ* be completed.

It is then manifest from what was proved before that $MR$ is a mean proportional between $SN$, $NQ$ and is equal to $EL$, and that $MO$ is the "side" of the area $AC$.

It is now to be proved that $MO$ is a first bimedial straight line.

Since $AE$ is commensurable in length with $ED$,
while $ED$ is commensurable with $AB$,
therefore $AE$ is incommensurable with $AB$. [x. 13]

And, since $AG$ is commensurable with $EG$,
$AE$ is also commensurable with each of the straight lines $AG$, $GE$. [x. 15]

But $AE$ is incommensurable in length with $AB$;
therefore $AG$, $GE$ are also incommensurable with $AB$. [x. 13]

Therefore $BA$, $AG$ and $BA$, $GE$ are pairs of rational straight lines commensurable in square only;
so that each of the rectangles $AH$, $GK$ is medial. [x. 21]

Hence each of the squares $SN$, $NQ$ is medial.

Therefore $MN$, $NO$ are also medial.

And, since $AG$ is commensurable in length with $GE$,
$AH$ is also commensurable with $GK$, [vi. 1, x. 11]
that is, $SN$ is commensurable with $NQ$,
that is, the square on $MN$ with the square on $NO$.

And, since $AE$ is incommensurable in length with $ED$,
while $AE$ is commensurable with $AG$,
and $ED$ is commensurable with $EF$,
therefore $AG$ is incommensurable with $EF$; [x. 13]
so that $AH$ is also incommensurable with $EL$,
that is, $SN$ is incommensurable with $MR$,
that is, $PN$ with $NR$, [vi. 1, x. 11]
that is, $MN$ is incommensurable in length with $NO$.

But $MN$, $NO$ were proved to be both medial and commensurable in square; therefore $MN$, $NO$ are medial straight lines commensurable in square only.

I say next that they also contain a rational rectangle.

For, since $DE$ is, by hypothesis, commensurable with each of the straight lines $AB$, $EF$,
therefore $EF$ is also commensurable with $EK$. [x. 12]

And each of them is rational;
therefore $EL$, that is, $MR$ is rational, [x. 19]
and $MR$ is the rectangle $MN$, $NO$.

But, if two medial straight lines commensurable in square only and containing a rational rectangle be added together, the whole is irrational and is called a first bimedial straight line. [x. 37]

Therefore $MO$ is a first bimedial straight line. Q. E. D.

## Proposition 56

*If an area be contained by a rational straight line and the third binomial, the "side" of the area is the irrational straight line called a second bimedial.*

For let the area $ABCD$ be contained by the rational straight line $AB$ and the third binomial $AD$ divided into its terms at $E$, of which terms $AE$ is the greater;

I say that the "side" of the area $AC$ is the irrational straight line called a second bimedial.

ELEMENTS X

For let the same construction be made as before.
Now, since $AD$ is a third binomial straight line,

therefore $AE$, $ED$ are rational straight lines commensurable in square only, the square on $AE$ is greater than the square on $ED$ by the square on a straight line commensurable with $AE$,
and neither of the terms $AE$, $ED$ is commensurable in length with $AB$.
[x. Deff. II. 3]

Then, in manner similar to the foregoing, we shall prove that $MO$ is the "side" of the area $AC$,
and $MN$, $NO$ are medial straight lines commensurable in square only;
so that $MO$ is bimedial.

It is next to be proved that it is also a second bimedial straight line.
Since $DE$ is incommensurable in length with $AB$, that is, with $EK$,
and $DE$ is commensurable with $EF$,
therefore $EF$ is incommensurable in length with $EK$. [x. 13]
And they are rational;
therefore $FE$, $EK$ are rational straight lines commensurable in square only.
Therefore $EL$, that is, $MR$, is medial. [x. 21]
And it is contained by $MN$, $NO$;
therefore the rectangle $MN$, $NO$ is medial.
Therefore $MO$ is a second bimedial straight line. [x. 38]
Q. E. D.

## Proposition 57

*If an area be contained by a rational straight line and the fourth binomial, the "side" of the area is the irrational straight line called major.*

For let the area $AC$ be contained by the rational straight line $AB$ and the fourth binomial $AD$ divided into its terms at $E$, of which terms let $AE$ be the greater;
I say that the "side" of the area $AC$ is the irrational straight line called major.
For, since $AD$ is a fourth binomial straight line,
therefore $AE$, $ED$ are rational straight lines commensurable in square only, the square on $AE$ is greater than the square on $ED$ by the square on a straight line incommensurable with $AE$,
and $AE$ is commensurable in length with $AB$. [x. Deff. II. 4]
Let $DE$ be bisected at $F$,
and let there be applied to $AE$ a parallelogram, the rectangle $AG$, $GE$, equal to the square on $EF$;
therefore $AG$ is incommensurable in length with $GE$. [x. 18]
Let $GH$, $EK$, $FL$ be drawn parallel to $AB$,

and let the rest of the construction be as before;
it is then manifest that $MO$ is the "side" of the area $AC$.

It is next to be proved that $MO$ is the irrational straight line called major.
Since $AG$ is incommensurable with $EG$,
$AH$ is also incommensurable with $GK$, that is, $SN$ with $NQ$;     [VI. 1, X. 11]
therefore $MN$, $NO$ are incommensurable in square.
And, since $AE$ is commensurable with $AB$,
$AK$ is rational;     [X. 19]
and it is equal to the squares on $MN$, $NO$;
therefore the sum of the squares on $MN$, $NO$ is also rational.
And, since $DE$ is incommensurable in length with $AB$, that is, with $EK$,
while $DE$ is commensurable with $EF$,
therefore $EF$ is incommensurable in length with $EK$.     [X. 13]
Therefore $EK$, $EF$ are rational straight lines commensurable in square only;
therefore $LE$, that is, $MR$, is medial.     [X. 21]
And it is contained by $MN$, $NO$;
therefore the rectangle $MN$, $NO$ is medial.
And the [sum] of the squares on $MN$, $NO$ is rational,
and $MN$, $NO$ are incommensurable in square.
But, if two straight lines incommensurable in square and making the sum of the squares on them rational, but the rectangle contained by them medial, be added together, the whole is irrational and is called major.     [X. 39]
Therefore $MO$ is the irrational straight line called major and is the "side" of the area $AC$.     Q. E. D.

## Proposition 58

*If an area be contained by a rational straight line and the fifth binomial, the "side" of the area is the irrational straight line called the side of a rational plus a medial area.*

For let the area $AC$ be contained by the rational straight line $AB$ and the fifth binomial $AD$ divided into its terms at $E$, so that $AE$ is the greater term;
I say that the "side" of the area $AC$ is the irrational straight line called the side of a rational plus a medial area.
For let the same construction be made as before shown;
it is then manifest that $MO$ is the "side" of the area $AC$.
It is then to be proved that $MO$ is the side of a rational plus a medial area.
For, since $AG$ is incommensurable with $GE$,     [X. 18]
therefore $AH$ is also commensurable with $HE$,     [VI. 1, X. 11]
that is, the square on $MN$ with the square on $NO$;
therefore $MN$, $NO$ are incommensurable in square.

ELEMENTS X                                                              241

And, since $AD$ is a fifth binomial straight line, and $ED$ the lesser segment, therefore $ED$ is commensurable in length with $AB$. [x. Deff. II. 5]

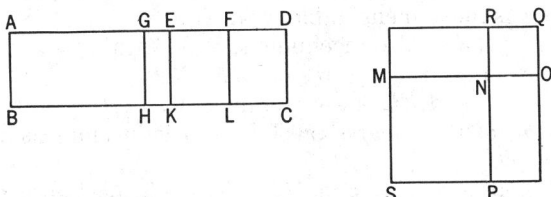

But $AE$ is incommensurable with $ED$;
  therefore $AB$ is also incommensurable in length with $AE$. [x. 13]
Therefore $AK$, that is, the sum of the squares on $MN$, $NO$, is medial. [x. 21]
And, since $DE$ is commensurable in length with $AB$, that is, with $EK$, while $DE$ is commensurable with $EF$,
  therefore $EF$ is also commensurable with $EK$. [x. 12]
And $EK$ is rational;
therefore $EL$, that is, $MR$, that is, the rectangle $MN$, $NO$, is also rational.
[x. 19]

Therefore $MN$, $NO$ are straight lines incommensurable in square which make the sum of the squares on them medial, but the rectangle contained by them rational.

Therefore $MO$ is the side of a rational plus a medial area [x. 40] and is the "side" of the area $AC$.                                    Q. E. D.

PROPOSITION 59

*If an area be contained by a rational straight line and the sixth binomial, the "side" of the area is the irrational straight line called the side of the sum of two medial areas.*

For let the area $ABCD$ be contained by the rational straight line $AB$ and the sixth binomial $AD$, divided into its terms at $E$, so that $AE$ is the greater term;

I say that the "side" of $AC$ is the side of the sum of two medial areas.

Let the same construction be made as before shown.

It is then manifest that $MO$ is the "side" of $AC$, and that $MN$ is incommensurable in square with $NO$.

Now, since $EA$ is incommensurable in length with $AB$, therefore $EA$, $AB$ are rational straight lines commensurable in square only; therefore $AK$, that is, the sum of the squares on $MN$, $NO$, is medial. [x. 21]

Again, since $ED$ is incommensurable in length with $AB$,

242    EUCLID

therefore $FE$ is also incommensurable with $EK$;    [x. 13]
therefore $FE$, $EK$ are rational straight lines commensurable in square only;
therefore $EL$, that is, $MR$, that is, the rectangle $MN$, $NO$, is medial.    [x. 21]
    And, since $AE$ is incommensurable with $EF$,
            $AK$ is also incommensurable with $EL$.    [vi. 1, x. 11]
But $AK$ is the sum of the squares on $MN$, $NO$,
            and $EL$ is the rectangle $MN$, $NO$;
therefore the sum of the squares on $MN$, $NO$ is incommensurable with the rectangle $MN$, $NO$.
    And each of them is medial, and $MN$, $NO$ are incommensurable in square.
    Therefore $MO$ is the side of the sum of two medial areas [x. 41], and is the "side" of $AC$.
                                    Q. E. D.

### Lemma

If a straight line be cut into unequal parts, the squares on the unequal parts are greater than twice the rectangle contained by the unequal parts.
    Let $AB$ be a straight line, and let it be cut into unequal parts at $C$, and let $AC$ be the greater;
I say that the squares on $AC$, $CB$ are greater than twice the rectangle $AC$, $CB$.
    For let $AB$ be bisected at $D$.
    Since, then, a straight line has been cut into equal parts at $D$, and into unequal parts at $C$,
therefore the rectangle $AC$, $CB$ together with the square on $CD$ is equal to the square on $AD$,    [ii. 5]
        so that the rectangle $AC$, $CB$ is less than the square on $AD$;
therefore twice the rectangle $AC$, $CB$ is less than double of the square on $AD$.
    But the squares on $AC$, $CB$ are double of the squares on $AD$, $DC$;    [ii. 9]
therefore the squares on $AC$, $CB$ are greater than twice the rectangle $AC$, $CB$.
                                    Q. E. D.

### Proposition 60

*The square on the binomial straight line applied to a rational straight line produces as breadth the first binomial.*

Let $AB$ be a binomial straight line divided into its terms at $C$, so that $AC$ is the greater term;
        let a rational straight line $DE$ be set out,
and let $DEFG$ equal to the square on $AB$ be applied to $DE$ producing $DG$ as its breadth;
    I say that $DG$ is a first binomial straight line.
    For let there be applied to $DE$ the rectangle $DH$ equal to the square on $AC$, and $KL$ equal to the square on $BC$;
therefore the remainder, twice the rectangle $AC$, $CB$, is equal to $MF$.
    Let $MG$ be bisected at $N$, and let $NO$ be drawn parallel [to $ML$ or $GF$].
    Therefore each of the rectangles $MO$, $NF$ is equal to once the rectangle $AC$, $CB$.
    Now, since $AB$ is a binomial divided into its terms at $C$,

therefore $AC$, $CB$ are rational straight lines commensurable in square only;
[x. 36]
therefore the squares on $AC$, $CB$ are rational and commensurable with one another,
> so that the sum of the squares on $AC$, $CB$ is also rational. [x. 15]

And it is equal to $DL$;
> therefore $DL$ is rational.

And it is applied to the rational straight line $DE$;
> therefore $DM$ is rational and commensurable in length with $DE$. [x. 20]

Again, since $AC$, $CB$ are rational straight lines commensurable in square only,
> therefore twice the rectangle $AC$, $CB$, that is $MF$, is medial. [x. 21]

And it is applied to the rational straight line $ML$;
therefore $MG$ is also rational and incommensurable in length with $ML$, that is, $DE$. [x. 22]

But $MD$ is also rational and is commensurable in length with $DE$;
> therefore $DM$ is incommensurable in length with $MG$. [x. 13]

And they are rational;
therefore $DM$, $MG$ are rational straight lines commensurable in square only;
> therefore $DG$ is binomial. [x. 36]

It is next to be proved that it is also a first binomial straight line.

Since the rectangle $AC$, $CB$ is a mean proportional between the squares on $AC$, $CB$, [cf. Lemma after x. 53]
> therefore $MO$ is also a mean proportional between $DH$, $KL$.

Therefore, as $DH$ is to $MO$, so is $MO$ to $KL$,
> that is, as $DK$ is to $MN$, so is $MN$ to $MK$; [vi. 1]
> therefore the rectangle $DK$, $KM$ is equal to the square on $MN$. [vi. 17]

And, since the square on $AC$ is commensurable with the square on $CB$,
> $DH$ is also commensurable with $KL$,
> so that $DK$ is also commensurable with $KM$. [vi. 1, x. 11]

And, since the squares on $AC$, $CB$ are greater than twice the rectangle $AC$, $CB$, [Lemma]
> therefore $DL$ is also greater than $MF$,
> so that $DM$ is also greater than $MG$. [vi. 1]

And the rectangle $DK$, $KM$ is equal to the square on $MN$, that is, to the fourth part of the square on $MG$,
> and $DK$ is commensurable with $KM$.

But, if there be two unequal straight lines, and to the greater there be applied a parallelogram equal to the fourth part of the square on the less and deficient by a square figure, and if it divide it into commensurable parts, the square on the greater is greater than the square on the less by the square on a straight line commensurable with the greater; [x. 17]
therefore the square on $DM$ is greater than the square on $MG$ by the square on a straight line commensurable with $DM$.

And $DM$, $MG$ are rational,
and $DM$, which is the greater term, is commensurable in length with the rational straight line $DE$ set out.

Therefore $DG$ is a first binomial straight line. [x. Deff. ii. 1]

Q. E. D.

## Proposition 61

*The square on the first bimedial straight line applied to a rational straight line produces as breadth the second binomial.*

Let $AB$ be a first bimedial straight line divided into its medials at $C$, of which medials $AC$ is the greater;
let a rational straight line $DE$ be set out,
and let there be applied to $DE$ the parallelogram $DF$ equal to the square on $AB$, producing $DG$ as its breadth;

I say that $DG$ is a second binomial straight line.

For let the same construction as before be made.

Then, since $AB$ is a first bimedial divided at $C$,
therefore $AC$, $CB$ are medial straight lines commensurable in square only, and containing a rational rectangle, [x. 37]
so that the squares on $AC$, $CB$ are also medial. [x. 21]

Therefore $DL$ is medial. [x. 15 and 13, Por.]

And it has been applied to the rational straight line $DE$;
therefore $MD$ is rational and incommensurable in length with $DE$. [x. 22]

Again, since twice the rectangle $AC$, $CB$ is rational, $MF$ is also rational.
And it is applied to the rational straight line $ML$;
therefore $MG$ is also rational and commensurable in length with $ML$, that is, $DE$; [x. 20]
therefore $DM$ is incommensurable in length with $MG$. [x. 13]

And they are rational;
therefore $DM$, $MG$ are rational straight lines commensurable in square only;
therefore $DG$ is binomial. [x. 36]

It is next to be proved that it is also a second binomial straight line.

For, since the squares on $AC$, $CB$ are greater than twice the rectangle $AC$, $CB$,
therefore $DL$ is also greater than $MF$,
so that $DM$ is also greater than $MG$. [vi. 1]

And, since the square on $AC$ is commensurable with the square on $CB$,
$DH$ is also commensurable with $KL$,
so that $DK$ is also commensurable with $KM$. [vi. 1, x. 11]

And the rectangle $DK$, $KM$ is equal to the square on $MN$;
therefore the square on $DM$ is greater than the square on $MG$ by the square on a straight line commensurable with $DM$. [x. 17]

And $MG$ is commensurable in length with $DE$.

Therefore $DG$ is a second binomial straight line. [x. Deff. ii. 2]

## Proposition 62

*The square on the second bimedial straight line applied to a rational straight line produces as breadth the third binomial.*

Let $AB$ be a second bimedial straight line divided into its medials at $C$, so that $AC$ is the greater segment;
let $DE$ be any rational straight line,
and to $DE$ let there be applied the parallelogram $DF$ equal to the square on $AB$ and producing $DG$ as its breadth;

ELEMENTS X 245

I say that *DG* is a third binomial straight line.
Let the same construction be made as before shown.

Then, since *AB* is a second bimedial divided at *C*,
therefore *AC*, *CB* are medial straight lines commensurable in square only and containing a medial rectangle, [x. 38]
so that the sum of the squares on *AC*, *CB* is also medial. [x. 15 and 23 Por.]
And it is equal to *DL*;
therefore *DL* is also medial.
And it is applied to the rational straight line *DE*;
therefore *MD* is also rational and incommensurable in length with *DE*. [x. 22]
For the same reason,
*MG* is also rational and incommensurable in length with *ML*, that is, with *DE*;
therefore each of the straight lines *DM*, *MG* is rational and incommensurable in length with *DE*.
And, since *AC* is incommensurable in length with *CB*,
and, as *AC* is to *CB*, so is the square on *AC* to the rectangle *AC*, *CB*,
therefore the square on *AC* is also incommensurable with the rectangle *AC*, *CB*. [x. 11]
Hence the sum of the squares on *AC*, *CB* is incommensurable with twice the rectangle *AC*, *CB*, [x. 12, 13]
that is, *DL* is incommensurable with *MF*,
so that *DM* is also incommensurable with *MG*. [vi. 1, x. 11]
And they are rational;
therefore *DG* is binomial. [x. 36]
It is to be proved that it is also a third binomial straight line.
In manner similar to the foregoing we may conclude that *DM* is greater than *MG*,
and that *DK* is commensurable with *KM*.
And the rectangle *DK*, *KM* is equal to the square on *MN*;
therefore the square on *DM* is greater than the square on *MG* by the square on a straight line commensurable with *DM*.
And neither of the straight lines *DM*, *MG* is commensurable in length with *DE*.
Therefore *DG* is a third binomial straight line. [x. Deff. II. 3]
Q. E. D.

PROPOSITION 63

*The square on the major straight line applied to a rational straight line produces as breadth the fourth binomial.*

Let *AB* be a major straight line divided at *C*, so that *AC* is greater than *CB*;
let *DE* be a rational straight line,
and to *DE* let there be applied the parallelogram *DF* equal to the square on *AB* and producing *DG* as its breadth;
I say that *DG* is a fourth binomial straight line.
Let the same construction be made as before shown.
Then, since *AB* is a major straight line divided at *C*,

*AC, CB* are straight lines incommensurable in square which make the sum of the squares on them rational, but the rectangle contained by them medial. [x. 39]

Since, then, the sum of the squares on *AC, CB* is rational, therefore *DL* is rational;
therefore *DM* is also rational and commensurable in length with *DE*. [x. 20]

Again, since twice the rectangle *AC, CB*, that is, *MF*, is medial,
and it is applied to the rational straight line *ML*,
therefore *MG* is also rational and incommensurable in length with *DE*; [x. 22]

therefore *DM* is also incommensurable in length with *MG*. [x. 13]

Therefore *DM, MG* are rational straight lines commensurable in square only;

therefore *DG* is binomial. [x. 36]

It is to be proved that it is also a fourth binomial straight line.

In manner similar to the foregoing we can prove that *DM* is greater than *MG*,
and that the rectangle *DK, KM* is equal to the square on *MN*.

Since then the square on *AC* is incommensurable with the square on *CB*,
therefore *DH* is also incommensurable with *KL*,
so that *DK* is also incommensurable with *KM*. [vi. 1, x. 11]

But, if there be two unequal straight lines, and to the greater there be applied a parallelogram equal to the fourth part of the square on the less and deficient by a square figure, and if it divide it into incommensurable parts, then the square on the greater will be greater than the square on the less by the square on a straight line incommensurable in length with the greater; [x. 18]
therefore the square on *DM* is greater than the square on *MG* by the square on a straight line incommensurable with *DM*.

And *DM, MG* are rational straight lines commensurable in square only, and *DM* is commensurable with the rational straight line *DE* set out.

Therefore *DG* is a fourth binomial straight line. [x. Deff. ii. 4]

Q. E. D.

## Proposition 64

*The square on the side of a rational plus a medial area applied to a rational straight line produces as breadth the fifth binomial.*

Let *AB* be the side of a rational plus a medial area, divided into its straight lines at *C*, so that *AC* is the greater;
let a rational straight line *DE* be set out,
and let there be applied to *DE* the parallelogram *DF* equal to the square on *AB*, producing *DG* as its breadth;
I say that *DG* is a fifth binomial straight line.

Let the same construction as before be made.

Since then *AB* is the side of a rational plus a medial area, divided at *C*,
therefore *AC, CB* are straight lines incommensurable in square which make

# ELEMENTS X

the sum of the squares on them medial, but the rectangle contained by them rational. [x. 40]

Since, then, the sum of the squares on $AC$, $CB$ is medial,
therefore $DL$ is medial,
so that $DM$ is rational and incommensurable in length with $DE$. [x. 22]

Again, since twice the rectangle $AC$, $CB$, that is $MF$, is rational,
therefore $MG$ is rational and commensurable with $DE$. [x. 20]

Therefore $DM$ is incommensurable with $MG$; [x. 13]
therefore $DM$, $MG$ are rational straight lines commensurable in square only;
therefore $DG$ is binomial. [x. 36]

I say next that it is also a fifth binomial straight line.

For it can be proved similarly that the rectangle $DK$, $KM$ is equal to the square on $MN$,
and that $DK$ is incommensurable in length with $KM$;
therefore the square on $DM$ is greater than the square on $MG$ by the square on a straight line incommensurable with $DM$. [x. 18]

And $DM$, $MG$ are commensurable in square only, and the less, $MG$, is commensurable in length with $DE$.

Therefore $DG$ is a fifth binomial. Q. E. D.

## PROPOSITION 65

*The square on the side of the sum of two medial areas applied to a rational straight line produces as breadth the sixth binomial.*

Let $AB$ be the side of the sum of two medial areas, divided at $C$,
let $DE$ be a rational straight line,
and let there be applied to $DE$ the parallelogram $DF$ equal to the square on $AB$, producing $DG$ as its breadth;

I say that $DG$ is a sixth binomial straight line.

For let the same construction be made as before.

Then, since $AB$ is the side of the sum of two medial areas, divided at $C$,
therefore $AC$, $CB$ are straight lines incommensurable in square which make the sum of the squares on them medial, the rectangle contained by them medial, and moreover the sum of the squares on them incommensurable with the rectangle contained by them, [x. 41]
so that, in accordance with what was before proved, each of the rectangles $DL$, $MF$ is medial.

And they are applied to the rational straight line $DE$;
therefore each of the straight lines $DM$, $MG$ is rational and incommensurable in length with $DE$. [x. 22]

And, since the sum of the squares on $AC$, $CB$ is incommensurable with twice the rectangle $AC$, $CB$,
therefore $DL$ is incommensurable with $MF$.

Therefore $DM$ is also incommensurable with $MG$; [vi. 1, x. 11]
therefore $DM$, $MG$ are rational straight lines commensurable in square only;
therefore $DG$ is binomial. [x. 36]

I say next that it is also a sixth binomial straight line.

Similarly again we can prove that the rectangle $DK$, $KM$ is equal to the square on $MN$,
and that $DK$ is incommensurable in length with $KM$;
and, for the same reason, the square on $DM$ is greater than the square on $MG$ by the square on a straight line incommensurable in length with $DM$.

And neither of the straight lines $DM$, $MG$ is commensurable in length with the rational straight line $DE$ set out.

Therefore $DG$ is a sixth binomial straight line. Q. E. D.

## PROPOSITION 66

*A straight line commensurable in length with a binomial straight line is itself also binomial and the same in order.*

Let $AB$ be binomial, and let $CD$ be commensurable in length with $AB$;
I say that $CD$ is binomial and the same in order with $AB$.

For, since $AB$ is binomial,
let it be divided into its terms at $E$,
and let $AE$ be the greater term;
therefore $AE$, $EB$ are rational straight lines commensurable in square only. [x. 36]

Let it be contrived that,
as $AB$ is to $CD$, so is $AE$ to $CF$; [vi. 12]
therefore also the remainder $EB$ is to the remainder $FD$ as $AB$ is to $CD$. [v. 19]
But $AB$ is commensurable in length with $CD$;
therefore $AE$ is also commensurable with $CF$, and $EB$ with $FD$. [x. 11]
And $AE$, $EB$ are rational;
therefore $CF$, $FD$ are also rational.
And, as $AE$ is to $CF$, so is $EB$ to $FD$. [v. 11]
Therefore, alternately, as $AE$ is to $EB$, so is $CF$ to $FD$. [v. 16]
But $AE$, $EB$ are commensurable in square only;
therefore $CF$, $FD$ are also commensurable in square only. [x. 11]
And they are rational;
therefore $CD$ is binomial. [x. 36]
I say next that it is the same in order with $AB$.

For the square on $AE$ is greater than the square on $EB$ either by the square on a straight line commensurable with $AE$ or by the square on a straight line incommensurable with it.

If then the square on $AE$ is greater than the square on $EB$ by the square on a straight line commensurable with $AE$,
the square on $CF$ will also be greater than the square on $FD$ by the square on a straight line commensurable with $CF$. [x. 14]

And, if $AE$ is commensurable with the rational straight line set out, $CF$ will also be commensurable with it, [x. 12]
and for this reason each of the straight lines $AB$, $CD$ is a first binomial, that is, the same in order. [x. Deff. II. 1]

But, if $EB$ is commensurable with the rational straight line set out, $FD$ is also commensurable with it, [x. 12]
and for this reason again $CD$ will be the same in order with $AB$,
for each of them will be a second binomial. [x. Deff. II. 2]

ELEMENTS X

But, if neither of the straight lines $AE$, $EB$ is commensurable with the rational straight line set out, neither of the straight lines $CF$, $FD$ will be commensurable with it, [x. 13]
and each of the straight lines $AB$, $CD$ is a third binomial. [x. Deff. II. 3]

But, if the square on $AE$ is greater than the square on $EB$ by the square on a straight line incommensurable with $AE$,
the square on $CF$ is also greater than the square on $FD$ by the square on a straight line incommensurable with $CF$. [x. 14]

And, if $AE$ is commensurable with the rational straight line set out, $CF$ is also commensurable with it,
and each of the straight lines $AB$, $CD$ is a fourth binomial. [x. Deff. II. 4]

But, if $EB$ is so commensurable, so is $FD$ also,
and each of the straight lines $AB$, $CD$ will be a fifth binomial. [x. Deff. II. 5]

But, if neither of the straight lines $AE$, $EB$ is so commensurable, neither of the straight lines $CF$, $FD$ is commensurable with the rational straight line set out,
and each of the straight lines $AB$, $CD$ will be a sixth binomial. [x. Deff. II. 6]

Hence a straight line commensurable in length with a binomial straight line is binomial and the same in order. Q. E. D.

PROPOSITION 67

*A straight line commensurable in length with a bimedial straight line is itself also bimedial and the same in order.*

Let $AB$ be bimedial, and let $CD$ be commensurable in length with $AB$;
I say that $CD$ is bimedial and the same in order with $AB$.
For, since $AB$ is bimedial,
let it be divided into its medials at $E$;
therefore $AE$, $EB$ are medial straight lines commensurable in square only. [x. 37, 38]

And let it be contrived that,
as $AB$ is to $CD$, so is $AE$ to $CF$;
therefore also the remainder $EB$ is to the remainder $FD$ as $AB$ is to $CD$. [v. 19]
But $AB$ is commensurable in length with $CD$;
therefore $AE$, $EB$ are also commensurable with $CF$, $FD$ respectively. [x. 11]
But $AE$, $EB$ are medial;
therefore $CF$, $FD$ are also medial. [x. 23]
And since, as $AE$ is to $EB$, so is $CF$ to $FD$. [v. 11]
and $AE$, $EB$ are commensurable in square only,
$CF$, $FD$ are also commensurable in square only. [x. 11]
But they were also proved medial;
therefore $CD$ is bimedial.

I say next that it is also the same in order with $AB$.
For since, as $AE$ is to $EB$, so is $CF$ to $FD$,
therefore also, as the square on $AE$ is to the rectangle $AE$, $EB$, so is the square on $CF$ to the rectangle $CF$, $FD$;
therefore, alternately,
as the square on $AE$ is to the square on $CF$, so is the rectangle $AE$, $EB$ to the rectangle $CF$, $FD$. [v. 16]
But the square on $AE$ is commensurable with the square on $CF$;

therefore the rectangle $AE$, $EB$ is also commensurable with the rectangle $CF$, $FD$.

If therefore the rectangle $AE$, $EB$ is rational,
the rectangle $CF$, $FD$ is also rational,
[and for this reason $CD$ is a first bimedial]; [x. 37]
but if medial, medial, [x. 23, Por.]
and each of the straight lines $AB$, $CD$ is a second bimedial. [x. 38]
And for this reason $CD$ will be the same in order with $AB$. Q. E. D.

## Proposition 68

*A straight line commensurable with a major straight line is itself also major.*

Let $AB$ be major, and let $CD$ be commensurable with $AB$;
I say that $CD$ is major.

Let $AB$ be divided at $E$;
therefore $AE$, $EB$ are straight lines incommensurable in square which make the sum of the squares on them rational, but the rectangle contained by them medial. [x. 39]

Let the same construction be made as before.

Then since, as $AB$ is to $CD$, so is $AE$ to $CF$, and $EB$ to $FD$,
therefore also, as $AE$ is to $CF$, so is $EB$ to $FD$. [v. 11]

But $AB$ is commensurable with $CD$;
therefore $AE$, $EB$ are also commensurable with $CF$, $FD$ respectively. [x. 11]

And since, as $AE$ is to $CF$, so is $EB$ to $FD$,
alternately also,
as $AE$ is to $EB$, so is $CF$ to $FD$; [v. 16]
therefore also, *componendo*,
as $AB$ is to $BE$, so is $CD$ to $DF$; [v. 18]
therefore also, as the square on $AB$ is to the square on $BE$, so is the square on $CD$ to the square on $DF$. [vi. 20]

Similarly we can prove that, as the square on $AB$ is to the square on $AE$, so also is the square on $CD$ to the square on $CF$.

Therefore also, as the square on $AB$ is to the squares on $AE$, $EB$, so is the square on $CD$ to the squares on $CF$, $FD$;
therefore also, alternately,
as the square on $AB$ is to the square on $CD$, so are the squares on $AE$, $EB$ to the squares on $CF$, $FD$. [v. 16]

But the square on $AB$ is commensurable with the square on $CD$;
therefore the squares on $AE$, $EB$ are also commensurable with the squares on $CF$, $FD$.

And the squares on $AE$, $EB$ together are rational;
therefore the squares on $CF$, $FD$ together are rational.

Similarly also twice the rectangle $AE$, $EB$ is commensurable with twice the rectangle $CF$, $FD$.

And twice the rectangle $AE$, $EB$ is medial;
therefore twice the rectangle $CF$, $FD$ is also medial. [x. 23, Por.]

Therefore $CF$, $FD$ are straight lines incommensurable in square which make, at the same time, the sum of the squares on them rational, but the rectangle contained by them medial; therefore the whole $CD$ is the irrational straight line called major. [x. 39]

Therefore a straight line commensurable with the major straight line is major. Q. E. D.

## Proposition 69

*A straight line commensurable with the side of a rational plus a medial area is itself also the side of a rational plus a medial area.*

Let $AB$ be the side of a rational plus a medial area, and let $CD$ be commensurable with $AB$;

it is to be proved that $CD$ is also the side of a rational plus a medial area.

Let $AB$ be divided into its straight lines at $E$;

therefore $AE$, $EB$ are straight lines incommensurable in square which make the sum of the squares on them medial, but the rectangle contained by them rational. [x. 40]

Let the same construction be made as before.

We can then prove similarly that

$CF$, $FD$ are incommensurable in square,

and the sum of the squares on $AE$, $EB$ is commensurable with the sum of the squares on $CF$, $FD$,

and the rectangle $AE$, $EB$ with the rectangle $CF$, $FD$;

so that the sum of the squares on $CF$, $FD$ is also medial, and the rectangle $CF$, $FD$ rational.

Therefore $CD$ is the side of a rational plus a medial area. Q. E. D.

## Proposition 70

*A straight line commensurable with the side of the sum of two medial areas is the side of the sum of two medial areas.*

Let $AB$ be the side of the sum of two medial areas, and $CD$ commensurable with $AB$;

it is to be proved that $CD$ is also the side of the sum of two medial areas.

For, since $AB$ is the side of the sum of two medial areas, let it be divided into its straight lines at $E$;

therefore $AE$, $EB$ are straight lines incommensurable in square which make the sum of the squares on them medial, the rectangle contained by them medial, and furthermore the sum of the squares on $AE$, $EB$ incommensurable with the rectangle $AE$, $EB$. [x. 41]

Let the same construction be made as before.

We can then prove similarly that

$CF$, $FD$ are also incommensurable in square,

the sum of the squares on $AE$, $EB$ is commensurable with the sum of the squares on $CF$, $FD$,

and the rectangle $AE$, $EB$ with the rectangle $CF$, $FD$;

so that the sum of the squares on $CF$, $FD$ is also medial,

the rectangle $CF$, $FD$ is medial,

and moreover the sum of the squares on $CF$, $FD$ is incommensurable with the rectangle $CF$, $FD$.

Therefore $CD$ is the side of the sum of two medial areas. Q. E. D.

## Proposition 71

*If a rational and a medial area be added together, four irrational straight lines arise, namely a binomial or a first bimedial or a major or a side of a rational plus a medial area.*

Let $AB$ be rational, and $CD$ medial;

I say that the "side" of the area $AD$ is a binomial or a first bimedial or a major or a side of a rational plus a medial area.

For $AB$ is either greater or less than $CD$.

First, let it be greater;

let a rational straight line $EF$ be set out, let there be applied to $EF$ the rectangle $EG$ equal to $AB$, producing $EH$ as breadth,

and let $HI$, equal to $DC$, be applied to $EF$, producing $HK$ as breadth.

Then, since $AB$ is rational and is equal to $EG$, therefore $EG$ is also rational.

And it has been applied to $EF$, producing $EH$ as breadth; therefore $EH$ is rational and commensurable in length with $EF$. [x. 20]

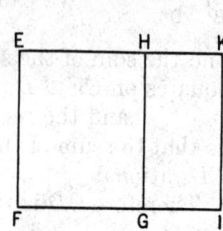

Again, since $CD$ is medial and is equal to $HI$,

therefore $HI$ is also medial.

And it is applied to the rational straight line $EF$, producing $HK$ as breadth; therefore $HK$ is rational and incommensurable in length with $EF$ [x. 22]

And, since $CD$ is medial,

while $AB$ is rational,

therefore $AB$ is incommensurable with $CD$,

so that $EG$ is also incommensurable with $HI$.

But, as $EG$ is to $HI$, so is $EH$ to $HK$; [vi. 1]

therefore $EH$ is also incommensurable in length with $HK$. [x. 11]

And both are rational;

therefore $EH$, $HK$ are rational straight lines commensurable in square only;

therefore $EK$ is a binomial straight line, divided at $H$. [x. 36]

And, since $AB$ is greater than $CD$,

while $AB$ is equal to $EG$ and $CD$ to $HI$,

therefore $EG$ is also greater than $HI$;

therefore $EH$ is also greater than $HK$.

The square, then, on $EH$ is greater than the square on $HK$ either by the square on a straight line commensurable in length with $EH$ or by the square on a straight line incommensurable with it.

First, let the square on it be greater by the square on a straight line commensurable with itself.

Now the greater straight line $HE$ is commensurable in length with the rational straight line $EF$ set out;

therefore $EK$ is a first binomial. [x. Deff. ii. 1]

But $EF$ is rational;
and, if an area be contained by a rational straight line and the first binomial, the side of the square equal to the area is binomial. [x. 54]

Therefore the "side" of $EI$ is binomial;
so that the "side" of $AD$ is also binomial.

Next, let the square on $EH$ be greater than the square on $HK$ by the square on a straight line incommensurable with $EH$.

Now the greater straight line $EH$ is commensurable in length with the rational straight line $EF$ set out;
therefore $EK$ is a fourth binomial. [x. Deff. II. 4]

But $EF$ is rational;
and, if an area be contained by a rational straight line and the fourth binomial, the "side" of the area is the irrational straight line called major. [x. 57]

Therefore the "side" of the area $EI$ is major;
so that the "side" of the area $AD$ is also major.

Next, let $AB$ be less than $CD$;
therefore $EG$ is also less than $HI$,
so that $EH$ is also less than $HK$.

Now the square on $HK$ is greater than the square on $EH$ either by the square on a straight line commensurable with $HK$ or by the square on a straight line incommensurable with it.

First, let the square on it be greater by the square on a straight line commensurable in length with itself.

Now the lesser straight line $EH$ is commensurable in length with the rational straight line $EF$ set out;
therefore $EK$ is a second binomial. [x. Deff. II. 2]

But $EF$ is rational,
and, if an area be contained by a rational straight line and the second binomial, the side of the square equal to it is a first bimedial; [x. 55]
therefore the "side" of the area $EI$ is a first bimedial,
so that the "side" of $AD$ is also a first bimedial.

Next, let the square on $HK$ be greater than the square on $HE$ by the square on a straight line incommensurable with $HK$.

Now the lesser straight line $EH$ is commensurable with the rational straight line $EF$ set out;
therefore $EK$ is a fifth binomial. [x. Deff. II. 5]

But $EF$ is rational;
and, if an area be contained by a rational straight line and the fifth binomial, the side of the square equal to the area is a side of a rational plus a medial area. [x. 58]

Therefore the "side" of the area $EI$ is a side of a rational plus a medial area, so that the "side" of the area $AD$ is also a side of a rational plus a medial area.

Therefore etc. Q. E. D.

## Proposition 72

*If two medial areas incommensurable with one another be added together, the remaining two irrational straight lines arise, namely either a second bimedial or a side of the sum of two medial areas.*

For let two medial areas $AB$, $CD$ incommensurable with one another be added together;

I say that the "side" of the area $AD$ is either a second bimedial or a side of the sum of two medial areas.

For $AB$ is either greater or less than $CD$.

First, if it so chance, let $AB$ be greater than $CD$.

Let the rational straight line $EF$ be set out,

and to $EF$ let there be applied the rectangle $EG$ equal to $AB$ and producing $EH$ as breadth, and the rectangle $HI$ equal to $CD$ and producing $HK$ as breadth.

Now, since each of the areas $AB$, $CD$ is medial,

therefore each of the areas $EG$, $HI$ is also medial.

And they are applied to the rational straight line $FE$, producing $EH$, $HK$ as breadth;

therefore each of the straight lines $EH$, $HK$ is rational and incommensurable in length with $EF$. [x. 22]

And, since $AB$ is incommensurable with $CD$,

and $AB$ is equal to $EG$, and $CD$ to $HI$,

therefore $EG$ is also incommensurable with $HI$.

But, as $EG$ is to $HI$, so is $EH$ to $HK$; [vi. 1]

therefore $EH$ is incommensurable in length with $HK$. [x. 11]

Therefore $EH$, $HK$ are rational straight lines commensurable in square only;

therefore $EK$ is binomial. [x. 36]

But the square on $EH$ is greater than the square on $HK$ either by the square on a straight line commensurable with $EH$ or by the square on a straight line incommensurable with it.

First, let the square on it be greater by the square on a straight line commensurable in length with itself.

Now neither of the straight lines $EH$, $HK$ is commensurable in length with the rational straight line $EF$ set out;

therefore $EK$ is a third binomial. [x. Deff. ii. 3]

But $EF$ is rational;

and, if an area be contained by a rational straight line and the third binomial, the "side" of the area is a second bimedial; [x. 56]

therefore the "side" of $EI$, that is, of $AD$, is a second bimedial.

Next, let the square on $EH$ be greater than the square on $HK$ by the square on a straight line incommensurable in length with $EH$.

Now each of the straight lines $EH$, $HK$ is incommensurable in length with $EF$;

therefore $EK$ is a sixth binomial. [x. Deff. ii. 6]

But, if an area be contained by a rational straight line and the sixth binomial, the "side" of the area is the side of the sum of two medial areas; [x. 59] so that the "side" of the area $AD$ is also the side of the sum of two medial areas.

Therefore etc.        Q. E. D.

The binomial straight line and the irrational straight lines after it are neither the same with the medial nor with one another.

For the square on a medial, if applied to a rational straight line, produces as breadth a straight line rational and incommensurable in length with that to which it is applied. [x. 22]

But the square on the binomial, if applied to a rational straight line, produces as breadth the first binomial. [x. 60]

The square on the first bimedial, if applied to a rational straight line, produces as breadth the second binomial. [x. 61]

The square on the second bimedial, if applied to a rational straight line, produces as breadth the third binomial. [x. 62]

The square on the major, if applied to a rational straight line, produces as breadth the fourth binomial. [x. 63]

The square on the side of a rational plus a medial area, if applied to a rational straight line, produces as breadth the fifth binomial. [x. 64]

The square on the side of the sum of two medial areas, if applied to a rational straight line, produces as breadth the sixth binomial. [x. 65]

And the said breadths differ both from the first and from one another: from the first because it is rational, and from one another because they are not the same in order;
so that the irrational straight lines themselves also differ from one another.

## Proposition 73

*If from a rational straight line there be subtracted a rational straight line commensurable with the whole in square only, the remainder is irrational; and let it be called an* apotome.

For from the rational straight line $AB$ let the rational straight line $BC$, commensurable with the whole in square only, be subtracted;

                  I say that the remainder $AC$ is the irrational straight
A    C         B   line called *apotome*.

For, since $AB$ is incommensurable in length with $BC$,
and, as $AB$ is to $BC$, so is the square on $AB$ to the rectangle $AB$, $BC$,
therefore the square on $AB$ is incommensurable with the rectangle $AB$, $BC$. [x. 11]

But the squares on $AB$, $BC$ are commensurable with the square on $AB$, [x. 15]

and twice the rectangle $AB$, $BC$ is commensurable with the rectangle $AB$, $BC$. [x. 6]

And, inasmuch as the squares on $AB$, $BC$ are equal to twice the rectangle $AB$, $BC$ together with the square on $CA$, [II. 7]
therefore the squares on $AB$, $BC$ are also incommensurable with the remainder, the square on $AC$. [x. 13, 16]

But the squares on $AB$, $BC$ are rational;
          therefore $AC$ is irrational.        [x. Def. 4]

And let it be called an *apotome*.        Q. E. D.

256                                EUCLID

## Proposition 74

*If from a medial straight line there be subtracted a medial straight line which is commensurable with the whole in square only, and which contains with the whole a rational rectangle, the remainder is irrational. And let it be called a* first apotome of a medial *straight line.*

For from the medial straight line $AB$ let there be subtracted the medial straight line $BC$ which is commensurable with $AB$ in square only and with $AB$ makes the rectangle $AB$, $BC$ rational;

I say that the remainder $AC$ is irrational; and let it be called a *first apotome of a medial* straight line.

For, since $AB$, $BC$ are medial,
            the squares on $AB$, $BC$ are also medial.
But twice the rectangle $AB$, $BC$ is rational;
therefore the squares on $AB$, $BC$ are incommensurable with twice the rectangle $AB$, $BC$;
therefore twice the rectangle $AB$, $BC$ is also incommensurable with the remainder, the square on $AC$,                                               [cf. II. 7]
since, if the whole is incommensurable with one of the magnitudes, the original magnitudes will also be incommensurable.                              [x. 16]
But twice the rectangle $AB$, $BC$ is rational;
            therefore the square on $AC$ is irrational;
                therefore $AC$ is irrational.                                [x. Def. 4]
And let it be called a *first apotome of a medial* straight line.       Q. E. D.

## Proposition 75

*If from a medial straight line there be subtracted a medial straight line which is commensurable with the whole in square only, and which contains with the whole a medial rectangle, the remainder is irrational; and let it be called a* second apotome of a medial *straight line.*

For from the medial straight line $AB$ let there be subtracted the medial straight line $CB$ which is commensurable with the whole $AB$ in square only and such that the rectangle $AB$, $BC$ which it contains with the whole $AB$, is medial;                                                          [x. 28]

I say that the remainder $AC$ is irrational; and let it be called a *second apotome of a medial* straight line.

For let a rational straight line $DI$ be set out,
let $DE$, equal to the squares on $AB$, $BC$, be applied to $DI$, producing $DG$ as breadth,

and let $DH$ equal to twice the rectangle $AB$, $BC$ be applied to $DI$, producing $DF$ as breadth;

therefore the remainder $FE$ is equal to the square on $AC$.  [II. 7]

Now, since the squares on $AB$, $BC$ are medial and commensurable,

therefore $DE$ is also medial.  [x. 15 and 23, Por.]

And it is applied to the rational straight line $DI$, producing $DG$ as breadth; therefore $DG$ is rational and incommensurable in length with $DI$.  [x. 22]

Again, since the rectangle $AB$, $BC$ is medial,

therefore twice the rectangle $AB$, $BC$ is also medial. [x. 23, Por.]

And it is equal to $DH$;

therefore $DH$ is also medial.

And it has been applied to the rational straight line $DI$, producing $DF$ as breadth;

therefore $DF$ is rational and incommensurable in length with $DI$. [x. 22]

And, since $AB$, $BC$ are commensurable in square only,

therefore $AB$ is incommensurable in length with $BC$;

therefore the square on $AB$ is also incommensurable with the rectangle $AB$, $BC$.  [x. 11]

But the squares on $AB$, $BC$ are commensurable with the square on $AB$,  [x. 15]

and twice the rectangle $AB$, $BC$ is commensurable with the rectangle $AB$, $BC$;  [x. 6]

therefore twice the rectangle $AB$, $BC$ is incommensurable with the squares on $AB$, $BC$.  [x. 13]

But $DE$ is equal to the squares on $AB$, $BC$,

and $DH$ to twice the rectangle $AB$, $BC$;

therefore $DE$ is incommensurable with $DH$.

But, as $DE$ is to $DH$, so is $GD$ to $DF$;  [VI. 1]

therefore $GD$ is incommensurable with $DF$.  [x. 11]

And both are rational;

therefore $GD$, $DF$ are rational straight lines commensurable in square only;

therefore $FG$ is an apotome.  [x. 73]

But $DI$ is rational,

and the rectangle contained by a rational and an irrational straight line is irrational,  [deduction from x. 20]

and its "side" is irrational.

And $AC$ is the "side" of $FE$;

therefore $AC$ is irrational.

And let it be called a *second apotome of a medial* straight line.  Q. E. D.

## Proposition 76

*If from a straight line there be subtracted a straight line which is incommensurable in square with the whole and which with the whole makes the squares on them added together rational, but the rectangle contained by them medial, the remainder is irrational; and let it be called* minor.

For from the straight line $AB$ let there be subtracted the straight line $BC$ which is incommensurable in square with the whole and fulfils the given conditions.  [x. 33]

I say that the remainder $AC$ is the irrational straight line called *minor*.

For, since the sum of the squares on $AB$, $BC$ is rational, while twice the rectangle $AB$, $BC$ is medial,

therefore the squares on $AB$, $BC$ are incommensurable with twice the rectangle $AB$, $BC$;

and, *convertendo*, the squares on $AB$, $BC$ are incommensurable with the remainder, the square on $AC$. [II. 7, X. 16]

But the squares on $AB$, $BC$ are rational;

therefore the square on $AC$ is irrational;

therefore $AC$ is irrational.

And let it be called *minor*.

Q. E. D.

## Proposition 77

*If from a straight line there be subtracted a straight line which is incommensurable in square with the whole, and which with the whole makes the sum of the squares on them medial, but twice the rectangle contained by them rational, the remainder is irrational; and let it be called* that which produces with a rational area a medial whole.

For from the straight line $AB$ let there be subtracted the straight line $BC$ which is incommensurable in square with $AB$ and fulfils the given conditions; [X. 34]

I say that the remainder $AC$ is the irrational straight line aforesaid.

For, since the sum of the squares on $AB$, $BC$ is medial,

while twice the rectangle $AB$, $BC$ is rational,

therefore the squares on $AB$, $BC$ are incommensurable with twice the rectangle $AB$, $BC$;

therefore the remainder also, the square on $AC$, is incommensurable with twice the rectangle $AB$, $BC$. [II. 7, X. 16]

And twice the rectangle $AB$, $BC$ is rational;

therefore the square on $AC$ is irrational;

therefore $AC$ is irrational.

And let it be called *that which produces with a rational area a medial whole*.

Q. E. D.

## Proposition 78

*If from a straight line there be subtracted a straight line which is incommensurable in square with the whole and which with the whole makes the sum of the squares on them medial, twice the rectangle contained by them medial, and further, the squares on them incommensurable with twice the rectangle contained by them, the remainder is irrational; and let it be called* that which produces with a medial area a medial whole.

For from the straight line $AB$ let there be subtracted the straight line $BC$ incommensurable in square with $AB$ and fulfilling the given conditions; [X. 35]

I say that the remainder $AC$ is the irrational straight line called *that which produces with a medial area a medial whole*.

For let a rational straight line $DI$ be set out, to $DI$ let there be applied $DE$ equal to the squares on $AB$, $BC$, producing $DG$ as breadth,

ELEMENTS X

and let $DH$ equal to twice the rectangle $AB$, $BC$ be subtracted.
Therefore the remainder $FE$ is equal to the square on $AC$, [II. 7]
so that $AC$ is the "side" of $FE$.

Now, since the sum of the squares on $AB$, $BC$ is medial and is equal to $DE$, therefore $DE$ is medial.

And it is applied to the rational straight line $DI$, producing $DG$ as breadth; therefore $DG$ is rational and incommensurable in length with $DI$. [x. 22]

Again, since twice the rectangle $AB$, $BC$ is medial and is equal to $DH$, therefore $DH$ is medial.

And it is applied to the rational straight line $DI$, producing $DF$ as breadth; therefore $DF$ is also rational and incommensurable in length with $DI$. [x. 22]

And, since the squares on $AB$, $BC$ are incommensurable with twice the rectangle $AB$, $BC$,
therefore $DE$ is also incommensurable with $DH$.
But, as $DE$ is to $DH$, so also is $DG$ to $DF$; [VI. 1]
therefore $DG$ is incommensurable with $DF$. [x. 11]

And both are rational;
therefore $GD$, $DF$ are rational straight lines commensurable in square only.
Therefore $FG$ is an apotome. [x. 73]

And $FH$ is rational;
but the rectangle contained by a rational straight line and an apotome is irrational, [deduction from x. 20]
and its "side" is irrational.
And $AC$ is the "side" of $FE$;
therefore $AC$ is irrational.

And let it be called *that which produces with a medial area a medial whole*.

Q. E. D.

PROPOSITION 79

*To an apotome only one rational straight line can be annexed which is commensurable with the whole in square only.*

Let $AB$ be an apotome, and $BC$ an annex to it;
therefore $AC$, $CB$ are rational straight lines commensurable in square only. [x. 73]

A———B————C—D

I say that no other rational straight line can be annexed to $AB$ which is commensurable with the whole in square only.

For, if possible, let $BD$ be so annexed;
therefore $AD$, $DB$ are also rational straight lines commensurable in square only. [x. 73]

Now, since the excess of the squares on $AD$, $DB$ over twice the rectangle $AD$, $DB$ is also the excess of the squares on $AC$, $CB$ over twice the rectangle $AC$, $CB$,
for both exceed by the same, the square on $AB$, [II. 7]
therefore, alternately, the excess of the squares on $AD$, $DB$ over the squares on $AC$, $CB$ is the excess of twice the rectangle $AD$, $DB$ over twice the rectangle $AC$, $CB$.

But the squares on $AD$, $DB$ exceed the squares on $AC$, $CB$ by a rational area, for both are rational;
therefore twice the rectangle $AD$, $DB$ also exceeds twice the rectangle $AC$, $CB$ by a rational area:

which is impossible,
for both are medial [x. 21], and a medial area does not exceed a medial by a rational area. [x. 26]

Therefore no other rational straight line can be annexed to $AB$ which is commensurable with the whole in square only.

Therefore only one rational straight line can be annexed to an apotome which is commensurable with the whole in square only. Q. E. D.

## Proposition 80

*To a first apotome of a medial straight line only one medial straight line can be annexed which is commensurable with the whole in square only and which contains with the whole a rational rectangle.*

For let $AB$ be a first apotome of a medial straight line, and let $BC$ be an annex to $AB$; therefore $AC$, $CB$ are medial straight lines commensurable in square only and such that the rectangle $AC$, $CB$ which they contain is rational; [x. 74]

I say that no other medial straight line can be annexed to $AB$ which is commensurable with the whole in square only and which contains with the whole a rational area.

For, if possible, let $DB$ also be so annexed;
therefore $AD$, $DB$ are medial straight lines commensurable in square only and such that the rectangle $AD$, $DB$ which they contain is rational. [x. 74]

Now, since the excess of the squares on $AD$, $DB$ over twice the rectangle $AD$, $DB$ is also the excess of the squares on $AC$, $CB$ over twice the rectangle $AC$, $CB$,
for they exceed by the same, the square on $AB$, [II. 7]
therefore, alternately, the excess of the squares on $AD$, $DB$ over the squares on $AC$, $CB$ is also the excess of twice the rectangle $AD$, $DB$ over twice the rectangle $AC$, $CB$.

But twice the rectangle $AD$, $DB$ exceeds twice the rectangle $AC$, $CB$ by a rational area,
for both are rational.

Therefore the squares on $AD$, $DB$ also exceed the squares on $AC$, $CB$ by a rational area:
which is impossible,
for both are medial [x. 15 and 23, Por.], and a medial area does not exceed a medial by a rational area. [x. 26]

Therefore etc. Q. E. D.

## Proposition 81

*To a second apotome of a medial straight line only one medial straight line can be annexed which is commensurable with the whole in square only and which contains with the whole a medial rectangle.*

Let $AB$ be a second apotome of a medial straight line and $BC$ an annex to $AB$;
therefore $AC$, $CB$ are medial straight lines commensurable in square only and such that the rectangle $AC$, $CB$ which they contain is medial. [x. 75]

I say that no other medial straight line can be annexed to $AB$ which is com-

ELEMENTS X                                                              261

mensurable with the whole in square only and which contains with the whole a medial rectangle.

For, if possible, let $BD$ also be so annexed;

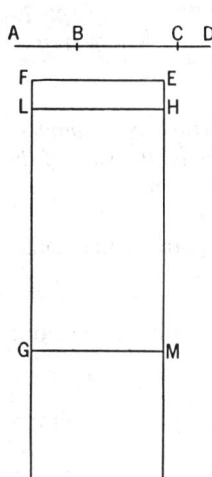

therefore $AD$, $DB$ are also medial straight lines commensurable in square only and such that the rectangle $AD$, $DB$ which they contain is medial.  [x. 75]

Let a rational straight line $EF$ be set out,
let $EG$ equal to the squares on $AC$, $CB$ be applied to $EF$, producing $EM$ as breadth,
and let $HG$ equal to twice the rectangle $AC$, $CB$ be subtracted, producing $HM$ as breadth;
therefore the remainder $EL$ is equal to the square on $AB$,  [II. 7]
so that $AB$ is the "side" of $EL$.

Again, let $EI$ equal to the squares on $AD$, $DB$ be applied to $EF$, producing $EN$ as breadth.

But $EL$ is also equal to the square on $AB$;
therefore the remainder $HI$ is equal to twice the rectangle $AD$, $DB$.  [II. 7]

Now, since $AC$, $CB$ are medial straight lines,
therefore the squares on $AC$, $CB$ are also medial.
And they are equal to $EG$;
therefore $EG$ is also medial.  [x. 15 and 23, Por.]

And it is applied to the rational straight line $EF$, producing $EM$ as breadth; therefore $EM$ is rational and incommensurable in length with $EF$.  [x. 22]

Again, since the rectangle $AC$, $CB$ is medial,
twice the rectangle $AC$, $CB$ is also medial.  [x. 23, Por.]
And it is equal to $HG$;
therefore $HG$ is also medial.
And it is applied to the rational straight line $EF$, producing $HM$ as breadth; therefore $HM$ is also rational and incommensurable in length with $EF$.  [x. 22]

And, since $AC$, $CB$ are commensurable in square only,
therefore $AC$ is incommensurable in length with $CB$.

But, as $AC$ is to $CB$, so is the square on $AC$ to the rectangle $AC$, $CB$; therefore the square on $AC$ is incommensurable with the rectangle $AC$, $CB$.  [x. 11]

But the squares on $AC$, $CB$ are commensurable with the square on $AC$, while twice the rectangle $AC$, $CB$ is commensurable with the rectangle $AC$, $CB$;  [x. 6]
therefore the squares on $AC$, $CB$ are incommensurable with twice the rectangle $AC$, $CB$.  [x. 13]

And $EG$ is equal to the squares on $AC$, $CB$,
while $GH$ is equal to twice the rectangle $AC$, $CB$;
therefore $EG$ is incommensurable with $HG$.

But, as $EG$ is to $HG$, so is $EM$ to $HM$;  [VI. 1]
therefore $EM$ is incommensurable in length with $MH$.  [x. 11]

And both are rational;
therefore $EM$, $MH$ are rational straight lines commensurable in square only;
therefore $EH$ is an apotome, and $HM$ an annex to it.  [x. 73]

Similarly we can prove that $HN$ is also an annex to it;
therefore to an apotome different straight lines are annexed which are commensurable with the wholes in square only:

which is impossible. [x. 79]

Therefore etc.
Q. E. D.

## Proposition 82

*To a minor straight line only one straight line can be annexed which is incommensurable in square with the whole and which makes, with the whole, the sum of the squares on them rational but twice the rectangle contained by them medial.*

Let $AB$ be the minor straight line, and let $BC$ be an annex to $AB$;
therefore $AC$, $CB$ are straight lines incommensurable in square which make the sum of the squares on them rational, but twice the rectangle contained by them medial. [x. 76]

I say that no other straight line can be annexed to $AB$ fulfilling the same conditions.

For, if possible, let $BD$ be so annexed;
therefore $AD$, $DB$ are also straight lines incommensurable in square which fulfil the aforesaid conditions. [x. 76]

Now, since the excess of the squares on $AD$, $DB$ over the squares on $AC$, $CB$ is also the excess of twice the rectangle $AD$, $DB$ over twice the rectangle $AC$, $CB$,
while the squares on $AD$, $DB$ exceed the squares on $AC$, $CB$ by a rational area, for both are rational,
therefore twice the rectangle $AD$, $DB$ also exceeds twice the rectangle $AC$, $CB$ by a rational area:

which is impossible, for both are medial. [x. 26]

Therefore to a minor straight line only one straight line can be annexed which is incommensurable in square with the whole and which makes the squares on them added together rational, but twice the rectangle contained by them medial.
Q. E. D.

## Proposition 83

*To a straight line which produces with a rational area a medial whole only one straight line can be annexed which is incommensurable in square with the whole straight line and which with the whole straight line makes the sum of the squares on them medial, but twice the rectangle contained by them rational.*

Let $AB$ be the straight line which produces with a rational area a medial whole,
and let $BC$ be an annex to $AB$;
therefore $AC$, $CB$ are straight lines incommensurable in square which fulfil the given conditions. [x. 77]

I say that no other straight line can be annexed to $AB$ which fulfils the same conditions.

For, if possible, let $BD$ be so annexed;
therefore $AD$, $DB$ are also straight lines incommensurable in square which fulfil the given conditions. [x. 77]

Since then, as in the preceding cases,
the excess of the squares on $AD$, $DB$ over the squares on $AC$, $CB$ is also the

ELEMENTS X

excess of twice the rectangle $AD, DB$ over twice the rectangle $AC, CB$, while twice the rectangle $AD, DB$ exceeds twice the rectangle $AC, CB$ by a rational area,

for both are rational,

therefore the squares on $AD, DB$ also exceed the squares on $AC, CB$ by a rational area:

which is impossible, for both are medial. [x. 26]

Therefore no other straight line can be annexed to $AB$ which is incommensurable in square with the whole and which with the whole fulfils the aforesaid conditions;

therefore only one straight line can be so annexed. Q. E. D.

PROPOSITION 84

*To a straight line which produces with a medial area a medial whole only one straight line can be annexed which is incommensurable in square with the whole straight line and which with the whole straight line makes the sum of the squares on them medial and twice the rectangle contained by them both medial and also incommensurable with the sum of the squares on them.*

Let $AB$ be the straight line which produces with a medial area a medial whole,

and $BC$ an annex to it;

therefore $AC, CB$ are straight lines incommensurable in square which fulfil the aforesaid conditions. [x. 78]

I say that no other straight line can be annexed to $AB$ which fulfils the aforesaid conditions.

For, if possible, let $BD$ be so annexed,

so that $AD, DB$ are also straight lines incommensurable in square which make the squares on $AD, DB$ added together medial, twice the rectangle $AD, DB$ medial, and also the squares on $AD, DB$ incommensurable with twice the rectangle $AD, DB$. [x. 78]

Let a rational straight line $EF$ be set out,

let $EG$ equal to the squares on $AC, CB$ be applied to $EF$, producing $EM$ as breadth,

and let $HG$ equal to twice the rectangle $AC, CB$ be applied to $EF$, producing $HM$ as breadth;

therefore the remainder, the square on $AB$ [II. 7], is equal to $EL$;

therefore $AB$ is the "side" of $EL$.

Again, let $EI$ equal to the squares on $AD, DB$ be applied to $EF$, producing $EN$ as breadth.

But the square on $AB$ is also equal to $EL$;

therefore the remainder, twice the rectangle $AD, DB$ [II. 7], is equal to $HI$.

Now, since the sum of the squares on $AC, CB$ is medial and is equal to $EG$,

therefore $EG$ is also medial.

And it is applied to the rational straight line $EF$, producing $EM$ as breadth;

therefore $EM$ is rational and incommensurable in length with $EF$. [x. 22]

Again, since twice the rectangle $AC$, $CB$ is medial and is equal to $HG$, therefore $HG$ is also medial.

And it is applied to the rational straight line $EF$, producing $HM$ as breadth;
therefore $HM$ is rational and incommensurable in length with $EF$. [x. 22]
And, since the squares on $AC$, $CB$ are incommensurable with twice the rectangle $AC$, $CB$,

$EG$ is also incommensurable with $HG$;
therefore $EM$ is also incommensurable in length with $MH$. [vi. 1, x. 11]
And both are rational;
therefore $EM$, $MH$ are rational straight lines commensurable in square only;
therefore $EH$ is an apotome, and $HM$ an annex to it. [x. 73]
Similarly we can prove that $EH$ is again an apotome and $HN$ an annex to it.
Therefore to an apotome different rational straight lines are annexed which are commensurable with the wholes in square only:
which was proved impossible. [x. 79]
Therefore no other straight line can be so annexed to $AB$.

Therefore to $AB$ only one straight line can be annexed which is incommensurable in square with the whole and which with the whole makes the squares on them added together medial, twice the rectangle contained by them medial, and also the squares on them incommensurable with twice the rectangle contained by them.

Q. E. D.

## DEFINITIONS III

1. Given a rational straight line and an apotome, if the square on the whole be greater than the square on the annex by the square on a straight line commensurable in length with the whole, and the whole be commensurable in length with the rational straight line set out, let the apotome be called a *first apotome*.

2. But if the annex be commensurable in length with the rational straight line set out, and the square on the whole be greater than that on the annex by the square on a straight line commensurable with the whole, let the apotome be called a *second apotome*.

3. But if neither be commensurable in length with the rational straight line set out, and the square on the whole be greater than the square on the annex by the square on a straight line commensurable with the whole, let the apotome be called a *third apotome*.

4. Again, if the square on the whole be greater than the square on the annex by the square on a straight line incommensurable with the whole, then, if the whole be commensurable in length with the rational straight line set out, let the apotome be called a *fourth apotome*;

5. if the annex be so commensurable, a *fifth*;

6. and, if neither, a *sixth*.

## Proposition 85

*To find the first apotome.*

Let a rational straight line $A$ be set out,
and let $BG$ be commensurable in length with $A$;
therefore $BG$ is also rational.

Let two square numbers $DE$, $EF$ be set out, and let their difference $FD$ not be square;

therefore neither has $ED$ to $DF$ the ratio which a square number has to a square number.

Let it be contrived that, as $ED$ is to $DF$, so is the square on $BG$ to the square on $GC$;  [x. 6, Por.]
therefore the square on $BG$ is commensurable with the square on $GC$.  [x. 6]

But the square on $BG$ is rational;
therefore the square on $GC$ is also rational;
therefore $GC$ is also rational.

And, since $ED$ has not to $DF$ the ratio which a square number has to a square number,
therefore neither has the square on $BG$ to the square on $GC$ the ratio which a square number has to a square number;
therefore $BG$ is incommensurable in length with $GC$.  [x. 9]

And both are rational;
therefore $BG$, $GC$ are rational straight lines commensurable in square only;
therefore $BC$ is an apotome.  [x. 73]

I say next that it is also a first apotome.

For let the square on $H$ be that by which the square on $BG$ is greater than the square on $GC$.

Now since, as $ED$ is to $FD$, so is the square on $BG$ to the square on $GC$,
therefore also, *convertendo*,  [v. 19, Por.]
as $DE$ is to $EF$, so is the square on $GB$ to the square on $H$.

But $DE$ has to $EF$ the ratio which a square number has to a square number, for each is square;
therefore the square on $GB$ also has to the square on $H$ the ratio which a square number has to a square number;
therefore $BG$ is commensurable in length with $H$.  [x. 9]

And the square on $BG$ is greater than the square on $GC$ by the square on $H$;
therefore the square on $BG$ is greater than the square on $GC$ by the square on a straight line commensurable in length with $BG$.

And the whole $BG$ is commensurable in length with the rational straight line $A$ set out.

Therefore $BC$ is a first apotome.  [x. Deff. III. 1]

Therefore the first apotome $BC$ has been found.

(Being) that which it was required to find.   Q. E. D.

PROPOSITION 86

*To find the second apotome.*

Let a rational straight line $A$ be set out, and $GC$ commensurable in length with $A$;
therefore $GC$ is rational.

Let two square numbers $DE$, $EF$ be set out, and let their difference $DF$ not be square.

Now let it be contrived that, as $FD$ is to $DE$, so is the square on $CG$ to the square on $GB$.  [x. 6, Por.]

Therefore the square on $CG$ is commensurable with the square on $GB$.  [x. 6]

266                                     EUCLID

But the square on $CG$ is rational;
   therefore the square on $GB$ is also rational;
    therefore $BG$ is rational.

And, since the square on $GC$ has not to the square on $GB$ the ratio which a square number has to a square number,
$CG$ is incommensurable in length with $GB$.
          [x. 9]

And both are rational;
therefore $CG$, $GB$ are rational straight lines commensurable in square only;
   therefore $BC$ is an apotome.   [x. 73]

I say next that it is also a second apotome.

For let the square on $H$ be that by which the square on $BG$ is greater than the square on $GC$.

Since then, as the square on $BG$ is to the square on $GC$, so is the number $ED$ to the number $DF$,
  therefore, *convertendo*,
as the square on $BG$ is to the square on $H$, so is $DE$ to $EF$.  [v. 19, Por.]

And each of the numbers $DE$, $EF$ is square;
therefore the square on $BG$ has to the square on $H$ the ratio which a square number has to a square number;
   therefore $BG$ is commensurable in length with $H$.  [x. 9]

And the square on $BG$ is greater than the square on $GC$ by the square on $H$;
therefore the square on $BG$ is greater than the square on $GC$ by the square on a straight line commensurable in length with $BG$.

And $CG$, the annex, is commensurable with the rational straight line $A$ set out.

Therefore $BC$ is a second apotome.   [x. Deff. III. 2]

Therefore the second apotome $BC$ has been found.   Q. E. D.

## Proposition 87

*To find the third apotome.*

Let a rational straight line $A$ be set out, let three numbers $E$, $BC$, $CD$ be set out which have not to one another the ratio which a square number has to a square number, but let $CB$ have to $BD$ the ratio which a square number has to a square number.

Let it be contrived that, as $E$ is to $BC$, so is the square on $A$ to the square on $FG$, and, as $BC$ is to $CD$, so is the square on $FG$ to the square on $GH$.  [x. 6, Por.]

Since then, as $E$ is to $BC$, so is the square on $A$ to the square on $FG$, therefore the square on $A$ is commensurable with the square on $FG$.  [x. 6]

But the square on $A$ is rational;
   therefore the square on $FG$ is also rational;
    therefore $FG$ is rational.

And, since $E$ has not to $BC$ the ratio which a square number has to a square number,
therefore neither has the square on $A$ to the square on $FG$ the ratio which a square number has to a square number;
> therefore $A$ is incommensurable in length with $FG$. [x. 9]

Again, since, as $BC$ is to $CD$, so is the square on $FG$ to the square on $GH$, therefore the square on $FG$ is commensurable with the square on $GH$. [x. 6]
But the square on $FG$ is rational;
> therefore the square on $GH$ is also rational;
> therefore $GH$ is rational.

And, since $BC$ has not to $CD$ the ratio which a square number has to a square number,
therefore neither has the square on $FG$ to the square on $GH$ the ratio which a square number has to a square number;
> therefore $FG$ is incommensurable in length with $GH$. [x. 9]

And both are rational;
therefore $FG$, $GH$ are rational straight lines commensurable in square only;
> therefore $FH$ is an apotome. [x. 73]

I say next that it is also a third apotome.
For since, as $E$ is to $BC$, so is the square on $A$ to the square on $FG$,
and, as $BC$ is to $CD$, so is the square on $FG$ to the square on $HG$,
therefore, *ex aequali*, as $E$ is to $CD$, so is the square on $A$ to the square on $HG$. [v. 22]

But $E$ has not to $CD$ the ratio which a square number has to a square number;
therefore neither has the square on $A$ to the square on $GH$ the ratio which a square number has to a square number;
> therefore $A$ is incommensurable in length with $GH$. [x. 9]

Therefore neither of the straight lines $FG$, $GH$ is commensurable in length with the rational straight line $A$ set out.

Now let the square on $K$ be that by which the square on $FG$ is greater than the square on $GH$.

Since then, as $BC$ is to $CD$, so is the square on $FG$ to the square on $GH$, therefore, *convertendo*, as $BC$ is to $BD$, so is the square on $FG$ to the square on $K$. [v. 19, Por.]

But $BC$ has to $BD$ the ratio which a square number has to a square number;
therefore the square on $FG$ also has to the square on $K$ the ratio which a square number has to a square number.

Therefore $FG$ is commensurable in length with $K$, [x. 9]
and the square on $FG$ is greater than the square on $GH$ by the square on a straight line commensurable with $FG$.

And neither of the straight lines $FG$, $GH$ is commensurable in length with the rational straight line $A$ set out;
> therefore $FH$ is a third apotome. [x. Deff. III. 3]

Therefore the third apotome $FH$ has been found. Q. E. D.

## Proposition 88

*To find the fourth apotome.*

Let a rational straight line $A$ be set out, and $BG$ commensurable in length with it;

therefore $BG$ is also rational.

Let two numbers $DF$, $FE$ be set out such that the whole $DE$ has not to either of the numbers $DF$, $EF$ the ratio which a square number has to a square number.

Let it be contrived that, as $DE$ is to $EF$, so is the square on $BG$ to the square on $GC$; [x. 6, Por.]
therefore the square on $BG$ is commensurable with the square on $GC$. [x. 6]

But the square on $BG$ is rational;
therefore the square on $GC$ is also rational;
therefore $GC$ is rational.

Now, since $DE$ has not to $EF$ the ratio which a square number has to a square number,
therefore neither has the square on $BG$ to the square on $GC$ the ratio which a square number has to a square number;
therefore $BG$ is incommensurable in length with $GC$. [x. 9]
And both are rational;
therefore $BG$, $GC$ are rational straight lines commensurable in square only;
therefore $BC$ is an apotome. [x. 73]

Now let the square on $H$ be that by which the square on $BG$ is greater than the square on $GC$.

Since then, as $DE$ is to $EF$, so is the square on $BG$ to the square on $GC$,
therefore also, *convertendo*, as $ED$ is to $DF$, so is the square on $GB$ to the square on $H$. [v. 19, Por.]

But $ED$ has not to $DF$ the ratio which a square number has to a square number;
therefore neither has the square on $GB$ to the square on $H$ the ratio which a square number has to a square number;
therefore $BG$ is incommensurable in length with $H$. [x. 9]
And the square on $BG$ is greater than the square on $GC$ by the square on $H$;
therefore the square on $BG$ is greater than the square on $GC$ by the square on a straight line incommensurable with $BG$.

And the whole $BG$ is commensurable in length with the rational straight line $A$ set out.

Therefore $BC$ is a fourth apotome. [x. Deff. III. 4]
Therefore the fourth apotome has been found. Q. E. D.

## Proposition 89

*To find the fifth apotome.*

Let a rational straight line $A$ be set out, and let $CG$ be commensurable in length with $A$;
therefore $CG$ is rational.

Let two numbers $DF$, $FE$ be set out such that $DE$ again has not to either of the numbers $DF$, $FE$ the ratio which a square number has to a square number;

ELEMENTS X 269

and let it be contrived that, as *FE* is to *ED*, so is the square on *CG* to the square on *GB*.

Therefore the square on *GB* is also rational; [x. 6]
therefore *BG* is also rational.

Now since, as *DE* is to *EF*, so is the square on *BG* to the square on *GC*,
while *DE* has not to *EF* the ratio which a square number has to a square number,
therefore neither has the square on *BG* to the square on *GC* the ratio which a square number has to a square number;
therefore *BG* is incommensurable in length with *GC*. [x. 9]

And both are rational;
therefore *BG*, *GC* are rational straight lines commensurable in square only;
therefore *BC* is an apotome. [x. 73]

I say next that it is also a fifth apotome.

For let the square on *H* be that by which the square on *BG* is greater than the square on *GC*.

Since then, as the square on *BG* is to the square on *GC*, so is *DE* to *EF*,
therefore, *convertendo*, as *ED* is to *DF*, so is the square on *BG* to the square on *H*. [v. 19, Por.]

But *ED* has not to *DF* the ratio which a square number has to a square number;
therefore neither has the square on *BG* to the square on *H* the ratio which a square number has to a square number;
therefore *BG* is incommensurable in length with *H*. [x. 9]

And the square on *BG* is greater than the square on *GC* by the square on *H*;
therefore the square on *GB* is greater than the square on *GC* by the square on a straight line incommensurable in length with *GB*.

And the annex *CG* is commensurable in length with the rational straight line *A* set out;
therefore *BC* is a fifth apotome. [x. Deff. III. 5]

Therefore the fifth apotome *BC* has been found. Q. E. D.

## Proposition 90

*To find the sixth apotome.*

Let a rational straight line *A* be set out, and three numbers *E*, *BC*, *CD* not having to one another the ratio which a square number has to a square number; and further let *CB* also not have to *BD* the ratio which a square number has to a square number.

Let it be contrived that, as *E* is to *BC*, so is the square on *A* to the square on *FG*,
and, as *BC* is to *CD*, so is the square on *FG* to the square on *GH*. [x. 6, Por.]

Now since, as *E* is to *BC*, so is the square on *A* to the square on *FG*,
therefore the square on *A* is commensurable with the square on *FG*. [x. 6]

But the square on *A* is rational;

therefore the square on $FG$ is also rational;

therefore $FG$ is also rational.

And, since $E$ has not to $BC$ the ratio which a square number has to a square number,

therefore neither has the square on $A$ to the square on $FG$ the ratio which a square number has to a square number;

therefore $A$ is incommensurable in length with $FG$. [x. 9]

Again, since, as $BC$ is to $CD$, so is the square on $FG$ to the square on $GH$, therefore the square on $FG$ is commensurable with the square on $GH$. [x. 6]

But the square on $FG$ is rational;

therefore the square on $GH$ is also rational;

therefore $GH$ is also rational.

And, since $BC$ has not to $CD$ the ratio which a square number has to a square number,

therefore neither has the square on $FG$ to the square on $GH$ the ratio which a square number has to a square number;

therefore $FG$ is incommensurable in length with $GH$. [x. 9]

And both are rational;

therefore $FG$, $GH$ are rational straight lines commensurable in square only;

therefore $FH$ is an apotome. [x. 73]

I say next that it is also a sixth apotome.

For since, as $E$ is to $BC$, so is the square on $A$ to the square on $FG$,

and, as $BC$ is to $CD$, so is the square on $FG$ to the square on $GH$,

therefore, *ex aequali*, as $E$ is to $CD$, so is the square on $A$ to the square on $GH$.

[v. 22]

But $E$ has not to $CD$ the ratio which a square number has to a square number;

therefore neither has the square on $A$ to the square on $GH$ the ratio which a square number has to a square number;

therefore $A$ is incommensurable in length with $GH$; [x. 9]

therefore neither of the straight lines $FG$, $GH$ is commensurable in length with the rational straight line $A$.

Now let the square on $K$ be that by which the square on $FG$ is greater than the square on $GH$.

Since then, as $BC$ is to $CD$, so is the square on $FG$ to the square on $GH$, therefore, *convertendo*, as $CB$ is to $BD$, so is the square on $FG$ to the square on $K$. [v. 19, Por.]

But $CB$ has not to $BD$ the ratio which a square number has to a square number;

therefore neither has the square on $FG$ to the square on $K$ the ratio which a square number has to a square number;

therefore $FG$ is incommensurable in length with $K$. [x. 9]

And the square on $FG$ is greater than the square on $GH$ by the square on $K$; therefore the square on $FG$ is greater than the square on $GH$ by the square on a straight line incommensurable in length with $FG$.

And neither of the straight lines $FG$, $GH$ is commensurable with the rational straight line $A$ set out.

Therefore $FH$ is a sixth apotome. [x. Deff. III. 6]

Therefore the sixth apotome $FH$ has been found. Q. E. D.

ELEMENTS X  271

## Proposition 91

*If an area be contained by a rational straight line and a first apotome, the "side" of the area is an apotome.*

For let the area $AB$ be contained by the rational straight line $AC$ and the first apotome $AD$;

I say that the "side" of the area $AB$ is an apotome.

For, since $AD$ is a first apotome, let $DG$ be its annex;
therefore $AG$, $GD$ are rational straight lines commensurable in square only.
[x. 73]

And the whole $AG$ is commensurable with the rational straight line $AC$ set out,
and the square on $AG$ is greater than the square on $GD$ by the square on a straight line commensurable in length with $AG$; [x. Deff. III. 1]
if therefore there be applied to $AG$ a parallelogram equal to the fourth part of the square on $DG$ and deficient by a square figure, it divides it into commensurable parts. [x. 17]

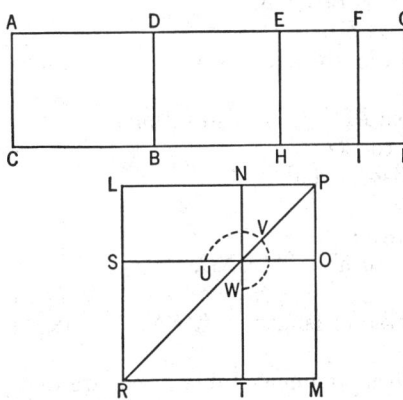

Let $DG$ be bisected at $E$,
let there be applied to $AG$ a parallelogram equal to the square on $EG$ and deficient by a square figure,
and let it be the rectangle $AF$, $FG$;
therefore $AF$ is commensurable with $FG$.

And through the points $E$, $F$, $G$ let $EH$, $FI$, $GK$ be drawn parallel to $AC$.

Now, since $AF$ is commensurable in length with $FG$,
therefore $AG$ is also commensurable in length with each of the straight lines $AF$, $FG$. [x. 15]
But $AG$ is commensurable with $AC$;
therefore each of the straight lines $AF$, $FG$ is commensurable in length with $AC$. [x. 12]

And $AC$ is rational;
therefore each of the straight lines $AF$, $FG$ is also rational,
so that each of the rectangles $AI$, $FK$ is also rational. [x. 19]

Now, since $DE$ is commensurable in length with $EG$,
therefore $DG$ is also commensurable in length with each of the straight lines $DE$, $EG$. [x. 15]

But $DG$ is rational and incommensurable in length with $AC$;
therefore each of the straight lines $DE$, $EG$ is also rational and incommensurable in length with $AC$; [x. 13]
therefore each of the rectangles $DH$, $EK$ is medial. [x. 21]

Now let the square $LM$ be made equal to $AI$, and let there be subtracted the square $NO$ having a common angle with it, the angle $LPM$, and equal to $FK$;
therefore the squares $LM$, $NO$ are about the same diameter. [VI. 26]
Let $PR$ be their diameter, and let the figure be drawn.

Since then the rectangle contained by $AF$, $FG$ is equal to the square on $EG$,
therefore, as $AF$ is to $EG$, so is $EG$ to $FG$. [VI. 17]
But, as $AF$ is to $EG$, so is $AI$ to $EK$,
and, as $EG$ is to $FG$, so is $EK$ to $KF$; [VI. 1]
therefore $EK$ is a mean proportional between $AI$, $KF$. [V. 11]
But $MN$ is also a mean proportional between $LM$, $NO$, as was before proved,
[Lemma after x. 53]
and $AI$ is equal to the square $LM$, and $KF$ to $NO$;
therefore $MN$ is also equal to $EK$.
But $EK$ is equal to $DH$, and $MN$ to $LO$;
therefore $DK$ is equal to the gnomon $UVW$ and $NO$.
But $AK$ is also equal to the squares $LM$, $NO$;
therefore the remainder $AB$ is equal to $ST$.
But $ST$ is the square on $LN$;
therefore the square on $LN$ is equal to $AB$;
therefore $LN$ is the "side" of $AB$.
I say next that $LN$ is an apotome.
For, since each of the rectangles $AI$, $FK$ is rational,
and they are equal to $LM$, $NO$,
therefore each of the squares $LM$, $NO$, that is, the squares on $LP$, $PN$ respectively, is also rational;
therefore each of the straight lines $LP$, $PN$ is also rational.
Again, since $DH$ is medial and is equal to $LO$,
therefore $LO$ is also medial.
Since, then, $LO$ is medial,
while $NO$ is rational,
therefore $LO$ is incommensurable with $NO$.
But, as $LO$ is to $NO$, so is $LP$ to $PN$; [VI. 1]
therefore $LP$ is incommensurable in length with $PN$. [X. 11]
And both are rational;
therefore $LP$, $PN$ are rational straight lines commensurable in square only;
therefore $LN$ is an apotome. [X. 73]
And it is the "side" of the area $AB$;
therefore the "side" of the area $AB$ is an apotome.
Therefore etc.
Q. E. D.

## Proposition 92

*If an area be contained by a rational straight line and a second apotome, the "side" of the area is a first apotome of a medial straight line.*

For let the area $AB$ be contained by the rational straight line $AC$ and the second apotome $AD$;
I say that the "side" of the area $AB$ is a first apotome of a medial straight line.
For let $DG$ be the annex to $AD$;
therefore $AG$, $GD$ are rational straight lines commensurable in square only,
[X. 73]
and the annex $DG$ is commensurable with the rational straight line $AC$ set out, while the square on the whole $AG$ is greater than the square on the annex $GD$ by the square on a straight line commensurable in length with $AG$.
[X. Deff. III. 2]

Since, then, the square on $AG$ is greater than the square on $GD$ by the square on a straight line commensurable with $AG$,

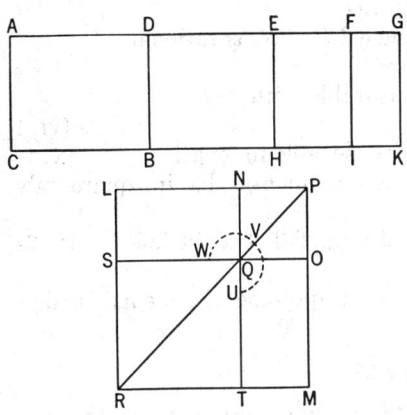

therefore, if there be applied to $AG$ a parallelogram equal to the fourth part of the square on $GD$ and deficient by a square figure, it divides it into commensurable parts. [x. 17]

Let then $DG$ be bisected at $E$,
let there be applied to $AG$ a parallelogram equal to the square on $EG$ and deficient by a square figure,
and let it be the rectangle $AF$, $FG$;
therefore $AF$ is commensurable in length with $FG$.

Therefore $AG$ is also commensurable in length with each of the straight lines $AF$, $FG$. [x. 15]

But $AG$ is rational and incommensurable in length with $AC$;
therefore each of the straight lines $AF$, $FG$ is also rational and incommensurable in length with $AC$; [x. 13]
therefore each of the rectangles $AI$, $FK$ is medial. [x. 21]

Again, since $DE$ is commensurable with $EG$,
therefore $DG$ is also commensurable with each of the straight lines $DE$, $EG$. [x. 15]

But $DG$ is commensurable in length with $AC$.
Therefore each of the rectangles $DH$, $EK$ is rational. [x. 19]

Let then the square $LM$ be constructed equal to $AI$,
and let there be subtracted $NO$ equal to $FK$ and being about the same angle with $LM$, namely the angle $LPM$;
therefore the squares $LM$, $NO$ are about the same diameter. [vi. 26

Let $PR$ be their diameter, and let the figure be drawn.
Since then $AI$, $FK$ are medial and are equal to the squares on $LP$, $PN$,
the squares on $LP$, $PN$ are also medial;
therefore $LP$, $PN$ are also medial straight lines commensurable in square only.

And, since the rectangle $AF$, $FG$ is equal to the square on $EG$,
therefore, as $AF$ is to $EG$, so is $EG$ to $FG$, [vi. 17]
while, as $AF$ is to $EG$, so is $AI$ to $EK$,
and, as $EG$ is to $FG$, so is $EK$ to $FK$; [vi. 1]
therefore $EK$ is a mean proportional between $AI$, $FK$. [v. 11]

But $MN$ is also a mean proportional between the squares $LM$, $NO$,
and $AI$ is equal to $LM$, and $FK$ to $NO$;
therefore $MN$ is also equal to $EK$.

But $DH$ is equal to $EK$, and $LO$ equal to $MN$;
therefore the whole $DK$ is equal to the gnomon $UVW$ and $NO$.

Since, then, the whole $AK$ is equal to $LM$, $NO$,
and, in these, $DK$ is equal to the gnomon $UVW$ and $NO$,
therefore the remainder $AB$ is equal to $TS$.

But $TS$ is the square on $LN$;
therefore the square on $LN$ is equal to the area $AB$;

therefore $LN$ is the "side" of the area $AB$.

I say that $LN$ is a first apotome of a medial straight line.

For, since $EK$ is rational and is equal to $LO$,
    therefore $LO$, that is, the rectangle $LP$, $PN$, is rational.
But $NO$ was proved medial;
    therefore $LO$ is incommensurable with $NO$.
But, as $LO$ is to $NO$, so is $LP$ to $PN$; [VI. 1]
    therefore $LP$, $PN$ are incommensurable in length. [X. 11]
Therefore $LP$, $PN$ are medial straight lines commensurable in square only, which contain a rational rectangle;
    therefore $LN$ is a first apotome of a medial straight line. [X. 74]
And it is the "side" of the area $AB$.

Therefore the "side" of the area $AB$ is a first apotome of a medial straight line.
Q. E. D.

## Proposition 93

*If an area be contained by a rational straight line and a third apotome, the "side" of the area is a second apotome of a medial straight line.*

For let the area $AB$ be contained by the rational straight line $AC$ and the third apotome $AD$;

I say that the "side" of the area $AB$ is a second apotome of a medial straight line.

For let $DG$ be the annex to $AD$;
therefore $AG$, $GD$ are rational straight lines commensurable in square only, and neither of the straight lines $AG$, $GD$ is commensurable in length with the rational straight line $AC$ set out,
while the square on the whole $AG$ is greater than the square on the annex $DG$ by the square on a straight line commensurable with $AG$. [X. Deff. III. 3]

Since, then, the square on $AG$ is greater than the square on $GD$ by the square on a straight line commensurable with $AG$,
therefore, if there be applied to $AG$ a parallelogram equal to the fourth part of the square on $DG$ and deficient by a square figure, it will divide it into commensurable parts. [X. 17]

Let then $DG$ be bisected at $E$, let there be applied to $AG$ a parallelogram equal to the square on $EG$ and deficient by a square figure,
and let it be the rectangle $AF$, $FG$.

Let $EH$, $FI$, $GK$ be drawn through the points $E$, $F$, $G$ parallel to $AC$.

Therefore $AF$, $FG$ are commensurable;
therefore $AI$ is also commensurable with $FK$. [VI. 1, X. 11]

And, since $AF$, $FG$ are commensurable in length,
therefore $AG$ is also commensurable in length with each of the straight lines $AF$, $FG$. [X. 15]

But $AG$ is rational and incommensurable in length with $AC$;
  so that $AF$, $FG$ are so also. [x. 13]
Therefore each of the rectangles $AI$, $FK$ is medial. [x. 21]

Again, since $DE$ is commensurable in length with $EG$,
therefore $DG$ is also commensurable in length with each of the straight lines $DE$, $EG$. [x. 15]
But $GD$ is rational and incommensurable in length with $AC$;
therefore each of the straight lines $DE$, $EG$ is also rational and incommensurable in length with $AC$; [x. 13]
  therefore each of the rectangles $DH$, $EK$ is medial. [x. 21]
And, since $AG$, $GD$ are commensurable in square only,
  therefore $AG$ is incommensurable in length with $GD$.
But $AG$ is commensurable in length with $AF$, and $DG$ with $EG$;
  therefore $AF$ is incommensurable in length with $EG$. [x. 13]
But, as $AF$ is to $EG$, so is $AI$ to $EK$; [vi. 1]
  therefore $AI$ is incommensurable with $EK$. [x. 11]

Now let the square $LM$ be constructed equal to $AI$,
and let there be subtracted $NO$ equal to $FK$ and being about the same angle with $LM$;
  therefore $LM$, $NO$ are about the same diameter. [vi. 26]
Let $PR$ be their diameter, and let the figure be drawn.
Now, since the rectangle $AF$, $FG$ is equal to the square on $EG$,
  therefore, as $AF$ is to $EG$, so is $EG$ to $FG$. [vi. 17]
But, as $AF$ is to $EG$, so is $AI$ to $EK$,
  and, as $EG$ is to $FG$, so is $EK$ to $FK$; [vi. 1]
  therefore also, as $AI$ is to $EK$, so is $EK$ to $FK$; [v. 11]
  therefore $EK$ is a mean proportional between $AI$, $FK$.
But $MN$ is also a mean proportional between the squares $LM$, $NO$,
  and $AI$ is equal to $LM$, and $FK$ to $NO$;
  therefore $EK$ is also equal to $MN$.
But $MN$ is equal to $LO$, and $EK$ equal to $DH$;
  therefore the whole $DK$ is also equal to the gnomon $UVW$ and $NO$.
But $AK$ is also equal to $LM$, $NO$;
therefore the remainder $AB$ is equal to $ST$, that is, to the square on $LN$;
  therefore $LN$ is the "side" of the area $AB$.
I say that $LN$ is a second apotome of a medial straight line.
For, since $AI$, $FK$ were proved medial, and are equal to the squares on $LP$, $PN$,
  therefore each of the squares on $LP$, $PN$ is also medial;
  therefore each of the straight lines $LP$, $PN$ is medial.
And, since $AI$ is commensurable with $FK$, [vi. 1, x. 11]
therefore the square on $LP$ is also commensurable with the square on $PN$.
Again, since $AI$ was proved incommensurable with $EK$,
  therefore $LM$ is also incommensurable with $MN$,
  that is, the square on $LP$ with the rectangle $LP$, $PN$;
so that $LP$ is also incommensurable in length with $PN$; [vi. 1, x. 11]
  therefore $LP$, $PN$ are medial straight lines commensurable in square only.
I say next that they also contain a medial rectangle.
For, since $EK$ was proved medial, and is equal to the rectangle $LP$, $PN$,

therefore the rectangle $LP$, $PN$ is also medial,
so that $LP$, $PN$ are medial straight lines commensurable in square only which contain a medial rectangle.

Therefore $LN$ is a second apotome of a medial straight line; [x. 75]
and it is the "side" of the area $AB$.

Therefore the "side" of the area $AB$ is a second apotome of a medial straight line.
Q. E. D.

## Proposition 94

*If an area be contained by a rational straight line and a fourth apotome, the "side" of the area is minor.*

For let the area $AB$ be contained by the rational straight line $AC$ and the fourth apotome $AD$;
I say that the "side" of the area $AB$ is minor.

For let $DG$ be the annex to $AD$;
therefore $AG$, $GD$ are rational straight lines commensurable in square only, $AG$ is commensurable in length with the rational straight line $AC$ set out, and the square on the whole $AG$ is greater than the square on the annex $DG$ by the square on a straight line incommensurable in length with $AG$,
[x. Deff. III. 4]

Since, then, the square on $AG$ is greater than the square on $GD$ by the square on a straight line incommensurable in length with $AG$, therefore, if there be applied to $AG$ a parallelogram equal to the fourth part of the square on $DG$ and deficient by a square figure, it will divide it into incommensurable parts. [x. 18]

Let then $DG$ be bisected at $E$, let there be applied to $AG$ a parallelogram equal to the square on $EG$ and deficient by a square figure,
and let it be the rectangle $AF$, $FG$;
therefore $AF$ is incommensurable in length with $FG$.

Let $EH$, $FI$, $GK$ be drawn through $E$, $F$, $G$ parallel to $AC$, $BD$.
Since, then, $AG$ is rational and commensurable in length with $AC$,
therefore the whole $AK$ is rational. [x. 19]

Again, since $DG$ is incommensurable in length with $AC$, and both are rational,
therefore $DK$ is medial. [x. 21]

Again, since $AF$ is incommensurable in length with $FG$,
therefore $AI$ is also incommensurable with $FK$. [vi. 1, x. 11]

Now let the square $LM$ be constructed equal to $AI$,
and let there be subtracted $NO$ equal to $FK$ and about the same angle, the angle $LPM$.

Therefore the squares $LM$, $NO$ are about the same diameter. [vi. 26]
Let $PR$ be their diameter, and let the figure be drawn.

Since, then, the rectangle $AF$, $FG$ is equal to the square on $EG$,
therefore, proportionally, as $AF$ is to $EG$, so is $EG$ to $FG$. [VI. 17]
But, as $AF$ is to $EG$, so is $AI$ to $EK$,
and, as $EG$ is to $FG$, so is $EK$ to $FK$; [VI. 1]
therefore $EK$ is a mean proportional between $AI$, $FK$. [V. 11]
But $MN$ is also a mean proportional between the squares $LM$, $NO$,
and $AI$ is equal to $LM$, and $FK$ to $NO$;
therefore $EK$ is also equal to $MN$.
But $DH$ is equal to $EK$, and $LO$ is equal to $MN$;
therefore the whole $DK$ is equal to the gnomon $UVW$ and $NO$.
Since, then, the whole $AK$ is equal to the squares $LM$, $NO$,
and, in these, $DK$ is equal to the gnomon $UVW$ and the square $NO$,
therefore the remainder $AB$ is equal to $ST$, that is, to the square on $LN$;
therefore $LN$ is the "side" of the area $AB$.
I say that $LN$ is the irrational straight line called minor.
For, since $AK$ is rational and is equal to the squares on $LP$, $PN$,
therefore the sum of the squares on $LP$, $PN$ is rational.
Again, since $DK$ is medial,
and $DK$ is equal to twice the rectangle $LP$, $PN$,
therefore twice the rectangle $LP$, $PN$ is medial.
And, since $AI$ was proved incommensurable with $FK$,
therefore the square on $LP$ is also incommensurable with the square on $PN$.

Therefore $LP$, $PN$ are straight lines incommensurable in square which make the sum of the squares on them rational, but twice the rectangle contained by them medial.

Therefore $LN$ is the irrational straight line called minor; [X. 76]
and it is the "side" of the area $AB$.

Therefore the "side" of the area $AB$ is minor.   Q. E. D.

## PROPOSITION 95

*If an area be contained by a rational straight line and a fifth apotome, the "side" of the area is a straight line which produces with a rational area a medial whole.*

For let the area $AB$ be contained by the rational straight line $AC$ and the fifth apotome $AD$;

I say that the "side" of the area $AB$ is a straight line which produces with a rational area a medial whole.

For let $DG$ be the annex to $AD$;
therefore $AG$, $GD$ are rational straight lines commensurable in square only, the annex $GD$ is commensurable in length with the rational straight line $AC$ set out,
and the square on the whole $AG$ is greater than the square on the annex $DG$ by the square on a straight line incommensurable with $AG$.  [X. Deff. III. 5]

Therefore, if there be applied to $AG$ a parallelogram equal to the fourth part of the square on $DG$ and deficient by a square figure, it will divide it into incommensurable parts. [X. 18]

Let then $DG$ be bisected at the point $E$,
let there be applied to $AG$ a parallelogram equal to the square on $EG$ and deficient by a square figure, and let it be the rectangle $AF$, $FG$;
therefore $AF$ is incommensurable in length with $FG$.

Now, since $AG$ is incommensurable in length with $CA$, and both are rational, therefore $AK$ is medial. [x. 21]

Again, since $DG$ is rational and commensurable in length with $AC$, $DK$ is rational. [x. 19]

Now let the square $LM$ be constructed equal to $AI$, and let the square $NO$ equal to $FK$ and about the same angle, the angle $LPM$, be subtracted;
therefore the squares $LM$, $NO$ are about the same diameter. [vi. 26]

Let $PR$ be their diameter, and let the figure be drawn.

Similarly then we can prove that $LN$ is the "side" of the area $AB$.

I say that $LN$ is the straight line which produces with a rational area a medial whole.

For, since $AK$ was proved medial and is equal to the squares on $LP$, $PN$, therefore the sum of the squares on $LP$, $PN$ is medial.

Again, since $DK$ is rational and is equal to twice the rectangle $LP$, $PN$, the latter is itself also rational.

And, since $AI$ is incommensurable with $FK$, therefore the square on $LP$ is also incommensurable with the square on $PN$; therefore $LP$, $PN$ are straight lines incommensurable in square which make the sum of the squares on them medial but twice the rectangle contained by them rational.

Therefore the remainder $LN$ is the irrational straight line called that which produces with a rational area a medial whole; [x. 77]
and it is the "side" of the area $AB$.

Therefore the "side" of the area $AB$ is a straight line which produces with a rational area a medial whole.

Q. E. D.

## Proposition 96

*If an area be contained by a rational straight line and a sixth apotome, the "side" of the area is a straight line which produces with a medial area a medial whole.*

For let the area $AB$ be contained by the rational straight line $AC$ and the sixth apotome $AD$;

I say that the "side" of the area $AB$ is a straight line which produces with a medial area a medial whole.

For let $DG$ be the annex to $AD$;
therefore $AG$, $GD$ are rational straight lines commensurable in square only, neither of them is commensurable in length with the rational straight line $AC$ set out,
and the square on the whole $AG$ is greater than the square on the annex $DG$ by the square on a straight line incommensurable in length with $AG$.

[x. Deff. III. 6]

Since, then, the square on $AG$ is greater than the square on $GD$ by the square on a straight line incommensurable in length with $AG$, therefore, if there be applied to $AG$ a parallelogram equal to the fourth part of the square on $DG$ and deficient by a square figure, it will divide it into incommensurable parts.  [x. 18]

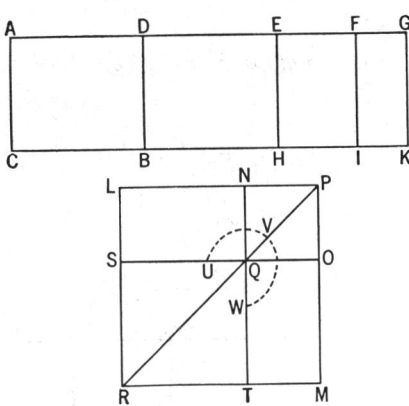

Let then $DG$ be bisected at $E$, let there be applied to $AG$ a parallelogram equal to the square on $EG$ and deficient by a square figure, and let it be the rectangle $AF$, $FG$; therefore $AF$ is incommensurable in length with $FG$.

But, as $AF$ is to $FG$, so is $AI$ to $FK$; [vi. 1]
therefore $AI$ is incommensurable with $FK$. [x. 11]

And, since $AG$, $AC$ are rational straight lines commensurable in square only,
$AK$ is medial. [x. 21]

Again, since $AC$, $DG$ are rational straight lines and incommensurable in length,
$DK$ is also medial. [x. 21]

Now, since $AG$, $GD$ are commensurable in square only,
therefore $AG$ is incommensurable in length with $GD$.
But, as $AG$ is to $GD$, so is $AK$ to $KD$; [vi. 1]
therefore $AK$ is incommensurable with $KD$. [x. 11]

Now let the square $LM$ be constructed equal to $AI$,
and let $NO$ equal to $FK$, and about the same angle, be subtracted;
therefore the squares $LM$, $NO$ are about the same diameter. [vi. 26]
Let $PR$ be their diameter, and let the figure be drawn.
Then in manner similar to the above we can prove that $LN$ is the "side" of the area $AB$.

I say that $LN$ is a straight line which produces with a medial area a medial whole.

For, since $AK$ was proved medial and is equal to the squares on $LP$, $PN$,
therefore the sum of the squares on $LP$, $PN$ is medial.
Again, since $DK$ was proved medial and is equal to twice the rectangle $LP$, $PN$,
twice the rectangle $LP$, $PN$ is also medial.
And, since $AK$ was proved incommensurable with $DK$,
the squares on $LP$, $PN$ are also incommensurable with twice the rectangle $LP$, $PN$.
And, since $AI$ is incommensurable with $FK$,
therefore the square on $LP$ is also incommensurable with the square on $PN$;
therefore $LP$, $PN$ are straight lines incommensurable in square which make the sum of the squares on them medial, twice the rectangle contained by them medial, and further, the squares on them incommensurable with twice the rectangle contained by them.

Therefore $LN$ is the irrational straight line called that which produces with a medial area a medial whole; [x. 78] and it is the "side" of the area $AB$.

Therefore the "side" of the area is a straight line which produces with a medial area a medial whole.

Q. E. D.

## Proposition 97

*The square on an apotome applied to a rational straight line produces as breadth a first apotome.*

Let $AB$ be an apotome, and $CD$ rational,
and to $CD$ let there be applied $CE$ equal to the square on $AB$ and producing $CF$ as breadth;

I say that $CF$ is a first apotome.

For let $BG$ be the annex to $AB$;
therefore $AG$, $GB$ are rational straight lines commensurable in square only. [x. 73]

To $CD$ let there be applied $CH$ equal to the square on $AG$, and $KL$ equal to the square on $BG$.

Therefore the whole $CL$ is equal to the squares on $AG$, $GB$, and, in these, $CE$ is equal to the square on $AB$;
therefore the remainder $FL$ is equal to twice the rectangle $AG$, $GB$. [II. 7]

Let $FM$ be bisected at the point $N$,
and let $NO$ be drawn through $N$ parallel to $CD$;
therefore each of the rectangles $FO$, $LN$ is equal to the rectangle $AG$, $GB$.

Now, since the squares on $AG$, $GB$ are rational,
and $DM$ is equal to the squares on $AG$, $GB$,
therefore $DM$ is rational.

And it has been applied to the rational straight line $CD$, producing $CM$ as breadth;
therefore $CM$ is rational and commensurable in length with $CD$. [x. 20]

Again, since twice the rectangle $AG$, $GB$ is medial, and $FL$ is equal to twice the rectangle $AG$, $GB$,
therefore $FL$ is medial.

And it is applied to the rational straight line $CD$, producing $FM$ as breadth;
therefore $FM$ is rational and incommensurable in length with $CD$. [x. 22]

And, since the squares on $AG$, $GB$ are rational,
while twice the rectangle $AG$, $GB$ is medial,
therefore the squares on $AG$, $GB$ are incommensurable with twice the rectangle $AG$, $GB$.

And $CL$ is equal to the squares on $AG$, $GB$,
and $FL$ to twice the rectangle $AG$, $GB$,
therefore $DM$ is incommensurable with $FL$.

But, as $DM$ is to $FL$, so is $CM$ to $FM$; [VI. 1]
therefore $CM$ is incommensurable in length with $FM$. [x. 11]

And both are rational;
therefore $CM$, $MF$ are rational straight lines commensurable in square only;
therefore $CF$ is an apotome. [x. 73]

ELEMENTS X

I say next that it is also a first apotome.

For, since the rectangle $AG$, $GB$ is a mean proportional between the squares on $AG$, $GB$,

and $CH$ is equal to the square on $AG$,
$KL$ equal to the square on $BG$,
and $NL$ equal to the rectangle $AG$, $GB$,
therefore $NL$ is also a mean proportional between $CH$, $KL$;
therefore, as $CH$ is to $NL$, so is $NL$ to $KL$.

But, as $CH$ is to $NL$, so is $CK$ to $NM$,
and, as $NL$ is to $KL$, so is $NM$ to $KM$; [VI. 1]
therefore the rectangle $CK$, $KM$ is equal to the square on $NM$ [VI. 17], that is, to the fourth part of the square on $FM$.

And, since the square on $AG$ is commensurable with the square on $GB$,
$CH$ is also commensurable with $KL$.

But, as $CH$ is to $KL$, so is $CK$ to $KM$; [VI. 1]
therefore $CK$ is commensurable with $KM$. [X. 11]

Since, then, $CM$, $MF$ are two unequal straight lines,
and to $CM$ there has been applied the rectangle $CK$, $KM$ equal to the fourth part of the square on $FM$ and deficient by a square figure,
while $CK$ is commensurable with $KM$,
therefore the square on $CM$ is greater than the square on $MF$ by the square on a straight line commensurable in length with $CM$. [X. 17]

And $CM$ is commensurable in length with the rational straight line $CD$ set out;

therefore $CF$ is a first apotome. [X. Deff. III. 1]

Therefore etc. Q. E. D.

PROPOSITION 98

*The square on a first apotome of a medial straight line applied to a rational straight line produces as breadth a second apotome.*

Let $AB$ be a first apotome of a medial straight line and $CD$ a rational straight line,
and to $CD$ let there be applied $CE$ equal to the square on $AB$, producing $CF$ as breadth;

I say that $CF$ is a second apotome.

For let $BG$ be the annex to $AB$;
therefore $AG$, $GB$ are medial straight lines commensurable in square only which contain a rational rectangle. [X. 74]

To $CD$ let there be applied $CH$ equal to the square on $AG$, producing $CK$ as breadth, and $KL$ equal to the square on $GB$, producing $KM$ as breadth;
therefore the whole $CL$ is equal to the squares on $AG$, $GB$;
therefore $CL$ is also medial. [X. 15 and 23, Por.]
And it is applied to the rational straight line $CD$, producing $CM$ as breadth;
therefore $CM$ is rational and incommensurable in length with $CD$. [X. 22]

Now, since $CL$ is equal to the squares on $AG$, $GB$,

and, in these, the square on $AB$ is equal to $CE$,

therefore the remainder, twice the rectangle $AG$, $GB$, is equal to $FL$. [II. 7]

But twice the rectangle $AG$, $GB$ is rational;

therefore $FL$ is rational.

And it is applied to the rational straight line $FE$, producing $FM$ as breadth;

therefore $FM$ is also rational and commensurable in length with $CD$. [x. 20]

Now, since the sum of the squares on $AG$, $GB$, that is, $CL$, is medial, while twice the rectangle $AG$, $GB$, that is, $FL$, is rational,

therefore $CL$ is incommensurable with $FL$.

But, as $CL$ is to $FL$, so is $CM$ to $FM$; [VI. 1]

therefore $CM$ is incommensurable in length with $FM$. [x. 11]

And both are rational;

therefore $CM$, $MF$ are rational straight lines commensurable in square only;

therefore $CF$ is an apotome. [x. 73]

I say next that it is also a second apotome.

For let $FM$ be bisected at $N$,

and let $NO$ be drawn through $N$ parallel to $CD$;

therefore each of the rectangles $FO$, $NL$ is equal to the rectangle $AG$, $GB$.

Now, since the rectangle $AG$, $GB$ is a mean proportional between the squares on $AG$, $GB$,

and the square on $AG$ is equal to $CH$,

the rectangle $AG$, $GB$ to $NL$,

and the square on $BG$ to $KL$,

therefore $NL$ is also a mean proportional between $CH$, $KL$;

therefore, as $CH$ is to $NL$, so is $NL$ to $KL$.

But, as $CH$ is to $NL$, so is $CK$ to $NM$,

and, as $NL$ is to $KL$, so is $NM$ to $MK$; [VI. 1]

therefore, as $CK$ is to $NM$, so is $NM$ to $KM$; [v. 11]

therefore the rectangle $CK$, $KM$ is equal to the square on $NM$ [VI. 17], that is, to the fourth part of the square on $FM$.

Since, then, $CM$, $MF$ are two unequal straight lines, and the rectangle $CK$, $KM$ equal to the fourth part of the square on $MF$ and deficient by a square figure has been applied to the greater, $CM$, and divides it into commensurable parts,

therefore the square on $CM$ is greater than the square on $MF$ by the square on a straight line commensurable in length with $CM$. [x. 17]

And the annex $FM$ is commensurable in length with the rational straight line $CD$ set out;

therefore $CF$ is a second apotome. [x. Deff. III. 2]

Therefore etc.

Q. E. D.

## Proposition 99

*The square on a second apotome of a medial straight line applied to a rational straight line produces as breadth a third apotome.*

Let $AB$ be a second apotome of a medial straight line, and $CD$ rational, and to $CD$ let there be applied $CE$ equal to the square on $AB$, producing $CF$ as breadth;

I say that $CF$ is a third apotome.

ELEMENTS X

For let $BG$ be the annex to $AB$;
therefore $AG$, $GB$ are medial straight lines commensurable in square only which contain a medial rectangle. [x. 75]

Let $CH$ equal to the square on $AG$ be applied to $CD$, producing $CK$ as breadth, and let $KL$ equal to the square on $BG$ be applied to $KH$, producing $KM$ as breadth;
therefore the whole $CL$ is equal to the squares on $AG$, $GB$;
therefore $CL$ is also medial. [x. 15 and 23, Por.]

And it is applied to the rational straight line $CD$, producing $CM$ as breadth;
therefore $CM$ is rational and incommensurable in length with $CD$. [x. 22]

Now, since the whole $CL$ is equal to the squares on $AG$, $GB$, and, in these, $CE$ is equal to the square on $AB$,
therefore the remainder $LF$ is equal to twice the rectangle $AG$, $GB$. [II. 7]

Let then $FM$ be bisected at the point $N$,
and let $NO$ be drawn parallel to $CD$;
therefore each of the rectangles $FO$, $NL$ is equal to the rectangle $AG$, $GB$.

But the rectangle $AG$, $GB$ is medial;
therefore $FL$ is also medial.

And it is applied to the rational straight line $EF$, producing $FM$ as breadth;
therefore $FM$ is also rational and incommensurable in length with $CD$. [x. 22]

And, since $AG$, $GB$ are commensurable in square only,
therefore $AG$ is incommensurable in length with $GB$;
therefore the square on $AG$ is also incommensurable with the rectangle $AG$, $GB$. [VI. 1, x. 11]

But the squares on $AG$, $GB$ are commensurable with the square on $AG$,
and twice the rectangle $AG$, $GB$ with the rectangle $AG$, $GB$;
therefore the squares on $AG$, $GB$ are incommensurable with twice the rectangle $AG$, $GB$. [x. 13]

But $CL$ is equal to the squares on $AG$, $GB$,
and $FL$ is equal to twice the rectangle $AG$, $GB$;
therefore $CL$ is also incommensurable with $FL$.

But, as $CL$ is to $FL$, so is $CM$ to $FM$; [VI. 1]
therefore $CM$ is incommensurable in length with $FM$. [x. 11]

And both are rational;
therefore $CM$, $MF$ are rational straight lines commensurable in square only;
therefore $CF$ is an apotome. [x. 73]

I say next that it is also a third apotome.

For, since the square on $AG$ is commensurable with the square on $GB$,
therefore $CH$ is also commensurable with $KL$,
so that $CK$ is also commensurable with $KM$. [VI. 1, x. 11]

And, since the rectangle $AG$, $GB$ is a mean proportional between the squares on $AG$, $GB$,
and $CH$ is equal to the square on $AG$,
$KL$ equal to the square on $GB$,
and $NL$ equal to the rectangle $AG$, $GB$;

therefore *NL* is also a mean proportional between *CH*, *KL*;
therefore, as *CH* is to *NL*, so is *NL* to *KL*.

But, as *CH* is to *NL*, so is *CK* to *NM*,
and, as *NL* is to *KL*, so is *NM* to *KM*; [VI. 1]
therefore, as *CK* is to *MN*, so is *MN* to *KM*; [V. 11]
therefore the rectangle *CK*, *KM* is equal to [the square on *MN*, that is, to] the fourth part of the square on *FM*.

Since, then, *CM*, *MF* are two unequal straight lines, and a parallelogram equal to the fourth part of the square on *FM* and deficient by a square figure has been applied to *CM*, and divides it into commensurable parts,
therefore the square on *CM* is greater than the square on *MF* by the square on a straight line commensurable with *CM*. [x. 17]

And neither of the straight lines *CM*, *MF* is commensurable in length with the rational straight line *CD* set out;
therefore *CF* is a third apotome. [x. Deff. III. 3]
Therefore etc.
Q. E. D.

## Proposition 100

*The square on a minor straight line applied to a rational straight line produces as breadth a fourth apotome.*

Let *AB* be a minor and *CD* a rational straight line, and to the rational straight line *CD* let *CE* be applied equal to the square on *AB* and producing *CF* as breadth;
I say that *CF* is a fourth apotome.

For let *BG* be the annex to *AB*;
therefore *AG*, *GB* are straight lines incommensurable in square which make the sum of the squares on *AG*, *GB* rational, but twice the rectangle *AG*, *GB* medial. [x. 76]

To *CD* let there be applied *CH* equal to the square on *AG* and producing *CK* as breadth,
and *KL* equal to the square on *BG*, producing *KM* as breadth;
therefore the whole *CL* is equal to the squares on *AG*, *GB*.

And the sum of the squares on *AG*, *GB* is rational;
therefore *CL* is also rational.

And it is applied to the rational straight line *CD*, producing *CM* as breadth;
therefore *CM* is also rational and commensurable in length with *CD*. [x. 20]

And, since the whole *CL* is equal to the squares on *AG*, *GB*, and, in these, *CE* is equal to the square on *AB*,
therefore the remainder *FL* is equal to twice the rectangle *AG*, *GB*. [II. 7]

Let then *FM* be bisected at the point *N*,
and let *NO* be drawn through *N* parallel to either of the straight lines *CD*, *ML*;
therefore each of the rectangles *FO*, *NL* is equal to the rectangle *AG*, *GB*.

And, since twice the rectangle *AG*, *GB* is medial and is equal to *FL*,
therefore *FL* is also medial.

And it is applied to the rational straight line *FE*, producing *FM* as breadth;

therefore $FM$ is rational and incommensurable in length with $CD$. [x. 22]

And, since the sum of the squares on $AG$, $GB$ is rational,
while twice the rectangle $AG$, $GB$ is medial,
the squares on $AG$, $GB$ are incommensurable with twice the rectangle $AG$, $GB$.

But $CL$ is equal to the squares on $AG$, $GB$,
and $FL$ equal to twice the rectangle $AG$, $GB$;
therefore $CL$ is incommensurable with $FL$.

But, as $CL$ is to $FL$, so is $CM$ to $MF$; [VI. 1]
therefore $CM$ is incommensurable in length with $MF$. [x. 11]

And both are rational;
therefore $CM$, $MF$ are rational straight lines commensurable in square only;
therefore $CF$ is an apotome. [x. 73]

I say that it is also a fourth apotome.

For, since $AG$, $GB$ are incommensurable in square,
therefore the square on $AG$ is also incommensurable with the square on $GB$.

And $CH$ is equal to the square on $AG$,
and $KL$ equal to the square on $GB$;
therefore $CH$ is incommensurable with $KL$.

But, as $CH$ is to $KL$, so is $CK$ to $KM$; [VI. 1]
therefore $CK$ is incommensurable in length with $KM$. [x. 11]

And, since the rectangle $AG$, $GB$ is a mean proportional between the squares on $AG$, $GB$,
and the square on $AG$ is equal to $CH$,
the square on $GB$ to $KL$,
and the rectangle $AG$, $GB$ to $NL$,
therefore $NL$ is a mean proportional between $CH$, $KL$;
therefore, as $CH$ is to $NL$, so is $NL$ to $KL$.

But, as $CH$ is to $NL$, so is $CK$ to $NM$,
and, as $NL$ is to $KL$, so is $NM$ to $KM$; [VI. 1]
therefore, as $CK$ is to $MN$, so is $MN$ to $KM$; [V. 11]
therefore the rectangle $CK$, $KM$ is equal to the square on $MN$ [VI. 17], that is, to the fourth part of the square on $FM$.

Since then $CM$, $MF$ are two unequal straight lines, and the rectangle $CK$, $KM$ equal to the fourth part of the square on $MF$ and deficient by a square figure has been applied to $CM$ and divides it into incommensurable parts, therefore the square on $CM$ is greater than the square on $MF$ by the square on a straight line incommensurable with $CM$. [x. 18]

And the whole $CM$ is commensurable in length with the rational straight line $CD$ set out;
therefore $CF$ is a fourth apotome. [x. Deff. III. 4]

Therefore etc.  Q. E. D.

## Proposition 101

*The square on the straight line which produces with a rational area a medial whole, if applied to a rational straight line, produces as breadth a fifth apotome.*

Let $AB$ be the straight line which produces with a rational area a medial whole, and $CD$ a rational straight line, and to $CD$ let $CE$ be applied equal to the square on $AB$ and producing $CF$ as breadth;
I say that $CF$ is a fifth apotome.

For let $BG$ be the annex to $AB$;

therefore $AG$, $GB$ are straight lines incommensurable in square which make the sum of the squares on them medial but twice the rectangle contained by them rational.  [x. 77]

To $CD$ let there be applied $CH$ equal to the square on $AG$, and $KL$ equal to the square on $GB$;
therefore the whole $CL$ is equal to the squares on $AG$, $GB$.

But the sum of the squares on $AG$, $GB$ together is medial;
therefore $CL$ is medial.

And it is applied to the rational straight line $CD$, producing $CM$ as breadth;
therefore $CM$ is rational and incommensurable with $CD$.  [x. 22]

And, since the whole $CL$ is equal to the squares on $AG$, $GB$,
and, in these, $CE$ is equal to the square on $AB$,
therefore the remainder $FL$ is equal to twice the rectangle $AG$, $GB$.  [II. 7]

Let then $FM$ be bisected at $N$,
and through $N$ let $NO$ be drawn parallel to either of the straight lines $CD$, $ML$;
therefore each of the rectangles $FO$, $NL$ is equal to the rectangle $AG$, $GB$.

And, since twice the rectangle $AG$, $GB$ is rational and equal to $FL$,
therefore $FL$ is rational.

And it is applied to the rational straight line $EF$, producing $FM$ as breadth;
therefore $FM$ is rational and commensurable in length with $CD$.  [x. 20]

Now, since $CL$ is medial, and $FL$ rational,
therefore $CL$ is incommensurable with $FL$.

But, as $CL$ is to $FL$, so is $CM$ to $MF$;  [VI. 1]
therefore $CM$ is incommensurable in length with $MF$.  [x. 11]

And both are rational;
therefore $CM$, $MF$ are rational straight lines commensurable in square only;
therefore $CF$ is an apotome.  [x. 73]

I say next that it is also a fifth apotome.

For we can prove similarly that the rectangle $CK$, $KM$ is equal to the square on $NM$, that is, to the fourth part of the square on $FM$.

And, since the square on $AG$ is incommensurable with the square on $GB$,
while the square on $AG$ is equal to $CH$,
and the square on $GB$ to $KL$,
therefore $CH$ is incommensurable with $KL$.

But, as $CH$ is to $KL$, so is $CK$ to $KM$;  [VI. 1]
therefore $CK$ is incommensurable in length with $KM$.  [x. 11]

Since then $CM$, $MF$ are two unequal straight lines,
and a parallelogram equal to the fourth part of the square on $FM$ and deficient by a square figure has been applied to $CM$, and divides it into incommensurable parts,
therefore the square on $CM$ is greater than the square on $MF$ by the square on a straight line incommensurable with $CM$.  [x. 18]

And the annex $FM$ is commensurable with the rational straight line $CD$ set out;
therefore $CF$ is a fifth apotome.  [x. Deff. III. 5]

Q. E. D.

## Proposition 102

*The square on the straight line which produces with a medial area a medial whole, if applied to a rational straight line, produces as breadth a sixth apotome.*

Let $AB$ be the straight line which produces with a medial area a medial whole, and $CD$ a rational straight line,
and to $CD$ let $CE$ be applied equal to the square on $AB$ and producing $CF$ as breadth;
I say that $CF$ is a sixth apotome.

For let $BG$ be the annex to $AB$;

therefore $AG$, $GB$ are straight lines incommensurable in square which make the sum of the squares on them medial, twice the rectangle $AG$, $GB$ medial, and the squares on $AG$, $GB$ incommensurable with twice the rectangle $AG$, $GB$. [x. 78]

Now to $CD$ let there be applied $CH$ equal to the square on $AG$ and producing $CK$ as breadth,
and $KL$ equal to the square on $BG$;
therefore the whole $CL$ is equal to the squares on $AG$, $GB$;
therefore $CL$ is also medial.

And it is applied to the rational straight line $CD$, producing $CM$ as breadth; therefore $CM$ is rational and incommensurable in length with $CD$. [x. 22]
Since now $CL$ is equal to the squares on $AG$, $GB$,
and, in these, $CE$ is equal to the square on $AB$,
therefore the remainder $FL$ is equal to twice the rectangle $AG$, $GB$. [II. 7]
And twice the rectangle $AG$, $GB$ is medial;
therefore $FL$ is also medial.

And it is applied to the rational straight line $FE$, producing $FM$ as breadth; therefore $FM$ is rational and incommensurable in length with $CD$. [x. 22]
And, since the squares on $AG$, $GB$ are incommensurable with twice the rectangle $AG$, $GB$,
and $CL$ is equal to the squares on $AG$, $GB$,
and $FL$ equal to twice the rectangle $AG$, $GB$,
therefore $CL$ is incommensurable with $FL$.
But, as $CL$ is to $FL$, so is $CM$ to $MF$; [VI. 1]
therefore $CM$ is incommensurable in length with $MF$. [x. 11]
And both are rational.
Therefore $CM$, $MF$ are rational straight lines commensurable in square only;
therefore $CF$ is an apotome. [x. 73]
I say next that it is also a sixth apotome.
For, since $FL$ is equal to twice the rectangle $AG$, $GB$,
let $FM$ be bisected at $N$,
and let $NO$ be drawn through $N$ parallel to $CD$;
therefore each of the rectangles $FO$, $NL$ is equal to the rectangle $AG$, $GB$.
And, since $AG$, $GB$ are incommensurable in square,

therefore the square on $AG$ is incommensurable with the square on $GB$.
But $CH$ is equal to the square on $AG$,
> and $KL$ is equal to the square on $GB$;
> > therefore $CH$ is incommensurable with $KL$.

But, as $CH$ is to $KL$, so is $CK$ to $KM$; [vi. 1]
> therefore $CK$ is incommensurable with $KM$. [x. 11]

And, since the rectangle $AG, GB$ is a mean proportional between the squares on $AG, GB$,
> and $CH$ is equal to the square on $AG$,
> > $KL$ equal to the square on $GB$,
> and $NL$ equal to the rectangle $AG, GB$,
> > therefore $NL$ is also a mean proportional between $CH, KL$;
> > > therefore, as $CH$ is to $NL$, so is $NL$ to $KL$.

And for the same reason as before the square on $CM$ is greater than the square on $MF$ by the square on a straight line incommensurable with $CM$. [x. 18]

And neither of them is commensurable with the rational straight line $CD$ set out;
> > therefore $CF$ is a sixth apotome. [x. Deff. iii. 6]

Q. E. D.

## Proposition 103

*A straight line commensurable in length with an apotome is an apotome and the same in order.*

Let $AB$ be an apotome,
and let $CD$ be commensurable in length with $AB$;
I say that $CD$ is also an apotome and the same in order with $AB$.

For, since $AB$ is an apotome, let $BE$ be the annex to it;
therefore $AE, EB$ are rational straight lines commensurable in square only. [x. 73]

Let it be contrived that the ratio of $BE$ to $DF$ is the same as the ratio of $AB$ to $CD$; [vi. 12]
> therefore also, as one is to one, so are all to all; [v. 12]
> therefore also, as the whole $AE$ is to the whole $CF$, so is $AB$ to $CD$.

But $AB$ is commensurable in length with $CD$.
Therefore $AE$ is also commensurable with $CF$, and $BE$ with $DF$. [x. 11]

And $AE, EB$ are rational straight lines commensurable in square only;
therefore $CF, FD$ are also rational straight lines commensurable in square only. [x. 13]

Now since, as $AE$ is to $CF$, so is $BE$ to $DF$,
> alternately therefore, as $AE$ is to $EB$, so is $CF$ to $FD$. [v. 16]

And the square on $AE$ is greater than the square on $EB$ either by the square on a straight line commensurable with $AE$ or by the square on a straight line incommensurable with it.

If then the square on $AE$ is greater than the square on $EB$ by the square on a straight line commensurable with $AE$, the square on $CF$ will also be greater than the square on $FD$ by the square on a straight line commensurable with $CF$. [x. 14]

And, if $AE$ is commensurable in length with the rational straight line set out,
$CF$ is so also, [x. 12]
if $BE$, then $DF$ also, [*id.*]
and, if neither of the straight lines $AE$, $EB$, then neither of the straight lines $CF$, $FD$. [x. 13]

But, if the square on $AE$ is greater than the square on $EB$ by the square on a straight line incommensurable with $AE$,
the square on $CF$ will also be greater than the square on $FD$ by the square on a straight line incommensurable with $CF$. [x. 14]

And, if $AE$ is commensurable in length with the rational straight line set out,
$CF$ is so also, [x. 12]
if $BE$, then $DF$ also, [x. 12]
and, if neither of the straight lines $AE$, $EB$, then neither of the straight lines $CF$, $FD$. [x. 13]

Therefore $CD$ is an apotome and the same in order with $AB$. Q. E. D.

## Proposition 104

*A straight line commensurable with an apotome of a medial straight line is an apotome of a medial straight line and the same in order.*

Let $AB$ be an apotome of a medial straight line,
and let $CD$ be commensurable in length with $AB$;
I say that $CD$ is also an apotome of a medial straight line and the same in order with $AB$.

For, since $AB$ is an apotome of a medial straight line, let $EB$ be the annex to it.

Therefore $AE$, $EB$ are medial straight lines commensurable in square only. [x. 74, 75]

Let it be contrived that, as $AB$ is to $CD$, so is $BE$ to $DF$; [vi. 12]
therefore $AE$ is also commensurable with $CF$, and $BE$ with $DF$. [v. 12, x. 11]

But $AE$, $EB$ are medial straight lines commensurable in square only;
therefore $CF$, $FD$ are also medial straight lines [x. 23] commensurable in square only; [x. 13]

therefore $CD$ is an apotome of a medial straight line. [x. 74, 75]

I say next that it is also the same in order with $AB$.

Since, as $AE$ is to $EB$, so is $CF$ to $FD$,
therefore also, as the square on $AE$ is to the rectangle $AE$, $EB$, so is the square on $CF$ to the rectangle $CF$, $FD$.

But the square on $AE$ is commensurable with the square on $CF$;
therefore the rectangle $AE$, $EB$ is also commensurable with the rectangle $CF$, $FD$. [v. 16, x. 11]

Therefore, if the rectangle $AE$, $EB$ is rational, the rectangle $CF$, $FD$ will also be rational, [x. Def. 4]
and if the rectangle $AE$, $EB$ is medial, the rectangle $CF$, $FD$ is also medial. [x. 23, Por.]

Therefore $CD$ is an apotome of a medial straight line and the same in order with $AB$. [x. 74, 75]

Q. E. D.

## Proposition 105

*A straight line commensurable with a minor straight line is minor.*

Let $AB$ be a minor straight line, and $CD$ commensurable with $AB$;
I say that $CD$ is also minor.

Let the same construction be made as before;
then, since $AE$, $EB$ are incommensurable in square, [x. 76]

therefore $CF$, $FD$ are also incommensurable in square. [x. 13]

Now since, as $AE$ is to $EB$, so is $CF$ to $FD$, [v. 12, v. 16]
therefore also, as the square on $AE$ is to the square on $EB$, so is the square on $CF$ to the square on $FD$. [vi. 22]

Therefore, *componendo*, as the squares on $AE$, $EB$ are to the square on $EB$, so are the squares on $CF$, $FD$ to the square on $FD$. [v. 18]

But the square on $BE$ is commensurable with the square on $DF$;
therefore the sum of the squares on $AE$, $EB$ is also commensurable with the sum of the squares on $CF$, $FD$. [v. 16, x. 11]

But the sum of the squares on $AE$, $EB$ is rational; [x. 76]

therefore the sum of the squares on $CF$, $FD$ is also rational. [x. Def. 4]

Again, since, as the square on $AE$ is to the rectangle $AE$, $EB$, so is the square on $CF$ to the rectangle $CF$, $FD$,

while the square on $AE$ is commensurable with the square on $CF$,
therefore the rectangle $AE$, $EB$ is also commensurable with the rectangle $CF$, $FD$.

But the rectangle $AE$, $EB$ is medial; [x. 76]

therefore the rectangle $CF$, $FD$ is also medial; [x. 23, Por.]
therefore $CF$, $FD$ are straight lines incommensurable in square which make the sum of the squares on them rational, but the rectangle contained by them medial.

Therefore $CD$ is minor. [x. 76]

Q. E. D.

## Proposition 106

*A straight line commensurable with that which produces with a rational area a medial whole is a straight line which produces with a rational area a medial whole.*

Let $AB$ be a straight line which produces with a rational area a medial whole, and $CD$ commensurable with $AB$;
I say that $CD$ is also a straight line which produces with a rational area a medial whole.

For let $BE$ be the annex to $AB$;
therefore $AE$, $EB$ are straight lines incommensurable in square which make the sum of the squares on $AE$, $EB$ medial, but the rectangle contained by them rational. [x. 77]

Let the same construction be made.

Then we can prove, in manner similar to the foregoing, that $CF$, $FD$ are in the same ratio as $AE$, $EB$,
the sum of the squares on $AE$, $EB$ is commensurable with the sum of the squares on $CF$, $FD$,
and the rectangle $AE$, $EB$ with the rectangle $CF$, $FD$;

ELEMENTS X

so that *CF*, *FD* are also straight lines incommensurable in square which make the sum of the squares on *CF*, *FD* medial, but the rectangle contained by them rational.

Therefore *CD* is a straight line which produces with a rational area a medial whole. [x. 77]

Q. E. D.

## Proposition 107

*A straight line commensurable with that which produces with a medial area a medial whole is itself also a straight line which produces with a medial area a medial whole.*

Let *AB* be a straight line which produces with a medial area a medial whole, and let *CD* be commensurable with *AB*;

I say that *CD* is also a straight line which produces with a medial area a medial whole.

For let *BE* be the annex to *AB*, and let the same construction be made;

therefore *AE*, *EB* are straight lines incommensurable in square which make the sum of the squares on them medial, the rectangle contained by them medial, and further, the sum of the squares on them incommensurable with the rectangle contained by them. [x. 78]

Now, as was proved, *AE*, *EB* are commensurable with *CF*, *FD*,

the sum of the squares on *AE*, *EB* with the sum of the squares on *CF*, *FD*,

and the rectangle *AE*, *EB* with the rectangle *CF*, *FD*;

therefore *CF*, *FD* are also straight lines incommensurable in square which make the sum of the squares on them medial, the rectangle contained by them medial, and further, the sum of the squares on them incommensurable with the rectangle contained by them.

Therefore *CD* is a straight line which produces with a medial area a medial whole. [x. 78]

Q. E. D.

## Proposition 108

*If from a rational area a medial area be subtracted, the "side" of the remaining area becomes one of two irrational straight lines, either an apotome or a minor straight line.*

For from the rational area *BC* let the medial area *BD* be subtracted;

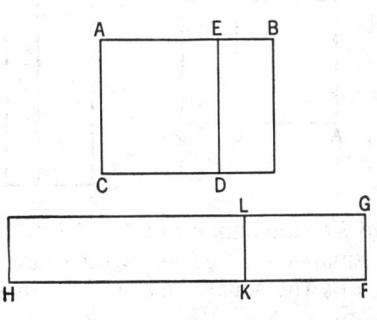

I say that the "side" of the remainder *EC* becomes one of two irrational straight lines, either an apotome or a minor straight line.

For let a rational straight line *FG* be set out,

to *FG* let there be applied the rectangular parallelogram *GH* equal to *BC*,

and let *GK* equal to *DB* be subtracted;

therefore the remainder *EC* is equal to *LH*.

Since, then, *BC* is rational, and *BD* medial,

while $BC$ is equal to $GH$, and $BD$ to $GK$,
therefore $GH$ is rational, and $GK$ medial.

And they are applied to the rational straight line $FG$;
therefore $FH$ is rational and commensurable in length with $FG$, [x. 20]
while $FK$ is rational and incommensurable in length with $FG$; [x. 22]
therefore $FH$ is incommensurable in length with $FK$. [x. 13]

Therefore $FH$, $FK$ are rational straight lines commensurable in square only;
therefore $KH$ is an apotome [x. 73], and $KF$ the annex to it.

Now the square on $HF$ is greater than the square on $FK$ by the square on a straight line either commensurable with $HF$ or not commensurable.

First, let the square on it be greater by the square on a straight line commensurable with it.

Now the whole $HF$ is commensurable in length with the rational straight line $FG$ set out;
therefore $KH$ is a first apotome. [x. Deff. III. 1]

But the "side" of the rectangle contained by a rational straight line and a first apotome is an apotome. [x. 91]

Therefore the "side" of $LH$, that is, of $EC$, is an apotome.

But, if the square on $HF$ is greater than the square on $FK$ by the square on a straight line incommensurable with $HF$,
while the whole $FH$ is commensurable in length with the rational straight line $FG$ set out,
$KH$ is a fourth apotome. [x. Deff. III. 4]

But the "side" of the rectangle contained by a rational straight line and a fourth apotome is minor. [x. 94]

Q. E. D.

## Proposition 109

*If from a medial area a rational area be subtracted, there arise two other irrational straight lines, either a first apotome of a medial straight line or a straight line which produces with a rational area a medial whole.*

For from the medial area $BC$ let the rational area $BD$ be subtracted.

I say that the "side" of the remainder $EC$ becomes one of two irrational straight lines, either a first apotome of a medial straight line or a straight line which produces with a rational area a medial whole.

For let a rational straight line $FG$ be set out,
and let the areas be similarly applied.

It follows then that $FH$ is rational and incommensurable in length with $FG$,
while $KF$ is rational and commensurable in length with $FG$;
therefore $FH$, $FK$ are rational straight lines commensurable in square only; [x. 13]

therefore $KH$ is an apotome, and $FK$ the annex to it. [x. 73]

Now the square on $HF$ is greater than the square on $FK$ either by the square on a straight line commensurable with $HF$ or by the square on a straight line incommensurable with it.

If then the square on $HF$ is greater than the square on $FK$ by the square on a straight line commensurable with $HF$,
while the annex $FK$ is commensurable in length with the rational straight line $FG$ set out,

$KH$ is a second apotome. [x. Deff. iii. 2]

But $FG$ is rational;
so that the "side" of $LH$, that is, of $EC$, is a first apotome of a medial straight line. [x. 92]

But, if the square on $HF$ is greater than the square on $FK$ by the square on a straight line incommensurable with $HF$,
while the annex $FK$ is commensurable in length with the rational straight line $FG$ set out,

$KH$ is a fifth apotome; [x. Deff. iii. 5]
so that the "side" of $EC$ is a straight line which produces with a rational area a medial whole. [x. 95]

Q. E. D.

## Proposition 110

*If from a medial area there be subtracted a medial area incommensurable with the whole, the two remaining irrational straight lines arise, either a second apotome of a medial straight line or a straight line which produces with a medial area a medial whole.*

For, as in the foregoing figures, let there be subtracted from the medial area $BC$ the medial area $BD$ incommensurable with the whole;

I say that the "side" of $EC$ is one of two irrational straight lines, either a second apotome of a medial straight line or a straight line which produces with a medial area a medial whole.

For, since each of the rectangles $BC$, $BD$ is medial,
and $BC$ is incommensurable with $BD$,
it follows that each of the straight lines $FH$, $FK$ will be rational and incommensurable in length with $FG$. [x. 22]

And, since $BC$ is incommensurable with $BD$,
that is, $GH$ with $GK$,
$HF$ is also incommensurable with $FK$; [vi. 1, x. 11]
therefore $FH$, $FK$ are rational straight lines commensurable in square only;
therefore $KH$ is an apotome. [x. 73]

If then the square on $FH$ is greater than the square on $FK$ by the square on a straight line commensurable with $FH$,
while neither of the straight lines $FH$, $FK$ is commensurable in length with the rational straight line $FG$ set out,

$KH$ is a third apotome. [x. Deff. iii. 3]

But $KL$ is rational,
and the rectangle contained by a rational straight line and a third apotome is irrational,

and the "side" of it is irrational, and is called a second apotome of a medial straight line; [x. 93]
so that the "side" of $LH$, that is, of $EC$, is a second apotome of a medial straight line.

But, if the square on $FH$ is greater than the square on $FK$ by the square on a straight line incommensurable with $FH$,
while neither of the straight lines $HF$, $FK$ is commensurable in length with $FG$, $KH$ is a sixth apotome. [x. Deff. III. 6]

But the "side" of the rectangle contained by a rational straight line and a sixth apotome is a straight line which produces with a medial area a medial whole. [x. 96]

Therefore the "side" of $LH$, that is, of $EC$, is a straight line which produces with a medial area a medial whole.

Q. E. D.

## Proposition 111

*The apotome is not the same with the binomial straight line.*

Let $AB$ be an apotome;
I say that $AB$ is not the same with the binomial straight line.

For, if possible, let it be so;
let a rational straight line $DC$ be set out, and to $CD$ let there be applied the rectangle $CE$ equal to the square on $AB$ and producing $DE$ as breadth.

Then, since $AB$ is an apotome,
$\qquad DE$ is a first apotome. [x. 97]

Let $EF$ be the annex to it;
therefore $DF$, $FE$ are rational straight lines commensurable in square only,
the square on $DF$ is greater than the square on $FE$ by the square on a straight line commensurable with $DF$,
and $DF$ is commensurable in length with the rational straight line $DC$ set out.
[x. Deff. III. 1]

Again, since $AB$ is binomial,
$\qquad$ therefore $DE$ is a first binomial straight line. [x. 60]

Let it be divided into its terms at $G$,
$\qquad$ and let $DG$ be the greater term;
therefore $DG$, $GE$ are rational straight lines commensurable in square only, the square on $DG$ is greater than the square on $GE$ by the square on a straight line commensurable with $DG$, and the greater term $DG$ is commensurable in length with the rational straight line $DC$ set out. [x. Deff. II. 1]

Therefore $DF$ is also commensurable in length with $DG$; [x. 12]
therefore the remainder $GF$ is also commensurable in length with $DF$. [x. 15]

But $DF$ is incommensurable in length with $EF$;
$\qquad$ therefore $FG$ is also incommensurable in length with $EF$. [x. 13]

Therefore $GF$, $FE$ are rational straight lines commensurable in square only;
$\qquad$ therefore $EG$ is an apotome. [x. 73]

But it is also rational:
$\qquad$ which is impossible.

ELEMENTS X 295

Therefore the apotome is not the same with the binomial straight line.
Q. E. D.

*The apotome and the irrational straight lines following it are neither the same with the medial straight line nor with one another.*

For the square on a medial straight line, if applied to a rational straight line, produces as breadth a straight line rational and incommensurable in length with that to which it is applied, [x. 22]
while the square on an apotome, if applied to a rational straight line, produces as breadth a first apotome, [x. 97]
the square on a first apotome of a medial straight line, if applied to a rational straight line, produces as breadth a second apotome, [x. 98]
the square on a second apotome of a medial straight line, if applied to a rational straight line, produces as breadth a third apotome, [x. 99]
the square on a minor straight line, if applied to a rational straight line, produces as breadth a fourth apotome, [x. 100]
the square on the straight line which produces with a rational area a medial whole, if applied to a rational straight line, produces as breadth a fifth apotome, [x. 101]
and the square on the straight line which produces with a medial area a medial whole, if applied to a rational straight line, produces as breadth a sixth apotome. [x. 102]

Since then the said breadths differ from the first and from one another, from the first because it is rational, and from one another since they are not the same in order,
it is clear that the irrational straight lines themselves also differ from one another.

And, since the apotome has been proved not to be the same as the binomial straight line, [x. 111]
but, if applied to a rational straight line, the straight lines following the apotome produce, as breadths, each according to its own order, apotomes, and those following the binomial straight line themselves also, according to their order, produce the binomials as breadths,
therefore those following the apotome are different, and those following the binomial straight line are different, so that there are, in order, thirteen irrational straight lines in all,

> Medial,
> Binomial,
> First bimedial,
> Second bimedial,
> Major,
> "Side" of a rational plus a medial area,
> "Side" of the sum of two medial areas,
> Apotome,
> First apotome of a medial straight line,
> Second apotome of a medial straight line,
> Minor,
> Producing with a rational area a medial whole,
> Producing with a medial area a medial whole.

## Proposition 112

*The square on a rational straight line applied to the binomial straight line produces as breadth an apotome the terms of which are commensurable with the terms of the binomial and moreover in the same ratio; and further, the apotome so arising will have the same order as the binomial straight line.*

Let $A$ be a rational straight line,
  let $BC$ be a binomial, and let $DC$ be its greater term;
  let the rectangle $BC$, $EF$ be equal to the square on $A$;

I say that $EF$ is an apotome the terms of which are commensurable with $CD$, $DB$, and in the same ratio, and further, $EF$ will have the same order as $BC$.

For again let the rectangle $BD$, $G$ be equal to the square on $A$.
Since, then, the rectangle $BC$, $EF$ is equal to the rectangle $BD$, $G$,
   therefore, as $CB$ is to $BD$, so is $G$ to $EF$.  [vi. 16]
But $CB$ is greater than $BD$;
   therefore $G$ is also greater than $EF$.  [v. 16, v. 14]
Let $EH$ be equal to $G$;
   therefore, as $CB$ is to $BD$, so is $HE$ to $EF$;
   therefore, *separando*, as $CD$ is to $BD$, so is $HF$ to $FE$.  [v. 17]
Let it be contrived that, as $HF$ is to $FE$, so is $FK$ to $KE$;
therefore also the whole $HK$ is to the whole $KF$ as $FK$ is to $KE$;
for, as one of the antecedents is to one of the consequents, so are all the antecedents to all the consequents.  [v. 12]
But, as $FK$ is to $KE$, so is $CD$ to $DB$;  [v. 11]
   therefore also, as $HK$ is to $KF$, so is $CD$ to $DB$.  [*id.*]
But the square on $CD$ is commensurable with the square on $DB$;  [x. 36]
therefore the square on $HK$ is also commensurable with the square on $KF$.
                  [vi. 22, x. 11]
And, as the square on $HK$ is to the square on $KF$, so is $HK$ to $KE$, since the three straight lines $HK$, $KF$, $KE$ are proportional.  [v. Def. 9]
Therefore $HK$ is commensurable in length with $KE$,
  so that $HE$ is also commensurable in length with $EK$.  [x. 15]
Now, since the square on $A$ is equal to the rectangle $EH$, $BD$,
  while the square on $A$ is rational,
   therefore the rectangle $EH$, $BD$ is also rational.
And it is applied to the rational straight line $BD$;
  therefore $EH$ is rational and commensurable in length with $BD$; [x. 20]
so that $EK$, being commensurable with it, is also rational and commensurable in length with $BD$.
Since, then, as $CD$ is to $DB$, so is $FK$ to $KE$,
  while $CD$, $DB$ are straight lines commensurable in square only,
   therefore $FK$, $KE$ are also commensurable in square only.  [x. 11]

ELEMENTS X

But *KE* is rational;
therefore *FK* is also rational.
Therefore *FK*, *KE* are rational straight lines commensurable in square only;
therefore *EF* is an apotome. [x. 73]

Now the square on *CD* is greater than the square on *DB* either by the square on a straight line commensurable with *CD* or by the square on a straight line incommensurable with it.

If then the square on *CD* is greater than the square on *DB* by the square on a straight line commensurable with *CD*, the square on *FK* is also greater than the square on *KE* by the square on a straight line commensurable with *FK*. [x. 14]

And, if *CD* is commensurable in length with the rational straight line set out,
so also is *FK*; [x. 11, 12]
if *BD* is so commensurable,
so also is *KE*; [x. 12]
but, if neither of the straight lines *CD*, *DB* is so commensurable,
neither of the straight lines *FK*, *KE* is so.

But, if the square on *CD* is greater than the square on *DB* by the square on a straight line incommensurable with *CD*,
the square on *FK* is also greater than the square on *KE* by the square on a straight line incommensurable with *FK*. [x. 14]

And, if *CD* is commensurable with the rational straight line set out,
so also is *FK*;
if *BD* is so commensurable,
so also is *KE*;
but, if neither of the straight lines *CD*, *DB* is so commensurable,
neither of the straight lines *FK*, *KE* is so;
so that *FE* is an apotome, the terms of which, *FK*, *KE* are commensurable with the terms *CD*, *DB* of the binomial straight line and in the same ratio, and it has the same order as *BC*. Q. E. D.

## Proposition 113

*The square on a rational straight line, if applied to an apotome, produces as breadth the binomial straight line the terms of which are commensurable with the terms of the apotome and in the same ratio; and further, the binomial so arising has the same order as the apotome.*

Let *A* be a rational straight line and *BD* an apotome, and let the rectangle *BD*, *KH* be equal to the square on *A*, so that the square on the rational straight line *A* when applied to the apotome *BD* produces *KH* as breadth;
I say that *KH* is a binomial straight line the terms of which are commensurable with the terms of *BD* and in the same ratio; and further, *KH* has the same order as *BD*.

For let *DC* be the annex to *BD*;
therefore *BC*, *CD* are rational straight lines commensurable in square only. [x. 73]
Let the rectangle *BC*, *G* be also equal to the square on *A*.
But the square on *A* is rational;

therefore the rectangle $BC$, $G$ is also rational.
And it has been applied to the rational straight line $BC$;
therefore $G$ is rational and commensurable in length with $BC$. [x. 20]
Since now the rectangle $BC$, $G$ is equal to the rectangle $BD$, $KH$,
therefore, proportionally, as $CB$ is to $BD$, so is $KH$ to $G$. [vi. 16]
But $BC$ is greater than $BD$;
therefore $KH$ is also greater than $G$. [v. 16, v. 14]
Let $KE$ be made equal to $G$;
therefore $KE$ is commensurable in length with $BC$.
And since, as $CB$ is to $BD$, so is $HK$ to $KE$,
therefore, *convertendo*, as $BC$ is to $CD$, so is $KH$ to $HE$. [v. 19, Por.]
Let it be contrived that, as $KH$ is to $HE$, so is $HF$ to $FE$;
therefore also the remainder $KF$ is to $FH$ as $KH$ is to $HE$, that is, as $BC$ is to $CD$. [v. 19]
But $BC$, $CD$ are commensurable in square only;
therefore $KF$, $FH$ are also commensurable in square only. [x. 11]
And since, as $KH$ is to $HE$, so is $KF$ to $FH$,
while, as $KH$ is to $HE$, so is $HF$ to $FE$,
therefore also, as $KF$ is to $FH$, so is $HF$ to $FE$, [v. 11]
so that also, as the first is to the third, so is the square on the first to the square on the second; [v. Def. 9]
therefore also, as $KF$ is to $FE$, so is the square on $KF$ to the square on $FH$.
But the square on $KF$ is commensurable with the square on $FH$,
for $KF$, $FH$ are commensurable in square;
therefore $KF$ is also commensurable in length with $FE$, [x. 11]
so that $KF$ is also commensurable in length with $KE$. [x. 15]
But $KE$ is rational and commensurable in length with $BC$;
therefore $KF$ is also rational and commensurable in length with $BC$. [x. 12]
And, since, as $BC$ is to $CD$, so is $KF$ to $FH$,
alternately, as $BC$ is to $KF$, so is $DC$ to $FH$. [v. 16]
But $BC$ is commensurable with $KF$;
therefore $FH$ is also commensurable in length with $CD$. [x. 11]
But $BC$, $CD$ are rational straight lines commensurable in square only;
therefore $KF$, $FH$ are also rational straight lines [x. Def. 3] commensurable in square only;
therefore $KH$ is binomial. [x. 36]

If now the square on $BC$ is greater than the square on $CD$ by the square on a straight line commensurable with $BC$,
the square on $KF$ will also be greater than the square on $FH$ by the square on a straight line commensurable with $KF$. [x. 14]
And, if $BC$ is commensurable in length with the rational straight line set out,
so also is $KF$;
if $CD$ is commensurable in length with the rational straight line set out,
so also is $FH$,
but, if neither of the straight lines $BC$, $CD$,
then neither of the straight lines $KF$, $FH$.
But, if the square on $BC$ is greater than the square on $CD$ by the square on a straight line incommensurable with $BC$,
the square on $KF$ is also greater than the square on $FH$ by the square on a

ELEMENTS X

straight line incommensurable with *KF*. [x. 14]
  And, if *BC* is commensurable with the rational straight line set out,
    so also is *KF*;
      if *CD* is so commensurable,
        so also is *FH*;
      but, if neither of the straight lines *BC*, *CD*,
        then neither of the straight lines *KF*, *FH*.
  Therefore *KH* is a binomial straight line, the terms of which *KF*, *FH* are commensurable with the terms *BC*, *CD* of the apotome and in the same ratio, and further, *KH* has the same order as *BD*.   Q. E. D.


## PROPOSITION 114

*If an area be contained by an apotome and the binomial straight line the terms of which are commensurable with the terms of the apotome and in the same ratio, the "side" of the area is rational.*

For let an area, the rectangle *AB*, *CD*, be contained by the apotome *AB* and the binomial straight line *CD*,

and let *CE* be the greater term of the latter; let the terms *CE*, *ED* of the binomial straight line be commensurable with the terms *AF*, *FB* of the apotome and in the same ratio; and let the "side" of the rectangle *AB*, *CD* be *G*; I say that *G* is rational.

For let a rational straight line *H* be set out, and to *CD* let there be applied a rectangle equal to the square on *H* and producing *KL* as breadth,
  Therefore *KL* is an apotome.
  Let its terms be *KM*, *ML* commensurable with the terms *CE*, *ED* of the binomial straight line and in the same ratio. [x. 112]
  But *CE*, *ED* are also commensurable with *AF*, *FB* and in the same ratio;
    therefore, as *AF* is to *FB*, so is *KM* to *ML*.
  Therefore, alternately, as *AF* is to *KM*, so is *BF* to *LM*;
therefore also the remainder *AB* is to the remainder *KL* as *AF* is to *KM*. [v. 19]
  But *AF* is commensurable with *KM*; [x. 12]
    therefore *AB* is also commensurable with *KL*. [x. 11]
  And, as *AB* is to *KL*, so is the rectangle *CD*, *AB* to the rectangle *CD*, *KL*;
[vi. 1]
therefore the rectangle *CD*, *AB* is also commensurable with the rectangle *CD*, *KL*. [x. 11]
  But the rectangle *CD*, *KL* is equal to the square on *H*;
therefore the rectangle *CD*, *AB* is commensurable with the square on *H*.
  But the square on *G* is equal to the rectangle *CD*, *AB*;
    therefore the square on *G* is commensurable with the square on *H*.
  But the square on *H* is rational;
      therefore the square on *G* is also rational;
        therefore *G* is rational.
  And it is the "side" of the rectangle *CD*, *AB*.
  Therefore etc.

PORISM. And it is made manifest to us by this also that it is possible for a rational area to be contained by irrational straight lines.   Q. E. D.

## PROPOSITION 115

*From a medial straight line there arise irrational straight lines infinite in number, and none of them is the same as any of the preceding.*

Let $A$ be a medial straight line;

I say that from $A$ there arise irrational straight lines infinite in number, and none of them is the same as any of the preceding.

Let a rational straight line $B$ be set out, and let the square on $C$ be equal to the rectangle $B, A$;

therefore $C$ is irrational; [x. Def. 4]
for that which is contained by an irrational and a rational straight line is irrational.                                                                                                                   [deduction from x. 20]

And it is not the same with any of the preceding;
for the square on none of the preceding, if applied to a rational straight line produces as breadth a medial straight line.

Again, let the square on $D$ be equal to the rectangle $B, C$;
therefore the square on $D$ is irrational.                               [deduction from x. 20]

Therefore $D$ is irrational;                                                                  [x. Def. 4]
and it is not the same with any of the preceding, for the square on none of the preceding, if applied to a rational straight line, produces $C$ as breadth.

Similarly, if this arrangement proceeds *ad infinitum*, it is manifest that from the medial straight line there arise irrational straight lines infinite in number, and none is the same with any of the preceding.   Q. E. D.

# BOOK ELEVEN

## DEFINITIONS

1. A *solid* is that which has length, breadth, and depth.
2. An extremity of a solid is a surface.
3. A *straight line* is *at right angles to a plane*, when it makes right angles with all the straight lines which meet it and are in the plane.
4. A *plane* is *at right angles to a plane* when the straight lines drawn, in one of the planes, at right angles to the common section of the planes are at right angles to the remaining plane.
5. The *inclination of a straight line to a plane* is, assuming a perpendicular drawn from the extremity of the straight line which is elevated above the plane to the plane, and a straight line joined from the point thus arising to the extremity of the straight line which is in the plane, the angle contained by the straight line so drawn and the straight line standing up.
6. The *inclination of a plane to a plane* is the acute angle contained by the straight lines drawn at right angles to the common section at the same point, one in each of the planes.
7. A plane is said to be *similarly inclined* to a plane as another is to another when the said angles of the inclinations are equal to one another.
8. *Parallel planes* are those which do not meet.
9. *Similar solid figures* are those contained by similar planes equal in multitude.
10. *Equal and similar solid figures* are those contained by similar planes equal in multitude and in magnitude.
11. A *solid angle* is the inclination constituted by more than two lines which meet one another and are not in the same surface, towards all the lines. Otherwise: A *solid angle* is that which is contained by more than two plane angles which are not in the same plane and are constructed to one point.
12. A *pyramid* is a solid figure, contained by planes, which is constructed from one plane to one point.
13. A *prism* is a solid figure contained by planes two of which, namely those which are opposite, are equal, similar and parallel, while the rest are parallelograms.
14. When, the diameter of a semicircle remaining fixed, the semicircle is carried round and restored again to the same position from which it began to be moved, the figure so comprehended is a *sphere*.
15. The *axis of the sphere* is the straight line which remains fixed and about which the semicircle is turned.
16. The *centre of the sphere* is the same as that of the semicircle.
17. A *diameter of the sphere* is any straight line drawn through the centre and

terminated in both directions by the surface of the sphere.

18. When, one side of those about the right angle in a right-angled triangle remaining fixed, the triangle is carried round and restored again to the same position from which it began to be moved, the figure so comprehended is a *cone*.

And, if the straight line which remains fixed be equal to the remaining side about the right angle which is carried round, the cone will be *right-angled*; if less, *obtuse-angled*; and if greater, *acute-angled*.

19. The *axis of the cone* is the straight line which remains fixed and about which the triangle is turned.

20. And the *base* is the circle described by the straight line which is carried round.

21. When, one side of those about the right angle in a rectangular parallelogram remaining fixed, the parallelogram is carried round and restored again to the same position from which it began to be moved, the figure so comprehended is a *cylinder*.

22. The *axis of the cylinder* is the straight line which remains fixed and about which the parallelogram is turned.

23. And the *bases* are the circles described by the two sides opposite to one another which are carried round.

24. *Similar cones and cylinders* are those in which the axes and the diameters of the bases are proportional.

25. A *cube* is a solid figure contained by six equal squares.

26. An *octahedron* is a solid figure contained by eight equal and equilateral triangles.

27. An *icosahedron* is a solid figure contained by twenty equal and equilateral triangles.

28. A *dodecahedron* is a solid figure contained by twelve equal, equilateral, and equiangular pentagons.

## BOOK XI. PROPOSITIONS

### Proposition 1

*A part of a straight line cannot be in the plane of reference and a part in a plane more elevated.*

For, if possible, let a part $AB$ of the straight line $ABC$ be in the plane of reference, and a part $BC$ in a plane more elevated.

There will then be in the plane of reference some straight line continuous with $AB$ in a straight line.

Let it be $BD$;
therefore $AB$ is a common segment of the two straight lines $ABC$, $ABD$:
which is impossible, inasmuch as, if we describe a circle with centre $B$ and distance $AB$, the diameters will cut off unequal circumferences of the circle.

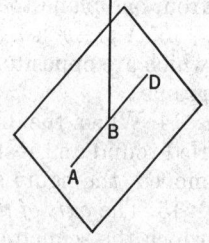

Therefore a part of a straight line cannot be in the plane of reference, and a part in a plane more elevated.

Q. E. D.

## PROPOSITION 2

*If two straight lines cut one another, they are in one plane, and every triangle is in one plane.*

For let the two straight lines $AB$, $CD$ cut one another at the point $E$;
I say that $AB$, $CD$ are in one plane, and every triangle is in one plane.
For let points $F$, $G$ be taken at random on $EC$, $EB$,
let $CB$, $FG$ be joined,
and let $FH$, $GK$ be drawn across;
I say first that the triangle $ECB$ is in one plane.
For, if part of the triangle $ECB$, either $FHC$ or $GBK$, is in the plane of reference, and the rest in another,

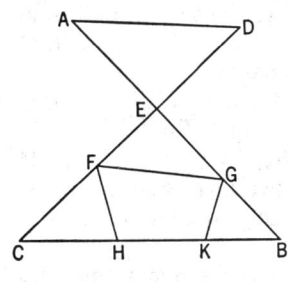

a part also of one of the straight lines $EC$, $EB$ will be in the plane of reference, and a part in another.
But, if the part $FCBG$ of the triangle $ECB$ be in the plane of reference, and the rest in another,
a part also of both the straight lines $EC$, $EB$ will be in the plane of reference and a part in another: which was proved absurd. [XI. 1]
Therefore the triangle $ECB$ is in one plane.
But, in whatever plane the triangle $ECB$ is, in that plane also is each of the straight lines $EC$, $EB$, and, in whatever plane each of the straight lines $EC$, $EB$ is, in that plane are $AB$, $CD$ also. [XI. 1]
Therefore the straight lines $AB$, $CD$ are in one plane,
and every triangle is in one plane.    Q. E. D.

## PROPOSITION 3

*If two planes cut one another, their common section is a straight line.*

For let the two planes $AB$, $BC$ cut one another,
and let the line $DB$ be their common section;
I say that the line $DB$ is a straight line.

For, if not, from $D$ to $B$ let the straight line $DEB$ be joined in the plane $AB$,
and in the plane $BC$ the straight line $DFB$.
Then the two straight lines $DEB$, $DFB$ will have the same extremities, and will clearly enclose an area: which is absurd.
Therefore $DEB$, $DFB$ are not straight lines.
Similarly we can prove that neither will there be any other straight line joined from $D$ to $B$ except $DB$ the common section of the planes $AB$, $BC$.
Therefore etc.    Q. E. D.

## PROPOSITION 4

*If a straight line be set up at right angles to two straight lines which cut one another, at their common point of section, it will also be at right angles to the plane through them.*

For let a straight line $EF$ be set up at right angles to the two straight lines $AB$, $CD$, which cut one another at the point $E$, from $E$;

I say that $EF$ is also at right angles to the plane through $AB$, $CD$.

For let $AE$, $EB$, $CE$, $ED$ be cut off equal to one another,

and let any straight line $GEH$ be drawn across through $E$, at random;

let $AD$, $CB$ be joined,

and further, let $FA$, $FG$, $FD$, $FC$, $FH$, $FB$ be joined from the point $F$ taken at random <on $EF$>.

Now, since the two straight lines $AE$, $ED$ are equal to the two straight lines $CE$, $EB$, and contain equal angles, [I. 15]

therefore the base $AD$ is equal to the base $CB$,

and the triangle $AED$ will be equal to the triangle $CEB$; [I. 4]

so that the angle $DAE$ is also equal to the angle $EBC$.

But the angle $AEG$ is also equal to the angle $BEH$; [I. 15]

therefore $AGE$, $BEH$ are two triangles which have two angles equal to two angles respectively, and one side equal to one side, namely that adjacent to the equal angles, that is to say, $AE$ to $EB$;

therefore they will also have the remaining sides equal to the remaining sides. [I. 26]

Therefore $GE$ is equal to $EH$, and $AG$ to $BH$.

And, since $AE$ is equal to $EB$,

while $FE$ is common and at right angles,

therefore the base $FA$ is equal to the base $FB$. [I. 4]

For the same reason

$FC$ is also equal to $FD$.

And, since $AD$ is equal to $CB$,

and $FA$ is also equal to $FB$,

the two sides $FA$, $AD$ are equal to the two sides $FB$, $BC$ respectively;

and the base $FD$ was proved equal to the base $FC$;

therefore the angle $FAD$ is also equal to the angle $FBC$. [I. 8]

And since, again, $AG$ was proved equal to $BH$,

and further, $FA$ also equal to $FB$,

the two sides $FA$, $AG$ are equal to the two sides $FB$, $BH$.

And the angle $FAG$ was proved equal to the angle $FBH$;

therefore the base $FG$ is equal to the base $FH$. [I. 4]

Now since, again, $GE$ was proved equal to $EH$,

and $EF$ is common,

the two sides $GE$, $EF$ are equal to the two sides $HE$, $EF$;

and the base $FG$ is equal to the base $FH$;

therefore the angle $GEF$ is equal to the angle $HEF$. [I. 8]

Therefore each of the angles $GEF$, $HEF$ is right.

Therefore $FE$ is at right angles to $GH$ drawn at random through $E$.

Similarly we can prove that $FE$ will also make right angles with all the straight lines which meet it and are in the plane of reference.

But a straight line is at right angles to a plane when it makes right angles

with all the straight lines which meet it and are in that same plane; [XI. Def. 3]
therefore $FE$ is at right angles to the plane of reference.
But the plane of reference is the plane through the straight lines $AB$, $CD$.
Therefore $FE$ is at right angles to the plane through $AB$, $CD$.
Therefore etc. Q. E. D.

## Proposition 5

*If a straight line be set up at right angles to three straight lines which meet one another, at their common point of section, the three straight lines are in one plane.*

For let a straight line $AB$ be set up at right angles to the three straight lines $BC$, $BD$, $BE$, at their point of meeting at $B$;

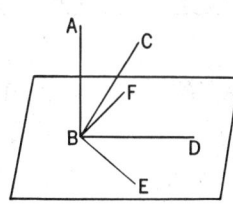

I say that $BC$, $BD$, $BE$ are in one plane.

For suppose they are not, but, if possible, let $BD$, $BE$ be in the plane of reference and $BC$ in one more elevated;

let the plane through $AB$, $BC$ be produced;

it will thus make, as common section in the plane of reference, a straight line. [XI. 3]

Let it make $BF$.

Therefore the three straight lines $AB$, $BC$, $BF$ are in one plane, namely that drawn through $AB$, $BC$.

Now, since $AB$ is at right angles to each of the straight lines $BD$, $BE$, therefore $AB$ is also at right angles to the plane through $BD$, $BE$. [XI. 4]

But the plane through $BD$, $BE$ is the plane of reference;

therefore $AB$ is at right angles to the plane of reference.

Thus $AB$ will also make right angles with all the straight lines which meet it and are in the plane of reference. [XI. Def. 3]

But $BF$ which is in the plane of reference meets it;

therefore the angle $ABF$ is right.

But, by hypothesis, the angle $ABC$ is also right;

therefore the angle $ABF$ is equal to the angle $ABC$.

And they are in one plane:

which is impossible.

Therefore the straight line $BC$ is not in a more elevated plane;

therefore the three straight lines $BC$, $BD$, $BE$ are in one plane.

Therefore, if a straight line be set up at right angles to three straight lines, at their point of meeting, the three straight lines are in one plane. Q. E. D.

## Proposition 6

*If two straight lines be at right angles to the same plane, the straight lines will be parallel.*

For let the two straight lines $AB$, $CD$ be at right angles to the plane of reference;

I say that $AB$ is parallel to $CD$.

For let them meet the plane of reference at the points $B$, $D$,
let the straight line $BD$ be joined,
let $DE$ be drawn, in the plane of reference, at right angles to $BD$,
let $DE$ be made equal to $AB$,

and let $BE$, $AE$, $AD$ be joined.

Now, since $AB$ is at right angles to the plane of reference, it will also make right angles with all the straight lines which meet it and are in the plane of reference. [XI. Def. 3]

But each of the straight lines $BD$, $BE$ is in the plane of reference and meets $AB$;

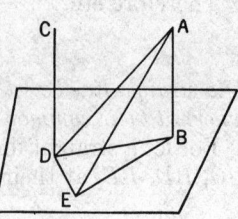

therefore each of the angles $ABD$, $ABE$ is right.

For the same reason

each of the angles $CDB$, $CDE$ is also right.

And, since $AB$ is equal to $DE$,

and $BD$ is common,

the two sides $AB$, $BD$ are equal to the two sides $ED$, $DB$;

and they include right angles;

therefore the base $AD$ is equal to the base $BE$. [I. 4]

And, since $AB$ is equal to $DE$,

while $AD$ is also equal to $BE$,

the two sides $AB$, $BE$ are equal to the two sides $ED$, $DA$;

and $AE$ is their common base;

therefore the angle $ABE$ is equal to the angle $EDA$. [I. 8]

But the angle $ABE$ is right;

therefore the angle $EDA$ is also right;

therefore $ED$ is at right angles to $DA$.

But it is also at right angles to each of the straight lines $BD$, $DC$;

therefore $ED$ is set up at right angles to the three straight lines $BD$, $DA$, $DC$ at their point of meeting;

therefore the three straight lines $BD$, $DA$, $DC$ are in one plane. [XI. 5]

But, in whatever plane $DB$, $DA$ are, in that plane is $AB$ also,

for every triangle is in one plane; [XI. 2]

therefore the straight lines $AB$, $BD$, $DC$ are in one plane.

And each of the angles $ABD$, $BDC$ is right;

therefore $AB$ is parallel to $CD$. [I. 28]

Therefore etc.

Q. E. D.

## Proposition 7

*If two straight lines be parallel and points be taken at random on each of them, the straight line joining the points is in the same plane with the parallel straight lines.*

Let $AB$, $CD$ be two parallel straight lines,

and let points $E$, $F$ be taken at random on them respectively;

I say that the straight line joining the points $E$, $F$ is in the same plane with the parallel straight lines.

For suppose it is not, but, if possible, let it be in a more elevated plane as $EGF$,

and let a plane be drawn through $EGF$;

it will then make, as section in the plane of reference, a straight line. [XI. 3]

Let it make it, as $EF$;

therefore the two straight lines $EGF$, $EF$ will enclose an area:

which is impossible.

# ELEMENTS XI

Therefore the straight line joined from $E$ to $F$ is not in a plane more elevated; therefore the straight line joined from $E$ to $F$ is in the plane through the parallel straight lines $AB$, $CD$.

Therefore etc.  Q. E. D.

## PROPOSITION 8

*If two straight lines be parallel, and one of them be at right angles to any plane, the remaining one will also be at right angles to the same plane.*

Let $AB$, $CD$ be two parallel straight lines,

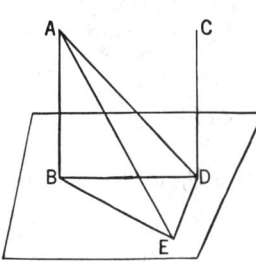

and let one of them, $AB$, be at right angles to the plane of reference;

I say that the remaining one, $CD$, will also be at right angles to the same plane.

For let $AB$, $CD$ meet the plane of reference at the points $B$, $D$,

and let $BD$ be joined;

therefore $AB$, $CD$, $BD$ are in one plane. [XI. 7]

Let $DE$ be drawn, in the plane of reference, at right angles to $BD$,

let $DE$ be made equal to $AB$,

and let $BE$, $AE$, $AD$ be joined.

Now, since $AB$ is at right angles to the plane of reference,
therefore $AB$ is also at right angles to all the straight lines which meet it and are in the plane of reference; [XI. Def. 3]

therefore each of the angles $ABD$, $ABE$ is right.

And, since the straight line $BD$ has fallen on the parallels $AB$, $CD$,

therefore the angles $ABD$, $CDB$ are equal to two right angles. [I. 29]

But the angle $ABD$ is right;

therefore the angle $CDB$ is also right;

therefore $CD$ is at right angles to $BD$.

And, since $AB$ is equal to $DE$,

and $BD$ is common,

the two sides $AB$, $BD$ are equal to the two sides $ED$, $DB$;

and the angle $ABD$ is equal to the angle $EDB$,

for each is right;

therefore the base $AD$ is equal to the base $BE$.

And, since $AB$ is equal to $DE$,

and $BE$ to $AD$,

the two sides $AB$, $BE$ are equal to the two sides $ED$, $DA$ respectively,

and $AE$ is their common base;

therefore the angle $ABE$ is equal to the angle $EDA$.

But the angle $ABE$ is right;

therefore the angle $EDA$ is also right;

therefore $ED$ is at right angles to $AD$.

But it is also at right angles to $DB$;

therefore $ED$ is also at right angles to the plane through $BD$, $DA$. [XI. 4]

Therefore $ED$ will also make right angles with all the straight lines which meet it and are in the plane through $BD$, $DA$.

But $DC$ is in the plane through $BD$, $DA$, inasmuch as $AB$, $BD$ are in the

plane through *BD*, *DA*, [XI. 2]
and *DC* is also in the plane in which *AB*, *BD* are.
Therefore *ED* is at right angles to *DC*,
so that *CD* is also at right angles to *DE*.
But *CD* is also at right angles to *BD*.
Therefore *CD* is set up at right angles to the two straight lines *DE*, *DB* which cut one another, from the point of section at *D*;
so that *CD* is also at right angles to the plane through *DE*, *DB*. [XI. 4]
But the plane through *DE*, *DB* is the plane of reference;
therefore *CD* is at right angles to the plane of reference.
Therefore etc. Q. E. D.

## Proposition 9

*Straight lines which are parallel to the same straight line and are not in the same plane with it are also parallel to one another.*

For let each of the straight lines *AB*, *CD* be parallel to *EF*, not being in the same plane with it;
I say that *AB* is parallel to *CD*.

For let a point *G* be taken at random on *EF*,
and from it let there be drawn *GH*, in the plane through *EF*, *AB*, at right angles to *EF*, and *GK* in the plane through *FE*, *CD* again at right angles to *EF*.

Now, since *EF* is at right angles to each of the straight lines *GH*, *GK*,
therefore *EF* is also at right angles to the plane through *GH*, *GK*. [XI. 4]
And *EF* is parallel to *AB*;
therefore *AB* is also at right angles to the plane through *HG*, *GK*. [XI. 8]
For the same reason
*CD* is also at right angles to the plane through *HG*, *GK*;
therefore each of the straight lines *AB*, *CD* is at right angles to the plane through *HG*, *GK*.

But, if two straight lines be at right angles to the same plane, the straight lines are parallel; [XI. 6]
therefore *AB* is parallel to *CD*. Q. E. D.

## Proposition 10

*If two straight lines meeting one another be parallel to two straight lines meeting one another not in the same plane, they will contain equal angles.*

For let the two straight lines *AB*, *BC* meeting one another be parallel to the two straight lines *DE*, *EF* meeting one another, not in the same plane;
I say that the angle *ABC* is equal to the angle *DEF*.

For let *BA*, *BC*, *ED*, *EF* be cut off equal to one another, and let *AD*, *CF*, *BE*, *AC*, *DF* be joined.

Now, since *BA* is equal and parallel to *ED*,
therefore *AD* is also equal and parallel to *BE*. [I. 33]
For the same reason
*CF* is also equal and parallel to *BE*.

ELEMENTS XI

Therefore each of the straight lines AD, CF is equal and parallel to BE.

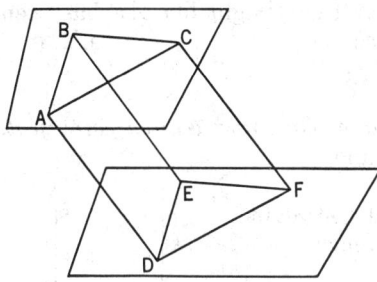

But straight lines which are parallel to the same straight line and are not in the same plane with it are parallel to one another; [XI. 9]
therefore AD is parallel and equal to CF.

And AC, DF join them;
therefore AC is also equal and parallel to DF. [I. 33]

Now, since the two sides AB, BC are equal to the two sides DE, EF,
and the base AC is equal to the base DF,
therefore the angle ABC is equal to the angle DEF. [I. 8]

Therefore etc.
Q. E. D.

## Proposition 11

*From a given elevated point to draw a straight line perpendicular to a given plane.*

Let A be the given elevated point, and the plane of reference the given plane; thus it is required to draw from the point A a straight line perpendicular to the plane of reference.

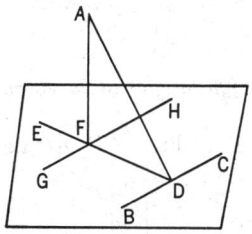

Let any straight line BC be drawn, at random, in the plane of reference,
and let AD be drawn from the point A perpendicular to BC. [I. 12]

If then AD is also perpendicular to the plane of reference, that which was enjoined will have been done.

But, if not, let DE be drawn from the point D at right angles to BC and in the plane of reference, [I. 11]
let AF be drawn from A perpendicular to DE, [I. 12]
and let GH be drawn through the point F parallel to BC. [I. 31]

Now, since BC is at right angles to each of the straight lines DA, DE,
therefore BC is also at right angles to the plane through ED, DA. [XI. 4]

And GH is parallel to it;
but, if two straight lines be parallel, and one of them be at right angles to any plane, the remaining one will also be at right angles to the same plane; [XI. 8]
therefore GH is also at right angles to the plane through ED, DA.

Therefore GH is also at right angles to all the straight lines which meet it and are in the plane through ED, DA. [XI. Def. 3]

But AF meets it and is in the plane through ED, DA;
therefore GH is at right angles to FA,
so that FA is also at right angles to GH.

But AF is also at right angles to DE;
therefore AF is at right angles to each of the straight lines GH, DE.

But, if a straight line be set up at right angles to two straight lines which cut one another, at the point of section, it will also be at right angles to the plane through them; [XI. 4]
therefore FA is at right angles to the plane through ED, GH.

But the plane through ED, GH is the plane of reference;

therefore $AF$ is at right angles to the plane of reference.

Therefore from the given elevated point $A$ the straight line $AF$ has been drawn perpendicular to the plane of reference.     Q. E. F.

## Proposition 12

*To set up a straight line at right angles to a given plane from a given point in it.*

Let the plane of reference be the given plane,
and $A$ the point in it;
thus it is required to set up from the point $A$ a straight line at right angles to the plane of reference.

Let any elevated point $B$ be conceived,
from $B$ let $BC$ be drawn perpendicular to
the plane of reference,          [XI. 11]
and through the point $A$ let $AD$ be drawn
parallel to $BC$.          [I. 31]

Then, since $AD$, $CB$ are two parallel straight lines, while one of them, $BC$, is at right angles to the plane of reference, therefore the remaining one, $AD$, is also at right angles to the plane of reference.          [XI. 8]

Therefore $AD$ has been set up at right angles to the given plane from the point $A$ in it.     Q. E. F.

## Proposition 13

*From the same point two straight lines cannot be set up at right angles to the same plane on the same side.*

For, if possible, from the same point $A$ let the two straight lines $AB$, $AC$ be set up at right angles to the plane of reference and on the same side,
and let a plane be drawn through $BA$, $AC$;
it will then make, as section through $A$ in the plane of reference, a straight line.          [XI. 3]

Let it make $DAE$;
therefore the straight lines $AB$, $AC$,
$DAE$ are in one plane.

And, since $CA$ is at right angles to the plane of reference, it will also make right angles with all the straight lines which meet it and are in the plane of reference.          [XI. Def. 3]

But $DAE$ meets it and is in the plane of reference;
therefore the angle $CAE$ is right.

For the same reason
the angle $BAE$ is also right;
therefore the angle $CAE$ is equal to the angle $BAE$.

And they are in one plane:
which is impossible.

Therefore etc.     Q. E. D.

## Proposition 14

*Planes to which the same straight line is at right angles will be parallel.*

For let any straight line $AB$ be at right angles to each of the planes $CD$, $EF$;

ELEMENTS XI 311

I say that the planes are parallel.
For, if not, they will meet when produced.

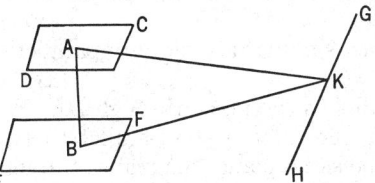

Let them meet;
they will then make, as common section,
a straight line. [XI. 3]
Let them make *GH*;
let a point *K* be taken at random on *GH*,
and let *AK*, *BK* be joined.
Now, since *AB* is at right angles to
the plane *EF*,
therefore *AB* is also at right angles to *BK* which is a straight line in the plane
*EF* produced; [XI. Def. 3]
therefore the angle *ABK* is right.
For the same reason
the angle *BAK* is also right.
Thus, in the triangle *ABK*, the two angles *ABK*, *BAK* are equal to two
right angles:
which is impossible. [I. 17]
Therefore the planes *CD*, *EF* will not meet when produced;
therefore the planes *CD*, *EF* are parallel. [XI. Def. 8]
Therefore planes to which the same straight line is at right angles are parallel.
Q. E. D.

PROPOSITION 15

*If two straight lines meeting one another be parallel to two straight lines meeting one another, not being in the same plane, the planes through them are parallel.*

For let the two straight lines *AB*, *BC* meeting one another be parallel to the

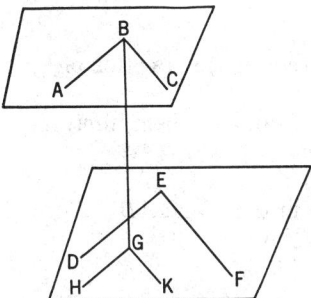

two straight lines *DE*, *EF* meeting one another, not being in the same plane; I say that the planes produced through *AB*, *BC* and *DE*, *EF* will not meet one another.
For let *BG* be drawn from the point *B* perpendicular to the plane through *DE*, *EF* [XI. 11],
and let it meet the plane at the point *G*;
through *G* let *GH* be drawn parallel to *ED*, and
*GK* parallel to *EF*. [I. 31]
Now, since *BG* is at right angles to the plane
through *DE*, *EF*,
therefore it will also make right angles with all the straight lines which meet it
and are in the plane through *DE*, *EF*. [XI. Def. 3]
But each of the straight lines *GH*, *GK* meets it and is in the plane through
*DE*, *EF*;
therefore each of the angles *BGH*, *BGK* is right.
And, since *BA* is parallel to *GH*, [XI. 9]
therefore the angles *GBA*, *BGH* are equal to two right angles. [I. 29]
But the angle *BGH* is right;
therefore the angle *GBA* is also right;
therefore *GB* is at right angles to *BA*.
For the same reason

*GB* is also at right angles to *BC*.

Since then the straight line *GB* is set up at right angles to the two straight lines *BA*, *BC* which cut one another, therefore *GB* is also at right angles to the plane through *BA*, *BC*. [XI. 4]

But planes to which the same straight line is at right angles are parallel; [XI. 14]

therefore the plane through *AB*, *BC* is parallel to the plane through *DE*, *EF*.

Therefore, if two straight lines meeting one another be parallel to two straight lines meeting one another, not in the same plane, the planes through them are parallel. Q. E. D.

## Proposition 16

*If two parallel planes be cut by any plane, their common sections are parallel.*

For let the two parallel planes *AB*, *CD* be cut by the plane *EFGH*, and let *EF*, *GH* be their common sections;

I say that *EF* is parallel to *GH*.

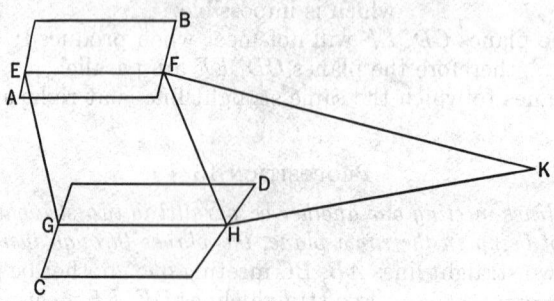

For, if not, *EF*, *GH* will, when produced, meet either in the direction of *F*, *H* or of *E*, *G*.

Let them be produced, as in the direction of *F*, *H*, and let them, first, meet at *K*.

Now, since *EFK* is in the plane *AB*,

therefore all the points on *EFK* are also in the plane *AB*. [XI. 1]

But *K* is one of the points on the straight line *EFK*;

therefore *K* is in the plane *AB*.

For the same reason

*K* is also in the plane *CD*;

therefore the planes *AB*, *CD* will meet when produced.

But they do not meet, because they are, by hypothesis, parallel;

therefore the straight lines *EF*, *GH* will not meet when produced in the direction of *F*, *H*.

Similarly we can prove that neither will the straight lines *EF*, *GH* meet when produced in the direction of *E*, *G*.

But straight lines which do not meet in either direction are parallel. [I. Def. 23]

Therefore *EF* is parallel to *GH*.

Therefore etc. Q. E. D.

## Proposition 17

*If two straight lines be cut by parallel planes, they will be cut in the same ratios.*

For let the two straight lines $AB$, $CD$ be cut by the parallel planes $GH$, $KL$, $MN$ at the points $A$, $E$, $B$ and $C$, $F$, $D$;

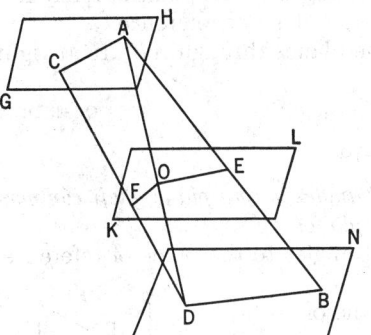

I say that, as the straight line $AE$ is to $EB$, so is $CF$ to $FD$.

For let $AC$, $BD$, $AD$ be joined,
let $AD$ meet the plane $KL$ at the point $O$,
and let $EO$, $OF$ be joined.

Now, since the two parallel planes $KL$, $MN$ are cut by the plane $EBDO$,
their common sections $EO$, $BD$ are parallel. [XI. 16]

For the same reason, since the two parallel planes $GH$, $KL$ are cut by the plane $AOFC$,
their common sections $AC$, $OF$ are parallel. [id.]

And, since the straight line $EO$ has been drawn parallel to $BD$, one of the sides of the triangle $ABD$,

therefore, proportionally, as $AE$ is to $EB$, so is $AO$ to $OD$. [VI. 2]

Again, since the straight line $OF$ has been drawn parallel to $AC$, one of the sides of the triangle $ADC$,

proportionally, as $AO$ is to $OD$, so is $CF$ to $FD$. [id.]

But it was also proved that, as $AO$ is to $OD$, so is $AE$ to $EB$;

therefore also, as $AE$ is to $EB$, so is $CF$ to $FD$. [V. 11]

Therefore etc.

Q. E. D.

## Proposition 18

*If a straight line be at right angles to any plane, all the planes through it will also be at right angles to the same plane.*

For let any straight line $AB$ be at right angles to the plane of reference;

I say that all the planes through $AB$ are also at right angles to the plane of reference.

For let the plane $DE$ be drawn through $AB$, let $CE$ be the common section of the plane $DE$ and the plane of reference,

let a point $F$ be taken at random on $CE$,
and from $F$ let $FG$ be drawn in the plane $DE$ at right angles to $CE$. [I. 11]

Now, since $AB$ is at right angles to the plane of reference, $AB$ is also at right angles to all the straight lines which meet it and are in the plane of reference; [XI. Def. 3]

so that it is also at right angles to $CE$;
therefore the angle $ABF$ is right.

But the angle $GFB$ is also right;

therefore $AB$ is parallel to $FG$. [I. 28]

But $AB$ is at right angles to the plane of reference;

therefore *FG* is also at right angles to the plane of reference.  [XI. 8]

Now a plane is at right angles to a plane, when the straight lines drawn, in one of the planes, at right angles to the common section of the planes are at right angles to the remaining plane.  [XI. Def. 4]

And *FG*, drawn in one of the planes *DE* at right angles to *CE*, the common section of the planes, was proved to be at right angles to the plane of reference; therefore the plane *DE* is at right angles to the plane of reference.

Similarly also it can be proved that all the planes through *AB* are at right angles to the plane of reference.

Therefore etc.

Q. E. D.

## Proposition 19

*If two planes which cut one another be at right angles to any plane, their common section will also be at right angles to the same plane.*

For let the two planes *AB*, *BC* be at right angles to the plane of reference, and let *BD* be their common section;

I say that *BD* is at right angles to the plane of reference.

For suppose it is not, and from the point *D* let *DE* be drawn in the plane *AB* at right angles to the straight line *AD*, and *DF* in the plane *BC* at right angles to *CD*.

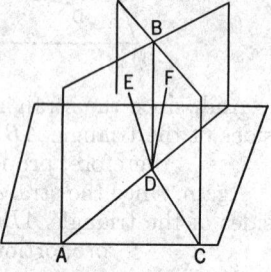

Now, since the plane *AB* is at right angles to the plane of reference, and *DE* has been drawn in the plane *AB* at right angles to *AD*, their common section, therefore *DE* is at right angles to the plane of reference.  [XI. Def. 4]

Similarly we can prove that *DF* is also at right angles to the plane of reference.

Therefore from the same point *D* two straight lines have been set up at right angles to the plane of reference on the same side:

which is impossible.  [XI. 13]

Therefore no straight line except the common section *DB* of the planes *AB*, *BC* can be set up from the point *D* at right angles to the plane of reference.

Therefore etc.

Q. E. D.

## Proposition 20

*If a solid angle be contained by three plane angles, any two, taken together in any manner, are greater than the remaining one.*

For let the solid angle at *A* be contained by the three plane angles *BAC*, *CAD*, *DAB*;

I say that any two of the angles *BAC*, *CAD*, *DAB*, taken together in any manner, are greater than the remaining one.

If now the angles *BAC*, *CAD*, *DAB* are equal to one another, it is manifest that any two are greater than the remaining one.

But, if not, let *BAC* be greater, and on the straight line *AB*, and at the point *A* on it, let the angle *BAE* be

ELEMENTS XI

constructed, in the plane through $BA$, $AC$, equal to the angle $DAB$;
let $AE$ be made equal to $AD$,
and let $BEC$, drawn across through the point $E$, cut the straight lines $AB$, $AC$ at the points $B$, $C$;
let $DB$, $DC$ be joined.
Now, since $DA$ is equal to $AE$,
and $AB$ is common,
two sides are equal to two sides;
and the angle $DAB$ is equal to the angle $BAE$;
therefore the base $DB$ is equal to the base $BE$. [I. 4]
And, since the two sides $BD$, $DC$ are greater than $BC$, [I. 20]
and of these $DB$ was proved equal to $BE$,
therefore the remainder $DC$ is greater than the remainder $EC$.
Now, since $DA$ is equal to $AE$,
and $AC$ is common,
and the base $DC$ is greater than the base $EC$,
therefore the angle $DAC$ is greater than the angle $EAC$. [I. 25]
But the angle $DAB$ was made equal to the angle $BAE$;
therefore the angles $DAB$, $DAC$ are greater than the angle $BAC$.

Similarly we can prove that the remaining angles also, taken together two and two, are greater than the remaining one.

Therefore etc.        Q. E. D.

## Proposition 21

*Any solid angle is contained by plane angles less than four right angles.*

Let the angle at $A$ be a solid angle contained by the plane angles $BAC$, $CAD$, $DAB$;

I say that the angles $BAC$, $CAD$, $DAB$ are less than four right angles.

For let points $B$, $C$, $D$ be taken at random on the straight lines $AB$, $AC$, $AD$ respectively,
and let $BC$, $CD$, $DB$ be joined.

Now, since the solid angle at $B$ is contained by the three plane angles $CBA$, $ABD$, $CBD$,
any two are greater than the remaining one;
[XI. 20]

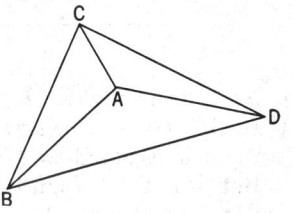

therefore the angles $CBA$, $ABD$ are greater than the angle $CBD$.
For the same reason
the angles $BCA$, $ACD$ are also greater than the angle $BCD$, and the angles $CDA$, $ADB$ are greater than the angle $CDB$;
therefore the six angles $CBA$, $ABD$, $BCA$, $ACD$, $CDA$, $ADB$ are greater than the three angles $CBD$, $BCD$, $CDB$.

But the three angles $CBD$, $BDC$, $BCD$ are equal to two right angles; [I. 32]
therefore the six angles $CBA$, $ABD$, $BCA$, $ACD$, $CDA$, $ADB$ are greater than two right angles.

And, since the three angles of each of the triangles $ABC$, $ACD$, $ADB$ are equal to two right angles,
therefore the nine angles of the three triangles, the angles $CBA$, $ACB$, $BAC$, $ACD$, $CDA$, $CAD$, $ADB$, $DBA$, $BAD$ are equal to six right angles;

316    EUCLID

and of them the six angles $ABC, BCA, ACD, CDA, ADB, DBA$ are greater than two right angles;

therefore the remaining three angles $BAC, CAD, DAB$ containing the solid angle are less than four right angles.

Therefore etc.                                             Q. E. D.

## Proposition 22

*If there be three plane angles of which two, taken together in any manner, are greater than the remaining one, and they are contained by equal straight lines, it is possible to construct a triangle out of the straight lines joining the extremities of the equal straight lines.*

Let there be three plane angles $ABC, DEF, GHK$, of which two, taken together in any manner, are greater than the remaining one, namely

the angles $ABC, DEF$ greater than the angle $GHK$,
the angles $DEF, GHK$ greater than the angle $ABC$,
and, further, the angles $GHK, ABC$ greater than the angle $DEF$;
let the straight lines $AB, BC, DE, EF, GH, HK$ be equal,
and let $AC, DF, GK$ be joined;

I say that it is possible to construct a triangle out of straight lines equal to $AC$, $DF$, $GK$, that is, that any two of the straight lines $AC, DF, GK$ are greater than the remaining one.

Now, if the angles $ABC, DEF, GHK$ are equal to one another, it is manifest that, $AC, DF, GK$ being equal also, it is possible to construct a triangle out of straight lines equal to $AC, DF, GK$.

But, if not, let them be unequal,
and on the straight line $HK$, and at the point $H$ on it, let the angle $KHL$ be constructed equal to the angle $ABC$;
let $HL$ be made equal to one of the straight lines $AB$, $BC, DE, EF, GH, HK$,
and let $KL, GL$ be joined.

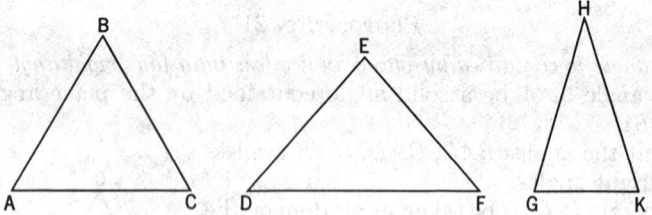

Now, since the two sides $AB, BC$ are equal to the two sides $KH, HL$,
and the angle at $B$ is equal to the angle $KHL$,
therefore the base $AC$ is equal to the base $KL$.    [I. 4]

And, since the angles $ABC, GHK$ are greater than the angle $DEF$,
while the angle $ABC$ is equal to the angle $KHL$,
therefore the angle $GHL$ is greater than the angle $DEF$.

And, since the two sides $GH, HL$ are equal to the two sides $DE, EF$,

ELEMENTS XI

and the angle *GHL* is greater than the angle *DEF*,
therefore the base *GL* is greater than the base *DF*.   [I. 24]
But *GK*, *KL* are greater than *GL*.
Therefore *GK*, *KL* are much greater than *DF*.
But *KL* is equal to *AC*;
therefore *AC*, *GK* are greater than the remaining straight line *DF*.
Similarly we can prove that
*AC*, *DF* are greater than *GK*,
and further, *DF*, *GK* are greater than *AC*.
Therefore it is possible to construct a triangle out of straight lines equal to *AC*, *DF*, *GK*.   Q. E. D.

## Proposition 23

*To construct a solid angle out of three plane angles two of which, taken together in any manner, are greater than the remaining one: thus the three angles must be less than four right angles.*

Let the angles *ABC*, *DEF*, *GHK* be the three given plane angles, and let two of these, taken together in any manner, be greater than the remaining one, while, further, the three are less than four right angles;
thus it is required to construct a solid angle out of angles equal to the angles *ABC*, *DEF*, *GHK*.

Let *AB*, *BC*, *DE*, *EF*, *GH*, *HK* be cut off equal to one another,
and let *AC*, *DF*, *GK* be joined;
it is therefore possible to construct a triangle out of straight lines equal to *AC*, *DF*, *GK*.   [XI. 22]

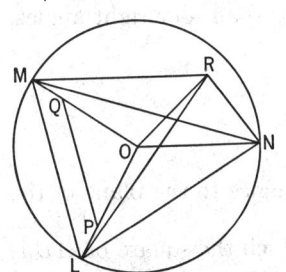

Let *LMN* be so constructed that *AC* is equal to *LM*, *DF* to *MN*, and further, *GK* to *NL*,
let the circle *LMN* be described about the triangle *LMN*,
let its centre be taken, and let it be *O*;
let *LO*, *MO*, *NO* be joined;
I say that *AB* is greater than *LO*.
For, if not, *AB* is either equal to *LO*, or less.
First, let it be equal.
Then, since *AB* is equal to *LO*,
while *AB* is equal to *BC*, and *OL* to *OM*,
the two sides *AB*, *BC* are equal to the two sides *LO*, *OM* respectively;
and, by hypothesis, the base *AC* is equal to the base *LM*;
therefore the angle *ABC* is equal to the angle *LOM*.   [I. 8]
For the same reason

the angle $DEF$ is also equal to the angle $MON$,
and further the angle $GHK$ to the angle $NOL$;
therefore the three angles $ABC$, $DEF$, $GHK$ are equal to the three angles $LOM$, $MON$, $NOL$.

But the three angles $LOM$, $MON$, $NOL$ are equal to four right angles; therefore the angles $ABC$, $DEF$, $GKH$ are equal to four right angles.

But they are also, by hypothesis, less than four right angles:
which is absurd.

Therefore $AB$ is not equal to $LO$.

I say next that neither is $AB$ less than $LO$.

For, if possible, let it be so,
and let $OP$ be made equal to $AB$, and $OQ$ equal to $BC$,
and let $PQ$ be joined.

Then, since $AB$ is equal to $BC$,
$OP$ is also equal to $OQ$,
so that the remainder $LP$ is equal to $QM$.

Therefore $LM$ is parallel to $PQ$, [VI. 2]
and $LMO$ is equiangular with $PQO$; [I. 29]
therefore, as $OL$ is to $LM$, so is $OP$ to $PQ$; [VI. 4]
and alternately, as $LO$ is to $OP$, so is $LM$ to $PQ$. [V. 16]

But $LO$ is greater than $OP$;
therefore $LM$ is also greater than $PQ$.

But $LM$ was made equal to $AC$;
therefore $AC$ is also greater than $PQ$.

Since, then, the two sides $AB$, $BC$ are equal to the two sides $PO$, $OQ$,
and the base $AC$ is greater than the base $PQ$,
therefore the angle $ABC$ is greater than the angle $POQ$. [I. 25]

Similarly we can prove that
the angle $DEF$ is also greater than the angle $MON$,
and the angle $GHK$ greater than the angle $NOL$.

Therefore the three angles $ABC$, $DEF$, $GHK$ are greater than the three angles $LOM$, $MON$, $NOL$.

But, by hypothesis, the angles $ABC$, $DEF$, $GHK$ are less than four right angles;
therefore the angles $LOM$, $MON$, $NOL$ are much less than four right angles.

But they are also equal to four right angles:
which is absurd.

Therefore $AB$ is not less than $LO$.

And it was proved that neither is it equal;
therefore $AB$ is greater than $LO$.

Let then $OR$ be set up from the point $O$ at right angles to the plane of the circle $LMN$, [XI. 12]
and let the square on $OR$ be equal to that area by which the square on $AB$ is greater than the square on $LO$; [Lemma]
let $RL$, $RM$, $RN$ be joined.

Then, since $RO$ is at right angles to the plane of the circle $LMN$, therefore $RO$ is also at right angles to each of the straight lines $LO$, $MO$, $NO$.

And, since $LO$ is equal to $OM$,
while $OR$ is common and at right angles,

therefore the base $RL$ is equal to the base $RM$.  [I. 4]

For the same reason
$RN$ is also equal to each of the straight lines $RL$, $RM$;
therefore the three straight lines $RL$, $RM$, $RN$ are equal to one another.

Next, since by hypothesis the square on $OR$ is equal to that area by which the square on $AB$ is greater than the square on $LO$,
therefore the square on $AB$ is equal to the squares on $LO$, $OR$.

But the square on $LR$ is equal to the squares on $LO$, $OR$, for the angle $LOR$ is right;  [I. 47]
therefore the square on $AB$ is equal to the square on $RL$;
therefore $AB$ is equal to $RL$.

But each of the straight lines $BC$, $DE$, $EF$, $GH$, $HK$ is equal to $AB$,
while each of the straight lines $RM$, $RN$ is equal to $RL$;
therefore each of the straight lines $AB$, $BC$, $DE$, $EF$, $GH$, $HK$
is equal to each of the straight lines $RL$, $RM$, $RN$.

And, since the two sides $LR$, $RM$ are equal to the two sides $AB$, $BC$,
and the base $LM$ is by hypothesis equal to the base $AC$,
therefore the angle $LRM$ is equal to the angle $ABC$.  [I. 8]

For the same reason
the angle $MRN$ is also equal to the angle $DEF$,
and the angle $LRN$ to the angle $GHK$.

Therefore, out of the three plane angles $LRM$, $MRN$, $LRN$, which are equal to the three given angles $ABC$, $DEF$, $GHK$, the solid angle at $R$ has been constructed, which is contained by the angles $LRM$, $MRN$, $LRN$.  Q. E. F.

### Lemma

But how it is possible to take the square on $OR$ equal to that area by which the square on $AB$ is greater than the square on $LO$, we can show as follows.

Let the straight lines $AB$, $LO$ be set out,
and let $AB$ be the greater;
let the semicircle $ABC$ be described on $AB$,
and into the semicircle $ABC$ let $AC$ be fitted equal to the straight line $LO$, not being greater than the diameter $AB$;  [IV. 1]
let $CB$ be joined

Since then the angle $ACB$ is an angle in the semicircle $ACB$,
therefore the angle $ACB$ is right.  [III. 31]

Therefore the square on $AB$ is equal to the squares on $AC$, $CB$.  [I. 47]

Hence the square on $AB$ is greater than the square on $AC$ by the square on $CB$.

But $AC$ is equal to $LO$.

Therefore the square on $AB$ is greater than the square on $LO$ by the square on $CB$.

If then we cut off $OR$ equal to $BC$, the square on $AB$ will be greater than the square on $LO$ by the square on $OR$.  Q. E. F.

### Proposition 24

*If a solid be contained by parallel planes, the opposite planes in it are equal and parallelogrammic.*

For let the solid $CDHG$ be contained by the parallel planes $AC$, $GF$, $AH$, $DF$, $BF$, $AE$;

I say that the opposite planes in it are equal and parallelogrammic.

For, since the two parallel planes $BG$, $CE$ are cut by the plane $AC$, their common sections are parallel. [XI. 16]

Therefore $AB$ is parallel to $DC$.

Again, since the two parallel planes $BF$, $AE$ are cut by the plane $AC$, their common sections are parallel. [XI. 16]

Therefore $BC$ is parallel to $AD$.

But $AB$ was also proved parallel to $DC$;

therefore $AC$ is a parallelogram.

Similarly we can prove that each of the planes $DF$, $FG$, $GB$, $BF$, $AE$ is a parallelogram.

Let $AH$, $DF$ be joined.

Then, since $AB$ is parallel to $DC$, and $BH$ to $CF$, the two straight lines $AB$, $BH$ which meet one another are parallel to the two straight lines $DC$, $CF$ which meet one another, not in the same plane;

therefore they will contain equal angles; [XI. 10]

therefore the angle $ABH$ is equal to the angle $DCF$.

And, since the two sides $AB$, $BH$ are equal to the two sides $DC$, $CF$,

[I. 34]

and the angle $ABH$ is equal to the angle $DCF$,

therefore the base $AH$ is equal to the base $DF$,

and the triangle $ABH$ is equal to the triangle $DCF$. [I. 4]

And the parallelogram $BG$ is double of the triangle $ABH$, and the parallelogram $CE$ double of the triangle $DCF$; [I. 34]

therefore the parallelogram $BG$ is equal to the parallelogram $CE$.

Similarly we can prove that

$AC$ is also equal to $GF$,

and $AE$ to $BF$.

Therefore etc.

Q. E. D.

## Proposition 25

*If a parallelepipedal solid be cut by a plane which is parallel to the opposite planes, then, as the base is to the base, so will the solid be to the solid.*

For let the parallelepipedal solid $ABCD$ be cut by the plane $FG$ which is parallel to the opposite planes $RA$, $DH$;

I say that, as the base $AEFV$ is to the base $EHCF$, so is the solid $ABFU$ to the solid $EGCD$.

For let $AH$ be produced in each direction,

let any number of straight lines whatever, $AK$, $KL$, be made equal to $AE$,

and any number whatever, $HM$, $MN$, equal to $EH$;

and let the parallelograms $LP$, $KV$, $HW$, $MS$ and the solids $LQ$, $KR$, $DM$, $MT$ be completed.

Then, since the straight lines $LK$, $KA$, $AE$ are equal to one another,

the parallelograms $LP$, $KV$, $AF$ are also equal to one another,

*KO, KB, AG* are equal to one another,
and further, *LX, KQ, AR* are equal to one another, for they are opposite.
[XI. 24]

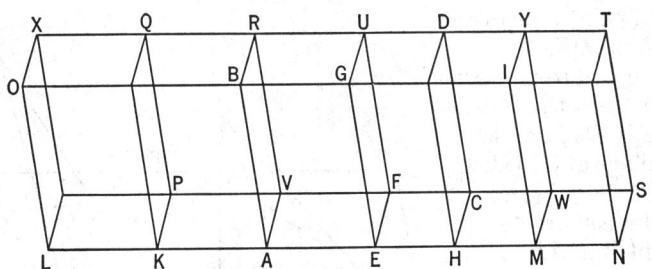

For the same reason
the parallelograms *EC, HW, MS* are also equal to one another,
*HG, HI, IN* are equal to one another,
and further, *DH, MY, NT* are equal to one another.
Therefore in the solids *LQ, KR, AU* three planes are equal to three planes.
But the three planes are equal to the three opposite;
therefore the three solids *LQ, KR, AU* are equal to one another.
For the same reason
the three solids *ED, DM, MT* are also equal to one another.
Therefore, whatever multiple the base *LF* is of the base *AF*, the same multiple also is the solid *LU* of the solid *AU*.
For the same reason,
whatever multiple the base *NF* is of the base *FH*, the same multiple also is the solid *NU* of the solid *HU*.
And, if the base *LF* is equal to the base *NF*, the solid *LU* is also equal to the solid *NU*;
if the base *LF* exceeds the base *NF*, the solid *LU* also exceeds the solid *NU*;
and, if one falls short, the other falls short.
Therefore, there being four magnitudes, the two bases *AF, FH*, and the two solids *AU, UH*,
equimultiples have been taken of the base *AF* and the solid *AU*, namely the base *LF* and the solid *LU*,
and equimultiples of the base *HF* and the solid *HU*, namely the base *NF* and the solid *NU*,
and it has been proved that, if the base *LF* exceeds the base *FN*, the solid *LU* also exceeds the solid *NU*,
if the bases are equal, the solids are equal,
and if the base falls short, the solid falls short.
Therefore, as the base *AF* is to the base *FH*, so is the solid *AU* to the solid *UH*. [v. Def. 5]

Q. E. D.

## PROPOSITION 26

*On a given straight line, and at a given point on it, to construct a solid angle equal to a given solid angle.*

Let $AB$ be the given straight line, $A$ the given point on it, and the angle at $D$, contained by the angles $EDC$, $EDF$, $FDC$, the given solid angle;
thus it is required to construct on the straight line $AB$, and at the point $A$ on it, a solid angle equal to the solid angle at $D$.

For let a point $F$ be taken at random on $DF$,
let $FG$ be drawn from $F$ perpendicular to the plane through $ED$, $DC$, and let it meet the plane at $G$, [XI. 11]

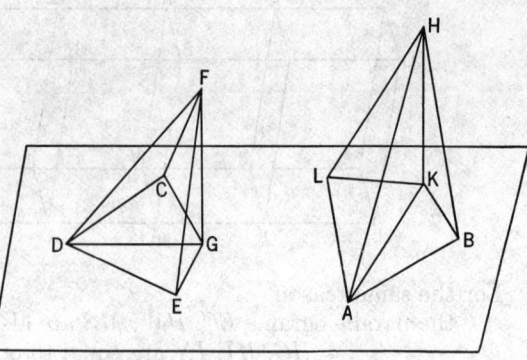

let $DG$ be joined,
let there be constructed on the straight line $AB$ and at the point $A$ on it the angle $BAL$ equal to the angle $EDC$, and the angle $BAK$ equal to the angle $EDG$,
[I. 23]

let $AK$ be made equal to $DG$,
let $KH$ be set up from the point $K$ at right angles to the plane through $BA$, $AL$, [XI. 12]

let $KH$ be made equal to $GF$,
and let $HA$ be joined;
I say that the solid angle at $A$, contained by the angles $BAL$, $BAH$, $HAL$ is equal to the solid angle at $D$ contained by the angles $EDC$, $EDF$, $FDC$.

For let $AB$, $DE$ be cut off equal to one another,
and let $HB$, $KB$, $FE$, $GE$ be joined.

Then, since $FG$ is at right angles to the plane of reference, it will also make right angles with all the straight lines which meet it and are in the plane of reference; [XI. Def. 3]

therefore each of the angles $FGD$, $FGE$ is right.
For the same reason
each of the angles $HKA$, $HKB$ is also right.
And, since the two sides $KA$, $AB$ are equal to the two sides $GD$, $DE$ respectively,
and they contain equal angles,
therefore the base $KB$ is equal to the base $GE$. [I. 4]
But $KH$ is also equal to $GF$,
and they contain right angles;
therefore $HB$ is also equal to $FE$. [I. 4]
Again, since the two sides $AK$, $KH$ are equal to the two sides $DG$, $GF$,
and they contain right angles,
therefore the base $AH$ is equal to the base $FD$. [I. 4]
But $AB$ is also equal to $DE$;
therefore the two sides $HA$, $AB$ are equal to the two sides $DF$, $DE$.
And the base $HB$ is equal to the base $FE$;
therefore the angle $BAH$ is equal to the angle $EDF$. [I. 8]
For the same reason
the angle $HAL$ is also equal to the angle $FDC$.

And the angle *BAL* is also equal to the angle *EDC*.

Therefore on the straight line *AB*, and at the point *A* on it, a solid angle has been constructed equal to the given solid angle at *D*.  Q. E. F.

## Proposition 27

*On a given straight line to describe a parallelepipedal solid similar and similarly situated to a given parallelepipedal solid.*

Let *AB* be the given straight line and *CD* the given parallelepipedal solid; thus it is required to describe on the given straight line *AB* a parallelepipedal solid similar and similarly situated to the given parallelepipedal solid *CD*.

For on the straight line *AB* and at the point *A* on it let the solid angle, contained by the angles *BAH*, *HAK*, *KAB*, be constructed equal to the solid angle at *C*, so that the angle *BAH* is equal to the angle *ECF*, the angle *BAK* equal to the angle *ECG*, and the angle *KAH* to the angle *GCF*;

and let it be contrived that,

as *EC* is to *CG*, so is *BA* to *AK*,

and, as *GC* is to *CF*, so is *KA* to *AH*.   [VI. 12]

Therefore also, *ex aequali*,

as *EC* is to *CF*, so is *BA* to *AH*.   [V. 22]

Let the parallelogram *HB* and the solid *AL* be completed.

Now since, as *EC* is to *CG*, so is *BA* to *AK*,

and the sides about the equal angles *ECG*, *BAK* are thus proportional,

therefore the parallelogram *GE* is similar to the parallelogram *KB*.

For the same reason

the parallelogram *KH* is also similar to the parallelogram *GF*, and further, *FE* to *HB*;

therefore three parallelograms of the solid *CD* are similar to three parallelograms of the solid *AL*.

But the former three are both equal and similar to the three opposite parallelograms,

and the latter three are both equal and similar to the three opposite parallelograms;

therefore the whole solid *CD* is similar to the whole solid *AL*.   [XI. Def. 9]

Therefore on the given straight line *AB* there has been described *AL* similar and similarly situated to the given parallelepipedal solid *CD*.   Q. E. F.

## Proposition 28

*If a parallelepipedal solid be cut by a plane through the diagonals of the opposite planes, the solid will be bisected by the plane.*

For let the parallelepipedal solid *AB* be cut by the plane *CDEF* through the diagonals *CF*, *DE* of opposite planes;

I say that the solid *AB* will be bisected by the plane *CDEF*.

For, since the triangle *CGF* is equal to the triangle *CFB*,   [I. 34]

and *ADE* to *DEH*,
while the parallelogram *CA* is also equal to the parallelogram *EB*, for they are opposite, and *GE* to *CH*,
therefore the prism contained by the two triangles *CGF*, *ADE* and the three parallelograms *GE*, *AC*, *CE* is also equal to the prism contained by the two triangles *CFB*, *DEH* and the three parallelograms *CH*, *BE*, *CE*;
for they are contained by planes equal both in multitude and in magnitude. [XI. Def. 10]

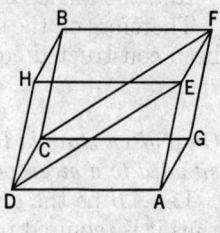

Hence the whole solid *AB* is bisected by the plane *CDEF*.  Q. E. D.

## Proposition 29

*Parallelepipedal solids which are on the same base and of the same height, and in which the extremities of the sides which stand up are on the same straight lines, are equal to one another.*

Let *CM*, *CN* be parallelepipedal solids on the same base *AB* and of the same height,
and let the extremities of their sides which stand up, namely *AG*, *AF*, *LM*, *LN*, *CD*, *CE*, *BH*, *BK*, be on the same straight lines *FN*, *DK*;
I say that the solid *CM* is equal to the solid *CN*.

For, since each of the figures *CH*, *CK* is a parallelogram, *CB* is equal to each of the straight lines *DH*, *EK*, [I. 34]
hence *DH* is also equal to *EK*.
Let *EH* be subtracted from each;
therefore the remainder *DE* is equal to the remainder *HK*.
Hence the triangle *DCE* is also equal to the triangle *HBK*, [I. 8, 4]
and the parallelogram *DG* to the parallelogram *HN*. [I. 36]
For the same reason
the triangle *AFG* is also equal to the triangle *MLN*.
But the parallelogram *CF* is equal to the parallelogram *BM*, and *CG* to *BN*, for they are opposite;
therefore the prism contained by the two triangles *AFG*, *DCE* and the three parallelograms *AD*, *DG*, *CG* is equal to the prism contained by the two triangles *MLN*, *HBK* and the three parallelograms *BM*, *HN*, *BN*.
Let there be added to each the solid of which the parallelogram *AB* is the base and *GEHM* its opposite;
therefore the whole parallelepipedal solid *CM* is equal to the whole parallelepipedal solid *CN*.
Therefore etc.

Q. E. D.

## Proposition 30

*Parallelepipedal solids which are on the same base and of the same height, and in which the extremities of the sides which stand up are not on the same straight lines, are equal to one another.*

Let $CM$, $CN$ be parallelepipedal solids on the same base $AB$ and of the same height,
and let the extremities of their sides which stand up, namely $AF$, $AG$, $LM$, $LN$, $CD$, $CE$, $BH$, $BK$, not be on the same straight lines;

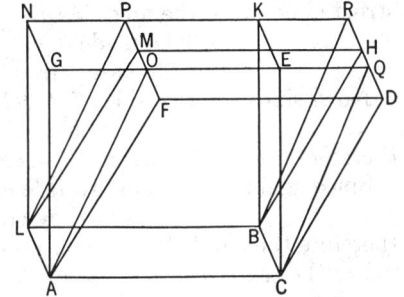

I say that the solid $CM$ is equal to the solid $CN$.

For let $NK$, $DH$ be produced and meet one another at $R$,
and further, let $FM$, $GE$ be produced to $P$, $Q$;
let $AO$, $LP$, $CQ$, $BR$ be joined.

Then the solid $CM$, of which the parallelogram $ACBL$ is the base, and $FDHM$ its opposite, is equal to the solid $CP$, of which the parallelogram $ACBL$ is the base, and $OQRP$ its opposite;
for they are on the same base $ACBL$ and of the same height, and the extremities of their sides which stand up, namely $AF$, $AO$, $LM$, $LP$, $CD$, $CQ$, $BH$, $BR$, are on the same straight lines $FP$, $DR$. [XI. 29]

But the solid $CP$, of which the parallelogram $ACBL$ is the base, and $OQRP$ its opposite, is equal to the solid $CN$, of which the parallelogram $ACBL$ is the base and $GEKN$ its opposite;
for they are again on the same base $ACBL$ and of the same height, and the extremities of their sides which stand up, namely $AG$, $AO$, $CE$, $CQ$, $LN$, $LP$, $BK$, $BR$, are on the same straight lines $GQ$, $NR$.

Hence the solid $CM$ is also equal to the solid $CN$.
Therefore etc. Q. E. D.

## PROPOSITION 31

*Parallelepipedal solids which are on equal bases and of the same height are equal to one another.*

Let the parallelepipedal solids $AE$, $CF$, of the same height, be on equal bases $AB$, $CD$.

I say that the solid $AE$ is equal to the solid $CF$.

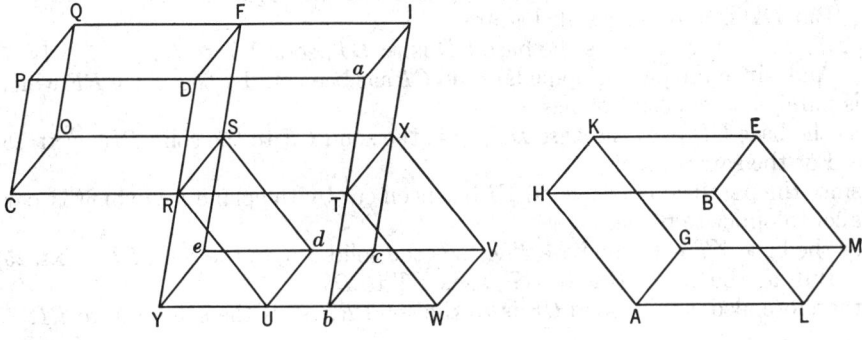

First, let the sides which stand up, $HK$, $BE$, $AG$, $LM$, $PQ$, $DF$, $CO$, $RS$, be at right angles to the bases $AB$, $CD$;

let the straight line $RT$ be produced in a straight line with $CR$;
on the straight line $RT$, and at the point $R$ on it, let the angle $TRU$ be constructed equal to the angle $ALB$, [I. 23]
let $RT$ be made equal to $AL$, and $RU$ equal to $LB$,
and let the base $RW$ and the solid $XU$ be completed.

Now, since the two sides $TR$, $RU$ are equal to the two sides $AL$, $LB$,
and they contain equal angles,
therefore the parallelogram $RW$ is equal and similar to the parallelogram $HL$.
Since again $AL$ is equal to $RT$, and $LM$ to $RS$,
and they contain right angles,
therefore the parallelogram $RX$ is equal and similar to the parallelogram $AM$.
For the same reason
$LE$ is also equal and similar to $SU$;
therefore three parallelograms of the solid $AE$ are equal and similar to three parallelograms of the solid $XU$.

But the former three are equal and similar to the three opposite, and the latter three to the three opposite; [XI. 24]
therefore the whole parallelepipedal solid $AE$ is equal to the whole parallelepipedal solid $XU$. [XI. Def. 10]

Let $DR$, $WU$ be drawn through and meet one another at $Y$,
let $aTb$ be drawn through $T$ parallel to $DY$,
let $PD$ be produced to $a$,
and let the solids $YX$, $RI$ be completed.

Then the solid $XY$, of which the parallelogram $RX$ is the base and $Yc$ its opposite, is equal to the solid $XU$ of which the parallelogram $RX$ is the base and $UV$ its opposite,
for they are on the same base $RX$ and of the same height, and the extremities of their sides which stand up, namely $RY$, $RU$, $Tb$, $TW$, $Se$, $Sd$, $Xc$, $XV$, are on the same straight lines $YW$, $eV$. [XI. 29]

But the solid $XU$ is equal to $AE$;
therefore the solid $XY$ is also equal to the solid $AE$.

And, since the parallelogram $RUWT$ is equal to the parallelogram $YT$,
for they are on the same base $RT$ and in the same parallels $RT$, $YW$, [I. 35]
while $RUWT$ is equal to $CD$, since it is also equal to $AB$,
therefore the parallelogram $YT$ is also equal to $CD$.
But $DT$ is another parallelogram;
therefore, as the base $CD$ is to $DT$, so is $YT$ to $DT$. [V. 7]

And, since the parallelepipedal solid $CI$ has been cut by the plane $RF$ which is parallel to opposite planes,
as the base $CD$ is to the base $DT$, so is the solid $CF$ to the solid $RI$. [XI. 25]
For the same reason,
since the parallelepipedal solid $YI$ has been cut by the plane $RX$ which is parallel to opposite planes,
as the base $YT$ is to the base $TD$, so is the solid $YX$ to the solid $RI$. [XI. 25]
But, as the base $CD$ is to $DT$, so is $YT$ to $DT$;
therefore also, as the solid $CF$ is to the solid $RI$, so is the solid $YX$ to $RI$.
[V. 11]

Therefore each of the solids $CF$, $YX$ has to $RI$ the same ratio;
therefore the solid $CF$ is equal to the solid $YX$. [V. 9]

But $YX$ was proved equal to $AE$;

therefore $AE$ is also equal to $CF$.

Next, let the sides standing up, $AG, HK, BE, LM, CN, PQ, DF, RS$, not be at right angles to the bases $AB, CD$;

I say again that the solid $AE$ is equal to the solid $CF$.

For from the points $K, E, G, M, Q, F, N, S$ let $KO, ET, GU, MV, QW, FX, NY, SI$ be drawn perpendicular to the plane of reference, and let them meet the plane at the points $O, T, U, V, W, X, Y, I$,

and let $OT, OU, UV, TV, WX, WY, YI, IX$ be joined.

Then the solid $KV$ is equal to the solid $QI$,

for they are on the equal bases $KM, QS$ and of the same height, and their sides which stand up are at right angles to their bases. [First part of this Prop.]

But the solid $KV$ is equal to the solid $AE$,

and $QI$ to $CF$;

for they are on the same base and of the same height, while the extremities of their sides which stand up are not on the same straight lines. [xi. 30]

Therefore the solid $AE$ is also equal to the solid $CF$.

Therefore etc.

Q. E. D.

## Proposition 32

*Parallelepipedal solids which are of the same height are to one another as their bases.*

Let $AB, CD$ be parallelepipedal solids of the same height;

I say that the parallelepipedal solids $AB, CD$ are to one another as their bases, that is, that, as the base $AE$ is to the base $CF$, so is the solid $AB$ to the solid $CD$.

 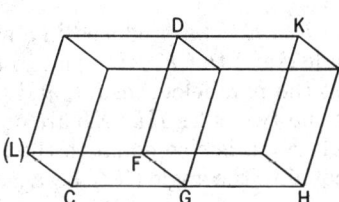

For let $FH$ equal to $AE$ be applied to $FG$, [i. 45]

and, on $FH$ as base, and with the same height as that of $CD$, let the parallelepipedal solid $GK$ be completed.

Then the solid $AB$ is equal to the solid $GK$;

for they are on equal bases $AE, FH$ and of the same height. [xi. 31]

And, since the parallelepipedal solid $CK$ is cut by the plane $DG$ which is parallel to opposite planes, therefore, as the base $CF$ is to the base $FH$, so is the solid $CD$ to the solid $DH$.

[XI. 25]

But the base $FH$ is equal to the base $AE$,
and the solid $GK$ to the solid $AB$;
therefore also, as the base $AE$ is to the base $CF$, so is the solid $AB$ to the solid $CD$.

Therefore etc.

Q. E. D.

## Proposition 33

*Similar parallelepipedal solids are to one another in the triplicate ratio of their corresponding sides.*

Let $AB$, $CD$ be similar parallelepipedal solids,
and let $AE$ be the side corresponding to $CF$;
I say that the solid $AB$ has to the solid $CD$ the ratio triplicate of that which $AE$ has to $CF$.

For let $EK$, $EL$, $EM$ be produced in a straight line with $AE$, $GE$, $HE$, let $EK$ be made equal to $CF$, $EL$ equal to $FN$, and further, $EM$ equal to $FR$,
and let the parallelogram $KL$ and the solid $KP$ be completed.

Now, since the two sides $KE$, $EL$ are equal to the two sides $CF$, $FN$, while the angle $KEL$ is also equal to the angle $CFN$, inasmuch as the angle $AEG$ is also equal to the angle $CFN$ because of the similarity of the solids $AB$, $CD$,
therefore the parallelogram $KL$ is equal &lt;and similar&gt; to the parallelogram $CN$.

For the same reason
the parallelogram $KM$ is also equal and similar to $CR$,
and further, $EP$ to $DF$;
therefore three parallelograms of the solid $KP$ are equal and similar to three parallelograms of the solid $CD$.

But the former three parallelograms are equal and similar to their opposites, and the latter three to their opposites; [XI. 24]
therefore the whole solid $KP$ is equal and similar to the whole solid $CD$.
[XI. Def. 10]

Let the parallelogram $GK$ be completed,
and on the parallelograms $GK$, $KL$ as bases, and with the same height as that of $AB$, let the solids $EO$, $LQ$ be completed.

Then since owing to the similarity of the solids $AB$, $CD$,
    as $AE$ is to $CF$, so is $EG$ to $FN$, and $EH$ to $FR$,
while $CF$ is equal to $EK$, $FN$ to $EL$, and $FR$ to $EM$,
therefore, as $AE$ is to $EK$, so is $GE$ to $EL$, and $HE$ to $EM$.
But, as $AE$ is to $EK$, so is $AG$ to the parallelogram $GK$,
    as $GE$ is to $EL$, so is $GK$ to $KL$,
    and, as $HE$ is to $EM$, so is $QE$ to $KM$; [VI. 1]
therefore also, as the parallelogram $AG$ is to $GK$, so is $GK$ to $KL$, and $QE$ to $KM$.
But, as $AG$ is to $GK$, so is the solid $AB$ to the solid $EO$,
    as $GK$ is to $KL$, so is the solid $OE$ to the solid $QL$,
    and, as $QE$ is to $KM$, so is the solid $QL$ to the solid $KP$; [XI. 32]
therefore also, as the solid $AB$ is to $EO$, so is $EO$ to $QL$, and $QL$ to $KP$.

But, if four magnitudes be continuously proportional, the first has to the fourth the ratio triplicate of that which it has to the second; [V. Def. 10]
therefore the solid $AB$ has to $KP$ the ratio triplicate of that which $AB$ has to $EO$.

But, as $AB$ is to $EO$, so is the parallelogram $AG$ to $GK$, and the straight line $AE$ to $EK$ [VI. 1];
hence the solid $AB$ has also to $KP$ the ratio triplicate of that which $AE$ has to $EK$.

But the solid $KP$ is equal to the solid $CD$,
    and the straight line $EK$ to $CF$;
therefore the solid $AB$ has also to the solid $CD$ the ratio triplicate of that which the corresponding side of it, $AE$, has to the corresponding side $CF$.

Therefore etc. Q. E. D.

PORISM. From this it is manifest that, if four straight lines be <continuously> proportional, as the first is to the fourth, so will a parallelepipedal solid on the first be to the similar and similarly described parallelepipedal solid on the second, inasmuch as the first has to the fourth the ratio triplicate of that which it has to the second.

## PROPOSITION 34

*In equal parallelepipedal solids the bases are reciprocally proportional to the heights; and those parallelepipedal solids in which the bases are reciprocally proportional to the heights are equal.*

Let $AB$, $CD$ be equal parallelepipedal solids;
I say that in the parallelepipedal solids $AB$, $CD$ the bases are reciprocally proportional to the heights,
that is, as the base $EH$ is to the base $NQ$, so is the height of the solid $CD$ to the height of the solid $AB$.

First, let the sides which stand up, namely $AG$, $EF$, $LB$, $HK$, $CM$, $NO$, $PD$,

$QR$, be at right angles to their bases;

I say that, as the base $EH$ is to the base $NQ$, so is $CM$ to $AG$.

If now the base $EH$ is equal to the base $NQ$,

while the solid $AB$ is also equal to the solid $CD$,

$CM$ will also be equal to $AG$.

For parallelepipedal solids of the same height are to one another as the bases; [XI. 32]

and, as the base $EH$ is to $NQ$, so will $CM$ be to $AG$,

and it is manifest that in the parallelepipedal solids $AB$, $CD$ the bases are reciprocally proportional to the heights.

Next, let the base $EH$ not be equal to the base $NQ$,

but let $EH$ be greater.

Now the solid $AB$ is equal to the solid $CD$;

therefore $CM$ is also greater than $AG$.

Let then $CT$ be made equal to $AG$,

and let the parallelepipedal solid $VC$ be completed on $NQ$ as base and with $CT$ as height.

Now, since the solid $AB$ is equal to the solid $CD$,

and $CV$ is outside them,

while equals have to the same the same ratio, [v. 7]

therefore, as the solid $AB$ is to the solid $CV$, so is the solid $CD$ to the solid $CV$.

But, as the solid $AB$ is to the solid $CV$, so is the base $EH$ to the base $NQ$,

for the solids $AB$, $CV$ are of equal height; [XI. 32]

and, as the solid $CD$ is to the solid $CV$, so is the base $MQ$ to the base $TQ$ [XI. 25] and $CM$ to $CT$ [VI. 1];

therefore also, as the base $EH$ is to the base $NQ$, so is $MC$ to $CT$.

But $CT$ is equal to $AG$;

therefore also, as the base $EH$ is to the base $NQ$, so is $MC$ to $AG$.

Therefore in the parallelepipedal solids $AB$, $CD$ the bases are reciprocally proportional to the heights.

Again, in the parallelepipedal solids $AB$, $CD$ let the bases be reciprocally proportional to the heights, that is, as the base $EH$ is to the base $NQ$, so let the height of the solid $CD$ be to the height of the solid $AB$;

I say that the solid $AB$ is equal to the solid $CD$.

Let the sides which stand up be again at right angles to the bases.

Now, if the base $EH$ is equal to the base $NQ$,

ELEMENTS XI

and, as the base $EH$ is to the base $NQ$, so is the height of the solid $CD$ to the height of the solid $AB$,
therefore the height of the solid $CD$ is also equal to the height of the solid $AB$.

But parallelepipedal solids on equal bases and of the same height are equal to one another; [XI. 31]
therefore the solid $AB$ is equal to the solid $CD$.

Next, let the base $EH$ not be equal to the base $NQ$,
but let $EH$ be greater;
therefore the height of the solid $CD$ is also greater than the height of the solid $AB$,
that is, $CM$ is greater than $AG$.

Let $CT$ be again made equal to $AG$,
and let the solid $CV$ be similarly completed.

Since, as the base $EH$ is to the base $NQ$, so is $MC$ to $AG$,
while $AG$ is equal to $CT$,
therefore, as the base $EH$ is to the base $NQ$, so is $CM$ to $CT$.

But, as the base $EH$ is to the base $NQ$, so is the solid $AB$ to the solid $CV$,
for the solids $AB$, $CV$ are of equal height; [XI. 32]
and, as $CM$ is to $CT$, so is the base $MQ$ to the base $QT$ [VI. 1]
and the solid $CD$ to the solid $CV$. [XI. 25]

Therefore also, as the solid $AB$ is to the solid $CV$, so is the solid $CD$ to the solid $CV$;
therefore each of the solids $AB$, $CD$ has to $CV$ the same ratio.

Therefore the solid $AB$ is equal to the solid $CD$. [V. 9]

Now let the sides which stand up, $FE$, $BL$, $GA$, $HK$, $ON$, $DP$, $MC$, $RQ$, not be at right angles to their bases;
let perpendiculars be drawn from the points $F$, $G$, $B$, $K$, $O$, $M$, $D$, $R$ to the planes through $EH$, $NQ$,
and let them meet the planes at $S$, $T$, $U$, $V$, $W$, $X$, $Y$, $a$,
and let the solids $FV$, $Oa$ be completed;

I say that, in this case too, if the solids $AB$, $CD$ are equal, the bases are reciprocally proportional to the heights, that is, as the base $EH$ is to the base $NQ$, so is the height of the solid $CD$ to the height of the solid $AB$.

Since the solid $AB$ is equal to the solid $CD$,

 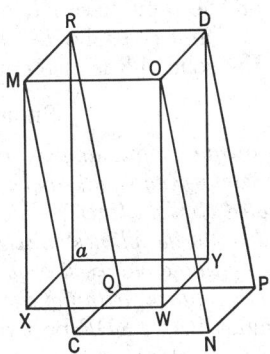

while $AB$ is equal to $BT$,
for they are on the same base $FK$ and of the same height; [XI. 29, 30]

and the solid $CD$ is equal to $DX$,

for they are again on the same base $RO$ and of the same height; [*id.*]

therefore the solid $BT$ is also equal to the solid $DX$.

Therefore, as the base $FK$ is to the base $OR$, so is the height of the solid $DX$ to the height of the solid $BT$. [Part I.]

But the base $FK$ is equal to the base $EH$,

and the base $OR$ to the base $NQ$;

therefore, as the base $EH$ is to the base $NQ$, so is the height of the solid $DX$ to the height of the solid $BT$.

But the solids $DX$, $BT$ and the solids $DC$, $BA$ have the same heights respectively;

therefore, as the base $EH$ is to the base $NQ$, so is the height of the solid $DC$ to the height of the solid $AB$.

Therefore in the parallelepipedal solids $AB$, $CD$ the bases are reciprocally proportional to the heights.

Again, in the parallelepipedal solids $AB$, $CD$ let the bases be reciprocally proportional to the heights,

that is, as the base $EH$ is to the base $NQ$, so let the height of the solid $CD$ be to the height of the solid $AB$;

I say that the solid $AB$ is equal to the solid $CD$.

For, with the same construction,

since, as the base $EH$ is to the base $NQ$, so is the height of the solid $CD$ to the height of the solid $AB$,

while the base $EH$ is equal to the base $FK$,

and $NQ$ to $OR$,

therefore, as the base $FK$ is to the base $OR$, so is the height of the solid $CD$ to the height of the solid $AB$.

But the solids $AB$, $CD$ and $BT$, $DX$ have the same heights respectively;

therefore, as the base $FK$ is to the base $OR$, so is the height of the solid $DX$ to the height of the solid $BT$.

Therefore in the parallelepipedal solids $BT$, $DX$ the bases are reciprocally proportional to the heights;

therefore the solid $BT$ is equal to the solid $DX$. [Part I.]

But $BT$ is equal to $BA$,

for they are on the same base $FK$ and of the same height; [XI. 29, 30]

and the solid $DX$ is equal to the solid $DC$. [*id.*]

Therefore the solid $AB$ is also equal to the solid $CD$.

Q. E. D.

## Proposition 35

*If there be two equal plane angles, and on their vertices there be set up elevated straight lines containing equal angles with the original straight lines respectively, if on the elevated straight lines points be taken at random and perpendiculars be drawn from them to the planes in which the original angles are, and if from the points so arising in the planes straight lines be joined to the vertices of the original angles, they will contain, with the elevated straight lines, equal angles.*

Let the angles $BAC$, $EDF$ be two equal rectilineal angles, and from the points $A$, $D$ let the elevated straight lines $AG$, $DM$ be set up containing, with the original straight lines, equal angles respectively, namely, the angle $MDE$ to the angle $GAB$ and the angle $MDF$ to the angle $GAC$,

ELEMENTS XI

let points G, M be taken at random on AG, DM,
let GL, MN be drawn from the points G, M perpendicular to the planes through BA, AC and ED, DF, and let them meet the planes at L, N,
and let LA, ND be joined;
I say that the angle GAL is equal to the angle MDN.

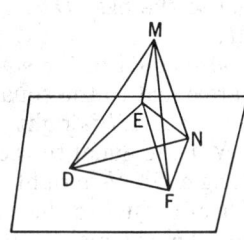

Let AH be made equal to DM,
and let HK be drawn through the point H parallel to GL.

But GL is perpendicular to the plane through BA, AC;
therefore HK is also perpendicular to the plane through BA, AC. [XI. 8]

From the points K, N let KC, NF, KB, NE be drawn perpendicular to the straight lines AC, DF, AB, DE,
and let HC, CB, MF, FE be joined.
Since the square on HA is equal to the squares on HK, KA,
and the squares on KC, CA are equal to the square on KA, [I. 47]
therefore the square on HA is also equal to the squares on HK, KC, CA.
But the square on HC is equal to the squares on HK, KC; [I. 47]
therefore the square on HA is equal to the squares on HC, CA.
Therefore the angle HCA is right. [I. 48]
For the same reason
the angle DFM is also right.
Therefore the angle ACH is equal to the angle DFM.
But the angle HAC is also equal to the angle MDF.
Therefore MDF, HAC are two triangles which have two angles equal to two angles respectively, and one side equal to one side, namely, that subtending one of the equal angles, that is, HA equal to MD;
therefore they will also have the remaining sides equal to the remaining sides respectively. [I. 26]
Therefore AC is equal to DF.
Similarly we can prove that AB is also equal to DE.
Since then AC is equal to DF, and AB to DE,
the two sides CA, AB are equal to the two sides FD, DE.
But the angle CAB is also equal to the angle FDE;
therefore the base BC is equal to the base EF, the triangle to the triangle, and the remaining angles to the remaining angles; [I. 4]
therefore the angle ACB is equal to the angle DFE.
But the right angle ACK is also equal to the right angle DFN;
therefore the remaining angle BCK is also equal to the remaining angle EFN.
For the same reason
the angle CBK is also equal to the angle FEN.
Therefore BCK, EFN are two triangles which have two angles equal to two angles respectively, and one side equal to one side, namely, that adjacent to the equal angles, that is, BC equal to EF;

therefore they will also have the remaining sides equal to the remaining sides.
[I. 26]

Therefore $CK$ is equal to $FN$.

But $AC$ is also equal to $DF$;

therefore the two sides $AC$, $CK$ are equal to the two sides $DF$, $FN$;
and they contain right angles.

Therefore the base $AK$ is equal to the base $DN$. [I. 4]

And, since $AH$ is equal to $DM$,
the square on $AH$ is also equal to the square on $DM$.

But the squares on $AK$, $KH$ are equal to the square on $AH$,
for the angle $AKH$ is right; [I. 47]
and the squares on $DN$, $NM$ are equal to the square on $DM$,
for the angle $DNM$ is right; [I. 47]

therefore the squares on $AK$, $KH$ are equal to the squares on $DN$, $NM$;
and of these the square on $AK$ is equal to the square on $DN$;

therefore the remaining square on $KH$ is equal to the square on $NM$;
therefore $HK$ is equal to $MN$.

And, since the two sides $HA$, $AK$ are equal to the two sides $MD$, $DN$ respectively,
and the base $HK$ was proved equal to the base $MN$,
therefore the angle $HAK$ is equal to the angle $MDN$. [I. 8]

Therefore etc.

PORISM. From this it is manifest that, if there be two equal plane angles, and if there be set up on them elevated straight lines which are equal and contain equal angles with the original straight lines respectively, the perpendiculars drawn from their extremities to the planes in which are the original angles are equal to one another.

Q. E. D.

## PROPOSITION 36

*If three straight lines be proportional, the parallelepipedal solid formed out of the three is equal to the parallelepipedal solid on the mean which is equilateral, but equiangular with the aforesaid solid.*

Let $A$, $B$, $C$ be three straight lines in proportion, so that, as $A$ is to $B$, so is $B$ to $C$;

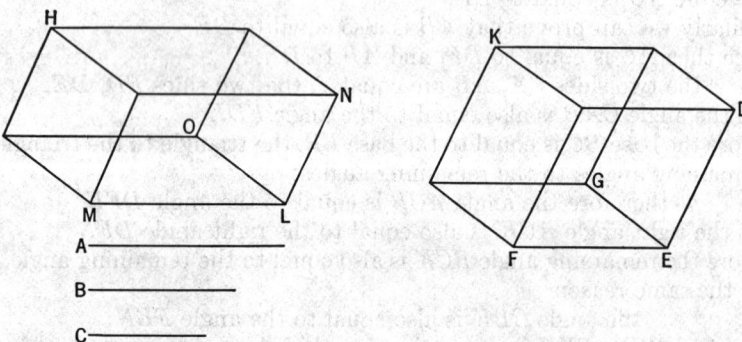

I say that the solid formed out of $A$, $B$, $C$ is equal to the solid on $B$ which is equilateral, but equiangular with the aforesaid solid.

Let there be set out the solid angle at $E$ contained by the angles $DEG$, $GEF$, $FED$,
let each of the straight lines $DE$, $GE$, $EF$ be made equal to $B$, and let the parallelepipedal solid $EK$ be completed,
      let $LM$ be made equal to $A$,
and on the straight line $LM$, and at the point $L$ on it, let there be constructed a solid angle equal to the solid angle at $E$, namely that contained by $NLO$, $OLM$, $MLN$;
    let $LO$ be made equal to $B$, and $LN$ equal to $C$.
 Now, since, as $A$ is to $B$, so is $B$ to $C$,
while $A$ is equal to $LM$, $B$ to each of the straight lines $LO$, $ED$, and $C$ to $LN$,
    therefore, as $LM$ is to $EF$, so is $DE$ to $LN$.
 Thus the sides about the equal angles $NLM$, $DEF$ are reciprocally proportional;
therefore the parallelogram $MN$ is equal to the parallelogram $DF$.  [VI. 14]
 And, since the angles $DEF$, $NLM$ are two plane rectilineal angles, and on them the elevated straight lines $LO$, $EG$ are set up which are equal to one another and contain equal angles with the original straight lines respectively,
therefore the perpendiculars drawn from the points $G$, $O$ to the planes through $NL$, $LM$ and $DE$, $EF$ are equal to one another;  [XI. 35, Por.]
   hence the solids $LH$, $EK$ are of the same height.
 But parallelepipedal solids on equal bases and of the same height are equal to one another;  [XI. 31]
    therefore the solid $HL$ is equal to the solid $EK$.
 And $LH$ is the solid formed out of $A$, $B$, $C$, and $EK$ the solid on $B$;
therefore the parallelepipedal solid formed out of $A$, $B$, $C$ is equal to the solid on $B$ which is equilateral, but equiangular with the aforesaid solid.
                 Q. E. D.

## PROPOSITION 37

*If four straight lines be proportional, the parallelepipedal solids on them which are similar and similarly described will also be proportional; and, if the parallelepipedal solids on them which are similar and similarly described be proportional, the straight lines will themselves also be proportional.*

 Let $AB$, $CD$, $EF$, $GH$ be four straight lines in proportion, so that, as $AB$ is to $CD$, so is $EF$ to $GH$;
and let there be described on $AB$, $CD$, $EF$, $GH$ the similar and similarly situ-

ated parallelepipedal solids $KA$, $LC$, $ME$, $NG$;
 I say that, as $KA$ is to $LC$, so is $ME$ to $NG$.

For, since the parallelepipedal solid $KA$ is similar to $LC$,
therefore $KA$ has to $LC$ the ratio triplicate of that which $AB$ has to $CD$.

[XI. 33]

For the same reason
$ME$ also has to $NG$ the ratio triplicate of that which $EF$ has to $GH$. [*id.*]

And, as $AB$ is to $CD$, so is $EF$ to $GH$.

Therefore also, as $AK$ is to $LC$, so is $ME$ to $NG$.

Next, as the solid $AK$ is to the solid $LC$, so let the solid $ME$ be to the solid $NG$;

I say that, as the straight line $AB$ is to $CD$, so is $EF$ to $GH$.

For since, again, $KA$ has to $LC$ the ratio triplicate of that which $AB$ has to $CD$, [XI. 33]
and $ME$ also has to $NG$ the ratio triplicate of that which $EF$ has to $GH$, [*id.*]

and, as $KA$ is to $LC$, so is $ME$ to $NG$,

therefore also, as $AB$ is to $CD$, so is $EF$ to $GH$.

Therefore etc.

Q. E. D.

## PROPOSITION 38

*If the sides of the opposite planes of a cube be bisected, and planes be carried through the points of section, the common section of the planes and the diameter of the cube bisect one another.*

For let the sides of the opposite planes $CF$, $AH$ of the cube $AF$ be bisected at the points $K$, $L$, $M$, $N$, $O$, $Q$, $P$, $R$, and through the points of section let the planes $KN$, $OR$ be carried;
let $US$ be the common section of the planes, and $DG$ the diameter of the cube $AF$.

I say that $UT$ is equal to $TS$, and $DT$ to $TG$.

For let $DU$, $UE$, $BS$, $SG$ be joined.

Then, since $DO$ is parallel to $PE$,

the alternate angles $DOU$, $UPE$ are equal to one another. [I. 29]

And, since $DO$ is equal to $PE$, and $OU$ to $UP$,

and they contain equal angles,
therefore the base $DU$ is equal to the base $UE$,

the triangle $DOU$ is equal to the triangle $PUE$,

and the remaining angles are equal to the remaining angles; [I. 4]

therefore the angle $OUD$ is equal to the angle $PUE$.

For this reason $DUE$ is a straight line. [I. 14]

For the same reason, $BSG$ is also a straight line,

and $BS$ is equal to $SG$.

Now, since $CA$ is equal and parallel to $DB$,

while $CA$ is also equal and parallel to $EG$,

# ELEMENTS XI

therefore $DB$ is also equal and parallel to $EG$. [XI. 9]
And the straight lines $DE$, $BG$ join their extremities;
therefore $DE$ is parallel to $BG$. [I. 33]
Therefore the angle $EDT$ is equal to the angle $BGT$,
for they are alternate; [I. 29]
and the angle $DTU$ is equal to the angle $GTS$. [I. 15]
Therefore $DTU$, $GTS$ are two triangles which have two angles equal to two angles, and one side equal to one side, namely that subtending one of the equal angles, that is, $DU$ equal to $GS$,
for they are the halves of $DE$, $BG$;
therefore they will also have the remaining sides equal to the remaining sides. [I. 26]

Therefore $DT$ is equal to $TG$, and $UT$ to $TS$.
Therefore etc. Q. E. D.

## Proposition 39

*If there be two prisms of equal height, and one have a parallelogram as base and the other a triangle, and if the parallelogram be double of the triangle, the prisms will be equal.*

Let $ABCDEF$, $GHKLMN$ be two prisms of equal height,
let one have the parallelogram $AF$ as base, and the other the triangle $GHK$,
and let the parallelogram $AF$ be double of the triangle $GHK$;
I say that the prism $ABCDEF$ is equal to the prism $GHKLMN$.

For let the solids $AO$, $GP$ be completed.
Since the parallelogram $AF$ is double of the triangle $GHK$,
while the parallelogram $HK$ is also double of the triangle $GHK$, [I. 34]
therefore the parallelogram $AF$ is equal to the parallelogram $HK$.
But parallelepipedal solids which are on equal bases and of the same height are equal to one another; [XI. 31]
therefore the solid $AO$ is equal to the solid $GP$.
And the prism $ABCDEF$ is half of the solid $AO$,
and the prism $GHKLMN$ is half of the solid $GP$; [XI. 28]
therefore the prism $ABCDEF$ is equal to the prism $GHKLMN$.
Therefore etc. Q. E. D.

# BOOK TWELVE

## PROPOSITIONS

### Proposition 1

*Similar polygons inscribed in circles are to one another as the squares on the diameters.*

Let $ABC$, $FGH$ be circles,
let $ABCDE$, $FGHKL$ be similar polygons inscribed in them, and let $BM$, $GN$ be diameters of the circles;

I say that, as the square on $BM$ is to the square on $GN$, so is the polygon $ABCDE$ to the polygon $FGHKL$.

For let $BE$, $AM$, $GL$, $FN$ be joined.

Now, since the polygon $ABCDE$ is similar to the polygon $FGHKL$,

 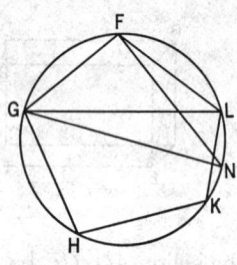

the angle $BAE$ is equal to the angle $GFL$,
and, as $BA$ is to $AE$, so is $GF$ to $FL$. [VI. Def. 1]

Thus $BAE$, $GFL$ are two triangles which have one angle equal to one angle, namely the angle $BAE$ to the angle $GFL$, and the sides about the equal angles proportional;

therefore the triangle $ABE$ is equiangular with the triangle $FGL$. [VI. 6]

Therefore the angle $AEB$ is equal to the angle $FLG$.

But the angle $AEB$ is equal to the angle $AMB$,
for they stand on the same circumference; [III. 27]
and the angle $FLG$ to the angle $FNG$;

therefore the angle $AMB$ is also equal to the angle $FNG$.

But the right angle $BAM$ is also equal to the right angle $GFN$; [III. 31]
therefore the remaining angle is equal to the remaining angle. [I. 32]

Therefore the triangle $ABM$ is equiangular with the triangle $FGN$.

Therefore, proportionally, as $BM$ is to $GN$, so is $BA$ to $GF$. [VI. 4]

ELEMENTS XII

But the ratio of the square on $BM$ to the square on $GN$ is duplicate of the ratio of $BM$ to $GN$,
and the ratio of the polygon $ABCDE$ to the polygon $FGHKL$ is duplicate of the ratio of $BA$ to $GF$; [VI. 20]
therefore also, as the square on $BM$ is to the square on $GN$, so is the polygon $ABCDE$ to the polygon $FGHKL$.

Therefore etc.                                                              Q. E. D.

## PROPOSITION 2

*Circles are to one another as the squares on the diameters.*

Let $ABCD$, $EFGH$ be circles, and $BD$, $FH$ their diameters;
I say that, as the circle $ABCD$ is to the circle $EFGH$, so is the square on $BD$ to the square on $FH$.

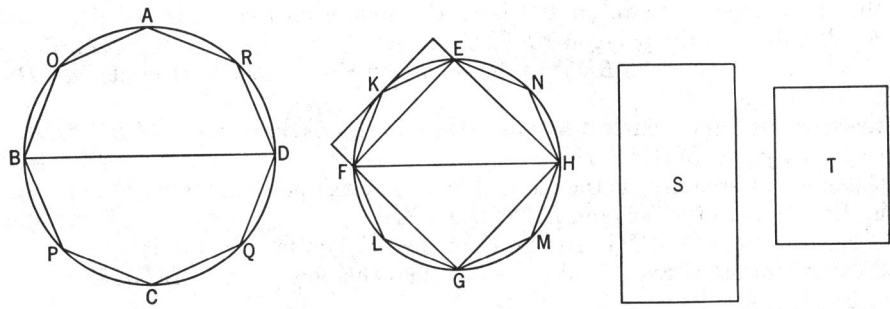

For, if the square on $BD$ is not to the square on $FH$ as the circle $ABCD$ is to the circle $EFGH$,
then, as the square on $BD$ is to the square on $FH$, so will the circle $ABCD$ be either to some less area than the circle $EFGH$, or to a greater.

First, let it be in that ratio to a less area $S$.

Let the square $EFGH$ be inscribed in the circle $EFGH$; then the inscribed square is greater than the half of the circle $EFGH$, inasmuch as, if through the points $E$, $F$, $G$, $H$ we draw tangents to the circle, the square $EFGH$ is half the square circumscribed about the circle, and the circle is less than the circumscribed square;
hence the inscribed square $EFGH$ is greater than the half of the circle $EFGH$.

Let the circumferences $EF$, $FG$, $GH$, $HE$ be bisected at the points $K$, $L$, $M$, $N$,
            and let $EK$, $KF$, $FL$, $LG$, $GM$, $MH$, $HN$, $NE$ be joined;
therefore each of the triangles $EKF$, $FLG$, $GMH$, $HNE$ is also greater than the half of the segment of the circle about it, inasmuch as, if through the points $K$, $L$, $M$, $N$ we draw tangents to the circle and complete the parallelograms on the straight lines $EF$, $FG$, $GH$, $HE$, each of the triangles $EKF$, $FLG$, $GMH$, $HNE$ will be half of the parallelogram about it,
          while the segment about it is less than the parallelogram;
hence each of the triangles $EKF$, $FLG$, $GMH$, $HNE$ is greater than the half of the segment of the circle about it.

Thus, by bisecting the remaining circumferences and joining straight lines, and by doing this continually, we shall leave some segments of the circle which will be less than the excess by which the circle $EFGH$ exceeds the area $S$.

For it was proved in the first theorem of the tenth book that, if two unequal magnitudes be set out, and if from the greater there be subtracted a magnitude greater than the half, and from that which is left a greater than the half, and if this be done continually, there will be left some magnitude which will be less than the lesser magnitude set out.

Let segments be left such as described, and let the segments of the circle $EFGH$ on $EK$, $KF$, $FL$, $LG$, $GM$, $MH$, $HN$, $NE$ be less than the excess by which the circle $EFGH$ exceeds the area $S$.

Therefore the remainder, the polygon $EKFLGMHN$, is greater than the area $S$.

Let there be inscribed, also, in the circle $ABCD$ the polygon $AOBPCQDR$ similar to the polygon $EKFLGMHN$;
therefore, as the square on $BD$ is to the square on $FH$, so is the polygon $AOBPCQDR$ to the polygon $EKFLGMHN$. [XII. 1]

But, as the square on $BD$ is to the square on $FH$, so also is the circle $ABCD$ to the area $S$;
therefore also, as the circle $ABCD$ is to the area $S$, so is the polygon $AOBPCQDR$ to the polygon $EKFLGMHN$; [v. 11]
therefore, alternately, as the circle $ABCD$ is to the polygon inscribed in it, so is the area $S$ to the polygon $EKFLGMHN$. [v. 16]

But the circle $ABCD$ is greater than the polygon inscribed in it;
therefore the area $S$ is also greater than the polygon $EKFLGMHN$.
But it is also less:
which is impossible.

Therefore, as the square on $BD$ is to the square on $FH$, so is not the circle $ABCD$ to any area less than the circle $EFGH$.

Similarly we can prove that neither is the circle $EFGH$ to any area less than the circle $ABCD$ as the square on $FH$ is to the square on $BD$.

I say next that neither is the circle $ABCD$ to any area greater than the circle $EFGH$ as the square on $BD$ is to the square on $FH$.

For, if possible, let it be in that ratio to a greater area $S$.

Therefore, inversely, as the square on $FH$ is to the square on $DB$, so is the area $S$ to the circle $ABCD$.

But, as the area $S$ is to the circle $ABCD$, so is the circle $EFGH$ to some area less than the circle $ABCD$;
therefore also, as the square on $FH$ is to the square on $BD$, so is the circle $EFGH$ to some area less than the circle $ABCD$: [v. 11]
which was proved impossible.

Therefore, as the square on $BD$ is to the square on $FH$, so is not the circle $ABCD$ to any area greater than the circle $EFGH$.

And it was proved that neither is it in that ratio to any area less than the circle $EFGH$;
therefore, as the square on $BD$ is to the square on $FH$, so is the circle $ABCD$ to the circle $EFGH$.

Therefore etc. Q. E. D.

## Lemma

I say that, the area $S$ being greater than the circle $EFGH$, as the area $S$ is to the circle $ABCD$, so is the circle $EFGH$ to some area less than the circle $ABCD$.

For let it be contrived that, as the area $S$ is to the circle $ABCD$, so is the circle $EFGH$ to the area $T$.

I say that the area $T$ is less than the circle $ABCD$.

For since, as the area $S$ is to the circle $ABCD$, so is the circle $EFGH$ to the area $T$,

therefore, alternately, as the area $S$ is to the circle $EFGH$, so is the circle $ABCD$ to the area $T$. [v. 16]

But the area $S$ is greater than the circle $EFGH$;

therefore the circle $ABCD$ is also greater than the area $T$.

Hence, as the area $S$ is to the circle $ABCD$, so is the circle $EFGH$ to some area less than the circle $ABCD$.  Q. E. D.

## Proposition 3

*Any pyramid which has a triangular base is divided into two pyramids equal and similar to one another, similar to the whole and having triangular bases, and into two equal prisms; and the two prisms are greater than the half of the whole pyramid.*

Let there be a pyramid of which the triangle $ABC$ is the base and the point $D$ the vertex;

I say that the pyramid $ABCD$ is divided into two pyramids equal to one another, having triangular bases and similar to the whole pyramid, and into two equal prisms; and the two prisms are greater than the half of the whole pyramid.

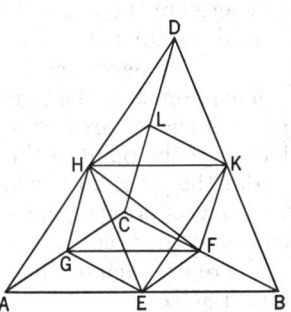

For let $AB, BC, CA, AD, DB, DC$ be bisected at the points $E, F, G, H, K, L$, and let $HE, EG, GH, HK, KL, LH, KF, FG$ be joined.

Since $AE$ is equal to $EB$, and $AH$ to $DH$,
 therefore $EH$ is parallel to $DB$. [vi. 2]
For the same reason
 $HK$ is also parallel to $AB$.
Therefore $HEBK$ is a parallelogram;
 therefore $HK$ is equal to $EB$. [i. 34]
But $EB$ is equal to $EA$;
 therefore $AE$ is also equal to $HK$.
But $AH$ is also equal to $HD$;
therefore the two sides $EA, AH$ are equal to the two sides $KH, HD$ respectively,
 and the angle $EAH$ is equal to the angle $KHD$;
 therefore the base $EH$ is equal to the base $KD$. [i. 4]
Therefore the triangle $AEH$ is equal and similar to the triangle $HKD$.
For the same reason
 the triangle $AHG$ is also equal and similar to the triangle $HLD$.
Now, since two straight lines $EH, HG$ meeting one another are parallel to two straight lines $KD, DL$ meeting one another, and are not in the same plane, they will contain equal angles. [xi. 10]

Therefore the angle $EHG$ is equal to the angle $KDL$.

And, since the two straight lines $EH$, $HG$ are equal to the two $KD$, $DL$ respectively,

and the angle $EHG$ is equal to the angle $KDL$,

therefore the base $EG$ is equal to the base $KL$; [I. 4]

therefore the triangle $EHG$ is equal and similar to the triangle $KDL$.

For the same reason

the triangle $AEG$ is also equal and similar to the triangle $HKL$.

Therefore the pyramid of which the triangle $AEG$ is the base and the point $H$ the vertex is equal and similar to the pyramid of which the triangle $HKL$ is the base and the point $D$ the vertex. [XI. Def. 10]

And, since $HK$ has been drawn parallel to $AB$, one of the sides of the triangle $ADB$,

the triangle $ADB$ is equiangular to the triangle $DHK$, [I. 29]

and they have their sides proportional;

therefore the triangle $ADB$ is similar to the triangle $DHK$. [VI. Def. 1]

For the same reason

the triangle $DBC$ is also similar to the triangle $DKL$, and the triangle $ADC$ to the triangle $DLH$.

Now, since the two straight lines $BA$, $AC$ meeting one another are parallel to the two straight lines $KH$, $HL$ meeting one another, not in the same plane, they will contain equal angles. [XI. 10]

Therefore the angle $BAC$ is equal to the angle $KHL$.

And, as $BA$ is to $AC$, so is $KH$ to $HL$;

therefore the triangle $ABC$ is similar to the triangle $HKL$.

Therefore also the pyramid of which the triangle $ABC$ is the base and the point $D$ the vertex is similar to the pyramid of which the triangle $HKL$ is the base and the point $D$ the vertex.

But the pyramid of which the triangle $HKL$ is the base and the point $D$ the vertex was proved similar to the pyramid of which the triangle $AEG$ is the base and the point $H$ the vertex.

Therefore each of the pyramids $AEGH$, $HKLD$ is similar to the whole pyramid $ABCD$.

Next, since $BF$ is equal to $FC$,

the parallelogram $EBFG$ is double of the triangle $GFC$.

And since, if there be two prisms of equal height, and one have a parallelogram as base, and the other a triangle, and if the parallelogram be double of the triangle, the prisms are equal, [XI. 39]

therefore the prism contained by the two triangles $BKF$, $EHG$, and the three parallelograms $EBFG$, $EBKH$, $HKFG$ is equal to the prism contained by the two triangles $GFC$, $HKL$ and the three parallelograms $KFCL$, $LCGH$, $HKFG$.

And it is manifest that each of the prisms, namely that in which the parallelogram $EBFG$ is the base and the straight line $HK$ is its opposite, and that in which the triangle $GFC$ is the base and the triangle $HKL$ its opposite, is greater than each of the pyramids of which the triangles $AEG$, $HKL$ are the bases and the points $H$, $D$ the vertices,

inasmuch as, if we join the straight lines $EF$, $EK$, the prism in which the parallelogram $EBFG$ is the base and the straight line $HK$ its opposite is greater than the pyramid of which the triangle $EBF$ is the base and the point $K$ the vertex.

But the pyramid of which the triangle $EBF$ is the base and the point $K$ the vertex is equal to the pyramid of which the triangle $AEG$ is the base and the point $H$ the vertex;
for they are contained by equal and similar planes.

Hence also the prism in which the parallelogram $EBFG$ is the base and the straight line $HK$ its opposite is greater than the pyramid of which the triangle $AEG$ is the base and the point $H$ the vertex.

But the prism in which the parallelogram $EBFG$ is the base and the straight line $HK$ its opposite is equal to the prism in which the triangle $GFC$ is the base and the triangle $HKL$ its opposite,
and the pyramid of which the triangle $AEG$ is the base and the point $H$ the vertex is equal to the pyramid of which the triangle $HKL$ is the base and the point $D$ the vertex.

Therefore the said two prisms are greater than the said two pyramids of which the triangles $AEG$, $HKL$ are the bases and the points $H$, $D$ the vertices.

Therefore the whole pyramid, of which the triangle $ABC$ is the base and the point $D$ the vertex, has been divided into two pyramids equal to one another and into two equal prisms, and the two prisms are greater than the half of the whole pyramid.    Q. E. D.

## Proposition 4

*If there be two pyramids of the same height which have triangular bases, and each of them be divided into two pyramids equal to one another and similar to the whole, and into two equal prisms, then, as the base of the one pyramid is to the base of the other pyramid, so will all the prisms in the one pyramid be to all the prisms, being equal in multitude, in the other pyramid.*

Let there be two pyramids of the same height which have the triangular bases $ABC$, $DEF$, and vertices the points $G$, $H$,
and let each of them be divided into two pyramids equal to one another and similar to the whole and into two equal prisms;    [XII. 3]

I say that, as the base $ABC$ is to the base $DEF$, so are all the prisms in the pyramid $ABCG$ to all the prisms, being equal in multitude, in the pyramid $DEFH$,

 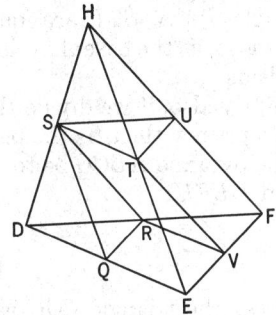

For, since $BO$ is equal to $OC$, and $AL$ to $LC$,
therefore $LO$ is parallel to $AB$,
and the triangle $ABC$ is similar to the triangle $LOC$.

For the same reason

the triangle *DEF* is also similar to the triangle *RVF*.

And, since *BC* is double of *CO*, and *EF* of *FV*,

therefore, as *BC* is to *CO*, so is *EF* to *FV*.

And on *BC*, *CO* are described the similar and similarly situated rectilineal figures *ABC*, *LOC*,

and on *EF*, *FV* the similar and similarly situated figures *DEF*, *RVF*;

therefore, as the triangle *ABC* is to the triangle *LOC*, so is the triangle *DEF* to the triangle *RVF*; [VI. 22]

therefore, alternately, as the triangle *ABC* is to the triangle *DEF*, so is the triangle *LOC* to the triangle *RVF*. [V. 16]

But, as the triangle *LOC* is to the triangle *RVF*, so is the prism in which the triangle *LOC* is the base and *PMN* its opposite, to the prism in which the triangle *RVF* is the base and *STU* its opposite; [Lemma following]

therefore also, as the triangle *ABC* is to the triangle *DEF*, so is the prism in which the triangle *LOC* is the base and *PMN* its opposite, to the prism in which the triangle *RVF* is the base and *STU* its opposite.

But, as the said prisms are to one another, so is the prism in which the parallelogram *KBOL* is the base and the straight line *PM* its opposite, to the prism in which the parallelogram *QEVR* is the base and the straight line *ST* its opposite. [XI. 39; cf. XII. 3]

Therefore also the two prisms, that in which the parallelogram *KBOL* is the base and *PM* its opposite, and that in which the triangle *LOC* is the base and *PMN* its opposite, are to the prisms in which *QEVR* is the base and the straight line *ST* its opposite and in which the triangle *RVF* is the base and *STU* its opposite in the same ratio. [V. 12]

Therefore also, as the base *ABC* is to the base *DEF*, so are the said two prisms to the said two prisms.

And similarly, if the pyramids *PMNG*, *STUH* be divided into two prisms and two pyramids,

as the base *PMN* is to the base *STU*, so will the two prisms in the pyramid *PMNG* be to the two prisms in the pyramid *STUH*.

But, as the base *PMN* is to the base *STU*, so is the base *ABC* to the base *DEF*;

for the triangles *PMN*, *STU* are equal to the triangles *LOC*, *RVF* respectively.

Therefore also, as the base *ABC* is to the base *DEF*, so are the four prisms to the four prisms.

And similarly also, if we divide the remaining pyramids into two pyramids and into two prisms, then, as the base *ABC* is to base the *DEF*, so will all the prisms in the pyramid *ABCG* be to all the prisms, being equal in multitude, in the pyramid *DEFH*. Q. E. D.

### Lemma

But that, as the triangle *LOC* is to the triangle *RVF*, so is the prism in which the triangle *LOC* is the base and *PMN* its opposite, to the prism in which the triangle *RVF* is the base and *STU* its opposite, we must prove as follows.

For in the same figure let perpendiculars be conceived drawn from *G*, *H* to the planes $ABC$, $DEF$; these are of course equal because, by hypothesis, the pyramids are of equal height.

Now, since the two straight lines $GC$ and the perpendicular from $G$ are cut by the parallel planes $ABC$, $PMN$;
they will be cut in the same ratios. [XI. 17]

And $GC$ is bisected by the plane $PMN$ at $N$;
therefore the perpendicular from $G$ to the plane $ABC$ will also be bisected by the plane $PMN$.

For the same reason
the perpendicular from $H$ to the plane $DEF$ will also be bisected by the plane $STU$.

And the perpendiculars from $G$, $H$ to the planes $ABC$, $DEF$ are equal;
therefore the perpendiculars from the triangles $PMN$, $STU$ to the planes $ABC$, $DEF$ are also equal.

Therefore the prisms in which the triangles $LOC$, $RVF$ are bases, and $PMN$, $STU$ their opposites, are of equal height.

Hence also the parallelepipedal solids described from the said prisms are of equal height and are to one another as their bases; [XI. 32]
therefore their halves, namely the said prisms, are to one another as the base $LOC$ is to the base $RVF$. Q. E. D.

## Proposition 5

*Pyramids which are of the same height and have triangular bases are to one another as the bases.*

Let there by pyramids of the same height, of which the triangles $ABC$, $DEF$ are the bases and the points $G$, $H$ the vertices;

I say that, as the base $ABC$ is to the base $DEF$, so is the pyramid $ABCG$ to the pyramid $DEFH$.

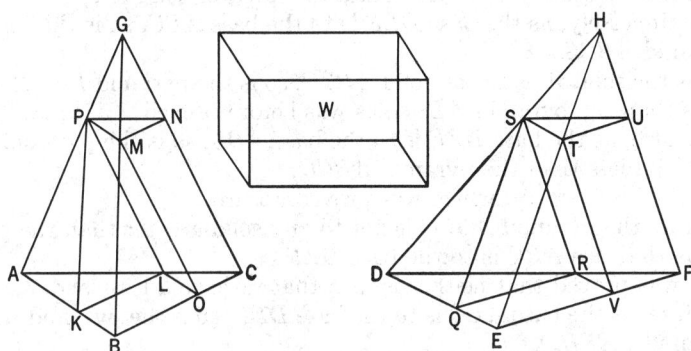

For, if the pyramid $ABCG$ is not to the pyramid $DEFH$ as the base $ABC$ is to the base $DEF$,
then, as the base $ABC$ is to the base $DEF$, so will the pyramid $ABCG$ be either to some solid less than the pyramid $DEFH$ or to a greater.

Let it, first, be in that ratio to a less solid $W$, and let the pyramid $DEFH$ be divided into two pyramids equal to one another and similar to the whole and into two equal prisms;

then the two prisms are greater than the half of the whole pyramid. [XII. 3]

Again, let the pyramids arising from the division be similarly divided, and let this be done continually until there are left over from the pyramid $DEFH$ some pyramids which are less than the excess by which the pyramid $DEFH$ exceeds the solid $W$. [X. 1]

Let such be left, and let them be, for the sake of argument, $DQRS$, $STUH$; therefore the remainders, the prisms in the pyramid $DEFH$, are greater than the solid $W$.

Let the pyramid $ABCG$ also be divided similarly, and a similar number of times, with the pyramid $DEFH$;
therefore, as the base $ABC$ is to the base $DEF$, so are the prisms in the pyramid $ABCG$ to the prisms in the pyramid $DEFH$. [XII. 4]

But, as the base $ABC$ is to the base $DEF$, so also is the pyramid $ABCG$ to the solid $W$;
therefore also, as the pyramid $ABCG$ is to the solid $W$, so are the prisms in the pyramid $ABCG$ to the prisms in the pyramid $DEFH$; [V. 11]
therefore, alternately, as the pyramid $ABCG$ is to the prisms in it, so is the solid $W$ to the prisms in the pyramid $DEFH$. [V. 16]

But the pyramid $ABCG$ is greater than the prisms in it;
therefore the solid $W$ is also greater than the prisms in the pyramid $DEFH$.
But it is also less:

which is impossible.

Therefore the prism $ABCG$ is not to any solid less than the pyramid $DEFH$ as the base $ABC$ is to the base $DEF$.

Similarly it can be proved that neither is the pyramid $DEFH$ to any solid less than the pyramid $ABCG$ as the base $DEF$ is to the base $ABC$.

I say next that neither is the pyramid $ABCG$ to any solid greater than the pyramid $DEFH$ as the base $ABC$ is to the base $DEF$.

For, if possible, let it be in that ratio to a greater solid $W$;
therefore, inversely, as the base $DEF$ is to the base $ABC$, so is the solid $W$ to the pyramid $ABCG$.

But, as the solid $W$ is to the solid $ABCG$, so is the pyramid $DEFH$ to some solid less than the pyramid $ABCG$, as was before proved; [XII. 2, Lemma]
therefore also, as the base $DEF$ is to the base $ABC$, so is the pyramid $DEFH$ to some solid less than the pyramid $ABCG$: [V. 11]

which was proved absurd.

Therefore the pyramid $ABCG$ is not to any solid greater than the pyramid $DEFH$ as the base $ABC$ is to the base $DEF$.

But it was proved that neither is it in that ratio to a less solid.

Therefore, as the base $ABC$ is to the base $DEF$, so is the pyramid $ABCG$ to the pyramid $DEFH$.
Q. E. D.

PROPOSITION 6

*Pyramids which are of the same height and have polygonal bases are to one another as the bases.*

Let there be pyramids of the same height of which the polygons $ABCDE$, $FGHKL$ are the bases and the points $M$, $N$ the vertices;

I say that, as the base $ABCDE$ is to the base $FGHKL$, so is the pyramid $ABCDEM$ to the pyramid $FGHKLN$.

ELEMENTS XII

For let $AC$, $AD$, $FH$, $FK$ be joined.

Since then $ABCM$, $ACDM$ are two pyramids which have triangular bases and equal height,

they are to one another as the bases; [xii. 5]

therefore, as the base $ABC$ is to the base $ACD$, so is the pyramid $ABCM$ to the pyramid $ACDM$.

And, *componendo*, as the base $ABCD$ is to the base $ACD$, so is the pyramid $ABCDM$ to the pyramid $ACDM$. [v. 18]

But also, as the base $ACD$ is to the base $ADE$, so is the pyramid $ACDM$ to the pyramid $ADEM$. [xii. 5]

Therefore, *ex aequali*, as the base $ABCD$ is to the base $ADE$, so is the pyramid $ABCDM$ to the pyramid $ADEM$. [v. 22]

And again, *componendo*, as the base $ABCDE$ is to the base $ADE$, so is the pyramid $ABCDEM$ to the pyramid $ADEM$. [v. 18]

Similarly also it can be proved that, as the base $FGHKL$ is to the base $FGH$, so is the pyramid $FGHKLN$ to the pyramid $FGHN$.

And, since $ADEM$, $FGHN$ are two pyramids which have triangular bases and equal height,

therefore, as the base $ADE$ is to the base $FGH$, so is the pyramid $ADEM$ to the pyramid $FGHN$. [xii. 5]

But, as the base $ADE$ is to the base $ABCDE$, so was the pyramid $ADEM$ to the pyramid $ABCDEM$.

Therefore also, *ex aequali*, as the base $ABCDE$ is to the base $FGH$, so is the pyramid $ABCDEM$ to the pyramid $FGHN$. [v. 22]

But further, as the base $FGH$ is to the base $FGHKL$, so also was the pyramid $FGHN$ to the pyramid $FGHKL$.

Therefore also, *ex aequali*, as the base $ABCDE$ is to the base $FGHKL$, so is the pyramid $ABCDEM$ to the pyramid $FGHKLN$. [v. 22]

Q. E. D.

Proposition 7

*Any prism which has a triangular base is divided into three pyramids equal to one another which have triangular bases.*

Let there be a prism in which the triangle $ABC$ is the base and $DEF$ its opposite;

I say that the prism $ABCDEF$ is divided into three pyramids equal to one another, which have triangular bases.

For let $BD$, $EC$, $CD$ be joined.

Since $ABED$ is a parallelogram, and $BD$ is its diameter,

therefore the triangle $ABD$ is equal to the triangle $EBD$; [i. 34]

therefore also the pyramid of which the triangle $ABD$ is the base and the point $C$ the vertex is equal to the pyramid of which the triangle $DEB$ is the base and the point $C$ the vertex. [XII. 5]

But the pyramid of which the triangle $DEB$ is the base and the point $C$ the vertex is the same with the pyramid of which the triangle $EBC$ is the base and the point $D$ the vertex;

for they are contained by the same planes.

Therefore the pyramid of which the triangle $ABD$ is the base and the point $C$ the vertex is also equal to the pyramid of which the triangle $EBC$ is the base and the point $D$ the vertex.

Again, since $FCBE$ is a parallelogram,
 and $CE$ is its diameter,
  the triangle $CEF$ is equal to the triangle $CBE$. [I. 34]

Therefore also the pyramid of which the triangle $BCE$ is the base and the point $D$ the vertex is equal to the pyramid of which the triangle $ECF$ is the base and the point $D$ the vertex. [XII. 5]

But the pyramid of which the triangle $BCE$ is the base and the point $D$ the vertex was proved equal to the pyramid of which the triangle $ABD$ is the base and the point $C$ the vertex;

therefore also the pyramid of which the triangle $CEF$ is the base and the point $D$ the vertex is equal to the pyramid of which the triangle $ABD$ is the base and the point $C$ the vertex;

therefore the prism $ABCDEF$ has been divided into three pyramids equal to one another which have triangular bases.

And, since the pyramid of which the triangle $ABD$ is the base and the point $C$ the vertex is the same with the pyramid of which the triangle $CAB$ is the base and the point $D$ the vertex,

for they are contained by the same planes,

while the pyramid of which the triangle $ABD$ is the base and the point $C$ the vertex was proved to be a third of the prism in which the triangle $ABC$ is the base and $DEF$ its opposite,

therefore also the pyramid of which the triangle $ABC$ is the base and the point $D$ the vertex is a third of the prism which has the same base, the triangle $ABC$, and $DEF$ as its opposite.

PORISM. From this it is manifest that any pyramid is a third part of the prism which has the same base with it and equal height. Q. E. D.

## PROPOSITION 8

*Similar pyramids which have triangular bases are in the triplicate ratio of their corresponding sides.*

Let there be similar and similarly situated pyramids of which the triangles $ABC$, $DEF$ are the bases and the points $G$, $H$ the vertices;

I say that the pyramid $ABCG$ has to the pyramid $DEFH$ the ratio triplicate of that which $BC$ has to $EF$.

For let the parallelepipedal solids $BGML$, $EHQP$ be completed.

Now, since the pyramid $ABCG$ is similar to the pyramid $DEFH$,
 therefore the angle $ABC$ is equal to the angle $DEF$,
  the angle $GBC$ to the angle $HEF$,
   and the angle $ABG$ to the angle $DEH$;

and, as AB is to DE, so is BC to EF, and BG to EH.
And since, as AB is to DE, so is BC to EF,
and the sides are proportional about equal angles,

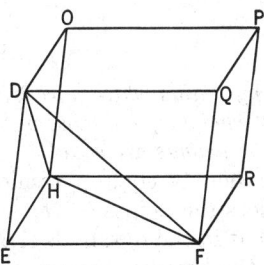

therefore the parallelogram BM is similar to the parallelogram EQ.
For the same reason
BN is also similar to ER, and BK to EO;
therefore the three parallelograms MB, BK, BN are similar to the three EQ, EO, ER.
But the three parallelograms MB, BK, BN are equal and similar to their three opposites,
and the three EQ, EO, ER are equal and similar to their three opposites. [XI. 24]

Therefore the solids BGML, EHQP are contained by similar planes equal in multitude.
Therefore the solid BGML is similar to the solid EHQP.
But similar parallelepipedal solids are in the triplicate ratio of their corresponding sides. [XI. 33]
Therefore the solid BGML has to the solid EHQP the ratio triplicate of that which the corresponding side BC has to the corresponding side EF.
But, as the solid BGML is to the solid EHQP, so is the pyramid ABCG to the pyramid DEFH,
inasmuch as the pyramid is a sixth part of the solid, because the prism which is half of the parallelepipedal solid [XI. 28] is also triple of the pyramid. [XII. 7]
Therefore the pyramid ABCG also has to the pyramid DEFH the ratio triplicate of that which BC has to EF. Q. E. D.

PORISM. From this it is manifest that similar pyramids which have polygonal bases are also to one another in the triplicate ratio of their corresponding sides.
For, if they are divided into the pyramids contained in them which have triangular bases, by virtue of the fact that the similar polygons forming their bases are also divided into similar triangles equal in multitude and corresponding to the wholes, [VI. 20]
then, as the one pyramid which has a triangular base in the one complete pyramid is to the one pyramid which has a triangular base in the other complete pyramid, so also will all the pyramids which have triangular bases contained in the one pyramid be to all the pyramids which have triangular bases contained in the other pyramid [V. 12], that is, the pyramid itself which has a polygonal base, to the pyramid which has a polygonal base.

But the pyramid which has a triangular base is to the pyramid which has a triangular base in the triplicate ratio of the corresponding sides;

therefore also the pyramid which has a polygonal base has to the pyramid which has a similar base the ratio triplicate of that which the side has to the side.

## Proposition 9

*In equal pyramids which have triangular bases the bases are reciprocally proportional to the heights; and those pyramids in which the bases are reciprocally proportional to the heights are equal.*

For let there be equal pyramids which have the triangular bases $ABC$, $DEF$ and vertices the points $G$, $H$;

I say that in the pyramids $ABCG$, $DEFH$ the bases are reciprocally proportional to the heights, that is, as the base $ABC$ is to the base $DEF$, so is the height of the pyramid $DEFH$ to the height of the pyramid $ABCG$.

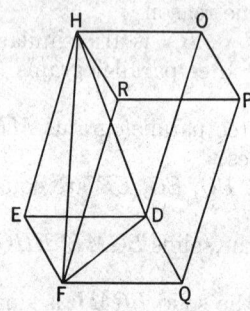

For let the parallelepipedal solids $BGML$, $EHQP$ be completed.

Now, since the pyramid $ABCG$ is equal to the pyramid $DEFH$,

and the solid $BGML$ is six times the pyramid $ABCG$,

and the solid $EHQP$ six times the pyramid $DEFH$,

therefore the solid $BGML$ is equal to the solid $EHQP$.

But in equal parallelepipedal solids the bases are reciprocally proportional to the heights; [XI. 34]

therefore, as the base $BM$ is to the base $EQ$, so is the height of the solid $EHQP$ to the height of the solid $BGML$.

But, as the base $BM$ is to $EQ$, so is the triangle $ABC$ to the triangle $DEF$. [I. 34]

Therefore also, as the triangle $ABC$ is to the triangle $DEF$, so is the height of the solid $EHQP$ to the height of the solid $BGML$. [V. 11]

But the height of the solid $EHQP$ is the same with the height of the pyramid $DEFH$,

and the height of the solid $BGML$ is the same with the height of the pyramid $ABCG$,

therefore, as the base $ABC$ is to the base $DEF$, so is the height of the pyramid $DEFH$ to the height of the pyramid $ABCG$.

Therefore in the pyramids $ABCG$, $DEFH$ the bases are reciprocally proportional to the heights.

Next, in the pyramids $ABCG$, $DEFH$ let the bases be reciprocally proportional to the heights;
that is, as the base $ABC$ is to the base $DEF$, so let the height of the pyramid $DEFH$ be to the height of the pyramid $ABCG$;
I say that the pyramid $ABCG$ is equal to the pyramid $DEFH$.

For, with the same construction,
since, as the base $ABC$ is to the base $DEF$, so is the height of the pyramid $DEFH$ to the height of the pyramid $ABCG$,
while, as the base $ABC$ is to the base $DEF$, so is the parallelogram $BM$ to the parallelogram $EQ$,
therefore also, as the parallelogram $BM$ is to the parallelogram $EQ$, so is the height of the pyramid $DEFH$ to the height of the pyramid $ABCG$. [v. 11]

But the height of the pyramid $DEFH$ is the same with the height of the parallelepiped $EHQP$,
and the height of the pyramid $ABCG$ is the same with the height of the parallelepiped $BGML$;
therefore, as the base $BM$ is to the base $EQ$, so is the height of the parallelepiped $EHQP$ to the height of the parallelepiped $BGML$.

But those parallelepipedal solids in which the bases are reciprocally proportional to the heights are equal; [xi. 34]
therefore the parallelepipedal solid $BGML$ is equal to the parallelepipedal solid $EHQP$.

And the pyramid $ABCG$ is a sixth part of $BGML$, and the pyramid $DEFH$ a sixth part of the parallelepiped $EHQP$;
therefore the pyramid $ABCG$ is equal to the pyramid $DEFH$.
Therefore etc. Q. E. D.

## Proposition 10

*Any cone is a third part of the cylinder which has the same base with it and equal height.*

For let a cone have the same base, namely the circle $ABCD$, with a cylinder and equal height;

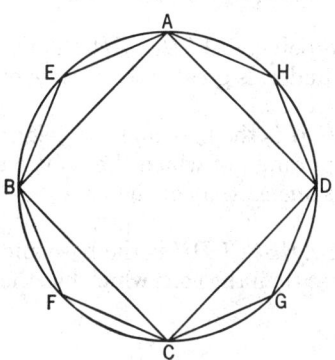

I say that the cone is a third part of the cylinder, that is, that the cylinder is triple of the cone.

For if the cylinder is not triple of the cone, the cylinder will be either greater than triple or less than triple of the cone.

First let it be greater than triple,
and let the square $ABCD$ be inscribed in the circle $ABCD$; [iv. 6]
then the square $ABCD$ is greater than the half of the circle $ABCD$.

From the square $ABCD$ let there be set up a prism of equal height with the cylinder.
Then the prism so set up is greater than the half of the cylinder,
inasmuch as, if we also circumscribe a square about the circle $ABCD$ [iv. 7], the square inscribed in the circle $ABCD$ is half of that circumscribed about it, and the solids set up from them are parallelepipedal prisms of equal height,

while parallelepipedal solids which are of the same height are to one another as their bases; [xi. 32]
therefore also the prism set up on the square $ABCD$ is half of the prism set up from the square circumscribed about the circle $ABCD$;

[cf. xi. 28, or xii. 6 and 7, Por.]
and the cylinder is less than the prism set up from the square circumscribed about the circle $ABCD$;

therefore the prism set up from the square $ABCD$ and of equal height with the cylinder is greater than the half of the cylinder.

Let the circumferences $AB$, $BC$, $CD$, $DA$ be bisected at the points $E$, $F$, $G$, $H$,
and let $AE$, $EB$, $BF$, $FC$, $CG$, $GD$, $DH$, $HA$ be joined;
then each of the triangles $AEB$, $BFC$, $CGD$, $DHA$ is greater than the half of that segment of the circle $ABCD$ which is about it, as we proved before.

[xii. 2]
On each of the triangles $AEB$, $BFC$, $CGD$, $DHA$ let prisms be set up of equal height with the cylinder;
then each of the prisms so set up is greater than the half part of that segment of the cylinder which is about it,
inasmuch as, if we draw through the points $E$, $F$, $G$, $H$ parallels to $AB$, $BC$, $CD$, $DA$, complete the parallelograms on $AB$, $BC$, $CD$, $DA$, and set up from them parallelepipedal solids of equal height with the cylinder, the prisms on the triangles $AEB$, $BFC$, $CGD$, $DHA$ are halves of the several solids set up;
and the segments of the cylinder are less than the parallelepipedal solids set up;
hence also the prisms on the triangles $AEB$, $BFC$, $CGD$, $DHA$ are greater than the half of the segments of the cylinder about them.

Thus, bisecting the circumferences that are left, joining straight lines, setting up on each of the triangles prisms of equal height with the cylinder,
and doing this continually,
we shall leave some segments of the cylinder which will be less than the excess by which the cylinder exceeds the triple of the cone. [x. 1]

Let such segments be left, and let them be $AE$, $EB$, $BF$, $FC$, $CG$, $GD$, $DH$, $HA$;
therefore the remainder, the prism of which the polygon $AEBFCGDH$ is the base and the height is the same as that of the cylinder, is greater than triple of the cone.

But the prism of which the polygon $AEBFCGDH$ is the base and the height the same as that of the cylinder is triple of the pyramid of which the polygon $AEBFCGDH$ is the base and the vertex is the same as that of the cone;

[xii. 7, Por.]
therefore also the pyramid of which the polygon $AEBFCGDH$ is the base and the vertex is the same as that of the cone is greater than the cone which has the circle $ABCD$ as base.

But it is also less, for it is enclosed by it:
which is impossible.

Therefore the cylinder is not greater than triple of the cone.

I say next that neither is the cylinder less than triple of the cone,
For, if possible, let the cylinder be less than triple of the cone,
therefore, inversely, the cone is greater than a third part of the cylinder.

Let the square $ABCD$ be inscribed in the circle $ABCD$;
therefore the square $ABCD$ is greater than the half of the circle $ABCD$.

Now let there be set up from the square $ABCD$ a pyramid having the same vertex with the cone;
therefore the pyramid so set up is greater than the half part of the cone, seeing that, as we proved before, if we circumscribe a square about the circle, the square $ABCD$ will be half of the square circumscribed about the circle, and if we set up from the squares parallelepipedal solids of equal height with the cone, which are also called prisms, the solid set up from the square $ABCD$ will be half of that set up from the square circumscribed about the circle;

for they are to one another as their bases. [XI. 32]

Hence also the thirds of them are in that ratio;
therefore also the pyramid of which the square $ABCD$ is the base is half of the pyramid set up from the square circumscribed about the circle.

And the pyramid set up from the square about the circle is greater than the cone,

for it encloses it.

Therefore the pyramid of which the square $ABCD$ is the base and the vertex is the same with that of the cone is greater than the half of the cone.

Let the circumferences $AB$, $BC$, $CD$, $DA$ be bisected at the points $E$, $F$, $G$, $H$,

and let $AE$, $EB$, $BF$, $FC$, $CG$, $GD$, $DH$, $HA$ be joined;
therefore also each of the triangles $AEB$, $BFC$, $CGD$, $DHA$ is greater than the half part of that segment of the circle $ABCD$ which is about it.

Now, on each of the triangles $AEB$, $BFC$, $CGD$, $DHA$ let pyramids be set up which have the same vertex as the cone;
therefore also each of the pyramids so set up is, in the same manner, greater than the half part of that segment of the cone which is about it.

Thus, by bisecting the circumferences that are left, joining straight lines, setting up on each of the triangles a pyramid which has the same vertex as the cone,

and doing this continually,

we shall leave some segments of the cone which will be less than the excess by which the cone exceeds the third part of the cylinder. [X. 1]

Let such be left, and let them be the segments on $AE$, $EB$, $BF$, $FC$, $CG$, $GD$, $DH$, $HA$;
therefore the remainder, the pyramid of which the polygon $AEBFCGDH$ is the base and the vertex the same with that of the cone, is greater than a third part of the cylinder.

But the pyramid of which the polygon $AEBFCGDH$ is the base and the vertex the same with that of the cone is a third part of the prism of which the polygon $AEBFCGDH$ is the base and the height is the same with that of the cylinder;
therefore the prism of which the polygon $AEBFCGDH$ is the base and the height is the same with that of the cylinder is greater than the cylinder of which the circle $ABCD$ is the base.

But it is also less, for it is enclosed by it:

which is impossible.

Therefore the cylinder is not less than triple of the cone.

But it was proved that neither is it greater than triple;
therefore the cylinder is triple of the cone;
hence the cone is a third part of the cylinder.
Therefore etc.

Q. E. D.

## PROPOSITION 11

*Cones and cylinders which are of the same height are to one another as their bases.*

Let there be cones and cylinders of the same height,
let the circles $ABCD$, $EFGH$ be their bases, $KL$, $MN$ their axes and $AC$, $EG$ the diameters of their bases;

I say that, as the circle $ABCD$ is to the circle $EFGH$, so is the cone $AL$ to the cone $EN$.

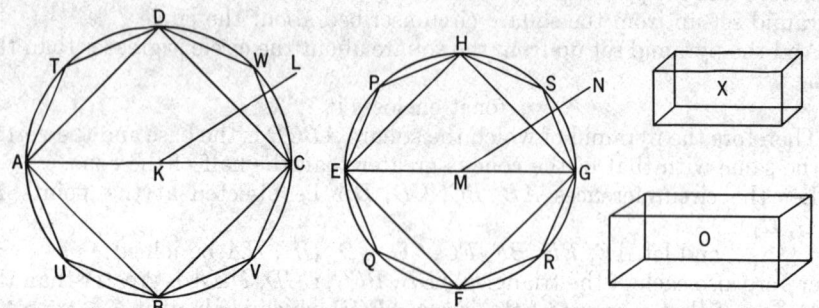

For, if not, then, as the circle $ABCD$ is to the circle $EFGH$, so will the cone $AL$ be either to some solid less than the cone $EN$ or to a greater.

First, let it be in that ratio to a less solid $O$, and let the solid $X$ be equal to that by which the solid $O$ is less than the cone $EN$;
therefore the cone $EN$ is equal to the solids $O$, $X$.

Let the square $EFGH$ be inscribed in the circle $EFGH$;
therefore the square is greater than the half of the circle.

Let there be set up from the square $EFGH$ a pyramid of equal height with the cone;
therefore the pyramid so set up is greater than the half of the cone,
inasmuch as, if we circumscribe a square about the circle, and set up from it a pyramid of equal height with the cone, the inscribed pyramid is half of the circumscribed pyramid,
for they are to one another as their bases, [XII. 6]
while the cone is less than the circumscribed pyramid.

Let the circumferences $EF$, $FG$, $GH$, $HE$ be bisected at the points $P$, $Q$, $R$, $S$, and let $HP$, $PE$, $EQ$, $QF$, $FR$, $RG$, $GS$, $SH$ be joined.

Therefore each of the triangles $HPE$, $EQF$, $FRG$, $GSH$ is greater than the half of that segment of the circle which is about it.

On each of the triangles $HPE$, $EQF$, $FRG$, $GSH$ let there be set up a pyramid of equal height with the cone;
therefore, also, each of the pyramids so set up is greater than the half of that segment of the cone which is about it.

Thus, bisecting the circumferences which are left, joining straight lines, set-

ting up on each of the triangles pyramids of equal height with the cone, and doing this continually,
we shall leave some segments of the cone which will be less than the solid $X$. [x. 1]

Let such be left, and let them be the segments on $HP$, $PE$, $EQ$, $QF$, $FR$, $RG$, $GS$, $SH$;
therefore the remainder, the pyramid of which the polygon $HPEQFRGS$ is the base and the height the same with that of the cone, is greater than the solid $O$.

Let there also be inscribed in the circle $ABCD$ the polygon $DTAUBVCW$ similar and similarly situated to the polygon $HPEQFRGS$,
and on it let a pyramid be set up of equal height with the cone $AL$.

Since then, as the square on $AC$ is to the square on $EG$, so is the polygon $DTAUBVCW$ to the polygon $HPEQFRGS$, [xii. 1]
while, as the square on $AC$ is to the square on $EG$, so is the circle $ABCD$ to the circle $EFGH$, [xii. 2]
therefore also, as the circle $ABCD$ is to the circle $EFGH$, so is the polygon $DTAUBVCW$ to the polygon $HPEQFRGS$.

But, as the circle $ABCD$ is to the circle $EFGH$, so is the cone $AL$ to the solid $O$,
and, as the polygon $DTAUBVCW$ is to the polygon $HPEQFRGS$, so is the pyramid of which the polygon $DTAUBVCW$ is the base and the point $L$ the vertex to the pyramid of which the polygon $HPEQFRGS$ is the base and the point $N$ the vertex. [xii. 6]

Therefore also, as the cone $AL$ is to the solid $O$, so is the pyramid of which the polygon $DTAUBVCW$ is the base and the point $L$ the vertex to the pyramid of which the polygon $HPEQFRGS$ is the base and the point $N$ the vertex; [v. 11]
therefore, alternately, as the cone $AL$ is to the pyramid in it, so is the solid $O$ to the pyramid in the cone $EN$. [v. 16]

But the cone $AL$ is greater than the pyramid in it;
therefore the solid $O$ is also greater than the pyramid in the cone $EN$.
But it is also less:
which is absurd.

Therefore the cone $AL$ is not to any solid less than the cone $EN$ as the circle $ABCD$ is to the circle $EFGH$.

Similarly we can prove that neither is the cone $EN$ to any solid less than the cone $AL$ as the circle $EFGH$ is to the circle $ABCD$.

I say next that neither is the cone $AL$ to any solid greater than the cone $EN$ as the circle $ABCD$ is to the circle $EFGH$.

For, if possible, let it be in that ratio to a greater solid $O$;
therefore, inversely, as the circle $EFGH$ is to the circle $ABCD$, so is the solid $O$ to the cone $AL$.

But, as the solid $O$ is to the cone $AL$, so is the cone $EN$ to some solid less than the cone $AL$;
therefore also, as the circle $EFGH$ is to the circle $ABCD$, so is the cone $EN$ to some solid less than the cone $AL$:
which was proved impossible.

Therefore the cone $AL$ is not to any solid greater than the cone $EN$ as the circle $ABCD$ is to the circle $EFGH$.

356   EUCLID

But it was proved that neither is it in this ratio to a less solid;
therefore, as the circle $ABCD$ is to the circle $EFGH$, so is the cone $AL$ to the cone $EN$.

But, as the cone is to the cone, so is the cylinder to the cylinder,
for each is triple of each;   [XII. 10]

Therefore also, as the circle $ABCD$ is to the circle $EFGH$, so are the cylinders on them which are of equal height.

Therefore etc.

Q. E. D.

## Proposition 12

*Similar cones and cylinders are to one another in the triplicate ratio of the diameters in their bases.*

Let there be similar cones and cylinders,
let the circles $ABCD$, $EFGH$ be their bases, $BD$, $FH$ the diameters of the bases, and $KL$, $MN$ the axes of the cones and cylinders;

I say that the cone of which the circle $ABCD$ is the base and the point $L$ the vertex has to the cone of which the circle $EFGH$ is the base and the point $N$ the vertex the ratio triplicate of that which $BD$ has to $FH$.

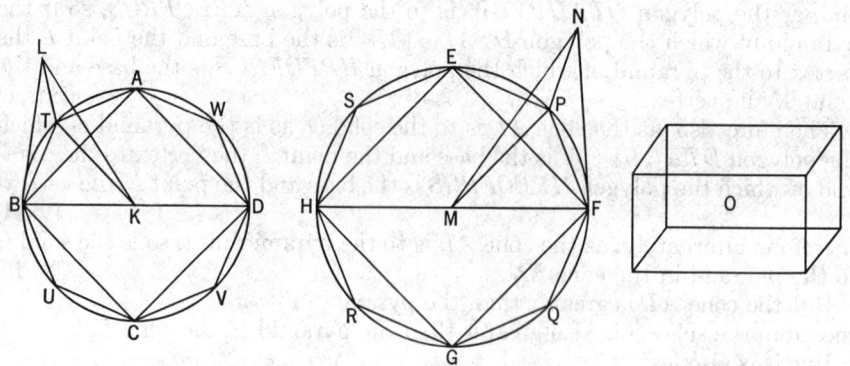

For, if the cone $ABCDL$ has not to the cone $EFGHN$ the ratio triplicate of that which $BD$ has to $FH$,
the cone $ABCDL$ will have that triplicate ratio either to some solid less than the cone $EFGHN$ or to a greater.

First, let it have that triplicate ratio to a less solid $O$.

Let the square $EFGH$ be inscribed in the circle $EFGH$;   [IV. 6]
therefore the square $EFGH$ is greater than the half of the circle $EFGH$.

Now let there be set up on the square $EFGH$ a pyramid having the same vertex with the cone;
therefore the pyramid so set up is greater than the half part of the cone.

Let the circumferences $EF$, $FG$, $GH$, $HE$ be bisected at the points $P$, $Q$, $R$, $S$,
and let $EP$, $PF$, $FQ$, $QG$, $GR$, $RH$, $HS$, $SE$ be joined.

Therefore each of the triangles $EPF$, $FQG$, $GRH$, $HSE$ is also greater than the half part of that segment of the circle $EFGH$ which is about it.

Now on each of the triangles $EPF$, $FQG$, $GRH$, $HSE$ let a pyramid be set up having the same vertex with the cone;

therefore each of the pyramids so set up is also greater than the half part of that segment of the cone which is about it.

Thus, bisecting the circumferences so left, joining straight lines, setting up on each of the triangles pyramids having the same vertex with the cone,
and doing this continually,
we shall leave some segments of the cone which will be less than the excess by which the cone $EFGHN$ exceeds the solid $O$. [x. 1]

Let such be left, and let them be the segments on $EP$, $PF$, $FQ$, $QG$, $GR$, $RH$, $HS$, $SE$;
therefore the remainder, the pyramid of which the polygon $EPFQGRHS$ is the base and the point $N$ the vertex, is greater than the solid $O$.

Let there be also inscribed in the circle $ABCD$ the polygon $ATBUCVDW$ similar and similarly situated to the polygon $EPFQGRHS$,
and let there be set up on the polygon $ATBUCVDW$ a pyramid having the same vertex with the cone;
of the triangles containing the pyramid of which the polygon $ATBUCVDW$ is the base and the point $L$ the vertex let $LBT$ be one,
and of the triangles containing the pyramid of which the polygon $EPFQGRHS$ is the base and the point $N$ the vertex let $NFP$ be one;
and let $KT$, $MP$ be joined.

Now, since the cone $ABCDL$ is similar to the cone $EFGHN$,
therefore, as $BD$ is to $FH$, so is the axis $KL$ to the axis $MN$. [xi. Def. 24]
But, as $BD$ is to $FH$, so is $BK$ to $FM$;
therefore also, as $BK$ is to $FM$, so is $KL$ to $MN$.
And, alternately, as $BK$ is to $KL$, so is $FM$ to $MN$. [v. 16]
And the sides are proportional about equal angles, namely the angles $BKL$, $FMN$;
therefore the triangle $BKL$ is similar to the triangle $FMN$. [vi. 6]
Again, since, as $BK$ is to $KT$, so is $FM$ to $MP$,
and they are about equal angles, namely the angles $BKT$, $FMP$,
inasmuch as, whatever part the angle $BKT$ is of the four right angles at the centre $K$, the same part also is the angle $FMP$ of the four right angles at the centre $M$;
since then the sides are proportional about equal angles,
therefore the triangle $BKT$ is similar to the triangle $FMP$. [vi. 6]
Again, since it was proved that, as $BK$ is to $KL$, so is $FM$ to $MN$,
while $BK$ is equal to $KT$, and $FM$ to $PM$,
therefore, as $TK$ is to $KL$, so is $PM$ to $MN$;
and the sides are proportional about equal angles, namely the angles $TKL$, $PMN$, for they are right;
therefore the triangle $LKT$ is similar to the triangle $NMP$. [vi. 6]
And since, owing to the similarity of the triangles $LKB$, $NMF$,
as $LB$ is to $BK$, so is $NF$ to $FM$,
and, owing to the similarity of the triangles $BKT$, $FMP$,
as $KB$ is to $BT$, so is $MF$ to $FP$,
therefore, *ex aequali*, as $LB$ is to $BT$, so is $NF$ to $FP$. [v. 22]
Again, since, owing to the similarity of the triangles $LTK$, $NPM$,
as $LT$ is to $TK$, so is $NP$ to $PM$,
and, owing to the similarity of the triangles $TKB$, $PMF$,

as $KT$ is to $TB$, so is $MP$ to $PF$;

therefore, *ex aequali*, as $LT$ is to $TB$, so is $NP$ to $PF$. [v. 22]

But it was also proved that, as $TB$ is to $BL$, so is $PF$ to $FN$.

Therefore, *ex aequali*, as $TL$ is to $LB$, so is $PN$ to $NF$. [v. 22]

Therefore in the triangles $LTB$, $NPF$ the sides are proportional;

therefore the triangles $LTB$, $NPF$ are equiangular; [vi. 5]

hence they are also similar. [vi. Def. 1]

Therefore the pyramid of which the triangle $BKT$ is the base and the point $L$ the vertex is also similar to the pyramid of which the triangle $FMP$ is the base and the point $N$ the vertex,

for they are contained by similar planes equal in multitude. [xi. Def. 9]

But similar pyramids which have triangular bases are to one another in the triplicate ratio of their corresponding sides. [xii. 8]

Therefore the pyramid $BKTL$ has to the pyramid $FMPN$ the ratio triplicate of that which $BK$ has to $FM$.

Similarly, by joining straight lines from $A$, $W$, $D$, $V$, $C$, $U$ to $K$, and from $E$, $S$, $H$, $R$, $G$, $Q$ to $M$, and setting up on each of the triangles pyramids which have the same vertex with the cones,

we can prove that each of the similarly arranged pyramids will also have to each similarly arranged pyramid the ratio triplicate of that which the corresponding side $BK$ has to the corresponding side $FM$, that is, which $BD$ has to $FH$.

And, as one of the antecedents is to one of the consequents, so are all the antecedents to all the consequents; [v. 12]

therefore also, as the pyramid $BKTL$ is to the pyramid $FMPN$, so is the whole pyramid of which the polygon $ATBUCVDW$ is the base and the point $L$ the vertex to the whole pyramid of which the polygon $EPFQGRHS$ is the base and the point $N$ the vertex;

hence also the pyramid of which $ATBUCVDW$ is the base and the point $L$ the vertex has to the pyramid of which the polygon $EPFQGRHS$ is the base and the point $N$ the vertex the ratio triplicate of that which $BD$ has to $FH$.

But, by hypothesis, the cone of which the circle $ABCD$ is the base and the point $L$ the vertex has also to the solid $O$ the ratio triplicate of that which $BD$ has to $FH$;

therefore, as the cone of which the circle $ABCD$ is the base and the point $L$ the vertex is to the solid $O$, so is the pyramid of which the polygon $ATBUCVDW$ is the base and $L$ the vertex to the pyramid of which the polygon $EPFQGRHS$ is the base and the point $N$ the vertex;

therefore, alternately, as the cone of which the circle $ABCD$ is the base and $L$ the vertex is to the pyramid contained in it of which the polygon $ATBUCVDW$ is the base and $L$ the vertex, so is the solid $O$ to the pyramid of which the polygon $EPFQGRHS$ is the base and $N$ the vertex. [v. 16]

But the said cone is greater than the pyramid in it;

for it encloses it.

Therefore the solid $O$ is also greater than the pyramid of which the polygon $EPFQGRHS$ is the base and $N$ the vertex.

But it is also less:

which is impossible.

Therefore the cone of which the circle $ABCD$ is the base and $L$ the vertex has not to any solid less than the cone of which the circle $EFGH$ is the base and the point $N$ the vertex the ratio triplicate of that which $BD$ has to $FH$.

Similarly we can prove that neither has the cone $EFGHN$ to any solid less than the cone $ABCDL$ the ratio triplicate of that which $FH$ has to $BD$.

I say next that neither has the cone $ABCDL$ to any solid greater than the cone $EFGHN$ the ratio triplicate of that which $BD$ has to $FH$.

For, if possible, let it have that ratio to a greater solid $O$.

Therefore, inversely, the solid $O$ has to the cone $ABCDL$ the ratio triplicate of that which $FH$ has to $BD$.

But, as the solid $O$ is to the cone $ABCDL$, so is the cone $EFGHN$ to some solid less than the cone $ABCDL$.

Therefore the cone $EFGHN$ also has to some solid less than the cone $ABCDL$ the ratio triplicate of that which $FH$ has to $BD$:
    which was proved impossible.

Therefore the cone $ABCDL$ has not to any solid greater than the cone $EFGHN$ the ratio triplicate of that which $BD$ has to $FH$.

But it was proved that neither has it this ratio to a less solid than the cone $EFGHN$.

Therefore the cone $ABCDL$ has to the cone $EFGHN$ the ratio triplicate of that which $BD$ has to $FH$.

But, as the cone is to the cone, so is the cylinder to the cylinder,
for the cylinder which is on the same base as the cone and of equal height with it is triple of the cone; [XII. 10]
therefore the cylinder also has to the cylinder the ratio triplicate of that which $BD$ has to $FH$.

Therefore etc.
Q. E. D.

## Proposition 13

*If a cylinder be cut by a plane which is parallel to its opposite planes, then, as the cylinder is to the cylinder, so will the axis be to the axis.*

For let the cylinder $AD$ be cut by the plane $GH$ which is parallel to the opposite planes $AB$, $CD$,
    and let the plane $GH$ meet the axis at the point $K$;
I say that, as the cylinder $BG$ is to the cylinder $GD$, so is the axis $EK$ to the axis $KF$.

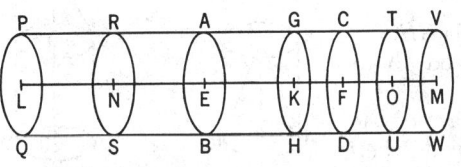

For let the axis $EF$ be produced in both directions to the points $L$, $M$,
and let there be set out any number whatever of axes $EN$, $NL$ equal to the axis $EK$, and any number whatever $FO$, $OM$ equal to $FK$;
and let the cylinder $PW$ on the axis $LM$ be conceived of which the circles $PQ$, $VW$ are the bases.

Let planes be carried through the points $N$, $O$ parallel to $AB$, $CD$ and to the bases of the cylinder $PW$,
    and let them produce the circles $RS$, $TU$ about the centres $N$, $O$.

Then, since the axes $LN$, $NE$, $EK$ are equal to one another, therefore the cylinders $QR$, $RB$, $BG$ are to one another as their bases. [XII. 11]

But the bases are equal;

therefore the cylinders $QR$, $RB$, $BG$ are also equal to one another.

Since then the axes $LN$, $NE$, $EK$ are equal to one another,

and the cylinders $QR$, $RB$, $BG$ are also equal to one another,

and the multitude of the former is equal to the multitude of the latter,

therefore, whatever multiple the axis $KL$ is of the axis $EK$, the same multiple also will the cylinder $QG$ be of the cylinder $GB$.

For the same reason, whatever multiple the axis $MK$ is of the axis $KF$, the same multiple also is the cylinder $WG$ of the cylinder $GD$.

And, if the axis $KL$ is equal to the axis $KM$, the cylinder $QG$ will also be equal to the cylinder $GW$,

if the axis is greater than the axis, the cylinder will also be greater than the cylinder,

and if less, less.

Thus, there being four magnitudes, the axes $EK$, $KF$ and the cylinders $BG$, $GD$,

there have been taken equimultiples of the axis $EK$ and of the cylinder $BG$, namely the axis $LK$ and the cylinder $QG$,

and equimultiples of the axis $KF$ and of the cylinder $GD$, namely the axis $KM$ and the cylinder $GW$;

and it has been proved that,

if the axis $KL$ is in excess of the axis $KM$, the cylinder $QG$ is also in excess of the cylinder $GW$,

if equal, equal,

and if less, less.

Therefore, as the axis $EK$ is to the axis $KF$, so is the cylinder $BG$ to the cylinder $GD$. [v. Def. 5]

Q. E. D.

## Proposition 14

*Cones and cylinders which are on equal bases are to one another as their heights.*

For let $EB$, $FD$ be cylinders on equal bases, the circles $AB$, $CD$;

I say that, as the cylinder $EB$ is to the cylinder $FD$, so is the axis $GH$ to the axis $KL$.

For let the axis $KL$ be produced to the point $N$,

let $LN$ be made equal to the axis $GH$, and let the cylinder $CM$ be conceived about $LN$ as axis.

Since then the cylinders $EB$, $CM$ are of the same height, they are to one another as their bases [XII. 11]

But the bases are equal to one another:

therefore the cylinders $EB$, $CM$ are also equal.

And, since the cylinder $FM$ has been cut by the plane $CD$ which is parallel to its opposite planes,

therefore, as the cylinder $CM$ is to the cylinder $FD$, so is the axis $LN$ to the axis $KL$. [XII. 13]

But the cylinder $CM$ is equal to the cylinder $EB$,
and the axis $LN$ to the axis $GH$;
therefore, as the cylinder $EB$ is to the cylinder $FD$, so is the axis $GH$ to the axis $KL$.

But, as the cylinder $EB$ is to the cylinder $FD$, so is the cone $ABG$ to the cone $CDK$. [XII. 10]

Therefore also, as the axis $GH$ is to the axis $KL$, so is the cone $ABG$ to the cone $CDK$ and the cylinder $EB$ to the cylinder $FD$. Q. E. D.

## PROPOSITION 15

*In equal cones and cylinders the bases are reciprocally proportional to the heights; and those cones and cylinders in which the bases are reciprocally proportional to the heights are equal.*

Let there be equal cones and cylinders of which the circles $ABCD$, $EFGH$ are the bases;
let $AC$, $EG$ be the diameters of the bases,
and $KL$, $MN$ the axes, which are also the heights of the cones or cylinders;
let the cylinders $AO$, $EP$ be completed.

I say that in the cylinders $AO$, $EP$ the bases are reciprocally proportional to the heights,
that is, as the base $ABCD$ is to the base $EFGH$, so is the height $MN$ to the height $KL$.

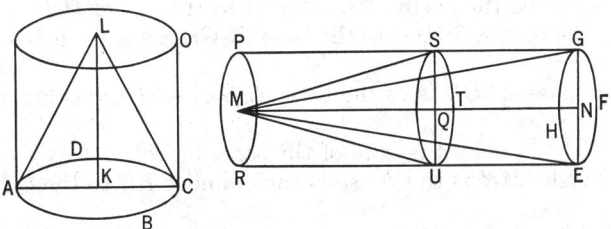

For the height $LK$ is either equal to the height $MN$ or not equal.
First, let it be equal.
Now the cylinder $AO$ is also equal to the cylinder $EP$.
But cones and cylinders which are of the same height are to one another as their bases; [XII. 11]
therefore the base $ABCD$ is also equal to the base $EFGH$.
Hence also, reciprocally, as the base $ABCD$ is to the base $EFGH$, so is the height $MN$ to the height $KL$.
Next, let the height $LK$ not be equal to $MN$,
but let $MN$ be greater;
from the height $MN$ let $QN$ be cut off equal to $KL$,
through the point $Q$ let the cylinder $EP$ be cut by the plane $TUS$ parallel to the planes of the circles $EFGH$, $RP$,
and let the cylinder $ES$ be conceived erected from the circle $EFGH$ as base and with height $NQ$.

Now, since the cylinder $AO$ is equal to the cylinder $EP$,
therefore, as the cylinder $AO$ is to the cylinder $ES$, so is the cylinder $EP$ to the cylinder $ES$. [V. 7]

But, as the cylinder $AO$ is to the cylinder $ES$, so is the base $ABCD$ to the base $EFGH$,

for the cylinders $AO$, $ES$ are of the same height; [XII. 11]
and, as the cylinder $EP$ is to the cylinder $ES$, so is the height $MN$ to the height $QN$,
for the cylinder $EP$ has been cut by a plane which is parallel to its opposite planes. [XII. 13]

Therefore also, as the base $ABCD$ is to the base $EFGH$, so is the height $MN$ to the height $QN$. [V. 11]

But the height $QN$ is equal to the height $KL$;
therefore, as the base $ABCD$ is to the base $EFGH$, so is the height $MN$ to the height $KL$.

Therefore in the cylinders $AO$, $EP$ the bases are reciprocally proportional to the heights.

Next, in the cylinders $AO$, $EP$ let the bases be reciprocally proportional to the heights,
that is, as the base $ABCD$ is to the base $EFGH$, so let the height $MN$ be to the height $KL$;

I say that the cylinder $AO$ is equal to the cylinder $EP$.

For, with the same construction,
since, as the base $ABCD$ is to the base $EFGH$, so is the height $MN$ to the height $KL$,

while the height $KL$ is equal to the height $QN$,
therefore, as the base $ABCD$ is to the base $EFGH$, so is the height $MN$ to the height $QN$.

But, as the base $ABCD$ is to the base $EFGH$, so is the cylinder $AO$ to the cylinder $ES$,

for they are of the same height; [XII. 11]
and, as the height $MN$ is to $QN$, so is the cylinder $EP$ to the cylinder $ES$; [XII. 13]
therefore, as the cylinder $AO$ is to the cylinder $ES$, so is the cylinder $EP$ to the cylinder $ES$. [V. 11]

Therefore the cylinder $AO$ is equal to the cylinder $EP$. [V. 9]
And the same is true for the cones also. Q. E. D.

## PROPOSITION 16

*Given two circles about the same centre, to inscribe in the greater circle an equilateral polygon with an even number of sides which does not touch the lesser circle.*

Let $ABCD$, $EFGH$ be the two given circles about the same centre $K$;
thus it is required to inscribe in the greater circle $ABCD$ an equilateral polygon with an even number of sides which does not touch the circle $EFGH$.

For let the straight line $BKD$ be drawn through the centre $K$,
and from the point $G$ let $GA$ be drawn at right angles to the straight line $BD$ and carried through to $C$;

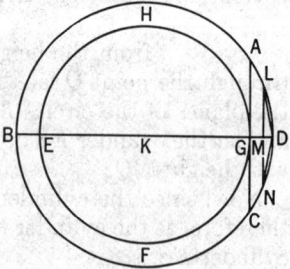

therefore $AC$ touches the circle $EFGH$. [III. 16, Por.]

Then, bisecting the circumference $BAD$, bisecting the half of it, and doing this continually, we shall leave a circumference less than $AD$. [X. 1]

Let such be left, and let it be $LD$;
from $L$ let $LM$ be drawn perpendicular to $BD$ and carried through to $N$,
and let $LD$, $DN$ be joined;
therefore $LD$ is equal to $DN$. [III. 3, I. 4]

Now, since $LN$ is parallel to $AC$,
and $AC$ touches the circle $EFGH$,
therefore $LN$ does not touch the circle $EFGH$;
therefore $LD$, $DN$ are far from touching the circle $EFGH$.

If then we fit into the circle $ABCD$ straight lines equal to the straight line $LD$ and placed continuously, there will be inscribed in the circle $ABCD$ an equilateral polygon with an even number of sides which does not touch the lesser circle $EFGH$.
Q. E. F.

## Proposition 17

*Given two spheres about the same centre, to inscribe in the greater sphere a polyhedral solid which does not touch the lesser sphere at its surface.*

Let two spheres be conceived about the same centre $A$;
thus it is required to inscribe in the greater sphere a polyhedral solid which does not touch the lesser sphere at its surface.

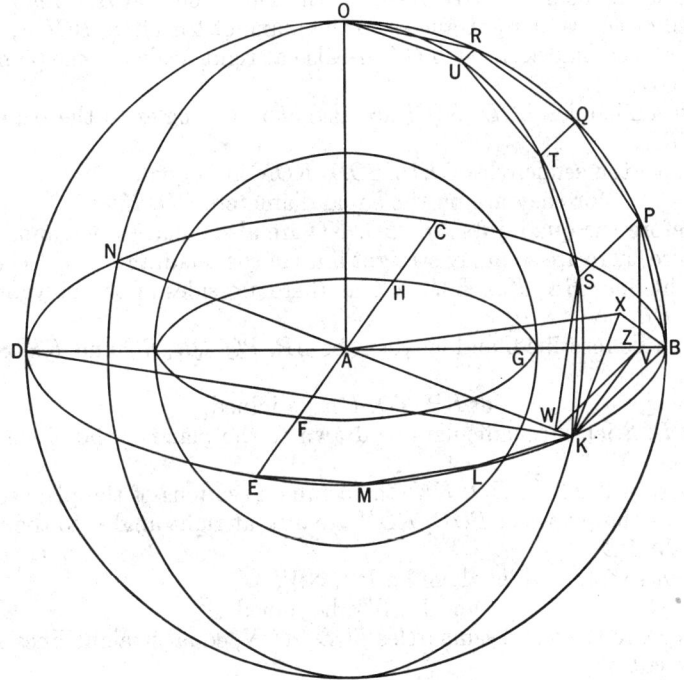

Let the spheres be cut by any plane through the centre;
then the sections will be circles,

inasmuch as the sphere was produced by the diameter remaining fixed and the semicircle being carried round it; [XI. Def. 14]
hence, in whatever position we conceive the semicircle to be, the plane carried through it will produce a circle on the circumference of the sphere.

And it is manifest that this circle is the greatest possible,
inasmuch as the diameter of the sphere, which is of course the diameter both of the semicircle and of the circle, is greater than all the straight lines drawn across in the circle or the sphere.

Let then $BCDE$ be the circle in the greater sphere,
and $FGH$ the circle in the lesser sphere;
let two diameters in them, $BD$, $CE$, be drawn at right angles to one another; then, given the two circles $BCDE$, $FGH$ about the same centre, let there be inscribed in the greater circle $BCDE$ an equilateral polygon with an even number of sides which does not touch the lesser circle $FGH$,
let $BK$, $KL$, $LM$, $ME$ be its sides in the quadrant $BE$,
let $KA$ be joined and carried through to $N$,
let $AO$ be set up from the point $A$ at right angles to the plane of the circle $BCDE$, and let it meet the surface of the sphere at $O$,
and through $AO$ and each of the straight lines $BD$, $KN$ let planes be carried; they will then make greatest circles on the surface of the sphere, for the reason stated.

Let them make such,
and in them let $BOD$, $KON$ be the semicircles on $BD$, $KN$.

Now, since $OA$ is at right angles to the plane of the circle $BCDE$,
therefore all the planes through $OA$ are also at right angles to the plane of the circle $BCDE$; [XI. 18]
hence the semicircles $BOD$, $KON$ are also at right angles to the plane of the circle $BCDE$.

And, since the semicircles $BED$, $BOD$, $KON$ are equal,
for they are on the equal diameters $BD$, $KN$,
therefore the quadrants $BE$, $BO$, $KO$ are also equal to one another.

Therefore there are as many straight lines in the quadrants $BO$, $KO$ equal to the straight lines $BK$, $KL$, $LM$, $ME$ as there are sides of the polygon in the quadrant $BE$.

Let them be inscribed, and let them be $BP$, $PQ$, $QR$, $RO$ and $KS$, $ST$, $TU$, $UO$,
let $SP$, $TQ$, $UR$ be joined,
and from $P$, $S$ let perpendiculars be drawn to the plane of the circle $BCDE$; [XI. 11]
these will fall on $BD$, $KN$, the common sections of the planes,
inasmuch as the planes of $BOD$, $KON$ are also at right angles to the plane of the circle $BCDE$. [cf. XI. Def. 4]

Let them so fall, and let them be $PV$, $SW$,
and let $WV$ be joined.

Now since, in the equal semicircles $BOD$, $KON$, equal straight lines $BP$, $KS$ have been cut off,
and the perpendiculars $PV$, $SW$ have been drawn,
therefore $PV$ is equal to $SW$, and $BV$ to $KW$. [III. 27, I. 26]
But the whole $BA$ is also equal to the whole $KA$;

therefore the remainder $VA$ is also equal to the remainder $WA$;
            therefore, as $BV$ is to $VA$, so is $KW$ to $WA$;
                        therefore $WV$ is parallel to $KB$. [vi. 2]
And, since each of the straight lines $PV$, $SW$ is at right angles to the plane of the circle $BCDE$,
                        therefore $PV$ is parallel to $SW$. [xi. 6]
But it was also proved equal to it;
            therefore $WV$, $SP$ are also equal and parallel. [i. 33]
And, since $WV$ is parallel to $SP$,
            while $WV$ is parallel to $KB$,
                        therefore $SP$ is also parallel to $KB$. [xi. 9]
And $BP$, $KS$ join their extremities;
            therefore the quadrilateral $KBPS$ is in one plane,
inasmuch as, if two straight lines be parallel, and points be taken at random on each of them, the straight line joining the points is in the same plane with the parallels. [xi. 7]

For the same reason
    each of the quadrilaterals $SPQT$, $TQRU$ is also in one plane.
But the triangle $URO$ is also in one plane. [xi. 2]
If then we conceive straight lines joined from the points $P$, $S$, $Q$, $T$, $R$, $U$ to $A$, there will be constructed a certain polyhedral solid figure between the circumferences $BO$, $KO$, consisting of pyramids of which the quadrilaterals $KBPS$, $SPQT$, $TQRU$ and the triangle $URO$ are the bases and the point $A$ the vertex.

And, if we make the same construction in the case of each of the sides $KL$, $LM$, $ME$ as in the case of $BK$, and further, in the case of the remaining three quadrants,
there will be constructed a certain polyhedral figure inscribed in the sphere and contained by pyramids, of which the said quadrilaterals and the triangle $URO$, and the others corresponding to them, are the bases and the point $A$ the vertex.

I say that the said polyhedron will not touch the lesser sphere at the surface on which the circle $FGH$ is.

Let $AX$ be drawn from the point $A$ perpendicular to the plane of the quadrilateral $KBPS$, and let it meet the plane at the point $X$; [xi. 11]
            let $XB$, $XK$ be joined.

Then, since $AX$ is at right angles to the plane of the quadrilateral $KBPS$, therefore it is also at right angles to all the straight lines which meet it and are in the plane of the quadrilateral. [xi. Def. 3]

Therefore $AX$ is at right angles to each of the straight lines $BX$, $XK$.
And, since $AB$ is equal to $AK$,
            the square on $AB$ is also equal to the square on $AK$.
And the squares on $AX$, $XB$ are equal to the square on $AB$,
            for the angle at $X$ is right; [i. 47]
            and the squares on $AX$, $XK$ are equal to the square on $AK$. [*id.*]
Therefore the squares on $AX$, $XB$ are equal to the squares on $AX$, $XK$.
Let the square on $AX$ be subtracted from each;
therefore the remainder, the square on $BX$, is equal to the remainder, the square on $XK$;
            therefore $BX$ is equal to $XK$.

Similarly we can prove that the straight lines joined from $X$ to $P$, $S$ are equal to each of the straight lines $BX$, $XK$.

Therefore the circle described with centre $X$ and distance one of the straight lines $XB$, $XK$ will pass through $P$, $S$ also,

and $KBPS$ will be a quadrilateral in a circle.

Now, since $KB$ is greater than $WV$,

while $WV$ is equal to $SP$,

therefore $KB$ is greater than $SP$.

But $KB$ is equal to each of the straight lines $KS$, $BP$;

therefore each of the straight lines $KS$, $BP$ is greater than $SP$.

And, since $KBPS$ is a quadrilateral in a circle,

and $KB$, $BP$, $KS$ are equal, and $PS$ less,

and $BX$ is the radius of the circle,

therefore the square on $KB$ is greater than double of the square on $BX$.

Let $KZ$ be drawn from $K$ perpendicular to $BV$.

Then, since $BD$ is less than double of $DZ$,

and, as $BD$ is to $DZ$, so is the rectangle $DB$, $BZ$ to the rectangle $DZ$, $ZB$, if a square be described upon $BZ$ and the parallelogram on $ZD$ be completed, then the rectangle $DB$, $BZ$ is also less than double of the rectangle $DZ$, $ZB$.

And, if $KD$ be joined,

the rectangle $DB$, $BZ$ is equal to the square on $BK$,

and the rectangle $DZ$, $ZB$ equal to the square on $KZ$; [III. 31, VI. 8 and Por.]

therefore the square on $KB$ is less than double of the square on $KZ$.

But the square on $KB$ is greater than double of the square on $BX$;

therefore the square on $KZ$ is greater than the square on $BX$.

And, since $BA$ is equal to $KA$,

the square on $BA$ is equal to the square on $AK$.

And the squares on $BX$, $XA$ are equal to the square on $BA$,

and the squares on $KZ$, $ZA$ equal to the square on $KA$; [I. 47]

therefore the squares on $BX$, $XA$ are equal to the squares on $KZ$, $ZA$.

and of these the square on $KZ$ is greater than the square on $BX$;

therefore the remainder, the square on $ZA$, is less than the square on $XA$.

Therefore $AX$ is greater than $AZ$;

therefore $AX$ is much greater than $AG$.

And $AX$ is the perpendicular on one base of the polyhedron,

and $AG$ on the surface of the lesser sphere;

hence the polyhedron will not touch the lesser sphere on its surface.

Therefore, given two spheres about the same centre, a polyhedral solid has been inscribed in the greater sphere which does not touch the lesser sphere at its surface.

Q. E. F.

PORISM. But if in another sphere also a polyhedral solid be inscribed similar to the solid in the sphere $BCDE$,

the polyhedral solid in the sphere $BCDE$ has to the polyhedral solid in the other sphere the ratio triplicate of that which the diameter of the sphere $BCDE$ has to the diameter of the other sphere.

For, the solids being divided into their pyramids similar in multitude and arrangement, the pyramids will be similar.

But similar pyramids are to one another in the triplicate ratio of their corresponding sides; [XII. 8, Por.]

therefore the pyramid of which the quadrilateral $KBPS$ is the base, and the point $A$ the vertex, has to the similarly arranged pyramid in the other sphere the ratio triplicate of that which the corresponding side has to the corresponding side, that is, of that which the radius $AB$ of the sphere about $A$ as centre has to the radius of the other sphere.

Similarly also each pyramid of those in the sphere about $A$ as centre has to each similarly arranged pyramid of those in the other sphere the ratio triplicate of that which $AB$ has to the radius of the other sphere.

And, as one of the antecedents is to one of the consequents, so are all the antecedents to all the consequents; [v. 12]
hence the whole polyhedral solid in the sphere about $A$ as centre has to the whole polyhedral solid in the other sphere the ratio triplicate of that which $AB$ has to the radius of the other sphere, that is, of that which the diameter $BD$ has to the diameter of the other sphere. Q. E. D.

## Proposition 18

*Spheres are to one another in the triplicate ratio of their respective diameters.*

Let the spheres $ABC$, $DEF$ be conceived,
and let $BC$, $EF$ be their diameters;
I say that the sphere $ABC$ has to the sphere $DEF$ the ratio triplicate of that which $BC$ has to $EF$.

For, if the sphere $ABC$ has not to the sphere $DEF$ the ratio triplicate of that which $BC$ has to $EF$,
then the sphere $ABC$ will have either to some less sphere than the sphere $DEF$, or to a greater, the ratio triplicate of that which $BC$ has to $EF$.

First, let it have that ratio to a less sphere $GHK$,

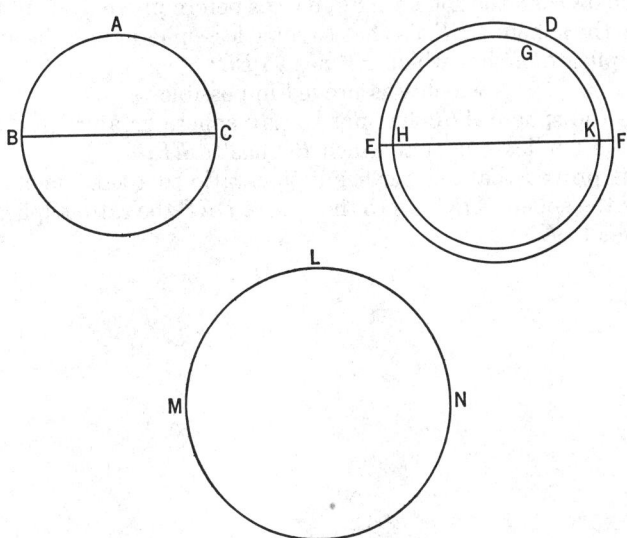

let $DEF$ be conceived about the same centre with $GHK$,
let there be inscribed in the greater sphere $DEF$ a polyhedral solid which does not touch the lesser sphere $GHK$ at its surface, [xii. 17]

and let there also be inscribed in the sphere $ABC$ a polyhedral solid similar to the polyhedral solid in the sphere $DEF$;

therefore the polyhedral solid in $ABC$ has to the polyhedral solid in $DEF$ the ratio triplicate of that which $BC$ has to $EF$. [XII. 17, Por.]

But the sphere $ABC$ also has to the sphere $GHK$ the ratio triplicate of that which $BC$ has to $EF$;

therefore, as the sphere $ABC$ is to the sphere $GHK$, so is the polyhedral solid in the sphere $ABC$ to the polyhedral solid in the sphere $DEF$;

and, alternately, as the sphere $ABC$ is to the polyhedron in it, so is the sphere $GHK$ to the polyhedral solid in the sphere $DEF$. [V. 16]

But the sphere $ABC$ is greater than the polyhedron in it;

therefore the sphere $GHK$ is also greater than the polyhedron in the sphere $DEF$.

But it is also less,
for it is enclosed by it.

Therefore the sphere $ABC$ has not to a less sphere than the sphere $DEF$ the ratio triplicate of that which the diameter $BC$ has to $EF$.

Similarly we can prove that neither has the sphere $DEF$ to a less sphere than the sphere $ABC$ the ratio triplicate of that which $EF$ has to $BC$.

I say next that neither has the sphere $ABC$ to any greater sphere than the sphere $DEF$ the ratio triplicate of that which $BC$ has to $EF$.

For, if possible, let it have that ratio to a greater, $LMN$;

therefore, inversely, the sphere $LMN$ has to the sphere $ABC$ the ratio triplicate of that which the diameter $EF$ has to the diameter $BC$.

But, inasmuch as $LMN$ is greater than $DEF$,

therefore, as the sphere $LMN$ is to the sphere $ABC$, so is the sphere $DEF$ to some less sphere than the sphere $ABC$, as was before proved. [XII. 2, Lemma]

Therefore the sphere $DEF$ also has to some less sphere than the sphere $ABC$ the ratio triplicate of that which $EF$ has to $BC$:
which was proved impossible.

Therefore the sphere $ABC$ has not to any sphere greater than the sphere $DEF$ the ratio triplicate of that which $BC$ has to $EF$.

But it was proved that neither has it that ratio to a less sphere.

Therefore the sphere $ABC$ has to the sphere $DEF$ the ratio triplicate of that which $BC$ has to $EF$.

Q. E. D.

# BOOK THIRTEEN

## PROPOSITIONS

### Proposition 1

*If a straight line be cut in extreme and mean ratio, the square on the greater segment added to the half of the whole is five times the square on the half.*

For let the straight line $AB$ be cut in extreme and mean ratio at the point $C$,
and let $AC$ be the greater segment;
let the straight line $AD$ be produced in a straight line with $CA$,
and let $AD$ be made half of $AB$;
I say that the square on $CD$ is five times the square on $AD$.

For let the squares $AE$, $DF$ be described on $AB$, $DC$,
and let the figure in $DF$ be drawn;
let $FC$ be carried through to $G$.

Now, since $AB$ has been cut in extreme and mean ratio at $C$,
therefore the rectangle $AB$, $BC$ is equal to the square on $AC$. [VI. Def. 3, VI. 17]

And $CE$ is the rectangle $AB$, $BC$, and $FH$ the square on $AC$;
therefore $CE$ is equal to $FH$.

And, since $BA$ is double of $AD$,
while $BA$ is equal to $KA$, and $AD$ to $AH$,
therefore $KA$ is also double of $AH$.

But, as $KA$ is to $AH$, so is $CK$ to $CH$; [VI. 1]
therefore $CK$ is double of $CH$.

But $LH$, $HC$ are also double of $CH$.
Therefore $KC$ is equal to $LH$, $HC$.

But $CE$ was also proved equal to $HF$;
therefore the whole square $AE$ is equal to the gnomon $MNO$.
And, since $BA$ is double of $AD$,
the square on $BA$ is quadruple of the square on $AD$,
that is, $AE$ is quadruple of $DH$.

But $AE$ is equal to the gnomon $MNO$;
therefore the gnomon $MNO$ is also quadruple of $AP$;
therefore the whole $DF$ is five times $AP$.

And $DF$ is the square on $DC$, and $AP$ the square on $DA$;
therefore the square on $CD$ is five times the square on $DA$.
Therefore etc.

Q. E. D.

## Proposition 2

*If the square on a straight line be five times the square on a segment of it, then, when the double of the said segment is cut in extreme and mean ratio, the greater segment is the remaining part of the original straight line.*

For let the square on the straight line $AB$ be five times the square on the segment $AC$ of it,
        and let $CD$ be double of $AC$;
I say that, when $CD$ is cut in extreme and mean ratio, the greater segment is $CB$.

Let the squares $AF$, $CG$ be described on $AB$, $CD$ respectively,
        let the figure in $AF$ be drawn,
        and let $BE$ be drawn through.

Now, since the square on $BA$ is five times the square on $AC$,
        $AF$ is five times $AH$.

Therefore the gnomon $MNO$ is quadruple of $AH$.

And, since $DC$ is double of $CA$, therefore the square on $DC$ is quadruple of the square on $CA$, that is, $CG$ is quadruple of $AH$.

But the gnomon $MNO$ was also proved quadruple of $AH$;
        therefore the gnomon $MNO$ is equal to $CG$.

And, since $DC$ is double of $CA$,
        while $DC$ is equal to $CK$, and $AC$ to $CH$,
        therefore $KB$ is also double of $BH$.        [VI. 1]

But $LH$, $HB$ are also double of $HB$;
        therefore $KB$ is equal to $LH$, $HB$.

But the whole gnomon $MNO$ was also proved equal to the whole $CG$;
        therefore the remainder $HF$ is equal to $BG$.

And $BG$ is the rectangle $CD$, $DB$,
        for $CD$ is equal to $DG$;
        and $HF$ is the square on $CB$;
therefore the rectangle $CD$, $DB$ is equal to the square on $CB$.

Therefore, as $DC$ is to $CB$, so is $CB$ to $BD$.

But $DC$ is greater than $CB$;
        therefore $CB$ is also greater than $BD$.

Therefore, when the straight line $CD$ is cut in extreme and mean ratio, $CB$ is the greater segment.

Therefore etc.
        Q. E. D.

## Lemma

That the double of $AC$ is greater than $BC$ is to be proved thus.

If not, let $BC$ be, if possible, double of $CA$.

Therefore the square on $BC$ is quadruple of the square on $CA$;
    therefore the squares on $BC$, $CA$ are five times the square on $CA$.

But, by hypothesis, the square on $BA$ is also five times the square on $CA$;

therefore the square on $BA$ is equal to the squares on $BC, CA$: which is impossible. [II. 4]

Therefore $CB$ is not double of $AC$.

Similarly we can prove that neither is a straight line less than $CB$ double of $CA$;

for the absurdity is much greater.

Therefore the double of $AC$ is greater than $CB$.  Q. E. D.

## Proposition 3

*If a straight line be cut in extreme and mean ratio, the square on the lesser segment added to the half of the greater segment is five times the square on the half of the greater segment.*

For let any straight line $AB$ be cut in extreme and mean ratio at the point $C$, let $AC$ be the greater segment, and let $AC$ be bisected at $D$;

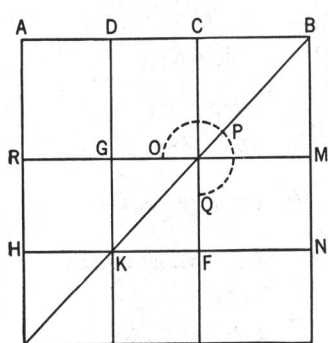

I say that the square on $BD$ is five times the square on $DC$.

For let the square $AE$ be described on $AB$, and let the figure be drawn double.

Since $AC$ is double of $DC$, therefore the square on $AC$ is quadruple of the square on $DC$, that is, $RS$ is quadruple of $FG$.

And, since the rectangle $AB, BC$ is equal to the square on $AC$, and $CE$ is the rectangle $AB, BC$, therefore $CE$ is equal to $RS$.

But $RS$ is quadruple of $FG$;

therefore $CE$ is also quadruple of $FG$.

Again, since $AD$ is equal to $DC$,

$HK$ is also equal to $KF$.

Hence the square $GF$ is also equal to the square $HL$.

Therefore $GK$ is equal to $KL$, that is $MN$ to $NE$;

hence $MF$ is also equal to $FE$.

But $MF$ is equal to $CG$;

therefore $CG$ is also equal to $FE$.

Let $CN$ be added to each;

therefore the gnomon $OPQ$ is equal to $CE$.

But $CE$ was proved quadruple of $GF$;

therefore the gnomon $OPQ$ is also quadruple of the square $FG$.

Therefore the gnomon $OPQ$ and the square $FG$ are five times $FG$.

But the gnomon $OPQ$ and the square $FG$ are the square $DN$.

And $DN$ is the square on $DB$, and $GF$ the square on $DC$.

Therefore the square on $DB$ is five times the square on $DC$. Q. E. D.

## Proposition 4

*If a straight line be cut in extreme and mean ratio, the square on the whole and the square on the lesser segment together are triple of the square on the greater segment.*

Let $AB$ be a straight line,

let it be cut in extreme and mean ratio at $C$, and let $AC$ be the greater segment;

I say that the squares on $AB$, $BC$ are triple of the square on $CA$.

For let the square $ADEB$ be described on $AB$, and let the figure be drawn.

Since, then, $AB$ has been cut in extreme and mean ratio at $C$,

and $AC$ is the greater segment,
therefore the rectangle $AB$, $BC$ is equal to the square on $AC$. [VI. Def. 3, VI. 17]

And $AK$ is the rectangle $AB$, $BC$, and $HG$ the square on $AC$;

therefore $AK$ is equal to $HG$.

And, since $AF$ is equal to $FE$,

let $CK$ be added to each;

therefore the whole $AK$ is equal to the whole $CE$;

therefore $AK$, $CE$ are double of $AK$.

But $AK$, $CE$ are the gnomon $LMN$ and the square $CK$;

therefore the gnomon $LMN$ and the square $CK$ are double of $AK$.

But, further, $AK$ was also proved equal to $HG$;

therefore the gnomon $LMN$ and the squares $CK$, $HG$ are triple of the square $HG$.

And the gnomon $LMN$ and the squares $CK$, $HG$ are the whole square $AE$ and $CK$, which are the squares on $AB$, $BC$,

while $HG$ is the square on $AC$.

Therefore the squares on $AB$, $BC$ are triple of the square on $AC$.

Q. E. D.

## Proposition 5

*If a straight line be cut in extreme and mean ratio, and there be added to it a straight line equal to the greater segment, the whole straight line has been cut in extreme and mean ratio, and the original straight line is the greater segment.*

For let the straight line $AB$ be cut in extreme and mean ratio at the point $C$, let $AC$ be the greater segment, and let $AD$ be equal to $AC$.

I say that the straight line $DB$ has been cut in extreme and mean ratio at $A$, and the original straight line $AB$ is the greater segment.

For let the square $AE$ be described on $AB$, and let the figure be drawn.

Since $AB$ has been cut in extreme and mean ratio at $C$,
therefore the rectangle $AB$, $BC$ is equal to the square on $AC$. [VI. Def. 3, VI. 17]

And $CE$ is the rectangle $AB$, $BC$, and $CH$ the square on $AC$;

therefore $CE$ is equal to $HC$.

But $HE$ is equal to $CE$,

and $DH$ is equal to $HC$;
therefore $DH$ is also equal to $HE$.
Therefore the whole $DK$ is equal to the whole $AE$.
And $DK$ is the rectangle $BD$, $DA$,
for $AD$ is equal to $DL$;
and $AE$ is the square on $AB$;
therefore the rectangle $BD$, $DA$ is equal to the square on $AB$.
Therefore, as $DB$ is to $BA$, so is $BA$ to $AD$. [vi. 17]
And $DB$ is greater than $BA$;
therefore $BA$ is also greater than $AD$. [v. 14]
Therefore $DB$ has been cut in extreme and mean ratio at $A$, and $AB$ is the greater segment. Q. E. D.

## Proposition 6

*If a rational straight line be cut in extreme and mean ratio, each of the segments is the irrational straight line called apotome.*

Let $AB$ be a rational straight line, let it be cut in extreme and mean ratio at $C$, and let $AC$ be the greater segment;
I say that each of the straight lines $AC$, $CB$ is the irrational straight line called apotome.

For let $BA$ be produced, and let $AD$ be made half of $BA$.
Since, then, the straight line $AB$ has been cut in extreme and mean ratio,
and to the greater segment $AC$ is added $AD$ which is half of $AB$,
therefore the square on $CD$ is five times the square on $DA$. [xiii. 1]
Therefore the square on $CD$ has to the square on $DA$ the ratio which a number has to a number;
therefore the square on $CD$ is commensurable with the square on $DA$. [x. 6]
But the square on $DA$ is rational,
for $DA$ is rational, being half of $AB$ which is rational;
therefore the square on $CD$ is also rational; [x. Def. 4]
therefore $CD$ is also rational.
And, since the square on $CD$ has not to the square on $DA$ the ratio which a square number has to a square number,
therefore $CD$ is incommensurable in length with $DA$; [x. 9]
therefore $CD$, $DA$ are rational straight lines commensurable in square only;
therefore $AC$ is an apotome. [x. 73]
Again, since $AB$ has been cut in extreme and mean ratio,
and $AC$ is the greater segment,
therefore the rectangle $AB$, $BC$ is equal to the square on $AC$. [vi. Def. 3, vi. 17]
Therefore the square on the apotome $AC$, if applied to the rational straight line $AB$, produces $BC$ as breadth.
But the square on an apotome, if applied to a rational straight line, produces as breadth a first apotome; [x. 97]
therefore $CB$ is a first apotome.
And $CA$ was also proved to be an apotome.
Therefore etc. Q. E. D.

## Proposition 7

*If three angles of an equilateral pentagon, taken either in order or not in order, be equal, the pentagon will be equiangular.*

For in the equilateral pentagon $ABCDE$ let, first, three angles taken in order, those at $A$, $B$, $C$, be equal to one another;

I say that the pentagon $ABCDE$ is equiangular.

For let $AC$, $BE$, $FD$ be joined.

Now, since the two sides $CB$, $BA$ are equal to the two sides $BA$, $AE$ respectively,

and the angle $CBA$ is equal to the angle $BAE$,

therefore the base $AC$ is equal to the base $BE$,

the triangle $ABC$ is equal to the triangle $ABE$,

and the remaining angles will be equal to the remaining angles, namely those which the equal sides subtend, [I. 4]

that is, the angle $BCA$ to the angle $BEA$, and the angle $ABE$ to the angle $CAB$;

hence the side $AF$ is also equal to the side $BF$. [I. 6]

But the whole $AC$ was also proved equal to the whole $BE$;

therefore the remainder $FC$ is also equal to the remainder $FE$.

But $CD$ is also equal to $DE$.

Therefore the two sides $FC$, $CD$ are equal to the two sides $FE$, $ED$;

and the base $FD$ is common to them;

therefore the angle $FCD$ is equal to the angle $FED$. [I. 8]

But the angle $BCA$ was also proved equal to the angle $AEB$;

therefore the whole angle $BCD$ is also equal to the whole angle $AED$.

But, by hypothesis, the angle $BCD$ is equal to the angles at $A$, $B$;

therefore the angle $AED$ is also equal to the angles at $A$, $B$.

Similarly we can prove that the angle $CDE$ is also equal to the angles at $A$, $B$, $C$;

therefore the pentagon $ABCDE$ is equiangular.

Next, let the given equal angles not be angles taken in order, but let the angles at the points $A$, $C$, $D$ be equal;

I say that in this case too the pentagon $ABCDE$ is equiangular.

For let $BD$ be joined.

Then, since the two sides $BA$, $AE$ are equal to the two sides $BC$, $CD$,

and they contain equal angles,

therefore the base $BE$ is equal to the base $BD$,

the triangle $ABE$ is equal to the triangle $BCD$,

and the remaining angles will be equal to the remaining angles,

namely those which the equal sides subtend; [I. 4]

therefore the angle $AEB$ is equal to the angle $CDB$.

But the angle $BED$ is also equal to the angle $BDE$,

since the side $BE$ is also equal to the side $BD$. [I. 5]

Therefore the whole angle $AED$ is equal to the whole angle $CDE$.

But the angle $CDE$ is, by hypothesis, equal to the angles at $A$, $C$;

therefore the angle $AED$ is also equal to the angles at $A$, $C$.

For the same reason

the angle $ABC$ is also equal to the angles at $A$, $C$, $D$.

Therefore the pentagon $ABCDE$ is equiangular. Q. E. D.

## Proposition 8

*If in an equilateral and equiangular pentagon straight lines subtend two angles taken in order, they cut one another in extreme and mean ratio, and their greater segments are equal to the side of the pentagon.*

For in the equilateral and equiangular pentagon $ABCDE$ let the straight lines $AC$, $BE$, cutting one another at the point $H$, subtend two angles taken in order, the angles at $A$, $B$;

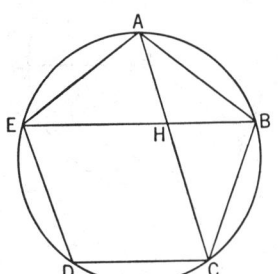

I say that each of them has been cut in extreme and mean ratio at the point $H$, and their greater segments are equal to the side of the pentagon.

For let the circle $ABCDE$ be circumscribed about the pentagon $ABCDE$. [IV. 14]

Then, since the two straight lines $EA$, $AB$ are equal to the two $AB$, $BC$,
and they contain equal angles,
therefore the base $BE$ is equal to the base $AC$,
the triangle $ABE$ is equal to the triangle $ABC$,
and the remaining angles will be equal to the remaining angles respectively, namely those which the equal sides subtend. [I. 4]

Therefore the angle $BAC$ is equal to the angle $ABE$;
therefore the angle $AHE$ is double of the angle $BAH$. [I. 32]
But the angle $EAC$ is also double of the angle $BAC$,
inasmuch as the circumference $EDC$ is also double of the circumference $CB$;
[III. 28, VI. 33]
therefore the angle $HAE$ is equal to the angle $AHE$;
hence the straight line $HE$ is also equal to $EA$, that is, to $AB$. [I. 6]
And, since the straight line $BA$ is equal to $AE$,
the angle $ABE$ is also equal to the angle $AEB$. [I. 5]
But the angle $ABE$ was proved equal to the angle $BAH$;
therefore the angle $BEA$ is also equal to the angle $BAH$.
And the angle $ABE$ is common to the two triangles $ABE$ and $ABH$;
therefore the remaining angle $BAE$ is equal to the remaining angle $AHB$; [I. 32]
therefore the triangle $ABE$ is equiangular with the triangle $ABH$;
therefore, proportionally, as $EB$ is to $BA$, so is $AB$ to $BH$. [VI. 4]
But $BA$ is equal to $EH$;
therefore, as $BE$ is to $EH$, so is $EH$ to $HB$.
And $BE$ is greater than $EH$;
therefore $EH$ is also greater than $HB$. [V. 14]
Therefore $BE$ has been cut in extreme and mean ratio at $H$, and the greater segment $HE$ is equal to the side of the pentagon.

Similarly we can prove that $AC$ has also been cut in extreme and mean ratio at $H$, and its greater segment $CH$ is equal to the side of the pentagon. Q. E. D.

## Proposition 9

*If the side of the hexagon and that of the decagon inscribed in the same circle be added together, the whole straight line has been cut in extreme and mean ratio, and its greater segment is the side of the hexagon.*

Let $ABC$ be a circle;
of the figures inscribed in the circle $ABC$ let $BC$ be the side of a decagon, $CD$ that of a hexagon,
and let them be in a straight line;
I say that the whole straight line $BD$ has been cut in extreme and mean ratio, and $CD$ is its greater segment.

For let the centre of the circle, the point $E$, be taken,
let $EB$, $EC$, $ED$ be joined,
and let $BE$ be carried through to $A$.

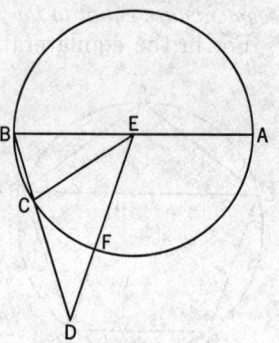

Since $BC$ is the side of an equilateral decagon, therefore the circumference $ACB$ is five times the circumference $BC$;
therefore the circumference $AC$ is quadruple of $CB$.

But, as the circumference $AC$ is to $CB$, so is the angle $AEC$ to the angle $CEB$;     [VI. 33]
therefore the angle $AEC$ is quadruple of the angle $CEB$.

And, since the angle $EBC$ is equal to the angle $ECB$,     [I. 5]
therefore the angle $AEC$ is double of the angle $ECB$.     [I. 32]

And, since the straight line $EC$ is equal to $CD$, for each of them is equal to the side of the hexagon inscribed in the circle $ABC$,     [IV. 15, Por.]
the angle $CED$ is also equal to the angle $CDE$;     [I. 5]
therefore the angle $ECB$ is double of the angle $EDC$.     [I. 32]

But the angle $AEC$ was proved double of the angle $ECB$;
therefore the angle $AEC$ is quadruple of the angle $EDC$.

But the angle $AEC$ was also proved quadruple of the angle $BEC$;
therefore the angle $EDC$ is equal to the angle $BEC$.

But the angle $EBD$ is common to the two triangles $BEC$ and $BED$;
therefore the remaining angle $BED$ is also equal to the remaining angle $ECB$;     [I. 32]
therefore the triangle $EBD$ is equiangular with the triangle $EBC$.

Therefore, proportionally, as $DB$ is to $BE$, so is $EB$ to $BC$.     [VI. 4]
But $EB$ is equal to $CD$.
Therefore, as $BD$ is to $DC$, so is $DC$ to $CB$.
And $BD$ is greater than $DC$;
therefore $DC$ is also greater than $CB$.

Therefore the straight line $BD$ has been cut in extreme and mean ratio, and $DC$ is its greater segment.     Q. E. D.

## PROPOSITION 10

*If an equilateral pentagon be inscribed in a circle, the square on the side of the pentagon is equal to the squares on the side of the hexagon and on that of the decagon inscribed in the same circle.*

Let $ABCDE$ be a circle,
and let the equilateral pentagon $ABCDE$ be inscribed in the circle $ABCDE$.
I say that the square on the side of the pentagon $ABCDE$ is equal to the

squares on the side of the hexagon and on that of the decagon inscribed in the circle $ABCDE$.

For let the centre of the circle, the point $F$, be taken,
  let $AF$ be joined and carried through to the point $G$,
    let $FB$ be joined,
let $FH$ be drawn from $F$ perpendicular to $AB$ and be carried through to $K$,
    let $AK$, $KB$ be joined,
let $FL$ be again drawn from $F$ perpendicular to $AK$, and be carried through to $M$,

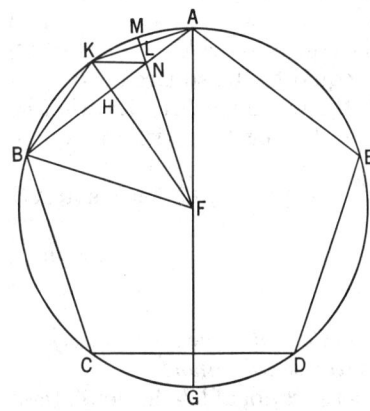

and let $KN$ be joined.
Since the circumference $ABCG$ is equal to the circumference $AEDG$,
 and in them $ABC$ is equal to $AED$,
therefore the remainder, the circumference $CG$, is equal to the remainder $GD$.
But $CD$ belongs to a pentagon;
 therefore $CG$ belongs to a decagon.
And, since $FA$ is equal to $FB$,
 and $FH$ is perpendicular,
therefore the angle $AFK$ is also equal to the angle $KFB$.  [I. 5, I. 26]
Hence the circumference $AK$ is also equal to $KB$;  [III. 26]
therefore the circumference $AB$ is double of the circumference $BK$;
 therefore the straight line $AK$ is a side of a decagon.
For the same reason
    $AK$ is also double of $KM$.
Now, since the circumference $AB$ is double of the circumference $BK$,
 while the circumference $CD$ is equal to the circumference $AB$,
therefore the circumference $CD$ is also double of the circumference $BK$.
But the circumference $CD$ is also double of $CG$;
 therefore the circumference $CG$ is equal to the circumference $BK$.
But $BK$ is double of $KM$, since $KA$ is so also;
   therefore $CG$ is also double of $KM$.
But, further, the circumference $CB$ is also double of the circumference $BK$,
  for the circumference $CB$ is equal to $BA$.
Therefore the whole circumference $GB$ is also double of $BM$;
  hence the angle $GFB$ is also double of the angle $BFM$.  [VI. 33]
But the angle $GFB$ is also double of the angle $FAB$,
  for the angle $FAB$ is equal to the angle $ABF$.
Therefore the angle $BFN$ is also equal to the angle $FAB$.
But the angle $ABF$ is common to the two triangles $ABF$ and $BFN$;
herefore the remaining angle $AFB$ is equal to the remaining angle $BNF$; [I. 32]
 therefore the triangle $ABF$ is equiangular with the triangle $BFN$.
Therefore, proportionally, as the straight line $AB$ is to $BF$, so is $FB$ to $BN$;
                [VI. 4]
 therefore the rectangle $AB$, $BN$ is equal to the square on $BF$. [VI. 17]
Again, since $AL$ is equal to $LK$,

while $LN$ is common and at right angles,
therefore the base $KN$ is equal to the base $AN$; [I. 4]
therefore the angle $LKN$ is also equal to the angle $LAN$.
But the angle $LAN$ is equal to the angle $KBN$;
therefore the angle $LKN$ is also equal to the angle $KBN$.
And the angle at $A$ is common to the two triangles $AKB$ and $AKN$.
Therefore the remaining angle $AKB$ is equal to the remaining angle $KNA$; [I. 32]
therefore the triangle $KBA$ is equiangular with the triangle $KNA$.
Therefore, proportionally, as the straight line $BA$ is to $AK$, so is $KA$ to $AN$; [VI. 4]
therefore the rectangle $BA$, $AN$ is equal to the square on $AK$. [VI. 17]
But the rectangle $AB$, $BN$ was also proved equal to the square on $BF$;
therefore the rectangle $AB$, $BN$ together with the rectangle $BA$, $AN$, that is, the square on $BA$ [II. 2], is equal to the square on $BF$ together with the square on $AK$.
And $BA$ is a side of the pentagon, $BF$ of the hexagon [IV. 15, Por.], and $AK$ of the decagon.
Therefore etc.
Q. E. D.

## Proposition 11

*If in a circle which has its diameter rational an equilateral pentagon be inscribed, the side of the pentagon is the irrational straight line called minor.*

For in the circle $ABCDE$ which has its diameter rational let the equilateral pentagon $ABCDE$ be inscribed;
I say that the side of the pentagon is the irrational straight line called minor.

For let the centre of the circle, the point $F$, be taken,
let $AF$, $FB$ be joined and carried through to the points, $G$, $H$,
let $AC$ be joined,
and let $FK$ be made a fourth part of $AF$.

Now $AF$ is rational;
therefore $FK$ is also rational.
But $BF$ is also rational;
therefore the whole $BK$ is rational.

And, since the circumference $ACG$ is equal to the circumference $ADG$,
and in them $ABC$ is equal to $AED$,
therefore the remainder $CG$ is equal to the remainder $GD$.

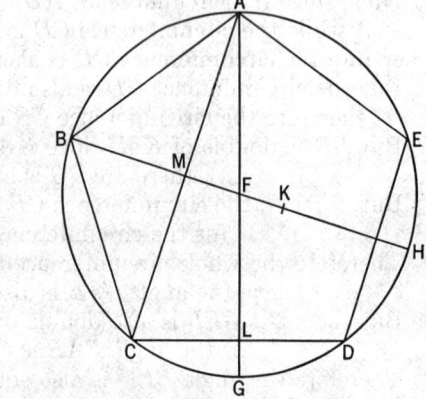

And, if we join $AD$, we conclude that the angles at $L$ are right,
and $CD$ is double of $CL$.
For the same reason
the angles at $M$ are also right,
and $AC$ is double of $CM$.
Since then the angle $ALC$ is equal to the angle $AMF$,

ELEMENTS XIII

and the angle $LAC$ is common to the two triangles $ACL$ and $AMF$,
therefore the remaining angle $ACL$ is equal to the remaining angle $MFA$;
[I. 32]
therefore the triangle $ACL$ is equiangular with the triangle $AMF$;
therefore, proportionally, as $LC$ is to $CA$, so is $MF$ to $FA$.

And the doubles of the antecedents may be taken;
therefore, as the double of $LC$ is to $CA$, so is the double of $MF$ to $FA$.

But, as the double of $MF$ is to $FA$, so is $MF$ to the half of $FA$;
therefore also, as the double of $LC$ is to $CA$, so is $MF$ to the half of $FA$.

And the halves of the consequents may be taken;
therefore, as the double of $LC$ is to the half of $CA$, so is $MF$ to the fourth of $FA$.

And $DC$ is double of $LC$, $CM$ is half of $CA$, and $FK$ a fourth part of $FA$;
therefore, as $DC$ is to $CM$, so is $MF$ to $FK$.

*Componendo* also, as the sum of $DC$, $CM$ is to $CM$, so is $MK$ to $KF$; [v. 18]
therefore also, as the square on the sum of $DC$, $CM$ is to the square on $CM$, so is the square on $MK$ to the square on $KF$.

And since, when the straight line subtending two sides of the pentagon, as $AC$, is cut in extreme and mean ratio, the greater segment is equal to the side of the pentagon, that is, to $DC$, [XIII. 8]
while the square on the greater segment added to the half of the whole is five times the square on the half of the whole, [XIII. 1]
and $CM$ is half of the whole $AC$,
therefore the square on $DC$, $CM$ taken as one straight line is five times the square on $CM$.

But it was proved that, as the square on $DC$, $CM$ taken as one straight line is to the square on $CM$, so is the square on $MK$ to the square on $KF$;
therefore the square on $MK$ is five times the square on $KF$.

But the square on $KF$ is rational,
for the diameter is rational;
therefore the square on $MK$ is also rational;
therefore $MK$ is rational.

And, since $BF$ is quadruple of $FK$,
therefore $BK$ is five times $KF$;
therefore the square on $BK$ is twenty-five times the square on $KF$.

But the square on $MK$ is five times the square on $KF$;
therefore the square on $BK$ is five times the square on $KM$;
therefore the square on $BK$ has not to the square on $KM$ the ratio which a square number has to a square number;
therefore $BK$ is incommensurable in length with $KM$. [x. 9]
And each of them is rational.

Therefore $BK$, $KM$ are rational straight lines commensurable in square only.

But, if from a rational straight line there be subtracted a rational straight line which is commensurable with the whole in square only, the remainder is irrational, namely an apotome;
therefore $MB$ is an apotome and $MK$ the annex to it. [x. 73]

I say next that $MB$ is also a fourth apotome.

Let the square on $N$ be equal to that by which the square on $BK$ is greater than the square on $KM$;
therefore the square on $BK$ is greater than the square on $KM$ by the square on $N$.

And, since *KF* is commensurable with *FB*,
  *componendo* also, *KB* is commensurable with *FB*.  [x. 15]
But *BF* is commensurable with *BH*;
  therefore *BK* is also commensurable with *BH*.  [x. 12]
And, since the square on *BK* is five times the square on *KM*,
therefore the square on *BK* has to the square on *KM* the ratio which 5 has to 1.

Therefore, *convertendo*, the square on *BK* has to the square on *N* the ratio which 5 has to 4 [v. 19, Por.], and this is not the ratio which a square number has to a square number;
  therefore *BK* is incommensurable with *N*;  [x. 9]
therefore the square on *BK* is greater than the square on *KM* by the square on a straight line incommensurable with *BK*.

Since then the square on the whole *BK* is greater than the square on the annex *KM* by the square on a straight line incommensurable with *BK*,
and the whole *BK* is commensurable with the rational straight line, *BH*, set out,
  therefore *MB* is a fourth apotome.  [x. Deff. iii. 4]

But the rectangle contained by a rational straight line and a fourth apotome is irrational,
  and its square root is irrational, and is called minor.  [x. 94]

But the square on *AB* is equal to the rectangle *HB*, *BM*,
because, when *AH* is joined, the triangle *ABH* is equiangular with the triangle *ABM*, and, as *HB* is to *BA*, so is *AB* to *BM*.

Therefore the side *AB* of the pentagon is the irrational straight line called minor.  Q. E. D.

## Proposition 12

*If an equilateral triangle be inscribed in a circle, the square on the side of the triangle is triple of the square on the radius of the circle.*

Let *ABC* be a circle,
and let the equilateral triangle *ABC* be inscribed in it;
I say that the square on one side of the triangle *ABC* is triple of the square on the radius of the circle.

For let the centre *D* of the circle *ABC* be taken,
  let *AD* be joined and carried through to *E*,
    and let *BE* be joined.

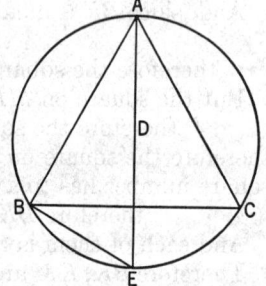

Then, since the triangle *ABC* is equilateral,
therefore the circumference *BEC* is a third part of
  the circumference of the circle *ABC*.

Therefore the circumference *BE* is a sixth part of
the circumference of the circle;
therefore the straight line *BE* belongs to a hexagon;
  therefore it is equal to the radius *DE*.  [iv. 15, Por.]

And, since *AE* is double of *DE*,
the square on *AE* is quadruple of the square on *ED*, that is, of the square on *BE*.

But the square on *AE* is equal to the squares on *AB*, *BE*;  [iii. 31, i. 47]
therefore the squares on *AB*, *BE* are quadruple of the square on *BE*.

Therefore, *separando*, the square on *AB* is triple of the square on *BE*.

ELEMENTS XIII 381

But *BE* is equal to *DE*;
        therefore the square on *AB* is triple of the square on *DE*.
Therefore the square on the side of the triangle is triple of the square on the radius.                                Q. E. D.

## Proposition 13

*To construct a pyramid, to comprehend it in a given sphere, and to prove that the square on the diameter of the sphere is one and a half times the square on the side of the pyramid.*

Let the diameter *AB* of the given sphere be set out,
    and let it be cut at the point *C* so that *AC* is double of *CB*;
        let the semicircle *ADB* be described on *AB*,
    let *CD* be drawn from the point *C* at right angles to *AB*,
            and let *DA* be joined;
    let the circle *EFG* which has its radius equal to *DC* be set out,
let the equilateral triangle *EFG* be inscribed in the circle *EFG*,         [IV. 2]
        let the centre of the circle, the point *H*, be taken,         [III. 1]
            let *EH*, *HF*, *HG* be joined;
from the point *H* let *HK* be set up at right angles to the plane of the circle *EFG*,         [XI. 12]
        let *HK* equal to the straight line *AC* be cut off from *HK*,
            and let *KE*, *KF*, *KG* be joined.

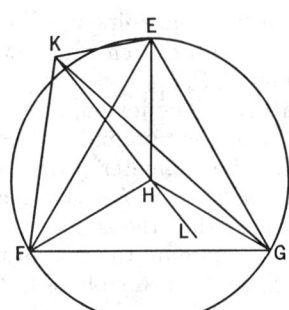

Now, since *KH* is at right angles to the plane of the circle *EFG*,
therefore it will also make right angles with all the straight lines which meet it and are in the plane of the circle *EFG*.         [XI. Def. 3]
    But each of the straight lines *HE*, *HF*, *HG* meets it:
therefore *HK* is at right angles to each of the straight lines *HE*, *HF*, *HG*.
    And, since *AC* is equal to *HK*, and *CD* to *HE*,
            and they contain right angles,
        therefore the base *DA* is equal to the base *KE*.         [I. 4]
    For the same reason
        each of the straight lines *KF*, *KG* is also equal to *DA*;
therefore the three straight lines *KE*, *KF*, *KG* are equal to one another.
    And, since *AC* is double of *CB*,
            therefore *AB* is triple of *BC*.

But, as $AB$ is to $BC$, so is the square on $AD$ to the square on $DC$, as will be proved afterwards.

Therefore the square on $AD$ is triple of the square on $DC$.

But the square on $FE$ is also triple of the square on $EH$,   [XIII. 12]

and $DC$ is equal to $EH$;

therefore $DA$ is also equal to $EF$.

But $DA$ was proved equal to each of the straight lines $KE$, $KF$, $KG$; therefore each of the straight lines $EF$, $FG$, $GE$ is also equal to each of the straight lines $KE$, $KF$, $KG$;

therefore the four triangles $EFG$, $KEF$, $KFG$, $KEG$ are equilateral.

Therefore a pyramid has been constructed out of four equilateral triangles, the triangle $EFG$ being its base and the point $K$ its vertex.

It is next required to comprehend it in the given sphere and to prove that the square on the diameter of the sphere is one and a half times the square on the side of the pyramid.

For let the straight line $HL$ be produced in a straight line with $KH$,

and let $HL$ be made equal to $CB$.

Now, since, as $AC$ is to $CD$, so is $CD$ to $CB$,   [VI. 8, Por.]

while $AC$ is equal to $KH$, $CD$ to $HE$, and $CB$ to $HL$,

therefore, as $KH$ is to $HE$, so is $EH$ to $HL$;

therefore the rectangle $KH$, $HL$ is equal to the square on $EH$.   [VI. 17]

And each of the angles $KHE$, $EHL$ is right;

therefore the semicircle described on $KL$ will pass through $E$ also.

[cf. VI. 8, III. 31]

If then, $KL$ remaining fixed, the semicircle be carried round and restored to the same position from which it began to be moved, it will also pass through the points $F$, $G$,

since, if $FL$, $LG$ be joined, the angles at $F$, $G$ similarly become right angles;

and the pyramid will be comprehended in the given sphere.

For $KL$, the diameter of the sphere, is equal to the diameter $AB$ of the given sphere, inasmuch as $KH$ was made equal to $AC$, and $HL$ to $CB$.

I say next that the square on the diameter of the sphere is one and a half times the square on the side of the pyramid.

For, since $AC$ is double of $CB$,

therefore $AB$ is triple of $BC$;

and, *convertendo*, $BA$ is one and a half times $AC$.

But, as $BA$ is to $AC$, so is the square on $BA$ to the square on $AD$.

Therefore the square on $BA$ is also one and a half times the square on $AD$.

And $BA$ is the diameter of the given sphere, and $AD$ is equal to the side of the pyramid.

Therefore the square on the diameter of the sphere is one and a half times the square on the side of the pyramid.   Q. E. D.

LEMMA

It is to be proved that, as $AB$ is to $BC$, so is the square on $AD$ to the square on $DC$.

For let the figure of the semicircle be set out,

let $DB$ be joined,

let the square $EC$ be described on $AC$,

and let the parallelogram $FB$ be completed.

Since then, because the triangle $DAB$ is equiangular with the triangle $DAC$, as $BA$ is to $AD$, so is $DA$ to $AC$, [vi. 8, vi. 4] therefore the rectangle $BA$, $AC$ is equal to the square on $AD$. [vi. 17]

And since, as $AB$ is to $BC$, so is $EB$ to $BF$, [vi. 1] and $EB$ is the rectangle $BA$, $AC$, for $EA$ is equal to $AC$,

and $BF$ is the rectangle $AC$, $CB$,

therefore, as $AB$ is to $BC$, so is the rectangle $BA$, $AC$ to the rectangle $AC$, $CB$.

And the rectangle $BA$, $AC$ is equal to the square on $AD$, and the rectangle $AC$, $CB$ to the square on $DC$,

for the perpendicular $DC$ is a mean proportional between the segments $AC$, $CB$ of the base, because the angle $ADB$ is right. [vi. 8, Por.]

Therefore, as $AB$ is to $BC$, so is the square on $AD$ to the square on $DC$.

Q. E. D.

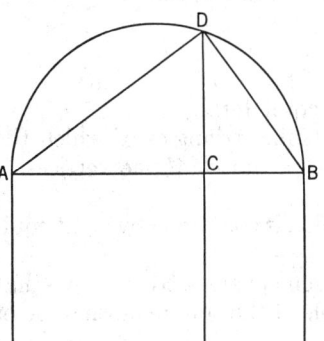

## Proposition 14

*To construct an octahedron and comprehend it in a sphere, as in the preceding case; and to prove that the square on the diameter of the sphere is double of the square on the side of the octahedron.*

Let the diameter $AB$ of the given sphere be set out,

and let it be bisected at $C$;

let the semicircle $ADB$ be described on $AB$,

let $CD$ be drawn from $C$ at right angles to $AB$,

let $DB$ be joined;

let the square $EFGH$, having each of its sides equal to $DB$, be set out,

let $HF$, $EG$ be joined,

from the point $K$ let the straight line $KL$ be set up at right angles to the plane of the square $EFGH$ [xi. 12], and let it be carried through to the other side of the plane, as $KM$;

from the straight lines $KL$, $KM$ let $KL$, $KM$ be respectively cut off equal to one of the straight lines $EK$, $FK$, $GK$, $HK$,

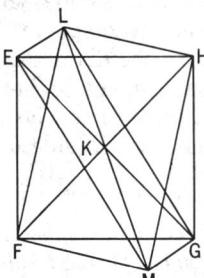

and let $LE$, $LF$, $LG$, $LH$, $ME$, $MF$, $MG$, $MH$ be joined.

Then, since $KE$ is equal to $KH$,

and the angle $EKH$ is right,

therefore the square on $HE$ is double of the square on $EK$. [I. 47]

Again, since $LK$ is equal to $KE$,

and the angle $LKE$ is right,

therefore the square on $EL$ is double of the square on $EK$. [*id.*]

But the square on $HE$ was also proved double of the square on $EK$;

therefore the square on $LE$ is equal to the square on $EH$;

therefore $LE$ is equal to $EH$.

For the same reason

$LH$ is also equal to $HE$;

therefore the triangle $LEH$ is equilateral.

Similarly we can prove that each of the remaining triangles of which the sides of the square $EFGH$ are the bases, and the points $L$, $M$ the vertices, is equilateral;

therefore an octahedron has been constructed which is contained by eight equilateral triangles.

It is next required to comprehend it in the given sphere, and to prove that the square on the diameter of the sphere is double of the square on the side of the octahedron.

For, since the three straight lines $LK$, $KM$, $KE$ are equal to one another,

therefore the semicircle described on $LM$ will also pass through $E$.

And for the same reason,

if, $LM$ remaining fixed, the semicircle be carried round and restored to the same position from which it began to be moved,

it will also pass through the points $F$, $G$, $H$,

and the octahedron will have been comprehended in a sphere.

I say next that it is also comprehended in the given sphere.

For, since $LK$ is equal to $KM$,

while $KE$ is common,

and they contain right angles,

therefore the base $LE$ is equal to the base $EM$. [I. 4]

And, since the angle $LEM$ is right, for it is in a semicircle, [III. 31]

therefore the square on $LM$ is double of the square on $LE$. [I. 47]

Again, since $AC$ is equal to $CB$,

$AB$ is double of $BC$.

But, as $AB$ is to $BC$, so is the square on $AB$ to the square on $BD$;

therefore the square on $AB$ is double of the square on $BD$.

But the square on $LM$ was also proved double of the square on $LE$.

And the square on $DB$ is equal to the square on $LE$, for $EH$ was made equal to $DB$.

Therefore the square on $AB$ is also equal to the square on $LM$;

therefore $AB$ is equal to $LM$.

And $AB$ is the diameter of the given sphere;

therefore $LM$ is equal to the diameter of the given sphere.

Therefore the octahedron has been comprehended in the given sphere, and it has been demonstrated at the same time that the square on the diameter of the sphere is double of the square on the side of the octahedron. Q. E. D.

## PROPOSITION 15

*To construct a cube and comprehend it in a sphere, like the pyramid; and to prove that the square on the diameter of the sphere is triple of the square on the side of the cube.*

Let the diameter $AB$ of the given sphere be set out,

and let it be cut at $C$ so that $AC$ is double of $CB$;
let the semicircle $ADB$ be described on $AB$,
let $CD$ be drawn from $C$ at right angles to $AB$,
and let $DB$ be joined;
let the square $EFGH$ having its side equal to $DB$ be set out,
from $E, F, G, H$ let $EK, FL, GM, HN$ be drawn at right angles to the plane of the square $EFGH$,
from $EK, FL, GM, HN$ let $EK, FL, GM, HN$ respectively be cut off equal to one of the straight lines $EF, FG, GH, HE$,
and let $KL, LM, MN, NK$ be joined;
therefore the cube $FN$ has been constructed which is contained by six equal squares.

It is then required to comprehend it in the given sphere, and to prove that the square on the diameter of the sphere is triple of the square on the side of the cube.

For let $KG, EG$ be joined.
Then, since the angle $KEG$ is right, because $KE$ is also at right angles to the plane $EG$ and of course to the straight line $EG$ also, [XI. Def. 3]
therefore the semicircle described on $KG$ will also pass through the point $E$.

Again, since $GF$ is at right angles to each of the straight lines $FL, FE$,
 $GF$ is also at right angles to the plane $FK$;
hence also, if we join $FK$, $GF$ will be at right angles to $FK$;
and for this reason again the semicircle described on $GK$ will also pass through $F$.

Similarly it will also pass through the remaining angular points of the cube.

If then, $KG$ remaining fixed, the semicircle be carried round and restored to the same position from which it began to be moved,
the cube will be comprehended in a sphere.

I say next that it is also comprehended in the given sphere.
For, since $GF$ is equal to $FE$,
and the angle at $F$ is right,
therefore the square on $EG$ is double of the square on $EF$.
But $EF$ is equal to $EK$;
therefore the square on $EG$ is double of the square on $EK$;
hence the squares on $GE, EK$, that is the square on $GK$ [I. 47], is triple of the square on $EK$.

And, since $AB$ is triple of $BC$,
while, as $AB$ is to $BC$, so is the square on $AB$ to the square on $BD$,
therefore the square on $AB$ is triple of the square on $BD$.
But the square on $GK$ was also proved triple of the square on $KE$.
And $KE$ was made equal to $DB$;
therefore $KG$ is also equal to $AB$.
And $AB$ is the diameter of the given sphere;
therefore $KG$ is also equal to the diameter of the given sphere.

# EUCLID

Therefore the cube has been comprehended in the given sphere; and it has been demonstrated at the same time that the square on the diameter of the sphere is triple of the square on the side of the cube.  Q. E. D.

## PROPOSITION 16

*To construct an icosahedron and comprehend it in a sphere, like the aforesaid figures; and to prove that the side of the icosahedron is the irrational straight line called minor.*

Let the diameter $AB$ of the given sphere be set out,
and let it be cut at $C$ so that $AC$ is quadruple of $CB$,
let the semicircle $ADB$ be described on $AB$,
let the straight line $CD$ be drawn from $C$ at right angles to $AB$,
and let $DB$ be joined;

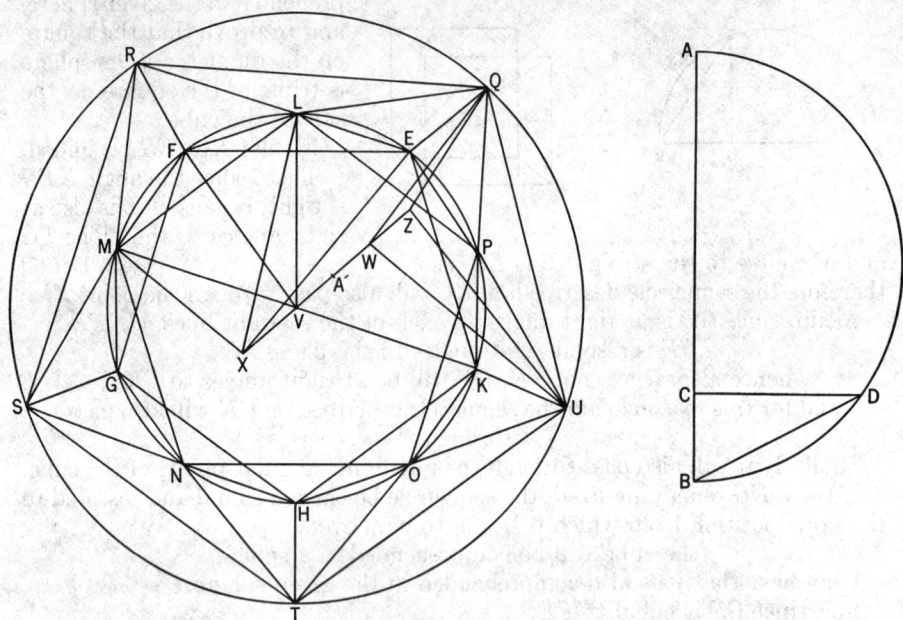

let the circle $EFGHK$ be set out and let its radius be equal to $DB$,
let the equilateral and equiangular pentagon $EFGHK$ be inscribed in the circle $EFGHK$,
let the circumferences $EF$, $FG$, $GH$, $HK$, $KE$ be bisected at the points $L$, $M$, $N$, $O$, $P$,
and let $LM$, $MN$, $NO$, $OP$, $PL$, $EP$ be joined.

Therefore the pentagon $LMNOP$ is also equilateral,
and the straight line $EP$ belongs to a decagon.

Now from the points $E$, $F$, $G$, $H$, $K$ let the straight lines $EQ$, $FR$, $GS$, $HT$, $KU$ be set up at right angles to the plane of the circle, and let them be equal to the radius of the circle $EFGHK$,
let $QR$, $RS$, $ST$, $TU$, $UQ$, $QL$, $LR$, $RM$, $MS$, $SN$, $NT$, $TO$, $OU$, $UP$, $PQ$ be joined.

## ELEMENTS XIII

Now, since each of the straight lines $EQ$, $KU$ is at right angles to the same plane,

therefore $EQ$ is parallel to $KU$. [XI. 6]

But it is also equal to it;
and the straight lines joining those extremities of equal and parallel straight lines which are in the same direction are equal and parallel. [I. 33]

Therefore $QU$ is equal and parallel to $EK$.

But $EK$ belongs to an equilateral pentagon;
therefore $QU$ also belongs to the equilateral pentagon inscribed in the circle $EFGHK$.

For the same reason
each of the straight lines $QR$, $RS$, $ST$, $TU$ also belongs to the equilateral pentagon inscribed in the circle $EFGHK$;

therefore the pentagon $QRSTU$ is equilateral.

And, since $QE$ belongs to a hexagon,

and $EP$ to a decagon,

and the angle $QEP$ is right,

therefore $QP$ belongs to a pentagon;
for the square on the side of the pentagon is equal to the square on the side of the hexagon and the square on the side of the decagon inscribed in the same circle. [XIII. 10]

For the same reason

$PU$ is also a side of a pentagon.

But $QU$ also belongs to a pentagon;

therefore the triangle $QPU$ is equilateral.

For the same reason
each of the triangles $QLR$, $RMS$, $SNT$, $TOU$ is also equilateral.

And, since each of the straight lines $QL$, $QP$ was proved to belong to a pentagon,

and $LP$ also belongs to a pentagon,

therefore the triangle $QLP$ is equilateral.

For the same reason
each of the triangles $LRM$, $MSN$, $NTO$, $OUP$ is also equilateral.

Let the centre of the circle $EFGHK$, the point $V$, be taken;

from $V$ let $VZ$ be set up at right angles to the plane of the circle,

let it be produced in the other direction, as $VX$,

let there be cut off $VW$, the side of a hexagon, and each of the straight lines $VX$, $WZ$, being sides of a decagon,

and let $QZ$, $QW$, $UZ$, $EV$, $LV$, $LX$, $XM$ be joined.

Now, since each of the straight lines $VW$, $QE$ is at right angles to the plane of the circle,

therefore $VW$ is parallel to $QE$. [XI. 6]

But they are also equal;

therefore $EV$, $QW$ are also equal and parallel. [I. 33]

But $EV$ belongs to a hexagon;

therefore $QW$ also belongs to a hexagon.

And, since $QW$ belongs to a hexagon,

and $WZ$ to a decagon,

and the angle $QWZ$ is right,

therefore $QZ$ belongs to a pentagon. [XIII. 10]

For the same reason

$UZ$ also belongs to a pentagon,

inasmuch as, if we join $VK$, $WU$, they will be equal and opposite, and $VK$, being a radius, belongs to a hexagon; [IV. 15, Por.]

therefore $WU$ also belongs to a hexagon.

But $WZ$ belongs to a decagon,

and the angle $UWZ$ is right;

therefore $UZ$ belongs to a pentagon. [XIII. 10]

But $QU$ also belongs to a pentagon;

therefore the triangle $QUZ$ is equilateral.

For the same reason

each of the remaining triangles of which the straight lines $QR$, $RS$, $ST$, $TU$ are the bases, and the point $Z$ the vertex, is also equilateral.

Again, since $VL$ belongs to a hexagon,

and $VX$ to a decagon,

and the angle $LVX$ is right,

therefore $LX$ belongs to a pentagon. [XIII. 10]

For the same reason,

if we join $MV$, which belongs to a hexagon,

$MX$ is also inferred to belong to a pentagon.

But $LM$ also belongs to a pentagon;

therefore the triangle $LMX$ is equilateral.

Similarly it can be proved that each of the remaining triangles of which $MN$, $NO$, $OP$, $PL$ are the bases, and the point $X$ the vertex, is also equilateral.

Therefore an icosahedron has been constructed which is contained by twenty equilateral triangles.

It is next required to comprehend it in the given sphere, and to prove that the side of the icosahedron is the irrational straight line called minor.

For, since $VW$ belongs to a hexagon,

and $WZ$ to a decagon,

therefore $VZ$ has been cut in extreme and mean ratio at $W$,

and $VW$ is its greater segment; [XIII. 9]

therefore as $ZV$ is to $VW$, so is $VW$ to $WZ$.

But $VW$ is equal to $VE$, and $WZ$ to $VX$;

therefore, as $ZV$ is to $VE$, so is $EV$ to $VX$.

And the angles $ZVE$, $EVX$ are right;

therefore, if we join the straight line $EZ$, the angle $XEZ$ will be right because of the similarity of the triangles $XEZ$, $VEZ$.

For the same reason,

since, as $ZV$ is to $VW$, so is $VW$ to $WZ$,

and $ZV$ is equal to $XW$, and $VW$ to $WQ$,

therefore, as $XW$ is to $WQ$, so is $QW$ to $WZ$.

And for this reason again,

if we join $QX$, the angle at $Q$ will be right; [VI. 8]

therefore the semicircle described on $XZ$ will also pass through $Q$. [III. 31]

And if, $XZ$ remaining fixed, the semicircle be carried round and restored to the same position from which it began to be moved, it will also pass through $Q$ and the remaining angular points of the icosahedron, and the icosahedron will have been comprehended in a sphere.

I say next that it is also comprehended in the given sphere.

For let $VW$ be bisected at $A'$.

Then, since the straight line $VZ$ has been cut in extreme and mean ratio at $W$,

and $ZW$ is its lesser segment,

therefore the square on $ZW$ added to the half of the greater segment, that is $WA'$, is five times the square on the half of the greater segment; [XIII. 3]

therefore the square on $ZA'$ is five times the square on $A'W$.

And $ZX$ is double of $ZA'$, and $VW$ double of $A'W$;

therefore the square on $ZX$ is five times the square on $WV$.

And, since $AC$ is quadruple of $CB$,

therefore $AB$ is five times $BC$.

But, as $AB$ is to $BC$, so is the square on $AB$ to the square on $BD$;

[VI. 8, V. Def. 9]

therefore the square on $AB$ is five times the square on $BD$.

But the square on $ZX$ was also proved to be five times the square on $VW$.

And $DB$ is equal to $VW$,

for each of them is equal to the radius of the circle $EFGHK$;

therefore $AB$ is also equal to $XZ$.

And $AB$ is the diameter of the given sphere;

therefore $XZ$ is also equal to the diameter of the given sphere.

Therefore the icosahedron has been comprehended in the given sphere.

I say next that the side of the icosahedron is the irrational straight line called minor.

For, since the diameter of the sphere is rational,

and the square on it is five times the square on the radius of the circle $EFGHK$,

therefore the radius of the circle $EFGHK$ is also rational;

hence its diameter is also rational.

But, if an equilateral pentagon be inscribed in a circle which has its diameter rational, the side of the pentagon is the irrational straight line called minor.

[XIII. 11]

And the side of the pentagon $EFGHK$ is the side of the icosahedron.

Therefore the side of the icosahedron is the irrational straight line called minor.

PORISM. From this it is manifest that the square on the diameter of the sphere is five times the square on the radius of the circle from which the icosahedron has been described, and that the diameter of the sphere is composed of the side of the hexagon and two of the sides of the decagon inscribed in the same circle.
Q. E. D.

## PROPOSITION 17

*To construct a dodecahedron and comprehend it in a sphere, like the aforesaid figures, and to prove that the side of the dodecahedron is the irrational straight line called apotome.*

Let $ABCD$, $CBEF$, two planes of the aforesaid cube at right angles to one another, be set out,

let the sides $AB$, $BC$, $CD$, $DA$, $EF$, $EB$, $FC$ be bisected at $G, H, K, L, M, N, O$ respectively,

let $GK, HL, MH, NO$ be joined.
let the straight lines $NP, PO, HQ$ be cut in extreme and mean ratio at the points $R, S, T$ respectively,
and let $RP, PS, TQ$ be their greater segments;
from the points $R, S, T$ let $RU, SV, TW$ be set up at right angles to the planes of the cube towards the outside of the cube,
let them be made equal to $RP, PS, TQ$,
and let $UB, BW, WC, CV, VU$ be joined.

I say that the pentagon $UBWCV$ is equilateral, and in one plane, and is further equiangular.

For let $RB, SB, VB$ be joined.

Then, since the straight line $NP$ has been cut in extreme and mean ratio at $R$,
and $RP$ is the greater segment,
therefore the squares on $PN, NR$ are triple of the square on $RP$. [XIII. 4]
But $PN$ is equal to $NB$, and $PR$ to $RU$;
therefore the squares on $BN, NR$ are triple of the square on $RU$.
But the square on $BR$ is equal to the squares on $BN, NR$; [I. 47]
therefore the square on $BR$ is triple of the square on $RU$;
hence the squares on $BR, RU$ are quadruple of the square on $RU$.
But the square on $BU$ is equal to the squares on $BR, RU$;
therefore the square on $BU$ is quadruple of the square on $RU$;
therefore $BU$ is double of $RU$.
But $VU$ is also double of $UR$,
inasmuch as $SR$ is also double of $PR$, that is, of $RU$;
therefore $BU$ is equal to $UV$.

Similarly it can be proved that each of the straight lines $BW, WC, CV$ is also equal to each of the straight lines $BU, UV$.

Therefore the pentagon $BUVCW$ is equilateral.

I say next that it is also in one plane.

For let $PX$ be drawn from $P$ parallel to each of the straight lines $RU, SV$ and towards the outside of the cube, and let $XH, HW$ be joined;
I say that $XHW$ is a straight line.

For, since $HQ$ has been cut in extreme and mean ratio at $T$, and $QT$ is its greater segment,
therefore, as $HQ$ is to $QT$, so is $QT$ to $TH$.
But $HQ$ is equal to $HP$, and $QT$ to each of the straight lines $TW, PX$;
therefore, as $HP$ is to $PX$, so is $WT$ to $TH$.

And $HP$ is parallel to $TW$,
for each of them is at right angles to the plane $BD$; [XI. 6]
and $TH$ is parallel to $PX$,

for each of them is at right angles to the plane $BF$. [id.]

But if two triangles, as $XPH$, $HTW$, which have two sides proportional to two sides be placed together at one angle so that their corresponding sides are also parallel,

the remaining straight lines will be in a straight line; [VI. 32]

therefore $XH$ is in a straight line with $HW$.

But every straight line is in one plane; [XI. 1]

therefore the pentagon $UBWCV$ is in one plane.

I say next that it is also equiangular.

For, since the straight line $NP$ has been cut in extreme and mean ratio at $R$, and $PR$ is the greater segment,

while $PR$ is equal to $PS$,

therefore $NS$ has also been cut in extreme and mean ratio at $P$,

and $NP$ is the greater segment; [XIII. 5]

therefore the squares on $NS$, $SP$ are triple of the square on $NP$. [XIII. 4]

But $NP$ is equal to $NB$, and $PS$ to $SV$;

therefore the squares on $NS$, $SV$ are triple of the square on $NB$;

hence the squares on $VS$, $SN$, $NB$ are quadruple of the square on $NB$.

But the square on $SB$ is equal to the squares on $SN$, $NB$;

therefore the squares on $BS$, $SV$, that is, the square on $BV$—for the angle $VSB$ is right—is quadruple of the square on $NB$;

therefore $VB$ is double of $BN$.

But $BC$ is also double of $BN$;

therefore $BV$ is equal to $BC$.

And, since the two sides $BU$, $UV$ are equal to the two sides $BW$, $WC$,

and the base $BV$ is equal to the base $BC$,

therefore the angle $BUV$ is equal to the angle $BWC$. [I. 8]

Similarly we can prove that the angle $UVC$ is also equal to the angle $BWC$; therefore the three angles $BWC$, $BUV$, $UVC$ are equal to one another.

But if in an equilateral pentagon three angles are equal to one another, the pentagon will be equiangular, [XIII. 7]

therefore the pentagon $BUVCW$ is equiangular.

And it was also proved equilateral;

therefore the pentagon $BUVCW$ is equilateral and equiangular, and it is on one side $BC$ of the cube.

Therefore, if we make the same construction in the case of each of the twelve sides of the cube,

a solid figure will have been constructed which is contained by twelve equilateral and equiangular pentagons, and which is called a dodecahedron.

It is then required to comprehend it in the given sphere, and to prove that the side of the dodecahedron is the irrational straight line called apotome.

For let $XP$ be produced, and let the produced straight line be $XZ$;

therefore $PZ$ meets the diameter of the cube, and they bisect one another, for this has been proved in the last theorem but one of the eleventh book.

[XI. 38]

Let them cut at $Z$;

therefore $Z$ is the centre of the sphere which comprehends the cube,

and $ZP$ is half of the side of the cube.

Let $UZ$ be joined.

Now, since the straight line $NS$ has been cut in extreme and mean ratio at $P$,

and $NP$ is its greater segment,

therefore the squares on $NS$, $SP$ are triple of the square on $NP$. [XIII. 4]

But $NS$ is equal to $XZ$,

inasmuch as $NP$ is also equal to $PZ$, and $XP$ to $PS$.

But further, $PS$ is also equal to $XU$,

since it is also equal to $RP$;

therefore the squares on $ZX$, $XU$ are triple of the square on $NP$.

But the square on $UZ$ is equal to the squares on $ZX$, $XU$;

therefore the square on $UZ$ is triple of the square on $NP$.

But the square on the radius of the sphere which comprehends the cube is also triple of the square on the half of the side of the cube,

for it has previously been shown how to construct a cube and comprehend it in a sphere, and to prove that the square on the diameter of the sphere is triple of the square on the side of the cube. [XIII. 15]

But, if whole is so related to whole, so is half to half also;

and $NP$ is half of the side of the cube;

therefore $UZ$ is equal to the radius of the sphere which comprehends the cube.

And $Z$ is the centre of the sphere which comprehends the cube;

therefore the point $U$ is on the surface of the sphere.

Similarly we can prove that each of the remaining angles of the dodecahedron is also on the surface of the sphere;

therefore the dodecahedron has been comprehended in the given sphere.

I say next that the side of the dodecahedron is the irrational straight line called apotome.

For since, when $NP$ has been cut in extreme and mean ratio, $RP$ is the greater segment,

and, when $PO$ has been cut in extreme and mean ratio, $PS$ is the greater segment,

therefore, when the whole $NO$ is cut in extreme and mean ratio, $RS$ is the greater segment.

[Thus, since, as $NP$ is to $PR$, so is $PR$ to $RN$,

the same is true of the doubles also,

for parts have the same ratio as their equimultiples; [v. 15]

therefore as $NO$ is to $RS$, so is $RS$ to the sum of $NR$, $SO$.

But $NO$ is greater than $RS$;

therefore $RS$ is also greater than the sum of $NR$, $SO$;

therefore $NO$ has been cut in extreme and mean ratio,

and $RS$ is its greater segment.]

But $RS$ is equal to $UV$;

therefore, when $NO$ is cut in extreme and mean ratio, $UV$ is the greater segment.

And, since the diameter of the sphere is rational,

and the square on it is triple of the square on the side of the cube,

therefore $NO$, being a side of the cube, is rational.

[But if a rational line be cut in extreme and mean ratio, each of the segments is an irrational apotome.]

Therefore $UV$, being a side of the dodecahedron, is an irrational apotome.

[XIII. 6]

PORISM. From this it is manifest that, when the side of the cube is cut in extreme and mean ratio, the greater segment is the side of the dodecahedron.

Q. E. D.

## PROPOSITION 18

*To set out the sides of the five figures and to compare them with one another.*

Let $AB$, the diameter of the given sphere, be set out,
and let it be cut at $C$ so that $AC$ is equal to $CB$, and at $D$ so that $AD$ is double of $DB$; let the semicircle $AEB$ be described on $AB$, from $C$, $D$ let $CE$, $DF$ be drawn at right angles to $AB$,
and let $AF$, $FB$, $EB$ be joined.
Then, since $AD$ is double of $DB$,
therefore $AB$ is triple of $BD$.
*Convertendo*, therefore, $BA$ is one and a half times $AD$.
But, as $BA$ is to $AD$, so is the square on $BA$ to the square on $AF$, [v. Def. 9, vi. 8]
for the triangle $AFB$ is equiangular with the triangle $AFD$;
therefore the square on $BA$ is one and a half times the square on $AF$.
But the square on the diameter of the sphere is also one and a half times the square on the side of the pyramid. [XIII. 13]
And $AB$ is the diameter of the sphere;
therefore $AF$ is equal to the side of the pyramid.
Again, since $AD$ is double of $DB$,
therefore $AB$ is triple of $BD$.
But, as $AB$ is to $BD$, so is the square on $AB$ to the square on $BF$;
[VI. 8, v. Def. 9]
therefore the square on $AB$ is triple of the square on $BF$.
But the square on the diameter of the sphere is also triple of the square on the side of the cube. [XIII. 15]
And $AB$ is the diameter of the sphere;
therefore $BF$ is the side of the cube.
And, since $AC$ is equal to $CB$,
therefore $AB$ is double of $BC$.
But, as $AB$ is to $BC$, so is the square on $AB$ to the square on $BE$;
therefore the square on $AB$ is double of the square on $BE$.
But the square on the diameter of the sphere is also double of the square on the side of the octahedron. [XIII. 14]
And $AB$ is the diameter of the given sphere;
therefore $BE$ is the side of the octahedron.
Next, let $AG$ be drawn from the point $A$ at right angles to the straight line $AB$,
let $AG$ be made equal to $AB$,
let $GC$ be joined,
and from $H$ let $HK$ be drawn perpendicular to $AB$.
Then, since $GA$ is double of $AC$,

for $GA$ is equal to $AB$,
and, as $GA$ is to $AC$, so is $HK$ to $KC$,
therefore $HK$ is also double of $KC$.

Therefore the square on $HK$ is quadruple of the square on $KC$; therefore the squares on $HK$, $KC$, that is, the square on $HC$, is five times the square on $KC$.

But $HC$ is equal to $CB$;
therefore the square on $BC$ is five times the square on $CK$.

And, since $AB$ is double of $CB$,
and, in them, $AD$ is double of $DB$,
therefore the remainder $BD$ is double of the remainder $DC$.

Therefore $BC$ is triple of $CD$;
therefore the square on $BC$ is nine times the square on $CD$.

But the square on $BC$ is five times the square on $CK$;
therefore the square on $CK$ is greater than the square on $CD$;
therefore $CK$ is greater than $CD$.

Let $CL$ be made equal to $CK$,
from $L$ let $LM$ be drawn at right angles to $AB$,
and let $MB$ be joined.

Now, since the square on $BC$ is five times the square on $CK$,
and $AB$ is double of $BC$, and $KL$ double of $CK$,
therefore the square on $AB$ is five times the square on $KL$.

But the square on the diameter of the sphere is also five times the square on the radius of the circle from which the icosahedron has been described.

[XIII. 16, Por.]

And $AB$ is the diameter of the sphere;
therefore $KL$ is the radius of the circle from which the icosahedron has been described;
therefore $KL$ is a side of the hexagon in the said circle. [IV. 15, Por.]

And, since the diameter of the sphere is made up of the side of the hexagon and two of the sides of the decagon inscribed in the same circle,

[XIII. 16, Por.]

and $AB$ is the diameter of the sphere,
while $KL$ is a side of the hexagon,
and $AK$ is equal to $LB$,
therefore each of the straight lines $AK$, $LB$ is a side of the decagon inscribed in the circle from which the icosahedron has been described.

And, since $LB$ belongs to a decagon, and $ML$ to a hexagon,
for $ML$ is equal to $KL$, since it is also equal to $HK$, being the same distance from the centre, and each of the straight lines $HK$, $KL$ is double of $KC$,
therefore $MB$ belongs to a pentagon. [XIII. 10]

But the side of the pentagon is the side of the icosahedron; [XIII. 16]
therefore $MB$ belongs to the icosahedron.

Now, since $FB$ is a side of the cube,
let it be cut in extreme and mean ratio at $N$,
and let $NB$ be the greater segment;
therefore $NB$ is a side of the dodecahedron. [XIII. 17, Por.]

And, since the square on the diameter of the sphere was proved to be one and a half times the square on the side $AF$ of the pyramid, double of the square on the side $BE$ of the octahedron and triple of the side $FB$ of the cube, therefore, of parts of which the square on the diameter of the sphere contains six, the square on the side of the pyramid contains four, the square on the side of the octahedron three, and the square on the side of the cube two.

Therefore the square on the side of the pyramid is four-thirds of the square on the side of the octahedron, and double of the square on the side of the cube; and the square on the side of the octahedron is one and a half times the square on the side of the cube.

The said sides, therefore, of the three figures, I mean the pyramid, the octahedron and the cube, are to one another in rational ratios.

But the remaining two, I mean the side of the icosahedron and the side of the dodecahedron, are not in rational ratios either to one another or to the aforesaid sides;

for they are irrational, the one being minor [XIII. 16] and the other an apotome [XIII. 17].

That the side $MB$ of the icosahedron is greater than the side $NB$ of the dodecahedron we can prove thus.

For, since the triangle $FDB$ is equiangular with the triangle $FAB$, [VI. 8]
        proportionally, as $DB$ is to $BF$, so is $BF$ to $BA$. [VI. 4]
And, since the three straight lines are proportional,
as the first is to the third, so is the square on the first to the square on the second; [V. Def. 9, VI. 20, Por.]
therefore, as $DB$ is to $BA$, so is the square on $DB$ to the square on $BF$;
therefore, inversely, as $AB$ is to $BD$, so is the square on $FB$ to the square on $BD$.

But $AB$ is triple of $BD$;
    therefore the square on $FB$ is triple of the square on $BD$.
But the square on $AD$ is also quadruple of the square on $DB$,
        for $AD$ is double of $DB$;
    therefore the square on $AD$ is greater than the square on $FB$;
        therefore $AD$ is greater than $FB$;
        therefore $AL$ is by far greater than $FB$.
And, when $AL$ is cut in extreme and mean ratio,
        $KL$ is the greater segment,
inasmuch as $LK$ belongs to a hexagon, and $KA$ to a decagon; [XIII. 9]
and, when $FB$ is cut in extreme and mean ratio, $NB$ is the greater segment;
        therefore $KL$ is greater than $NB$.
But $KL$ is equal to $LM$;
        therefore $LM$ is greater than $NB$.
Therefore $MB$, which is a side of the icosahedron, is by far greater than $NB$ which is a side of the dodecahedron. Q. E. D.

---

I say next that *no other figure, besides the said five figures, can be constructed which is contained by equilateral and equiangular figures equal to one another.*

For a solid angle cannot be constructed with two triangles, or indeed planes.

With three triangles the angle of the pyramid is constructed, with four the angle of the octahedron, and with five the angle of the icosahedron;

but a solid angle cannot be formed by six equilateral and equiangular triangles placed together at one point,

for, the angle of the equilateral triangle being two-thirds of a right angle, the six will be equal to four right angles:

which is impossible, for any solid angle is contained by angles less than four right angles. [XI. 21]

For the same reason, neither can a solid angle be constructed by more than six plane angles.

By three squares the angle of the cube is contained, but by four it is impossible for a solid angle to be contained,

for they will again be four right angles.

By three equilateral and equiangular pentagons the angle of the dodecahedron is contained;

but by four such it is impossible for any solid angle to be contained,

for, the angle of the equilateral pentagon being a right angle and a fifth, the four angles will be greater than four right angles:

which is impossible.

Neither again will a solid angle be contained by other polygonal figures by reason of the same absurdity.

Therefore etc.

Q. E. D.

## Lemma

But that *the angle of the equilateral and equiangular pentagon is a right angle and a fifth* we must prove thus.

Let $ABCDE$ be an equilateral and equiangular pentagon,
let the circle $ABCDE$ be circumscribed about it,
let its centre $F$ be taken,
and let $FA, FB, FC, FD, FE$ be joined.

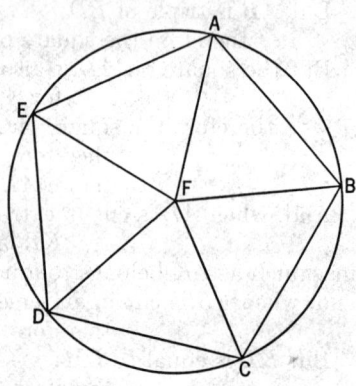

Therefore they bisect the angles of the pentagon at $A, B, C, D, E$.

And, since the angles at $F$ are equal to four right angles and are equal,

therefore one of them, as the angle $AFB$, is
one right angle less a fifth;

therefore the remaining angles $FAB, ABF$
consist of one right angle and a fifth.

But the angle $FAB$ is equal to the angle $FBC$;

therefore the whole angle $ABC$ of the pentagon consists of one right angle and a fifth.

Q. E. D.

# THE WORKS OF ARCHIMEDES
# INCLUDING THE METHOD

# BIOGRAPHICAL NOTE
## Archimedes, c. 287–212 b.c.

Archimedes was a citizen of Syracuse, in Sicily, where he was born around the year 287 b.c. He was intimate with Hiero, King of Syracuse, and with his son, Gelo, and Plutarch says that he was related to them. In his *Sand-Reckoner*, which was dedicated to Gelo, Archimedes speaks of his father, Pheidias, as an astronomer who investigated the sizes and distances of the sun and moon.

As a young man Archimedes seems to have spent some time in Egypt, where he invented the water-screw as a means of drawing water out of the Nile for irrigating the fields, though it is also said that he invented this machine to drain bilge water from a huge ship built for King Hiero. He may have studied with the pupils of Euclid in Alexandria. It was probably there that he made the friendship of Conon of Samos and Eratosthenes. To Conon he was in the habit of communicating his discoveries before their publication, and it was for Eratosthenes that he wrote the *Method* and through him that he addressed the famous *Cattle-Problem* to the mathematicians of Alexandria—if the tradition is to be credited that associates Archimedes with this problem. After the death of Conon, Archimedes sent his discoveries to Conon's friend and pupil, Dositheus of Pelusium, to whom four of the extant treatises are dedicated.

His mechanical inventions won great fame for Archimedes and figure largely in the traditions about him. After discovering the solution of the problem *To move a given weight by a given force*, he boasted to King Hiero: "Give me a place to stand on and I can move the earth." Asked for a practical demonstration, he contrived a machine by which with the use of only one arm he drew out of the dock a large ship, laden with passengers and goods, which the combined strength of the Syracusans could scarcely move. From that day Hiero ordered that "Archimedes was to be believed in everything he might say." At the king's request Archimedes then made for him catapults, battering rams, cranes, and many other engines of war, which were later used with such success in the defense of Syracuse against the Romans that they were unable to take the city except by treachery. There is also a story in Lucian that Archimedes set fire to the Roman ships by an arrangement of burning glasses.

Although Archimedes acquired by his mechanical inventions "the renown of more than human sagacity," according to Plutarch, he "would not deign to leave behind him any commentary or writing on such subjects," since he considered them "sordid and ignoble." He did, however, write a description, now lost, of an apparatus, composed of concentric glass spheres moved by water power, representing the Eudoxian system of the world. This astronomical machine, which survived to be seen and described by Cicero in his *Republic*, was sufficiently accurate to show the eclipses of the sun and the moon. Except for this lost work *On Sphere-making*, Archimedes wrote only on strictly mathematical subjects. He took all the mathematical sciences for his province: arithmetic, geometry, astronomy, mechanics, and hydrostatics. Unlike Euclid and Apollonius he wrote no textbooks. Of his writings, although some have been lost, the most important have survived.

The absorption of Archimedes in his mathematical investigations was so great that he forgot his food and neglected his person, and when carried by force to the bath, Plutarch records, "he used to trace geometrical figures in the ashes of the fire and diagrams in the oil on his body." Asked by Hiero to discover whether a goldsmith had alloyed with silver the gold of his crown, Archimedes found the answer while bathing by considering the water displaced by his body, whereupon he is reported to have run home in his excitement without his clothes, shouting, "Eureka" (I have found it).

Archimedes' preoccupation with mathematics is even said to have been the cause of his death. In the general massacre which followed the capture of Syracuse by Marcellus in 212 B.C., Archimedes was so intent upon a mathematical diagram that he took no notice, and when ordered by a soldier to attend the victorious general, he refused until he should have solved his problem, whereupon he was slain by the enraged soldier. No blame attaches to the Roman general, Marcellus, since he had given orders to spare the house and person of the mathematician, and in the midst of his triumph he lamented the death of Archimedes, provided him with an honorable burial, and befriended his surviving relatives. In accordance with the expressed desire of Archimedes, his family and friends inscribed on his tomb the figure of his favorite theorem, on the sphere and the circumscribed cylinder, and the ratio of the containing solid to the contained. When Cicero was in Sicily as quaestor in 75 B.C., he discovered the neglected and forgotten tomb of Archimedes near the Agrigentine Gate and piously restored it.

# CONTENTS

Biographical Note, 399
On the sphere and cylinder, book i, 403
On the sphere and cylinder, book ii, 434
Measurement of a circle, 447
On conoids and spheroids, 452
On spirals, 482
On the equilibrium of planes, book i, 502
On the equilibrium of planes, book ii, 510
The sand-reckoner, 520
Quadrature of the parabola, 527
On floating bodies, book i, 538
On floating bodies, book ii, 543
Book of lemmas, 561
The method treating of mechanical problems, 569

# ON THE SPHERE AND CYLINDER
## BOOK ONE

ARCHIMEDES to DOSITHEUS greeting

"On a former occasion I sent you the investigations which I had up to that time completed, including the proofs, showing that any segment bounded by a straight line and a section of a right-angled cone [a parabola] is four-thirds of the triangle which has the same base with the segment and equal height. Since then certain theorems not hitherto demonstrated have occurred to me, and I have worked out the proofs of them. They are these: first, that the surface of any sphere is four times its greatest circle; next, that the surface of any segment of a sphere is equal to a circle whose radius is equal to the straight line drawn from the vertex of the segment to the circumference of the circle which is the base of the segment; and, further, that any cylinder having its base equal to the greatest circle of those in the sphere, and height equal to the diameter of the sphere, is itself [*i.e.* in content] half as large again as the sphere, and its surface also [including its bases] is half as large again as the surface of the sphere. Now these properties were all along naturally inherent in the figures referred to, but remained unknown to those who were before my time engaged in the study of geometry. Having, however, now discovered that the properties are true of these figures, I cannot feel any hesitation in setting them side by side both with my former investigations and with those of the theorems of Eudoxus on solids which are held to be most irrefragably established, namely, that any pyramid is one third part of the prism which has the same base with the pyramid and equal height, and that any cone is one third part of the cylinder which has the same base with the cone and equal height. For, though these properties also were naturally inherent in the figures all along, yet they were in fact unknown to all the many able geometers who lived before Eudoxus, and had not been observed by any one. Now, however, it will be open to those who possess the requisite ability to examine these discoveries of mine. They ought to have been published while Conon was still alive, for I should conceive that he would best have been able to grasp them and to pronounce upon them the appropriate verdict; but, as I judge it well to communicate them to those who are conversant with mathematics, I send them to you with the proofs written out, which it will be open to mathematicians to examine. Farewell.

"I first set out the axioms and the assumptions which I have used for the proofs of my propositions."

## DEFINITIONS

1. "There are in a plane certain terminated bent lines, which either lie wholly on the same side of the straight lines joining their extremities, or have no part of them on the other side."

2. "I apply the term *concave in the same direction* to a line such that, if any two points on it are taken, either all the straight lines connecting the points fall on the same side of the line, or some fall on one and the same side while others fall on the line itself, but none on the other side."

3. "Similarly also there are certain terminated surfaces, not themselves being in a plane but having their extremities in a plane, and such that they will either be wholly on the same side of the plane containing their extremities, or have no part of them on the other side."

4. "I apply the term *concave in the same direction* to surfaces such that, if any two points on them are taken, the straight lines connecting the points either all fall on the same side of the surface, or some fall on one and the same side of it while some fall upon it, but none on the other side."

5. "I use the term *solid sector*, when a cone cuts a sphere, and has its apex at the centre of the sphere, to denote the figure comprehended by the surface of the cone and the surface of the sphere included within the cone."

6. "I apply the term *solid rhombus*, when two cones with the same base have their apices on opposite sides of the plane of the base in such a position that their axes lie in a straight line, to denote the solid figure made up of both the cones."

## ASSUMPTIONS

1. "*Of all lines which have the same extremities the straight line is the least.*"

2. "Of other lines in a plane and having the same extremities, [any two] such are unequal whenever both are concave in the same direction and one of them is either wholly included between the other and the straight line which has the same extremities with it, or is partly included by, and is partly common with, the other; and that [line] which is included is the lesser [of the two]."

3. "Similarly, of surfaces which have the same extremities, if those extremities are in a plane, the plane is the least [in area]."

4. "Of other surfaces with the same extremities, the extremities being in a plane, [any two] such are unequal whenever both are concave in the same direction and one surface is either wholly included between the other and the plane which has the same extremities with it, or is partly included by, and partly common with, the other; and that [surface] which is included is the lesser [of the two in area]."

5. "Further, of unequal lines, unequal surfaces, and unequal solids, the greater exceeds the less by such a magnitude as, when added to itself, can be made to exceed any assigned magnitude among those which are comparable with [it and with] one another.

"These things being premised, *if a polygon be inscribed in a circle, it is plain that the perimeter of the inscribed polygon is less than the circumference of the circle;* for each of the sides of the polygon is less than that part of the circumference of the circle which is cut off by it."

# ON THE SPHERE AND CYLINDER I

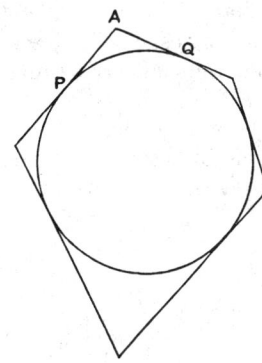

## Proposition 1

*If a polygon be circumscribed about a circle, the perimeter of the circumscribed polygon is greater than the perimeter of the circle.*

Let any two adjacent sides, meeting in $A$, touch the circle at $P$, $Q$ respectively.

Then [*Assumptions*, 2]
$$PA + AQ > (\text{arc } PQ).$$
A similar inequality holds for each angle of the polygon; and, by addition, the required result follows.

## Proposition 2

*Given two unequal magnitudes, it is possible to find two unequal straight lines such that the greater straight line has to the less a ratio less than the greater magnitude has to the less.*

Let $AB, D$ represent the two unequal magnitudes, $AB$ being the greater.

Suppose $BC$ measured along $BA$ equal to $D$, and let $GH$ be any straight line.

Then, if $CA$ be added to itself a sufficient number of times, the sum will exceed $D$. Let $AF$ be this sum, and take $E$ on $GH$ produced such that $GH$ is the same multiple of $HE$ that $AF$ is of $AC$.

Thus $$EH : HG = AC : AF.$$
But, since $AF > D$ (or $CB$),
$$AC : AF < AC : CB.$$
Therefore, *componendo*,
$$EG : GH < AB : D.$$
Hence $EG$, $GH$ are two lines satisfying the given condition.

## Proposition 3

*Given two unequal magnitudes and a circle, it is possible to inscribe a polygon in the circle and to describe another about it so that the side of the circumscribed polygon may have to the side of the inscribed polygon a ratio less than that of the greater magnitude to the less.*

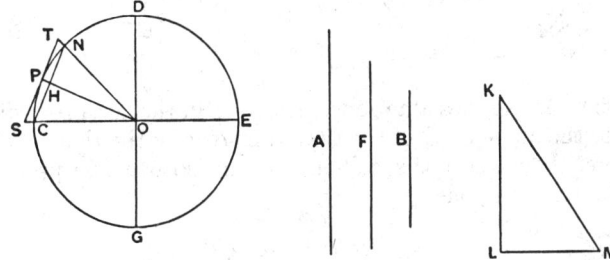

Let $A$, $B$ represent the given magnitudes, $A$ being the greater.

Find [Prop. 2] two straight lines $F$, $KL$, of which $F$ is the greater, such that
$$F : KL < A : B. \qquad (1).$$

Draw $LM$ perpendicular to $LK$ and of such length that $KM = F$.

In the given circle let $CE$, $DG$ be two diameters at right angles. Then, bisecting the angle $DOC$, bisecting the half again, and so on, we shall arrive ultimately at an angle (as $NOC$) less than twice the angle $LKM$.

Join $NC$, which (by the construction) will be the side of a regular polygon inscribed in the circle. Let $OP$ be the radius of the circle bisecting the angle $NOC$ (and therefore bisecting $NC$ at right angles, in $H$, say), and let the tangent at $P$ meet $OC$, $ON$ produced in $S$, $T$ respectively.

Now, since
$$\angle CON < 2 \angle LKM,$$
$$\angle HOC < \angle LKM,$$
and the angles at $H$, $L$ are right;
therefore $MK : LK > OC : OH$
$$> OP : OH.$$
Hence $ST : CN < MK : LK$
$$< F : LK;$$
therefore, *a fortiori*, by (1),
$$ST : CN < A : B.$$
Thus two polygons are found satisfying the given condition.

## Proposition 4

*Again, given two unequal magnitudes and a sector, it is possible to describe a polygon about the sector and to inscribe another in it so that the side of the circumscribed polygon may have to the side of the inscribed polygon a ratio less than the greater magnitude has to the less.*

[The "inscribed polygon" found in this proposition is one which has for two sides the two radii bounding the sector, while the remaining sides (the number of which is, by construction, some power of 2) subtend equal parts of the arc of the sector; the "circumscribed polygon" is formed by the tangents parallel to the sides of the inscribed polygon and by the two bounding radii produced.]

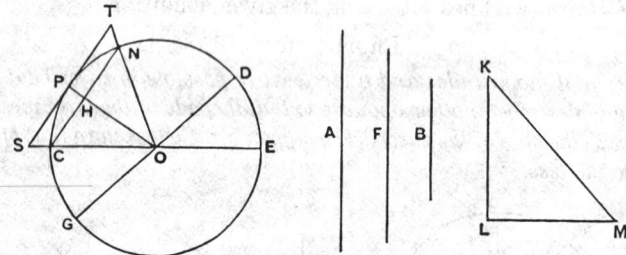

In this case we make the same construction as in the last proposition except that we bisect the angle $COD$ of the sector, instead of the right angle between two diameters, then bisect the half again, and so on. The proof is exactly similar to the preceding one.

## Proposition 5

*Given a circle and two unequal magnitudes, to describe a polygon about the circle and inscribe another in it, so that the circumscribed polygon may have to the inscribed a ratio less than the greater magnitude has to the less.*

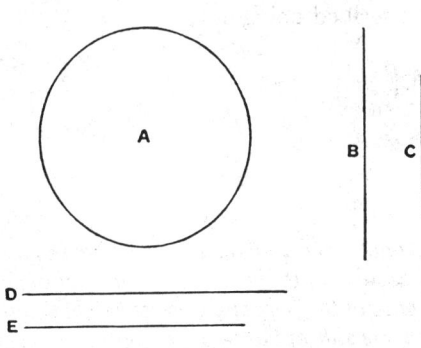

Let $A$ be the given circle and $B$, $C$ the given magnitudes, $B$ being the greater.

Take two unequal straight lines $D$, $E$, of which $D$ is the greater, such that $D:E<B:C$ [Prop. 2], and let $F$ be a mean proportional between $D$, $E$ so that $D$ is also greater than $F$.

Describe (in the manner of Prop. 3) one polygon about the circle, and inscribe another in it, so that the side of the former has to the side of the latter a ratio less than the ratio $D:F$.

Thus the duplicate ratio of the side of the former polygon to the side of the latter is less than the ratio $D^2:F^2$.

But the said duplicate ratio of the sides is equal to the ratio of the areas of the polygons, since they are similar;

therefore the area of the circumscribed polygon has to the area of the inscribed polygon a ratio less than the ratio $D^2:F^2$, or $D:E$, and *a fortiori* less than the ratio $B:C$.

## Proposition 6

"Similarly we can show that, *given two unequal magnitudes and a sector, it is possible to circumscribe a polygon about the sector and inscribe in it another similar one so that the circumscribed may have to the inscribed a ratio less than the greater magnitude has to the less.*

"And it is likewise clear that, *if a circle or a sector, as well as a certain area, be given, it is possible, by inscribing regular polygons in the circle or sector, and by continually inscribing such in the remaining segments, to leave segments of the circle or sector which are* [together] *less than the given area.* For this is proved in the *Elements* [Eucl. XII. 2].

"But it is yet to be proved that, *given a circle or sector and an area, it is possible to describe a polygon about the circle or sector, such that the area remaining between the circumference and the circumscribed figure is less than the given area.*"

The proof for the circle (which, as Archimedes says, can be equally applied to a sector) is as follows.

Let $A$ be the given circle and $B$ the given area.

Now, there being two unequal magnitudes $A+B$ and $A$, let a polygon $(C)$ be circumscribed about the circle and a polygon $(I)$ inscribed in it [as in Prop. 5],

so that

$$C:I<A+B:A. \qquad (1).$$

The circumscribed polygon $(C)$ shall be that required.

For the circle $(A)$ is greater than the inscribed polygon $(I)$.

Therefore, from (1), *a fortiori*,
$$C : A < A+B : A,$$
whence
$$C < A+B,$$
or
$$C-A < B.$$

## Proposition 7

*If in an isosceles cone* [i.e. *a right circular cone*] *a pyramid be inscribed having an equilateral base, the surface of the pyramid excluding the base is equal to a triangle having its base equal to the perimeter of the base of the pyramid and its height equal to the perpendicular drawn from the apex on one side of the base.*

Since the sides of the base of the pyramid are equal, it follows that the perpendiculars from the apex to all the sides of the base are equal; and the proof of the proposition is obvious.

## Proposition 8

*If a pyramid be circumscribed about an isosceles cone, the surface of the pyramid excluding its base is equal to a triangle having its base equal to the perimeter of the base of the pyramid and its height equal to the side* [i.e. *a generator*] *of the cone.*

The base of the pyramid is a polygon circumscribed about the circular base of the cone, and the line joining the apex of the cone or pyramid to the point of contact of any side of the polygon is perpendicular to that side. Also all these perpendiculars, being generators of the cone, are equal; whence the proposition follows immediately.

## Proposition 9

*If in the circular base of an isosceles cone a chord be placed, and from its extremities straight lines be drawn to the apex of the cone, the triangle so formed will be less than the portion of the surface of the cone intercepted between the lines drawn to the apex.*

Let $ABC$ be the circular base of the cone, and $O$ its apex.

Draw a chord $AB$ in the circle, and join $OA$, $OB$. Bisect the arc $ACB$ in $C$, and join $AC$, $BC$, $OC$.

Then
$$\triangle OAC + \triangle OBC > \triangle OAB.$$

Let the excess of the sum of the first two triangles over the third be equal to the area $D$.

Then $D$ is either less than the sum of the segments $AEC$, $CFB$, or not less.

I. Let $D$ be not less than the sum of the segments referred to.

We have now two surfaces

(1) that consisting of the portion $OAEC$ of the surface of the cone together with the segment $AEC$, and

(2) the triangle $OAC$;

and, since the two surfaces have the same extremities (the perimeter of the triangle $OAC$), the former surface is greater than the latter, which is *included* by it [*Assumptions*, 3 or 4].

Hence (surface $OAEC$)+(segment $AEC$)>$\triangle OAC$.
Similarly (surface $OCFB$)+(segment $CFB$)>$\triangle OBC$.

Therefore, since $D$ is not less than the sum of the segments, we have, by addition,
$$(\text{surface } OAECFB)+D>\triangle OAC+\triangle OBC$$
$$>\triangle OAB+D, \text{ by hypothesis.}$$

Taking away the common part $D$, we have the required result.

II. Let $D$ be less than the sum of the segments $AEC$, $CFB$.

If now we bisect the arcs $AC$, $CB$, then bisect the halves, and so on, we shall ultimately leave segments which are together less than $D$. [Prop. 6]

Let $AGE$, $EHC$, $CKF$, $FLB$ be those segments, and join $OE$, $OF$.

Then, as before,

(surface $OAGE$)+(segment $AGE$)>$\triangle OAE$
and (surface $OEHC$)+(segment $EHC$)>$\triangle OEC$.

Therefore (surface $OAGHC$)+(segments $AGE$, $EHC$)
$$>\triangle OAE+\triangle OEC$$
$$>\triangle OAC, \textit{ a fortiori}.$$

Similarly for the part of the surface of the cone bounded by $OC$, $OB$ and the arc $CFB$.

Hence, by addition,
(surface $OAGEHCKFLB$)+(segments $AGE$, $EHC$, $CKF$, $FLB$)
$$>\triangle OAC+\triangle OBC$$
$$>\triangle OAB+D, \text{ by hypothesis.}$$

But the sum of the segments is less than $D$, and the required result follows.

## PROPOSITION 10

*If in the plane of the circular base of an isosceles cone two tangents be drawn to the circle meeting in a point, and the points of contact and the point of concourse of the tangents be respectively joined to the apex of the cone, the sum of the two triangles formed by the joining lines and the two tangents are together greater than the included portion of the surface of the cone.*

Let $ABC$ be the circular base of the cone, $O$ its apex, $AD$, $BD$ the two tangents to the circle meeting in $D$. Join $OA$, $OB$, $OD$.

Let $ECF$ be drawn touching the circle at $C$, the middle point of the arc $ACB$, and therefore parallel to $AB$. Join $OE$, $OF$.

Then $ED+DF>EF$,

and, adding $AE+FB$ to each side,
$$AD+DB>AE+EF+FB.$$

Now $OA$, $OC$, $OB$, being generators of the cone, are equal, and they are respectively perpendicular to the tangents at $A$, $C$, $B$.

It follows that
$$\triangle OAD+\triangle ODB>\triangle OAE+\triangle OEF+\triangle OFB.$$

Let the area $G$ be equal to the excess of the first sum over the second.

$G$ is then either less, or not less, than the sum of the spaces $EAHC$, $FCKB$ remaining between the circle and the tangents, which sum we will call $L$.

I. Let $G$ be not less than $L$.

We have now two surfaces

(1) that of the pyramid with apex $O$ and base $AEFB$, excluding the face $OAB$,

(2) that consisting of the part $OACB$ of the surface of the cone together with the segment $ACB$.

These two surfaces have the same extremities, viz. the perimeter of the triangle $OAB$, and, since the former *includes* the latter, the former is the greater [*Assumptions*, 4].

That is, the surface of the pyramid exclusive of the face $OAB$ is greater than the sum of the surface $OACB$ and the segment $ACB$.

Taking away the segment from each sum, we have

$$\triangle OAE + \triangle OEF + \triangle OFB + L > \text{the surface } OAHCKB.$$

And $G$ is not less than $L$.

It follows that

$$\triangle OAE + \triangle OEF + \triangle OFB + G,$$

which is by hypothesis equal to $\triangle OAD + \triangle ODB$, is greater than the same surface.

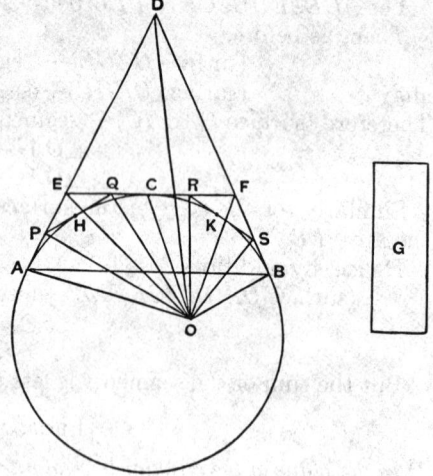

II. Let $G$ be less than $L$.

If we bisect the arcs $AC$, $CB$ and draw tangents at their middle points, then bisect the halves and draw tangents, and so on, we shall lastly arrive at a polygon such that the sum of the parts remaining between the sides of the polygon and the circumference of the segment is less than $G$.

Let the remainders be those between the segment and the polygon $APQRSB$, and let their sum be $M$. Join $OP$, $OQ$, etc.

Then, as before,

$$\triangle OAE + \triangle OEF + \triangle OFB > \triangle OAP + \triangle OPQ + \cdots + \triangle OSB.$$

Also, as before,

(surface of pyramid $OAPQRSB$ excluding the face $OAB$) > the part $OACB$ of the surface of the cone together with the segment $ACB$.

Taking away the segment from each sum,

$$\triangle OAP + \triangle OPQ + \cdots + M > \text{the part } OACB \text{ of the surface of the cone.}$$

Hence, *a fortiori*,

$$\triangle OAE + \triangle OEF + \triangle OFB + G,$$

which is by hypothesis equal to

$$\triangle OAD + \triangle ODB,$$

is greater than the part $OACB$ of the surface of the cone.

## Proposition 11

*If a plane parallel to the axis of a right cylinder cut the cylinder, the part of the surface of the cylinder cut off by the plane is greater than the area of the parallelogram in which the plane cuts it.*

# ON THE SPHERE AND CYLINDER I

## Proposition 12

*If at the extremities of two generators of any right cylinder tangents be drawn to the circular bases in the planes of those bases respectively, and if the pairs of tangents meet, the parallelograms formed by each generator and the two corresponding tangents respectively are together greater than the included portion of the surface of the cylinder between the two generators.*

[The proofs of these two propositions follow exactly the methods of Props. 9, 10 respectively, and it is therefore unnecessary to reproduce them.]

"From the properties thus proved it is clear (1) that, *if a pyramid be inscribed in an isosceles cone, the surface of the pyramid excluding the base is less than the surface of the cone* [*excluding the base*], and (2) that, *if a pyramid be circumscribed about an isosceles cone, the surface of the pyramid excluding the base is greater than the surface of the cone excluding the base.*

"It is also clear from what has been proved both (1) that, *if a prism be inscribed in a right cylinder, the surface of the prism made up of its parallelograms* [i.e. *excluding its bases*] *is less than the surface of the cylinder excluding its bases*, and (2) that, *if a prism be circumscribed about a right cylinder, the surface of the prism made up of its parallelograms is greater than the surface of the cylinder excluding its bases.*"

## Proposition 13

*The surface of any right cylinder excluding the bases is equal to a circle whose radius is a mean proportional between the side* [i.e. *a generator*] *of the cylinder and the diameter of its base.*

Let the base of the cylinder be the circle $A$, and make $CD$ equal to the diameter of this circle, and $EF$ equal to the height of the cylinder.

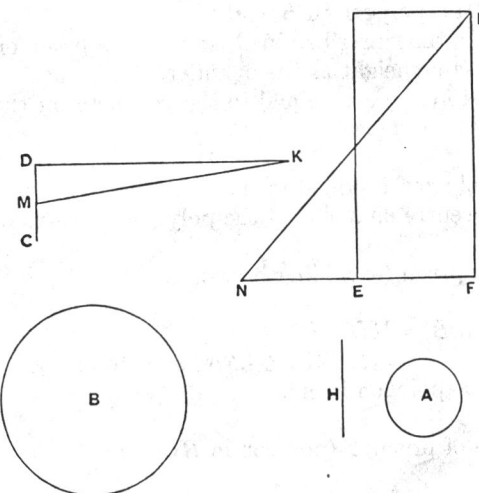

Let $H$ be a mean proportional between $CD$, $EF$, and $B$ a circle with radius equal to $H$.

Then the circle $B$ shall be equal to the surface of the cylinder (excluding the bases), which we will call $S$.

For, if not, $B$ must be either greater or less than $S$.

I. Suppose $B < S$.

Then it is possible to circumscribe a regular polygon about $B$, and to inscribe another in it, such that the ratio of the former to the latter is less than the ratio $S : B$.

Suppose this done, and circumscribe about $A$ a polygon similar to that described about $B$; then erect on the polygon about $A$ a prism of the same height as the cylinder. The prism will therefore be circumscribed to the cylinder.

Let $KD$, perpendicular to $CD$, and $FL$, perpendicular to $EF$, be each equal to the perimeter of the polygon about $A$. Bisect $CD$ in $M$, and join $MK$.

Then $\triangle KDM$ = the polygon about $A$.
Also $\square EL$ = surface of prism (excluding bases).
Produce $FE$ to $N$ so that $FE = EN$, and join $NL$.

Now the polygons about $A$, $B$, being similar, are in the duplicate ratio of the radii of $A$, $B$.

Thus
$$\triangle KDM : (\text{polygon about } B) = MD^2 : H^2$$
$$= MD^2 : CD \cdot EF$$
$$= MD : NF$$
$$= \triangle KDM : \triangle LFN$$

(since $DK = FL$).

Therefore (polygon about $B$) = $\triangle LFN$
$$= \square EL$$
$$= (\text{surface of prism about } A),$$

from above.

But (polygon about $B$) : (polygon in $B$) $< S : B$.
Therefore
(surface of prism about $A$) : (polygon in $B$) $< S : B$,
and, alternately,
(surface of prism about $A$) : $S <$ (polygon in $B$) : $B$;
which is impossible, since the surface of the prism is greater than $S$, while the polygon inscribed in $B$ is less than $B$.

Therefore $B \not< S$.

II. Suppose $B > S$.

Let a regular polygon be circumscribed about $B$ and another inscribed in it so that
(polygon about $B$) : (polygon in $B$) $< B : S$.

Inscribe in $A$ a polygon similar to that inscribed in $B$, and erect a prism on the polygon inscribed in $A$ of the same height as the cylinder.

Again, let $DK$, $FL$, drawn as before, be each equal to the perimeter of the polygon inscribed in $A$.

Then, in this case,
$$\triangle KDM > (\text{polygon inscribed in } A)$$
(since the perpendicular from the centre on a side of the polygon is less than the radius of $A$).

Also $\triangle LFN = \square EL =$ surface of prism (excluding bases).
Now
(polygon in $A$) : (polygon in $B$) = $MD^2 : H^2$,
$$= \triangle KDM : \triangle LFN, \text{ as before.}$$
And $\triangle KDM > $ (polygon in $A$).
Therefore
$\triangle LFN$, or (surface of prism) $>$ (polygon in $B$).
But this is impossible, because
(polygon about $B$) : (polygon in $B$) $< B : S$,
$<$ (polygon about $B$) : $S$, a fortiori,
so that (polygon in $B$) $> S$,
$>$ (surface of prism), a fortiori.

Hence $B$ is neither greater nor less than $S$, and therefore
$$B = S.$$

# ON THE SPHERE AND CYLINDER I

## PROPOSITION 14

*The surface of any isosceles cone excluding the base is equal to a circle whose radius is a mean proportional between the side of the cone [a generator] and the radius of the circle which is the base of the cone.*

Let the circle $A$ be the base of the cone; draw $C$ equal to the radius of the circle, and $D$ equal to the side of the cone, and let $E$ be a mean proportional between $C$, $D$.

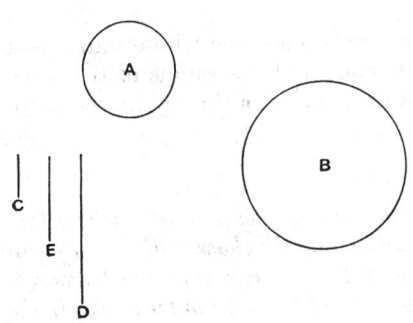

Draw a circle $B$ with radius equal to $E$.

Then shall $B$ be equal to the surface of the cone (excluding the base), which we will call $S$.

If not, $B$ must be either greater or less than $S$.

I. Suppose $B < S$.

Let a regular polygon be described about $B$ and a similar one inscribed in it such that the former has to the latter a ratio less than the ratio $S : B$.

Describe about $A$ another similar polygon, and on it set up a pyramid with apex the same as that of the cone.

Then (polygon about $A$) : (polygon about $B$)
$= C^2 : E^2$
$= C : D$
$=$ (polygon about $A$) : (surface of pyramid excluding base).

Therefore
(surface of pyramid = (polygon about $B$).

Now (polygon about $B$) : (polygon in $B$) $< S : B$.

Therefore
(surface of pyramid) : (polygon in $B$) $< S : B$,

which is impossible, (because the surface of the pyramid is greater than $S$, while the polygon in $B$ is less than $B$).

Hence $B \not< S$.

II. Suppose $B > S$.

Take regular polygons circumscribed and inscribed to $B$ such that the ratio of the former to the latter is less than the ratio $B : S$.

Inscribe in $A$ a similar polygon to that inscribed in $B$, and erect a pyramid on the polygon inscribed in $A$ with apex the same as that of the cone.

In this case
(polygon in $A$) : (polygon in $B$) $= C^2 : E^2$
$= C : D$
$>$ (polygon in $A$) : (surface of pyramid excluding base).

This is clear because the ratio of $C$ to $D$ is greater than the ratio of the perpendicular from the centre of $A$ on a side of the polygon to the perpendicular from the apex of the cone on the same side.

Therefore
(surface of pyramid) > (polygon in $B$).

But (polygon about $B$) : (polygon in $B$) $< B : S$.

Therefore, *a fortiori*,

(polygon about $B$) : (surface of pyramid) $< B : S$;

which is impossible.

Since therefore $B$ is neither greater nor less than $S$,
$$B = S.$$

## Proposition 15

*The surface of any isosceles cone has the same ratio to its base as the side of the cone has to the radius of the base.*

By Prop. 14, the surface of the cone is equal to a circle whose radius is a mean proportional between the side of the cone and the radius of the base.

Hence, since circles are to one another as the squares of their radii, the proposition follows.

## Proposition 16

*If an isosceles cone be cut by a plane parallel to the base, the portion of the surface of the cone between the parallel planes is equal to a circle whose radius is a mean proportional between (1) the portion of the side of the cone intercepted by the parallel planes and (2) the line which is equal to the sum of the radii of the circles in the parallel planes.*

Let $OAB$ be a triangle through the axis of a cone, $DE$ its intersection with the plane cutting off the frustum, and $OFC$ the axis of the cone.

Then the surface of the cone $OAB$ is equal to a circle whose radius is equal to $\sqrt{OA \cdot AC}$. [Prop. 14.]

Similarly the surface of the cone $ODE$ is equal to a circle whose radius is equal to $\sqrt{OD \cdot DF}$.

And the surface of the frustum is equal to the difference between the two circles.

Now
$$OA \cdot AC - OD \cdot DF = DA \cdot AC + OD \cdot AC - OD \cdot DF.$$
But
$$OD \cdot AC = OA \cdot DF,$$
since
$$OA : AC = OD : DF.$$
Hence
$$OA \cdot AC - OD \cdot DF = DA \cdot AC + DA \cdot DF$$
$$= DA \cdot (AC + DF).$$

And, since circles are to one another as the squares of their radii, it follows that the difference between the circles whose radii are $\sqrt{OA \cdot AC}$, $\sqrt{OD \cdot DF}$ respectively is equal to a circle whose radius is $\sqrt{DA \cdot (AC + DF)}$.

Therefore the surface of the frustum is equal to this circle.

## LEMMAS

"1. *Cones having equal height have the same ratio as their bases; and those having equal bases have the same ratio as their heights*[1].

2. *If a cylinder be cut by a plane parallel to the base, then, as the cylinder is to the cylinder, so is the axis to the axis*[2].

---

[1] Euclid XII. 11. "Cones and cylinders of equal height are to one another as their bases." Euclid XII. 14. "Cones and cylinders on equal bases are to one another as their heights."

[2] Euclid XII. 13. "If a cylinder be cut by a plane parallel to the opposite planes [the bases], then, as the cylinder is to the cylinder, so will the axis be to the axis."

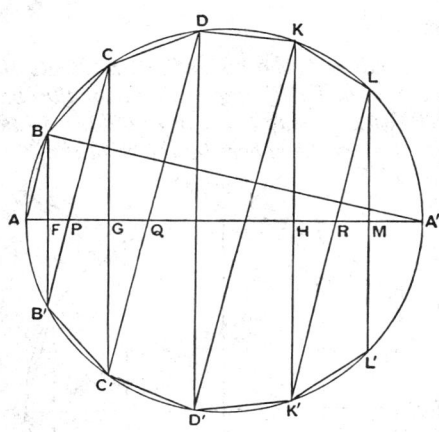

Joining $CB'$, $DC'$, $\cdots LK'$, as in the last proposition, and supposing that they meet $AM$ in $P$, $Q$, $\cdots R$, while $BB'$, $CC'$, $\cdots$, $KK'$ meet $AM$ in $F$, $G$, $\cdots H$, we have, by similar triangles,

$$BF : FA = B'F : FP$$
$$= CG : PG$$
$$= C'G : GQ$$
$$\cdots\cdots\cdots\cdots$$
$$= LM : RM;$$

and, summing the antecedents and consequents, we obtain

$$(BB' + CC' + \cdots + LM) : AM$$
$$= BF : FA$$
$$= A'B : BA.$$

PROPOSITION 23

Take a great circle $ABC \cdots$ of a sphere, and inscribe in it a regular polygon whose sides are a multiple of four in number. Let $AA'$, $MM'$ be diameters at right angles and joining opposite angular points of the polygon.

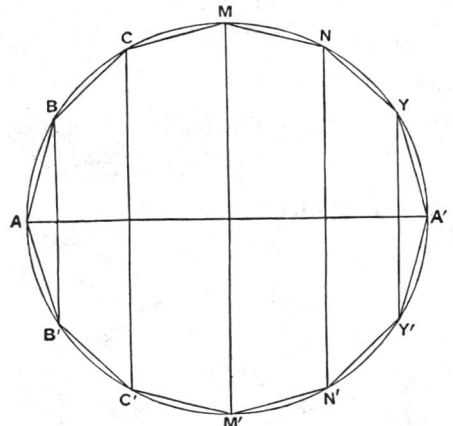

Then, if the polygon and great circle revolve together about the diameter $AA'$, the angular points of the polygon, except $A$, $A'$, will describe circles on the surface of the sphere at right angles to the diameter $AA'$. Also the sides of the polygon will describe portions of conical surfaces, e.g. $BC$ will describe a surface forming part of a cone whose base is a circle about $CC'$ as diameter and whose apex is the point in which $CB$, $C'B'$ produced meet each other and the diameter $AA'$.

Comparing the hemisphere $MAM'$ and that half of the figure described by the revolution of the polygon which is included in the hemisphere, we see that the surface of the hemisphere and the surface of the inscribed figure have the same boundaries in one plane (viz. the circle on $MM'$ as diameter), the former surface entirely includes the latter, and they are both concave in the same direction.

Therefore [*Assumptions*, 4] the surface of the hemisphere is greater than that of the inscribed figure; and the same is true of the other halves of the figures.

Hence *the surface of the sphere is greater than the surface described by the revolution of the polygon inscribed in the great circle about the diameter of the great circle.*

## Proposition 24

*If a regular polygon $AB \cdots A' \cdots B'A$, the number of whose sides is a multiple of four, be inscribed in a great circle of a sphere, and if $BB'$ subtending two sides be joined, and all the other lines parallel to $BB'$ and joining pairs of angular points be drawn, then the surface of the figure inscribed in the sphere by the revolution of the polygon about the diameter $AA'$ is equal to a circle the square of whose radius is equal to the rectangle*

$$BA(BB'+CC'+\cdots).$$

The surface of the figure is made up of the surfaces of parts of different cones.

Now the surface of the cone $ABB'$ is equal to a circle whose radius is $\sqrt{BA \cdot \tfrac{1}{2}BB'}$. [Prop. 14]

The surface of the frustum $BB'C'C$ is equal to a circle of radius

$\sqrt{BC \cdot \tfrac{1}{2}(BB'+CC')}$,  [Prop. 16]

and so on.

It follows, since $BA = BC = \cdots$, that the whole surface is equal to a circle whose radius is equal to
$$\sqrt{BA(BB'+CC'+\cdots+MM'+\cdots+YY')}.$$

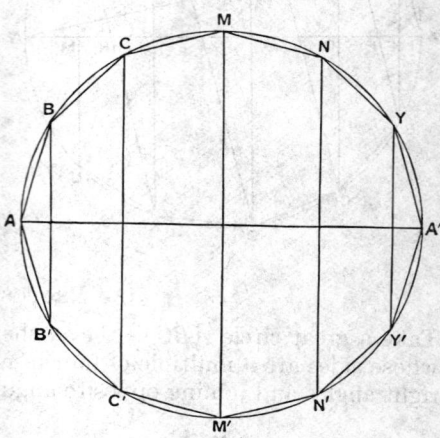

## Proposition 25

*The surface of the figure inscribed in a sphere as in the last propositions, consisting of portions of conical surfaces, is less than four times the greatest circle in the sphere.*

Let $AB \cdots A' \cdots B'A$ be a regular polygon inscribed in a great circle, the number of its sides being a multiple of four.

As before, let $BB'$ be drawn subtending two sides, and $CC', \cdots YY'$ parallel to $BB'$.

Let $R$ be a circle such that the square of its radius is equal to

$AB(BB'+CC'+\cdots+YY')$,

so that the surface of the figure inscribed in the sphere is equal to $R$. [Prop. 24]

Now
$(BB'+CC'+\cdots+YY') : AA'$
$\qquad = A'B : AB$,  [Prop. 21]
whence $AB(BB'+CC'+\cdots+YY')$
$\qquad = AA' \cdot A'B$.

Hence $(\text{radius of } R)^2 = AA' \cdot A'B$
$\qquad\qquad < AA'^2$.

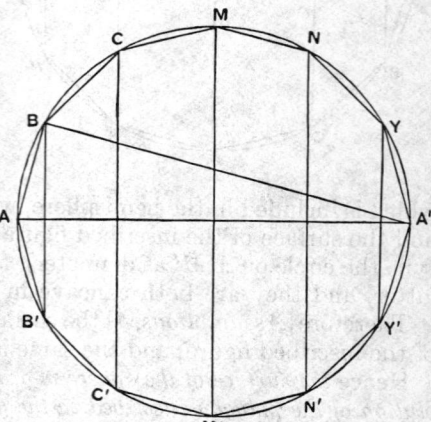

Therefore the surface of the inscribed figure, or the circle $R$, is less than four times the circle $AMA'M'$.

## Proposition 26

*The figure inscribed as above in a sphere is equal [in volume] to a cone whose base is a circle equal to the surface of the figure inscribed in the sphere and whose height is equal to the perpendicular drawn from the centre of the sphere to one side of the polygon.*

Suppose, as before, that $AB \cdots A' \cdots B'A$ is the regular polygon inscribed in a great circle, and let $BB'$, $CC'$, $\cdots$ be joined.

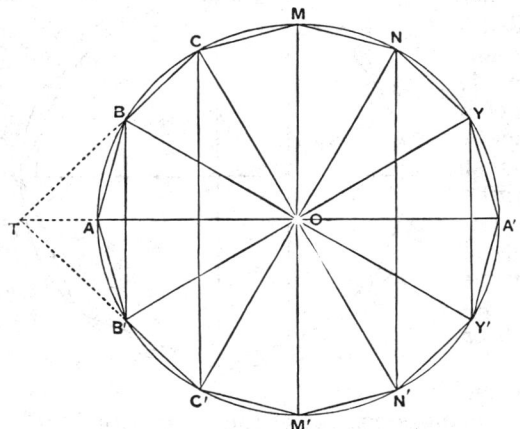

With apex $O$ construct cones whose bases are the circles on $BB'$, $CC'$, $\cdots$ as diameters in planes perpendicular to $AA'$.

Then $OBAB'$ is a solid rhombus, and its volume is equal to a cone whose base is equal to the surface of the cone $ABB'$ and whose height is equal to the perpendicular from $O$ on $AB$ [Prop. 18]. Let the length of the perpendicular be $p$.

Again, if $CB$, $C'B'$ produced meet in $T$, the portion of the solid figure which is described by the revolution of the triangle $BOC$ about $AA'$ is equal to the difference between the rhombi $OCTC'$ and $OBTB'$, i.e. to a cone whose base is equal to the surface of the frustum $BB'C'C$ and whose height is $p$ [Prop. 20].

Proceeding in this manner, and adding, we prove that, since cones of equal height are to one another as their bases, the volume of the solid of revolution is equal to a cone with height $p$ and base equal to the sum of the surfaces of the cone $BAB'$, the frustum $BB'C'C$, etc., i.e. a cone with height $p$ and base equal to the surface of the solid.

## Proposition 27

*The figure inscribed in the sphere as before is less than four times the cone whose base is equal to a great circle of the sphere and whose height is equal to the radius of the sphere.*

By Prop. 26 the volume of the solid figure is equal to a cone whose base is equal to the surface of the solid and whose height is $p$, the perpendicular from $O$ on any side of the polygon. Let $R$ be such a cone.

Take also a cone $S$ with base equal to the great circle, and height equal to the radius, of the sphere.

Now, since the surface of the inscribed solid is less than four times the great circle [Prop. 25], the base of the cone $R$ is less than four times the base of the cone $S$.

Also the height $(p)$ of $R$ is less than the height of $S$.

Therefore the volume of $R$ is less than four times that of $S$; and the proposition is proved.

## Proposition 28

Let a regular polygon, whose sides are a multiple of four in number, be circumscribed about a great circle of a given sphere, as $AB \cdots A' \cdots B'A$; and about the polygon describe another circle, which will therefore have the same centre as the great circle of the sphere. Let $AA'$ bisect the polygon and cut the sphere in $a$, $a'$.

If the great circle and the circumscribed polygon revolve together about $AA'$, the great circle will describe the surface of a sphere, the angular points of the polygon except $A$, $A'$ will move round the surface of a larger sphere, the points of contact of the sides of the polygon with the great circle of the inner sphere will describe circles on that sphere in planes perpendicular to $AA'$, and the sides of the polygon themselves will describe portions of conical surfaces. *The circumscribed figure will thus be greater than the sphere itself.*

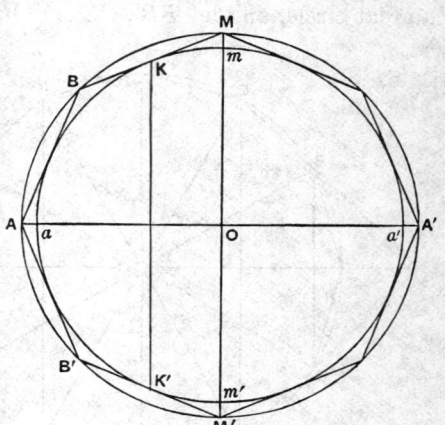

Let any side, as $BM$, touch the inner circle in $K$, and let $K'$ be the point of contact of the circle with $B'M'$.

Then the circle described by the revolution of $KK'$ about $AA'$ is the boundary in one plane of two surfaces

(1) the surface formed by the revolution of the circular segment $KaK'$, and

(2) the surface formed by the revolution of the part $KB \cdots A \cdots B'K'$ of the polygon.

Now the second surface entirely includes the first, and they are both concave in the same direction;

therefore [*Assumptions*, 4] the second surface is greater than the first.

The same is true of the portion of the surface on the opposite side of the circle on $KK'$ as diameter.

Hence, adding, we see that *the surface of the figure circumscribed to the given sphere is greater than that of the sphere itself.*

## Proposition 29

*In a figure circumscribed to a sphere in the manner shown in the previous proposition the surface is equal to a circle the square on whose radius is equal to*
$$AB(BB'+CC'+ \cdots).$$

For the figure circumscribed to the sphere is inscribed in a larger sphere, and the proof of Prop. 24 applies.

## Proposition 30

*The surface of a figure circumscribed as before about a sphere is greater than four times the great circle of the sphere.*

Let $AB \cdots A' \cdots B'A$ be the regular polygon of $4n$ sides which by its revolution about $AA'$ describes the figure circumscribing the sphere of which $ama'm'$ is a great circle. Suppose $aa'$, $AA'$ to be in one straight line.

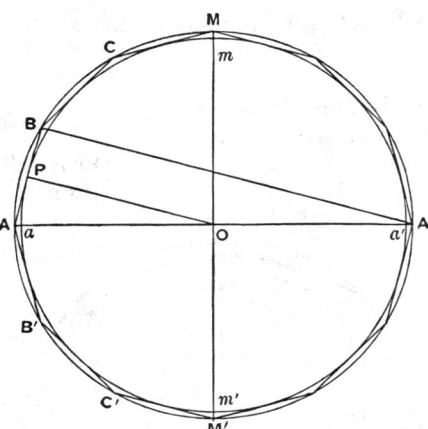

Let $R$ be a circle equal to the surface of the circumscribed solid.

Now
$$(BB'+CC'+ \cdots):AA'=A'B:BA,$$
[as in Prop. 21]
so that
$$AB(BB'+CC'+ \cdots)=AA' \cdot A'B.$$
Hence (radius of $R$) $=\sqrt{AA' \cdot A'B}$
[Prop. 29]
$$>A'B.$$

But $A'B=2OP$, where $P$ is the point in which $AB$ touches the circle $ama'm'$.

Therefore (radius of $R$) > (diameter of circle $ama'm'$);

whence $R$, and therefore the surface of the circumscribed solid, is greater than four times the great circle of the given sphere.

## Proposition 31

*The solid of revolution circumscribed as before about a sphere is equal to a cone whose base is equal to the surface of the solid and whose height is equal to the radius of the sphere.*

The solid is, as before, a solid inscribed in a larger sphere; and, since the perpendicular on any side of the revolving polygon is equal to the radius of the inner sphere, the proposition is identical with Prop. 26.

COR. *The solid circumscribed about the smaller sphere is greater than four times the cone whose base is a great circle of the sphere and whose height is equal to the radius of the sphere.*

For, since the surface of the solid is greater than four times the great circle of the inner sphere [Prop. 30], the cone whose base is equal to the surface of the solid and whose height is the radius of the sphere is greater than four times the cone of the same height which has the great circle for base. [*Lemma* 1.]

Hence, by the proposition, the volume of the solid is greater than four times the latter cone.

## Proposition 32

*If a regular polygon with $4n$ sides be inscribed in a great circle of a sphere, as $ab \cdots a' \cdots b'a$, and a similar polygon $AB \cdots A' \cdots B'A$ be described about the great circle, and if the polygons revolve with the great circle about the diameters $aa'$, $AA'$ respectively, so that they describe the surfaces of solid figures inscribed in and circumscribed to the sphere respectively, then*

*(1) the surfaces of the circumscribed and inscribed figures are to one another in the duplicate ratio of their sides, and*

*(2) the figures themselves [i.e. their volumes] are in the triplicate ratio of their sides.*

(1) Let $AA'$, $aa'$ be in the same straight line, and let $MmOm'M'$ be a diameter at right angles to them.

Join $BB'$, $CC'$, $\cdots$ and $bb'$, $cc'$, $\cdots$ which will all be parallel to one another and $MM'$.

Suppose $R$, $S$ to be circles such that
$$R = \text{(surface of circumscribed solid)},$$
$$S = \text{(surface of inscribed solid)}.$$
Then (radius of $R$)$^2 = AB(BB' + CC' + \cdots)$ [Prop. 29]
(radius of $S$)$^2 = ab(bb' + cc' + \cdots)$. [Prop. 24]

And, since the polygons are similar, the rectangles in these two equations are similar, and are therefore in the ratio of
$$AB^2 : ab^2.$$

Hence
(surface of circumscribed solid) : (surface of inscribed solid) $= AB^2 : ab^2$.

(2) Take a cone $V$ whose base is the circle $R$ and whose height is equal to $Oa$, and a cone $W$ whose base is the circle $S$ and whose height is equal to the perpendicular from $O$ on $ab$, which we will call $p$.

Then $V$, $W$ are respectively equal to the volumes of the circumscribed and inscribed figures. [Props. 31, 26]

Now, since the polygons are similar,
$$AB : ab = Oa : p$$
$$= \text{(height of cone } V\text{)} : \text{(height of cone } W\text{)};$$
and, as shown above, the bases of the cones (the circles $R$, $S$) are in the ratio of $AB^2$ to $ab^2$.

Therefore $V : W = AB^3 : ab^3$.

## Proposition 33

*The surface of any sphere is equal to four times the greatest circle in it.*

Let $C$ be a circle equal to four times the great circle.

Then, if $C$ is not equal to the surface of the sphere, it must either be less or greater.

I. Suppose $C$ less than the surface of the sphere.

It is then possible to find two lines $\beta$, $\gamma$, of which $\beta$ is the greater, such that
$$\beta : \gamma < \text{(surface of sphere)} : C.$$ [Prop. 2]
Take such lines, and let $\delta$ be a mean proportional between them.

Suppose similar regular polygons with $4n$ sides circumscribed about and inscribed in a great circle such that the ratio of their sides is less than the ratio $\beta : \delta$. [Prop. 3]

Let the polygons with the circle revolve together about a diameter common to all, describing solids of revolution as before.

Then    (surface of outer solid) : (surface of inner solid)
         = (side of outer)² : (side of inner)²        [Prop. 32]
         < β² : δ², or β : γ
         < (surface of sphere) : C, a fortiori.

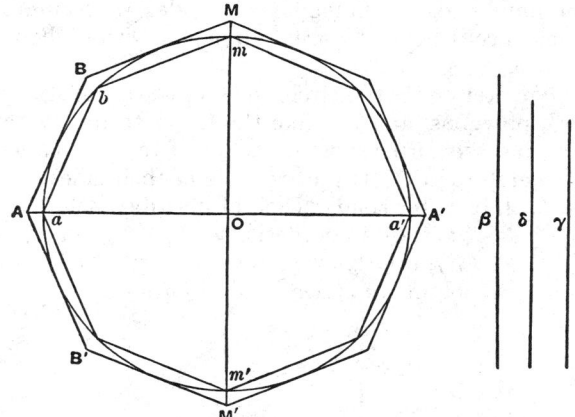

But this is impossible, since the surface of the circumscribed solid is greater than that of the sphere [Prop. 28], while the surface of the inscribed solid is less than C [Prop. 25].

Therefore C is not less than the surface of the sphere.

II. Suppose C greater than the surface of the sphere.

Take lines β, γ, of which β is the greater, such that
$$\beta : \gamma < C : \text{(surface of sphere)}.$$

Circumscribe and inscribe to the great circle similar regular polygons, as before, such that their sides are in a ratio less than that of β to δ, and suppose solids of revolution generated in the usual manner.

Then, in this case,
 (surface of circumscribed solid) : (surface of inscribed solid)
         < C : (surface of sphere).

But this is impossible, because the surface of the circumscribed solid is greater than C [Prop. 30], while the surface of the inscribed solid is less than that of the sphere [Prop. 23].

Thus C is not greater than the surface of the sphere.

Therefore, since it is neither greater nor less, C is equal to the surface of the sphere.

## PROPOSITION 34

*Any sphere is equal to four times the cone which has its base equal to the greatest circle in the sphere and its height equal to the radius of the sphere.*

Let the sphere be that of which $ama'm'$ is a great circle.

If now the sphere is not equal to four times the cone described, it is either greater or less.

I. If possible, let the sphere be greater than four times the cone.

Suppose V to be a cone whose base is equal to four times the great circle and whose height is equal to the radius of the sphere.

Then, by hypothesis, the sphere is greater than $V$; and two lines $\beta, \gamma$ can be found (of which $\beta$ is the greater) such that

$$\beta : \gamma < (\text{volume of sphere}) : V.$$

Between $\beta$ and $\gamma$ place two arithmetic means $\delta, \epsilon$.

As before, let similar regular polygons with sides $4n$ in number be circumscribed about and inscribed in the great circle, such that their sides are in a ratio less than $\beta : \delta$.

Imagine the diameter $aa'$ of the circle to be in the same straight line with a diameter of both polygons, and imagine the latter to revolve with the circle about $aa'$, describing the surfaces of two solids of revolution. The volumes of these solids are therefore in the triplicate ratio of their sides. [Prop. 32]

Thus (vol. of outer solid) : (vol. of inscribed solid)
$< \beta^3 : \delta^3$, by hypothesis,
$< \beta : \gamma$, *a fortiori* (since $\beta : \gamma > \beta^3 : \delta^3$),
$< (\text{volume of sphere}) : V$, *a fortiori*.

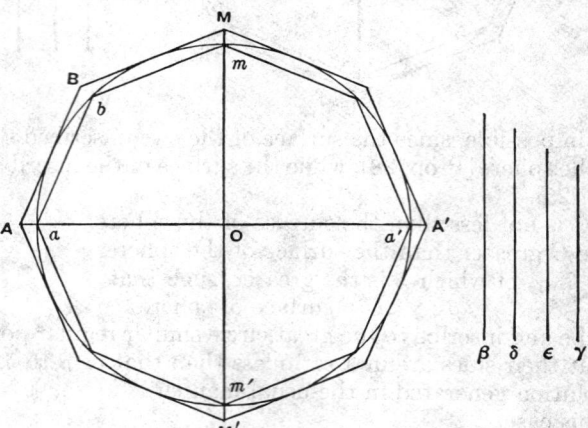

But this is impossible, since the volume of the circumscribed solid is greater than that of the sphere [Prop. 28], while the volume of the inscribed solid is less than $V$ [Prop. 27].

Hence the sphere is not greater than $V$, or four times the cone described in the enunciation.

II. If possible, let the sphere be less than $V$.

In this case we take $\beta, \gamma$ ($\beta$ being the greater) such that

$$\beta : \gamma < V : (\text{volume of sphere}).$$

The rest of the construction and proof proceeding as before, we have finally
(volume of outer solid) : (volume of inscribed solid)
$< V : (\text{volume of sphere})$.

But this is impossible, because the volume of the outer solid is greater than $V$ [Prop. 31, Cor.], and the volume of the inscribed solid is less than the volume of the sphere.

Hence the sphere is not less than $V$.

Since then the sphere is neither less nor greater than $V$, it is equal to $V$, or to four times the cone described in the enunciation.

Cor. From what has been proved it follows that *every cylinder whose base is the greatest circle in a sphere and whose height is equal to the diameter of the sphere is $\frac{3}{2}$ of the sphere, and its surface together with its bases is $\frac{3}{2}$ of the surface of the sphere.*

For the cylinder is three times the cone with the same base and height [Eucl. xii. 10], i.e. six times the cone with the same base and with height equal to the radius of the sphere.

But the sphere is four times the latter cone [Prop. 34]. Therefore the cylinder is $\frac{3}{2}$ of the sphere.

Again, the surface of a cylinder (excluding the bases) is equal to a circle whose radius is a mean proportional between the height of the cylinder and the diameter of its base [Prop. 13].

In this case the height is equal to the diameter of the base and therefore the circle is that whose radius is the diameter of the sphere, or a circle equal to four times the great circle of the sphere.

Therefore the surface of the cylinder with the bases is equal to six times the great circle.

And the surface of the sphere is four times the great circle [Prop. 33]; whence
(surface of cylinder with bases) = $\frac{3}{2}$ · (surface of sphere).

## Proposition 35

*If in a segment of a circle $LAL'$ (where $A$ is the middle point of the arc) a polygon $LK\cdots A\cdots K'L'$ be inscribed of which $LL'$ is one side, while the other sides are $2n$ in number and all equal, and if the polygon revolve with the segment about the diameter $AM$, generating a solid figure inscribed in a segment of a sphere, then the surface of the inscribed solid is equal to a circle the square on whose radius is equal to the rectangle*

$$AB\left(BB'+CC'+\cdots+KK'+\frac{LL'}{2}\right).$$

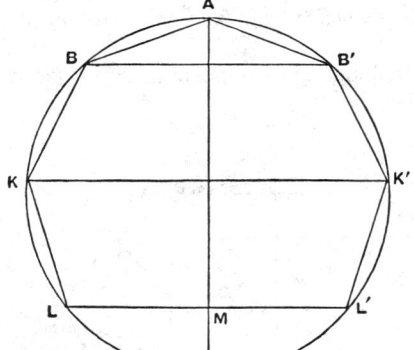

The surface of the inscribed figure is made up of portions of surfaces of cones.

If we take these successively, the surface of the cone $BAB'$ is equal to a circle whose radius is
$$\sqrt{AB\cdot\tfrac{1}{2}BB'}.\qquad\text{[Prop. 14]}$$
The surface of the frustum of a cone $BCC'B'$ is equal to a circle whose radius is
$$\sqrt{AB\cdot\frac{BB'+CC'}{2}};\quad\text{[Prop. 16]}$$
and so on.

Proceeding in this way and adding, we find, since circles are to one another as the squares of their radii, that the surface of the inscribed figure is equal to a circle whose radius is

$$\sqrt{AB\left(BB'+CC'+\ldots+KK'+\frac{LL'}{2}\right)}.$$

## Proposition 36

*The surface of the figure inscribed as before in the segment of a sphere is less than that of the segment of the sphere.*

This is clear, because the circular base of the segment is a common boundary of each of two surfaces, of which one, the segment, includes the other, the solid, while both are concave in the same direction [*Assumptions*, 4].

## Proposition 37

*The surface of the solid figure inscribed in the segment of the sphere by the revolution of* $LK \cdots A \cdots K'L'$ *about* $AM$ *is less than a circle with radius equal to* $AL$.

Let the diameter $AM$ meet the circle of which $LAL'$ is a segment again in $A'$. Join $A'B$.

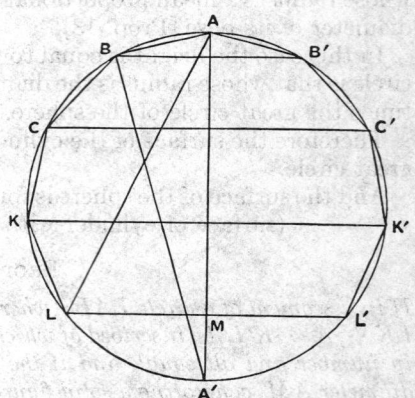

As in Prop. 35, the surface of the inscribed solid is equal to a circle the square on whose radius is
$$AB(BB'+CC'+ \cdots +KK'+LM).$$
But this rectangle
$$= A'B \cdot AM \quad [\text{Prop. 22}]$$
$$< A'A \cdot AM$$
$$< AL^2.$$
Hence the surface of the inscribed solid is less than the circle whose radius is $AL$.

## Proposition 38

*The solid figure described as before in a segment of a sphere less than a hemisphere, together with the cone whose base is the base of the segment and whose apex is the centre of the sphere, is equal to a cone whose base is equal to the surface of the inscribed solid and whose height is equal to the perpendicular from the centre of the sphere on any side of the polygon.*

Let $O$ be the centre of the sphere, and $p$ the length of the perpendicular from $O$ on $AB$.

Suppose cones described with $O$ as apex, and with the circles on $BB'$, $CC'$, $\cdots$ as diameters as bases.

Then the rhombus $OBAB'$ is equal to a cone whose base is equal to the surface of the cone $BAB'$, and whose height is $p$. [Prop. 18]

Again, if $CB$, $C'B'$ meet in $T$, the solid described by the triangle $BOC$ as the polygon revolves about $AO$ is the difference between the rhombi $OCTC'$ and $OBTB'$, and is therefore equal to a cone whose base is equal to the surface of

## ON THE SPHERE AND CYLINDER I

the frustum $BCC'B'$ and whose height is $p$. [Prop. 20]

Similarly for the part of the solid described by the triangle $COD$ as the polygon revolves; and so on.

Hence, by addition, the solid figure inscribed in the segment together with the cone $OLL'$ is equal to a cone whose base is the surface of the inscribed solid and whose height is $p$.

Cor. *The cone whose base is a circle with radius equal to $AL$ and whose height is equal to the radius of the sphere is greater than the sum of the inscribed solid and the cone $OLL'$.*

For, by the proposition, the inscribed solid together with the cone $OLL'$ is equal to a cone with base equal to the surface of the solid and with height $p$.

This latter cone is less than a cone with height equal to $OA$ and with base equal to the circle whose radius is $AL$, because the height $p$ is less than $OA$, while the surface of the solid is less than a circle with radius $AL$. [Prop. 37]

### Proposition 39

Let $lal'$ be a segment of a great circle of a sphere, being less than a semicircle. Let $O$ be the centre of the sphere, and join $Ol$, $Ol'$. Suppose a polygon circumscribed about the sector $Olal'$ such that its sides, excluding the two radii, are $2n$ in number and all equal, as $LK, \cdots BA, AB', \cdots K'L'$; and let $OA$ be that radius of the great circle which bisects the segment $lal'$.

The circle circumscribing the polygon will then have the same centre $O$ as the given great circle.

Now suppose the polygon and the two circles to revolve together about $OA$. The two circles will describe spheres, the angular points except $A$ will describe circles on the outer sphere, with diameters $BB'$ etc., the points of contact of the sides with the inner segment will describe circles on the inner sphere, the sides themselves will describe the surfaces of cones or frusta of cones, and the whole figure circumscribed to the segment of the inner sphere by the revolution of the equal sides of the polygon will have for its base the circle on $LL'$ as diameter.

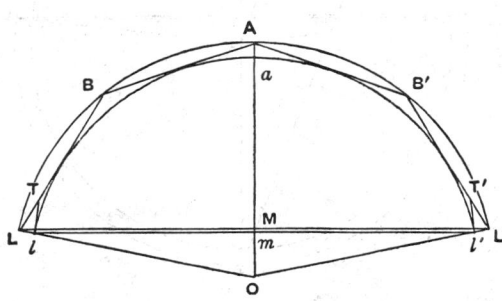

*The surface of the solid figure so circumscribed about the sector of the sphere [excluding its base] will be greater than that of the segment of the sphere whose base is the circle on $ll'$ as diameter.*

For draw the tangents $lT$, $l'T'$ to the inner segment at $l$, $l'$. These with the sides of the polygon will describe by their revolution a solid whose surface is greater than that of the segment [*Assumptions,* 4].

But the surface described by the revolution of $lT$ is less than that described by the revolution of $LT$, since the angle $TlL$ is a right angle, and therefore $LT > lT$.

Hence, *a fortiori*, the surface described by $LK \cdots A \cdots K'L'$ is greater than that of the segment.

Cor. *The surface of the figure so described about the sector of the sphere is equal to a circle the square on whose radius is equal to the rectangle*
$$AB\,(BB'+CC'+\cdots+KK'+\tfrac{1}{2}LL').$$

For the circumscribed figure is inscribed in the outer sphere, and the proof of Prop. 35 therefore applies.

## Proposition 40

*The surface of the figure circumscribed to the sector as before is greater than a circle whose radius is equal to al.*

Let the diameter $AaO$ meet the great circle and the circle circumscribing the revolving polygon again in $a'$, $A'$. Join $A'B$, and let $ON$ be drawn to $N$, the point of contact of $AB$ with the inner circle.

Now, by Prop. 39, Cor., the surface of the solid figure circumscribed to the sector $OlAl'$ is equal to a circle the square on whose radius is equal to the rectangle
$$AB\left(BB'+CC'+\cdots+KK'+\frac{LL'}{2}\right).$$

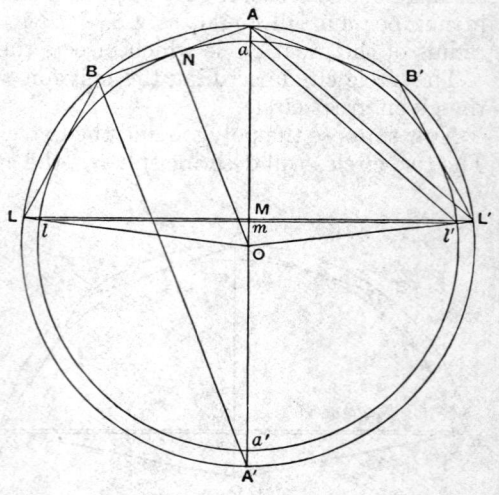

But this rectangle is equal to $A'B\cdot AM$ [as in Prop. 22].

Next, since $AL'$, $al'$ are parallel, the triangles $AML'$, $aml'$ are similar. And $AL' > al'$; therefore $AM > am$.

Also $\quad A'B = 2ON = aa'$.

Therefore $\quad A'B\cdot AM > am\cdot aa'$
$\qquad\qquad\qquad\qquad > al'^2.$

Hence the surface of the solid figure circumscribed to the sector is greater than a circle whose radius is equal to $al'$, or $al$.

Cor. 1. *The volume of the figure circumscribed about the sector together with the cone whose apex is $O$ and base the circle on $LL'$ as diameter, is equal to the volume of a cone whose base is equal to the surface of the circumscribed figure and whose height is $ON$.*

For the figure is inscribed in the outer sphere which has the same centre as the inner. Hence the proof of Prop. 38 applies.

Cor. 2. *The volume of the circumscribed figure with the cone $OLL'$ is greater than the cone whose base is a circle with radius equal to $al$ and whose height is equal to the radius $(Oa)$ of the inner sphere.*

For the volume of the figure with the cone $OLL'$ is equal to a cone whose base is equal to the surface of the figure and whose height is equal to $ON$.

And the surface of the figure is greater than a circle with radius equal to $al$ [Prop. 40], while the heights $Oa$, $ON$ are equal.

## Proposition 41

Let $lal'$ be a segment of a great circle of a sphere which is less than a semicircle.

Suppose a polygon inscribed in the sector $Olal'$ such that the sides $lk, \cdots ba, ab', \cdots k'l'$ are $2n$ in number and all equal. Let a similar polygon be circumscribed about the sector so that its sides are parallel to those of the first polygon; and draw the circle circumscribing the outer polygon.

Now let the polygons and circles revolve together about $OaA$, the radius bisecting the segment $lal'$.

Then (1) *the surfaces of the outer and inner solids of revolution so described are in the ratio of $AB^2$ to $ab^2$, and* (2) *their volumes together with the corresponding cones with the same base and with apex $O$ in each case are as $AB^3$ to $ab^3$.*

(1) For the surfaces are equal to circles the squares on whose radii are equal respectively to

$$AB\left(BB'+CC'+\cdots+KK'+\frac{LL'}{2}\right), \qquad \text{[Prop. 39, Cor.]}$$

and

$$ab\left(bb'+cc'+\cdots+kk'+\frac{ll'}{2}\right). \qquad \text{[Prop. 35]}$$

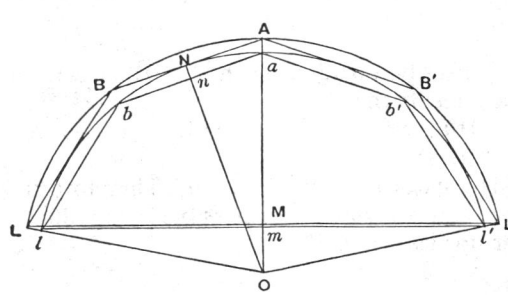

But these rectangles are in the ratio of $AB^2$ to $ab^2$. Therefore so are the surfaces.

(2) Let $OnN$ be drawn perpendicular to $ab$ and $AB$; and suppose the circles which are equal to the surfaces of the outer and inner solids of revolution to be denoted by $S$, $s$ respectively.

Now the volume of the circumscribed solid together with the cone $OLL'$ is equal to a cone whose base is $S$ and whose height is $ON$ [Prop. 40, Cor. 1].

And the volume of the inscribed figure with the cone $Oll'$ is equal to a cone with base $s$ and height $On$ [Prop. 38].

But $\qquad S : s = AB^2 : ab^2,$

and $\qquad ON : On = AB : ab.$

Therefore the volume of the circumscribed solid together with the cone $OLL'$ is to the volume of the inscribed solid together with the cone $Oll'$ as $AB^3$ is to $ab^3$ [Lemma 5].

## Proposition 42

*If $lal'$ be a segment of a sphere less than a hemisphere and $Oa$ the radius perpendicular to the base of the segment, the surface of the segment is equal to a circle whose radius is equal to $al$.*

Let $R$ be a circle whose radius is equal to $al$. Then the surface of the segment, which we will call $S$, must, if it be not equal to $R$, be either greater or less than $R$.

I. Suppose, if possible, $S > R$.

Let $lal'$ be a segment of a great circle which is less than a semicircle. Join $Ol$, $Ol'$, and let similar polygons with $2n$ equal sides be circumscribed and inscribed to the sector, as in the previous propositions, but such that
(circumscribed polygon) : (inscribed polygon) $< S : R$.

[Prop. 6]

Let the polygons now revolve with the segment about $OaA$, generating solids of revolution circumscribed and inscribed to the segment of the sphere.

Then
(surface of outer solid) : (surface of inner solid)
$= AB^2 : ab^2$                                                    [Prop. 41]
$=$ (circumscribed polygon) : (inscribed polygon)
$< S : R$, by hypothesis.

But the surface of the outer solid is greater than $S$ [Prop. 39].

Therefore the surface of the inner solid is greater than $R$; which is impossible, by Prop. 37.

II. Suppose, if possible, $S < R$.

In this case we circumscribe and inscribe polygons such that their ratio is less than $R : S$; and we arrive at the result that
(surface of outer solid) : (surface of inner solid)
$< R : S$.

But the surface of the outer solid is greater than $R$ [Prop. 40]. Therefore the surface of the inner solid is greater than $S$ : which is impossible [Prop. 36].

Hence, since $S$ is neither greater nor less than $R$,
$S = R$.

## Proposition 43

*Even if the segment of the sphere is greater than a hemisphere, its surface is still equal to a circle whose radius is equal to $al$.*

For let $lal'a'$ be a great circle of the sphere, $aa'$ being the diameter perpendicular to $ll'$; and let $la'l'$ be a segment less than a semicircle.

Then, by Prop. 42, the surface of the segment $la'l'$ of the sphere is equal to a circle with radius equal to $a'l$.

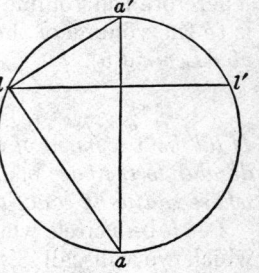

Also the surface of the whole sphere is equal to a circle with radius equal to $aa'$ [Prop. 33].

But $aa'^2 - a'l^2 = al^2$, and circles are to one another as the squares on their radii.

Therefore the surface of the segment $lal'$, being the difference between the surfaces of the sphere and of $la'l'$, is equal to a circle with radius equal to $al$.

## PROPOSITION 44

*The volume of any sector of a sphere is equal to a cone whose base is equal to the surface of the segment of the sphere included in the sector, and whose height is equal to the radius of the sphere.*

Let $R$ be a cone whose base is equal to the surface of the segment $lal'$ of a sphere and whose height is equal to the radius of the sphere; and let $S$ be the volume of the sector $Olal'$.

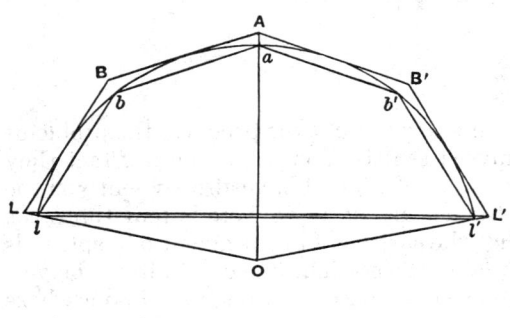

Then, if $S$ is not equal to $R$, it must be either greater or less.

I. Suppose, if possible, that $S > R$.

Find two straight lines $\beta$, $\gamma$, of which $\beta$ is the greater, such that
$$\beta : \gamma < S : R;$$
and let $\delta$, $\epsilon$ be two arithmetic means between $\beta$, $\gamma$.

Let $lal'$ be a segment of a great circle of the sphere. Join $Ol$, $Ol'$, and let similar polygons with $2n$ equal sides be circumscribed and inscribed to

the sector of the circle as before, but such that their sides are in a ratio less than $\beta : \delta$. [Prop. 4].

Then let the two polygons revolve with the segment about $OaA$, generating two solids of revolution.

Denoting the volumes of these solids by $V$, $v$ respectively, we have
$$(V + \text{cone } OLL') : (v + \text{cone } Oll') = AB^3 : ab^3 \quad \text{[Prop. 41]}$$
$$< \beta^3 : \delta^3$$
$$< \beta : \gamma, \text{ a fortiori,}$$
$$< S : R, \text{ by hypothesis.}$$

Now $(V + \text{cone } OLL') > S$.
Therefore also $(v + \text{cone } Oll') > R$.

But this is impossible, by Prop. 38, Cor. combined with Props. 42, 43.

Hence $S \not> R$.

II. Suppose, if possible, that $S < R$.

In this case we take $\beta$, $\gamma$ such that
$$\beta : \gamma < R : S,$$
and the rest of the construction proceeds as before.

We thus obtain the relation
$$(V + \text{cone } OLL') : (v + \text{cone } Oll') < R : S.$$

Now $(v + \text{cone } Oll') < S$.
Therefore $(V + \text{cone } OLL') < R$;
which is impossible, by Prop. 40, Cor. 2 combined with Props. 42, 43.

Since then $S$ is neither greater nor less than $R$,
$$S = R.$$

# ON THE SPHERE AND CYLINDER
# BOOK TWO

ARCHIMEDES to Dositheus greeting.

"On a former occasion you asked me to write out the proofs of the problems the enunciations of which I had myself sent to Conon. In point of fact they depend for the most part on the theorems of which I have already sent you the demonstrations, namely (1) that the surface of any sphere is four times the greatest circle in the sphere, (2) that the surface of any segment of a sphere is equal to a circle whose radius is equal to the straight line drawn from the vertex of the segment to the circumference of its base, (3) that the cylinder whose base is the greatest circle in any sphere and whose height is equal to the diameter of the sphere is itself in magnitude half as large again as the sphere, while its surface [including the two bases] is half as large again as the surface of the sphere, and (4) that any solid sector is equal to a cone whose base is the circle which is equal to the surface of the segment of the sphere included in the sector, and whose height is equal to the radius of the sphere. Such then of the theorems and problems as depend on these theorems I have written out in the book which I send herewith; those which are discovered by means of a different sort of investigation, those namely which relate to spirals and the conoids, I will endeavour to send you soon.

"The first of the problems was as follows: *Given a sphere, to find a plane area equal to the surface of the sphere.*

"The solution of this is obvious from the theorems aforesaid. For four times the greatest circle in the sphere is both a plane area and equal to the surface of the sphere.

"The second problem was the following."

### Proposition 1 (Problem)

*Given a cone or a cylinder, to find a sphere equal to the cone or to the cylinder.*

If $V$ be the given cone or cylinder, we can make a cylinder equal to $\frac{3}{2}V$. Let this cylinder be the cylinder whose base is the circle on $AB$ as diameter and whose height is $OD$.

Now, if we could make another cylinder, equal to the cylinder $(OD)$ but such that its height is equal to the diameter of its base, the problem would be solved, because this latter cylinder would be equal to $\frac{3}{2}V$, and the sphere whose diameter is equal to the height (or to the diameter of the base) of the same cylinder would then be the sphere required [I. 34, Cor.].

Suppose the problem solved, and let the cylinder $(CG)$ be equal to the cylinder $(OD)$, while $EF$, the diameter of the base, is equal to the height $CG$.

Then, since in equal cylinders the heights and bases are reciprocally proportional,
$$AB^2 : EF^2 = CG : OD$$
$$= EF : OD. \qquad (1)$$

Suppose $MN$ to be such a line that
$$EF^2 = AB \cdot MN. \qquad (2)$$
Hence $\qquad AB : EF = EF : MN$,
and, combining (1) and (2), we have
$$AB : MN = EF : OD,$$
or $\qquad AB : EF = MN : OD.$
Therefore $\qquad AB : EF = EF : MN = MN : OD,$
and $EF$, $MN$ are two mean proportionals between $AB$, $OD$.

The synthesis of the problem is therefore as follows. Take two mean proportionals $EF$, $MN$ between $AB$ and $OD$, and describe a cylinder whose base is a circle on $EF$ as diameter and whose height $CG$ is equal to $EF$.

Then, since
$$AB : EF = EF : MN = MN : OD,$$
$$EF^2 = AB \cdot MN,$$
and therefore $\qquad AB^2 : EF^2 = AB : MN$
$$= EF : OD$$
$$= CG : OD;$$
whence the bases of the two cylinders $(OD)$, $(CG)$ are reciprocally proportional to their heights.

Therefore the cylinders are equal, and it follows that
$$\text{cylinder } (CG) = \tfrac{3}{2} V.$$

The sphere on $EF$ as diameter is therefore the sphere required, being equal to $V$.

PROPOSITION 2

*If $BAB'$ be a segment of a sphere, $BB'$ a diameter of the base of the segment, and $O$ the centre of the sphere, and if $AA'$ be the diameter of the sphere bisecting $BB'$ in $M$, then the volume of the segment is equal to that of a cone whose base is the same as that of the segment and whose height is $h$, where*
$$h : AM = OA' + A'M : A'M.$$

Measure $MH$ along $MA$ equal to $h$, and $MH'$ along $MA'$ equal to $h'$, where
$$h' : A'M = OA + AM : AM.$$

Suppose the three cones constructed which have $O, H, H'$ for their apices and the base $(BB')$ of the segment for their common base. Join $AB, A'B$.

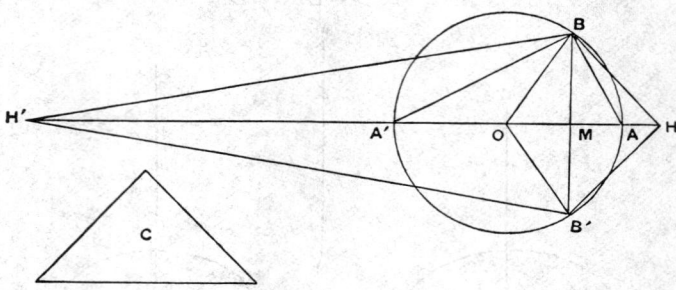

Let $C$ be a cone whose base is equal to the surface of the segment $BAB'$ of the sphere, i.e. to a circle with radius equal to $AB$ [I. 42], and whose height is equal to $OA$.

Then the cone $C$ is equal to the solid sector $OBAB'$ [I. 44].

Now, since $\qquad HM : MA = OA' + A'M : A'M,$
*dividendo*, $\qquad HA : AM = OA : A'M,$
and, alternately, $\qquad HA : AO = AM : MA',$
so that
$$HO : OA = AA' : A'M$$
$$= AB^2 : BM^2$$
$$= \text{(base of cone } C) : \text{(circle on } BB' \text{ as diameter)}.$$

But $OA$ is equal to the height of the cone $C$; therefore, since cones are equal if their bases and heights are reciprocally proportional, it follows that the cone $C$ (or the solid sector $OBAB'$) is equal to a cone whose base is the circle on $BB'$ as diameter and whose height is equal to $OH$.

And this latter cone is equal to the sum of two others having the same base and with heights $OM, MH$, i.e. to the solid rhombus $OBHB'$.

Hence the sector $OBAB'$ is equal to the rhombus $OBHB'$.

Taking away the common part, the cone $OBB'$,
$$\text{the segment } BAB' = \text{the cone } HBB'.$$

Similarly, by the same method, we can prove that
$$\text{the segment } BA'B' = \text{the cone } H'BB'.$$

*Alternative proof of the latter property.*

Suppose $D$ to be a cone whose base is equal to the surface of the whole sphere and whose height is equal to $OA$.

Thus $D$ is equal to the volume of the sphere. [I. 33, 34]

Now, since $\qquad OA' + A'M : A'M = HM : MA,$
*dividendo* and *alternando*, as before,
$$OA : AH = A'M : MA.$$

Again, since $\qquad H'M : MA' = OA + AM : AM,$
$$H'A' : OA = A'M : MA$$
$$= OA : AH, \text{ from above.}$$

*Componendo*, $\qquad H'O : OA = OH : HA,$ \hfill (1)
Alternately, $\qquad H'O : OH = OA : AH,$ \hfill (2)

and, *componendo*,  $HH' : HO = OH : HA$,
    $\qquad\qquad\qquad\qquad = H'O : OA$, from (1),
whence  $\qquad HH' \cdot OA = H'O \cdot OH$.  (3)
Next, since  $\qquad H'O : OH = OA : AH$, by (2),
    $\qquad\qquad\qquad\qquad = A'M : MA$,
    $(H'O+OH)^2 : H'O \cdot OH = (A'M+MA)^2 : A'M \cdot MA$,
whence, by means of (3),
    $\qquad HH'^2 : HH' \cdot OA = AA'^2 : A'M \cdot MA$,
or  $\qquad HH' : OA = AA'^2 : BM^2$.

Now the cone $D$, which is equal to the sphere, has for its base a circle whose radius is equal to $AA'$, and for its height a line equal to $OA$.

Hence this cone $D$ is equal to a cone whose base is the circle on $BB'$ as diameter and whose height is equal to $HH'$;
therefore  $\qquad$ the cone $D$ = the rhombus $HBH'B'$,
or  $\qquad$ the rhombus $HBH'B'$ = the sphere.
But  $\qquad$ the segment $BAB'$ = the cone $HBB'$;
therefore the remaining segment $BA'B'$ = the cone $H'BB'$.

Cor. *The segment $BAB'$ is to a cone with the same base and equal height in the ratio of $OA'+A'M$ to $A'M$.*

### Proposition 3 (Problem)

*To cut a given sphere by a plane so that the surfaces of the segments may have to one another a given ratio.*

Suppose the problem solved. Let $AA'$ be a diameter of a great circle of the sphere, and suppose that a plane perpendicular to $AA'$ cuts the plane of the great circle in the straight line $BB'$, and $AA'$ in $M$, and that it divides the sphere so that the surface of the segment $BAB'$ has to the surface of the segment $BA'B'$ the given ratio.

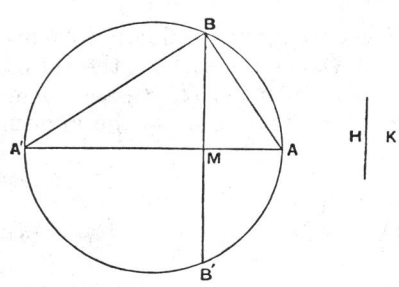

Now these surfaces are respectively equal to circles with radii equal to $AB$, $A'B$ [I. 42, 43].

Hence the ratio $AB^2 : A'B^2$ is equal to the given ratio, i.e. $AM$ is to $MA'$ in the given ratio.

Accordingly the synthesis proceeds as follows.
If $H : K$ be the given ratio, divide $AA'$ in $M$ so that
    $\qquad\qquad AM : MA' = H : K$.
Then $AM : MA' = AB^2 : A'B^2$
    $\qquad$ = (circle with radius $AB$) : (circle with radius $A'B$)
    $\qquad$ = (surface of segment $BAB'$) : (surface of segment $BA'B'$).
Thus the ratio of the surfaces of the segments is equal to the ratio $H : K$.

### Proposition 4 (Problem)

*To cut a given sphere by a plane so that the volumes of the segments are to one another in a given ratio.*

Suppose the problem solved, and let the required plane cut the great circle

$ABA'$ at right angles in the line $BB'$. Let $AA'$ be that diameter of the great circle which bisects $BB'$ at right angles (in $M$), and let $O$ be the centre of the sphere.

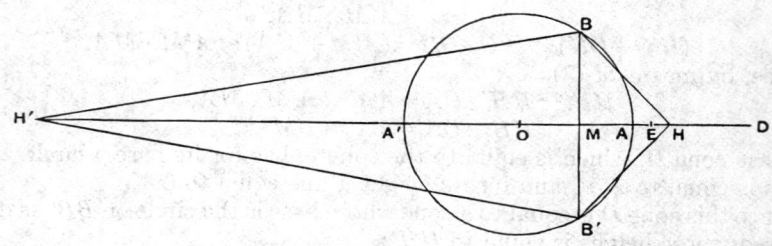

Take $H$ on $OA$ produced, and $H'$ on $OA'$ produced, such that
$$OA'+A'M : A'M = HM : MA, \quad (1)$$
and
$$OA+AM : AM = H'M : MA'. \quad (2)$$
Join $BH, B'H, BH', B'H'$.

Then the cones $HBB', H'BB'$ are respectively equal to the segments $BAB', BA'B'$ of the sphere [Prop. 2].

Hence the ratio of the cones, and therefore of their altitudes, is given, i.e.
$$HM : H'M = \text{the given ratio}. \quad (3)$$

We have now three equations (1), (2), (3), in which there appear three as yet undetermined points $M, H, H'$; and it is first necessary to find, by means of them, another equation in which only one of these points ($M$) appears, i.e. we have, so to speak, to *eliminate* $H, H'$.

Now, from (3), it is clear that $HH' : H'M$ is also a given ratio; and Archimedes' method of elimination is, *first*, to find values for each of the ratios $A'H' : H'M$ and $HH' : H'A'$ which are alike independent of $H, H'$, and then, *secondly*, to equate the ratio compounded of these two ratios to the known value of the ratio $HH' : H'M$.

(*a*) To find such a value for $A'H' : H'M$.

It is at once clear from equation (2) above that
$$A'H' : H'M = OA : OA+AM. \quad (4)$$

(*b*) To find such a value for $HH' : A'H'$.

From (1) we derive
$$A'M : MA = OA'+A'M : HM$$
$$= OA' : AH; \quad (5)$$
and, from (2), $\quad A'M : MA = H'M : OA+AM$
$$= A'H' : OA. \quad (6)$$

Thus $\quad HA : AO = OA' : A'H'$,
whence $\quad OH : OA' = OH' : A'H'$,
or $\quad OH : OH' = OA' : A'H'$.

It follows that
$$HH' : OH' = OH' : A'H',$$
or $\quad HH' \cdot H'A' = OH'^2$.

Therefore $\quad HH' : H'A' = OH'^2 : H'A'^2$
$$= AA'^2 : A'M^2, \text{ by means of (6)}.$$

(*c*) To express the ratios $A'H' : H'M$ and $HH' : H'M$ more simply we make

## ON THE SPHERE AND CYLINDER II

the following construction. Produce $OA$ to $D$ so that $OA = AD$. ($D$ will lie beyond $H$, for $A'M > MA$, and therefore, by (5), $OA > AH$.)
Then
$$A'H' : H'M = OA : OA + AM$$
$$= AD : DM. \qquad (7)$$
Now divide $AD$ at $E$ so that
$$HH' : H'M = AD : DE. \qquad (8)$$
Thus, using equations (8), (7) and the value of $HH' : H'A'$ above found, we have
$$AD : DE = HH' : H'M$$
$$= (HH' : H'A') \cdot (A'H' : H'M)$$
$$= (AA'^2 : A'M^2) \cdot (AD : DM).$$
But $\qquad AD : DE = (DM : DE) \cdot (AD : DM).$
Therefore $\qquad MD : DE = AA'^2 : A'M^2. \qquad (9)$
And $D$ is given, since $AD = OA$. Also $AD : DE$ (being equal to $HH' : H'M$) is a given ratio. Therefore $DE$ is given.

*Hence the problem reduces itself to the problem of dividing $A'D$ into two parts at $M$ so that*
$$MD : \text{(a given length)} = \text{(a given area)} : A'M^2.$$

Archimedes adds: "If the problem is propounded in this general form, it requires a διορισμός [i.e. it is necessary to investigate the limits of possibility], but, if there be added the conditions subsisting in the present case, it does not require a διορισμός."

In the present case the problem is:

*Given a straight line $A'A$ produced to $D$ so that $A'A = 2AD$, and given a point $E$ on $AD$, to cut $AA'$ in a point $M$ so that*
$$AA'^2 : A'M^2 = MD : DE.$$

"And the analysis and synthesis of both problems will be given at the end."[1]

The synthesis of the main problem will be as follows. Let $R : S$ be the given ratio, $R$ being less than $S$. $AA'$ being a diameter of a great circle, and $O$ the centre, produce $OA$ to $D$ so that $OA = AD$, and divide $AD$ in $E$ so that
$$AE : ED = R : S.$$
Then cut $AA'$ in $M$ so that
$$MD : DE = AA'^2 : A'M^2.$$

Through $M$ erect a plane perpendicular to $AA'$; this plane will then divide the sphere into segments which will be to one another as $R$ to $S$.

Take $H$ on $A'A$ produced, and $H'$ on $AA'$ produced, so that
$$OA' + A'M : A'M = HM : MA, \qquad (1)$$
$$OA + AM : AM = H'M : MA'. \qquad (2)$$
We have then to show that
$$HM : MH' = R : S, \text{ or } AE : ED.$$

(a) We first find the value of $HH' : H'A'$ as follows.
As was shown in the analysis (b),
$$HH' \cdot H'A' = OH'^2,$$
or $\qquad HH' : H'A' = OH'^2 : H'A'^2$
$$= AA'^2 : A'M^2$$
$$= MD : DE, \text{ by construction.}$$

---

[1]As Archimedes' commentator, Eutocius, notes: "... we do not find the promise kept in any of the copies." Sir Thomas Heath's translation of Eutocius' note on the matter, along with the solutions of Dionysodorus and Diocles, is omitted from this edition.—Ed.

($\beta$) Next we have
$$H'A' : H'M = OA : OA + AM$$
$$= AD : DM.$$
Therefore
$$HH' : H'M = (HH' : H'A') \cdot (H'A' : H'M)$$
$$= (MD : DE) \cdot (AD : DM)$$
$$= AD : DE,$$
whence
$$HM : MH' = AE : ED$$
$$= R : S.$$

Q. E. D.

## PROPOSITION 5 (PROBLEM)

*To construct a segment of a sphere similar to one segment and equal in volume to another.*

Let $ABB'$ be one segment whose vertex is $A$ and whose base is the circle on $BB'$ as diameter; and let $DEF$ be another segment whose vertex is $D$ and whose base is the circle on $EF$ as diameter. Let $AA'$, $DD'$ be diameters of the great circles passing through $BB'$, $EF$ respectively, and let $O$, $C$ be the respective centres of the spheres.

Suppose it required to draw a segment similar to $DEF$ and equal in volume to $ABB'$.

*Analysis.* Suppose the problem solved, and let $def$ be the required segment, $d$ being the vertex and $ef$ the diameter of the base. Let $dd'$ be the diameter of the sphere which bisects $ef$ at right angles, $c$ the centre of the sphere.

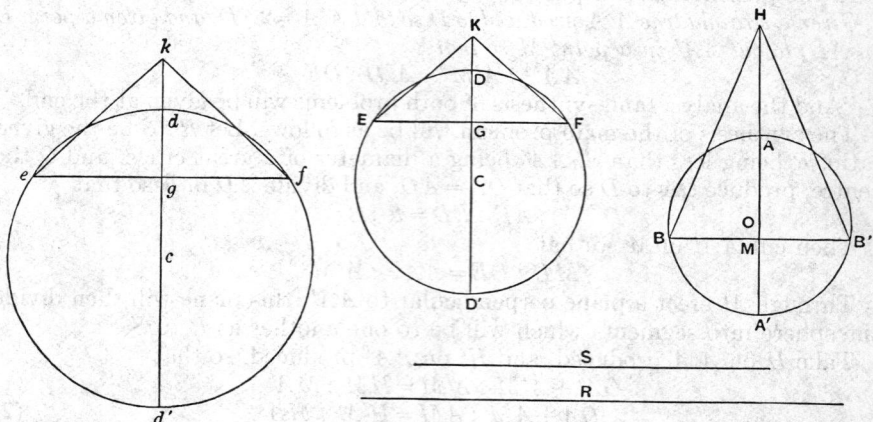

Let $M$, $G$, $g$ be the points where $BB'$, $EF$, $ef$ are bisected at right angles by $AA'$, $DD'$, $dd'$ respectively, and produce $OA$, $CD$, $cd$ respectively to $H$, $K$, $k$, so that
$$\left.\begin{array}{r}OA' + A'M : A'M = HM : MA\\ CD' + D'G : D'G = KG : GD\\ cd' + d'g : d'g = kg : gd\end{array}\right\},$$
and suppose cones formed with vertices $H$, $K$, $k$ and with the same bases as the respective segments. The cones will then be equal to the segments respectively [Prop. 2].

Therefore, by hypothesis,

the cone $HBB'$ = the cone $kef$.

Hence
$$(\text{circle on diameter } BB') : (\text{circle on diameter } ef) = kg : HM,$$
so that
$$BB'^2 : ef^2 = kg : HM \qquad (1)$$
But, since the segments $DEF$, $def$ are similar, so are the cones $KEF$, $kef$. Therefore
$$KG : EF = kg : ef.$$
And the ratio $KG : EF$ is given. Therefore the ratio $kg : ef$ is given.

Suppose a length $R$ taken such that
$$kg : ef = HM : R. \qquad (2)$$
Thus $R$ is given.

Again, since $kg : HM = BB'^2 : ef^2 = ef : R$, by (1) and (2), suppose a length $S$ taken such that
$$ef^2 = BB' \cdot S,$$
or
$$BB'^2 : ef^2 = BB' : S.$$
Thus
$$BB' : ef = ef : S = S : R,$$
and $ef$, $S$ are two mean proportionals in continued proportion between $BB'$, $R$.

*Synthesis.* Let $ABB'$, $DEF$ be great circles, $AA'$, $DD'$ the diameters bisecting $BB'$, $EF$ at right angles in $M$, $G$ respectively, and $O$, $C$ the centres.

Take $H$, $K$ in the same way as before, and construct the cones $HBB'$, $KEF$, which are therefore equal to the respective segments $ABB'$, $DEF$.

Let $R$ be a straight line such that
$$KG : EF = HM : R,$$
and between $BB'$, $R$ take two mean proportionals $ef$, $S$.

On $ef$ as base describe a segment of a circle with vertex $d$ and similar to the segment of a circle $DEF$. Complete the circle, and let $dd'$ be the diameter through $d$, and $c$ the centre. Conceive a sphere constructed of which $def$ is a great circle, and through $ef$ draw a plane at right angles to $dd'$.

Then shall $def$ be the required segment of a sphere.

For the segments $DEF$, $def$ of the spheres are similar, like the circular segments $DEF$, $def$.

Produce $cd$ to $k$ so that
$$cd' + d'g : d'g = kg : gd.$$
The cones $KEF$, $kef$ are then similar.

Therefore $\qquad kg : ef = KG : EF = HM : R,$
whence $\qquad kg : HM = ef : R.$

But, since $BB'$, $ef$, $S$, $R$ are in continued proportion,
$$BB'^2 : ef^2 = BB' : S$$
$$= ef : R$$
$$= kg : HM.$$

Thus the bases of the cones $HBB'$, $kef$ are reciprocally proportional to their heights. The cones are therefore equal, and $def$ is the segment required, being equal in volume to the cone $kef$. [Prop. 2]

## Proposition 6 (Problem)

*Given two segments of spheres, to find a third segment of a sphere similar to one of the given segments and having its surface equal to that of the other.*

Let $ABB'$ be the segment to whose surface the surface of the required segment is to be equal, $ABA'B'$ the great circle whose plane cuts the plane of the base of the segment $ABB'$ at right angles in $BB'$. Let $AA'$ be the diameter which bisects $BB'$ at right angles.

Let $DEF$ be the segment to which the required segment is to be similar, $DED'F$ the great circle cutting the base of the segment at right angles in $EF$. Let $DD'$ be the diameter bisecting $EF$ at right angles in $G$.

Suppose the problem solved, $def$ being a segment similar to $DEF$ and having its surface equal to that of $ABB'$; and complete the figure for $def$ as for $DEF$, corresponding points being denoted by small and capital letters respectively.

Join $AB$, $DF$, $df$.

Now, since the surfaces of the segments $def$, $ABB'$ are equal, so are the circles on $df$, $AB$ as diameters;

[I. 42, 43]

that is, $df = AB$.

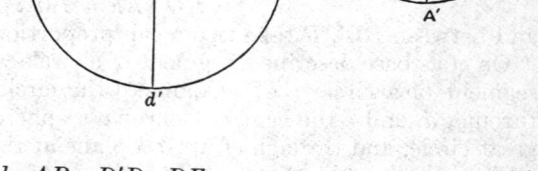

From the similarity of the segments $DEF$, $def$ we obtain
$$d'd : dg = D'D : DG,$$
and $dg : df = DG : DF$;
whence $d'd : df = D'D : DF$,
or $d'd : AB = D'D : DF$.
But $AB$, $D'D$, $DF$ are all given;

therefore $d'd$ is given.

Accordingly the synthesis is as follows.

Take $d'd$ such that
$$d'd : AB = D'D : DF. \tag{1}$$
Describe a circle on $d'd$ as diameter, and conceive a sphere constructed of which this circle is a great circle.

Divide $d'd$ at $g$ so that
$$d'g : gd = D'G : GD,$$
and draw through $g$ a plane perpendicular to $d'd$ cutting off the segment $def$ of the sphere and intersecting the plane of the great circle in $ef$. The segments $def$, $DEF$ are thus similar, and
$$dg : df = DG : DF.$$
But from above, *componendo*,
$$d'd : dg = D'D : DG.$$
Therefore, *ex aequali*, $d'd : df = D'D : DF$,
whence, by (1), $df = AB$.

Therefore the segment $def$ has its surface equal to the surface of the segment $ABB'$ [I. 42, 43], while it is also similar to the segment $DEF$.

## Proposition 7 (Problem)

*From a given sphere to cut off a segment by a plane so that the segment may have a given ratio to the cone which has the same base as the segment and equal height.*

Let $AA'$ be the diameter of a great circle of the sphere. It is required to draw a plane at right angles to $AA'$ cutting off a segment, as $ABB'$, such that the segment $ABB'$ has to the cone $ABB'$ a given ratio.

## Analysis.

Suppose the problem solved, and let the plane of section cut the plane of the great circle in $BB'$, and the diameter $AA'$ in $M$. Let $O$ be the centre of the sphere.

Produce $OA$ to $H$ so that
$$OA' + A'M : A'M = HM : MA. \qquad (1)$$

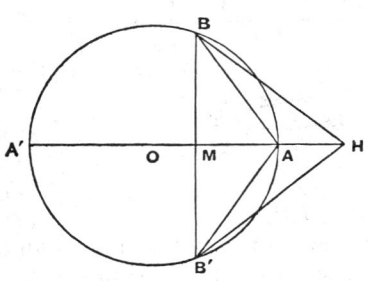

Thus the cone $HBB'$ is equal to the segment $ABB'$.

[Prop. 2]

Therefore the given ratio must be equal to the ratio of the cone $HBB'$ to the cone $ABB'$, i.e. to the ratio $HM : MA$.

Hence the ratio $OA' + A'M : A'M$ is given; and therefore $A'M$ is given.

διορισμός.

Now $\qquad OA' : A'M > OA' : A'A$,
so that $\qquad OA' + A'M : A'M > OA' + A'A : A'A$
$\qquad\qquad\qquad\qquad\qquad > 3 : 2$.

Thus, *in order that a solution may be possible, it is a necessary condition that the given ratio must be greater than* $3 : 2$.

The *synthesis* proceeds thus.

Let $AA'$ be a diameter of a great circle of the sphere, $O$ the centre.

Take a line $DE$, and a point $F$ on it, such that $DE : EF$ is equal to the given ratio, being greater than $3 : 2$.

Now, since $\qquad OA' + A'A : A'A = 3 : 2$,
$\qquad\qquad\qquad DE : EF > OA' + A'A : A'A$,
so that $\qquad DF : FE > OA' : A'A$.

Hence a point $M$ can be found on $AA'$ such that
$$DF : FE = OA' : A'M. \qquad (2)$$

Through $M$ draw a plane at right angles to $AA'$ intersecting the plane of the great circle in $BB'$, and cutting off from the sphere the segment $ABB'$.

As before, take $H$ on $OA$ produced such that
$$OA' + A'M : A'M = HM : MA.$$

Therefore $HM : MA = DE : EF$, by means of (2).

It follows that the cone $HBB'$, or the segment $ABB'$, is to the cone $ABB'$ in the given ratio $DE : EF$.

## Proposition 8

*If a sphere be cut by a plane not passing through the centre into two segments $A'BB'$, $ABB'$, of which $A'BB'$ is the greater, then the ratio*
$$(segmt.\ A'BB') : (segmt.\ ABB')$$
$$< (surface\ of\ A'BB')^2 : (surface\ of\ ABB')$$
$$but > (surface\ of\ A'BB')^{\frac{3}{2}} : (surface\ of\ ABB')^{\frac{3}{2}}.$$

Let the plane of section cut a great circle $A'BAB'$ at right angles in $BB'$, and let $AA'$ be the diameter bisecting $BB'$ at right angles in $M$.

Let $O$ be the centre of the sphere.

Join $A'B$, $AB$.

As usual, take $H$ on $OA$ produced, and $H'$ on $OA'$ produced, so that

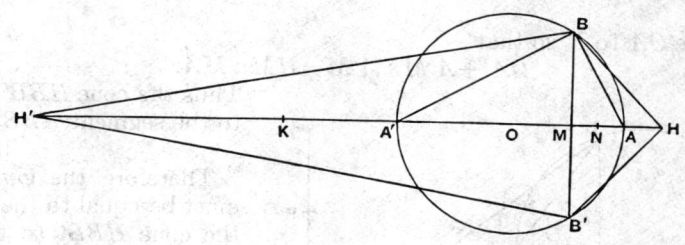

$$OA'+A'M : A'M = HM : MA, \qquad (1)$$
$$OA+AM : AM = H'M : MA', \qquad (2)$$

and conceive cones drawn each with the same base as the two segments and with apices $H$, $H'$ respectively. The cones are then respectively equal to the segments [Prop. 2], and they are in the ratio of their heights $HM$, $H'M$.

Also
$$(\text{surface of } A'BB') : (\text{surface of } ABB') = A'B^2 : AB^2 \quad [\text{I. 42, 43}]$$
$$= A'M : AM.$$

We have therefore to prove
(a) that $\qquad H'M : MH < A'M^2 : MA^2,$
(b) that $\qquad H'M : MH > A'M^{\frac{3}{2}} : MA^{\frac{3}{2}}.$

(a) From (2) above,
$$A'M : AM = H'M : OA+AM$$
$$= H'A' : OA', \text{ since } OA = OA'.$$

Since $A'M > AM$, $H'A' > OA'$; therefore, if we take $K$ on $H'A'$ so that $OA' = A'K$, $K$ will fall between $H'$ and $A'$.

And, by (1), $\qquad A'M : AM = KM : MH.$

Thus $\qquad KM : MH = H'A' : A'K$, since $A'K = OA'$,
$$> H'M : MK.$$

Therefore $\qquad H'M \cdot MH < KM^2.$

It follows that
$$H'M \cdot MH : MH^2 < KM^2 : MH^2,$$
or $\qquad H'M : MH < KM^2 : MH^2$
$$< A'M^2 : AM^2, \text{ by (1)}.$$

(b) Since $\qquad OA' = OA,$
$$A'M \cdot MA < A'O \cdot OA,$$
or $\qquad A'M : OA' < OA : AM$
$$< H'A' : A'M, \text{ by means of (2)}.$$

Therefore $\qquad A'M^2 < H'A' \cdot OA'$
$$< H'A' \cdot A'K.$$

Take a point $N$ on $A'A$ such that
$$A'N^2 = H'A' \cdot A'K.$$

Thus $\qquad H'A' : A'K = A'N^2 : A'K^2.$ $\qquad (3)$

Also $\qquad H'A' : A'N = A'N : A'K,$

and, *componendo*,
$$H'N : A'N = NK : A'K,$$

whence $\qquad A'N^2 : A'K^2 = H'N^2 : NK^2.$

Therefore, by (3),
$$H'A' : A'K = H'N^2 : NK^2.$$
Now $\qquad H'M : MK > H'N : NK.$
Therefore
$$\begin{aligned} H'M^2 : MK^2 &> H'A' : A'K \\ &> H'A' : OA' \\ &> A'M : MA, \text{ by (2), as above,} \\ &> OA' + A'M : MH, \text{ by (1),} \\ &> KM : MH. \end{aligned}$$

Hence $\qquad H'M^2 : MH^2 = (H'M^2 : MK^2) \cdot (KM^2 : MH^2)$
$$> (KM : MH) \cdot (KM^2 : MH^2).$$

It follows that
$$\begin{aligned} H'M : MH &> KM^{\frac{3}{2}} : MH^{\frac{3}{2}} \\ &> A'M^{\frac{3}{2}} : AM^{\frac{3}{2}}, \text{ by (1)}. \end{aligned}$$

## Proposition 9

*Of all segments of spheres which have equal surfaces the hemisphere is the greatest in volume.*

Let $ABA'B'$ be a great circle of a sphere, $AA'$ being a diameter, and $O$ the centre. Let the sphere be cut by a plane, not passing through $O$, perpendicular to $AA'$ (at $M$), and intersecting the plane of the great circle in $BB'$. The segment $ABB'$ may then be either less than a hemisphere as in Fig. 1, or greater than a hemisphere as in Fig. 2.

Let $DED'E'$ be a great circle of another sphere, $DD'$ being a diameter and $C$ the centre. Let the sphere be cut by a plane through $C$ perpendicular to $DD'$ and intersecting the plane of the great circle in the diameter $EE'$.

Suppose the surfaces of the segment $ABB'$ and of the hemisphere $DEE'$ to be equal.

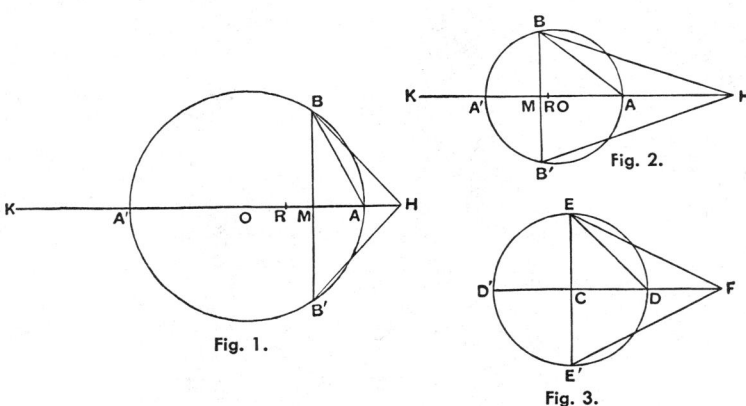

Fig. 1. Fig. 2. Fig. 3.

Since the surfaces are equal, $AB = DE$. [I. 42, 43]

Now, in Fig. 1, $\qquad AB^2 > 2AM^2$ and $< 2AO^2,$
and, in Fig. 2, $\qquad AB^2 < 2AM^2$ and $> 2AO^2.$

Hence, if $R$ be taken on $AA'$ such that
$$AR^2 = \tfrac{1}{2}AB^2,$$

$R$ will fall between $O$ and $M$.

Also, since $AB^2 = DE^2$, $AR = CD$.

Produce $OA'$ to $K$ so that $OA' = A'K$, and produce $A'A$ to $H$ so that
$$A'K : A'M = HA : AM,$$
or, *componendo*, $\qquad A'K + A'M : A'M = HM : MA. \qquad (1)$

Thus the cone $HBB'$ is equal to the segment $ABB'$. [Prop. 2]

Again, produce $CD$ to $F$ so that $CD = DF$, and the cone $FEE'$ will be equal to the hemisphere $DEE'$. [Prop. 2]

Now $\qquad\qquad AR \cdot RA' > AM \cdot MA',$
and $\qquad\qquad AR^2 = \tfrac{1}{2}AB^2 = \tfrac{1}{2}AM \cdot AA' = AM \cdot A'K.$

Hence
$$AR \cdot RA' + RA^2 > AM \cdot MA' + AM \cdot A'K,$$
or $\qquad\qquad AA' \cdot AR > AM \cdot MK$
$\qquad\qquad\qquad\qquad > HM \cdot A'M,$ by (1).

Therefore $\qquad AA' : A'M > HM : AR,$
or $\qquad\qquad AB^2 : BM^2 > HM : AR,$
i.e. $\qquad\qquad AR^2 : BM^2 > HM : 2AR,$ since $AB^2 = 2AR^2,$
$\qquad\qquad\qquad\qquad > HM : CF.$

Thus, since $AR = CD$, or $CE$,
$$\text{(circle on diam. } EE') : \text{(circle on diam. } BB') > HM : CF.$$

It follows that
$$\text{(the cone } FEE') > \text{(the cone } HBB'),$$
and therefore the hemisphere $DEE'$ is greater in volume than the segment $ABB'$.

# MEASUREMENT OF A CIRCLE

## Proposition 1

*The area of any circle is equal to a right-angled triangle in which one of the sides about the right angle is equal to the radius, and the other to the circumference, of the circle.*

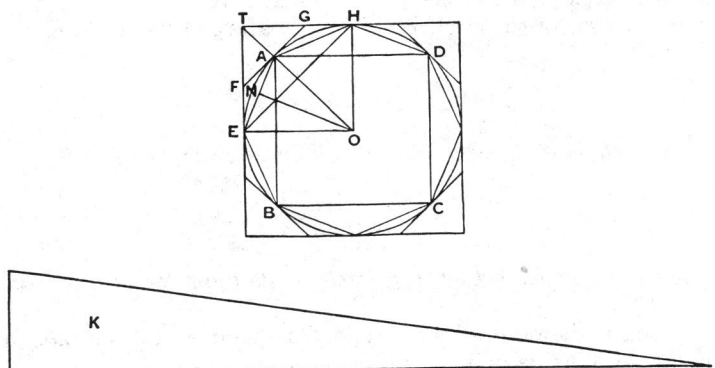

Let $ABCD$ be the given circle, $K$ the triangle described.

Then, if the circle is not equal to $K$, it must be either greater or less.

I. If possible, let the circle be greater than $K$.

Inscribe a square $ABCD$, bisect the arcs $AB$, $BC$, $CD$, $DA$, then bisect (if necessary) the halves, and so on, until the sides of the inscribed polygon whose angular points are the points of division subtend segments whose sum is less than the excess of the area of the circle over $K$.

Thus the area of the polygon is greater than $K$.

Let $AE$ be any side of it, and $ON$ the perpendicular on $AE$ from the centre $O$.

Then $ON$ is less than the radius of the circle and therefore less than one of the sides about the right angle in $K$. Also the perimeter of the polygon is less than the circumference of the circle, i.e. less than the other side about the right angle in $K$.

Therefore the area of the polygon is less than $K$; which is inconsistent with the hypothesis.

Thus the area of the circle is not greater than $K$.

II. If possible, let the circle be less than $K$.

Circumscribe a square, and let two adjacent sides, touching the circle in $E$, $H$, meet in $T$. Bisect the arcs between adjacent points of contact and draw the tangents at the points of bisection. Let $A$ be the middle point of the arc $EH$, and $FAG$ the tangent at $A$.

Then the angle $TAG$ is a right angle.

Therefore $$TG > GA$$
$$> GH.$$

It follows that the triangle $FTG$ is greater than half the area $TEAH$.

Similarly, if the arc $AH$ be bisected and the tangent at the point of bisection be drawn, it will cut off from the area $GAH$ more than one-half.

Thus, by continuing the process, we shall ultimately arrive at a circumscribed polygon such that the spaces intercepted between it and the circle are together less than the excess of $K$ over the area of the circle.

Thus the area of the polygon will be less than $K$.

Now, since the perpendicular from $O$ on any side of the polygon is equal to the radius of the circle, while the perimeter of the polygon is greater than the circumference of the circle, it follows that the area of the polygon is greater than the triangle $K$; which is impossible.

Therefore the area of the circle is not less than $K$.

Since then the area of the circle is neither greater nor less than $K$, it is equal to it.

## Proposition 2

*The area of a circle is to the square on its diameter as* 11 *to* 14[1].

## Proposition 3

*The ratio of the circumference of any circle to its diameter is less than* $3\frac{1}{7}$ *but greater than* $3\frac{10}{71}$ [2].

I. Let $AB$ be the diameter of any circle, $O$ its centre, $AC$ the tangent at $A$; and let the angle $AOC$ be one-third of a right angle.

Then $\qquad OA : AC [= \sqrt{3} : 1] > 265 : 153,$ \hfill (1)

and $\qquad OC : CA [= 2 : 1] = 306 : 153.$ \hfill (2)

*First,* draw $OD$ bisecting the angle $AOC$ and meeting $AC$ in $D$.

Now $\qquad CO : OA = CD : DA,$ \hfill [Eucl. VI. 3]

so that $\qquad [CO + OA : OA = CA : DA,$ or]
$$CO + OA : CA = OA : AD.$$

Therefore [by (1) and (2)]
$$OA : AD > 571 : 153. \qquad (3)$$

---

[1] The text of this proposition is not satisfactory, and Archimedes cannot have placed it before Proposition 3, as the approximation depends upon the result of that proposition.

[2] In view of the interesting questions arising out of the arithmetical content of this proposition of Archimedes, it is necessary, in reproducing it, to distinguish carefully the actual steps set out in the text as we have it from the intermediate steps (mostly supplied by Eutocius) which it is convenient to put in for the purpose of making the proof easier to follow. Accordingly all the steps not actually appearing in the text have been enclosed in square brackets, in order that it may be clearly seen how far Archimedes omits actual calculations and only gives results. It will be observed that he gives two fractional approximations to $\sqrt{3}$ (one being less and the other greater than the real value) without any explanation as to how he arrived at them; and in like manner approximations to the square roots of several large numbers which are not complete squares are merely stated.

MEASUREMENT OF A CIRCLE 449

Hence
$$OD^2 : AD^2 [= (OA^2 + AD^2) : AD^2$$
$$> (571^2 + 153^2) : 153^2]$$
$$> 349450 : 23409,$$

so that $\quad OD : DA > 591\tfrac{1}{8} : 153.$ (4)

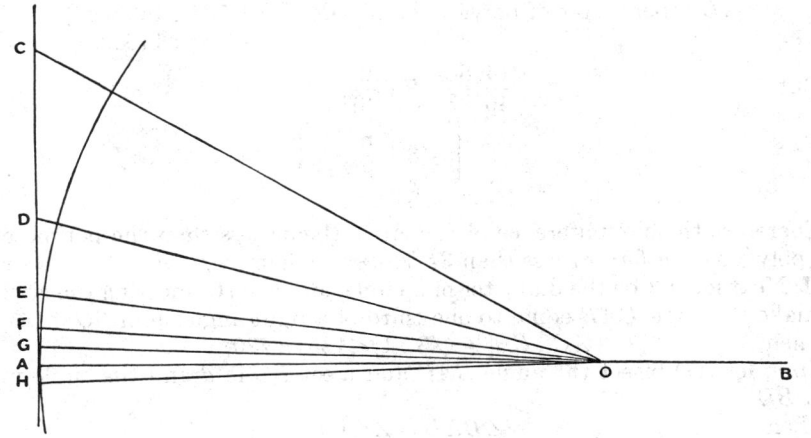

*Secondly*, let $OE$ bisect the angle $AOD$, meeting $AD$ in $E$.
[Then $\quad DO : OA = DE : EA$,
so that $\quad DO + OA : DA = OA : AE.$]
Therefore $\quad OA : AE [> (591\tfrac{1}{8} + 571) : 153$, by (3) and (4)]
$$> 1162\tfrac{1}{8} : 153.$$ (5)

[It follows that
$$OE^2 : EA^2 > \{(1162\tfrac{1}{8})^2 + 153^2\} : 153^2$$
$$> (1350534\tfrac{33}{64} + 23409) : 23409$$
$$> 1373943\tfrac{33}{64} : 23409.]$$

Thus $\quad OE : EA > 1172\tfrac{1}{8} : 153.$ (6)

*Thirdly*, let $OF$ bisect the angle $AOE$ and meet $AE$ in $F$.
We thus obtain the result [corresponding to (3) and (5) above] that
$$OA : AF [> (1162\tfrac{1}{8} + 1172\tfrac{1}{8}) : 153]$$
$$> 2334\tfrac{1}{4} : 153.$$ (7)

[Therefore $\quad OF^2 : FA^2 > \{(2334\tfrac{1}{4})^2 + 153^2\} : 153^2$
$$> 5472132\tfrac{1}{16} : 23409.]$$

Thus $\quad OF : FA > 2339\tfrac{1}{4} : 153.$ (8)

*Fourthly*, let $OG$ bisect the angle $AOF$, meeting $AF$ in $G$.
We have then
$$OA : AG [> (2334\tfrac{1}{4} + 2339\tfrac{1}{4}) : 153, \text{ by means of (7) and (8)}]$$
$$> 4673\tfrac{1}{2} : 153.$$

Now the angle $AOC$, which is one-third of a right angle, has been bisected four times, and it follows that
$$\angle AOG = \tfrac{1}{48} \text{ (a right angle)}.$$

Make the angle $AOH$ on the other side of $OA$ equal to the angle $AOG$, and let $GA$ produced meet $OH$ in $H$.
Then $\quad \angle GOH = \tfrac{1}{24}$ (a right angle).

Thus $GH$ is one side of a regular polygon of 96 sides circumscribed to the given circle.

And, since $\quad OA : AG > 4673\frac{1}{2} : 153,$
while $\quad AB = 2OA, \ GH = 2AG,$
it follows that
$$AB : (\text{perimeter of polygon of 96 sides})[> 4673\frac{1}{2} : 153 \times 96]$$
$$> 4673\frac{1}{2} : 14688.$$

But $\quad \dfrac{14688}{4673\frac{1}{2}} = 3 + \dfrac{667\frac{1}{2}}{4673\frac{1}{2}}$

$$\left[ < 3 + \dfrac{667\frac{1}{2}}{4672\frac{1}{2}} \right]$$
$$< 3\tfrac{1}{7}.$$

Therefore the circumference of the circle (being less than the perimeter of the polygon) is *a fortiori* less than $3\frac{1}{7}$ times the diameter $AB$.

II. Next let $AB$ be the diameter of a circle, and let $AC$, meeting the circle in $C$, make the angle $CAB$ equal to one-third of a right angle. Join $BC$.

Then $\quad AC : CB [= \sqrt{3} : 1] < 1351 : 780.$

*First*, let $AD$ bisect the angle $BAC$ and meet $BC$ in $d$ and the circle in $D$. Join $BD$.

Then
$$\angle BAD = \angle dAC$$
$$= \angle dBD,$$
and the angles at $D$, $C$ are both right angles.

It follows that the triangles $ADB$, $[ACd]$, $BDd$ are similar.

Therefore $\quad AD : DB = BD : Dd$
$$[= AC : Cd]$$
$$= AB : Bd \qquad \text{[Eucl. VI. 3]}$$
$$= AB + AC : Bd + Cd$$
$$= AB + AC : BC$$

or $\quad BA + AC : BC = AD : DB.$

[But $\quad AC : CB < 1351 : 780,$ from above,
while $\quad BA : BC = 2 : 1$
$$= 1560 : 780.]$$

Therefore $\quad AD : DB < 2911 : 780.$ \hfill (1)

[Hence $\quad AB^2 : BD^2 < (2911^2 + 780^2) : 780^2$
$$< 9082321 : 608400.]$$

Thus $\quad AB : BD < 3013\frac{3}{4} : 780.$ \hfill (2)

*Secondly*, let $AE$ bisect the angle $BAD$, meeting the circle in $E$; and let $BE$ be joined.

Then we prove, in the same way as before, that
$$AE : EB [= BA + AD : BD$$
$$< (3013\tfrac{3}{4} + 2911) : 780, \text{ by (1) and (2)}]$$
$$< 5924\tfrac{3}{4} : 780$$
$$< 5924\tfrac{3}{4} \times \tfrac{4}{13} : 780 \times \tfrac{4}{13}$$
$$< 1823 : 240. \qquad (3)$$

[Hence $\quad AB^2 : BE^2 < (1823^2 + 240^2) : 240^2$
$$< 3380929 : 57600.]$$

Therefore $\quad AB : BE < 1838\tfrac{9}{11} : 240.$ \hfill (4)

*Thirdly*, let $AF$ bisect the angle $BAE$, meeting the circle in $F$.

MEASUREMENT OF A CIRCLE        451

Thus  $AF : FB [= BA + AE : BE$
$< 3661\frac{9}{11} : 240$, by (3) and (4)]
$< 3661\frac{9}{11} \times \frac{11}{40} : 240 \times \frac{11}{40}$
$< 1007 : 66.$         (5)

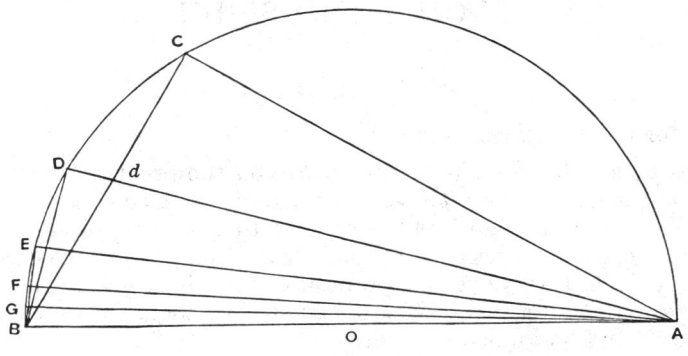

[It follows that
$$AB^2 : BF^2 < (1007^2 + 66^2) : 66^2$$
$$< 1018405 : 4356.]$$
Therefore   $AB : BF < 1009\frac{1}{6} : 66.$       (6)
*Fourthly*, let the angle $BAF$ be bisected by $AG$ meeting the circle in $G$.
Then   $AG : GB [= BA + AF : BF]$
$< 2016\frac{1}{6} : 66$, by (5) and (6).
[And   $AB^2 : BG^2 < \{(2016\frac{1}{6})^2 + 66^2\} : 66^2$
$< 4069284\frac{1}{36} : 4356.]$
Therefore   $AB : BG < 2017\frac{1}{4} : 66,$
whence   $BG : AB > 66 : 2017\frac{1}{4}.$       (7)
[Now the angle $BAG$ which is the result of the fourth bisection of the angle $BAC$, or of one-third of a right angle, is equal to one-fortyeighth of a right angle.

Thus the angle subtended by $BG$ at the centre is
$\frac{1}{24}$ (a right angle).]

Therefore $BG$ is a side of a regular inscribed polygon of 96 sides.
It follows from (7) that
(perimeter of polygon) $: AB [> 96 \times 66 : 2017\frac{1}{4}]$
$> 6336 : 2017\frac{1}{4}.$

And   $\dfrac{6336}{2017\frac{1}{4}} > 3\frac{10}{71}.$

Much more then is the circumference of the circle greater than $3\frac{10}{71}$ times the diameter.

Thus the ratio of the circumference to the diameter
$< 3\frac{1}{7}$ but $> 3\frac{10}{71}.$

# ON CONOIDS AND SPHEROIDS

## INTRODUCTION[1]

"ARCHIMEDES to Dositheus greeting.

"In this book I have set forth and send you the proofs of the remaining theorems not included in what I sent you before, and also of some others discovered later which, though I had often tried to investigate them previously, I had failed to arrive at because I found their discovery attended with some difficulty. And this is why even the propositions themselves were not published with the rest. But afterwards, when I had studied them with greater care, I discovered what I had failed in before.

"Now the remainder of the earlier theorems were propositions concerning the right-angled conoid [paraboloid of revolution]; but the discoveries which I have now added relate to an obtuse-angled conoid [hyperboloid of revolution] and to spheroidal figures, some of which I call *oblong* and others *flat*."

I. "Concerning the *right-angled conoid* it was laid down that, if a section of a right-angled cone [a parabola] be made to revolve about the diameter [axis] which remains fixed and return to the position from which it started, the figure comprehended by the section of the right-angled cone is called a *right-angled conoid*, and the diameter which has remained fixed is called its *axis*, while its *vertex* is the point in which the axis meets the surface of the conoid. And if a plane touch the right-angled conoid, and another plane drawn parallel to the tangent plane cut off a segment of the conoid, the *base* of the segment cut off is defined as the portion intercepted by the section of the conoid on the cutting plane, the *vertex* [of the segment] as the point in which the first plane touches the conoid, and the *axis* [of the segment] as the portion cut off within the segment from the line drawn through the vertex of the segment parallel to the axis of the conoid.

"The questions propounded for consideration were"

(1) "why, if a segment of the right-angled conoid be cut off by a plane at right angles to the axis, will the segment so cut off be half as large again as the cone which has the same base as the segment and the same axis, and"

(2) "why, if two segments be cut off from the right-angled conoid by planes drawn in any manner, will the segments so cut off have to one another the duplicate ratio of their axes."

II. "Respecting the *obtuse-angled conoid* we lay down the following premisses. If there be in a plane a section of an obtuse-angled cone [a hyperbola], its

---

[1] The whole of this introductory matter, including the definitions, is translated literally from the Greek text in order that the terminology of Archimedes may be faithfully represented. When this has once been set out, nothing will be lost by returning to modern phraseology and notation. These will accordingly be employed, as usual, when we come to the actual propositions of the treatise.

diameter [axis], and the nearest lines to the section of the obtuse-angled cone [*i.e.* the asymptotes of the hyperbola], and if, the diameter [axis] remaining fixed, the plane containing the aforesaid lines be made to revolve about it and return to the position from which it started, the nearest lines to the section of the obtuse-angled cone [the asymptotes] will clearly comprehend an isosceles cone whose vertex will be the point of concourse of the nearest lines and whose axis will be the diameter [axis] which has remained fixed. The figure comprehended by the section of the obtuse-angled cone is called an *obtuse-angled conoid* [hyperboloid of revolution], its *axis* is the diameter which has remained fixed, and its *vertex* the point in which the axis meets the surface of the conoid. The cone comprehended by the nearest lines to the section of the obtuse-angled cone is called [the cone] *enveloping the conoid*, and the straight line between the vertex of the conoid and the vertex of the cone enveloping the conoid is called [the line] *adjacent to the axis*. And if a plane touch the obtuse-angled conoid, and another plane drawn parallel to the tangent plane cut off a segment of the conoid, the *base* of the segment so cut off is defined as the portion intercepted by the section of the conoid on the cutting plane, the *vertex* [of the segment] as the point of contact of the plane which touches the conoid, the *axis* [of the segment] as the portion cut off within the segment from the line drawn through the vertex of the segment and the vertex of the cone enveloping the conoid; and the straight line between the said vertices is called *adjacent to the axis*.

"Right-angled conoids are all similar; but of obtuse-angled conoids let those be called similar in which the cones enveloping the conoids are similar.

"The following questions are propounded for consideration":

(1) "why, if a segment be cut off from the obtuse-angled conoid by a plane at right angles to the axis, the segment so cut off has to the cone which has the same base as the segment and the same axis the ratio which the line equal to the sum of the axis of the segment and three times the line adjacent to the axis bears to the line equal to the sum of the axis of the segment and twice the line adjacent to the axis, and"

(2) "why, if a segment of the obtuse-angled conoid be cut off by a plane not at right angles to the axis, the segment so cut off will bear to the figure which has the same base as the segment and the same axis, being a segment of a cone, the ratio which the line equal to the sum of the axis of the segment and three times the line adjacent to the axis bears to the line equal to the sum of the axis of the segment and twice the line adjacent to the axis."

III. "Concerning spheroidal figures we lay down the following premises. If a section of an acute-angled cone [ellipse] be made to revolve about the greater diameter [major axis] which remains fixed and return to the position from which it started, the figure comprehended by the section of the acute-angled cone is called an *oblong spheroid*. But if the section of the acute-angled cone revolve about the lesser diameter [minor axis] which remains fixed and return to the position from which it started, the figure comprehended by the section of the acute-angled cone is called a *flat spheroid*. In either of the spheroids the *axis* is defined as the diameter [axis] which has remained fixed, the *vertex* as the point in which the axis meets the surface of the spheroid, the *centre* as the middle point of the axis, and the *diameter* as the line drawn through the centre at right angles to the axis. And, if parallel planes touch, without cutting, either of the spheroidal figures, and if another plane be drawn parallel to the tangent planes and cutting the spheroid, the *base* of the resulting segments is defined as the portion intercepted by the section of the spheroid on the cutting plane, their *vertices* as the points in which the parallel planes touch the spheroid, and their *axes* as the portions cut off within the segments from the straight line joining their vertices. And that the planes touching the spheroid meet its surface at one point only, and that the straight line joining the points of contact passes through the centre of the spheroid, we shall prove. Those spheroidal figures are called *similar* in which the axes have the same ratio to the 'diameters.' And let segments of spheroidal figures and conoids be called *similar* if they are cut off from similar figures and have their bases similar, while their axes, being either at right angles to the planes of the bases or making equal angles with the corresponding diameters [axes] of the bases, have the same ratio to one another as the corresponding diameters [axes] of the bases.

"The following questions about spheroids are propounded for consideration,"

(1) "why, if one of the spheroidal figures be cut by a plane through the centre at right angles to the axis, each of the resulting segments will be double of the cone having the same base as the segment and the same axis; while, if the plane of section be at right angles to the axis without passing through the centre, (a) the greater of the resulting segments will bear to the cone which has the same base as the segment and the same axis the ratio which the line equal to the sum of half the straight line which is the axis of the spheroid and the axis of the lesser segment bears to the axis of the lesser segment, and (b) the lesser segment bears to the cone which has the same base as the segment and the same axis the ratio which the line equal to the sum of half the straight line which is the axis of the spheroid and the axis of the greater segment bears to the axis of the greater segment";

(2) "why, if one of the spheroids be cut by a plane passing through the centre but not at right angles to the axis, each of the resulting segments will be double of the figure having the same base as the segment and the same axis and consisting of a segment of a cone.

(3) "But, if the plane cutting the spheroid be neither through the centre nor at right angles to the axis, (a) the greater of the resulting segments will have to the figure which has the same base as the segment and the same axis the ratio which the line equal to the sum of half the line joining the vertices of the segments and the axis of the lesser segment bears to the axis of the lesser segment, and (b) the lesser segment will have to the figure with the same base as the segment and the same axis the ratio which the line equal to the sum of half the line joining the vertices of the segments and the axis of the greater segment bears to the axis of the greater segment. And the figure referred to is in these cases also a segment of a cone.

"When the aforesaid theorems are proved, there are discovered by means of them many theorems and problems.

"Such, for example, are the theorems":

(1) "that similar spheroids and similar segments both of spheroidal figures and conoids have to one another the triplicate ratio of their axes, and"

(2) "that in equal spheroidal figures the squares on the 'diameters' are reciprocally proportional to the axes, and, if in spheroidal figures the squares on

the 'diameters' are reciprocally proportional to the axes, the spheroids are equal.

"Such also is the problem, From a given spheroidal figure or conoid to cut off a segment by a plane drawn parallel to a given plane so that the segment cut off is equal to a given cone or cylinder or to a given sphere.

"After prefixing therefore the theorems and directions which are necessary for the proof of them, I will then proceed to expound the propositions themselves to you. Farewell."

## DEFINITIONS

"If a cone be cut by a plane meeting all the sides [generators] of the cone, the section will be either a circle or a section of an acute-angled cone [an ellipse]. If then the section be a circle, it is clear that the segment cut off from the cone towards the same parts as the vertex of the cone will be a cone. But, if the section be a section of an acute-angled cone [an ellipse], let the figure cut off from the cone towards the same parts as the vertex of the cone be called a *segment of a cone*. Let the *base* of the segment be defined as the plane comprehended by the section of the acute-angled cone, its *vertex* as the point which is also the vertex of the cone, and its *axis* as the straight line joining the vertex of the cone to the centre of the section of the acute-angled cone.

"And if a cylinder be cut by two parallel planes meeting all the sides [generators] of the cylinder, the sections will be either circles or sections of acute-angled cones [ellipses] equal and similar to one another. If then the sections be circles, it is clear that the figure cut off from the cylinder between the parallel planes will be a cylinder. But, if the sections be sections of acute-angled cones [ellipses], let the figure cut off from the cylinder between the parallel planes be called a *frustum of a cylinder*. And let the *bases* of the frustum be defined as the planes comprehended by the sections of the acute-angled cones [ellipses], and the *axis* as the straight line joining the centres of the sections of the acute-angled cones, so that the axis will be in the same straight line with the axis of the cylinder."

## LEMMA

*If in an ascending arithmetical progression consisting of the magnitudes $A_1$, $A_2, \cdots A_n$ the common difference be equal to the least term $A_1$, then*

$$n \cdot A_n < 2(A_1 + A_2 + \cdots + A_n),$$

and

$$> 2(A_1 + A_2 + \cdots + A_{n-1}).$$

[The proof of this is given incidentally in the treatise *On Spirals*, Prop. 11. By placing lines side by side to represent the terms of the progression and then producing each so as to make it equal to the greatest term, Archimedes gives the equivalent of the following proof.

If $\qquad S_n = A_1 + A_2 + \cdots + A_{n-1} + A_n,$
we have also $\qquad S_n = A_n + A_{n-1} + A_{n-2} + \cdots + A_1.$
And $\qquad A_1 + A_{n-1} = A_2 + A_{n-2} = \cdots = A_n.$
Therefore $\qquad 2S_n = (n+1)A_n,$
whence $\qquad n \cdot A_n < 2S_n,$
and $\qquad n \cdot A_n > 2S_{n-1}.$

Thus, if the progression is $a, 2a, \cdots na,$

$$S_n = \frac{n(n+1)}{2}a,$$

and $n^2 a < 2S_n,$
but $\qquad\qquad\qquad > 2S_{n-1}.$]

## Proposition 1

If $A_1, B_1, C_1, \ldots K_1$ and $A_2, B_2, C_2, \ldots K_2$ be two series of magnitudes such that
$$\left.\begin{aligned} A_1 : B_1 &= A_2 : B_2, \\ B_1 : C_1 &= B_2 : C_2, \text{ and so on,} \end{aligned}\right\} \qquad (\alpha)$$
and if $A_3, B_3, C_3, \ldots K_3$ and $A_4, B_4, C_4, \ldots K_4$ be two other series such that
$$\left.\begin{aligned} A_1 : A_3 &= A_2 : A_4, \\ B_1 : B_3 &= B_2 : B_4, \text{ and so on,} \end{aligned}\right\} \qquad (\beta)$$
then
$$(A_1+B_1+C_1+\cdots+K_1) : (A_3+B_3+C_3+\cdots+K_3)$$
$$= (A_2+B_2+C_2+\cdots+K_2) : (A_4+B_4+\cdots+K_4).$$

The proof is as follows.
Since $\qquad\qquad A_3 : A_1 = A_4 : A_2,$
and $\qquad\qquad A_1 : B_1 = A_2 : B_2,$
while $\qquad\qquad B_1 : B_3 = B_2 : B_4,$
we have, *ex aequali,* $\quad A_3 : B_3 = A_4 : B_4.$
Similarly $\qquad\qquad B_3 : C_3 = B_4 : C_4,$ and so on. $\Big\} \qquad (\gamma)$

Again, it follows from equations $(\alpha)$ that
$$A_1 : A_2 = B_1 : B_2 = C_1 : C_2 = \cdots$$
Therefore
$$A_1 : A_2 = (A_1+B_1+C_1+\cdots+K_1) : (A_2+B_2+\cdots+K_2),$$
or $\quad (A_1+B_1+C_1+\cdots+K_1) : A_1 = (A_2+B_2+C_2+\cdots+K_2) : A_2;$
and $\qquad\qquad A_1 : A_3 = A_2 : A_4,$
while from equations $(\gamma)$ it follows in like manner that
$$A_3 : (A_3+B_3+C_3+\cdots+K_3) = A_4 : (A_4+B_4+C_4+\cdots+K_4).$$
By the last three equations, *ex aequali,*
$$(A_1+B_1+C_1+\cdots+K_1) : (A_3+B_3+C_3+\cdots+K_3)$$
$$= (A_2+B_2+C_2+\cdots+K_2) : (A_4+B_4+C_4+\cdots+K_4).$$

Cor. If any terms in the third and fourth series corresponding to terms in the first and second be left out, the result is the same. For example, if the last terms $K_3, K_4$ are absent,
$$(A_1+B_1+C_1+\cdots+K_1) : (A_3+B_3+C_3+\cdots+I_3)$$
$$= (A_2+B_2+C_2+\cdots+K_2) : (A_4+B_4+C_4+\cdots+I_4),$$
where $I$ immediately precedes $K$ in each series.

## Lemma to Proposition 2

### [*On Spirals*, Prop. 10.]

If $A_1, A_2, A_3, \ldots A_n$ be $n$ lines forming an ascending arithmetical progression in which the common difference is equal to the least term $A_1$, then
$$(n+1)A_n^2 + A_1(A_1+A_2+A_3+\cdots+A_n) = 3(A_1^2+A_2^2+A_3^2+\cdots+A_n^2).$$

Let the lines $A_n, A_{n-1}, A_{n-2}, \ldots A_1$ be placed in a row from left to right. Produce $A_{n-1}, A_{n-2}, \ldots A_1$ until they are each equal to $A_n$, so that the parts produced are respectively equal to $A_1, A_2, \ldots A_{n-1}$.

Taking each line successively, we have
$$2A_n^2 = 2A_n^2,$$
$$(A_1+A_{n-1})^2 = A_1^2 + A_{n-1}^2 + 2A_1 \cdot A_{n-1},$$
$$(A_2+A_{n-2})^2 = A_2^2 + A_{n-2}^2 + 2A_2 \cdot A_{n-2},$$

$$(A_{n-1}+A_1)^2 = A^2{}_{n-1}+A_1{}^2+2A_{n-1}\cdot A_1.$$

And, by addition,
$$(n+1)A_n{}^2 = 2(A_1{}^2+A_2{}^2+\cdots+A_n{}^2)$$
$$+2A_1\cdot A_{n-1}+2A_2\cdot A_{n-2}+\cdots+2A_{n-1}\cdot A_1.$$

Therefore, in order to obtain the required result, we have to prove that
$$2(A_1\cdot A_{n-1}+A_2\cdot A_{n-2}+\cdots+A_{n-1}\cdot A_1)+$$
$$A_1(A_1+A_2+A_3+\cdots+A_n)$$
$$= A_1{}^2+A_2{}^2+\cdots+A_n{}^2. \qquad (\alpha)$$

Now
$$2A_2\cdot A_{n-2} = A_1\cdot 4A_{n-2}, \text{ because } A_2=2A_1,$$
$$2A_3\cdot A_{n-3} = A_1\cdot 6A_{n-3}, \text{ because } A_3=3A_1,$$
$$\cdots\cdots\cdots\cdots\cdots\cdots$$
$$2A_{n-1}\cdot A_1 = A_1\cdot 2(n-1)A_1.$$

It follows that
$$2(A_1\cdot A_{n-1}+A_2\cdot A_{n-2}+\cdots+A_{n-1}\cdot A_1)+$$
$$A_1(A_1+A_2+\cdots+A_n) = A_1\{A_n+3A_{n-1}+5A_{n-2}+\cdots+(2n-1)A_1\}.$$

And this last expression can be proved to be equal to
$$A_1{}^2+A_2{}^2+\cdots+A_n{}^2.$$

For
$$A_n{}^2 = A_1(n\cdot A_n)$$
$$= A_1\{A_n+(n-1)A_n\}$$
$$= A_1\{A_n+2(A_{n-1}+A_{n-2}+\cdots+A_1)\},$$
because $(n-1)A_n = A_{n-1}+A_1$
$$+A_{n-2}+A_2$$
$$+\cdots\cdots\cdots$$
$$+A_1+A_{n-1}.$$

Similarly $\quad A^2{}_{n-1} = A_1\{A_{n-1}+2(A_{n-2}+A_{n-3}+\cdots+A_1)\},$
$$\cdots\cdots\cdots\cdots\cdots\cdots$$
$$A_2{}^2 = A_1(A_2+2A_1),$$
$$A_1{}^2 = A_1\cdot A_1;$$

whence, by addition,
$$A_1{}^2+A_2{}^2+A_3{}^2+\cdots+A_n{}^2 = A_1\{A_n+3A_{n-1}+5A_{n-2}+\cdots+(2n-1)A_1\}.$$

Thus the equation marked ($\alpha$) above is true; and it follows that
$$(n+1)A_n{}^2+A_1(A_1+A_2+A_3+\cdots+A_n) = 3(A_1{}^2+A_2{}^2+\cdots+A_n{}^2).$$

COR. 1. *From this it is evident that*
$$n\cdot A_n{}^2 < 3(A_1{}^2+A_2{}^2+\cdots+A_n{}^2). \qquad (1)$$

Also $\quad A_n{}^2 = A_1\{A_n+2(A_{n-1}+A_{n-2}+\cdots+A_1)\},$ as above,
so that $\quad A_n{}^2 > A_1(A_n+A_{n-1}+\cdots+A_1),$
and therefore
$$A_n{}^2+A_1(A_1+A_2+\cdots+A_n) < 2A_n{}^2.$$

*It follows from the proposition that*
$$n\cdot A_n{}^2 > 3(A_1{}^2+A_2{}^2+\cdots+A^2{}_{n-1}). \qquad (2)$$

COR. 2. All these results will hold if we substitute *similar figures* for squares on all the lines; for similar figures are in the duplicate ratio of their sides.

## Proposition 2

If $A_1, A_2 \cdots A_n$ be any number of areas such that
$$A_1 = ax + x^2,$$
$$A_2 = a \cdot 2x + (2x)^2,$$
$$A_3 = a \cdot 3x + (3x)^2,$$
$$\cdots\cdots\cdots\cdots\cdots$$
$$A_n = a \cdot nx + (nx)^2,$$

then
$$n \cdot A_n : (A_1 + A_2 + \cdots + A_n) < (a + nx) : \left(\frac{a}{2} + \frac{nx}{3}\right),$$

and
$$n \cdot A_n : (A_1 + A_2 + \cdots + A_{n-1}) > (a + nx) : \left(\frac{a}{2} + \frac{nx}{3}\right).$$

For, by the Lemma immediately preceding Prop. 1,
$$n \cdot anx < (ax + a \cdot 2x + \cdots + a \cdot nx),$$
and
$$> 2(ax + a \cdot 2x + \cdots + a \cdot \overline{n-1}x).$$

Also, by the Lemma preceding this proposition,
$$n \cdot (nx)^2 < 3\{x^2 + (2x)^2 + (3x)^2 + \cdots + (nx)^2\}$$
and
$$> 3\{x^2 + (2x)^2 + \cdots + (\overline{n-1}x)^2\}.$$

Hence
$$\frac{an^2 x}{2} + \frac{n(nx)^2}{3} < [(ax + x^2) + \{a \cdot 2x + (2x)^2\} + \cdots + \{a \cdot nx + (nx)^2\}],$$

and
$$> [(ax + x^2) + \{a \cdot 2x + (2x)^2\} + \cdots + \{a \cdot \overline{n-1}x + (\overline{n-1}x)^2\}],$$

or
$$\frac{an^2 x}{2} + \frac{n(nx)^2}{3} < A_1 + A_2 + \cdots + A_n,$$

and
$$> A_1 + A_2 + \cdots + A_{n-1}.$$

It follows that
$$n \cdot A_n : (A_1 + A_2 + \cdots + A_n) < n\{a \cdot nx + (nx)^2\} : \left\{\frac{an^2 x}{2} + \frac{n(nx)^2}{3}\right\},$$

or
$$n \cdot A_n : (A_1 + A_2 + \cdots + A_n) < (a + nx) : \left(\frac{a}{2} + \frac{nx}{3}\right);$$

also
$$n \cdot A_n : (A_1 + A_2 + \cdots + A_{n-1}) > (a + nx) : \left(\frac{a}{2} + \frac{nx}{3}\right).$$

## Proposition 3

(1) *If TP, TP' be two tangents to any conic meeting in T, and if Qq, Q'q' be any two chords parallel respectively to TP, TP' and meeting in O, then*
$$QO \cdot Oq : Q'O \cdot Oq' = TP^2 : TP'^2.$$
"And this is proved in the elements of conics."[1]

(2) *If QQ' be a chord of a parabola bisected in V by the diameter PV, and if PV be of constant length, then the areas of the triangle PQQ' and of the segment PQQ' are both constant whatever be the direction of QQ'.*

Let $ABB'$ be the particular segment of the parabola whose vertex is $A$, so that $BB'$ is bisected perpendicularly by the axis at the point $H$, where $AH = PV$.

Draw $QD$ perpendicular to $PV$.

---

[1] In the treatises on conics by Aristaeus and Euclid.

ON CONOIDS AND SPHEROIDS 459

Let $p_a$ be the parameter of the principal ordinates, and let $p$ be another line of such length that

$$QV^2 : QD^2 = p : p_a;$$

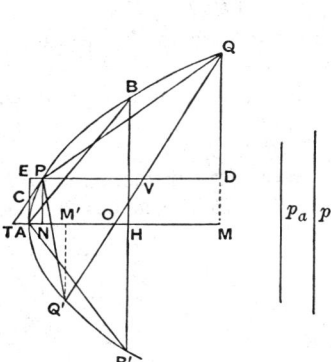

it will then follow that $p$ is equal to the parameter of the ordinates to the diameter $PV$, i.e. those which are parallel to $QV$.

"For this is proved in the conics."[1]

Thus $QV^2 = p \cdot PV$.

And $BH^2 = p_a \cdot AH$, while $AH = PV$.

Therefore $QV^2 : BH^2 = p : p_a$.

But $QV^2 : QD^2 = p : p_a$;

hence $BH = QD$.

Thus $BH \cdot AH = QD \cdot PV$,

and therefore $\triangle ABB' = \triangle PQQ'$;

that is, the area of the triangle $PQQ'$ is constant so long as $PV$ is of constant length.

Hence also the area of the segment $PQQ'$ is constant under the same conditions; for the segment is equal to $\frac{4}{3}\triangle PQQ'$. [*Quadrature of the Parabola*, Prop. 17 or 24.]

PROPOSITION 4

*The area of any ellipse is to that of the auxiliary circle as the minor axis to the major.*

Let $AA'$ be the major and $BB'$ the minor axis of the ellipse, and let $BB'$ meet the auxiliary circle in $b$, $b'$.

Suppose $O$ to be such a circle that

$$(\text{circle } AbA'b') : O = CA : CB.$$

Then shall $O$ be equal to the area of the ellipse.

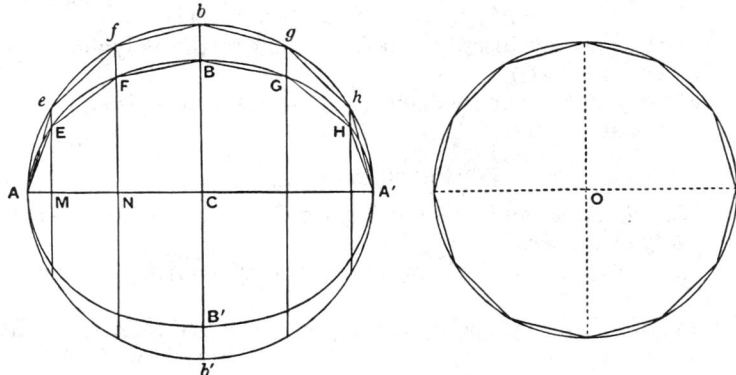

For, if not, $O$ must be either greater or less than the ellipse.

I. If possible, let $O$ be greater than the ellipse.

We can then inscribe in the circle $O$ an equilateral polygon of $4n$ sides such that its area is greater than that of the ellipse. [cf. *On the Sphere and Cylinder*, I. 6.]

[1]The theorem which is here assumed by Archimedes as known . . . is easily deduced from Apollonius I. 49. . . .

Let this be done, and inscribe in the auxiliary circle of the ellipse the polygon $AefbghA'\ldots$ similar to that inscribed in $O$. Let the perpendiculars $eM, fN, \ldots$ on $AA'$ meet the ellipse in $E, F, \ldots$ respectively. Join $AE, EF, FB, \ldots$.

Suppose that $P'$ denotes the area of the polygon inscribed in the auxiliary circle, and $P$ that of the polygon inscribed in the ellipse.

Then, since all the lines $eM, fN, \cdots$ are cut in the same proportions at $E, F, \ldots,$
i.e.
$$eM : EM = fN : FN = \cdots = bC : BC,$$
the pairs of triangles, as $eAM$, $EAM$, and the pairs of trapeziums, as $eMNf$, $EMNF$, are all in the same ratio to one another as $bC$ to $BC$, or as $CA$ to $CB$.

Therefore, by addition,
$$P' : P = CA : CB.$$

Now $P'$ : (polygon inscribed in $O$)
$$= (\text{circle } AbA'b') : O$$
$$= CA : CB, \text{ by hypothesis.}$$

Therefore $P$ is equal to the polygon inscribed in $O$.

But this is impossible, because the latter polygon is by hypothesis greater than the ellipse, and *a fortiori* greater than $P$.

Hence $O$ is not greater than the ellipse.

II. If possible, let $O$ be less than the ellipse.

In this case we inscribe in the *ellipse* a polygon $P$ with $4n$ equal sides such that $P > O$.

Let the perpendiculars from the angular points on the axis $AA'$ be produced to meet the auxiliary circle, and let the corresponding polygon ($P'$) in the circle be formed.

Inscribe in $O$ a polygon similar to $P'$.
Then $\qquad P' : P = CA : CB$
$$= (\text{circle } AbA'b') : O, \text{ by hypothesis,}$$
$$= P' : (\text{polygon inscribed in } O).$$

Therefore the polygon inscribed in $O$ is equal to the polygon $P$; which is impossible, because $P > O$.

Hence $O$, being neither greater nor less than the ellipse, is equal to it; and the required result follows.

## Proposition 5

*If $AA'$, $BB'$ be the major and minor axis of an ellipse respectively, and if $d$ be the diameter of any circle, then*
$$(\text{area of ellipse}) : (\text{area of circle}) = AA' \cdot BB' : d^2.$$

For
$$(\text{area of ellipse}) : (\text{area of auxiliary circle}) = BB' : AA' \qquad [\text{Prop. 4}]$$
$$= AA' \cdot BB' : AA'^2.$$

And
$$(\text{area of aux. circle}) : (\text{area of circle with diam. } d) = AA'^2 : d^2.$$
Therefore the required result follows *ex aequali*.

## Proposition 6

*The areas of ellipses are as the rectangles under their axes.*

This follows at once from Props. 4, 5.

Cor. *The areas of similar ellipses are as the squares of corresponding axes.*

## ON CONOIDS AND SPHEROIDS

### Proposition 7

*Given an ellipse with centre C, and a line CO drawn perpendicular to its plane, it is possible to find a circular cone with vertex O and such that the given ellipse is a section of it [or, in other words, to find the circular sections of the cone with vertex O passing through the circumference of the ellipse].*

Conceive an ellipse with $BB'$ as its minor axis and lying in a plane perpendicular to that of the paper. Let $CO$ be drawn perpendicular to the plane of the ellipse, and let $O$ be the vertex of the required cone. Produce $OB, OC, OB'$, and in the same plane with them draw $BED$ meeting $OC, OB'$ produced in $E, D$ respectively and in such a direction that
$$BE \cdot ED : EO^2 = CA^2 : CO^2,$$
where $CA$ is half the major axis of the ellipse.

"And this is possible, since
$$BE \cdot ED : EO^2 > BC \cdot CB' : CO^2."$$
[Both the construction and this proposition are assumed as known.]

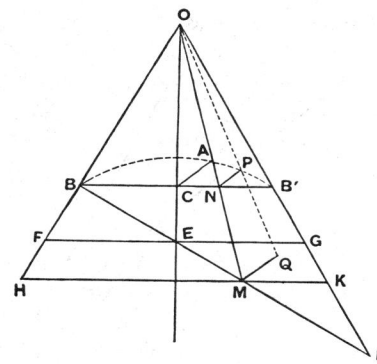

Now conceive a circle with $BD$ as diameter lying in a plane at right angles to that of the paper, and describe a cone with this circle for its base and with vertex $O$.

We have therefore to prove that the given ellipse is a section of the cone, or, if $P$ be any point on the ellipse, that $P$ lies on the surface of the cone.

Draw $PN$ perpendicular to $BB'$. Join $ON$ and produce it to meet $BD$ in $M$, and let $MQ$ be drawn in the plane of the circle on $BD$ as diameter perpendicular to $BD$ and meeting the circle in $Q$. Also let $FG$, $HK$ be drawn through $E, M$ respectively parallel to $BB'$.

We have then
$$QM^2 : HM \cdot MK = BM \cdot MD : HM \cdot MK$$
$$= BE \cdot ED : FE \cdot EG$$
$$= (BE \cdot ED : EO^2) \cdot (EO^2 : FE \cdot EG)$$
$$= (CA^2 : CO^2) \cdot (CO^2 : BC \cdot CB')$$
$$= CA^2 : CB^2$$
$$= PN^2 : BN \cdot NB'.$$
Therefore $\quad QM^2 : PN^2 = HM \cdot MK : BN \cdot NB'$
$$= OM^2 : ON^2;$$
whence, since $PN, QM$ are parallel, $OPQ$ is a straight line.

But $Q$ is on the circumference of the circle on $BD$ as diameter; therefore $OQ$ is a generator of the cone, and hence $P$ lies on the cone.

Thus the cone passes through all points on the ellipse.

### Proposition 8

*Given an ellipse, a plane through one of its axes $AA'$ and perpendicular to the plane of the ellipse, and a line CO drawn from C, the centre, in the given plane through $AA'$ but not perpendicular to $AA'$, it is possible to find a cone with vertex*

$O$ such that the given ellipse is a section of it [or, in other words, to find the circular sections of the cone with vertex $O$ whose surface passes through the circumference of the ellipse].

By hypothesis, $OA$, $OA'$ are unequal. Produce $OA'$ to $D$ so that $OA = OD$. Join $AD$, and draw $FG$ through $C$ parallel to it.

The given ellipse is to be supposed to lie in a plane perpendicular to the plane of the paper. Let $BB'$ be the other axis of the ellipse.

Conceive a plane through $AD$ perpendicular to the plane of the paper, and in it describe either (a), if $CB^2 = FC \cdot CG$, a circle with diameter $AD$, or (b), if not, an ellipse on $AD$ as axis such that, if $d$ be the other axis,
$$d^2 : AD^2 = CB^2 : FC \cdot CG.$$

Take a cone with vertex $O$ whose surface passes through the circle or ellipse just drawn. This is possible even when the curve is an ellipse, because the line from $O$ to the middle point of $AD$ is perpendicular to the plane of the ellipse, and the construction is effected by means of Prop. 7.

Let $P$ be any point on the given ellipse, and we have only to prove that $P$ lies on the surface of the cone so described.

Draw $PN$ perpendicular to $AA'$. Join $ON$, and produce it to meet $AD$ in $M$. Through $M$ draw $HK$ parallel to $A'A$.

Lastly, draw $MQ$ perpendicular to the plane of the paper (and therefore perpendicular to both $HK$ and $AD$) meeting the ellipse or circle about $AD$ (and therefore the surface of the cone) in $Q$.

Then
$$QM^2 : HM \cdot MK = (QM^2 : DM \cdot MA) \cdot (DM \cdot MA : HM \cdot MK)$$
$$= (d^2 : AD^2) \cdot (FC \cdot CG : A'C \cdot CA)$$
$$= (CB^2 : FC \cdot CG) \cdot (FC \cdot CG : A'C \cdot CA)$$
$$= CB^2 : CA^2$$
$$= PN^2 : A'N \cdot NA.$$

Therefore, alternately,
$$QM^2 : PN^2 = HM \cdot MK : A'N \cdot NA$$
$$= OM^2 : ON^2.$$

Thus, since $PN$, $QM$ are parallel, $OPQ$ is a straight line; and, $Q$ being on the surface of the cone, it follows that $P$ is also on the surface of the cone.

Similarly all points on the ellipse are also on the cone, and the ellipse is therefore a section of the cone.

## Proposition 9

*Given an ellipse, a plane through one of its axes and perpendicular to that of the ellipse, and a straight line $CO$ drawn from the centre $C$ of the ellipse in the given plane through the axis but not perpendicular to that axis, it is possible to find a* *cylinder with axis OC such that the ellipse is a section of it [or, in other words, to find the circular sections of the cylinder with axis OC whose surface passes through the circumference of the given ellipse].*

Let $AA'$ be an axis of the ellipse, and suppose the plane of the ellipse to be perpendicular to that of the paper, so that $OC$ lies in the plane of the paper.

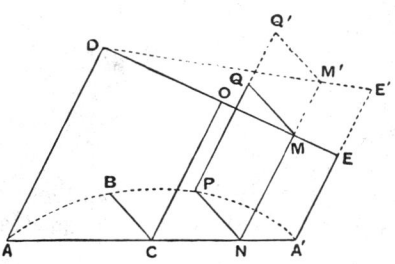

Draw $AD$, $A'E$ parallel to $CO$, and let $DE$ be the line through $O$ perpendicular to both $AD$ and $A'E$.

We have now three different cases according as the other axis $BB'$ of the ellipse is (1) equal to, (2) greater than, or (3) less than, $DE$.

(1) Suppose $BB' = DE$.

Draw a plane through $DE$ at right angles to $OC$, and in this plane describe a circle on $DE$ as diameter. Through this circle describe a cylinder with axis $OC$.

This cylinder shall be the cylinder required, or its surface shall pass through every point $P$ of the ellipse.

For, if $P$ be any point on the ellipse, draw $PN$ perpendicular to $AA'$; through $N$ draw $NM$ parallel to $CO$ meeting $DE$ in $M$, and through $M$, in the plane of the circle on $DE$ as diameter, draw $MQ$ perpendicular to $DE$, meeting the circle in $Q$.

Then, since 
$$DE = BB',$$
$$PN^2 : AN \cdot NA' = DO^2 : AC \cdot CA'.$$

And $$DM \cdot ME : AN \cdot NA' = DO^2 : AC^2,$$
since $AD$, $NM$, $CO$, $A'E$ are parallel.

Therefore 
$$PN^2 = DM \cdot ME$$
$$= QM^2,$$
by the property of the circle.

Hence, since $PN$, $QM$ are equal as well as parallel, $PQ$ is parallel to $MN$ and therefore to $CO$. It follows that $PQ$ is a generator of the cylinder, whose surface accordingly passes through $P$.

(2) If $BB' > DE$, we take $E'$ on $A'E$ such that $DE' = BB'$ and describe a circle on $DE'$ as diameter in a plane perpendicular to that of the paper; and the rest of the construction and proof is exactly similar to those given for case (1).

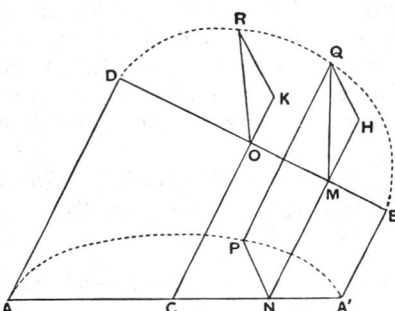

(3) Suppose $BB' < DE$.

Take a point $K$ on $CO$ produced such that 
$$DO^2 - CB^2 = OK^2.$$

From $K$ draw $KR$ perpendicular to the plane of the paper and equal to $CB$.

Thus $OR^2 = OK^2 + CB^2 = OD^2$.

In the plane containing $DE$, $OR$ describe a circle on $DE$ as diameter. Through this circle (which must pass through $R$) draw a cylinder with axis $OC$.

We have then to prove that, if $P$ be any point on the given ellipse, $P$ lies on the cylinder so described.

Draw $PN$ perpendicular to $AA'$, and through $N$ draw $NM$ parallel to $CO$ meeting $DE$ in $M$. In the plane of the circle on $DE$ as diameter draw $MQ$ perpendicular to $DE$ and meeting the circle in $Q$.

Lastly, draw $QH$ perpendicular to $NM$ produced. $QH$ will then be perpendicular to the plane containing $AC$, $DE$, i.e. the plane of the paper.

Now $\quad\quad QH^2 : QM^2 = KR^2 : OR^2$, by similar triangles.

And $\quad\quad QM^2 : AN \cdot NA' = DM \cdot ME : AN \cdot NA'$
$$= OD^2 : CA^2.$$

Hence, *ex aequali*, since $\quad OR = OD$,
$$QH^2 : AN \cdot NA' = KR^2 : CA^2$$
$$= CB^2 : CA^2$$
$$= PN^2 : AN \cdot NA'.$$

Thus $QH = PN$. And $QH$, $PN$ are also parallel. Accordingly $PQ$ is parallel to $MN$, and therefore to $CO$, so that $PQ$ is a generator, and the cylinder passes through $P$.

## Proposition 10

It was proved by the earlier geometers that *any two cones have to one another the ratio compounded of the ratios of their bases and of their heights*.[1] The same method of proof will show that *any segments of cones have to one another the ratio compounded of the ratios of their bases and of their heights*.

The proposition that *any 'frustum' of a cylinder is triple of the conical segment which has the same base as the frustum and equal height* is also proved in the same manner as the proposition that *the cylinder is triple of the cone which has the same base as the cylinder and equal height*.[2]

## Proposition 11

(1) *If a paraboloid of revolution be cut by a plane through, or parallel to, the axis, the section will be a parabola equal to the original parabola which by its revolution generates the paraboloid. And the axis of the section will be the intersection between the cutting plane and the plane through the axis of the paraboloid at right angles to the cutting plane.*

*If the paraboloid be cut by a plane at right angles to its axis, the section will be a circle whose centre is on the axis.*

(2) *If a hyperboloid of revolution be cut by a plane through the axis, parallel to the axis, or through the centre, the section will be a hyperbola, (a) if the section be through the axis, equal, (b) if parallel to the axis, similar, (c) if through the centre, not similar, to the original hyperbola which by its revolution generates the hyperboloid. And the axis of the section will be the intersection of the cutting plane and the plane through the axis of the hyperboloid at right angles to the cutting plane.*

*Any section of the hyperboloid by a plane at right angles to the axis will be a circle whose centre is on the axis.*

(3) *If any of the spheroidal figures be cut by a plane through the axis or parallel to the axis, the section will be an ellipse, (a) if the section be through the axis, equal, (b) if parallel to the axis, similar, to the ellipse which by its revolution gen-*

---

[1] This follows from Eucl. xii. 11 and 14 taken together. Cf. *On the Sphere and Cylinder* i, Lemma 1.

[2] This proposition was proved by Eudoxus, as stated in the preface to *On the Sphere and Cylinder* i. Cf. Eucl. xii. 10.

erates the figure. And the axis of the section will be the intersection of the cutting plane and the plane through the axis of the spheroid at right angles to the cutting plane.

If the section be by a plane at right angles to the axis of the spheroid, it will be a circle whose centre is on the axis.

(4) *If any of the said figures be cut by a plane through the axis, and if a perpendicular be drawn to the plane of section from any point on the surface of the figure but not on the section, that perpendicular will fall within the section.*

"And the proofs of all these propositions are evident."

## Proposition 12

*If a paraboloid of revolution be cut by a plane neither parallel nor pendicular to the axis, and if the plane through the axis perpendicular to the cutting plane intersect it in a straight line of which the portion intercepted within the paraboloid is $RR'$, the section of the paraboloid will be an ellipse whose major axis is $RR'$ and whose minor axis is equal to the perpendicular distance between the lines through $R$, $R'$ parallel to the axis of the paraboloid.*

Suppose the cutting plane to be perpendicular to the plane of the paper, and let the latter be the plane through the axis $ANF$ of the paraboloid which intersects the cutting plane at right angles in $RR'$. Let $RH$ be parallel to the axis of the paraboloid, and $R'H$ perpendicular to $RH$.

Let $Q$ be any point on the section made by the cutting plane, and from $Q$ draw $QM$ perpendicular to $RR'$. $QM$ will therefore be perpendicular to the plane of the paper.

Through $M$ draw $DMFE$ perpendicular to the axis $ANF$ meeting the parabolic section made by the plane of the paper in $D$, $E$. Then $QM$ is perpendicular to $DE$, and, if a plane be drawn through $DE$, $QM$, it will be perpendicular to the axis and will cut the paraboloid in a circular section.

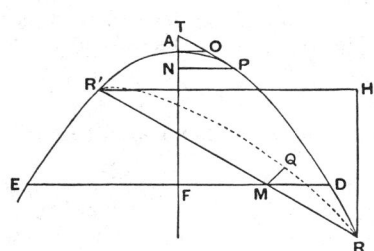

Since $Q$ is on this circle,
$$QM^2 = DM \cdot ME.$$

Again, if $PT$ be that tangent to the parabolic section in the plane of the paper which is parallel to $RR'$, and if the tangent at $A$ meet $PT$ in $O$, then, from the property of the parabola,

$DM \cdot ME : RM \cdot MR' = AO^2 : OP^2$ [Prop. 3 (1)]
$\qquad\qquad\qquad\qquad = AO^2 : OT^2$, since $AN = AT$.

Therefore $\quad QM^2 : RM \cdot MR' = AO^2 : OT^2$
$\qquad\qquad\qquad\qquad = R'H^2 : RR'^2,$
by similar triangles.

Hence $Q$ lies on an ellipse whose major axis is $RR'$ and whose minor axis is equal to $R'H$.

## Propositions 13, 14

*If a hyperboloid of revolution be cut by a plane meeting all the generators of the enveloping cone, or if an 'oblong' spheroid be cut by a plane not perpendicular to*

the axis,[1] *and if a plane through the axis intersect the cutting plane at right angles in a straight line on which the hyperboloid or spheroid intercepts a length* $RR'$, *then the section by the cutting plane will be an ellipse whose major axis is* $RR'$.

Suppose the cutting plane to be at right angles to the plane of the paper, and suppose the latter plane to be that through the axis $ANF$ which intersects the

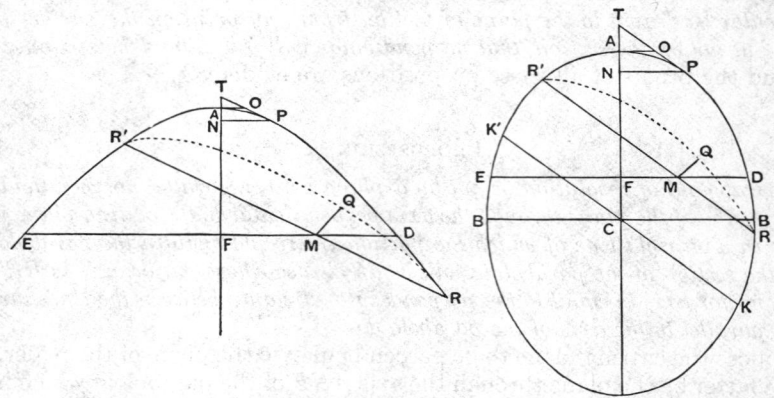

cutting plane at right angles in $RR'$. The section of the hyperboloid or spheroid by the plane of the paper is thus a hyperbola or ellipse having $ANF$ for its transverse or major axis.

Take any point on the section made by the cutting plane, as $Q$, and draw $QM$ perpendicular to $RR'$. $QM$ will then be perpendicular to the plane of the paper.

Through $M$ draw $DFE$ at right angles to the axis $ANF$ meeting the hyperbola or ellipse in $D$, $E$; and through $QM$, $DE$ let a plane be described. This plane will accordingly be perpendicular to the axis and will cut the hyperboloid or spheroid in a circular section.

Thus $\qquad QM^2 = DM \cdot ME$.

Let $PT$ be that tangent to the hyperbola or ellipse which is parallel to $RR'$, and let the tangent at $A$ meet $PT$ in $O$.

Then, by the property of the hyperbola or ellipse,
$$DM \cdot ME : RM \cdot MR' = OA^2 : OP^2,$$
or $\qquad QM^2 : RM \cdot MR' = OA^2 : OP^2$.

Now (1) in the hyperbola $OA < OP$, because $AT < AN$, and accordingly
$$OT < OP, \text{ while } OA < OT,$$

(2) in the ellipse, if $KK'$ be the diameter parallel to $RR'$, and $BB'$ the minor axis,
$$BC \cdot CB' : KC \cdot CK' = OA^2 : OP^2;$$
and $BC \cdot CB' < KC \cdot CK'$, so that $OA < OP$.

Hence in both cases the locus of $Q$ is an ellipse whose major axis is $RR'$.

Cor. 1. If the spheroid be a 'flat' spheroid, the section will be an ellipse, and everything will proceed as before except that $RR'$ will in this case be the *minor* axis.

[1] Archimedes begins Prop. 14 for the *spheroid* with the remark that, when the cutting plane passes through or is parallel to the axis, the case is clear. Cf. Prop. 11 (3).

COR 2. In all conoids or spheroids parallel sections will be similar, since the ratio $OA^2 : OP^2$ is the same for all the parallel sections.

## PROPOSITION 15

(1) *If from any point on the surface of a conoid a line be drawn, in the case of the paraboloid, parallel to the axis, and, in the case of the hyperboloid, parallel to any line passing through the vertex of the enveloping cone, the part of the straight line which is in the same direction as the convexity of the surface will fall without it, and the part which is in the other direction within it.*

For, if a plane be drawn, in the case of the paraboloid, through the axis and the point, and, in the case of the hyperboloid, through the given point and through the given straight line drawn through the vertex of the enveloping cone, the section by the plane will be (a) in the paraboloid a parabola whose axis is the axis of the paraboloid, (b) in the hyperboloid a hyperbola in which the given line through the vertex of the enveloping cone is a diameter.[1]

[Prop. 11]

Hence the property follows from the plane properties of the conics.

(2) *If a plane touch a conoid without cutting it, it will touch it at one point only, and the plane drawn through the point of contact and the axis of the conoid will be at right angles to the plane which touches it.*

For, if possible, let the plane touch at two points. Draw through each point a parallel to the axis. The plane passing through both parallels will therefore either pass through, or be parallel to, the axis. Hence the section of the conoid made by this plane will be a conic [Prop. 11 (1), (2)], the two points will lie on this conic, and the line joining them will lie within the conic and therefore within the conoid. But this line will be in the tangent plane, since the two points are in it. Therefore some portion of the tangent plane will be within the conoid; which is impossible, since the plane does not cut it.

Therefore the tangent plane touches in one point only.

That the plane through the point of contact and the axis is perpendicular to the tangent plane is evident in the particular case where the point of contact is the vertex of the conoid. For, if two planes through the axis cut it in two conics, the tangents at the vertex in both conics will be perpendicular to the axis of the conoid. And all such tangents will be in the tangent plane, which must therefore be perpendicular to the axis and to any plane through the axis.

If the point of contact $P$ is not the vertex, draw the plane passing through the axis $AN$ and the point $P$. It will cut the conoid in a conic whose axis is $AN$ and the tangent plane in a line $DPE$ touching the conic at $P$. Draw $PNP'$ perpendicular to the axis, and draw a plane through it also perpendicular to the axis. This plane will make a circular section and meet the tangent plane in a tangent to the circle, which will therefore be at right angles to $PN$. Hence the tangent to the circle will be at right angles to the plane containing $PN$, $AN$; and it follows that this last plane is perpendicular to the tangent plane.

---

[1]There seems to be some error in the text here, which says that "the *diameter*" (i.e. axis) of the hyperbola is "the straight line drawn in the conoid from the vertex of the cone." But this straight line is not, in general, the *axis* of the section.

## Proposition 16

(1) *If a plane touch any of the spheroidal figures without cutting it, it will touch at one point only, and the plane through the point of contact and the axis will be at right angles to the tangent plane.*

This is proved by the same method as the last proposition.

(2) *If any conoid or spheroid be cut by a plane through the axis, and if through any tangent to the resulting conic a plane be erected at right angles to the plane of section, the plane so erected will touch the conoid or spheroid in the same point as that in which the line touches the conic.*

For it cannot meet the surface at any other point. If it did, the perpendicular from the second point on the cutting plane would be perpendicular also to the tangent to the conic and would therefore fall outside the surface. But it must fall within it. [Prop. 11 (4)]

(3) *If two parallel planes touch any of the spheroidal figures, the line joining the points of contact will pass through the centre of the spheroid.*

If the planes are at right angles to the axis, the proposition is obvious. If not, the plane through the axis and one point of contact is at right angles to the tangent plane at that point. It is therefore at right angles to the parallel tangent plane, and therefore passes through the second point of contact. Hence both points of contact lie on one plane through the axis, and the proposition is reduced to a plane one.

## Proposition 17

*If two parallel planes touch any of the spheroidal figures, and another plane be drawn parallel to the tangent planes and passing through the centre, the line drawn through any point of the circumference of the resulting section parallel to the chord of contact of the tangent planes will fall outside the spheroid.*

This is proved at once by reduction to a plane proposition.

Archimedes adds that it is evident that, if the plane parallel to the tangent planes does not pass through the centre, a straight line drawn in the manner described will fall without the spheroid in the direction of the smaller segment but within it in the other direction.

## Proposition 18

*Any spheroidal figure which is cut by a plane through the centre is divided, both as regards its surface and its volume, into two equal parts by that plane.*

To prove this, Archimedes takes another equal and similar spheroid, divides it similarly by a plane through the centre, and then uses the method of application.

## Propositions 19, 20

*Given a segment cut off by a plane from a paraboloid or hyperboloid of revolution, or a segment of a spheroid less than half the spheroid also cut off by a plane, it is possible to inscribe in the segment one solid figure and to circumscribe about it another solid figure, each made up of cylinders or "frusta" of cylinders of equal height, and such that the circumscribed figure exceeds the inscribed figure by a volume less than that of any given solid.*

Let the plane base of the segment be perpendicular to the plane of the paper,

ON CONOIDS AND SPHEROIDS 469

and let the plane of the paper be the plane through the axis of the conoid or spheroid which cuts the base of the segment at right angles in $BC$. The section in the plane of the paper is then a conic $BAC$. [Prop. 11]

Let $EAF$ be that tangent to the conic which is parallel to $BC$, and let $A$ be the point of contact. Through $EAF$ draw a plane parallel to the plane through $BC$ bounding the segment. The plane so drawn will then touch the conoid or spheroid at $A$. [Prop. 16]

(1) If the base of the segment is at right angles to the axis of the conoid or spheroid, $A$ will be the vertex of the conoid or spheroid, and its axis $AD$ will bisect $BC$ at right angles.

(2) If the base of the segment is not at right angles to the axis of the conoid or spheroid, we draw $AD$

(a) in the paraboloid, parallel to the axis,

(b) in the hyperboloid, through the centre (or the vertex of the enveloping cone),

(c) in the spheroid, through the centre,

and in all the cases it will follow that $AD$ bisects $BC$ in $D$.

Then $A$ will be the vertex of the segment, and $AD$ will be its axis.

Further, the base of the segment will be a circle or an ellipse with $BC$ as diameter or as an axis respectively, and with centre $D$. We can therefore describe through this circle or ellipse a cylinder or a 'frustum' of a cylinder whose axis is $AD$. [Prop. 9]

Dividing this cylinder or frustum continually into equal parts by planes parallel to the base, we shall at length arrive at a cylinder or frustum less in volume than any given solid.

Let this cylinder or frustum be that whose axis is $OD$, and let $AD$ be divided into parts equal to $OD$, at $L, M, \ldots$.

Through $L, M, \ldots$ draw lines parallel to $BC$ meeting the conic in $P, Q, \ldots$, and through these lines draw planes parallel to the base of the segment. These will cut the conoid or spheroid in circles or similar ellipses. On each of these circles or ellipses describe two cylinders or frusta of cylinders each with axis equal to $OD$, one of them lying in the direction of $A$ and the other in the direction of $D$, as shown in the figure.

Then the cylinders or frusta of cylinders drawn in the direction of $A$ make up a circumscribed figure, and those in the direction of $D$ an inscribed figure, in relation to the segment.

Also the cylinder or frustum $PG$ in the circumscribed figure is equal to the cylinder or frustum $PH$ in the inscribed figure, $QI$ in the circumscribed figure is equal to $QK$ in the inscribed figure, and so on.

Therefore, by addition,

(circumscribed fig.) = (inscr. fig.) + (cylinder or frustum whose axis is $OD$).

But the cylinder or frustum whose axis is $OD$ is less than the given solid figure; whence the proposition follows.

"Having set out these preliminary propositions, let us proceed to demonstrate the theorems propounded with reference to the figures."

## Propositions 21, 22

*Any segment of a paraboloid of revolution is half as large again as the cone or segment of a cone which has the same base and the same axis.*

Let the base of the segment be perpendicular to the plane of the paper, and let the plane of the paper be the plane through the axis of the paraboloid which cuts the base of the segment at right angles in $BC$ and makes the parabolic section $BAC$.

Let $EF$ be that tangent to the parabola which is parallel to $BC$, and let $A$ be the point of contact.

Then (1), if the plane of the base of the segment is perpendicular to the axis of the paraboloid, that axis is the line $AD$ bisecting $BC$ at right angles in $D$.

(2) If the plane of the base is not perpendicular to the axis of the paraboloid, draw $AD$ parallel to the axis of the paraboloid. $AD$ will then bisect $BC$, but not at right angles.

Draw through $EF$ a plane parallel to the base of the segment. This will touch the paraboloid at $A$, and $A$ will be the vertex of the segment, $AD$ its axis.

The base of the segment will be a circle with diameter $BC$ or an ellipse with $BC$ as major axis.

Accordingly a cylinder or a frustum of a cylinder can be found passing through the circle or ellipse and having $AD$ for its axis [Prop. 9]; and likewise a cone or a segment of a cone can be drawn passing through the circle or ellipse and having $A$ for vertex and $AD$ for axis. [Prop. 8]

Suppose $X$ to be a cone equal to $\frac{3}{2}$ (cone or segment of cone $ABC$). The cone $X$ is therefore equal to half the cylinder or frustum of a cylinder $EC$.

[Cf. Prop. 10]

We shall prove that the volume of the segment of the paraboloid is equal to $X$.

If not, the segment must be either greater or less than $X$.

I. If possible, let the segment be greater than $X$.

We can then inscribe and circumscribe, as in the last proposition, figures made up of cylinders or frusta of cylinders with equal height and such that

(circumscribed fig.) − (inscribed fig.) < (segment) − $X$.

Let the greatest of the cylinders or frusta forming the circumscribed figure be that whose base is the circle or ellipse about $BC$ and whose axis is $OD$, and let the smallest of them be that whose base is the circle or ellipse about $PP'$ and whose axis is $AL$.

Let the greatest of the cylinders forming the inscribed figure be that whose base is the circle or ellipse about $RR'$ and whose axis is $OD$, and let the smallest be that whose base is the circle or ellipse about $PP'$ and whose axis is $LM$.

Produce all the plane bases of the cylinders or frusta to meet the surface of the complete cylinder or frustum $EC$.

Now, since

(circumscribed fig.) − (inscr. fig.) < (segment) − $X$,

it follows that (inscribed figure) $> X$. $(\alpha)$

Next, comparing successively the cylinders or frusta with heights equal to $OD$ and respectively forming parts of the complete cylinder or frustum $EC$ and of the inscribed figure, we have

(first cylinder or frustum in $EC$) : (first in inscr. fig.)
$$= BD^2 : RO^2$$
$$= AD : AO$$
$$= BD : TO, \text{ where } AB \text{ meets } OR \text{ in } T.$$

And (second cylinder or frustum in $EC$) : (second in inscr. fig.)
$$= HO : SN, \text{ in like manner,}$$

and so on.

Hence [Prop. 1] (cylinder or frustum $EC$) : (inscribed figure)
$$= (BD + HO + \cdots) : (TO + SN + \cdots),$$
where $BD, HO, \ldots$ are all equal, and $BD, TO, SN, \ldots$ diminish in arithmetical progression.

But [Lemma preceding Prop. 1]
$$BD + HO + \cdots > 2(TO + SN + \cdots).$$
Therefore (cylinder or frustum $EC$) $> 2$ (inscribed fig.),
or $X >$ (inscribed fig.);
which is impossible, by $(\alpha)$ above.

II. If possible, let the segment be less than $X$.

In this case we inscribe and circumscribe figures as before, but such that
(circumscr. fig.) $-$ (inscr. fig.) $< X -$ (segment),
whence it follows that
(circumscribed figure) $< X$. $(\beta)$

And, comparing the cylinders or frusta making up the complete cylinder or frustum $CE$ and the *circumscribed* figure respectively, we have

(first cylinder or frustum in $CE$) : (first in circumscr. fig.)
$$= BD^2 : BD^2$$
$$= BD : BD.$$
(second in $CE$) : (second in circumscr. fig.)
$$= HO^2 : RO^2$$
$$= AD : AO$$
$$= HO : TO,$$

and so on.

Hence [Prop. 1]
(cylinder or frustum $CE$) : (circumscribed fig.)
$$= (BD + HO + \cdots) : (BD + TO + \cdots),$$
$$< 2 : 1, \qquad \text{[Lemma preceding Prop. 1]}$$
and it follows that
$$X < (\text{circumscribed fig.});$$
which is impossible, by $(\beta)$.

Thus the segment, being neither greater nor less than $X$, is equal to it, and therefore to $\frac{3}{2}$ (cone or segment of cone $ABC$).

## Proposition 23

*If from a paraboloid of revolution two segments be cut off, one by a plane perpendicular to the axis, the other by a plane not perpendicular to the axis, and if the axes of the segments are equal, the segments will be equal in volume.*

472    ARCHIMEDES

Let the two planes be supposed perpendicular to the plane of the paper, and let the latter plane be the plane through the axis of the paraboloid cutting the other two planes at right angles in $BB'$, $QQ'$ respectively and the paraboloid itself in the parabola $QPQ'B'$.

Let $AN$, $PV$ be the equal axes of the segments, and $A$, $P$ their respective vertices.

Draw $QL$ parallel to $AN$ or $PV$ and $Q'L$ perpendicular to $QL$.

Now, since the segments of the parabolic section cut off by $BB'$, $QQ'$ have equal axes, the triangles $ABB'$, $PQQ'$ are equal [Prop. 3]. Also, if $QD$ be perpendicular to $PV$, $QD = BN$ (as in the same Prop. 3).

Conceive two cones drawn with the same bases as the segments and with $A$, $P$ as vertices respectively. The height of the cone $PQQ'$ is then $PK$, where $PK$ is perpendicular to $QQ'$.

Now the cones are in the ratio compounded of the ratios of their bases and of their heights, i.e. the ratio compounded of (1) the ratio of the circle about $BB'$ to the ellipse about $QQ'$, and (2) the ratio of $AN$ to $PK$.

That is to say, we have, by means of Props. 5, 12,
$$(\text{cone } ABB') : (\text{cone } PQQ') = (BB'^2 : QQ' \cdot Q'L) \cdot (AN : PK).$$
And $BB' = 2BN = 2QD = Q'L$, while $QQ' = 2QV$.
Therefore
$$(\text{cone } ABB') : (\text{cone } PQQ') = (QD : QV) \cdot (AN : PK)$$
$$= (PK : PV) \cdot (AN : PK)$$
$$= AN : PV.$$

Since $AN = PV$, the ratio of the cones is a ratio of equality; and it follows that the segments, being each half as large again as the respective cones [Prop. 22], are equal.

PROPOSITION 24

*If from a paraboloid of revolution two segments be cut off by planes drawn in any manner, the segments will be to one another as the squares on their axes.*

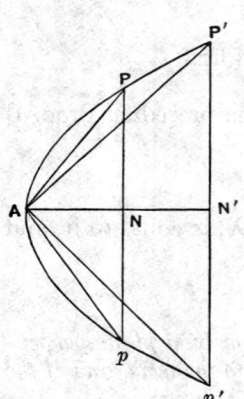

For let the paraboloid be cut by a plane through the axis in the parabolic section $P'PApp'$, and let the axis of the parabola and paraboloid be $ANN'$.

Measure along $ANN'$ the lengths $AN$, $AN'$ equal to the respective axes of the given segments, and through $N$, $N'$ draw planes perpendicular to the axis, making circular sections on $Pp$, $P'p'$ as diameters respectively. With these circles as bases and with the common vertex $A$ let two cones be described.

Now the segments of the paraboloid whose bases are the circles about $Pp$, $P'p'$ are equal to the given segments respectively, since their respective axes are equal [Prop. 23]; and, since the segments $APp$, $AP'p'$ are half as large again as the cones $APp$, $AP'p'$ respectively, we have only to show that the cones are in the ratio of $AN^2$ to $AN'^2$.

But
$$(\text{cone } APp) : (\text{cone } AP'p') = (PN^2 : P'N'^2) \cdot (AN : AN')$$
$$= (AN : AN') \cdot (AN : AN')$$
$$= AN^2 : AN'^2;$$
thus the proposition is proved.

## Propositions 25, 26

*In any hyperboloid of revolution, if $A$ be the vertex and $AD$ the axis of any segment cut off by a plane, and if $CA$ be the semidiameter of the hyperboloid through $A$ ($CA$ being of course in the same straight line with $AD$), then*
$$(segment) : (cone\ with\ same\ base\ and\ axis)$$
$$= (AD+3CA) : (AD+2CA).$$

Let the plane cutting off the segment be perpendicular to the plane of the paper, and let the latter plane be the plane through the axis of the hyperboloid which intersects the cutting plane at right angles in $BB'$, and makes the hyperbolic segment $BAB'$. Let $C$ be the centre of the hyperboloid (or the vertex of the enveloping cone).

Let $EF$ be that tangent to the hyperbolic section which is parallel to $BB'$. Let $EF$ touch at $A$, and join $CA$. Then $CA$ produced will bisect $BB'$ at $D$, $CA$ will be a semi-diameter of the hyperboloid, $A$ will be the vertex of the segment, and $AD$ its axis. Produce $AC$ to $A'$ and $H$, so that $AC = CA' = A'H$.

Through $EF$ draw a plane parallel to the base of the segment. This plane will touch the hyperboloid at $A$.

Then (1), if the base of the segment is at right angles to the axis of the hyperboloid, $A$ will be the vertex, and $AD$ the axis, of the hyperboloid as well as of the segment, and the base of the segment will be a circle on $BB'$ as diameter.

(2) If the base of the segment is not perpendicular to the axis of the hyperboloid, the base will be an ellipse on $BB'$ as major axis. [Prop. 13]

Then we can draw a cylinder or a frustum of a cylinder $EBB'F$ passing through the circle or ellipse about $BB'$ and having $AD$ for its axis; also we can describe a cone or a segment of a cone through the circle or ellipse and having $A$ for its vertex.

We have to prove that
(segment $ABB'$) : (cone or segment of cone $ABB'$) = $HD : A'D$.

Let $V$ be a cone such that
$$V : (\text{cone or segment of cone } ABB') = HD : A'D, \qquad (\alpha)$$
and we have to prove that $V$ is equal to the segment.

Now
(cylinder or frustum $EB'$) : (cone or segmt. of cone $ABB'$) = 3 : 1.

Therefore, by means of ($\alpha$), (cylinder or frustum $EB'$) $: V = A'D : \dfrac{HD}{3}$. ($\beta$)

If the segment is not equal to $V$, it must either be greater or less.

I. If possible, let the segment be greater than $V$.

Inscribe and circumscribe to the segment figures made up of cylinders or frusta of cylinders, with axes along $AD$ and all equal to one another, such that

474  ARCHIMEDES

(circumscribed fig.) − (inscr. fig.) < (segmt.) − V,

whence                    (inscribed figure) > V.                           (γ)

Produce all the planes forming the bases of the cylinders or frusta of cylinders to meet the surface of the complete cylinder or frustum EB'.

Then, if ND be the axis of the greatest cylinder or frustum in the circumscribed figure, the complete cylinder will be divided into cylinders or frusta each equal to this greatest cylinder or frustum.

Let there be a number of straight lines $a$ equal to $AA'$ and as many in number as the parts into which $AD$ is divided by the bases of the cylinders or frusta. To each line $a$ apply a rectangle which shall overlap it by a square, and let the greatest of the rectangles be equal to the rectangle $AD \cdot A'D$ and the least equal to the rectangle $AL \cdot A'L$; also let the sides of the overlapping squares $b, p, q, \ldots l$ be in descending arithmetical progression. Thus $b, p, q, \ldots l$ will be respectively equal to $AD, AN, AM, \ldots AL$, and the rectangles $(ab+b^2)$, $(ap+p^2), \ldots (al+l^2)$ will be respectively equal to $AD \cdot A'D, AN \cdot A'N, \ldots AL \cdot A'L$.

Suppose, further, that we have a series of spaces $S$ each equal to the largest rectangle $AD \cdot A'D$ and as many in number as the diminishing rectangles.

Comparing now the successive cylinders or frusta (1) in the complete cylinder or frustum $EB'$ and (2) in the inscribed figure, beginning from the base of the segment, we have

(first cylinder or frustum in $EB'$) : (first in inscr. figure)
$$= BD^2 : PN^2$$
$$= AD \cdot A'D : AN \cdot A'N, \text{ from the hyperbola,}$$
$$= S : (ap+p^2).$$

Again

(second cylinder or frustum in $EB'$) : (second in inscr. fig.)
$$= BD^2 : QM^2$$
$$= AD \cdot A'D : AM \cdot A'M$$
$$= S : (aq+q^2),$$

and so on.

The last cylinder or frustum in the complete cylinder or frustum $EB'$ has no cylinder or frustum corresponding to it in the inscribed figure.

Combining the proportions, we have [Prop. 1]
(cylinder or frustum $EB'$) : (inscribed figure)
$$= (\text{sum of all the spaces } S) : (ap+p^2)+(aq+q^2)+\cdots$$
$$> (a+b) : \left(\frac{a}{2}+\frac{b}{3}\right) \qquad \text{[Prop. 2]}$$

$$> A'D : \frac{HD}{3}, \text{ since } a = AA', b = AD,$$

$$> (EB') : V, \text{ by } (\beta) \text{ above.}$$

Hence (inscribed figure) $< V$.

But this is impossible, because, by ($\gamma$) above, the inscribed figure is greater than $V$.

II. Next suppose, if possible, that the segment is less than $V$.

In this case we circumscribe and inscribe figures such that
(circumscribed fig.) − (inscribed fig.) $< V −$ (segment),
whence we derive
$$V > (\text{circumscribed figure}). \qquad (\delta)$$

We now compare successive cylinders or frusta in the complete cylinder or frustum and in the *circumscribed* figure; and we have

(first cylinder or frustum in $EB'$) : (first in circumscribed fig.)
$$= S : S$$
$$= S : (ab+b^2),$$
(second in $EB'$) : (second in circumscribed fig.)
$$= S : (ap+p^2),$$

and so on.

Hence [Prop. 1]
(cylinder or frustum $EB'$) : (circumscribed fig.)
$$= (\text{sum of all spaces } S) : (ab+b^2)+(ap+p^2)+\cdots$$

$$< (a+b) : \left(\frac{a}{2}+\frac{b}{3}\right) \qquad \text{[Prop. 2]}$$

$$< A'D : \frac{HD}{3}$$

$$< (EB') : V, \text{ by } (\beta) \text{ above.}$$

476   ARCHIMEDES

Hence the circumscribed figure is greater than $V$; which is impossible, by ($\delta$) above.

Thus the segment is neither greater nor less than $V$, and is therefore equal to it.

Therefore, by ($\alpha$),

(segment $ABB'$) : (cone or segment of cone $ABB'$)
$$= (AD+3CA) : (AD+2CA).$$

### Propositions 27, 28, 29, 30

(1) *In any spheroid whose centre is $C$, if a plane meeting the axis cut off a segment not greater than half the spheroid and having $A$ for its vertex and $AD$ for its axis, and if $A'D$ be the axis of the remaining segment of the spheroid, then*

(first segmt.) : (cone or segmt. of cone with same base and axis)
$$= CA + A'D : A'D$$
$$[= 3CA - AD : 2CA - AD].$$

(2) *As a particular case, if the plane passes through the centre, so that the segment is half the spheroid, half the spheroid is double of the cone or segment of a cone which has the same vertex and axis.*

Let the plane cutting off the segment be at right angles to the plane of the paper, and let the latter plane be the plane through the axis of the spheroid which intersects the cutting plane in $BB'$ and makes the elliptic section $ABA'B'$.

Let $EF$, $E'F'$ be the two tangents to the ellipse which are parallel to $BB'$, let them touch it in $A$, $A'$, and through the tangents draw planes parallel to the base of the segment. These planes will touch the spheroid at $A$, $A'$, which will be the vertices of the two segments into which it is divided. Also $AA'$ will pass through the centre $C$ and bisect $BB'$ in $D$.

Then (1) if the base of the segments be perpendicular to the axis of the spheroid, $A$, $A'$ will be the vertices of the spheroid as well as of the segments, $AA'$ will be the axis of the spheroid, and the base of the segments will be a circle on $BB'$ as diameter;

(2) if the base of the segments be not perpendicular to the axis of the spheroid, the base of the segments will be an ellipse of which $BB'$ is one axis, and $AD$, $A'D$ will be the axes of the segments respectively.

## ON CONOIDS AND SPHEROIDS

We can now draw a cylinder or a frustum of a cylinder $EBB'F$ through the circle or ellipse about $BB'$ and having $AD$ for its axis; and we can also draw a cone or a segment of a cone passing through the circle or ellipse about $BB'$ and having $A$ for its vertex.

We have then to show that, if $CA'$ be produced to $H$ so that $CA' = A'H$,
(segment $ABB'$) : (cone or segment of cone $ABB'$) = $HD$ : $A'D$.

Let $V$ be such a cone that
$$V : \text{(cone or segment of cone } ABB') = HD : A'D; \qquad (\alpha)$$
and we have to show that the segment $ABB'$ is equal to $V$.

But, since
(cylinder or frustum $EB'$) : (cone or segment of cone $ABB'$) = 3 : 1,
we have, by the aid of $(\alpha)$,
$$\text{(cylinder or frustum } EB') : V = A'D : \frac{HD}{3} \qquad (\beta)$$

Now, if the segment $ABB'$ is not equal to $V$, it must be either greater or less.

I. Suppose, if possible, that the segment is greater than $V$.

Let figures be inscribed and circumscribed to the segment consisting of cylinders or frusta of cylinders, with axes along $AD$ and all equal to one another, such that
(circumscribed fig.) − (inscribed fig.) < (segment) − $V$,
whence it follows that
$$\text{(inscribed fig.)} > V. \qquad (\gamma)$$

Produce all the planes forming the bases of the cylinders or frusta to meet the surface of the complete cylinder or frustum $EB'$. Thus, if $ND$ be the axis of the greatest cylinder or frustum of a cylinder in the circumscribed figure, the complete cylinder or frustum $EB'$ will be divided into cylinders or frusta of cylinders each equal to the greatest of those in the circumscribed figure.

Take straight lines $da'$ each equal to $A'D$ and as many in number as the parts into which $AD$ is divided by the bases of the cylinders or frusta, and measure $da$ along $da'$ equal to $AD$. It follows that $aa' = 2CD$.

Apply to each of the lines $a'd$ rectangles with height equal to $ad$, and draw the squares on each of the lines $ad$ as in the figure. Let $S$ denote the area of each complete rectangle.

From the first rectangle take away a gnomon with breadth equal to $AN$ (i.e. with each end of a length equal to $AN$); take away from the second rectangle a gnomon with breadth equal to $AM$, and so on, the last rectangle having no gnomon taken from it.

Then
the first gnomon $= A'D \cdot AD - ND \cdot (A'D - AN)$
$= A'D \cdot AN + ND \cdot AN$
$= AN \cdot A'N$.

Similarly,
the second gnomon $= AM \cdot A'M$,
and so on.

And the last gnomon (that in the last rectangle but one) is equal to $AL \cdot A'L$.

Also, after the gnomons are taken away from the successive rectangles, the remainders (which we will call $R_1, R_2, \cdots R_n$, where $n$ is the number of rectangles and accordingly $R_n = S$) are rectangles applied to straight lines each of length $aa'$ and "exceeding by squares" whose sides are respectively equal to $DN, DM, \ldots DA$.

For brevity, let $DN$ be denoted by $x$, and $aa'$ or $2CD$ by $c$, so that
$$R_1 = cx + x^2, \quad R_2 = c \cdot 2x + (2x)^2, \cdots$$

Then, comparing successively the cylinders or frusta of cylinders (1) in the complete cylinder or frustum $EB'$ and (2) in the inscribed figure, we have

(first cylinder or frustum in $EB'$) : (first in inscribed fig.)
$$= BD^2 : PN^2$$
$$= AD \cdot A'D : AN \cdot A'N$$
$$= S : \text{(first gnomon)};$$

(second cylinder or frustum in $EB'$) : (second in inscribed fig.)
$$= S : \text{(second gnomon)},$$

and so on.

The last of the cylinders or frusta in the cylinder or frustum $EB'$ has none corresponding to it in the inscribed figure, and there is no corresponding gnomon.

Combining the proportions, we have [by Prop. 1]

(cylinder or frustum $EB'$) : (inscribed fig.)
= (sum of all spaces $S$) : (sum of gnomons).

Now the differences between $S$ and the successive gnomons are $R_1, R_2, \ldots R_n$, while
$$R_1 = cx + x^2,$$
$$R_2 = c \cdot 2x + (2x)^2,$$
$$\ldots\ldots\ldots\ldots\ldots\ldots$$
$$R_n = cb + b^2 = S,$$

where $b = nx = AD$.

Hence [Prop. 2]

(sum of all spaces $S$) : $(R_1 + R_2 + \cdots + R_n) < (c+b) : \left(\dfrac{c}{2} + \dfrac{b}{3}\right)$.

It follows that

(sum of all spaces $S$) : (sum of gnomons) $> (c+b) : \left(\dfrac{c}{2} + \dfrac{2b}{3}\right)$

$$> A'D : \dfrac{HD}{3}.$$

Thus        (cylinder or frustum $EB'$) : (inscribed fig.)

$$> A'D : \dfrac{HD}{3}$$

$>$ (cylinder or frustum $EB'$) : $V$,

from ($\beta$) above.

Therefore        (inscribed fig.) $< V$;

which is impossible, by ($\gamma$) above.

Hence the segment $ABB'$ is not greater than $V$.

II. If possible, let the segment $ABB'$ be less than $V$.

We then inscribe and circumscribe figures such that
(circumscribed fig.) $-$ (inscribed fig.) $< V -$ (segment),
whence        $V >$ (circumscribed fig.).        ($\delta$)

In this case we compare the cylinders or frusta in ($EB'$) with those in the *circumscribed* figure.

Thus
> (first cylinder or frustum in $EB'$) : (first in circumscribed fig.)
> $= S : S$;
> (second in $EB'$) : (second in circumscribed fig.)
> $= S$ : (first gnomon),

and so on.

Lastly
> (last in $EB'$) : (last in circumscribed fig.)
> $= S$ : (last gnomon).

Now
$$\{S+\text{(all the gnomons)}\} = nS - (R_1 + R_2 + \cdots + R_{n-1}).$$

And
$$nS : R_1 + R_2 + \cdots + R_{n-1} > (c+b) : \left(\frac{c}{2} + \frac{b}{3}\right), \qquad \text{[Prop. 2]}$$

so that
$$nS : \{S+\text{(all the gnomons)}\} < (c+b) : \left(\frac{c}{2} + \frac{2b}{3}\right).$$

It follows that, if we combine the above proportions as in Prop. 1, we obtain
> (cylinder or frustum $EB'$) : (circumscribed fig.)
> $< (c+b) : \left(\dfrac{c}{2} + \dfrac{2b}{3}\right)$
> $< A'D : \dfrac{HD}{3}$
> $< (EB') : V$, by ($\beta$) above.

Hence the circumscribed figure is greater than $V$; which is impossible, by ($\delta$) above.

Thus, since the segment $ABB'$ is neither greater nor less than $V$, it is equal to it; and the proposition is proved.

(2) The particular case [Props. 27, 28] where the segment is half the spheroid differs from the above in that the distance $CD$ or $c/2$ vanishes, and the rectangles $cb + b^2$ are simply squares ($b^2$), so that the gnomons are simply the differences between $b^2$ and $x^2$, $b^2$ and $(2x)^2$, and so on.

Instead therefore of Prop. 2 we use the *Lemma to Prop.* 2, *Cor.* 1, given above [*On Spirals*, Prop. 10], and instead of the ratio $(c+b) : \left(\dfrac{c}{2} + \dfrac{2b}{3}\right)$ we obtain the ratio $3 : 2$, whence (segment $ABB'$) : (cone or segment of cone $ABB'$) $= 2 : 1$.

## Propositions 31, 32

*If a plane divide a spheroid into two unequal segments, and if $AN$, $A'N$ be the axes of the lesser and greater segments respectively, while $C$ is the centre of the spheroid, then*
> *(greater segmt.) : (cone or segmt. of cone with same base and axis)*
> $= CA + AN : AN.$

Let the plane dividing the spheroid be that through $PP'$ perpendicular to the plane of the paper, and let the latter plane be that through the axis of the spheroid which intersects the cutting plane in $PP'$ and makes the elliptic section $PAP'A'$.

Draw the tangents to the ellipse which are parallel to $PP'$; let them touch the ellipse at $A$, $A'$, and through the tangents draw planes parallel to the base of the segments. These planes will touch the spheroid at $A$, $A'$, the line $AA'$

will pass through the centre $C$ and bisect $PP'$ in $N$, while $AN$, $A'N$ will be the axes of the segments.

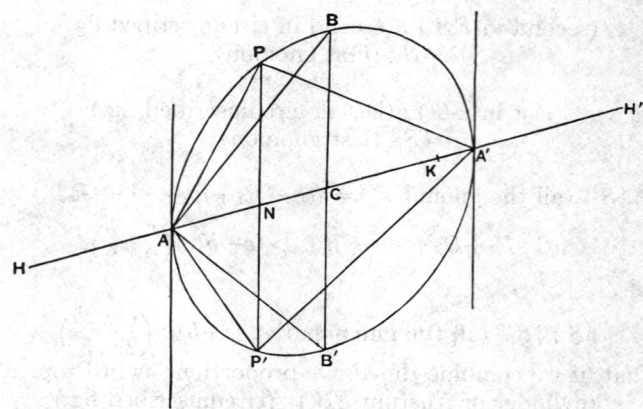

Then (1) if the cutting plane be perpendicular to the axis of the spheroid, $AA'$ will be that axis, and $A, A'$ will be the vertices of the spheroid as well as of the segments. Also the sections of the spheroid by the cutting plane and all planes parallel to it will be circles.

(2) If the cutting plane be not perpendicular to the axis, the base of the segments will be an ellipse of which $PP'$ is an axis, and the sections of the spheroid by all planes parallel to the cutting plane will be similar ellipses.

Draw a plane through $C$ parallel to the base of the segments and meeting the plane of the paper in $BB'$.

Construct three cones or segments of cones, two having $A$ for their common vertex and the plane sections through $PP'$, $BB'$ for their respective bases, and a third having the plane section through $PP'$ for its base and $A'$ for its vertex.

Produce $CA$ to $H$ and $CA'$ to $H'$ so that
$$AH = A'H' = CA.$$
We have then to prove that
(segment $A'PP'$) : (cone or segment of cone $A'PP'$)
$$= CA + AN : AN$$
$$= NH : AN.$$
Now half the spheroid is double of the cone or segment of a cone $ABB'$ [Props. 27, 28]. Therefore
(the spheroid) $= 4$(cone or segment of cone $ABB'$).
But
(cone or segmt. of cone $ABB'$) : (cone or segmt. of cone $APP'$)
$$= (CA : AN) \cdot (BC^2 : PN^2)$$
$$= (CA : AN) \cdot (CA \cdot CA' : AN \cdot A'N). \quad (\alpha)$$
If we measure $AK$ along $AA'$ so that
$$AK : AC = AC : AN,$$
we have $\quad AK \cdot A'N : AC \cdot A'N = CA : AN,$
and the compound ratio in ($\alpha$) becomes
$$(AK \cdot A'N : CA \cdot A'N) \cdot (CA \cdot CA' : AN \cdot A'N),$$
i.e. $\quad AK \cdot CA' : AN \cdot A'N.$

Thus
(cone or segmt. of cone $ABB'$) : (cone or segmt. of cone $APP'$)
$$= AK \cdot CA' : AN \cdot A'N.$$
But (cone or segment of cone $APP'$) : (segment $APP'$)
$$= A'N : NH' \qquad \text{[Props. 29, 30]}$$
$$= AN \cdot A'N : AN \cdot NH'.$$
Therefore, *ex aequali*,
(cone or segment of cone $ABB'$) : (segment $APP'$)
$$= AK \cdot CA' : AN \cdot NH',$$
so that (spheroid) : (segment $APP'$)
$$= HH' \cdot AK : AN \cdot NH',$$
since $HH' = 4CA'$.
Hence (segment $A'PP'$) : (segment $APP'$)
$$= (HH' \cdot AK - AN \cdot NH') : AN \cdot NH'$$
$$= (AK \cdot NH + NH' \cdot NK) : AN \cdot NH'.$$
Further,
(segment $APP'$) : (cone or segment of cone $APP'$)
$$= NH' : A'N$$
$$= AN \cdot NH' : AN \cdot A'N,$$
and
(cone or segmt. of cone $APP'$) : (cone or segmt. of cone $A'PP'$)
$$= AN : A'N$$
$$= AN \cdot A'N : A'N^2.$$
From the last three proportions we obtain, *ex aequali*,
(segment $A'PP'$) : (cone or segment of cone $A'PP'$)
$$= (AK \cdot NH + NH' \cdot NK) : A'N^2$$
$$= (AK \cdot NH + NH' \cdot NK) : (CA^2 + NH' \cdot CN)$$
$$= (AK \cdot NH + NH' \cdot NK) : (AK \cdot AN + NH' \cdot CN). \qquad (\beta)$$
But
$$AK \cdot NH : AK \cdot AN = NH : AN$$
$$= CA + AN : AN$$
$$= AK + CA : CA \text{ (since } AK : AC = AC : AN\text{)}$$
$$= HK : CA$$
$$= HK - NH : CA - AN$$
$$= NK : CN$$
$$= NH' \cdot NK : NH' \cdot CN.$$
Hence the ratio in ($\beta$) is equal to the ratio
$$AK \cdot NH : AK \cdot AN, \text{ or } NH : AN.$$
Therefore
(segment $A'PP'$) : (cone or segment of cone $A'PP'$)
$$= NH : AN$$
$$= CA + AN : AN.$$

# ON SPIRALS

"ARCHIMEDES to Dositheus greeting.

"Of most of the theorems which I sent to Conon, and of which you ask me from time to time to send you the proofs, the demonstrations are already before you in the books brought to you by Heracleides; and some more are also contained in that which I now send you. Do not be surprised at my taking a considerable time before publishing these proofs. This has been owing to my desire to communicate them first to persons engaged in mathematical studies and anxious to investigate them. In fact, how many theorems in geometry which have seemed at first impracticable are in time successfully worked out! Now Conon died before he had sufficient time to investigate the theorems referred to; otherwise he would have discovered and made manifest all these things, and would have enriched geometry by many other discoveries besides. For I know well that it was no common ability that he brought to bear on mathematics, and that his industry was extraordinary. But, though many years have elapsed since Conon's death, I do not find that any one of the problems has been stirred by a single person. I wish now to put them in review one by one, particularly as it happens that there are two included among them which are impossible of realisation [and which may serve as a warning] how those who claim to discover everything but produce no proofs of the same may be confuted as having actually pretended to discover the impossible.

"What are the problems I mean, and what are those of which you have already received the proofs, and those of which the proofs are contained in this book respectively, I think it proper to specify. The first of the problems was, Given a sphere, to find a plane area equal to the surface of the sphere; and this was first made manifest on the publication of the book concerning the sphere, for, when it is once proved that the surface of any sphere is four times the greatest circle in the sphere, it is clear that it is possible to find a plane area equal to the surface of the sphere. The second was, Given a cone or a cylinder, to find a sphere equal to the cone or cylinder; the third, To cut a given sphere by a plane so that the segments of it have to one another an assigned ratio; the fourth, To cut a given sphere by a plane so that the segments of the surface have to one another an assigned ratio; the fifth, To make a given segment of a sphere similar to a given segment of a sphere;[1] the sixth, Given two segments of either the same or different spheres, to find a segment of a sphere which shall be similar to one of the segments and have its surface equal to the surface of the other segment. The seventh was, From a given sphere to cut off a segment by a plane so that the segment bears to the cone which has the same base

---

[1] Cf. *On the Sphere and Cylinder*, II. 5.

as the segment and equal height an assigned ratio greater than that of three to two. Of all the propositions just enumerated Heracleides brought you the proofs. The proposition stated next after these was wrong, viz. that, if a sphere be cut by a plane into unequal parts, the greater segment will have to the less the duplicate ratio of that which the greater surface has to the less. That this is wrong is obvious by what I sent you before; for it included this proposition: If a sphere be cut into unequal parts by a plane at right angles to any diameter in the sphere, the greater segment of the surface will have to the less the same ratio as the greater segment of the diameter has to the less, while the greater segment of the sphere has to the less a ratio less than the duplicate ratio of that which the greater surface has to the less, but greater than the sesqui-alterate[1] of that ratio. The last of the problems was also wrong, viz. that, if the diameter of any sphere be cut so that the square on the greater segment is triple of the square on the lesser segment, and if through the point thus arrived at, a plane be drawn at right angles to the diameter and cutting the sphere, the figure in such a form as is the greater segment of the sphere is the greatest of all the segments which have an equal surface. That this is wrong is also clear from the theorems which I before sent you. For it was there proved that the hemisphere is the greatest of all the segments of a sphere bounded by an equal surface.

"After these theorems the following were propounded concerning the cone.[2] If a section of a right-angled cone [a parabola], in which the diameter [axis] remains fixed, be made to revolve so that the diameter [axis] is the axis [of revolution], let the figure described by the section of the right-angled cone be called a *conoid*. And if a plane touch the conoidal figure and another plane drawn parallel to the tangent plane cut off a segment of the conoid, let the *base* of the segment cut off be defined as the cutting plane, and the *vertex* as the point in which the other plane touches the conoid. Now, if the said figure be cut by a plane at right angles to the axis, it is clear that the section will be a circle; but it needs to be proved that the segment cut off will be half as large again as the cone which has the same base as the segment and equal height. And if two segments be cut off from the conoid by planes drawn in any manner, it is clear that the sections will be sections of acute-angled cones [ellipses] if the cutting planes be not at right angles to the axis; but it needs to be proved that the segments will bear to one another the ratio of the squares on the lines drawn from their vertices parallel to the axis to meet the cutting planes. The proofs of these propositions are not yet sent to you.

"After these came the following propositions about the *spiral*, which are as it were another sort of problem having nothing in common with the foregoing; and I have written out the proofs of them for you in this book. They are as follows. If a straight line of which one extremity remains fixed be made to revolve at a uniform rate in a plane until it returns to the position from which it started, and if, at the same time as the straight line revolves, a point move at a uniform rate along the straight line, starting from the fixed extremity, the point will describe a spiral in the plane. I say then that the area bounded by the spiral and the straight line which has returned to the position from which it started is a third part of the circle described with the fixed point as centre and with radius the length traversed by the point along the straight line during

[1] See *On the Sphere and Cylinder*, II. 8.
[2] This should be presumably "the *conoid*," not "the cone."

the one revolution. And, if a straight line touch the spiral at the extreme end of the spiral, and another straight line be drawn at right angles to the line which has revolved and resumed its position from the fixed extremity of it, so as to meet the tangent, I say that the straight line so drawn to meet it is equal to the circumference of the circle. Again, if the revolving line and the point moving along it make several revolutions and return to the position from which the straight line started, I say that the area added by the spiral in the third revolution will be double of that added in the second, that in the fourth three times, that in the fifth four times, and generally the areas added in the later revolutions will be multiples of that added in the second revolution according to the successive numbers, while the area bounded by the spiral in the first revolution is a sixth part of that added in the second revolution. Also, if on the spiral described in one revolution two points be taken and straight lines be drawn joining them to the fixed extremity of the revolving line, and if two circles be drawn with the fixed point as centre and radii the lines drawn to the fixed extremity of the straight line, and the shorter of the two lines be produced, I say that (1) the area bounded by the circumference of the greater circle in the direction of (the part of) the spiral included between the straight lines, the spiral (itself) and the produced straight line will bear to (2) the area bounded by the circumference of the lesser circle, the same (part of the) spiral and the straight line joining their extremities the ratio which (3) the radius of the lesser circle together with two thirds of the excess of the radius of the greater circle over the radius of the lesser bears to (4) the radius of the lesser circle together with one third of the said excess.

"The proofs then of these theorems and others relating to the spiral are given in the present book. Prefixed to them, after the manner usual in other geometrical works, are the propositions necessary to the proofs of them. And here too, as in the books previously published, I assume the following lemma, that, if there be (two) unequal lines or (two) unequal areas, the excess by which the greater exceeds the less can, by being [continually] added to itself, be made to exceed any given magnitude among those which are comparable with [it and with] one another."

## Proposition 1

*If a point move at a uniform rate along any line, and two lengths be taken on it, they will be proportional to the times of describing them.*

Two unequal lengths are taken on a straight line, and two lengths on another straight line representing the times; and they are proved to be proportional by taking equimultiples of each length and the corresponding time after the manner of Eucl. V, Def. 5.

## Proposition 2

*If each of two points on different lines respectively move along them each at a uniform rate, and if lengths be taken, one on each line, forming pairs, such that each pair are described in equal times, the lengths will be porportionals.*

This is proved at once by equating the ratio of the lengths taken on one line to that of the times of description, which must also be equal to the ratio of the lengths taken on the other line.

## ON SPIRALS

### Proposition 3

*Given any number of circles, it is possible to find a straight line greater than the sum of all their circumferences.*

For we have only to describe polygons about each and then take a straight line equal to the sum of the perimeters of the polygons.

### Proposition 4

*Given two unequal lines, viz. a straight line and the circumference of a circle, it is possible to find a straight line less than the greater of the two lines and greater than the less.*

For, by the Lemma, the excess can, by being added a sufficient number of times to itself, be made to exceed the lesser line.

Thus e.g., if $c > l$ (where $c$ is the circumference of the circle and $l$ the length of the straight line), we can find a number $n$ such that
$$n(c-l) > l.$$
Therefore
$$c - l > \frac{l}{n},$$
and
$$c > l + \frac{l}{n} > l.$$

Hence we have only to divide $l$ into $n$ equal parts and add one of them to $l$. The resulting line will satisfy the condition.

### Proposition 5

*Given a circle with centre $O$, and the tangent to it at a point $A$, it is possible to draw from $O$ a straight line $OPF$, meeting the circle in $P$ and the tangent in $F$, such that, if $c$ be the circumference of any given circle whatever,*
$$FP : OP < (\text{arc } AP) : c.$$

Take a straight line, as $D$, greater than the circumference $c$. [Prop. 3]

Through $O$ draw $OH$ parallel to the given tangent, and draw through $A$ a line $APH$, meeting the circle in $P$ and $OH$ in $H$, such that the portion $PH$ intercepted between the circle and the line $OH$ may be equal to $D$. Join $OP$ and produce it to meet the tangent in $F$.

Then $FP : OP = AP : PH$, by parallels,
$$= AP : D$$
$$< (\text{arc } AP) : c.$$

### Proposition 6

*Given a circle with centre $O$, a chord $AB$ less than the diameter, and $OM$ the perpendicular on $AB$ from $O$, it is possible to draw a straight line $OFP$, meeting the chord $AB$ in $F$ and the circle in $P$, such that*
$$FP : PB = D : E,$$
*where $D : E$ is any given ratio less than $BM : MO$.*

Draw $OH$ parallel to $AB$, and $BT$ perpendicular to $BO$ meeting $OH$ in $T$.

Then the triangles $BMO$, $OBT$ are similar, and therefore
$$BM:MO = OB:BT,$$
whence $\qquad D:E < OB:BT.$

Suppose that a line $PH$ (greater than $BT$) is taken such that
$$D:E = OB:PH,$$
and let $PH$ be so placed that it passes through $B$ and $P$ lies on the circumference of the circle, while $H$ is on the line $OH$. ($PH$ will fall outside $BT$, because $PH > BT$.) Join $OP$ meeting $AB$ in $F$.

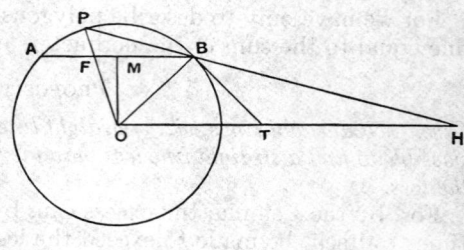

We now have
$$FP:PB = OP:PH$$
$$= OB:PH$$
$$= D:E.$$

## Proposition 7

*Given a circle with centre $O$, a chord $AB$ less than the diameter, and $OM$ the perpendicular on it from $O$, it is possible to draw from $O$ a straight line $OPF$, meeting the circle in $P$ and $AB$ produced in $F$, such that*
$$FP:PB = D:E,$$
*where $D:E$ is any given ratio greater than $BM:MO$.*

Draw $OT$ parallel to $AB$, and $BT$ perpendicular to $BO$ meeting $OT$ in $T$.
In this case,
$$D:E > BM:MO$$
$$> OB:BT, \text{ by similar triangles.}$$
Take a line $PH$ (less than $BT$) such that
$$D:E = OB:PH,$$
and place $PH$ so that $P$, $H$ are on the circle and on $OT$ respectively, while $HP$ produced passes through $B$.

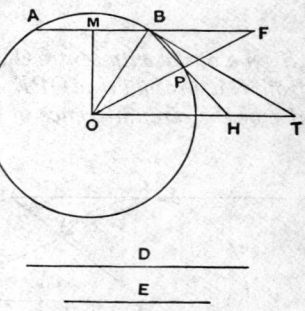

Then $\qquad FP:PB = OP:PH$
$$= D:E.$$

## Proposition 8

*Given a circle with centre $O$, a chord $AB$ less than the diameter, the tangent at $B$, and the perpendicular $OM$ from $O$ on $AB$, it is possible to draw from $O$ a straight line $OFP$, meeting the chord $AB$ in $F$, the circle in $P$ and the tangent in $G$, such that*
$$FP:BG = D:E,$$
*where $D:E$ is any given ratio less than $BM:MO$.*

If $OT$ be drawn parallel to $AB$ meeting the tangent at $B$ in $T$,
$$BM:MO = OB:BT,$$
so that $\qquad D:E < OB:BT.$

Take a point $C$ on $TB$ produced such that
$$D:E = OB:BC,$$
whence $\qquad BC > BT.$

ON SPIRALS 487

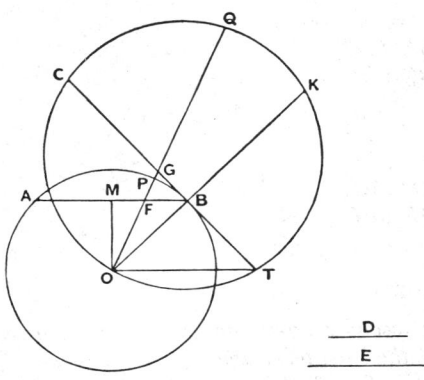

Through the points $O, T, C$ describe a circle, and let $OB$ be produced to meet this circle in $K$.

Then, since $BC > BT$, and $OB$ is perpendicular to $CT$, it is possible to draw from $O$ a straight line $OGQ$, meeting $CT$ in $G$ and the circle about $OTC$ in $Q$, such that $GQ = BK$.

Let $OGQ$ meet $AB$ in $F$ and the original circle in $P$.

Now $CG \cdot GT = OG \cdot GQ$;
and $OF : OG = BT : GT$,
so that $OF \cdot GT = OG \cdot BT$.

It follows that

$$CG \cdot GT : OF \cdot GT = OG \cdot GQ : OG \cdot BT,$$

or
$$CG : OF = GQ : BT$$
$$= BK : BT, \text{ by construction,}$$
$$= BC : OB$$
$$= BC : OP.$$

Hence $OP : OF = BC : CG$,
and therefore $PF : OP = BG : BC$,
or $PF : BG = OP : BC$
$$= OB : BC$$
$$= D : E.$$

PROPOSITION 9

*Given a circle with centre $O$, a chord $AB$ less than the diameter, the tangent at $B$, and the perpendicular $OM$ from $O$ on $AB$, it is possible to draw from $O$ a straight line $OPGF$, meeting the circle in $P$, the tangent in $G$, and $AB$ produced in $F$, such that*

$$FP : BG = D : E,$$

*where $D : E$ is any given ratio greater than $BM : MO$.*

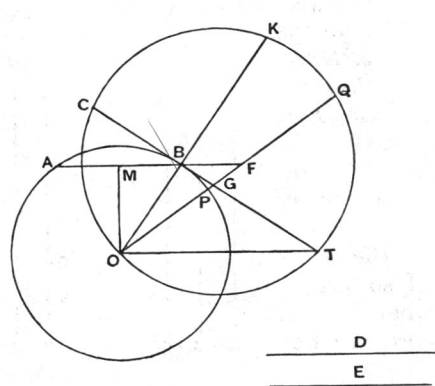

Let $OT$ be drawn parallel to $AB$ meeting the tangent at $B$ in $T$.

Then
$D : E > BM : MO$
$\qquad > OB : BT$, by similar triangles.

Produce $TB$ to $C$ so that
$$D : E = OB : BC,$$
whence $BC < BT$.

Describe a circle through the points $O, T, C$, and produce $OB$ to meet this circle in $K$.

Then, since $TB > BC$, and $OB$ is perpendicular to $CT$, it is possible to draw from $O$ a line $OGQ$, meeting $CT$ in $G$, and the circle about $OTC$ in $Q$, such that $GQ = BK$. Let $OQ$ meet the original circle in $P$ and $AB$ produced in $F$.

488                               ARCHIMEDES

We now prove, exactly as in the last proposition, that
$$CG : OF = BK : BT$$
$$= BC : OP.$$

Thus, as before,
$$OP : OF = BC : CG,$$
and
$$OP : PF = BC : BG,$$
whence
$$PF : BG = OP : BC$$
$$= OB : BC$$
$$= D : E.$$

## Proposition 10

If $A_1, A_2, A_3, \cdots A_n$ be $n$ lines forming an ascending arithmetical progression in which the common difference is equal to $A_1$, the least term, then
$$(n+1)A_n^2 + A_1(A_1 + A_2 + \cdots + A_n) = 3(A_1^2 + A_2^2 + \cdots + A_n^2).$$

[Archimedes' proof of this proposition is given above, pp. 456–7, and it is there pointed out that the result is equivalent to
$$1^2 + 2^2 + 3^2 + \cdots + n^2 = \frac{n(n+1)(2n+1)}{6}.]$$

Cor. 1. *It follows from this proposition that*
$$n \cdot A_n^2 < 3(A_1^2 + A_2^2 + \cdots + A_n^2),$$
*and also that*
$$n \cdot A_n^2 > 3(A_1^2 + A_2^2 + \cdots + A_{n-1}^2).$$

[For the proof of the latter inequality see p. 457 above.]

Cor. 2. *All the results will equally hold if similar figures are substituted for squares.*

## Proposition 11

If $A_1, A_2, \cdots A_n$ be $n$ lines forming an ascending arithmetical progression [in which the common difference is equal to the least term $A_1$], then
$$(n-1)A_n^2 : (A_n^2 + A_{n-1}^2 + \cdots + A_2^2) < A_n^2 : \{A_n \cdot A_1 + \tfrac{1}{3}(A_n - A_1)^2\};$$
but
$$(n-1)A_n^2 : (A_{n-1}^2 + A_{n-2}^2 + \cdots + A_1^2) > A_n^2 : \{A_n \cdot A_1 + \tfrac{1}{3}(A_n - A_1)^2\}.$$

[Archimedes sets out the terms side by side in the manner shown in the figure, where $BC = A_n$, $DE = A_{n-1}, \ldots RS = A_1$, and produces $DE$, $FG$, $\ldots RS$ until they are respectively equal to $BC$ or $A_n$, so that $EH$, $GI$, $\ldots SU$ in the figure are respectively equal to $A_1$, $A_2 \ldots A_{n-1}$. He further measures lengths $BK$, $DL$, $FM$, $\ldots PV$ along $BC$, $DE$, $FG$, $\ldots PQ$ respectively each equal to $RS$.

The figure makes the relations between the terms easier to see with the eye, but the use of so large a number of letters makes the proof somewhat difficult to follow, and it may be more clearly represented as follows.]

It is evident that $(A_n - A_1) = A_{n-1}$.

The following proportion is therefore obviously true, viz.
$$(n-1)A_n^2 : (n-1)(A_n \cdot A_1 + \tfrac{1}{3}A_{n-1}^2) = A_n^2 : \{A_n \cdot A_1 + \tfrac{1}{3}(A_n - A_1)^2\}.$$

In order therefore to prove the desired result, we have only to show that
$$(n-1)A_n \cdot A_1 + \tfrac{1}{3}(n-1)A_{n-1}^2 < (A_n^2 + A_{n-1}^2 + \cdots + A_2^2)$$
but
$$> (A_{n-1}^2 + A_{n-2}^2 + \cdots + A_1^2).$$

I. To prove the first inequality, we have
$$(n-1)A_n \cdot A_1 + \tfrac{1}{3}(n-1)A_{n-1}^2$$
$$= (n-1)A_1^2 + (n-1)A_1 \cdot A_{n-1} + \tfrac{1}{3}(n-1)A_{n-1}^2. \tag{1}$$

And
$$A_n^2 + A_{n-1}^2 + \cdots + A_2^2 = (A_{n-1} + A_1)^2 + (A_{n-2} + A_1)^2 + \cdots + (A_1 + A_1)^2$$
$$= (A_{n-1}^2 + A_{n-2}^2 + \cdots + A_1^2)$$
$$+ (n-1)A_1^2$$
$$+ 2A_1(A_{n-1} + A_{n-2} + \cdots + A_1)$$
$$= (A_{n-1}^2 + A_{n-2}^2 + \cdots + A_1^2)$$
$$+ (n-1)A_1^2$$
$$+ A_1\{A_{n-1} + A_{n-2} + A_{n-3} + \cdots + A_1$$
$$\qquad\qquad + A_1 + A_2 + \cdots + A_{n-2} + A_{n-1}\}$$
$$= (A_{n-1}^2 + A_{n-2}^2 + \cdots + A_1^2)$$
$$+ (n-1)A_1^2$$
$$+ nA_1 \cdot A_{n-1}. \tag{2}$$

Comparing the right-hand sides of (1) and (2), we see that $(n-1)A_1^2$ is common to both sides, and
$$(n-1)A_1 \cdot A_{n-1} < nA_1 \cdot A_{n-1},$$
while, by Prop. 10, Cor. 1,
$$\tfrac{1}{3}(n-1)A_{n-1}^2 < A_{n-1}^2 + A_{n-2}^2 + \cdots + A_1^2.$$
It follows therefore that
$$(n-1)A_n \cdot A_1 + \tfrac{1}{3}(n-1)A_{n-1}^2 < (A_n^2 + A_{n-1}^2 + \cdots + A_2^2);$$
and hence the first part of the proposition is proved.

II. We have now, in order to prove the second result, to show that
$$(n-1)A_n \cdot A_1 + \tfrac{1}{3}(n-1)A_{n-1}^2 > (A_{n-1}^2 + A_{n-2}^2 + \cdots + A_1^2).$$
The right-hand side is equal to
$$(A_{n-2} + A_1)^2 + (A_{n-3} + A_1)^2 + \cdots + (A_1 + A_1)^2 + A_1^2$$
$$= A_{n-2}^2 + A_{n-3}^2 + \cdots + A_1^2$$
$$+ (n-1)A_1^2$$
$$+ 2A_1(A_{n-2} + A_{n-3} + \cdots + A_1)$$
$$= (A_{n-2}^2 + A_{n-3}^2 + \cdots + A_1^2)$$
$$+ (n-1)A_1^2$$
$$+ A_1 \left\{ \begin{array}{l} A_{n-2} + A_{n-3} + \cdots + A_1 \\ + A_1 \ + A_2 \ + \cdots + A_{n-2} \end{array} \right\}$$
$$= (A_{n-2}^2 + A_{n-3}^2 + \cdots + A_1^2)$$
$$+ (n-1)A_1^2$$
$$+ (n-2)A_1 \cdot A_{n-1}. \tag{3}$$

Comparing this expression with the right-hand side of (1) above, we see that $(n-1)A_1^2$ is common to both sides, and
$$(n-1)A_1 \cdot A_{n-1} > (n-2)A_1 \cdot A_{n-1},$$
while, by Prop. 10, Cor. 1,
$$\tfrac{1}{3}(n-1)A_{n-1}^2 > (A_{n-2}^2 + A_{n-3}^2 + \cdots + A_1^2).$$
Hence $\quad (n-1)A_n \cdot A_1 + \tfrac{1}{3}(n-1)A_{n-1}^2 > (A_{n-1}^2 + A_{n-2}^2 + \cdots + A_1^2);$
and the second required result follows.

COR. *The results in the above proposition are equally true if similar figures be substituted for squares on the several lines.*

## DEFINITIONS

1. If a straight line drawn in a plane revolve at a uniform rate about one extremity which remains fixed and return to the position from which it started, and if, at the same time as the line revolves, a point move at a uniform rate along the straight line beginning from the extremity which remains fixed, the point will describe a *spiral* (ἕλιξ) in the plane.

2. Let the extremity of the straight line which remains fixed while the straight line revolves be called the *origin* of the spiral.

3. And let the position of the line from which the straight line began to revolve be called the *initial line* in the revolution.

4. Let the length which the point that moves along the straight line describes in one revolution be called the *first distance*, that which the same point describes in the second revolution the *second distance*, and similarly let the distances described in further revolutions be called after the number of the particular revolution.

5. Let the area bounded by the spiral described in the first revolution and the *first distance* be called the *first area*, that bounded by the spiral described in the second revolution and the *second distance* the *second area*, and similarly for the rest in order.

6. If from the origin of the spiral any straight line be drawn, let that side of it which is in the same direction as that of the revolution be called *forward* (προαγούμενα), and that which is in the other direction *backward* (ἑπόμενα).

7. Let the circle drawn with the *origin* as centre and the *first distance* as radius be called the *first circle*, that drawn with the same centre and twice the radius the *second circle*, and similarly for the succeeding circles.

## Proposition 12

*If any number of straight lines drawn from the origin to meet the spiral make equal angles with one another, the lines will be in arithmetical progression.*

[The proof is obvious.]

## Proposition 13

*If a straight line touch the spiral, it will touch it in one point only.*

Let $O$ be the origin of the spiral, and $BC$ a tangent to it.

If possible, let $BC$ touch the spiral in two points $P$, $Q$. Join $OP$, $OQ$, and bisect the angle $POQ$ by the straight line $OR$ meeting the spiral in $R$.

Then [Prop. 12] $OR$ is an arithmetic mean between $OP$ and $OQ$, or
$$OP+OQ=2OR.$$
But in any triangle $POQ$, if the bisector of the angle $POQ$ meets $PQ$ in $K$,
$$OP+OQ>2OK.$$

Therefore $OK<OR$, and it follows that some point on $BC$ between $P$ and $Q$ lies within the spiral. Hence $BC$ cuts the spiral; which is contrary to the hypothesis.

## Proposition 14

*If O be the origin, and P, Q two points on the first turn of the spiral, and if OP, OQ produced meet the "first circle" AKP'Q' in P', Q' respectively, OA being the initial line, then*

$$OP : OQ = (\text{arc } AKP') : (\text{arc } AKQ').$$

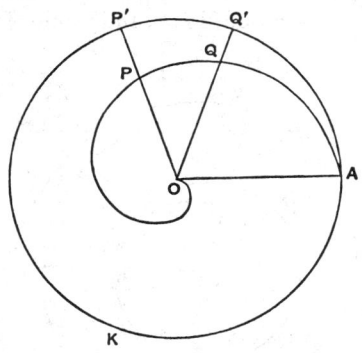

For, while the revolving line $OA$ moves about $O$, the point $A$ on it moves uniformly along the circumference of the circle $AKP'Q'$, and at the same time the point describing the spiral moves uniformly along $OA$.

Thus, while $A$ describes the arc $AKP'$, the moving point on $OA$ describes the length $OP$, and, while $A$ describes the arc $AKQ'$, the moving point on $OA$ describes the distance $OQ$.

Hence

$$OP : OQ = (\text{arc } AKP') : (\text{arc } AKQ').$$

[Prop. 2]

## Proposition 15

*If P, Q be points on the second turn of the spiral, and OP, OQ meet the "first circle" AKP'Q' in P', Q', as in the last proposition, and if c be the circumference of the "first circle," then*

$$OP : OQ = c + (\text{arc } AKP') : c + (\text{arc } AKQ').$$

For, while the moving point on $OA$ describes the distance $OP$, the point $A$ describes the whole of the circumference of the "first circle" together with the arc $AKP'$; and, while the moving point on $OA$ describes the distance $OQ$, the point $A$ describes the whole circumference of the "first circle" together with the arc $AKQ'$.

Cor. Similarly, if $P$, $Q$ are on the $n$th turn of the spiral,

$$OP : OQ = (n-1)c + (\text{arc } AKP') : (n-1)c + (\text{arc } AKQ').$$

## Propositions 16, 17

*If BC be the tangent at P, any point on the spiral, PC being the "forward" part of BC, and if OP be joined, the angle OPC is obtuse while the angle OPB is acute.*

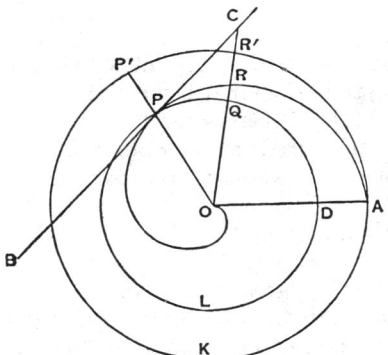

I. Suppose $P$ to be on the first turn of the spiral.

Let $OA$ be the initial line, $AKP'$ the "first circle." Draw the circle $DLP$ with centre $O$ and radius $OP$, meeting $OA$ in $D$. This circle must then, in the "forward" direction from $P$, fall within the spiral, and in the "backward" direction outside it, since the radii vectores of the spiral are on the "forward side" greater, and on the "backward" side less, than $OP$. Hence the angle $OPC$ cannot be acute, since it cannot be less than the angle between $OP$ and

492 ARCHIMEDES

the tangent to the circle at $P$, which is a right angle.

It only remains therefore to prove that $OPC$ is not a right angle.

If possible, let it be a right angle. $BC$ will then touch the circle at $P$.

Therefore [Prop. 5] it is possible to draw a line $OQC$ meeting the circle through $P$ in $Q$ and $BC$ in $C$, such that
$$CQ : OQ < (\text{arc } PQ) : (\text{arc } DLP). \qquad (1)$$

Suppose that $OC$ meets the spiral in $R$ and the "first circle" in $R'$; and produce $OP$ to meet the "first circle" in $P'$.

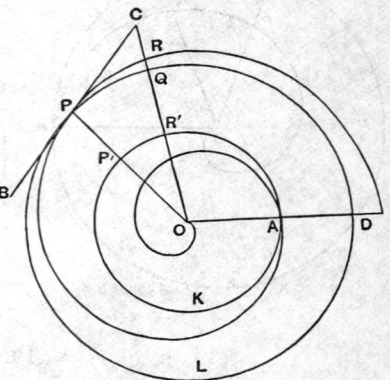

From (1) it follows, *componendo*, that
$$CO : OQ < (\text{arc } DLQ) : (\text{arc } DLP)$$
$$< (\text{arc } AKR') : (\text{arc } AKP')$$
$$< OR : OP. \qquad [\text{Prop. } 14]$$
But this is impossible, because $OQ = OP$, and $OR < OC$.

Hence the angle $OPC$ is not a right angle. It was also proved not to be acute.

Therefore the angle $OPC$ is obtuse, and the angle $OPB$ consequently acute.

II. If $P$ is on the second, or the $n$th turn, the proof is the same, except that in the proportion (1) above we have to substitute for the arc $DLP$ an arc equal to $(p + \text{arc } DLP)$ or $(n-1 \cdot p + \text{arc } DLP)$, where $p$ is the perimeter of the circle $DLP$ through $P$. Similarly, in the later steps, $p$ or $(n-1)p$ will be added to each of the arcs $DLQ$ and $DLP$, and $c$ or $(n-1)c$ to each of the arcs $AKR'$, $AKP'$, where $c$ is the circumference of the "first circle" $AKP'$.

## Propositions 18, 19

I. *If $OA$ be the initial line, $A$ the end of the first turn of the spiral, and if the tangent to the spiral at $A$ be drawn, the straight line $OB$ drawn from $O$ perpendicular to $OA$ will meet the said tangent in some point $B$, and $OB$ will be equal to the circumference of the "first circle."*

II. *If $A'$ be the end of the second turn, the perpendicular $OB$ will meet the tangent at $A'$ in some point $B'$, and $OB'$ will be equal to 2 (circumference of "second circle").*

III. *Generally, if $A_n$ be the end of the $n$th turn, and $OB$ meet the tangent at $A_n$ in $B_n$, then* $$OB_n = nc_n,$$
*where $c_n$ is the circumference of the "$n$th circle."*

I. Let $AKC$ be the "first circle." Then, since the "backward" angle between $OA$ and the tangent at $A$ is acute [Prop. 16], the tangent will meet the "first circle" in a second point $C$. And the angles $CAO$, $BOA$ are together less than two right angles; therefore $OB$ will meet $AC$ produced in some point $B$.

Then, if $c$ be the circumference of the first circle, we have to prove that
$$OB = c.$$

If not, $OB$ must be either greater or less than $c$.

(1) If possible, suppose $OB > c$.

Measure along $OB$ a length $OD$ less than $OB$ but greater than $c$.

We have then a circle $AKC$, a chord $AC$ in it less than the diameter, and a ratio $AO : OD$ which is greater than the ratio $AO : OB$ or (what is, by similar

ON SPIRALS    493

triangles, equal to it) the ratio of $\tfrac{1}{2}AC$ to the perpendicular from $O$ on $AC$. Therefore [Prop. 7] we can draw a straight line $OPF$, meeting the circle in $P$ and $CA$ produced in $F$, such that

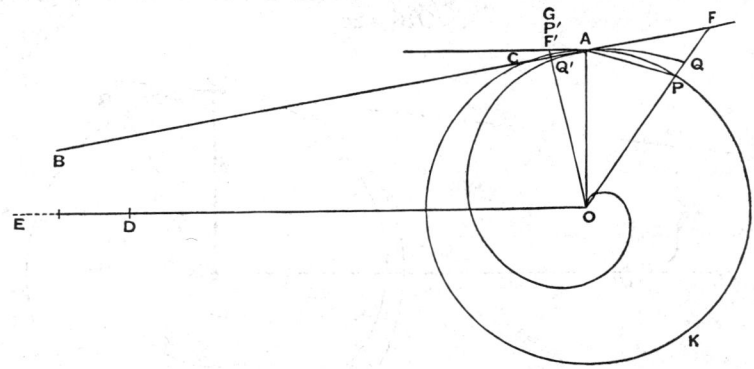

$$FP : PA = AO : OD.$$

Thus, alternately, since    $AO = PO$,
$$FP : PO = PA : OD$$
$$< (\text{arc } PA) : c,$$

since (arc $PA) > PA$, and $OD > c$.

*Componendo*,
$$FO : PO < (c + \text{arc } PA) : c$$
$$< OQ : OA,$$

where $OF$ meets the spiral in $Q$.    [Prop. 15]

Therefore, since $OA = OP$, $FO < OQ$; which is impossible.

Hence    $OB \not< c.$

(2) If possible, suppose    $OB < c.$

Measure $OE$ along $OB$ so that $OE$ is greater than $OB$ but less than $c$.

In this case, since the ratio $AO : OE$ is less than the ratio $AO : OB$ (or the ratio of $\tfrac{1}{2}AC$ to the perpendicular from $O$ on $AC$), we can [Prop. 8] draw a line $OF'P'G$, meeting $AC$ in $F'$, the circle in $P'$, and the tangent at $A$ to the circle in $G$, such that
$$F'P' : AG = AO : OE.$$

Let $OP'G$ cut the spiral in $Q'$.

Then we have, alternately,
$$F'P' : P'O = AG : OE$$
$$> (\text{arc } AP') : c,$$

because $AG > (\text{arc } AP')$, and $OE < c$.

Therefore
$$F'O : P'O < (\text{arc } AKP') : c$$
$$< OQ' : OA.$$    [Prop. 14]

But this is impossible, since $OA = OP'$, and $OQ' < OF'$.

Hence    $OB \not< c.$

Since therefore $OB$ is neither greater nor less than $c$,
$$OB = c.$$

II. Let $A'K'C'$ be the "second circle," $A'C'$ being the tangent to the spiral at $A'$ (which will cut the second circle, since the "backward" angle $OA'C'$ is acute). Thus, as before, the perpendicular $OB'$ to $OA'$ will meet $A'C'$ produced in some point $B'$.

If then $c'$ is the circumference of the "second circle," we have to prove that
$$OB' = 2c'.$$

For, if not, $OB'$ must be either greater or less than $2c'$.

(1) If possible, suppose $OB' > 2c'$.

Measure $OD'$ along $OB'$ so that $OD'$ is less than $OB'$ but greater than $2c'$.

Then, as in the case of the "first circle" above, we can draw a straight line $OPF$ meeting the "second circle" in $P$ and $C'A'$ produced in $F$, such that
$$FP : PA' = A'O : OD'.$$

Let $OF$ meet the spiral in $Q$.

We now have, since $\quad A'O = PO$,
$$FP : PO = PA' : OD'$$
$$< (\text{arc } A'P) : 2c',$$
because $(\text{arc } A'P) > A'P$ and $OD' > 2c'$.

Therefore $\quad FO : PO < (2c' + \text{arc } A'P) : 2c'$
$$< OQ : OA'. \qquad \text{[Prop. 15, Cor.]}$$

Hence $FO < OQ$; which is impossible.

Thus $\quad OB' \not> 2c'$.

Similarly, as in the case of the "first circle," we can prove that
$$OB' \not< 2c'.$$

Therefore $\quad OB' = 2c'$.

III. Proceeding, in like manner, to the "third" and succeeding circles, we shall prove that
$$OB_n = nc_n.$$

## Proposition 20

I. *If $P$ be any point on the first turn of the spiral and $OT$ be drawn perpendicular to $OP$, $OT$ will meet the tangent at $P$ to the spiral in some point $T$; and, if the circle drawn with centre $O$ and radius $OP$ meet the initial line in $K$, then $OT$ is equal to the arc of this circle between $K$ and $P$ measured in the "forward" direction of the spiral.*

II. *Generally, if P be a point on the nth turn, and the notation be as before, while p represents the circumference of the circle with radius OP,*

$$OT = (n-1)p + \text{arc } KP \quad (\text{measured "forward"}).$$

I. Let $P$ be a point on the first turn of the spiral, $OA$ the initial line, $PR$ the tangent at $P$ taken in the "backward" direction.

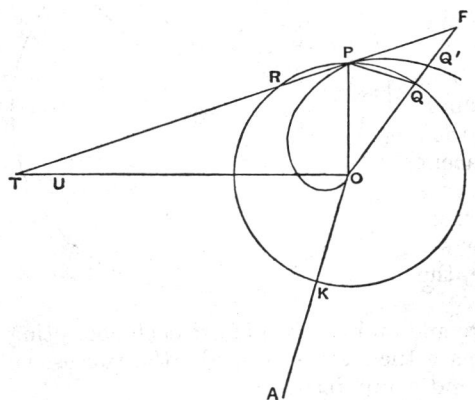

Then [Prop. 16] the angle $OPR$ is acute. Therefore $PR$ meets the circle through $P$ in some point $R$; and also $OT$ will meet $PR$ produced in some point $T$.

If now $OT$ is not equal to the arc $KRP$, it must be either greater or less.

(1) If possible, let $OT$ be greater than the arc $KRP$.

Measure $OU$ along $OT$ less than $OT$ but greater than the arc $KRP$.

Then, since the ratio $PO : OU$ is greater than the ratio $PO : OT$, or (what is, by similar triangles, equal to it) the ratio of $\frac{1}{2}PR$ to the perpendicular from $O$ on $PR$, we can draw a line $OQF$, meeting the circle in $Q$ and $RP$ produced in $F$, such that

$$FQ : PQ = PO : OU. \quad \text{[Prop. 7]}$$

Let $OF$ meet the spiral in $Q'$.

We have then
$$FQ : QO = PQ : OU$$
$$< (\text{arc } PQ) : (\text{arc } KRP), \text{ by hypothesis.}$$

*Componendo,*
$$FO : QO < (\text{arc } KRQ) : (\text{arc } KRP)$$
$$< OQ' : OP. \quad \text{[Prop. 14]}$$

But $\qquad QO = OP.$

Therefore $FO < OQ'$; which is impossible.

Hence $\qquad OT \not> (\text{arc } KRP).$

(2) The proof that $OT \not< (\text{arc } KRP)$ follows the method of Prop. 18, I. (2), exactly as the above follows that of Prop. 18, I. (1).

Since then $OT$ is neither greater nor less than the arc $KRP$, it is equal to it.

II. If $P$ be on the second turn, the same method shows that
$$OT = p + (\text{arc } KRP);$$
and, similarly, we have, for a point $P$ on the $n$th turn,
$$OT = (n-1)p + (\text{arc } KRP).$$

## Propositions 21, 22, 23

*Given an area bounded by any arc of a spiral and the lines joining the extremities of the arc to the origin, it is possible to circumscribe about the area one figure, and to inscribe in it another figure, each consisting of similar sectors of circles, and such that the circumscribed figure exceeds the inscribed by less than any assigned area.*

For let $BC$ be any arc of the spiral, $O$ the origin. Draw the circle with centre

$O$ and radius $OC$, where $C$ is the "forward" end of the arc.

Then, by bisecting the angle $BOC$, bisecting the resulting angles, and so on continually, we shall ultimately arrive at an angle $COr$ cutting off a sector of the circle less than any assigned area. Let $COr$ be this sector.

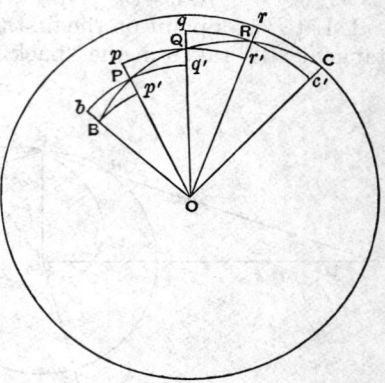

Let the other lines dividing the angle $BOC$ into equal parts meet the spiral in $P$, $Q$, and let $Or$ meet it in $R$. With $O$ as centre and radii $OB$, $OP$, $OQ$, $OR$ respectively describe arcs of circles $Bp'$, $bBq'$, $pQr'$, $qRc'$, each meeting the adjacent radii as shown in the figure. In each case the arc in the "forward" direction from each point will fall within, and the arc in the "backward" direction outside, the spiral.

We have now a circumscribed figure and an inscribed figure each consisting of similar sectors of circles. To compare their areas, we take the successive sectors of each, beginning from $OC$, and compare them.

The sector $OCr$ in the circumscribed figure stands alone.

And
$$(\text{sector } ORq) = (\text{sector } ORc'),$$
$$(\text{sector } OQp) = (\text{sector } OQr'),$$
$$(\text{sector } OPb) = (\text{sector } OPq'),$$
while the sector $OBp'$ in the inscribed figure stands alone.

Hence, if the equal sectors be taken away, the difference between the circumscribed and inscribed figures is equal to the difference between the sectors $OCr$ and $OBp'$; and this difference is less than the sector $OCr$, which is itself less than any assigned area.

The proof is exactly the same whatever be the number of angles into which the angle $BOC$ is divided, the only difference being that, when the arc begins from the origin, the smallest sectors $OPb$, $OPq'$ in each figure are equal, and there is therefore no inscribed sector standing by itself, so that the difference between the circumscribed and inscribed figures is equal to the sector $OCr$ itself.

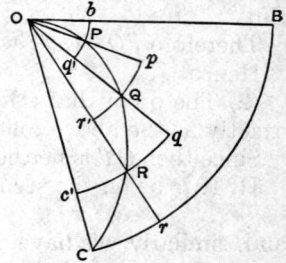

Thus the proposition is universally true.

COR. Since the area bounded by the spiral is intermediate in magnitude between the circumscribed and inscribed figures, it follows that

(1) *a figure can be circumscribed to the area such that it exceeds the area by less than any assigned space,*

(2) *a figure can be inscribed such that the area exceeds it by less than any assigned space.*

## Proposition 24

*The area bounded by the first turn of the spiral and the initial line is equal to one-third of the "first circle"* $[=\frac{1}{3}\pi(2\pi a)^2$, *where the spiral is* $r = a\theta]$.

ON SPIRALS

[*The same proof shows equally that, if OP be any radius vector in the first turn of the spiral, the area of the portion of the spiral bounded thereby is equal to one-third of that sector of the circle drawn with radius OP which is bounded by the initial line and OP, measured in the "forward" direction from the initial line.*]

Let $O$ be the origin, $OA$ the initial line, $A$ the extremity of the first turn.

Draw the "first circle," i.e. the circle with $O$ as centre and $OA$ as radius.

Then, if $C_1$ be the area of the first circle, $R_1$ that of the first turn of the spiral bounded by $OA$, we have to prove that
$$R_1 = \tfrac{1}{3}C_1.$$

For, if not, $R_1$ must be either greater or less than $C_1$.

I. If possible, suppose $R_1 < \tfrac{1}{3}C_1$.

We can then circumscribe a figure about $R_1$ made up of similar sectors of circles such that, if $F$ be the area of this figure,
$$F - R_1 < \tfrac{1}{3}C_1 - R_1,$$
whence $F < \tfrac{1}{3}C_1$.

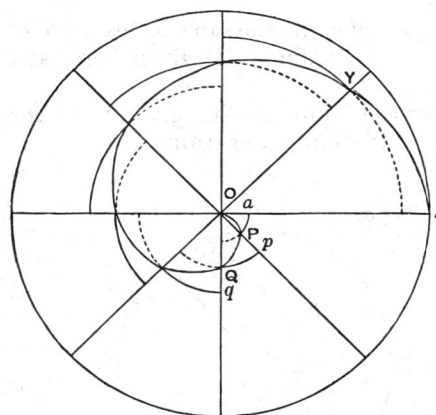

Let $OP$, $OQ$, $\cdots$ be the radii of the circular sectors, beginning from the smallest. The radius of the largest is of course $OA$.

The radii then form an ascending arithmetical progression in which the common difference is equal to the least term $OP$. If $n$ be the number of the sectors, we have [by Prop. 10, Cor. 1]
$$n \cdot OA^2 < 3(OP^2 + OQ^2 + \cdots + OA^2);$$
and, since the similar sectors are proportional to the squares on their radii, it follows that
$$C_1 < 3F,$$
or $$F > \tfrac{1}{3}C_1.$$

But this is impossible, since $F$ was less than $\tfrac{1}{3}C_1$.

Therefore $R_1 \not< \tfrac{1}{3}C_1$.

II. If possible, suppose $R_1 > \tfrac{1}{3}C_1$.

We can then *inscribe* a figure made up of similar sectors of circles such that, if $f$ be its area,
$$R_1 - f < R_1 - \tfrac{1}{3}C_1,$$
whence $f > \tfrac{1}{3}C_1$.

If there are $(n-1)$ sectors, their radii, as $OP$, $OQ$, $\cdots$, form an ascending arithmetical progression in which the least term is equal to the common difference, and the greatest term, as $OY$, is equal to $(n-1)OP$.

Thus [Prop. 10, Cor. 1]
$$n \cdot OA^2 > 3(OP^2 + OQ^2 + \cdots + OY^2),$$
whence $C_1 > 3f$,
or $f < \tfrac{1}{3}C_1$;
which is impossible, since $f > \tfrac{1}{3}C_1$.

Therefore $R_1 \not> \tfrac{1}{3}C_1$.

Since then $R_1$ is neither greater nor less than $\tfrac{1}{3}C_1$,
$$R_1 = \tfrac{1}{3}C_1.$$

## PROPOSITIONS 25, 26, 27

[Prop. 25.] *If $A_2$ be the end of the second turn of the spiral, the area bounded by the second turn and $OA_2$ is to the area of the "second circle" in the ratio of 7 to 12, being the ratio of $\{r_2 r_1 + \frac{1}{3}(r_2 - r_1)^2\}$ to $r_2^2$, where $r_1, r_2$ are the radii of the "first" and "second" circles respectively.*

[Prop. 26.] *If $BC$ be any arc measured in the "forward" direction on any turn of a spiral, not being greater than the complete turn, and if a circle be drawn with $O$ as centre and $OC$ as radius meeting $OB$ in $B'$, then*

(area of spiral between $OB$, $OC$) : (sector $OB'C$)
$= \{OC \cdot OB + \frac{1}{3}(OC - OB)^2\} : OC^2.$

[Prop. 27.] *If $R_1$ be the area of the first turn of the spiral bounded by the initial line, $R_2$ the area of the ring added by the second complete turn, $R_3$ that of the ring added by the third turn, and so on, then*

$$R_3 = 2R_2, \quad R_4 = 3R_2, \quad R_5 = 4R_2, \quad \cdots, \quad R_n = (n-1)R_2.$$

*Also* $\qquad\qquad R_2 = 6R_1.$

[Archimedes' proof of Prop. 25 is, *mutatis mutandis*, the same as his proof of the more general Prop. 26. The latter will accordingly be given here, and applied to Prop. 25 as a particular case.]

Let $BC$ be an arc measured in the "forward" direction on any turn of the spiral, $CKB'$ the circle drawn with $O$ as centre and $OC$ as radius.

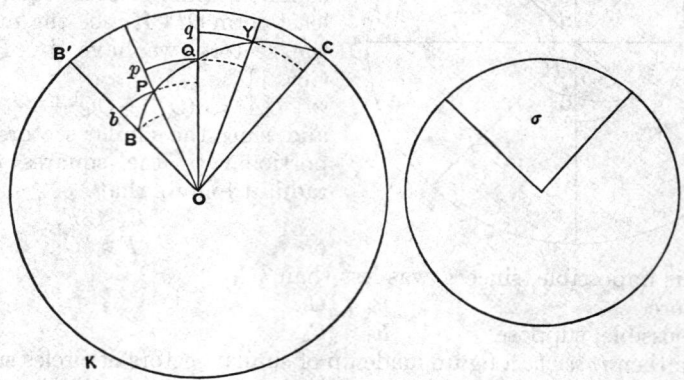

Take a circle such that the square of its radius is equal to
$$OC \cdot OB + \frac{1}{3}(OC - OB)^2,$$
and let $\sigma$ be a sector in it whose central angle is equal to the angle $BOC$.
Thus $\qquad \sigma : (\text{sector } OB'C) = \{OC \cdot OB + \frac{1}{3}(OC - OB)^2\} : OC^2,$
and we have therefore to prove that
$$(\text{area of spiral } OBC) = \sigma.$$

For, if not, the area of the spiral $OBC$ (which we will call $S$) must be either greater or less than $\sigma$.

I. Suppose, if possible, $S < \sigma$.

Circumscribe to the area $S$ a figure made up of similar sectors of circles, such that, if $F$ be the area of the figure,
$$F - S < \sigma - S,$$
whence $\qquad\qquad F < \sigma.$

ON SPIRALS 499

Let the radii of the successive sectors, starting from $OB$, be $OP$, $OQ$, $\cdots OC$. Produce $OP$, $OQ$, $\cdots$ to meet the circle $CKB'$, $\cdots$

If then the lines $OB$, $OP$, $OQ$, $\ldots OC$ be $n$ in number, the number of sectors in the circumscribed figure will be $(n-1)$, and the sector $OB'C$ will also be divided into $(n-1)$ equal sectors. Also $OB$, $OP$, $OQ$, $\cdots OC$ will form an ascending arithmetical progression of $n$ terms.

Therefore [see Prop. 11 and Cor.]
$$(n-1)OC^2 : (OP^2+OQ^2+\cdots+OC^2) < OC^2 : \{OC\cdot OB+\tfrac{1}{3}(OC-OB)^2\}$$
$$< (\text{sector } OB'C) : \sigma, \text{ by hypothesis.}$$

Hence, since similar sectors are as the squares of their radii,
$$(\text{sector } OB'C) : F < (\text{sector } OB'C) : \sigma,$$
so that $\qquad F > \sigma.$
But this is impossible, because $\quad F < \sigma.$
Therefore $\qquad S \not< \sigma.$

II. Suppose, if possible, $S > \sigma$.

Inscribe in the area $S$ a figure made up of similar sectors of circles such that, if $f$ be its area,
$$S-f < S-\sigma,$$
whence $\qquad f > \sigma.$

Suppose $OB$, $OP$, $\ldots OY$ to be the radii of the successive sectors making up the figure $f$, being $(n-1)$ in number.

We shall have in this case [see Prop. 11 and Cor.]
$$(n-1)OC^2 : (OB^2+OP^2+\cdots+OY^2) > OC^2 : \{OC\cdot OB+\tfrac{1}{3}(OC-OB)^2\},$$
whence $\qquad (\text{sector } OB'C) : f > (\text{sector } OB'C) : \sigma,$
so that $\qquad f < \sigma.$
But this is impossible, because $\quad f > \sigma.$
Therefore $\qquad S \not> \sigma.$

Since then $S$ is neither greater nor less than $\sigma$, it follows that
$$S = \sigma.$$

In the particular case where $B$ coincides with $A_1$, the end of the first turn of the spiral, and $C$ with $A_2$, the end of the second turn, the sector $OB'C$ becomes the complete "second circle," that, namely, with $OA_2$ (or $r_2$) as radius.

Thus (area of spiral bounded by $OA_2$) : ("second circle")
$$= \{r_2 r_1 + \tfrac{1}{3}(r_2-r_1)^2\} : r_2^2$$
$$= (2+\tfrac{1}{3}) : 4 \quad (\text{since } r_2 = 2r_1)$$
$$= 7 : 12.$$

Again, the area of the spiral bounded by $OA_2$ is equal to $R_1+R_2$ (i.e. the area bounded by the first turn and $OA_1$, together with the ring added by the second turn). Also the "second circle" is four times the "first circle," and therefore equal to $12 R_1$.

Hence $\qquad (R_1+R_2) : 12R_1 = 7 : 12,$
or $\qquad R_1+R_2 = 7R_1.$
Thus $\qquad R_2 = 6R_1.$ \hfill (1)

Next, for the third turn, we have
$$(R_1+R_2+R_3) : (\text{"third circle"}) = \{r_3\, r_2 + \tfrac{1}{3}(r_3-r_2)^2\} : r_3^2$$
$$= (3\cdot 2 + \tfrac{1}{3}) : 3^2$$
$$= 19 : 27,$$
and $\qquad$ ("third circle") $= 9($"first circle"$)$
$$= 27R_1;$$

therefore $R_1+R_2+R_3 = 19R_1$,
and, by (1) above, it follows that
$$R_3 = 12R_1$$
$$= 2R_2, \qquad (2)$$
and so on.

Generally, we have
$(R_1+R_2+\cdots+R_n) : (n\text{th circle}) = \{r_n r_{n-1} + \tfrac{1}{3}(r_n-r_{n-1})^2\} : r_n^2$,
$(R_1+R_2+\cdots+R_{n-1}) : (\overline{n-1}\text{th circle}) = \{r_{n-1}\,r_{n-2}+\tfrac{1}{3}(r_{n-1}-r_{n-2})^2\} : r_{n-1}^2$,
and
Therefore $(n\text{th circle}) : (\overline{n-1}\text{th circle}) = r_n^2 : r_{n-1}^2$.

$$(R_1+R_2+\cdots+R_n) : (R_1+R_2+\cdots+R_{n-1})$$
$$= \{n(n-1)+\tfrac{1}{3}\} : \{(n-1)(n-2)+\tfrac{1}{3}\}$$
$$= \{3n(n-1)+1\} : \{3(n-1)(n-2)+1\}.$$

*Dirimendo*,
$$R_n : (R_1+R_2+\cdots+R_{n-1}) = 6(n-1) : \{3(n-1)(n-2)+1\}. \qquad (\alpha)$$
Similarly
$$R_{n-1} : (R_1+R_2+\cdots+R_{n-2}) = 6(n-2) : \{3(n-2)(n-3)+1\},$$
from which we derive
$$R_{n-1} : (R_1+R_2+\cdots+R_{n-1})$$
$$= 6(n-2) : \{6(n-2)+3(n-2)(n-3)+1\}$$
$$= 6(n-2) : \{3(n-1)(n-2)+1\}. \qquad (\beta).$$

Combining ($\alpha$) and ($\beta$), we obtain
$$R_n : R_{n-1} = (n-1) : (n-2).$$
Thus
$R_2, R_3, R_4, \cdots R_n$ are in the ratio of the successive numbers $1, 2, 3 \cdots (n-1)$.

## Proposition 28

*If O be the origin and BC any arc measured in the "forward" direction on any turn of the spiral, let two circles be drawn (1) with centre O, and radius OB, meeting OC in $C'$, and (2) with centre O and radius OC, meeting OB produced in $B'$. Then, if E denote the area bounded by the larger circular arc $B'C$, the line $B'B$, and the spiral BC, while F denotes the area bounded by the smaller arc $BC'$, the line $CC'$ and the spiral BC,*
$$E : F = \{OB + \tfrac{2}{3}(OC-OB)\} : \{OB + \tfrac{1}{3}(OC-OB)\}.$$

Let $\sigma$ denote the area of the lesser sector $OBC'$; then the larger sector $OB'C$ is equal to $\sigma+F+E$. Thus [Prop. 26]
$(\sigma+F) : (\sigma+F+E) =$
$$\{OC \cdot OB + \tfrac{1}{3}(OC-OB)^2\} : OC^2, \quad (1)$$
whence
$$E : (\sigma+F) = \{OC(OC-OB) - \tfrac{1}{3}(OC-OB)^2\}$$
$$: \{OC \cdot OB + \tfrac{1}{3}(OC-OB)^2\}$$
$$= \{OB(OC-OB) + \tfrac{2}{3}(OC-OB)^2\}$$
$$: \{OC \cdot OB + \tfrac{1}{3}(OC-OB)^2\}. \quad (2)$$

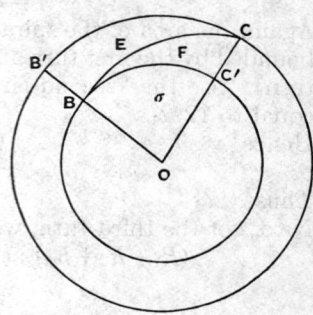

Again
$$(\sigma+F+E) : \sigma = OC^2 : OB^2.$$
Therefore, by the first proportion above, *ex aequali*,
$$(\sigma+F) : \sigma = \{OC \cdot OB + \tfrac{1}{3}(OC-OB)^2\} : OB^2,$$

whence
$$(\sigma+F) : F = \{OC \cdot OB + \tfrac{1}{3}(OC-OB)^2\} \\ : \{OB(OC-OB) + \tfrac{1}{3}(OC-OB)^2\}.$$

Combining this with (2) above, we obtain
$$E : F = \{OB(OC-OB) + \tfrac{2}{3}(OC-OB)^2\} : \{OB(OC-OB) + \tfrac{1}{3}(OC-OB)^2\} \\ = \{OB + \tfrac{2}{3}(OC-OB)\} : \{OB + \tfrac{1}{3}(OC-OB)\}.$$

# ON THE EQUILIBRIUM OF PLANES OR THE CENTRES OF GRAVITY OF PLANES

## BOOK ONE

"I POSTULATE the following":

1. "Equal weights at equal distances are in equilibrium, and equal weights at unequal distances are not in equilibrium but incline towards the weight which is at the greater distance."
2. "If, when weights at certain distances are in equilibrium, something be added to one of the weights, they are not in equilibrium but incline towards that weight to which the addition was made."
3. "Similarly, if anything be taken away from one of the weights, they are not in equilibrium but incline towards the weight from which nothing was taken."
4. "When equal and similar plane figures coincide if applied to one another, their centres of gravity similarly coincide."
5. "In figures which are unequal but similar, the centres of gravity will be similarly situated. By points similarly situated in relation to similar figures I mean points such that, if straight lines be drawn from them to the equal angles, they make equal angles with the corresponding sides."
6. "If magnitudes at certain distances be in equilibrium, (other) magnitudes equal to them will also be in equilibrium at the same distances."
7. "In any figure whose perimeter is concave in (one and) the same direction the centre of gravity must be within the figure."

### PROPOSITION 1

*Weights which balance at equal distances are equal.*

For, if they are unequal, take away from the greater the difference between the two. The remainders will then not balance [*Post.* 3]; which is absurd.

Therefore the weights cannot be unequal.

### PROPOSITION 2

*Unequal weights at equal distances will not balance but will incline towards the greater weight.*

For take away from the greater the difference between the two. The equal remainders will therefore balance [*Post.* 1]. Hence, if we add the difference again, the weights will not balance but incline towards the greater [*Post.* 2].

### PROPOSITION 3

*Unequal weights will balance at unequal distances, the greater weight being at the lesser distance.*

Let $A$, $B$ be two unequal weights (of which $A$ is the greater) balancing about $C$ at distances $AC$, $BC$ respectively.

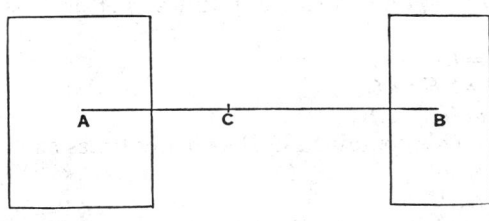

Then shall $AC$ be less than $BC$. For, if not, take away from $A$ the weight $(A-B)$. The remainders will then incline towards $B$ [*Post.* 3]. But this is impossible, for (1) if $AC = CB$, the equal remainders will balance, or (2) if $AC > CB$, they will incline towards $A$ at the greater distance [*Post.* 1].

Hence $AC < CB$.

*Conversely*, if the weights balance, and $AC < CB$, then $A > B$.

## Proposition 4

*If two equal weights have not the same centre of gravity, the centre of gravity of both taken together is at the middle point of the line joining their centres of gravity.*

[Proved from Prop. 3 by *reductio ad absurdum*.]

## Proposition 5

*If three equal magnitudes have their centres of gravity on a straight line at equal distances, the centre of gravity of the system will coincide with that of the middle magnitude.*

[This follows immediately from Prop. 4.]

Cor. 1. *The same is true of any odd number of magnitudes if those which are at equal distances from the middle one are equal, while the distances between their centres of gravity are equal.*

Cor. 2. *If there be an even number of magnitudes with their centres of gravity situated at equal distances on one straight line, and if the two middle ones be equal, while those which are equidistant from them (on each side) are equal respectively, the centre of gravity of the system is the middle point of the line joining the centres of gravity of the two middle ones.*

## Propositions 6, 7

*Two magnitudes, whether commensurable* [Prop. 6] *or incommensurable* [Prop. 7], *balance at distances reciprocally proportional to the magnitudes.*

I. Suppose the magnitudes $A$, $B$ to be commensurable, and the points $A$, $B$ to be their centres of gravity. Let $DE$ be a straight line so divided at $C$ that
$$A : B = DC : CE.$$

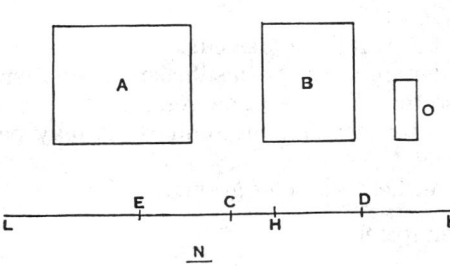

We have then to prove that, if $A$ be placed at $E$ and $B$ at $D$, $C$ is the centre of gravity of the two taken together.

Since $A$, $B$ are commensurable, so are $DC$, $CE$. Let $N$ be a common measure of $DC, CE$. Make $DH, DK$ each equal to $CE$, and $EL$ (on $CE$ produced) equal to $CD$. Then $EH = CD$, since $DH = CE$. Therefore $LH$ is bisected at $E$, as $HK$ is bisected at $D$.

Thus $LH$, $HK$ must each contain $N$ an even number of times.

Take a magnitude $O$ such that $O$ is contained as many times in $A$ as $N$ is contained in $LH$, whence
$$A : O = LH : N.$$
But
$$B : A = CE : DC$$
$$= HK : LH.$$
Hence, *ex aequali*, $B : O = HK : N$, or $O$ is contained in $B$ as many times as $N$ is contained in $HK$.

Thus $O$ is a common measure of $A$, $B$.

Divide $LH$, $HK$ into parts each equal to $N$, and $A$, $B$ into parts each equal to $O$. The parts of $A$ will therefore be equal in number to those of $LH$, and the parts of $B$ equal in number to those of $HK$. Place one of the parts of $A$ at the middle point of each of the parts $N$ of $LH$, and one of the parts of $B$ at the middle point of each of the parts $N$ of $HK$.

Then the centre of gravity of the parts of $A$ placed at equal distances on $LH$ will be at $E$, the middle point of $LH$ [Prop. 5, Cor. 2], and the centre of gravity of the parts of $B$ placed at equal distances along $HK$ will be at $D$, the middle point of $HK$.

Thus we may suppose $A$ itself applied at $E$, and $B$ itself applied at $D$.

But the system formed by the parts $O$ of $A$ and $B$ together is a system of equal magnitudes even in number and placed at equal distances along $LK$. And, since $LE = CD$, and $EC = DK$, $LC = CK$, so that $C$ is the middle point of $LK$. Therefore $C$ is the centre of gravity of the system ranged along $LK$.

Therefore $A$ acting at $E$ and $B$ acting at $D$ balance about the point $C$.

II. Suppose the magnitudes to be incommensurable, and let them be $(A+a)$ and $B$ respectively. Let $DE$ be a line divided at $C$ so that
$$(A+a) : B = DC : CE.$$
Then, if $(A+a)$ placed at $E$ and $B$ placed at $D$ do not balance about $C$, $(A+a)$ is either too great to balance $B$, or not great enough.

Suppose, if possible, that $(A+a)$ is too great to balance $B$. Take from $(A+a)$ a magnitude $a$ smaller than the deduction which would make the remainder balance $B$, but such that the remainder $A$ and the magnitude $B$ are commensurable.

Then, since $A$, $B$ are commensurable, and
$$A : B < DC : CE,$$
$A$ and $B$ will not balance [Prop. 6], but $D$ will be depressed.

But this is impossible, since the deduction $a$ was an insufficient deduction from $(A+a)$ to produce equilibrium, so that $E$ was still depressed.

Therefore $(A+a)$ is not too great to balance $B$; and similarly it may be proved that $B$ is not too great to balance $(A+a)$.

Hence $(A+a)$, $B$ taken together have their centre of gravity at $C$.

## Proposition 8

*If $AB$ be a magnitude whose centre of gravity is $C$, and $AD$ a part of it whose centre of gravity is $F$, then the centre of gravity of the remaining part will be a point $G$ on $FC$ produced such that*

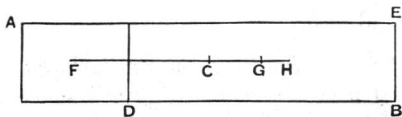

$GC : CF = (AD) : (DE)$.

For, if the centre of gravity of the remainder $(DE)$ be not $G$, let it be a point $H$. Then an absurdity follows at once from Props. 6, 7.

## Proposition 9

*The centre of gravity of any parallelogram lies on the straight line joining the middle points of opposite sides.*

Let $ABCD$ be a parallelogram, and let $EF$ join the middle points of the opposite sides $AD$, $BC$.

If the centre of gravity does not lie on $EF$, suppose it to be $H$, and draw $HK$ parallel to $AD$ or $BC$ meeting $EF$ in $K$.

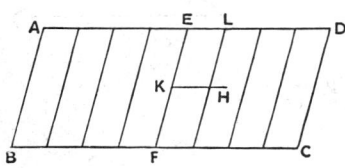

Then it is possible, by bisecting $ED$, then bisecting the halves, and so on continually, to arrive at a length $EL$ less than $KH$. Divide both $AE$ and $ED$ into parts each equal to $EL$, and through the points of division draw parallels to $AB$ or $CD$.

We have then a number of equal and similar parallelograms, and, if any one be applied to any other, their centres of gravity coincide [*Post.* 4]. Thus we have an even number of equal magnitudes whose centres of gravity lie at equal distances along a straight line. Hence the centre of gravity of the whole parallelogram will lie on the line joining the centres of gravity of the two middle parallelograms [Prop. 5, Cor. 2].

But this is impossible, for $H$ is outside the middle parallelograms.

Therefore the centre of gravity cannot but lie on $EF$.

## Proposition 10

*The centre of gravity of a parallelogram is the point of intersection of its diagonals.*

For, by the last proposition, the centre of gravity lies on each of the lines which bisect opposite sides. Therefore it is at the point of their intersection; and this is also the point of intersection of the diagonals.

*Alternative proof.*

Let $ABCD$ be the given parallelogram, and $BD$ a diagonal. Then the triangles $ABD$, $CDB$ are equal and similar, so that [*Post.* 4], if one be applied to the other, their centres of gravity will fall one upon the other.

Suppose $F$ to be the centre of gravity of the triangle $ABD$. Let $G$ be the middle point of $BD$. Join $FG$ and produce it to $H$, so that $FG = GH$.

If we then apply the triangle $ABD$ to the triangle $CDB$ so that $AD$ falls on $CB$ and $AB$ on $CD$, the point $F$ will fall on $H$.

But [by *Post.* 4] $F$ will fall on the centre of gravity of $CDB$. Therefore $H$ is the centre of gravity of $CDB$.

Hence, since $F$, $H$ are the centres of gravity of the two equal triangles, the centre of gravity of the whole parallelogram is at the middle point of $FH$, i.e. at the middle point of $BD$, which is the intersection of the two diagonals.

## Proposition 11

*If abc, ABC be two similar triangles, and g, G two points in them similarly situated with respect to them respectively, then, if g be the centre of gravity of the triangle abc, G must be the centre of gravity of the triangle ABC.*

Suppose
$$ab : bc : ca = AB : BC : CA.$$

The proposition is proved by an obvious *reductio ad absurdum*. For, if G be not the centre of gravity of the triangle ABC, suppose H to be its centre of gravity.

*Post.* 5 requires that g, H shall be similarly situated with respect to the triangles respectively; and this leads at once to the absurdity that the angles HAB, GAB are equal.

## Proposition 12

*Given two similar triangles abc, ABC, and d, D the middle points of bc, BC respectively, then, if the centre of gravity of abc lie on ad, that of ABC will lie on AD.*

Let g be the point on ad which is the centre of gravity of abc.

Take G on AD such that
$$ad : ag = AD : AG,$$
and join gb, gc, GB, GC.

Then, since the triangles are similar, and bd, BD are the halves of bc, BC respectively,
$$ab : bd = AB : BD,$$
and the angles abd, ABD are equal.

Therefore the triangles abd, ABD are similar, and
$$\angle bad = \angle BAD.$$

Also
$$ba : ad = BA : AD,$$
while, from above,
$$ad : ag = AD : AG.$$

Therefore $ba : ag = BA : AG$, while the angles bag, BAG are equal.

Hence the triangles bag, BAG are similar, and
$$\angle abg = \angle ABG.$$

And, since the angles abd, ABD are equal, it follows that
$$\angle gbd = \angle GBD.$$

In exactly the same manner we prove that
$$\angle gac = \angle GAC,$$
$$\angle acg = \angle ACG,$$
$$\angle gcd = \angle GCD.$$

Therefore g, G are similarly situated with respect to the triangles respectively; whence [Prop. 11] G is the centre of gravity of ABC.

## Proposition 13

*In any triangle the centre of gravity lies on the straight line joining any angle to the middle point of the opposite side.*

Let $ABC$ be a triangle and $D$ the middle point of $BC$. Join $AD$. Then shall the centre of gravity lie on $AD$.

For, if possible, let this not be the case, and let $H$ be the centre of gravity. Draw $HI$ parallel to $CB$ meeting $AD$ in $I$.

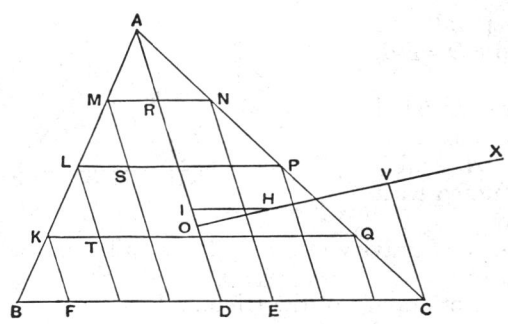

Then, if we bisect $DC$, then bisect the halves, and so on, we shall at length arrive at a length, as $DE$, less than $HI$. Divide both $BD$ and $DC$ into lengths each equal to $DE$, and through the points of division draw lines each parallel to $DA$ meeting $BA$ and $AC$ in points as $K, L, M$ and $N, P, Q$ respectively.

Join $MN, LP, KQ$, which lines will then be each parallel to $BC$.

We have now a series of parallelograms as $FQ, TP, SN$, and $AD$ bisects opposite sides in each. Thus the centre of gravity of each parallelogram lies on $AD$ [Prop. 9], and therefore the centre of gravity of the figure made up of them all lies on $AD$.

Let the centre of gravity of all the parallelograms taken together be $O$. Join $OH$ and produce it; also draw $CV$ parallel to $DA$ meeting $OH$ produced in $V$.

Now, if $n$ be the number of parts into which $AC$ is divided,

$\triangle ADC$ : (sum of triangles on $AN, NP, \cdots$) = $AC^2 : (AN^2 + NP^2 + \cdots)$
$$= n^2 : n$$
$$= n : 1$$
$$= AC : AN.$$

Similarly
$\triangle ABD$ : (sum of triangles on $AM, ML, \cdots$) = $AB : AM$.
And $AC : AN = AB : AM$.
It follows that
$\triangle ABC$ : (sum of all the small $\triangle$s) = $CA : AN$
$> VO : OH$, by parallels.

Suppose $OV$ produced to $X$ so that
$\triangle ABC$ : (sum of small $\triangle$s) = $XO : OH$,
whence, *dividendo*,
(sum of parallelograms) : (sum of small $\triangle$s) = $XH : HO$.

Since then the centre of gravity of the triangle $ABC$ is at $H$, and the centre of gravity of the part of it made up of the parallelograms is at $O$, it follows from Prop. 8 that the centre of gravity of the remaining portion consisting of all the small triangles taken together is at $X$.

But this is impossible, since all the triangles are on one side of the line through $X$ parallel to $AD$.

Therefore the centre of gravity of the triangle cannot but lie on $AD$.

*Alternative proof.*

Suppose, if possible, that $H$, not lying on $AD$, is the centre of gravity of the triangle $ABC$. Join $AH$, $BH$, $CH$. Let $E$, $F$ be the middle points of $CA$, $AB$ respectively, and join $DE$, $EF$, $FD$. Let $EF$ meet $AD$ in $M$.

Draw $FK$, $EL$ parallel to $AH$ meeting $BH$, $CH$ in $K$, $L$ respectively. Join $KD$, $HD$, $LD$, $KL$. Let $KL$ meet $DH$ in $N$, and join $MN$.

Since $DE$ is parallel to $AB$, the triangles $ABC$, $EDC$ are similar.

And, since $CE = EA$, and $EL$ is parallel to $AH$, it follows that $CL = LH$. And $CD = DB$. Therefore $BH$ is parallel to $DL$.

Thus in the similar and similarly situated triangles $ABC$, $EDC$ the straight lines $AH$, $BH$ are respectively parallel to $EL$, $DL$; and it follows that $H$, $L$ are similarly situated with respect to the triangles respectively.

But $H$ is, by hypothesis, the centre of gravity of $ABC$. Therefore $L$ is the centre of gravity of $EDC$. [Prop. 11]

Similarly the point $K$ is the centre of gravity of the triangle $FBD$.

And the triangles $FBD$, $EDC$ are equal, so that the centre of gravity of both together is at the middle point of $KL$, i.e. at the point $N$.

The remainder of the triangle $ABC$, after the triangles $FBD$, $EDC$ are deducted, is the parallelogram $AFDE$, and the centre of gravity of this parallelogram is at $M$, the intersection of its diagonals.

It follows that the centre of gravity of the whole triangle $ABC$ must lie on $MN$; that is, $MN$ must pass through $H$, which is impossible (since $MN$ is parallel to $AH$).

Therefore the centre of gravity of the triangle $ABC$ cannot but lie on $AD$.

## Proposition 14

It follows at once from the last proposition that *the centre of gravity of any triangle is at the intersection of the lines drawn from any two angles to the middle points of the opposite sides respectively.*

## Proposition 15

*If $AD$, $BC$ be the two parallel sides of a trapezium $ABCD$, $AD$ being the smaller, and if $AD$, $BC$ be bisected at $E$, $F$ respectively, then the centre of gravity of the trapezium is at a point $G$ on $EF$ such that*
$$GE : GF = (2BC + AD) : (2AD + BC).$$

Produce $BA$, $CD$ to meet at $O$. Then $FE$ produced will also pass through $O$, since $AE = ED$, and $BF = FC$.

Now the centre of gravity of the triangle $OAD$ will lie on $OE$, and that of the triangle $OBC$ will lie on $OF$. [Prop. 13]

It follows that the centre of gravity of the remainder, the trapezium $ABCD$, will also lie on $OF$. [Prop. 8]

Join $BD$, and divide it at $L$, $M$ into three equal parts. Through $L$, $M$ draw $PQ$, $RS$ parallel to $BC$ meeting $BA$ in $P$, $R$, $FE$ in $W$, $V$, and $CD$ in $Q$, $S$ respectively.

Join $DF$, $BE$ meeting $PQ$ in $H$ and $RS$ in $K$ respectively.
Now, since
$$BL = \tfrac{1}{3}BD,$$
$$FH = \tfrac{1}{3}FD.$$

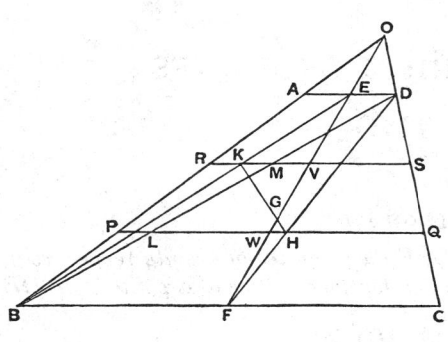

Therefore $H$ is the centre of gravity of the triangle $DBC$.

Similarly, since $EK = \tfrac{1}{3}BE$, it follows that $K$ is the centre of gravity of the triangle $ADB$.

Therefore the centre of gravity of the triangles $DBC$, $ADB$ together, i.e. of the trapezium, lies on the line $HK$.

But it also lies on $OF$.

Therefore, if $OF$, $HK$ meet in $G$, $G$ is the centre of gravity of the trapezium.

Hence [Props. 6, 7]
$$\triangle DBC : \triangle ABD = KG : GH$$
$$= VG : GW.$$
But $\triangle DBC : \triangle ABD = BC : AD.$
Therefore $BC : AD = VG : GW.$
It follows that
$$(2BC + AD) : (2AD + BC) = (2VG + GW) : (2GW + VG)$$
$$= EG : GF.$$

Q.E.D.

# ON THE EQUILIBRIUM OF PLANES
## BOOK TWO

### Proposition 1

*If $P$, $P'$ be two parabolic segments and $D$, $E$ their centres of gravity respectively, the centre of gravity of the two segments taken together will be at a point $C$ on $DE$ determined by the relation*
$$P : P' = CE : CD.$$

In the same straight line with $DE$ measure $EH$, $EL$ each equal to $DC$, and $DK$ equal to $DH$; whence it follows at once that $DK = CE$, and also that
$$KC = CL.$$

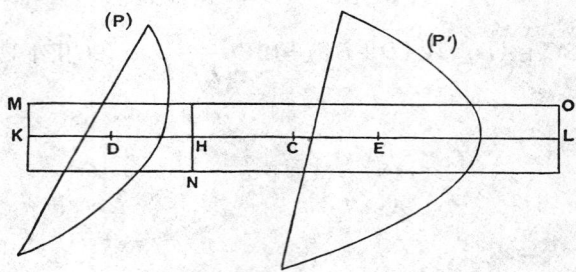

Apply a rectangle $MN$ equal in area to the parabolic segment $P$ to a base equal to $KH$, and place the rectangle so that $KH$ bisects it, and is parallel to its base.

Then $D$ is the centre of gravity of $MN$, since $KD = DH$.

Produce the sides of the rectangle which are parallel to $KH$, and complete the rectangle $NO$ whose base is equal to $HL$. Then $E$ is the centre of gravity of the rectangle $NO$.

Now
$$(MN) : (NO) = KH : HL$$
$$= DH : EH$$
$$= CE : CD$$
$$= P : P'.$$
But $(MN) = P$.
Therefore $(NO) = P'$.

Also, since $C$ is the middle point of $KL$, $C$ is the centre of gravity of the whole parallelogram made up of the two parallelograms $(MN)$, $(NO)$, which are equal to, and have the same centres of gravity as, $P$, $P'$ respectively.

Hence $C$ is the centre of gravity of $P$, $P'$ taken together.

## ON THE EQUILIBRIUM OF PLANES II

## DEFINITION AND LEMMAS PRELIMINARY TO PROPOSITION 2

"If in a segment bounded by a straight line and a section of a right-angled cone [a parabola] a triangle be inscribed having the same base as the segment and equal height, if again triangles be inscribed in the remaining segments having the same bases as the segments and equal height, and if in the remaining segments triangles be inscribed in the same manner, let the resulting figure be said to be *inscribed in the recognised manner* in the segment.

"And it is plain"

(1) "that *the lines joining the two angles of the figure so inscribed which are nearest to the vertex of the segment, and the next pairs of angles in order, will be parallel to the base of the segment,*"

(2) "that *the said lines will be bisected by the diameter of the segment,* and"

(3) "that *they will cut the diameter in the proportions of the successive odd numbers, the number one having reference to* [*the length adjacent to*] *the vertex of the segment.*

"And these properties will have to be proved in their proper places."

### Proposition 2

*If a figure be "inscribed in the recognised manner" in a parabolic segment, the centre of gravity of the figure so inscribed will lie on the diameter of the segment.*

For, in the figure of the foregoing lemmas, the centre of gravity of the trapezium $BRrb$ must lie on $XO$, that of the trapezium $RQqr$ on $WX$, and so on, while the centre of gravity of the triangle $PAp$ lies on $AV$.

Hence the centre of gravity of the whole figure lies on $AO$.

### Proposition 3

*If $BAB'$, $bab'$ be two similar parabolic segments whose diameters are $AO$, $ao$ respectively, and if a figure be inscribed in each segment "in the recognised manner," the number of sides in each figure being equal, the centres of gravity of the inscribed figures will divide $AO$, $ao$ in the same ratio.*[1]

Suppose $BRQPAP'Q'R'B'$, $brqpap'q'r'b'$ to be the two figures inscribed "in the recognised manner." Join $PP'$, $QQ'$, $RR'$ meeting $AO$ in $L$, $M$, $N$, and $pp'$, $qq'$, $rr'$ meeting $ao$ in $l$, $m$, $n$.

Then [Lemma (3)]
$$AL : LM : MN : NO = 1 : 3 : 5 : 7$$
$$= al : lm : mn : no,$$
so that $AO$, $ao$ are divided in the same proportion.

Also, by reversing the proof of Lemma (3), we see that
$$PP' : pp' = QQ' : qq' = RR' : rr' = BB' : bb'.$$

Since then $RR' : BB' = rr' : bb'$, and these ratios respectively determine the proportion in which $NO$, $no$ are divided by the centres of gravity of the trapezia $BRR'B'$, $brr'b'$ [I. 15], it follows that the centres of gravity of the trapezia divide $NO$, $no$ in the same ratio.

Similarly the centres of gravity of the trapezia $RQQ'R'$, $rqq'r'$ divide $MN$, $mn$ in the same ratio respectively, and so on.

---

[1] Archimedes enunciates this proposition as true of *similar* segments, but it is equally true of segments which are not similar, as the course of the proof will show.

Lastly, the centres of gravity of the triangles *PAP'*, *pap'* divide *AL*, *al* respectively in the same ratio.

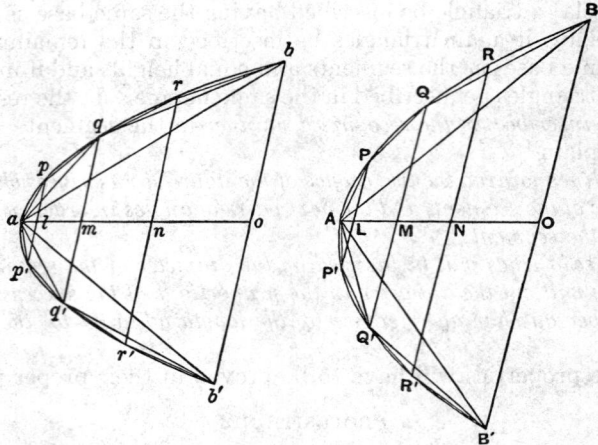

Moreover the corresponding trapezia and triangles are, each to each, in the same proportion (since their sides and heights are respectively proportional), while *AO*, *ao* are divided in the same proportion.

Therefore the centres of gravity of the complete inscribed figures divide *AO*, *ao* in the same proportion.

## Proposition 4

*The centre of gravity of any parabolic segment cut off by a straight line lies on the diameter of the segment.*

Let *BAB'* be a parabolic segment, *A* its vertex and *AO* its diameter.

Then, if the centre of gravity of the segment does not lie on *AO*, suppose it to be, if possible, the point *F*. Draw *FE* parallel to *AO* meeting *BB'* in *E*.

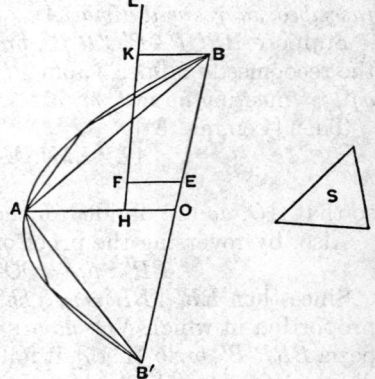

Inscribe in the segment the triangle *ABB'* having the same vertex and height as the segment, and take an area *S* such that

$$\triangle ABB' : S = BE : EO.$$

We can then inscribe in the segment "in the recognised manner" a figure such that the segments of the parabola left over are together less than *S*.[1]

---

[1]For Prop. 20 of the *Quadrature of the Parabola* proves that, if in any segment the triangle with the same base and height be inscribed, the triangle is greater than half the segment; whence it appears that, each time that we increase the number of the sides of the figure inscribed "in the recognised manner," we take away more than half of the remaining segments.

Let the inscribed figure be drawn accordingly; its centre of gravity then lies on $AO$ [Prop. 2]. Let it be the point $H$.

Join $HF$ and produce it to meet in $K$ the line through $B$ parallel to $AO$. Then we have

(inscribed figure) : (remainder of segmt.) $> \triangle ABB' : S$
$> BE : EO$
$> KF : FH$.

Suppose $L$ taken on $HK$ produced so that the former ratio is equal to the ratio $LF : FH$.

Then, since $H$ is the centre of gravity of the inscribed figure, and $F$ that of the segment, $L$ must be the centre of gravity of all the segments taken together which form the remainder of the original segment. [I. 8]

But this is impossible, since all these segments lie on one side of the line drawn through $L$ parallel to $AO$ (Cf. *Post.* 7).

Hence the centre of gravity of the segment cannot but lie on $AO$.

PROPOSITION 5

*If in a parabolic segment a figure be inscribed "in the recognised manner," the centre of gravity of the segment is nearer to the vertex of the segment than the centre of gravity of the inscribed figure is.*

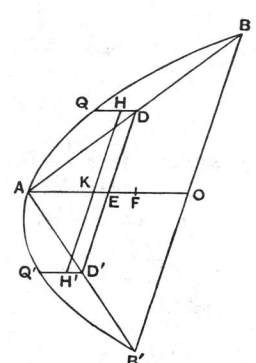

Let $BAB'$ be the given segment, and $AO$ its diameter. *First,* let $ABB'$ be the *triangle* inscribed "in the recognised manner."

Divide $AO$ in $F$ so that $AF = 2FO$; $F$ is then the centre of gravity of the triangle $ABB'$.

Bisect $AB$, $AB'$ in $D, D'$ respectively, and join $DD'$ meeting $AO$ in $E$. Draw $DQ$, $D'Q'$ parallel to $OA$ to meet the curve. $QD, Q'D'$ will then be the diameters of the segments whose bases are $AB$, $AB'$, and the centres of gravity of those segments will lie respectively on $QD$, $Q'D'$ [Prop. 4]. Let them be $H$, $H'$, and join $HH'$ meeting $AO$ in $K$.

Now $QD$, $Q'D'$ are equal,[1] and therefore the segments of which they are the diameters are equal [*On Conoids and Spheroids*, Prop. 3].

Also, since $QD$, $Q'D'$ are parallel, and $DE = ED'$, $K$ is the middle point of $HH'$.

Hence the centre of gravity of the equal segments $AQB$, $AQ'B'$ taken together is $K$, where $K$ lies between $E$ and $A$. And the centre of gravity of the triangle $ABB'$ is $F$.

It follows that the centre of gravity of the whole segment $BAB'$ lies between $K$ and $F$, and is therefore nearer to the vertex $A$ than $F$ is.

*Secondly,* take the *five-sided* figure $BQAQ'B'$ inscribed "in the recognised manner," $QD$, $Q'D'$ being, as before, the diameters of the segments $AQB$, $AQ'B'$.

Then, by the first part of this proposition, the centre of gravity of the segment $AQB$ (lying of course on $QD$) is nearer to $Q$ than the centre of gravity of

[1]This may either be inferred from Lemma (1) above (since $QQ'$, $DD'$ are both parallel to $BB'$), or from Prop. 19 of the *Quadrature of the Parabola*, which applies equally to $Q$ or $Q'$.

the triangle $AQB$ is. Let the centre of gravity of the segment be $H$, and that of the triangle $I$.

Similarly let $H'$ be the centre of gravity of the segment $AQ'B'$, and $I'$ that of the triangle $AQ'B'$.

It follows that the centre of gravity of the two segments $AQB$, $AQ'B'$ taken together is $K$, the middle point of $HH'$, and that of the two triangles $AQB$, $AQ'B'$ is $L$, the middle point of $II'$.

If now the centre of gravity of the triangle $ABB'$ be $F$, the centre of gravity of the whole segment $BAB'$ (i.e. that of the triangle $ABB'$ and the two segments $AQB$, $AQ'B'$ taken together) is a point $G$ on $KF$ determined by the proportion

(sum of segments $AQB$, $AQ'B'$) : $\triangle ABB' = FG : GK$.

[I. 6, 7]

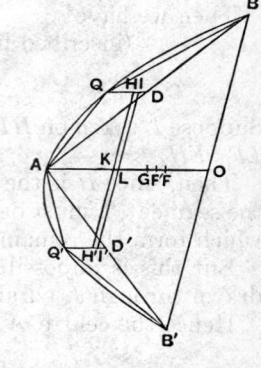

And the centre of gravity of the inscribed figure $BQAQ'B'$ is a point $F'$ on $LF$ determined by the proportion

$$(\triangle AQB + \triangle AQ'B') : \triangle ABB' = FF' : F'L.$$ [I. 6, 7]

[Hence      $FG : GK > FF' : F'L$,

or      $GK : FG < F'L : FF'$,

and, *componendo*,    $FK : FG < FL : FF'$, while $FK > FL$.]

Therefore $FG > FF'$, or $G$ lies nearer than $F'$ to the vertex $A$.

Using this last result, and proceeding in the same way, we can prove the proposition for *any* figure inscribed "in the recognised manner."

## Proposition 6

*Given a segment of a parabola cut off by a straight line, it is possible to inscribe in it "in the recognised manner" a figure such that the distance between the centres of gravity of the segment and of the inscribed figure is less than any assigned length.*

Let $BAB'$ be the segment, $AO$ its diameter, $G$ its centre of gravity, and $ABB'$ the triangle inscribed "in the recognised manner."

Let $D$ be the assigned length and $S$ an area such that

$$AG : D = \triangle ABB' : S.$$

In the segment inscribe "in the recognised manner" a figure such that the sum of the segments left over is less than $S$. Let $F$ be the centre of gravity of the inscribed figure.

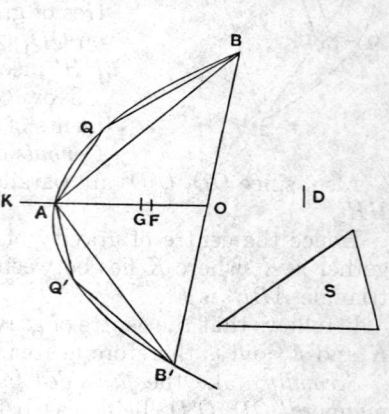

We shall prove that $FG < D$.

For, if not, $FG$ must be either equal to, or greater than, $D$.

And clearly

       (inscribed fig.) : (sum of remaining segmts.)

       $> \triangle ABB' : S$

       $> AG : D$

       $> AG : FG$, by hypothesis (since $FG \not< D$).

Let the first ratio be equal to the ratio $KG : FG$ (where $K$ lies on $GA$ produced); and it follows that $K$ is the centre of gravity of the small segments taken together. [I. 8]

But this is impossible, since the segments are all on the same side of a line drawn through $K$ parallel to $BB'$.

Hence $FG$ cannot but be less than $D$.

## PROPOSITION 7

*If there be two similar parabolic segments, their centres of gravity divide their diameters in the same ratio.*

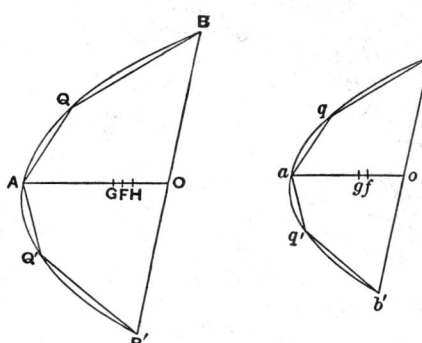

Let $BAB'$, $bab'$ be the two similar segments, $AO$, $ao$ their diameters, and $G$, $g$ their centres of gravity respectively.

Then, if $G$, $g$ do not divide $AO$, $ao$ respectively in the same ratio, suppose $H$ to be such a point on $AO$ that
$$AH : HO = ag : go;$$
and inscribe in the segment $BAB'$ "in the recognised manner" a figure such that, if $F$ be its centre of gravity,
$$GF < GH. \quad [\text{Prop. 6}]$$
Inscribe in the segment $bab'$ "in the recognised manner" a similar figure; then, if $f$ be the centre of gravity of this figure,
$$ag < af. \qquad [\text{Prop. 5}]$$
And, by Prop. 3,    $af : fo = AF : FO$.
But            $AF : FO < AH : HO$
                    $< ag : go$, by hypothesis.
Therefore      $af : fo < ag : go$; which is impossible.

It follows that $G$, $g$ cannot but divide $AO$, $ao$ in the same ratio.

## PROPOSITION 8

*If $AO$ be the diameter of a parabolic segment, and $G$ its centre of gravity, then*
$$AG = \tfrac{3}{2} GO.$$

Let the segment be $BAB'$. Inscribe the triangle $ABB'$ "in the recognised manner," and let $F$ be its centre of gravity.

Bisect $AB$, $AB'$ in $D$, $D'$, and draw $DQ$, $D'Q'$ parallel to $OA$ to meet the curve, so that $QD$, $Q'D'$ are the diameters of the segments $AQB$, $AQ'B'$ respectively.

Let $H$, $H'$ be the centres of gravity of the segments $AQB$, $AQ'B'$ respectively. Join $QQ'$, $HH'$ meeting $AO$ in $V$, $K$ respectively.

$K$ is then the centre of gravity of the two segments $AQB$, $AQ'B'$ taken together.

Now           $AG : GO = QH : HD$,            [Prop. 7]
whence         $AO : OG = QD : HD$.
But $AO = 4QD$ [as is easily proved by means of Lemma (3), p. 511].

Therefore        $OG = 4HD$;
and, by subtraction,   $AG = 4QH$.

Also, by Lemma (2), $QQ'$ is parallel to $BB'$ and therefore to $DD'$. It follows from Prop. 7 that $HH'$ is also parallel to $QQ'$ or $DD'$,
and hence $\qquad QH = VK$.
Therefore $\qquad AG = 4VK$,
and $\qquad AV + KG = 3VK$.

Measuring $VL$ along $VK$ so that $VL = \tfrac{1}{3}AV$, we have
$$KG = 3LK. \qquad (1)$$
Again $\qquad AO = 4AV \qquad$ [Lemma (3)]
$\qquad\qquad = 3AL$, since $AV = 3VL$,
whence $\qquad AL = \tfrac{1}{3}AO = OF$. $\qquad (2)$

Now, by I. 6, 7,
$\triangle ABB'$ : (sum of segmts. $AQB, AQ'B'$) $= KG : GF$,
and $\quad \triangle ABB' = 3$(sum of segments $AQB, AQ'B'$)
[since the segment $ABB'$ is equal to $\tfrac{4}{3}\triangle ABB'$ (*Quadrature of the Parabola*, Props. 17, 24)].
Hence $\qquad KG = 3GF$.
But $\qquad KG = 3LK$, from (1) above.
Therefore $\qquad LF = LK + KG + GF$
$\qquad\qquad\qquad = 5GF$.
And, from (2),
$$LF = (AO - AL - OF) = \tfrac{1}{3}AO = OF.$$
Therefore $\qquad OF = 5GF$,
and $\qquad OG = 6GF$.
But $\qquad AO = 3OF = 15GF$.
Therefore, by subtraction,
$$AG = 9GF$$
$$= \tfrac{3}{2}GO.$$

### Proposition 9 (Lemma)

*If $a, b, c, d$ be four lines in continued proportion and in descending order of magnitude, and if*
$$d : (a-d) = x : \tfrac{3}{5}(a-c),$$
*and* $\qquad (2a + 4b + 6c + 3d) : (5a + 10b + 10c + 5d) = y : (a-c)$,
*it is required to prove that*
$$x + y = \tfrac{2}{5}a.$$

[The following is the proof given by Archimedes, with the only difference that it is set out in algebraical instead of geometrical notation. This is done in the particular case simply in order to make the proof easier to follow. Archimedes exhibits his lines in the figure reproduced in the margin, but, now that it is possible to use algebraical notation, there is no advantage in using the figure and the more cumbrous notation which only obscures the course of the proof. The relation between Archimedes' figure and the letters used below is as follows:
$AB = a$, $\Gamma B = b$, $\Delta B = c$, $EB = d$, $ZH = x$, $H\Theta = y$, $\Delta O = z$.]

We have $\qquad\qquad \dfrac{a}{b} = \dfrac{b}{c} = \dfrac{c}{d} \qquad\qquad (1)$

## ON THE EQUILIBRIUM OF PLANES II

whence
$$\frac{a-b}{b}=\frac{b-c}{c}=\frac{c-d}{d},$$

and therefore
$$\frac{a-b}{b-c}=\frac{b-c}{c-d}=\frac{a}{b}=\frac{b}{c}=\frac{c}{d} \quad (2)$$

Now
$$\frac{2(a+b)}{2c}=\frac{a+b}{c}=\frac{a+b}{b}\cdot\frac{b}{c}=\frac{a-c}{b-c}\cdot\frac{b-c}{c-d}=\frac{a-c}{c-d}$$

And, in like manner,
$$\frac{b+c}{d}=\frac{b+c}{c}\cdot\frac{c}{d}=\frac{a-c}{c-d}.$$

It follows from the last two relations that
$$\frac{a-c}{c-d}=\frac{2a+3b+c}{2c+d} \quad (3)$$

Suppose $z$ to be so taken that
$$\frac{2a+4b+4c+2d}{2c+d}=\frac{a-c}{z} \quad (4)$$

so that $z<(c-d)$.

Therefore
$$\frac{a-c+z}{a-c}=\frac{2a+4b+6c+3d}{2(a+d)+4(b+c)}.$$

And, by hypothesis,
$$\frac{a-c}{y}=\frac{5(a+d)+10(b+c)}{2a+4b+6c+3d},$$

so that
$$\frac{a-c+z}{y}=\frac{5(a+d)+10(b+c)}{2(a+d)+4(b+c)}=\frac{5}{2} \quad (5)$$

Again, dividing (3) by (4) crosswise, we obtain
$$\frac{z}{c-d}=\frac{2a+3b+c}{2(a+d)+4(b+c)},$$

whence
$$\frac{c-d-z}{c-d}=\frac{b+3c+2d}{2(a+d)+4(b+c)} \quad (6)$$

But, by (2),
$$\frac{c-d}{d}=\frac{a-b}{b}=\frac{3(b-c)}{3c}=\frac{2(c-d)}{2d},$$

so that
$$\frac{c-d}{d}=\frac{(a-b)+3(b-c)+2(c-d)}{b+3c+2d} \quad (7)$$

Combining (6) and (7), we have
$$\frac{c-d-z}{d}=\frac{(a-b)+3(b-c)+2(c-d)}{2(a+d)+4(b+c)},$$

whence
$$\frac{c-z}{d}=\frac{3a+6b+3c}{2(a+d)+4(b+c)} \quad (8)$$

And, since [by (1)]
$$\frac{c-d}{c+d}=\frac{b-c}{b+c}=\frac{a-b}{a+b},$$

we have
$$\frac{c-d}{a-c}=\frac{c+d}{b+c+a+b},$$

whence
$$\frac{a-d}{a-c}=\frac{a+2b+2c+d}{a+2b+c}=\frac{2(a+d)+4(b+c)}{2(a+c)+4b} \quad (9)$$

Thus
$$\frac{a-d}{\tfrac{3}{5}(a-c)} = \frac{2(a+d)+4(b+c)}{\tfrac{3}{5}\{2(a+c)+4b\}},$$
and therefore, by hypothesis,
$$\frac{d}{x} = \frac{2(a+d)+4(b+c)}{\tfrac{3}{5}\{2(a+c)+4b\}}.$$
But, by (8),
$$\frac{c-z}{d} = \frac{3a+6b+3c}{2(a+d)+4(b+c)};$$
and it follows, *ex aequali*, that
$$\frac{c-z}{x} = \frac{3(a+c)+6b}{\tfrac{3}{5}\{2(a+c)+4b\}} = \frac{5}{3} \cdot \frac{3}{2} = \frac{5}{2}.$$
And, by (5),
$$\frac{a-c+z}{y} = \frac{5}{2}.$$
Therefore
$$\frac{5}{2} = \frac{a}{x+y},$$
or
$$x+y = \tfrac{2}{5}a.$$

## PROPOSITION 10

*If PP'B'B be the portion of a parabola intercepted between two parallel chords PP', BB' bisected respectively in N, O by the diameter ANO (N being nearer than O to A, the vertex of the segments), and if NO be divided into five equal parts of which LM is the middle one (L being nearer than M to N), then, if G be a point on LM such that*
$$LG : GM = BO^2 \cdot (2PN+BO) : PN^2 \cdot (2BO+PN),$$
*G will be the centre of gravity of the area PP'B'B.*

Take a line $ao$ equal to $AO$, and $an$ on it equal to $AN$. Let $p, q$ be points on the line $ao$ such that
$$ao : aq = aq : an, \qquad (1)$$
$$ao : an = aq : ap, \qquad (2)$$
[whence $ao : aq = aq : an = an : ap$, or $ao, aq, an, ap$ are lines in continued proportion and in descending order of magnitude].

Measure along $GA$ a length $GF$ such that
$$op : ap = OL : GF. \qquad (3)$$
Then, since $PN, BO$ are ordinates to $ANO$,
$$BO^2 : PN^2 = AO : AN$$
$$= ao : an$$
$$= ao^2 : aq^2, \text{ by (1)},$$
so that
$$BO : PN = ao : aq, \qquad (4)$$
and
$$BO^3 : PN^3 = ao^3 : aq^3$$
$$= (ao : aq) \cdot (aq : an) \cdot (an : ap)$$
$$= ao : ap. \qquad (5)$$
Thus
$$(\text{segment } BAB') : (\text{segment } PAP')$$
$$= \triangle BAB' : \triangle PAP'$$
$$= BO^3 : PN^3$$
$$= ao : ap,$$
whence
$$(\text{area } PP'B'B) : (\text{segment } PAP') = op : ap.$$

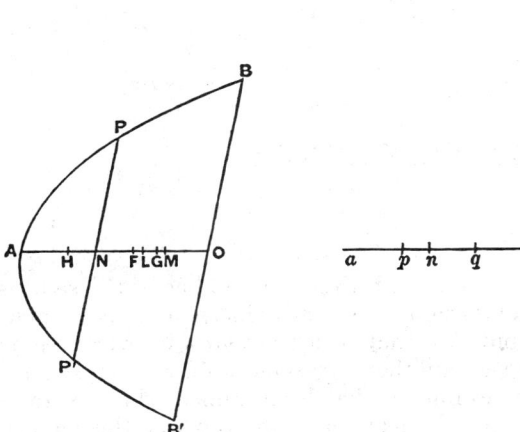

$$= OL : GF, \text{ by (3)},$$
$$= \tfrac{3}{5}ON : GF. \quad (6)$$

Now
$$BO^2 \cdot (2PN+BO) : BO^3$$
$$= (2PN+BO) : BO$$
$$= (2aq+ao) : ao, \text{ by (4)},$$
$$BO^3 : PN^3$$
$$= ao : ap, \text{ by (5)},$$
and
$$PN^3 : PN^2 \cdot (2BO+PN)$$
$$= PN : (2BO+PN)$$
$$= aq : (2ao+aq), \text{ by (4)},$$
$$= ap : (2an+ap), \text{ by (2)}.$$
Hence, *ex aequali*,
$$BO^2 \cdot (2PN+BO) : PN^2 \cdot (2BO+PN) = (2aq+ao) : (2an+ap),$$

so that, by hypothesis,
$$LG : GM = (2aq+ao) : (2an+ap).$$
*Componendo*, and multiplying the antecedents by 5,
$$ON : GM = \{5(ao+ap)+10(aq+an)\} : (2an+ap).$$
But
$$ON : OM = 5 : 2 = \{5(ao+ap)+10(aq+an)\} : \{2(ao+ap)+4(aq+an)\}.$$
It follows that
$$ON : OG = \{5(ao+ap)+10(aq+an)\} : (2ao+4aq+6an+3ap).$$
Therefore
$$(2ao+4aq+6an+3ap) : \{5(ao+ap)+10(aq+an)\} = OG : ON$$
$$= OG : on.$$
And
$$ap : (ao-ap) = ap : op$$
$$= GF : OL, \text{ by hypothesis},$$
$$= GF : \tfrac{3}{5}on,$$
while $ao, aq, an, ap$ are in continued proportion.

Therefore, by Prop. 9,
$$GF+OG = OF = \tfrac{2}{5}ao = \tfrac{2}{5}OA.$$

Thus $F$ is the centre of gravity of the segment $BAB'$.  [Prop. 8]

Let $H$ be the centre of gravity of the segment $PAP'$, so that $AH = \tfrac{3}{5}AN$.

And, since $AF = \tfrac{3}{5}AO$,

we have, by subtraction, $HF = \tfrac{3}{5}ON$.

But, by (6) above,
$$(\text{area } PP'B'B) : (\text{segment } PAP') = \tfrac{3}{5}ON : GF$$
$$= HF : FG.$$

Thus, since $F$, $H$ are the centres of gravity of the segments $BAB'$, $PAP'$ respectively, it follows [by I. 6, 7] that $G$ is the centre of gravity of the area $PP'B'B$.

# THE SAND-RECKONER

"THERE are some, King Gelon, who think that the number of the sand is infinite in multitude; and I mean by the sand not only that which exists about Syracuse and the rest of Sicily but also that which is found in every region whether inhabited or uninhabited. Again there are some who, without regarding it as infinite, yet think that no number has been named which is great enough to exceed its multitude. And it is clear that they who hold this view, if they imagined a mass made up of sand in other respects as large as the mass of the earth, including in it all the seas and the hollows of the earth filled up to a height equal to that of the highest of the mountains, would be many times further still from recognising that any number could be expressed which exceeded the multitude of the sand so taken. But I will try to show you by means of geometrical proofs, which you will be able to follow, that, of the numbers named by me and given in the work which I sent to Zeuxippus, some exceed not only the number of the mass of sand equal in magnitude to the earth filled up in the way described, but also that of a mass equal in magnitude to the universe. Now you are aware that 'universe' is the name given by most astronomers to the sphere whose centre is the centre of the earth and whose radius is equal to the straight line between the centre of the sun and the centre of the earth. This is the common account (τὰ γραφόμενα), as you have heard from astronomers. But Aristarchus of Samos brought out a book consisting of some hypotheses, in which the premisses lead to the result that the universe is many times greater than that now so called. His hypotheses are that the fixed stars and the sun remain unmoved, that the earth revolves about the sun in the circumference of a circle, the sun lying in the middle of the orbit, and that the sphere of the fixed stars, situated about the same centre as the sun, is so great that the circle in which he supposes the earth to revolve bears such a proportion to the distance of the fixed stars as the centre of the sphere bears to its surface. Now it is easy to see that this is impossible; for, since the centre of the sphere has no magnitude, we cannot conceive it to bear any ratio whatever to the surface of the sphere. We must however take Aristarchus to mean this: since we conceive the earth to be, as it were, the centre of the universe, the ratio which the earth bears to what we describe as the 'universe' is the same as the ratio which the sphere containing the circle in which he supposes the earth to revolve bears to the sphere of the fixed stars. For he adapts the proofs of his results to a hypothesis of this kind, and in particular he appears to suppose the magnitude of the sphere in which he represents the earth as moving to be equal to what we call the 'universe.'

"I say then that, even if a sphere were made up of the sand, as great as Aristarchus supposes the sphere of the fixed stars to be, I shall still prove that,

## THE SAND-RECKONER

of the numbers named in the *Principles*,[1] some exceed in multitude the number of the sand which is equal in magnitude to the sphere referred to, provided that the following assumptions be made."

1. *"The perimeter of the earth is about 3,000,000 stadia and not greater.*

"It is true that some have tried, as you are of course aware, to prove that the said perimeter is about 300,000 stadia. But I go further and, putting the magnitude of the earth at ten times the size that my predecessors thought it, I suppose its perimeter to be about 3,000,000 stadia and not greater."

2. *"The diameter of the earth is greater than the diameter of the moon, and the diameter of the sun is greater than the diameter of the earth.*

"In this assumption I follow most of the earlier astronomers."

3. *"The diameter of the sun is about 30 times the diameter of the moon and not greater.*

"It is true that, of the earlier astronomers, Eudoxus declared it to be about nine times as great, and Pheidias my father twelve times, while Aristarchus tried to prove that the diameter of the sun is greater than 18 times but less than 20 times the diameter of the moon. But I go even further than Aristarchus, in order that the truth of my proposition may be established beyond dispute, and I suppose the diameter of the sun to be about 30 times that of the moon and not greater."

4. *"The diameter of the sun is greater than the side of the chiliagon inscribed in the greatest circle in the (sphere of the) universe.*

"I make this assumption because Aristarchus discovered that the sun appeared to be about $\frac{1}{720}$th part of the circle of the zodiac, and I myself tried, by a method which I will now describe, to find experimentally (ὀργανικῶς) the angle subtended by the sun and having its vertex at the eye."

[Up to this point the treatise has been literally translated because of the historical interest attaching to the *ipsissima verba* of Archimedes on such a subject. The rest of the work can now be more freely reproduced, and, before proceeding to the mathematical contents of it, it is only necessary to remark that Archimedes next describes how he arrived at a higher and a lower limit for the angle subtended by the sun. This he did by taking a long rod or ruler, fastening on the end of it a small cylinder or disc, pointing the rod in the direction of the sun just after its rising (so that it was possible to look directly at it), then putting the cylinder at such a distance that it just concealed, and just failed to conceal, the sun, and lastly measuring the angles subtended by the cylinder. He explains also the correction which he thought it necessary to make because "the eye does not see from one point but from a certain area."]

The result of the experiment was to show that the angle subtended by the diameter of the sun was less than $\frac{1}{164}$th part, and greater than $\frac{1}{200}$th part, of a right angle.

*To prove that (on this assumption) the diameter of the sun is greater than the side of a chiliagon, or figure with* 1000 *equal sides, inscribed in a great circle of the "universe."*

Suppose the plane of the paper to be the plane passing through the centre of the sun, the centre of the earth and the eye, at the time when the sun has

---
[1] A lost work of Archimedes.

just risen above the horizon. Let the plane cut the earth in the circle $EHL$ and the sun in the circle $FKG$, the centres of the earth and sun being $C, O$ respectively, and $E$ being the position of the eye.

Further, let the plane cut the sphere of the "universe" (i.e. the sphere whose centre is $C$ and radius $CO$) in the great circle $AOB$.

Draw from $E$ two tangents to the circle $FKG$ touching it at $P, Q$, and from $C$ draw two other tangents to the same circle touching it in $F, G$ respectively.

Let $CO$ meet the sections of the earth and sun in $H, K$ respectively; and let $CF, CG$ produced meet the great circle $AOB$ in $A, B$.

Join $EO, OF, OG, OP, OQ, AB$, and let $AB$ meet $CO$ in $M$.

Now $CO > EO$, since the sun is just above the horizon.
Therefore $\angle PEQ > \angle FCG$.

And $\angle PEQ > \frac{1}{200}R$ } where $R$ represents a right angle.
but $< \frac{1}{164}R$

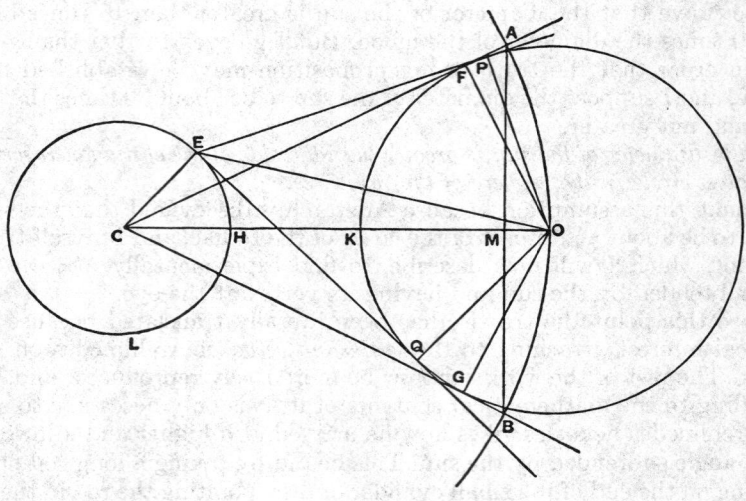

Thus $\angle FCG < \frac{1}{164}R$, a fortiori,
and the chord $AB$ subtends an arc of the great circle which is less than $\frac{1}{656}$th of the circumference of that circle, i.e.

$AB <$ (side of 656-sided polygon inscribed in the circle).

Now the perimeter of any polygon inscribed in the great circle is less than $\frac{44}{7}CO$. [Cf. *Measurement of a circle*, Prop. 3.]
Therefore $AB : CO < 11 : 1148$,
and, a fortiori, $AB < \frac{1}{100}CO$. ($\alpha$)

Again, since $CA = CO$, and $AM$ is perpendicular to $CO$, while $OF$ is perpendicular to $CA$, $AM = OF$.
Therefore $AB = 2AM =$ (diameter of sun).
Thus (diameter of sun) $< \frac{1}{100}CO$, by ($\alpha$),
and, a fortiori, (diameter of earth) $< \frac{1}{100}CO$. [Assumption 2]
Hence $CH + OK < \frac{1}{100}CO$,
so that $HK > \frac{99}{100}CO$,

or $\qquad CO:HK<100:99.$
And $\qquad CO>CF,$
while $\qquad HK<EQ.$
Therefore $\qquad CF:EQ<100:99. \qquad (\beta)$

Now in the right-angled triangles $CFO$, $EQO$, of the sides about the right angles, $\qquad OF=OQ$, but $EQ<CF$ (since $EO<CO$).
Therefore $\qquad \angle OEQ : \angle OCF > CO : EO,$
but $\qquad \qquad \qquad <CF : EQ.$[1]

Doubling the angles,
$$\angle PEQ : \angle ACB < CF : EQ$$
$$<100:99, \text{ by } (\beta) \text{ above.}$$
But $\qquad \angle PEQ > \frac{1}{200}R$, by hypothesis.
Therefore $\qquad \angle ACB > \frac{99}{20000}R$
$$> \frac{1}{203}R.$$

It follows that the arc $AB$ is greater than $\frac{1}{812}$th of the circumference of the great circle $AOB$.

Hence, *a fortiori*,
$$AB > \text{(side of chiliagon inscribed in great circle)},$$
and $AB$ is equal to the diameter of the sun, as proved above.

*The following results can now be proved:*
$$(\text{diameter of ``universe''}) < 10,000 \ (\text{diameter of earth}),$$
and $\qquad (\text{diameter of ``universe''}) < 10,000,000,000 \text{ stadia}.$

(1) Suppose, for brevity, that $d_u$ represents the diameter of the "universe," $d_s$ that of the sun, $d_e$ that of the earth, and $d_m$ that of the moon.

By hypothesis, $\qquad d_s \not> 30 d_m,$ $\qquad$ [Assumption 3]
and $\qquad \qquad \qquad d_e > d_m;$ $\qquad$ [Assumption 2]
therefore $\qquad \qquad d_s < 30 d_e.$

Now, by the last proposition,
$$d_s > \text{(side of chiliagon inscribed in great circle)},$$
so that $\qquad (\text{perimeter of chiliagon}) < 1000 d_s$
$$< 30,000 d_e.$$

But the perimeter of any regular polygon with more sides than 6 inscribed in a circle is greater than that of the inscribed regular hexagon, and therefore greater than three times the diameter. Hence
$$(\text{perimeter of chiliagon}) > 3 d_u.$$
It follows that $\qquad d_u < 10,000 d_e.$

(2) $\qquad$ (Perimeter of earth) $\not> 3,000,000$ stadia. $\qquad$ [Assumption 1]
and $\qquad$ (perimeter of earth) $> 3 d_e.$
Therefore $\qquad d_e < 1,000,000$ stadia,
whence $\qquad d_u < 10,000,000,000$ stadia.

*Assumption 5*

Suppose a quantity of sand taken not greater than a poppy-seed, and suppose that it contains not more than 10,000 grains.

---

[1]The proposition here assumed is of course equivalent to the trigonometrical formula which states that, if $a$, $\beta$ are the circular measures of two angles, each less than a right angle, of which $a$ is the greater, then
$$\frac{\tan a}{\tan \beta} > \frac{a}{\beta} > \frac{\sin a}{\sin \beta}.$$

Next suppose the diameter of the poppy-seed to be not less than $\frac{1}{40}$th of a finger-breadth.

## Orders and Periods of Numbers

I. We have traditional names for numbers up to a myriad (10,000); we can therefore express numbers up to a myriad myriads (100,000,000). Let these numbers be called numbers of the *first order*.

Suppose the 100,000,000 to be the unit of the *second order*, and let the *second order* consist of the numbers from that unit up to $(100,000,000)^2$.

Let this again be the unit of the *third order* of numbers ending with $(100,000,000)^3$; and so on, until we reach the 100,000,000*th order* of numbers ending with $(100,000,000)^{100,000,000}$, which we will call $P$.

II. Suppose the numbers from 1 to $P$ just described to form the *first period*.

Let $P$ be the unit of the *first order of the second period*, and let this consist of the numbers from $P$ up to $100,000,000P$.

Let the last number be the unit of the *second order of the second period*, and let this end with $(100,000,000)^2 P$.

We can go on in this way till we reach the 100,000,000*th order of the second period* ending with $(100,000,000)^{100,000,000} P$, or $P^2$.

III. Taking $P^2$ as the unit of the *first order of the third period*, we proceed in the same way till we reach the 100,000,000*th order of the third period* ending with $P^3$.

IV. Taking $P^3$ as the unit of the *first order of the fourth period*, we continue the same process until we arrive at the 100,000,000*th order of the* 100,000,000*th period* ending with $P^{100,000,000}$. This last number is expressed by Archimedes as "a myriad-myriad units of the myriad-myriad-th order of the myriad-myriad-th period (αἱ μυριακισμυριοστᾶς περιόδου μυριακισμυριοστῶν ἀριθμῶν μυρίαι μυριάδες)," which is easily seen to be 100,000,000 times the product of $(100,000,000)^{99,999,999}$ and $P^{99,999,999}$, i.e. $P^{100,000,000}$.

## Octads

Consider the series of terms in continued proportion of which the first is 1 and the second 10 [i.e. the geometrical progression $1, 10^1, 10^2, 10^3, \cdots$]. The *first octad* of these terms [*i.e.* $1, 10^1, 10^2, \cdots 10^7$] fall accordingly under the *first order of the first period* above described, the *second octad* [i.e. $10^8, 10^9, \cdots 10^{15}$] under the *second order of the first period*, the first term of the octad being the unit of the corresponding order in each case. Similarly for the *third octad*, and so on. We can, in the same way, place any number of octads.

## Theorem

*If there be any number of terms of a series in continued proportion, say $A_1$, $A_2$, $A_3, \cdots A_m, \cdots A_n, \cdots A_{m+n-1}, \cdots$ of which $A_1 = 1$, $A_2 = 10$ [so that the series forms the geometrical progression $1, 10^1, 10^2, \cdots 10^{m-1}, \cdots 10^{n-1}, \cdots 10^{m+n-2}, \cdots$], and if any two terms as $A_m$, $A_n$ be taken and multiplied, the product $A_m \cdot A_n$ will be a term in the same series and will be as many terms distant from $A_n$ as $A_m$ is distant from $A_1$; also it will be distant from $A_1$ by a number of terms less by one than the sum of the numbers of terms by which $A_m$ and $A_n$ respectively are distant from $A_1$.*

Take the term which is distant from $A_n$ by the same number of terms as $A_m$

THE SAND-RECKONER

is distant from $A_1$. This number of terms is $m$ (the first and last being both counted). Thus the term to be taken is $m$ terms distant from $A_n$, and is therefore the term $A_{m+n-1}$.

We have therefore to prove that
$$A_m \cdot A_n = A_{m+n-1}.$$
Now terms equally distant from other terms in the continued proportion are proportional.

Thus $$\frac{A_m}{A_1} = \frac{A_{m+n-1}}{A_n}.$$
But $A_m = A_m \cdot A_1$, since $A_1 = 1$.
Therefore $A_{m+n-1} = A_m \cdot A_n$. (1)

The second result is now obvious, since $A_m$ is $m$ terms distant from $A_1$, $A_n$ is $n$ terms distant from $A_1$, and $A_{m+n-1}$ is $(m+n-1)$ terms distant from $A_1$.

APPLICATION TO THE NUMBER OF THE SAND

By Assumption 5 [p. 523],
(diam. of poppy-seed) $\not< \frac{1}{40}$(finger-breadth);
and, since spheres are to one another in the triplicate ratio of their diameters, it follows that
(sphere of diam. 1 finger-breadth) $\not> 64{,}000$ poppy-seeds
$\not> 64{,}000 \times 10{,}000$
$\not> 640{,}000{,}000$
$\not> 6$ units of *second order* $+ 40{,}000{,}000$ units of *first order* grains of sand.
(*a fortiori*) $< 10$ units of *second order* of numbers.

We now gradually increase the diameter of the supposed sphere, multiplying it by 100 each time. Thus, remembering that the sphere is thereby multiplied by $100^3$ or $1{,}000{,}000$, the number of grains of sand which would be contained in a sphere with each successive diameter may be arrived at as follows.

| Diameter of sphere. | Corresponding number of grains of sand. |
|---|---|
| (1) 100 finger-breadths | $< 1{,}000{,}000 \times 10$ units of *second order* |
| | $< $ (7th term of series) $\times$ (10th term of series) |
| | $< $ 16th term of series [i.e. $10^{15}$] |
| | $< [10^7$ or] $10{,}000{,}000$ units of the *second order*. |
| (2) 10,000 finger-breadths | $< 1{,}000{,}000 \times$ (last number) |
| | $< $ (7th term of series) $\times$ (16th term) |
| | $< $ 22nd term of series [i.e. $10^{21}$] |
| | $< [10^5$ or] $100{,}000$ units of *third order*. |
| (3) 1 stadium ($<10{,}000$ finger-breadths) | $< 100{,}000$ units of *third order*. |
| (4) 100 stadia | $< 1{,}000{,}000 \times$ (last number) |
| | $< $ (7th term of series) $\times$ (22nd term) |
| | $< $ 28th term of series [$10^{27}$] |
| | $< [10^3$ or] $1{,}000$ units of *fourth order*. |
| (5) 10,000 stadia | $< 1{,}000{,}000 \times$ (last number) |
| | $< $ (7th term of series) $\times$ (28th term) |
| | $< $ 34th term of series [$10^{33}$] |
| | $< 10$ units of *fifth order*. |

| | |
|---|---|
| (6) 1,000,000 stadia | <(7th term of series)×(34th term) |
| | <40th term                    [$10^{39}$] |
| | <[$10^7$ or] 10,000,000 units of *fifth order*. |
| (7) 100,000,000 stadia | <(7th term of series)×(40th term) |
| | <46th term                    [$10^{45}$] |
| | <[$10^5$ or] 100,000 units of *sixth order*. |
| (8) 10,000,000,000 stadia | <(7th term of series)×(46th term) |
| | <52nd term of series         [$10^{51}$] |
| | <[$10^3$ or] 1,000 units of *seventh order*. |

But, by the proposition above [p. 523],

        (diameter of "universe") < 10,000,000,000 stadia.

Hence *the number of grains of sand which could be contained in a sphere of the size of our "universe" is less than 1,000 units of the seventh order of numbers* [or $10^{51}$].

From this we can prove further that *a sphere of the size attributed by Aristarchus to the sphere of the fixed stars would contain a number of grains of sand less than* 10,000,000 *units of the eighth order of numbers* [or $10^{56+7} = 10^{63}$].

For, by hypothesis,

        (earth) : ("universe") = ("universe") : (sphere of fixed stars).

And [p. 523]

        (diameter of "universe") < 10,000 (diam. of earth);

whence

        (diam. of sphere of fixed stars) < 10,000 (diam. of "universe").

Therefore

        (sphere of fixed stars) < $(10,000)^3$ · ("universe").

It follows that the number of grains of sand which would be contained in a sphere equal to the sphere of the fixed stars

        < $(10,000)^3$ × 1,000 units of *seventh order*

        < (13th term of series) × (52nd term of series)

        < 64th term of series                              [i.e. $10^{63}$]

        < [$10^7$ or] 10,000,000 units of *eighth order* of numbers.

CONCLUSION.

"I conceive that these things, King Gelon, will appear incredible to the great majority of people who have not studied mathematics, but that to those who are conversant therewith and have given thought to the question of the distances and sizes of the earth, the sun and moon and the whole universe, the proof will carry conviction. And it was for this reason that I thought the subject would be not inappropriate for your consideration."

# QUADRATURE OF THE PARABOLA

"Archimedes to Dositheus greeting.

"When I heard that Conon, who was my friend in his lifetime, was dead, but that you were acquainted with Conon and withal versed in geometry, while I grieved for the loss not only of a friend but of an admirable mathematician, I set myself the task of communicating to you, as I had intended to send to Conon, a certain geometrical theorem which had not been investigated before but has now been investigated by me, and which I first discovered by means of mechanics and then exhibited by means of geometry. Now some of the earlier geometers tried to prove it possible to find a rectilineal area equal to a given circle and a given segment of a circle; and after that they endeavoured to square the area bounded by the section of the whole cone and a straight line, assuming lemmas not easily conceded, so that it was recognised by most people that the problem was not solved. But I am not aware that any one of my predecessors has attempted to square the segment bounded by a straight line and a section of a right-angled cone [a parabola], of which problem I have now discovered the solution. For it is here shown that every segment bounded by a straight line and a section of a right-angled cone [a parabola] is four-thirds of the triangle which has the same base and equal height with the segment, and for the demonstration of this property the following lemma is assumed: that the excess by which the greater of (two) unequal areas exceeds the less can, by being added to itself, be made to exceed any given finite area. The earlier geometers have also used this lemma; for it is by the use of this same lemma that they have shown that circles are to one another in the duplicate ratio of their diameters, and that spheres are to one another in the triplicate ratio of their diameters, and further that every pyramid is one third part of the prism which has the same base with the pyramid and equal height; also, that every cone is one third part of the cylinder having the same base as the cone and equal height they proved by assuming a certain lemma similar to that aforesaid. And, in the result, each of the aforesaid theorems has been accepted no less than those proved without the lemma. As therefore my work now published has satisfied the same test as the propositions referred to, I have written out the proof and send it to you, first as investigated by means of mechanics, and afterwards too as demonstrated by geometry. Prefixed are, also, the elementary propositions in conics which are of service in the proof. Farewell."

## Proposition 1

*If from a point on a parabola a straight line be drawn which is either itself the axis or parallel to the axis, as PV, and if QQ' be a chord parallel to the tangent to the parabola at P and meeting PV in V, then*
$$QV = VQ'.$$
Conversely, *if $QV = VQ'$, the chord $QQ'$ will be parallel to the tangent at P.*

## Proposition 2

*If in a parabola QQ' be a chord parallel to the tangent at P, and if a straight line be drawn through P which is either itself the axis or parallel to the axis, and which meets QQ' in V and the tangent at Q to the parabola in T, then*
$$PV = PT.$$

## Proposition 3

*If from a point on a parabola a straight line be drawn which is either itself the axis or parallel to the axis, as PV, and if from two other points Q, Q' on the parabola straight lines be drawn parallel to the tangent at P and meeting PV in V, V' respectively, then* $\qquad PV : PV' = QV^2 : Q'V'^2.$

"And these propositions are proved in the elements of conics.[1]"

## Proposition 4

*If Qq be the base of any segment of a parabola, and P the vertex of the segment, and if the diameter through any other point R meet Qq in O and QP (produced if necessary) in F, then* $\qquad QV : VO = OF : FR.$

Draw the ordinate $RW$ to $PV$, meeting $QP$ in $K$.
Then $\qquad PV : PW = QV^2 : RW^2;$
whence, by parallels, $\qquad PQ : PK = PQ^2 : PF^2.$

[1] i.e. in the treatises on conics by Euclid and Aristaeus.

In other words, $PQ, PF, PK$ are in continued proportion; therefore

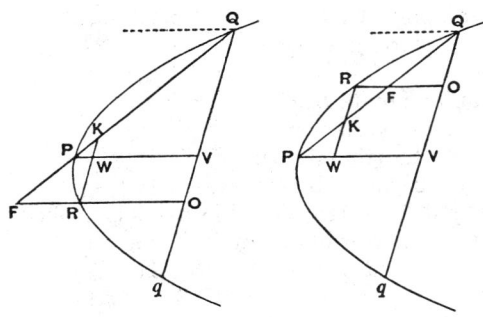

$$PQ : PF = PF : PK$$
$$= PQ \pm PF : PF \pm PK$$
$$= QF : KF.$$

Hence, by parallels, $QV : VO = OF : FR$.

## Proposition 5

*If $Qq$ be the base of any segment of a parabola, $P$ the vertex of the segment, and $PV$ its diameter, and if the diameter of the parabola through any other point $R$ meet $Qq$ in $O$ and the tangent at $Q$ in $E$, then*

$$QO : Oq = ER : RO.$$

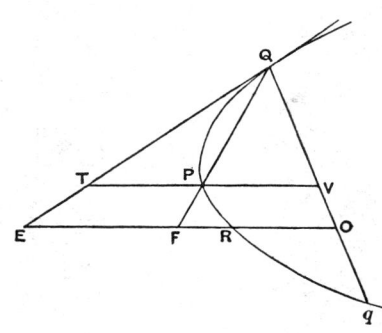

Let the diameter through $R$ meet $QP$ in $F$.

Then, by Prop. 4,
$$QV : VO = OF : FR.$$
Since $QV = Vq$, it follows that
$$QV : qO = OF : OR. \quad (1)$$
Also, if $VP$ meet the tangent in $T$,
$PT = PV$, and therefore $EF = OF$.

Accordingly, doubling the antecedents in (1), we have
$$Qq : qO = OE : OR,$$
whence $\quad QO : Oq = ER : RO.$

## Propositions 6, 7[1]

*Suppose a lever $AOB$ placed horizontally and supported at its middle point $O$. Let a triangle $BCD$ in which the angle $C$ is right or obtuse be suspended from $B$ and $O$, so that $C$ is attached to $O$ and $CD$ is in the same vertical line with $O$. Then, if $P$ be such an area as, when suspended from $A$, will keep the system in equilibrium,*
$$P = \tfrac{1}{3} \triangle BCD.$$

---

[1] In Prop. 6 Archimedes takes the separate case in which the angle $BCD$ of the triangle is a right angle so that $C$ coincides with $O$ in the figure and $F$ with $E$. He then proves, in Prop. 7, the same property for the triangle in which $BCD$ is an obtuse angle, by treating the triangle as the difference between two right-angled triangles $BOD, BOC$ and using the result of Prop. 6. I have combined the two propositions in one proof, for the sake of brevity. The same remark applies to the propositions following Props. 6, 7.

Take a point $E$ on $OB$ such that $BE = 2OE$, and draw $EFH$ parallel to $OCD$ meeting $BC$, $BD$ in $F$, $H$ respectively.

Let $G$ be the middle point of $FH$.

Then $G$ is the centre of gravity of the triangle $BCD$.

Hence, if the angular points $B$, $C$ be set free and the triangle be suspended by attaching $F$ to $E$, the triangle will hang in the same position as before, because $EFG$ is a vertical straight line. "For this is proved."[1]

Therefore, as before, there will be equilibrium.

Thus $\qquad P : \triangle BCD = OE : AO$
$\qquad\qquad\qquad\qquad = 1 : 3,$
or $\qquad\qquad P = \tfrac{1}{3} \triangle BCD.$

## Propositions 8, 9

Suppose a lever $AOB$ placed horizontally and supported at its middle point $O$. Let a triangle $BCD$, right-angled or obtuse-angled at $C$, be suspended from the points $B$, $E$ on $OB$, the angular point $C$ being so attached to $E$ that the side $CD$ is in the same vertical line with $E$. Let $Q$ be an area such that
$$AO : OE = \triangle BCD : Q.$$

Then, if an area $P$ suspended from $A$ keep the system in equilibrium,
$\qquad P < \triangle BCD$ but $> Q$.

Take $G$ the centre of gravity of the triangle $BCD$, and draw $GH$ parallel to $DC$, i.e. vertically, meeting $BO$ in $H$.

We may now suppose the triangle $BCD$ suspended from $H$, and, since there is equilibrium,
$$\triangle BCD : P = AO : OH, \qquad\qquad (1)$$
whence $\qquad\qquad P < \triangle BCD.$
Also $\qquad\qquad \triangle BCD : Q = AO : OE.$
Therefore, by (1), $\qquad \triangle BCD : Q > \triangle BCD : P,$
and $\qquad\qquad P > Q.$

## Propositions 10, 11

Suppose a lever $AOB$ placed horizontally and supported at $O$, its middle point. Let $CDEF$ be a trapezium which can be so placed that its parallel sides $CD$, $FE$ are vertical, while $C$ is vertically below $O$, and the other sides $CF$, $DE$ meet in $B$. Let $EF$ meet $BO$ in $H$, and let the trapezium be suspended by attaching $F$ to $H$ and $C$ to $O$. Further, suppose $Q$ to be an area such that
$$AO : OH = (\text{trapezium } CDEF) : Q.$$
Then, if $P$ be the area which, when suspended from $A$, keeps the system in equilibrium,
$$P < Q.$$

---

[1] Doubtless in the lost book περὶ ζυγῶν.

## QUADRATURE OF THE PARABOLA

*The same is true in the particular case where the angles at C, F are right, and consequently C, F coincide with O, H respectively.*

Divide $OH$ in $K$ so that
$$(2CD+FE) : (2FE+CD) = HK : KO.$$

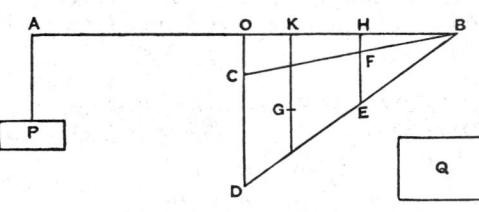

Draw $KG$ parallel to $OD$, and let $G$ be the middle point of the portion of $KG$ intercepted within the trapezium. Then $G$ is the centre of gravity of the trapezium [*On the equilibrium of planes*, I. 15].

Thus we may suppose the trapezium suspended from $K$, and the equilibrium will remain undisturbed.

Therefore $AO : OK = $ (trapezium $CDEF$) $: P$,
and, by hypothesis, $AO : OH = $ (trapezium $CDEF$) $: Q$.
Since $OK < OH$, it follows that
$$P < Q.$$

### Propositions 12, 13

*If the trapezium CDEF be placed as in the last propositions, except that CD is vertically below a point L on OB instead of being below O, and the trapezium is suspended from L, H, suppose that Q, R are areas such that*
$$AO : OH = (\text{trapezium } CDEF) : Q,$$
and
$$AO : OL = (\text{trapezium } CDEF) : R.$$

*If then an area P suspended from A keep the system in equilibrium,*
$$P > R \text{ but} < Q.$$

Take the centre of gravity $G$ of the trapezium, as in the last propositions, and let the line through $G$ parallel to $DC$ meet $OB$ in $K$.

Then we may suppose the trapezium suspended from $K$, and there will still be equilibrium.

Therefore (trapezium $CDEF$) $: P = AO : OK$.
Hence (trapezium $CDEF$) $: P >$ (trapezium $CDEF$) $: Q$,
but $<$ (trapezium $CDEF$) $: R$.
It follows that $P < Q$ but $> R$.

### Propositions 14, 15

Let $Qq$ be the base of any segment of a parabola. Then, if two lines be drawn from $Q$, $q$, each parallel to the axis of the parabola and on the same side of $Qq$ as the segment is, either (1) the angles so formed at $Q$, $q$ are both right angles, or (2) one is acute and the other obtuse. In the latter case let the angle at $q$ be the obtuse angle.

Divide $Qq$ into any number of equal parts at the points $O_1, O_2, \cdots O_n$. Draw through $q, O_1, O_2, \cdots O_n$ diameters of the parabola meeting the tangent at $Q$ in $E, E_1, E_2, \cdots E_n$ and the parabola itself in $q, R_1, R_2, \cdots R_n$. Join $QR_1, QR_2, \cdots QR_n$ meeting $qE, O_1E_1, O_2E_2, \cdots O_{n-1}E_{n-1}$ in $F, F_1, F_2, \cdots F_{n-1}$.

Let the diameters $Eq, E_1O_1, \cdots E_nO_n$ meet a straight line $QOA$ drawn through $Q$ perpendicular to the diameters in the points $O, H_1, H_2, \cdots H_n$ respectively. (In the particular case where $Qq$ is itself perpendicular to the diameters $q$ will coincide with $O$, $O_1$ with $H_1$, and so on.)

*It is required to prove that*
(1) $\triangle EqQ < 3(\text{sum of trapezia } FO_1, F_1O_2, \cdots F_{n-1}O_n \text{ and } \triangle E_nO_nQ)$,
(2) $\triangle EqQ > 3(\text{sum of trapezia } R_1O_2, R_2O_3, \cdots R_{n-1}O_n \text{ and } \triangle R_nO_nQ)$.

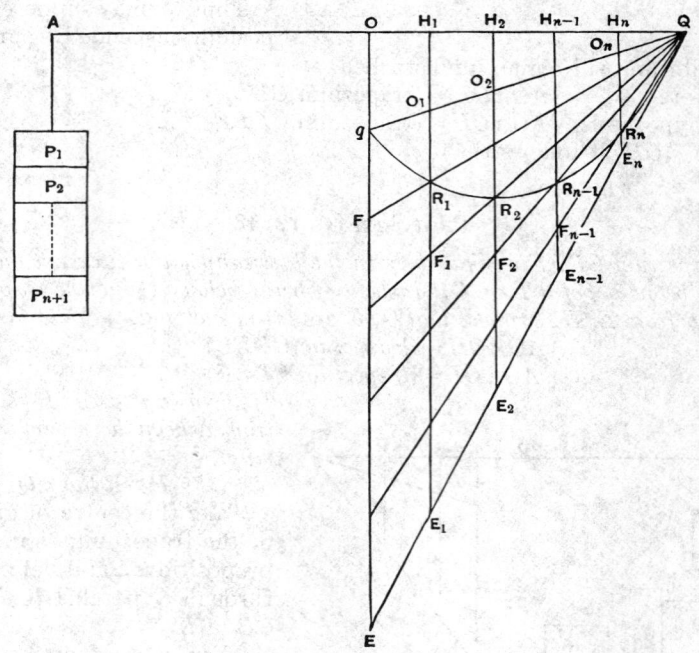

Suppose $AO$ made equal to $OQ$, and conceive $QOA$ as a lever placed horizontally and supported at $O$. Suppose the triangle $EqQ$ suspended from $OQ$ in the position drawn, and suppose that the trapezium $EO_1$ in the position drawn is balanced by an area $P_1$ suspended from $A$, the trapezium $E_1O_2$ in the position drawn is balanced by the area $P_2$ suspended from $A$, and so on, the triangle $E_nO_nQ$ being in like manner balanced by $P_{n+1}$.

Then $P_1+P_2+\cdots+P_{n+1}$ will balance the whole triangle $EqQ$ as drawn, and therefore $\qquad P_1+P_2+\cdots+P_{n+1} = \frac{1}{3}\triangle EqQ$. [Props. 6, 7]

Again $\qquad AO : OH_1 = QO : OH_1$
$\qquad\qquad\qquad\quad = Qq : qO_1$
$\qquad\qquad\qquad\quad = E_1O_1 : O_1R_1$ [by means of Prop. 5]
$\qquad\qquad\qquad\quad = (\text{trapezium } EO_1) : (\text{trapezium } FO_1)$;
whence [Props. 10, 11] $\qquad (FO_1) > P_1$.

## QUADRATURE OF THE PARABOLA

Next
$$AO : OH_1 = E_1O_1 : O_1R_1$$
$$= (E_1O_2) : (R_1O_2), \qquad (\alpha)$$

while
$$AO : OH_2 = E_2O_2 : O_2R_2$$
$$= (E_1O_2) : (F_1O_2); \qquad (\beta)$$

and, since $(\alpha)$ and $(\beta)$ are simultaneously true, we have, by Props. 12, 13,
$$(F_1O_2) > P_2 > (R_1O_2).$$

Similarly it may be proved that
$$(F_2O_3) > P_3 > (R_2O_3),$$
and so on.

Lastly [Props. 8, 9]     $\triangle E_nO_nQ > P_{n+1} > \triangle R_nO_nQ.$

By addition, we obtain

(1)     $(FO_1) + (F_1O_2) + \cdots + (F_{n-1}O_n) + \triangle E_nO_nQ > P_1 + P_2 + \cdots + P_{n+1}$
$$> \tfrac{1}{3}\triangle EqQ,$$

or     $\triangle EqQ < 3(FO_1 + F_1O_2 + \cdots + F_{n-1}O_n + \triangle E_nO_nQ).$

(2)     $(R_1O_2) + (R_2O_3) + \cdots + (R_{n-1}O_n) + \triangle R_nO_nQ < P_2 + P_3 + \cdots + P_{n+1}$
$$< P_1 + P_2 + \cdots + P_{n+1}, \text{ a fortiori,}$$
$$< \tfrac{1}{3}\triangle EqQ,$$

or     $\triangle EqQ > 3(R_1O_2 + R_2O_3 + \cdots + R_{n-1}O_n + \triangle R_nO_nQ).$

### Proposition 16

*Suppose $Qq$ to be the base of a parabolic segment, $q$ being not more distant than $Q$ from the vertex of the parabola. Draw through $q$ the straight line $qE$ parallel to the axis of the parabola to meet the tangent at $Q$ in $E$. It is required to prove that*
$$(\text{area of segment}) = \tfrac{1}{3}\triangle EqQ.$$

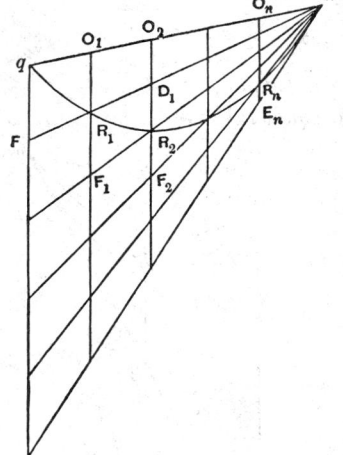

For, if not, the area of the segment must be either greater or less than $\tfrac{1}{3}\triangle EqQ$.

I. Suppose the area of the segment greater than $\tfrac{1}{3}\triangle EqQ$. Then the excess can, if continually added to itself, be made to exceed $\triangle EqQ$. And it is possible to find a submultiple of the triangle $EqQ$ less than the said excess of the segment over $\tfrac{1}{3}\triangle EqQ$.

Let the triangle $FqQ$ be such a submultiple of the triangle $EqQ$. Divide $Eq$ into equal parts each equal to $qF$, and let all the points of division including $F$ be joined to $Q$ meeting the parabola in $R_1, R_2, \cdots R_n$ respectively. Through $R_1, R_2, \cdots R_n$ draw diameters of the parabola meeting $qQ$ in $O_1, O_2, \cdots O_n$ respectively.

Let $O_1R_1$ meet $QR_2$ in $F_1$.
Let $O_2R_2$ meet $QR_1$ in $D_1$ and $QR_3$ in $F_2$.
Let $O_3R_3$ meet $QR_2$ in $D_2$ and $QR_4$ in $F_3$,
and so on.

We have, by hypothesis,
$$\triangle FqQ < (\text{area of segment}) - \tfrac{1}{3}\triangle EqQ,$$
or     $(\text{area of segment}) - \triangle FqQ > \tfrac{1}{3}\triangle EqQ.$ $\qquad (\alpha)$

Now, since all the parts of $qE$, as $qF$ and the rest, are equal, $O_1R_1 = R_1F_1$, $O_2D_1 = D_1R_2 = R_2F_2$, and so on; therefore

$$\triangle FqQ = (FO_1 + R_1O_2 + D_1O_3 + \cdots)$$
$$= (FO_1 + F_1D_1 + F_2D_2 + \cdots + F_{n-1}D_{n-1} + \triangle E_nR_nQ). \quad (\beta)$$

But (area of segment) $< (FO_1 + F_1O_2 + \cdots + F_{n-1}O_n + \triangle E_nO_nQ)$.

Subtracting, we have
$$\text{(area of segment)} - \triangle FqQ < (R_1O_2 + R_2O_3 + \cdots + R_{n-1}O_n + \triangle R_nO_nQ),$$
whence, *a fortiori*, by $(\alpha)$,
$$\tfrac{1}{3}\triangle EqQ < (R_1O_2 + R_2O_3 + \cdots + R_{n-1}O_n + \triangle R_nO_nQ).$$
But this is impossible, since [Props. 14, 15]
$$\tfrac{1}{3}\triangle EqQ > (R_1O_2 + R_2O_3 + \cdots + R_{n-1}O_n + \triangle R_nO_nQ).$$

Therefore (area of segment) $\not> \tfrac{1}{3}\triangle EqQ$.

II. If possible, suppose the area of the segment less than $\tfrac{1}{3}\triangle EqQ$.

Take a submultiple of the triangle $EqQ$, as the triangle $FqQ$, less than the excess of $\tfrac{1}{3}\triangle EqQ$ over the area of the segment, and make the same construction as before.

Since
$$\triangle FqQ < \tfrac{1}{3}\triangle EqQ - \text{(area of segment)},$$
it follows that
$$\triangle FqQ + \text{(area of segment)} < \tfrac{1}{3}\triangle EqQ$$
$$< (FO_1 + F_1O_2 + \cdots + F_{n-1}O_n + \triangle E_nO_nQ).$$
[Props. 14, 15]

Subtracting from each side the area of the segment, we have
$$\triangle FqQ < \text{(sum of spaces } qFR_1, R_1F_1R_2, \cdots E_nR_nQ\text{)}$$
$$< (FO_1 + F_1D_1 + \cdots + F_{n-1}D_{n-1} + \triangle E_nR_nQ), \text{ a } \textit{fortiori};$$
which is impossible, because, by $(\beta)$ above,
$$\triangle FqQ = FO_1 + F_1D_1 + \cdots + F_{n-1}D_{n-1} + \triangle E_nR_nQ.$$

Hence (area of segment) $\not< \tfrac{1}{3}\triangle EqQ$.

Since then the area of the segment is neither less nor greater than $\tfrac{1}{3}\triangle EqQ$, it is equal to it.

## Proposition 17

It is now manifest that *the area of any segment of a parabola is four-thirds of the triangle which has the same base as the segment and equal height.*

Let $Qq$ be the base of the segment, $P$ its vertex. Then $PQq$ is the inscribed triangle with the same base as the segment and equal height.

Since $P$ is the vertex of the segment, the diameter through $P$ bisects $Qq$. Let $V$ be the point of bisection.

Let $VP$, and $qE$ drawn parallel to it, meet the tangent at $Q$ in $T$, $E$ respectively.

Then, by parallels,
$$qE = 2VT,$$
and $PV = PT,$ [Prop. 2]
so that $VT = 2PV.$

Hence $\triangle EqQ = 4\triangle PQq.$

But, by Prop. 16, the area of the segment is equal to $\tfrac{1}{3}\triangle EqQ$.

Therefore (area of segment) $= \tfrac{4}{3}\triangle PQq$.

---

Def. "In segments bounded by a straight line and any curve I call the

## QUADRATURE OF THE PARABOLA

straight line the *base*, and the *height* the greatest perpendicular drawn from the curve to the base of the segment, and the *vertex* the point from which the greatest perpendicular is drawn."

### PROPOSITION 18

*If $Qq$ be the base of a segment of a parabola, and $V$ the middle point of $Qq$, and if the diameter through $V$ meet the curve in $P$, then $P$ is the vertex of the segment.*

For $Qq$ is parallel to the tangent at $P$ [Prop. 1]. Therefore, of all the perpendiculars which can be drawn from points on the segment to the base $Qq$, that from $P$ is the greatest. Hence, by the definition, $P$ is the vertex of the segment.

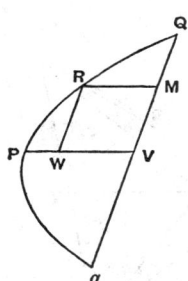

### PROPOSITION 19

*If $Qq$ be a chord of a parabola bisected in $V$ by the diameter $PV$, and if $RM$ be a diameter bisecting $QV$ in $M$, and $RW$ be the ordinate from $R$ to $PV$, then*
$$PV = \tfrac{4}{3}RM.$$
For, by the property of the parabola,
$$PV : PW = QV^2 : RW^2$$
$$= 4RW^2 : RW^2,$$
so that $\qquad PV = 4PW,$
whence $\qquad PV = \tfrac{4}{3}RM.$

### PROPOSITION 20

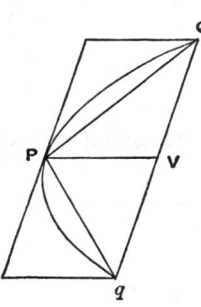

*If $Qq$ be the base, and $P$ the vertex, of a parabolic segment, then the triangle $PQq$ is greater than half the segment $PQq$.*

For the chord $Qq$ is parallel to the tangent at $P$, and the triangle $PQq$ is half the parallelogram formed by $Qq$, the tangent at $P$, and the diameters through $Q$, $q$.

Therefore the triangle $PQq$ is greater than half the segment.

COR. It follows that *it is possible to inscribe in the segment a polygon such that the segments left over are together less than any assigned area.*

### PROPOSITION 21

*If $Qq$ be the base, and $P$ the vertex, of any parabolic segment, and if $R$ be the vertex of the segment cut off by $PQ$, then*
$$\triangle PQq = 8 \triangle PRQ.$$
The diameter through $R$ will bisect the chord $PQ$, and therefore also $QV$, where $PV$ is the diameter bisecting $Qq$. Let the diameter through $R$ bisect $PQ$ in $Y$ and $QV$ in $M$. Join $PM$.

By Prop. 19, $\qquad PV = \tfrac{4}{3}RM.$
Also $\qquad PV = 2YM.$
Therefore $\qquad YM = 2RY,$

and
$$\triangle PQM = 2\triangle PRQ.$$
Hence
$$\triangle PQV = 4\triangle PRQ,$$
and
$$\triangle PQq = 8\triangle PRQ.$$

Also, if $RW$, the ordinate from $R$ to $PV$, be produced to meet the curve again in $r$,
$$RW = rW,$$
and the same proof shows that
$$\triangle PQq = 8\triangle Prq.$$

## Proposition 22

*If there be a series of areas $A, B, C, D, \cdots$ each of which is four times the next in order, and if the largest, $A$, be equal to the triangle $PQq$ inscribed in a parabolic segment $PQq$ and having the same base with it and equal height, then*
$$(A+B+C+D+\cdots) < (\text{area of segment } PQq).$$

For, since $\triangle PQq = 8\triangle PRQ = 8\triangle Pqr$, where $R, r$ are the vertices of the segments cut off by $PQ, Pq$, as in the last proposition,
$$\triangle PQq = 4(\triangle PQR + \triangle Pqr).$$
Therefore, since $\triangle PQq = A$,
$$\triangle PQR + \triangle Pqr = B.$$

In like manner we prove that the triangles similarly inscribed in the remaining segments are together equal to the area $C$, and so on.

Therefore $A+B+C+D+\cdots$ is equal to the area of a certain inscribed polygon, and is therefore less than the area of the segment.

## Proposition 23

*Given a series of areas $A, B, C, D, \cdots Z$, of which $A$ is the greatest, and each is equal to four times the next in order, then*
$$A+B+C+\cdots+Z+\tfrac{1}{3}Z = \tfrac{4}{3}A.$$

Take areas $b, c, d, \cdots$ such that
$$b = \tfrac{1}{3}B,$$
$$c = \tfrac{1}{3}C,$$
$$d = \tfrac{1}{3}D, \text{ and so on.}$$
Then, since $b = \tfrac{1}{3}B$,
and $B = \tfrac{1}{4}A$,
$$B + b = \tfrac{1}{3}A.$$
Similarly $C + c = \tfrac{1}{3}B.$
. . . . . . . . . .

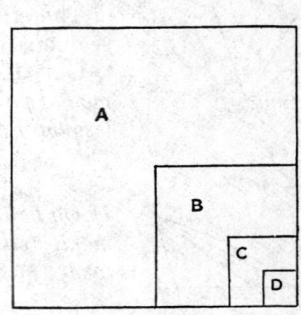

Therefore
$$B+C+D+\cdots+Z+b+c+d+\cdots+z = \tfrac{1}{3}(A+B+C+\cdots+Y).$$
But
$$b+c+d+\cdots+y = \tfrac{1}{3}(B+C+D+\cdots+Y).$$
Therefore, by subtraction,
$$B+C+D+\cdots+Z+z = \tfrac{1}{3}A$$
or
$$A+B+C+\cdots+Z+\tfrac{1}{3}Z = \tfrac{4}{3}A.$$

## Proposition 24

*Every segment bounded by a parabola and a chord Qq is equal to four-thirds of the triangle which has the same base as the segment and equal height.*

Suppose $K = \frac{4}{3} \triangle PQq,$

where $P$ is the vertex of the segment; and we have then to prove that the area of the segment is equal to $K$.

For, if the segment be not equal to $K$, it must either be greater or less.

I. Suppose the area of the segment greater than $K$.

If then we inscribe in the segments cut off by $PQ$, $Pq$ triangles which have the same base and equal height, i.e. triangles with the same vertices $R$, $r$ as those of the segments, and if in the remaining segments we inscribe triangles in the same manner, and so on, we shall finally have segments remaining whose sum is less than the area by which the segment $PQq$ exceeds $K$.

Therefore the polygon so formed must be greater than the area $K$; which is impossible, since [Prop. 23]

$$A+B+C+ \cdots +Z < \tfrac{4}{3}A,$$

where $A = \triangle PQq.$

Thus the area of the segment cannot be greater than $K$.

II. Suppose, if possible, that the area of the segment is less than $K$.

If then $\triangle PQq = A$, $B = \frac{1}{4}A$, $C = \frac{1}{4}B$, and so on, until we arrive at an area $X$ such that $X$ is less than the difference between $K$ and the segment, we have

$$A+B+C+ \cdots +X+\tfrac{1}{3}X = \tfrac{4}{3}A \qquad \text{[Prop. 23]}$$
$$= K.$$

Now, since $K$ exceeds $A+B+C+ \cdots +X$ by an area less than $X$, and the area of the segment by an area greater than $X$, it follows that

$$A+B+C+ \cdots +X > \text{(the segment)};$$

which is impossible, by Prop. 22 above.

Hence the segment is not less than $K$.

Thus, since the segment is neither greater nor less than $K$,

(area of segment $PQq$) $= K = \tfrac{4}{3} \triangle PQq.$

# ON FLOATING BODIES

## BOOK ONE

### POSTULATE 1

"Let it be supposed that a fluid is of such a character that, its parts lying evenly and being continuous, that part which is thrust the less is driven along by that which is thrust the more; and that each of its parts is thrust by the fluid which is above it in a perpendicular direction if the fluid be sunk in anything and compressed by anything else."

### PROPOSITION 1

*If a surface be cut by a plane always passing through a certain point, and if the section be always a circumference [of a circle] whose centre is the aforesaid point, the surface is that of a sphere.*

For, if not, there will be some two lines drawn from the point to the surface which are not equal.

Suppose $O$ to be the fixed point, and $A$, $B$ to be two points on the surface such that $OA$, $OB$ are unequal. Let the surface be cut by a plane passing through $OA$, $OB$. Then the section is, by hypothesis, a circle whose centre is $O$.

Thus $OA = OB$; which is contrary to the assumption. Therefore the surface cannot but be a sphere.

### PROPOSITION 2

*The surface of any fluid at rest is the surface of a sphere whose centre is the same as that of the earth.*

Suppose the surface of the fluid cut by a plane through $O$, the centre of the earth, in the curve $ABCD$.

$ABCD$ shall be the circumference of a circle.

For, if not, some of the lines drawn from $O$ to the curve will be unequal. Take one of them, $OB$, such that $OB$ is greater than some of the lines from $O$ to the curve and less than others. Draw a circle with $OB$ as radius. Let it be $EBF$, which will therefore fall partly within and partly without the surface of the fluid.

Draw $OGH$ making with $OB$ an angle equal to the angle $EOB$, and meeting the surface in $H$ and the circle in $G$. Draw also in the plane an arc of a circle $PQR$ with centre $O$ and within the fluid.

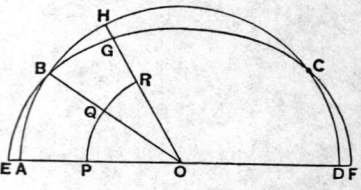

Then the parts of the fluid along $PQR$ are uniform and continuous, and the part $PQ$ is compressed by the part between it and $AB$, while the part $QR$ is compressed by the part between $QR$ and $BH$.

Therefore the parts along $PQ$, $QR$ will be unequally compressed, and the part which is compressed the less will be set in motion by that which is compressed the more.

Therefore there will not be rest; which is contrary to the hypothesis.

Hence the section of the surface will be the circumference of a circle whose centre is $O$; and so will all other sections by planes through $O$.

Therefore the surface is that of a sphere with centre $O$.

### Proposition 3

*Of solids those which, size for size, are of equal weight with a fluid will, if let down into the fluid, be immersed so that they do not project above the surface but do not sink lower.*

If possible, let a certain solid $EFHG$ of equal weight, volume for volume, with the fluid remain immersed in it so that part of it, $EBCF$, projects above the surface.

Draw through $O$, the centre of the earth, and through the solid a plane cutting the surface of the fluid in the circle $ABCD$.

Conceive a pyramid with vertex $O$ and base a parallelogram at the surface of the fluid, such that it includes the immersed portion of the solid. Let this

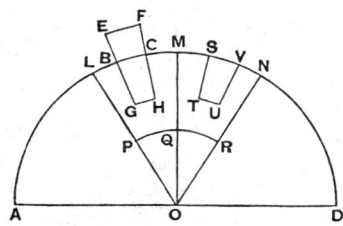

pyramid be cut by the plane of $ABCD$ in $OL$, $OM$. Also let a sphere within the fluid and below $GH$ be described with centre $O$, and let the plane of $ABCD$ cut this sphere in $PQR$.

Conceive also another pyramid in the fluid with vertex $O$, continuous with the former pyramid and equal and similar to it. Let the pyramid so described be cut in $OM$, $ON$ by the plane of $ABCD$.

Lastly, let $STUV$ be a part of the fluid within the second pyramid equal and similar to the part $BGHC$ of the solid, and let $SV$ be at the surface of the fluid.

Then the pressures on $PQ$, $QR$ are unequal, that on $PQ$ being the greater. Hence the part at $QR$ will be set in motion by that at $PQ$, and the fluid will not be at rest; which is contrary to the hypothesis.

Therefore the solid will not stand out above the surface.

Nor will it sink further, because all the parts of the fluid will be under the same pressure.

### Proposition 4

*A solid lighter than a fluid will, if immersed in it, not be completely submerged, but part of it will project above the surface.*

In this case, after the manner of the previous proposition, we assume the solid, if possible, to be completely submerged and the fluid to be at rest in that position, and we conceive (1) a pyramid with its vertex at $O$, the centre of the earth, including the solid, (2) another pyramid continuous with the former and equal and similar to it, with the same vertex $O$, (3) a portion of the fluid within this latter pyramid equal to the immersed solid in the other pyramid, (4) a sphere with centre $O$ whose surface is below the immersed solid and the part of the fluid in the second pyramid corresponding thereto. We suppose a plane to be drawn through the centre $O$ cutting the surface of the fluid in the circle

$ABC$, the solid in $S$, the first pyramid in $OA$, $OB$, the second pyramid in $OB$, $OC$, the portion of the fluid in the second pyramid in $K$, and the inner sphere in $PQR$.

Then the pressures on the parts of the fluid at $PQ$, $QR$ are unequal, since $S$ is lighter than $K$. Hence there will not be rest; which is contrary to the hypothesis.

Therefore the solid $S$ cannot, in a condition of rest, be completely submerged.

## Proposition 5

*Any solid lighter than a fluid will, if placed in the fluid, be so far immersed that the weight of the solid will be equal to the weight of the fluid displaced.*

For let the solid be $EGHF$, and let $BGHC$ be the portion of it immersed when the fluid is at rest. As in Prop. 3, conceive a pyramid with vertex $O$ including the solid, and another pyramid with the same vertex continuous with the former and equal and similar to it. Suppose a portion of the fluid $STUV$ at the base of the second pyramid to be equal and similar to the immersed portion of the solid; and let the construction be the same as in Prop. 3.

Then, since the pressure on the parts of the fluid at $PQ$, $QR$ must be equal in order that the fluid may be at rest, it follows that the weight of the portion $STUV$ of the fluid must be equal to the weight of the solid $EGHF$. And the former is equal to the weight of the fluid displaced by the immersed portion of the solid $BGHC$.

## Proposition 6

*If a solid lighter than a fluid be forcibly immersed in it, the solid will be driven upwards by a force equal to the difference between its weight and the weight of the fluid displaced.*

For let $A$ be completely immersed in the fluid, and let $G$ represent the weight of $A$, and $(G+H)$ the weight of an equal volume of the fluid. Take a solid $D$, whose weight is $H$ and add it to $A$. Then the weight of $(A+D)$ is less than that of an equal volume of the fluid; and, if $(A+D)$ is immersed in the fluid, it will project so that its weight will be equal to the weight of the fluid displaced. But its weight is $(G+H)$.

Therefore the weight of the fluid displaced is $(G+H)$, and hence the volume of the fluid displaced is the volume of the solid $A$. There will accordingly be rest with $A$ immersed and $D$ projecting.

Thus the weight of $D$ balances the upward force exerted by the fluid on $A$, and therefore the latter force is equal to $H$, which is the difference between the weight of $A$ and the weight of the fluid which $A$ displaces.

## Proposition 7

*A solid heavier than a fluid will, if placed in it, descend to the bottom of the fluid, and the solid will, when weighed in the fluid, be lighter than its true weight by the weight of the fluid displaced.*

(1) The first part of the proposition is obvious, since the part of the fluid under the solid will be under greater pressure, and therefore the other parts will give way until the solid reaches the bottom.

(2) Let $A$ be a solid heavier than the same volume of the fluid, and let $(G+H)$ represent its weight, while $G$ represents the weight of the same volume of the fluid.

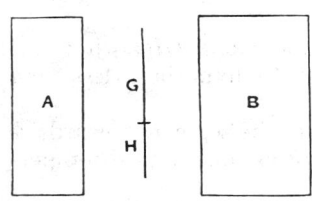

Take a solid $B$ lighter than the same volume of the fluid, and such that the weight of $B$ is $G$, while the weight of the same volume of the fluid is $(G+H)$.

Let $A$ and $B$ be now combined into one solid and immersed. Then, since $(A+B)$ will be of the same weight as the same volume of fluid, both weights being equal to $(G+H)+G$, it follows that $(A+B)$ will remain stationary in the fluid.

Therefore the force which causes $A$ by itself to sink must be equal to the upward force exerted by the fluid on $B$ by itself. This latter is equal to the difference between $(G+H)$ and $G$ [Prop. 6]. Hence $A$ is depressed by a force equal to $H$, i.e. its weight in the fluid is $H$, or the difference between $(G+H)$ and $G$.

## Postulate 2

"Let it be granted that bodies which are forced upwards in a fluid are forced upwards along the perpendicular [to the surface] which passes through their centre of gravity."

## Proposition 8

*If a solid in the form of a segment of a sphere, and of a substance lighter than a fluid, be immersed in it so that its base does not touch the surface, the solid will rest in such a position that its axis is perpendicular to the surface; and, if the solid be forced into such a position that its base touches the fluid on one side and be then set free, it will not remain in that position but will return to the symmetrical position.*

## Proposition 9

*If a solid in the form of a segment of a sphere, and of a substance lighter than a fluid, be immersed in it so that its base is completely below the surface, the solid will rest in such a position that its axis is perpendicular to the surface.*

[The proof of this proposition has only survived in a mutilated form. It deals moreover with only one case out of three which are distinguished at the beginning, viz. that in which the segment is greater than a hemisphere. . . .]

Suppose, first, that the segment is greater than a hemisphere. Let it be cut by a plane through its axis and the centre of the earth; and, if possible, let it be at rest in the position shown in the figure, where $AB$ is the intersection of the plane with the base of the segment, *DE* its axis, *C* the centre of the sphere of which the segment is a part, *O* the centre of the earth.

The centre of gravity of the portion of the segment outside the fluid, as *F*, lies on *OC* produced, its axis passing through *C*.

Let *G* be the centre of gravity of the segment. Join *FG*, and produce it to *H* so that

*FG* : *GH* = (volume of immersed portion) : (rest of solid).

Join *OH*.

Then the weight of the portion of the solid outside the fluid acts along *FO*, and the pressure of the fluid on the immersed portion along *OH*, while the weight of the immersed portion acts along *HO* and is by hypothesis less than the pressure of the fluid acting along *OH*.

Hence there will not be equilibrium, but the part of the segment towards *A* will ascend and the part towards *B* descend, until *DE* assumes a position perpendicular to the surface of the fluid.

# ON FLOATING BODIES

# BOOK TWO

### Proposition 1

*If a solid lighter than a fluid be at rest in it, the weight of the solid will be to that of the same volume of the fluid as the immersed portion of the solid is to the whole.*

Let $(A+B)$ be the solid, $B$ the portion immersed in the fluid.

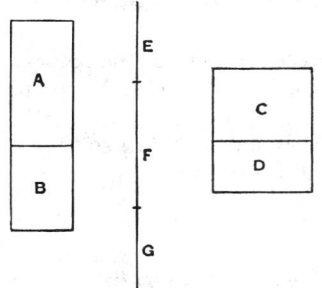

Let $(C+D)$ be an equal volume of the fluid, $C$ being equal in volume to $A$ and $B$ to $D$.

Further suppose the line $E$ to represent the weight of the solid $(A+B)$, $(F+G)$ to represent the weight of $(C+D)$, and $G$ that of $D$.

Then

weight of $(A+B)$ : weight of $(C+D)$ =
$$E : (F+G). \qquad (1)$$

And the weight of $(A+B)$ is equal to the weight of a volume $B$ of the fluid [I. 5], i.e. to the weight of $D$.

That is to say, $E=G$.

Hence, by (1),

$$\begin{aligned}\text{weight of } (A+B) : \text{weight of } (C+D) &= G : F+G \\ &= D : C+D \\ &= B : A+B.\end{aligned}$$

### Proposition 2

*If a right segment of a paraboloid of revolution whose axis is not greater than $\frac{3}{4}p$ (where p is the principal parameter of the generating parabola), and whose specific gravity is less than that of a fluid, be placed in the fluid with its axis inclined to the vertical at any angle, but so that the base of the segment does not touch the surface of the fluid, the segment of the paraboloid will not remain in that position but will return to the position in which its axis is vertical.*

Let the axis of the segment of the paraboloid be $AN$, and through $AN$ draw a plane perpendicular to the surface of the fluid. Let the plane intersect the paraboloid in the parabola $BAB'$, the base of the segment of the paraboloid in $BB'$, and the plane of the surface of the fluid in the chord $QQ'$ of the parabola.

Then, since the axis $AN$ is placed in a position not perpendicular to $QQ'$, $BB'$ will not be parallel to $QQ'$.

Draw the tangent $PT$ to the parabola which is parallel to $QQ'$, and let $P$ be the point of contact.[1]

[1] The rest of the proof ... is given in brackets as supplied by Commandinus.

[From $P$ draw $PV$ parallel to $AN$ meeting $QQ'$ in $V$. Then $PV$ will be a diameter of the parabola, and also the axis of the portion of the paraboloid immersed in the fluid.

Let $C$ be the centre of gravity of the paraboloid $BAB'$, and $F$ that of the portion immersed in the fluid. Join $FC$ and produce it to $H$ so that $H$ is the centre of gravity of the remaining portion of the paraboloid above the surface.

Then, since $\quad AN = \tfrac{3}{2}AC$,
and $\quad\quad\quad\quad AN \not> \tfrac{3}{4}p$,

it follows that $\quad AC \not> \dfrac{p}{2}$.

Therefore, if $CP$ be joined, the angle $CPT$ is acute. Hence, if $CK$ be drawn perpendicular to $PT$, $K$ will fall between $P$ and $T$. And, if $FL$, $HM$ be drawn parallel to $CK$ to meet $PT$, they will each be perpendicular to the surface of the fluid.

Now the force acting on the immersed portion of the segment of the paraboloid will act upwards along $LF$, while the weight of the portion outside the fluid will act downwards along $HM$.

Therefore there will not be equilibrium, but the segment will turn so that $B$ will rise and $B'$ will fall, until $AN$ takes the vertical position.]

## Proposition 3

*If a right segment of a paraboloid of revolution whose axis is not greater than $\tfrac{3}{4}p$ (where $p$ is the parameter), and whose specific gravity is less than that of a fluid, be placed in the fluid with its axis inclined at any angle to the vertical, but so that its base is entirely submerged, the solid will not remain in that position but will return to the position in which the axis is vertical.*

Let the axis of the paraboloid be $AN$, and through $AN$ draw a plane perpendicular to the surface of the fluid intersecting the paraboloid in the parabola $BAB'$, the base of the segment in $BNB'$, and the plane of the surface of the fluid in the chord $QQ'$ of the parabola.

Then, since $AN$, as placed, is not perpendicular to the surface of the fluid, $QQ'$ and $BB'$ will not be parallel.

Draw $PT$ parallel to $QQ'$ and touching the parabola at $P$. Let $PT$ meet $NA$ produced in $T$. Draw the diameter $PV$ bisecting $QQ'$ in $V$. $PV$ is then the axis of the portion of the paraboloid above the surface of the fluid.

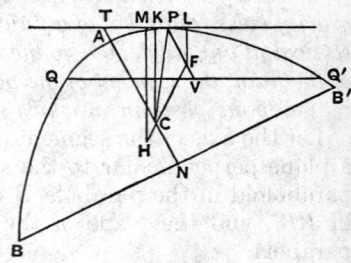

Let $C$ be the centre of gravity of the whole segment of the paraboloid, $F$ that of the portion above the surface. Join $FC$ and produce it to $H$ so that $H$ is the centre of gravity of the immersed portion.

Then, since $AC \not> \dfrac{p}{2}$, the angle $CPT$ is an acute angle, as in the last proposition.

Hence, if $CK$ be drawn perpendicular to $PT$, $K$ will fall between $P$ and $T$. Also, if $HM$, $FL$ be drawn parallel to $CK$, they will be perpendicular to the surface of the fluid.

And the force acting on the submerged portion will act upwards along $HM$, while the weight of the rest will act downwards along $LF$ produced.

Thus the paraboloid will turn until it takes the position in which $AN$ is vertical.

## Proposition 4

*Given a right segment of a paraboloid of revolution whose axis $AN$ is greater than $\frac{3}{4}p$ (where $p$ is the parameter), and whose specific gravity is less than that of a fluid but bears to it a ratio not less than $(AN-\frac{3}{4}p)^2 : AN^2$, if the segment of the paraboloid be placed in the fluid with its axis at any inclination to the vertical, but so that its base does not touch the surface of the fluid, it will not remain in that position but will return to the position in which its axis is vertical.*

Let the axis of the segment of the paraboloid be $AN$, and let a plane be drawn through $AN$ perpendicular to the surface of the fluid and intersecting the segment in the parabola $BAB'$, the base of the segment in $BB'$, and the surface of the fluid in the chord $QQ'$ of the parabola.

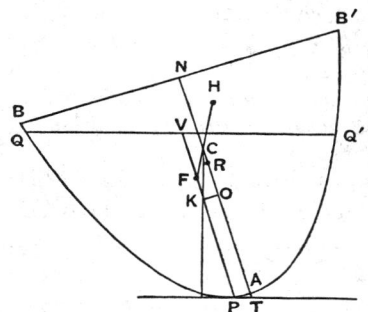

Then $AN$, as placed, will not be perpendicular to $QQ'$.

Draw $PT$ parallel to $QQ'$ and touching the parabola at $P$. Draw the diameter $PV$ bisecting $QQ'$ in $V$. Thus $PV$ will be the axis of the submerged portion of the solid.

Let $C$ be the centre of gravity of the whole solid, $F$ that of the immersed portion. Join $FC$ and produce it to $H$ so that $H$ is the centre of gravity of the remaining portion.

Now, since $\qquad AN = \frac{3}{2}AC$,
and $\qquad AN > \frac{3}{4}p$,
it follows that $\qquad AC > \frac{p}{2}$.

Measure $CO$ along $CA$ equal to $\frac{p}{2}$, and $OR$ along $OC$ equal to $\frac{1}{2}AO$.

Then, since $\qquad AN = \frac{3}{2}AC$,
and $\qquad AR = \frac{3}{2}AO$,
we have, by subtraction, $\qquad NR = \frac{3}{2}OC$.

That is, $\qquad AN - AR = \frac{3}{2}OC$
$\qquad\qquad\qquad = \frac{3}{4}p$,
or $\qquad AR = (AN - \frac{3}{4}p)$.

Thus $\qquad (AN - \frac{3}{4}p)^2 : AN^2 = AR^2 : AN^2$,
and therefore the ratio of the specific gravity of the solid to that of the fluid is, by the enunciation, not less than the ratio $AR^2 : AN^2$.

But, by Prop. 1, the former ratio is equal to the ratio of the immersed portion to the whole solid, i.e. to the ratio $PV^2 : AN^2$ [*On Conoids and Spheroids*, Prop. 24].

Hence $\qquad PV^2 : AN^2 \not< AR^2 : AN^2$,

or
$$PV \not< AR.$$
It follows that
$$PF(=\tfrac{2}{3}PV) \not< \tfrac{2}{3}AR$$
$$\not< AO.$$

If, therefore, $OK$ be drawn from $O$ perpendicular to $OA$, it will meet $PF$ between $P$ and $F$.

Also, if $CK$ be joined, the triangle $KCO$ is equal and similar to the triangle formed by the normal, the subnormal and the ordinate at $P$ (since $CO=\tfrac{1}{2}p$ or the subnormal, and $KO$ is equal to the ordinate).

Therefore $CK$ is parallel to the normal at $P$, and therefore perpendicular to the tangent at $P$ and to the surface of the fluid.

Hence, if parallels to $CK$ be drawn through $F$, $H$, they will be perpendicular to the surface of the fluid, and the force acting on the submerged portion of the solid will act upwards along the former, while the weight of the other portion will act downwards along the latter.

Therefore the solid will not remain in its position but will turn until $AN$ assumes a vertical position.

## Proposition 5

*Given a right segment of a paraboloid of revolution such that its axis $AN$ is greater than $\tfrac{3}{4}p$ (where $p$ is the parameter), and its specific gravity is less than that of a fluid but in a ratio to it not greater than the ratio $\{AN^2-(AN-\tfrac{3}{4}p)^2\} : AN^2$, if the segment be placed in the fluid with its axis inclined at any angle to the vertical, but so that its base is completely submerged, it will not remain in that position but will return to the position in which $AN$ is vertical.*

Let a plane be drawn through $AN$, as placed, perpendicular to the surface of the fluid and cutting the segment of the paraboloid in the parabola $BAB'$, the base of the segment in $BB'$, and the plane of the surface of the fluid in the chord $QQ'$ of the parabola.

Draw the tangent $PT$ parallel to $QQ'$, and the diameter $PV$, bisecting $QQ'$, will accordingly be the axis of the portion of the paraboloid above the surface of the fluid.

Let $F$ be the centre of gravity of the portion above the surface, $C$ that of the whole solid, and produce $FC$ to $H$, the centre of gravity of the immersed portion.

As in the last proposition, $AC > \dfrac{p}{2}$, and we measure $CO$ along $CA$ equal to $\dfrac{p}{2}$, and $OR$ along $OC$ equal to $\tfrac{1}{2}AO$.

Then $AN=\tfrac{3}{2}AC$, and $AR=\tfrac{3}{2}AO$;
and we derive, as before, $AR=(AN-\tfrac{3}{4}p)$.

Now, by hypothesis,

(spec. gravity of solid) : (spec. gravity of fluid)
$$\not> \{AN^2-(AN-\tfrac{3}{4}p)^2\} : AN^2$$
$$\not> (AN^2-AR^2) : AN^2.$$

Therefore
(portion submerged) : (whole solid)
$$\not> (AN^2-AR^2) : AN^2,$$

and
$$\text{(whole solid)} : \text{(portion above surface)}$$
$$> AN^2 : AR^2.$$
Thus $\qquad AN^2 : PV^2 > AN^2 : AR^2,$
whence $\qquad PV < AR,$
and $\qquad PF < \tfrac{2}{3}AR$
$\qquad\qquad\qquad < AO.$

Therefore, if a perpendicular to $AC$ be drawn from $O$, it will meet $PF$ in some point $K$ between $P$ and $F$.

And, since $CO = \tfrac{1}{2}p$, $CK$ will be perpendicular to $PT$, as in the last proposition.

Now the force acting on the submerged portion of the solid will act upwards through $H$, and the weight of the other portion downwards through $F$, in directions parallel in both cases to $CK$; whence the proposition follows.

PROPOSITION 6

*If a right segment of a paraboloid lighter than a fluid be such that its axis $AM$ is greater than $\tfrac{3}{4}p$, but $AM : \tfrac{1}{2}p < 15 : 4$, and if the segment be placed in the fluid with its axis so inclined to the vertical that its base touches the fluid, it will never remain in such a position that the base touches the surface in one point only.*

Suppose the segment of the paraboloid to be placed in the position described, and let the plane through the axis $AM$ perpendicular to the surface of the fluid intersect the segment of the paraboloid in the parabolic segment $BAB'$ and the plane of the surface of the fluid in $BQ$.

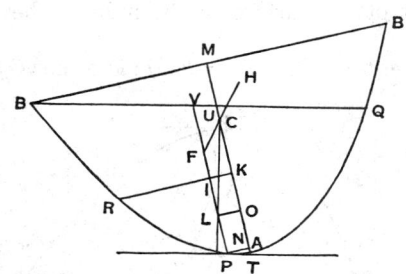

Take $C$ on $AM$ such that $AC = 2CM$ (or so that $C$ is the centre of gravity of the segment of the paraboloid), and measure $CK$ along $CA$ such that
$$AM : CK = 15 : 4.$$
Thus $AM : CK > AM : \tfrac{1}{2}p$, by hypothesis; therefore $CK < \tfrac{1}{2}p$.

Measure $CO$ along $CA$ equal to $\tfrac{1}{2}p$. Also draw $KR$ perpendicular to $AC$ meeting the parabola in $R$.

Draw the tangent $PT$ parallel to $BQ$, and through $P$ draw the diameter $PV$ bisecting $BQ$ in $V$ and meeting $KR$ in $I$.

Then $\qquad PV : PI \underset{\text{or}>}{=} KM : AK,$

"*for this is proved.*"

And
whence $\qquad CK = \tfrac{4}{15}AM = \tfrac{2}{5}AC;$
$\qquad AK = AC - CK = \tfrac{3}{5}AC = \tfrac{2}{5}AM.$
Thus $\qquad KM = \tfrac{3}{5}AM.$
Therefore $\qquad KM = \tfrac{3}{2}AK.$
It follows that $\qquad PV \underset{\text{or}>}{=} \tfrac{3}{2}PI,$
so that $\qquad PI \underset{\text{or}<}{=} 2IV.$

Let $F$ be the centre of gravity of the immersed portion of the paraboloid, so that $PF = 2FV$. Produce $FC$ to $H$, the centre of gravity of the portion above the surface.

Draw $OL$ perpendicular to $PV$.

Then, since $CO = \frac{1}{2}p$, $CL$ must be perpendicular to $PT$ and therefore to the surface of the fluid.

And the forces acting on the immersed portion of the paraboloid and the portion above the surface act respectively upwards and downwards along lines through $F$ and $H$ parallel to $CL$.

Hence the paraboloid cannot remain in the position in which $B$ just touches the surface, but must turn in the direction of increasing the angle $PTM$.

The proof is the same in the case where the point $I$ is not on $VP$ but on $VP$ produced, as in the second figure.

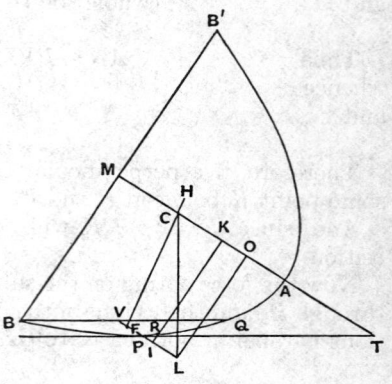

## Proposition 7

*Given a right segment of a paraboloid of revolution lighter than a fluid and such that its axis $AM$ is greater than $\frac{3}{4}p$, but $AM : \frac{1}{2}p < 15 : 4$, if the segment be placed in the fluid so that its base is entirely submerged, it will never rest in such a position that the base touches the surface of the fluid at one point only.*

Suppose the solid so placed that one point of the base only ($B$) touches the surface of the fluid. Let the plane through $B$ and the axis $AM$ cut the solid in the parabolic segment $BAB'$ and the plane of the surface of the fluid in the chord $BQ$ of the parabola.

Let $C$ be the centre of gravity of the segment, so that $AC = 2CM$; and measure $CK$ along $CA$ such that
$$AM : CK = 15 : 4.$$
It follows that $CK < \frac{1}{2}p$.

Measure $CO$ along $CA$ equal to $\frac{1}{2}p$. Draw $KR$ perpendicular to $AM$ meeting the parabola in $R$.

Let $PT$, touching at $P$, be the tangent to the parabola which is parallel to $BQ$, and $PV$ the diameter bisecting $BQ$, i.e. the axis of the portion of the paraboloid above the surface.

Then, as in the last proposition, we prove that
$$PV \underset{\text{or}>}{=} \tfrac{3}{2}PI,$$
and
$$PI \underset{\text{or}<}{=} 2IV.$$

Let $F$ be the centre of gravity of the portion of the solid above the surface; join $FC$ and produce it to $H$, the centre of gravity of the portion submerged.

Draw $OL$ perpendicular to $PV$; and, as before, since $CO = \frac{1}{2}p$, $CL$ is perpendicular to the tangent $PT$. And the lines through $H$, $F$ parallel to $CL$ are perpendicular to the surface of the fluid; thus the proposition is established as before.

The proof is the same if the point $I$ is not on $VP$ but on $VP$ produced.

## Proposition 8

*Given a solid in the form of a right segment of a paraboloid of revolution whose axis $AM$ is greater than $\frac{3}{4}p$, but such that $AM : \frac{1}{2}p < 15 : 4$, and whose specific gravity bears to that of a fluid a ratio less than $(AM - \frac{3}{4}p)^2 : AM^2$, then, if the solid be placed in the fluid so that its base does not touch the fluid and its axis is inclined at an angle to the vertical, the solid will not return to the position in which its axis is vertical and will not remain in any position except that in which its axis makes with the surface of the fluid a certain angle to be described.*

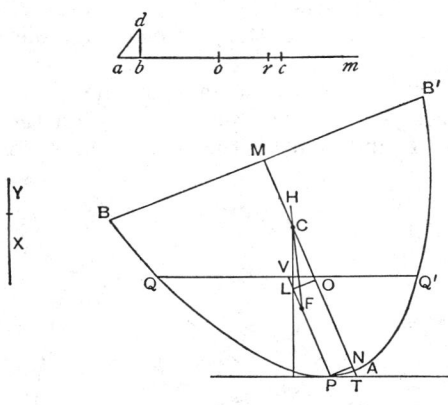

Let $am$ be taken equal to the axis $AM$, and let $c$ be a point on $am$ such that $ac = 2cm$. Measure $co$ along $ca$ equal to $\frac{1}{2}p$, and $or$ along $oc$ equal to $\frac{1}{3}ao$.

Let $X + Y$ be a straight line such that

(spec. gr. of solid) : (spec. gr. of fluid) $= (X+Y)^2 : am^2$,  ($\alpha$)

and suppose $X = 2Y$.

Now $ar = \frac{3}{2}ao = \frac{3}{2}(\frac{2}{3}am - \frac{1}{2}p)$
$= am - \frac{3}{4}p$
$= AM - \frac{3}{4}p$.

Therefore, by hypothesis,
$(X+Y)^2 : am^2 < ar^2 : am^2$,

whence $(X+Y) < ar$, and therefore $X < ao$.

Measure $ob$ along $oa$ equal to $X$, and draw $bd$ perpendicular to $ab$ and of such length that $bd^2 = \frac{1}{2}co \cdot ab$.  ($\beta$)
Join $ad$.

Now let the solid be placed in the fluid with its axis $AM$ inclined at an angle to the vertical. Through $AM$ draw a plane perpendicular to the surface of the fluid, and let this plane cut the paraboloid in the parabola $BAB'$ and the plane of the surface of the fluid in the chord $QQ'$ of the parabola.

Draw the tangent $PT$ parallel to $QQ'$, touching at $P$, and let $PV$ be the diameter bisecting $QQ'$ in $V$ (or the axis of the immersed portion of the solid), and $PN$ the ordinate from $P$.

Measure $AO$ along $AM$ equal to $ao$, and $OC$ along $OM$ equal to $oc$, and draw $OL$ perpendicular to $PV$.

I. Suppose the angle $OTP$ greater than the angle $dab$.

Thus $PN^2 : NT^2 > db^2 : ba^2$.
But $PN^2 : NT^2 = p : 4AN$
$= co : NT$,
and $db^2 : ba^2 = \frac{1}{2}co : ab$, by ($\beta$).
Therefore $NT < 2ab$,
or $AN < ab$,
whence $NO > bo$ (since $ao = AO$)
$> X$.

Now $(X+Y)^2 : am^2 =$ (spec. gr. of solid) : (spec. gr. of fluid)
$=$ (portion immersed) : (rest of solid)

$$= PV^2 : AM^2,$$
so that $\qquad X+Y=PV$
But $\qquad PL(=NO)>X$
$$>\tfrac{2}{3}(X+Y), \text{ since } X=2Y,$$
$$>\tfrac{2}{3}PV,$$
or $\qquad PV<\tfrac{3}{2}PL,$
and therefore $\qquad PL>2LV.$

Take a point $F$ on $PV$ so that $PF=2FV$, i.e. so that $F$ is the centre of gravity of the immersed portion of the solid.

Also $AC=ac=\tfrac{2}{3}am=\tfrac{2}{3}AM$, and therefore $C$ is the centre of gravity of the whole solid.

Join $FC$ and produce it to $H$, the centre of gravity of the portion of the solid above the surface.

Now, since $CO=\tfrac{1}{2}p$, $CL$ is perpendicular to the surface of the fluid; therefore so are the parallels to $CL$ through $F$ and $H$. But the force on the immersed portion acts upwards through $F$ and that on the rest of the solid downwards through $H$.

Therefore the solid will not rest but turn in the direction of diminishing the angle $MTP$.

II. Suppose the angle $OTP$ less than the angle $dab$. In this case, we shall have, instead of the above results, the following,
$$AN>ab,$$
$$NO<X.$$
Also $\qquad PV>\tfrac{3}{2}PL,$
and therefore $\qquad PL<2LV.$

Make $PF$ equal to $2FV$, so that $F$ is the centre of gravity of the immersed portion.

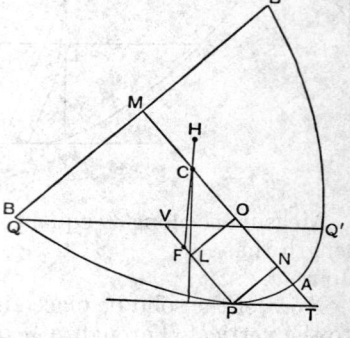

And, proceeding as before, we prove in this case that the solid will turn in the direction of *increasing* the angle $MTP$.

III. When the angle $MTP$ is equal to the angle $dab$, equalities replace inequalities in the results obtained, and $L$ is itself the centre of gravity of the immersed portion. Thus all the forces act in one straight line, the perpendicular $CL$; therefore there is equilibrium, and the solid will rest in the position described.

## Proposition 9

*Given a solid in the form of a right segment of a paraboloid of revolution whose axis $AM$ is greater than $\tfrac{3}{4}p$, but such that $AM : \tfrac{1}{2}p<15 : 4$, and whose specific gravity bears to that of a fluid a ratio greater than $\{AM^2-(AM-\tfrac{3}{4}p)^2\} : AM^2$, then, if the solid be placed in the fluid with its axis inclined at an angle to the vertical but so that its base is entirely below the surface, the solid will not return to the position in which its axis is vertical and will not remain in any position except that in which its axis makes with the surface of the fluid an angle equal to that described in the last proposition.*

Take $am$ equal to $AM$, and take $c$ on $am$ such that $ac=2cm$. Measure $co$ along $ca$ equal to $\tfrac{1}{2}p$, and $ar$ along $ac$ such that $ar=\tfrac{3}{2}ao$.

Let $X+Y$ be such a line that

(spec. gr. of solid) : (spec. gr. of fluid) = $\{am^2-(X+Y)^2\} : am^2$, and suppose $X=2Y$.

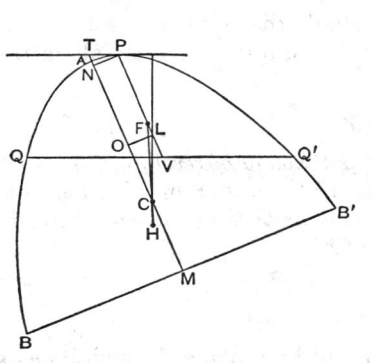

Now $ar = \frac{3}{2}ao$
$= \frac{3}{2}(\frac{2}{3}am - \frac{1}{2}p)$
$= AM - \frac{3}{4}p.$

Therefore, by hypothesis,
$am^2 - ar^2 : am^2 < \{am^2-(X+Y)^2\}: am^2$,
whence $X+Y < ar$,
and therefore $X < ao.$

Make $ob$ (measured along $oa$) equal to $X$, and draw $bd$ perpendicular to $ba$ and of such length that
$$bd^2 = \tfrac{1}{2}co \cdot ab.$$

Join $ad$.

Now suppose the solid placed as in the figure with its axis $AM$ inclined to the vertical. Let the plane through $AM$ perpendicular to the surface of the fluid cut the solid in the parabola $BAB'$ and the surface of the fluid in $QQ'$.

Let $PT$ be the tangent parallel to $QQ'$, $PV$ the diameter bisecting $QQ'$ or) the axis of the portion of the paraboloid above the surface), $PN$ the ordinate from $P$.

I. Suppose the angle $MTP$ greater than the angle $dab$. Let $AM$ be cut as before in $C$ and $O$ so that $AC=2CM$, $OC=\frac{1}{2}p$, and accordingly $AM$, $am$ are equally divided. Draw $OL$ perpendicular to $PV$.

Then, we have, as in the last proposition,
$$PN^2 : NT^2 > db^2 : ba^2,$$
whence $co : NT > \frac{1}{2}co : ab,$
and therefore $AN < ab.$
It follows that $NO > bo$
$> X.$

Again, since the specific gravity of the solid is to that of the fluid as the immersed portion of the solid to the whole,
$$AM^2-(X+Y)^2 : AM^2 = AM^2 - PV^2 : AM^2,$$
or $(X+Y)^2 : AM^2 = PV^2 : AM^2.$
That is, $X+Y = PV.$
And $PL$ (or $NO) > X$
$> \tfrac{2}{3}PV,$
so that $PL > 2LV.$

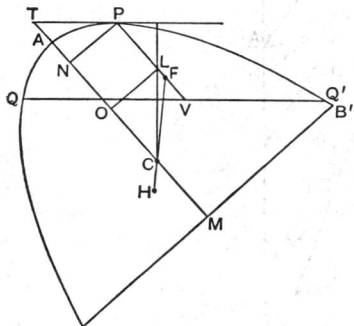

Take $F$ on $PV$ so that $PF=2FV$. Then $F$ is the centre of gravity of the portion of the solid above the surface.

Also $C$ is the centre of gravity of the whole solid. Join $FC$ and produce it to $H$, the centre of gravity of the immersed portion.

Then, since $CO=\tfrac{1}{2}p$, $CL$ is perpendicular to $PT$ and to the surface of the fluid; and the force acting on the immersed portion of the solid acts upwards along the parallel to $CL$ through $H$, while the weight of the rest of the solid acts downwards along the parallel to $CL$ through $F$.

Hence the solid will not rest but turn in the direction of diminishing the angle $MTP$.

II. Exactly as in the last proposition, we prove that, if the angle $MTP$ be less than the angle $dab$, the solid will not remain in its position but will turn in the direction of increasing the angle $MTP$.

III. If the angle $MTP$ is equal to the angle $dab$, the solid will rest in that position, because $L$ and $F$ will coincide, and all the forces will act along the one line $CL$.

## Proposition 10

*Given a solid in the form of a right segment of a paraboloid of revolution in which the axis $AM$ is of a length such that $AM : \frac{1}{2}p > 15 : 4$, and supposing the solid placed in a fluid of greater specific gravity so that its base is entirely above the surface of the fluid, to investigate the positions of rest.*

(Preliminary)

Suppose the segment of the paraboloid to be cut by a plane through its axis $AM$ in the parabolic segment $BAB_1$ of which $BB_1$ is the base.

Divide $AM$ at $C$ so that $AC = 2CM$, and measure $CK$ along $CA$ so that
$$AM : CK = 15 : 4, \qquad (\alpha)$$
whence, by the hypothesis, $CK > \frac{1}{2}p$.

Suppose $CO$ measured along $CA$ equal to $\frac{1}{2}p$, and take a point $R$ on $AM$ such that
$$MR = \tfrac{3}{2}CO.$$
Thus $AR = AM - MR$
$\phantom{Thus AR} = \tfrac{3}{2}(AC - CO)$
$\phantom{Thus AR} = \tfrac{3}{2}AO.$

Join $BA$, draw $KA_2$ perpendicular to $AM$ meeting $BA$ in $A_2$, bisect $BA$ in $A_3$, and draw $A_2M_2$, $A_3M_3$ parallel to $AM$ meeting $BM$ in $M_2$, $M_3$ respectively.

On $A_2M_2$, $A_3M_3$ as axes describe parabolic segments similar to the segment $BAB_1$. (It follows, by similar triangles, that $BM$ will be the base of the segment whose axis is $A_3M_3$ and $BB_2$ the base of that whose axis is $A_2M_2$, where $BB_2 = 2BM_2$.)

The parabola $BA_2B_2$ will then pass through $C$.

[For
$BM_2 : M_2M = BM_2 : A_2K$
$\phantom{BM_2 : M_2M} = KM : AK$

$$= CM + CK : AC - CK$$
$$= (\tfrac{1}{3} + \tfrac{4}{15})AM : (\tfrac{2}{3} - \tfrac{4}{15})AM$$
$$= 9 : 6 \qquad (\beta)$$
$$= MA : AC.$$

Thus $C$ is seen to be on the parabola $BA_2B_2$ by the converse of Prop. 4 of the *Quadrature of the Parabola*.]

Also, if a perpendicular to $AM$ be drawn from $O$, it will meet the parabola $BA_2B_2$ in two points, as $Q_2$, $P_2$. Let $Q_1Q_2Q_3D$ be drawn through $Q_2$ parallel to $AM$ meeting the parabolas $BAB_1$, $BA_3M$ respectively in $Q_1$, $Q_3$ and $BM$ in $D$; and let $P_1P_2P_3$ be the corresponding parallel to $AM$ through $P_2$. Let the tangents to the outer parabola at $P_1$, $Q_1$ meet $MA$ produced in $T_1$, $U$ respectively.

Then, since the three parabolic segments are similar and similarly situated, with their bases in the same straight line and having one common extremity, and since $Q_1Q_2Q_3D$ is a diameter common to all three segments, it follows that
$$Q_1Q_2 : Q_2Q_3 = (B_2B_1 : B_1B) \cdot (BM : MB_2).$$

Now $\qquad B_2B_1 : B_1B = MM_2 : BM \qquad$ (dividing by 2)
$\qquad\qquad\qquad = 2 : 5, \qquad$ by means of $(\beta)$ above.

And $\qquad BM : MB_2 = BM : (2BM_2 - BM)$
$\qquad\qquad\qquad = 5 : (6-5), \qquad$ by means of $(\beta)$,
$\qquad\qquad\qquad = 5 : 1.$

It follows that $\qquad Q_1Q_2 : Q_2Q_3 = 2 : 1,$
or $\qquad\qquad\qquad Q_1Q_2 = 2Q_2Q_3.$
Similarly $\qquad\qquad P_1P_2 = 2P_2P_3.$
Also, since $\qquad\qquad MR = \tfrac{3}{2}CO = \tfrac{3}{4}p,$
$\qquad\qquad\qquad AR = AM - MR$
$\qquad\qquad\qquad = AM - \tfrac{3}{4}p.$

(ENUNCIATION)

*If the segment of the paraboloid be placed in the fluid with its base entirely above the surface, then*

(I.) *if*
$$(spec.\ gr.\ of\ solid) : (spec.\ gr.\ of\ fluid) \not< AR^2 : AM^2$$
$$[\not< (AM - \tfrac{3}{4}p)^2 : AM^2],$$
*the solid will rest in the position in which its axis $AM$ is vertical;*

(II.) *if*
$$(spec.\ gr.\ of\ solid) : (spec.\ gr.\ of\ fluid) < AR^2 : AM^2$$
$$but > Q_1Q_3{}^2 : AM^2,$$
*the solid will not rest with its base touching the surface of the fluid in one point only, but in such a position that its base does not touch the surface at any point and its axis makes with the surface an angle greater than $U$;*

(III. a) *if*
$$(spec.\ gr.\ of\ solid) : (spec.\ gr.\ of\ fluid) = Q_1Q_3{}^2 : AM^2,$$
*the solid will rest and remain in the position in which the base touches the surface of the fluid at one point only and the axis makes with the surface an angle equal to $U$;*

(III. b) *if*
$$(spec.\ gr.\ of\ solid) : (spec.\ gr.\ of\ fluid) = P_1P_3{}^2 : AM^2,$$
*the solid will rest with its base touching the surface of the fluid at one point only and with its axis inclined to the surface at an angle equal to $T_1$;*

(IV.) *if*
$$(\text{spec. gr. of solid}) : (\text{spec. gr. of fluid}) > P_1P_3{}^2 : AM^2$$
$$\text{but} < Q_1Q_3{}^2 : AM^2,$$
*the solid will rest and remain in a position with its base more submerged;*

(V.) *if*
$$(\text{spec. gr. of solid}) : (\text{spec. gr. of fluid}) < P_1P_3{}^2 : AM^2,$$
*the solid will rest in a position in which its axis is inclined to the surface of the fluid at an angle less than $T_1$, but so that the base does not even touch the surface at one point.*

(PROOF)

(I.) Since $AM > \tfrac{3}{4}p$, and
$$(\text{spec. gr. of solid}) : (\text{spec. gr. of fluid}) \not< (AM - \tfrac{3}{4}p)^2 : AM^2,$$
it follows, by Prop. 4, that the solid will be in stable equilibrium with its axis vertical.

(II.) In this case
$$(\text{spec. gr. of solid}) : (\text{spec. gr. of fluid}) < AR^2 : AM^2$$
$$\text{but} > Q_1Q_3{}^2 : AM^2.$$

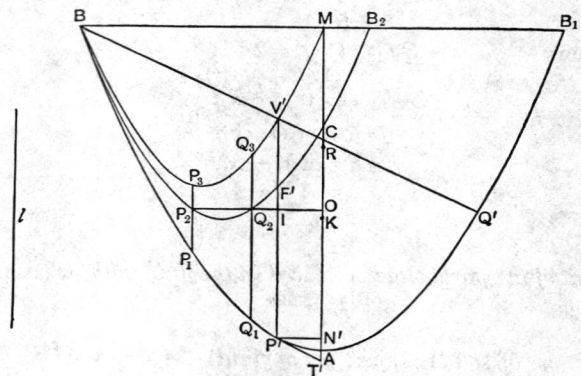

Suppose the ratio of the specific gravities to be equal to $l^2 : AM^2$, so that
$$l < AR \text{ but} > Q_1Q_3.$$

Place $P'V'$ between the two parabolas $BAB_1$, $BP_3 Q_3 M$ equal to $l$ and parallel to $AM$; and let $P'V'$ meet the intermediate parabola in $F'$.

Then, by the same proof as before, we obtain
$$P'F' = 2F'V'.$$

Let $P'T'$, the tangent at $P'$ to the outer parabola, meet $MA$ in $T'$, and let $P'N'$ be the ordinate at $P'$.

Join $BV'$ and produce it to meet the outer parabola in $Q'$. Let $OQ_2P_2$ meet $P'V'$ in $I$.

Now, since, in two similar and similarly situated parabolic segments with bases $BM$, $BB_1$ in the same straight line, $BV'$, $BQ'$ are drawn making the same angle with the bases,
$$BV' : BQ' = BM : BB_1$$
$$= 1 : 2,$$
so that
$$BV' = V'Q'.$$

Suppose the segment of the paraboloid placed in the fluid, as described, with its axis inclined at an angle to the vertical, and with its base touching the surface at one point $B$ only. Let the solid be cut by a plane through the axis and perpendicular to the surface of the fluid, and let the plane intersect the solid in the parabolic segment $BAB'$ and the plane of the surface of the fluid in $BQ$.

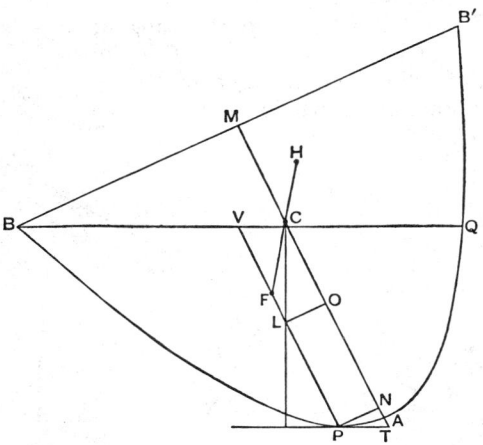

Take the points $C, O$ on $AM$ as before described. Draw the tangent parallel to $BQ$ touching the parabola in $P$ and meeting $AM$ in $T$; and let $PV$ be the diameter bisecting $BQ$ (i.e. the axis of the immersed portion of the solid).

Then $\quad l^2 : AM^2 = $ (spec. gr. of solid) : (spec. gr. of fluid)
$\quad\quad\quad = $ (portion immersed) : (whole solid)
$\quad\quad\quad = PV^2 : AM^2$,
whence $\quad\quad P'V' = l = PV$.

Thus the segments in the two figures, namely $BP'Q'$, $BPQ$, are equal and similar.

Therefore $\quad\quad\quad \angle PTN = \angle P'T'N'$.
Also $\quad\quad\quad AT = AT', AN = AN', PN = P'N'$.

Now, in the first figure, $P'I < 2IV'$.

Therefore, if $OL$ be perpendicular to $PV$ in the second figure,
$$PL < 2LV.$$

Take $F$ on $LV$ so that $PF = 2FV$, i.e. so that $F$ is the centre of gravity of the immersed portion of the solid. And $C$ is the centre of gravity of the whole solid. Join $FC$ and produce it to $H$, the centre of gravity of the portion above the surface.

Now, since $CO = \frac{1}{2}p$, $CL$ is perpendicular to the tangent at $P$ and to the surface of the fluid. Thus, as before, we prove that the solid will not rest with $B$ touching the surface, but will turn in the direction of increasing the angle $PTN$.

Hence, in the position of rest, the axis $AM$ must make with the surface of the fluid an angle greater than the angle $U$ which the tangent at $Q_1$ makes with $AM$.

(III. a) In this case
(spec. gr. of solid) : (spec. gr. of fluid) $= Q_1Q_3^2 : AM^2$.

Let the segment of the paraboloid be placed in the fluid so that its base nowhere touches the surface of the fluid, and its axis is inclined at an angle to the vertical.

Let the plane through $AM$ perpendicular to the surface of the fluid cut the paraboloid in the parabola $BAB'$ and the plane of the surface of the fluid in $QQ'$. Let $PT$ be the tangent parallel to $QQ'$, $PV$ the diameter bisecting $QQ'$, $PN$ the ordinate at $P$.

Divide $AM$ as before at $C$, $O$.

In the other figure let $Q_1N'$ be the ordinate at $Q_1$. Join $BQ_3$ and produce it to meet the outer parabola in $q$. Then $BQ_3 = Q_3q$, and the tangent $Q_1U$ is parallel to $Bq$. Now

$$Q_1Q_3{}^2 : AM^2 = \text{(spec. gr. of solid)} : \text{(spec. gr. of fluid)}$$
$$= \text{(portion immersed)} : \text{(whole solid)}$$
$$= PV^2 : AM^2.$$

Therefore $Q_1Q_3 = PV$; and the segments $QPQ'$, $BQ_1q$ of the paraboloid are equal in volume. And the base of one passes through $B$, while the base of the other passes through $Q$, a point nearer to $A$ than $B$ is.

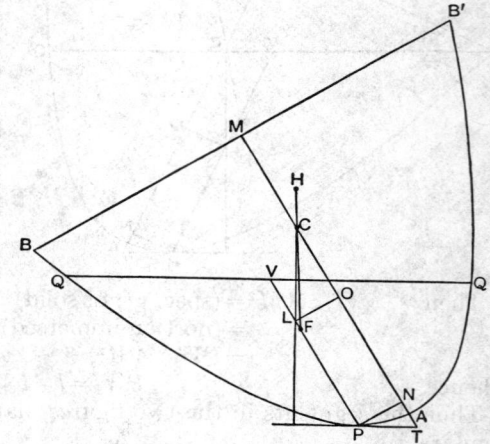

It follows that the angle between $QQ'$ and $BB'$ is less than the angle $B_1Bq$.

Therefore
$$\angle U < \angle PTN,$$
whence $AN' > AN$, and therefore
$$N'O (\text{or } Q_1Q_2) < PL,$$
where $OL$ is perpendicular to $PV$.

It follows, since $Q_1Q_2 = 2Q_2Q_3$, that
$$PL > 2LV.$$

Therefore $F$, the centre of gravity of the immersed portion of the solid, is between $P$ and $L$, while, as before, $CL$ is perpendicular to the surface of the fluid.

Producing $FC$ to $H$, the centre of gravity of the portion of the solid above the surface, we see that the solid must turn in the direction of diminishing the angle $PTN$ until one point $B$ of the base just touches the surface of the fluid.

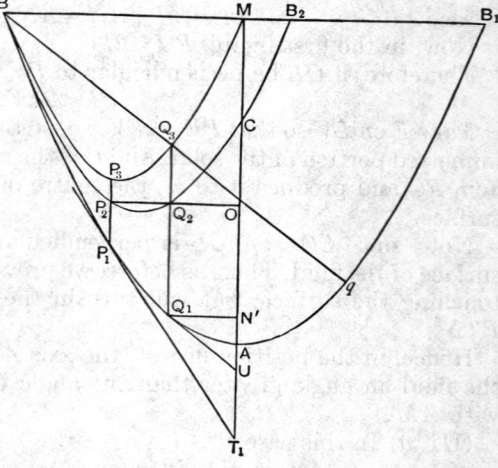

When this is the case, we shall have a segment $BPQ$ equal and similar to the segment $BQ_1q$, the angle $PTN$ will be equal to the angle $U$, and $AN$ will be equal to $AN'$.

Hence in this case $PL = 2LV$, and $F$, $L$ coincide, so that $F$, $C$, $H$ are all in one vertical straight line.

Thus the paraboloid will remain in the position in which one point $B$ of the base touches the surface of the fluid, and the axis makes with the surface an angle equal to $U$.

(III. b) In the case where
    (spec. gr. of solid) : (spec. gr. of fluid) $= P_1P_3^2 : AM^2$,
we can prove in the same way that, if the solid be placed in the fluid so that its axis is inclined to the vertical and its base does not anywhere touch the surface of the fluid, the solid will take up and rest in the position in which one point only of the base touches the surface, and the axis is inclined to it at an angle equal to $T_1$ (in the figure on p. 552).

(IV.) In this case
    (spec. gr. of solid) : (spec. gr. of fluid) $> P_1P_3^2 : AM^2$
                                             but $< Q_1Q_3^2 : AM^2$.

Suppose the ratio to be equal to $l^2 : AM^2$, so that $l$ is greater than $P_1P_3$ but less than $Q_1Q_3$.

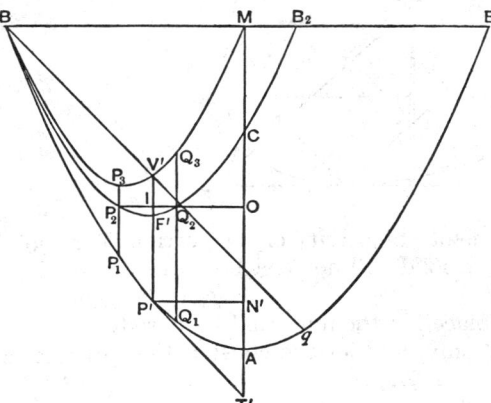

Place $P'V'$ between the parabolas $BP_1Q_1$, $BP_3Q_3$ so that $P'V'$ is equal to $l$ and parallel to $AM$, and let $P'V'$ meet the intermediate parabola in $F'$ and $OQ_2P_2$ in $I$.

Join $BV'$ and produce it to meet the outer parabola in $q$.

Then, as before, $BV' = V'q$, and accordingly the tangent $P'T'$ at $P'$ is parallel to $Bq$. Let $P'N'$ be the ordinate of $P'$.

1. Now let the segment be placed in the fluid, *first*, with its axis so inclined to the vertical that its base does not anywhere touch the surface of the fluid.

Let the plane through $AM$ perpendicular to the surface of the fluid cut the paraboloid in the parabola $BAB'$ and the plane of the surface of the fluid in $QQ'$. Let $PT$ be the tangent parallel to $QQ'$, $PV$ the diameter bisecting $QQ'$. Divide $AM$ at $C$, $O$ as before, and draw $OL$ perpendicular to $PV$.

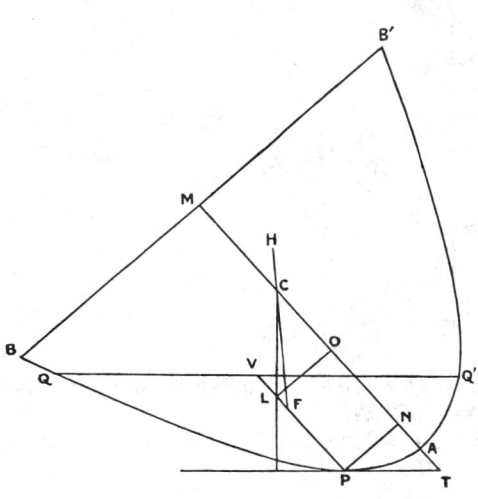

Then, as before, we have $PV = l = P'V'$.

Thus the segments $BP'q$, $QPQ'$ of the paraboloid are equal in volume; and it follows that the angle between $QQ'$ and $BB'$ is less than the angle $B_1Bq$.

Therefore
$$\angle P'T'N' < \angle PTN,$$
and hence $AN' > AN$,
so that $NO > N'O$,
i.e. $PL > P'I$
        $> P'F'$, a fortiori.

Thus $PL > 2LV$, so that $F$, the centre of gravity of the immersed portion of the solid, is between $L$ and $P$, while $CL$ is perpendicular to the surface of the fluid.

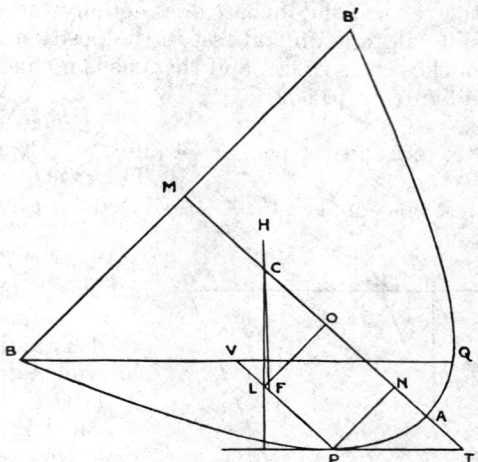

If then we produce $FC$ to $H$, the centre of gravity of the portion of the solid above the surface, we prove that the solid will not rest but turn in the direction of diminishing the angle $PTN$.

2. Next let the paraboloid be so placed in the fluid that its base touches the surface of the fluid at one point $B$ only, and let the construction proceed as before.

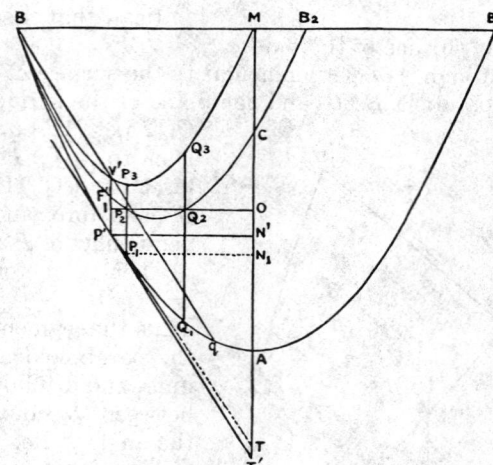

Then $PV = P'V'$, and the segments $BPQ$, $BP'q$ are equal and similar, so that
$$\angle PTN = \angle P'T'N'.$$
It follows that $\qquad AN = AN', \ NO = N'O,$
and therefore $\qquad P'I = PL,$
whence $\qquad PL > 2LV.$

Thus $F$ again lies between $P$ and $L$, and, as before, the paraboloid will turn in the direction of diminishing the angle $PTN$, i.e. so that the base will be more submerged.

(V.) In this case
$$\text{(spec. gr. of solid)} : \text{(spec. gr. of fluid)} < P_1P_3{}^2 : AM^2.$$
If then the ratio is equal to $l^2 : AM^2$, $l < P_1P_3$. Place $P'V'$ between the parabolas $BP_1Q_1$ and $BP_3Q_3$ equal in length to $l$ and parallel to $AM$. Let $P'V'$ meet the intermediate parabola in $F'$ and $OP_2$ in $I$.

Join $BV'$ and produce it to meet the outer parabola in $q$. Then, as before, $BV' = V'q$, and the tangent $P'T'$ is parallel to $Bq$.

1. Let the paraboloid be so placed in the fluid that its base touches the surface at one point only.

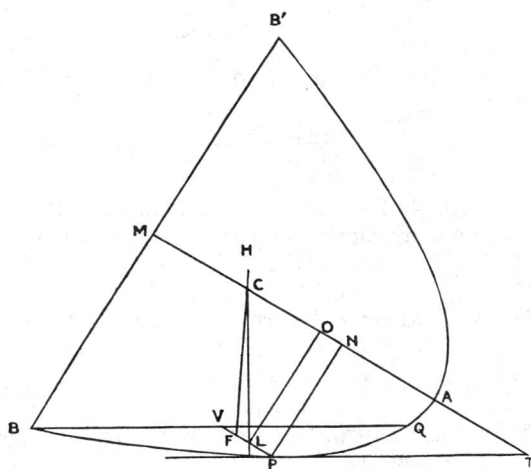

Let the plane through $AM$ perpendicular to the surface of the fluid cut the paraboloid in the parabolic section $BAB'$ and the plane of the surface of the fluid in $BQ$.

Making the usual construction, we find
$$PV = l = P'V',$$
and the segments $BPQ$, $BP_1q$ are equal and similar.

Therefore $\qquad \angle PTN = \angle P'T'N'$,
and $\qquad AN = AN'$, $N'O = NO$.
Therefore $\qquad PL = P'I$,
whence it follows that $\qquad PL < 2LV$.

Thus $F$, the centre of gravity of the immersed portion of the solid, lies between $L$ and $V$, while $CL$ is perpendicular to the surface of the fluid.

Producing $FC$ to $H$, the centre of gravity of the portion above the surface, we prove, as usual, that there will not be rest, but the solid will turn in the direction of increasing the angle $PTN$, so that the base will not anywhere touch the surface.

2. *The solid will however rest in a position where its axis makes with the surface of the fluid an angle less than* $T_1$.

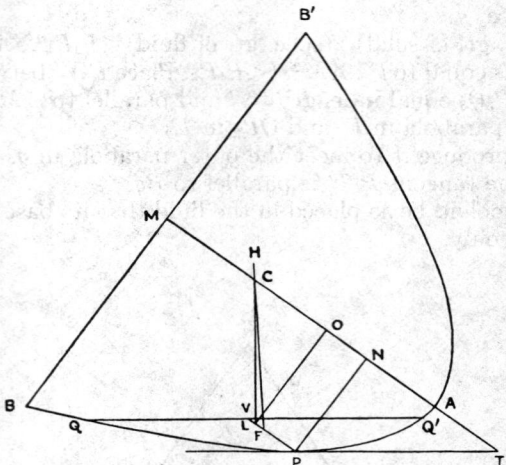

For let it be placed so that the angle $PTN$ is not less than $T_1$.
Then, with the same construction as before, $PV = l = P'V'$.
And, since
$$\angle T \not< \angle T_1,$$
$$AN \not> AN_1,$$
and therefore $NO \not< N_1O$, where $P_1N_1$ is the ordinate of $P_1$.
Hence $PL \not< P_1P_2$.
But $P_1P_2 > P'F'$.
Therefore $PL > \tfrac{2}{3}PV$,
so that $F$, the centre of gravity of the immersed portion of the solid, lies between $P$ and $L$.

Thus the solid will turn in the direction of diminishing the angle $PTN$ until that angle becomes less than $T_1$.

# BOOK OF LEMMAS

### PROPOSITION 1

*If two circles touch at A, and if BD, EF be parallel diameters in them, ADF is a straight line.*

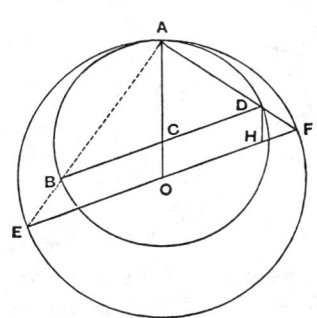

Let $O$, $C$ be the centres of the circles, and let $OC$ be joined and produced to $A$. Draw $DH$ parallel to $AO$ meeting $OF$ in $H$.

Then, since $\quad OH = CD = CA$,
and $\quad OF = OA$,
we have, by subtraction, $\quad HF = CO = DH$.
Therefore $\quad \angle HDF = \angle HFD$.

Thus both the triangles $CAD$, $HDF$ are isosceles, and the third angles $ACD$, $DHF$ in each are equal. Therefore the equal angles in each are equal to one another, and
$$\angle ADC = \angle DFH.$$
Add to each the angle $CDF$, and it follows that
$$\angle ADC + \angle CDF = \angle CDF + \angle DFH$$
$$= \text{(two right angles)}.$$

Hence $ADF$ is a straight line.

The same proof applies if the circles touch externally.

### PROPOSITION 2

*Let AB be the diameter of a semicircle, and let the tangents to it at B and at any other point D on it meet in T. If now DE be drawn perpendicular to AB, and if AT, DE meet in F,*
$$DF = FE.$$

Produce $AD$ to meet $BT$ produced in $H$. Then the angle $ADB$ in the semicircle is right; therefore the angle $BDH$ is also right. And $TB$, $TD$ are equal.

Therefore $T$ is the centre of the semicircle on $BH$ as diameter, which passes through $D$.

Hence $\quad HT = TB.$

And, since $DE$, $HB$ are parallel, it follows that $DF = FE$.

## Proposition 3

*Let P be any point on a segment of a circle whose base is AB, and let PN be perpendicular to AB. Take D on AB so that AN = ND. If now PQ be an arc equal to the arc PA, and BQ be joined,*

*BQ, BD shall be equal.*

Join PA, PQ, PD, DQ.
Then, since the arcs PA, PQ are equal,
$$PA = PQ.$$
But, since AN = ND, and the angles at N are right,
$$PA = PD.$$
Therefore $\quad PQ = PD,$
and $\quad\angle PQD = \angle PDQ.$

Now, since A, P, Q, B are concyclic,
$$\angle PAD + \angle PQB = \text{(two right angles)},$$
whence $\quad\angle PDA + \angle PQB = \text{(two right angles)}$
$$= \angle PDA + \angle PDB.$$
Therefore $\quad\angle PQB = \angle PDB;$
and, since the parts, the angles PQD, PDQ, are equal,
$$\angle BQD = \angle BDQ,$$
and $\quad BQ = BD.$

## Proposition 4

*If AB be the diameter of a semicircle and N any point on AB, and if semicircles be described within the first semicircle and having AN, BN as diameters respectively, the figure included between the circumferences of the three semicircles is "what Archimedes called an ἄρβηλος";[1] and its area is equal to the circle on PN as diameter, where PN is perpendicular to AB and meets the original semicircle in P.*

For
$$AB^2 = AN^2 + NB^2 + 2AN \cdot NB$$
$$= AN^2 + NB^2 + 2PN^2.$$
But circles (or semicircles) are to one another as the squares of their radii (or diameters).

Hence
(semicircle on AB) = (sum of semicircles on AN, NB) + 2(semicircle on PN).

That is, the circle on PN as diameter is equal to the difference between the semicircle on AB and the sum of the semicircles on AN, NB, i.e. is equal to the area of the ἄρβηλος.

## Proposition 5

*Let AB be the diameter of a semicircle, C any point on AB, and CD perpendicular to it, and let semicircles be described within the first semicircle and having AC, CB as diameters. Then, if two circles be drawn touching CD on different sides and each touching two of the semicircles, the circles so drawn will be equal.*

Let one of the circles touch CD at E, the semicircle on AB in F, and the semicircle on AC in G.

[1] ἄρβηλος is literally "a shoemaker's knife."

Draw the diameter $EH$ of the circle, which will accordingly be perpendicular to $CD$ and therefore parallel to $AB$.

Join $FH$, $HA$, and $FE$, $EB$. Then, by Prop. 1, $FHA$, $FEB$ are both straight lines, since $EH$, $AB$ are parallel.

For the same reason $AGE$, $CGH$ are straight lines.

Let $AF$ produced meet $CD$ in $D$, and let $AE$ produced meet the outer semicircle in $I$. Join $BI$, $ID$.

Then, since the angles $AFB$, $ACD$ are right, the straight lines $AD$, $AB$ are such that the perpendiculars on each from the extremity of the other meet in the point $E$. Therefore, by the properties of triangles, $AE$ is perpendicular to the line joining $B$ to $D$.

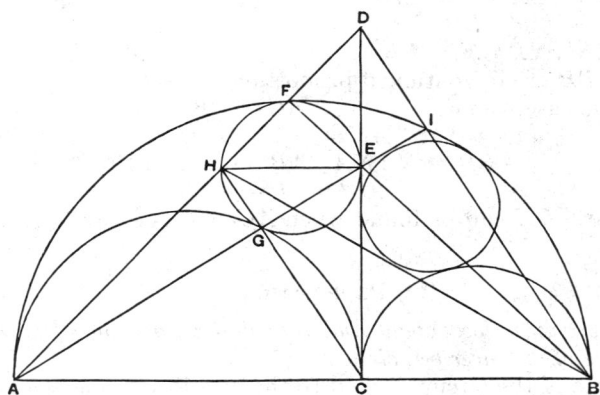

But $AE$ is perpendicular to $BI$.

Therefore $BID$ is a straight line.

Now, since the angles at $G$, $I$ are right, $CH$ is parallel to $BD$.

Therefore
$$AB : BC = AD : DH$$
$$= AC : HE,$$
so that
$$AC \cdot CB = AB \cdot HE.$$

In like manner, if $d$ is the diameter of the other circle, we can prove that
$$AC \cdot CB = AB \cdot d.$$

Therefore $d = HE$, and the circles are equal.

## Proposition 6

Let $AB$, the diameter of a semicircle, be divided at $C$ so that $AC = \frac{3}{2}CB$ [or in any ratio]. Describe semicircles within the first semicircle and on $AC$, $CB$ as diameters, and suppose a circle drawn touching all three semicircles. If $GH$ be the diameter of this circle, to find the relation between $GH$ and $AB$.

Let $GH$ be that diameter of the circle which is parallel to $AB$, and let the circle touch the semicircles on $AB$, $AC$, $CB$ in $D$, $E$, $F$ respectively.

Join $AG$, $GD$ and $BH$, $HD$. Then, by Prop. 1, $AGD$, $BHD$ are straight lines.

For a like reason $AEH$, $BFG$ are straight lines, as also are $CEG$, $CFH$.

Let $AD$ meet the semicircle on $AC$ in $I$, and let $BD$ meet the semicircle on $CB$ in $K$. Join $CI$, $CK$ meeting $AE$, $BF$ respectively in $L$, $M$, and let $GL$, $HM$ produced meet $AB$ in $N$, $P$ respectively.

Now, in the triangle $AGC$, the perpendiculars from $A$, $C$ on the opposite sides meet in $L$. Therefore, by the properties of triangles, $GLN$ is perpendicular to $AC$.

Similarly $HMP$ is perpendicular to $CB$.

Again, since the angles at $I$, $K$, $D$ are right, $CK$ is parallel to $AD$, and $CI$ to $BD$.

Therefore $AC : CB = AL : LH$
$\qquad\qquad\qquad = AN : NP$,
and $\qquad BC : CA = BM : MG$
$\qquad\qquad\qquad = BP : PN$.

Hence $\qquad AN : NP = NP : PB$,
or $AN$, $NP$, $PB$ are in continued proportion.

Now, in the case where $\qquad AC = \tfrac{3}{2}CB$,
$\qquad\qquad\qquad AN = \tfrac{3}{2}NP = \tfrac{9}{4}PB$,
whence $\qquad BP : PN : NA : AB = 4 : 6 : 9 : 19$.

Therefore $\qquad GH = NP = \tfrac{6}{19}AB$.

And similarly $GH$ can be found when $AC : CB$ is equal to any other given ratio.

## Proposition 7

*If circles be circumscribed about and inscribed in a square, the circumscribed circle is double of the inscribed circle.*

For the ratio of the circumscribed to the inscribed circle is equal to that of the square on the diagonal to the square itself, i.e. to the ratio $2 : 1$.

## Proposition 8

*If $AB$ be any chord of a circle whose centre is $O$, and if $AB$ be produced to $C$ so that $BC$ is equal to the radius; if further $CO$ meet the circle in $D$ and be produced to meet the circle a second time in $E$, the arc $AE$ will be equal to three times the arc $BD$.*

Draw the chord $EF$ parallel to $AB$, and join $OB$, $OF$.

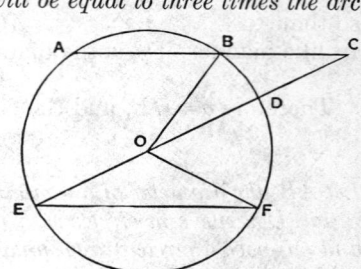

Then, since the angles $OEF$, $OFE$ are equal,
$\angle COF = 2\angle OEF$
$\qquad = 2\angle BCO$, by parallels,
$\qquad = 2\angle BOD$, since $BC = BO$.

Therefore
$\angle BOF = 3\angle BOD$,
so that the arc $BF$ is equal to three times the arc $BD$.

Hence the arc $AE$, which is equal to the arc $BF$, is equal to three times the arc $BD$.

## Proposition 9

*If in a circle two chords $AB$, $CD$ which do not pass through the centre intersect at right angles, then*

$(\text{arc } AD)+(\text{arc } CB)=(\text{arc } AC)+(\text{arc } DB).$

Let the chords intersect at $O$, and draw the diameter $EF$ parallel to $AB$ intersecting $CD$ in $H$. $EF$ will thus bisect $CD$ at right angles in $H$, and

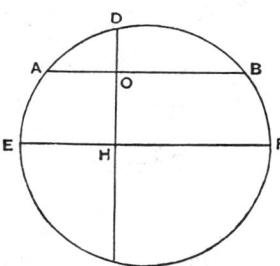

$$(\text{arc } ED) = (\text{arc } EC).$$

Also $EDF$, $ECF$ are semicircles, while
$$(\text{arc } ED) = (\text{arc } EA)+(\text{arc } AD).$$
Therefore
(sum of arcs $CF$, $EA$, $AD$) = (arc of a semicircle).
And the arcs $AE$, $BF$ are equal.
Therefore
$$(\text{arc } CB)+(\text{arc } AD) = (\text{arc of a semicircle}).$$

Hence the remainder of the circumference, the sum of the arcs $AC$, $DB$, is also equal to a semicircle; and the proposition is proved.

PROPOSITION 10

*Suppose that $TA$, $TB$ are two tangents to a circle, while $TC$ cuts it. Let $BD$ be the chord through $B$ parallel to $TC$, and let $AD$ meet $TC$ in $E$. Then, if $EH$ be drawn perpendicular to $BD$, it will bisect it in $H$.*

Let $AB$ meet $TC$ in $F$, and join $BE$.

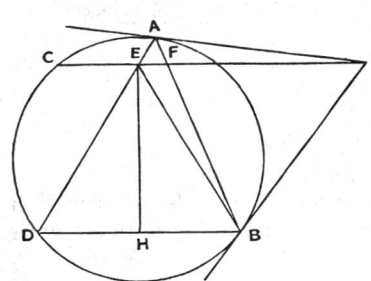

Now the angle $TAB$ is equal to the angle in the alternate segment, i.e.
$$\angle TAB = \angle ADB$$
$$= \angle AET, \text{ by parallels.}$$

Hence the triangles $EAT$, $AFT$ have one angle equal and another (at $T$) common. They are therefore similar, and
$$FT : AT = AT : ET.$$
Therefore $\quad ET \cdot TF = TA^2$
$$= TB^2.$$

It follows that the triangles $EBT$, $BFT$ are similar.

Therefore $\quad \angle TEB = \angle TBF$
$$= \angle TAB.$$

But the angle $TEB$ is equal to the angle $EBD$, and the angle $TAB$ was proved equal to the angle $EDB$.

Therefore $\quad\quad\quad\quad \angle EDB = \angle EBD.$

And the angles at $H$ are right angles.

It follows that $\quad\quad\quad BH = HD.$

PROPOSITION 11

*If two chords $AB$, $CD$ in a circle intersect at right angles in a point $O$, not being the centre, then*
$$AO^2+BO^2+CO^2+DO^2 = (\text{diameter})^2.$$

Draw the diameter $CE$, and join $AC$, $CB$, $AD$, $BE$.

Then the angle $CAO$ is equal to the angle $CEB$ in the same segment, and the angles $AOC$, $EBC$ are right; therefore the triangles $AOC$, $EBC$ are similar, and

$$\angle ACO = \angle ECB.$$

It follows that the subtended arcs, and therefore the chords $AD$, $BE$, are equal.

Thus $\quad (AO^2 + DO^2) + (BO^2 + CO^2) = AD^2 + BC^2$
$$= BE^2 + BC^2$$
$$= CE^2.$$

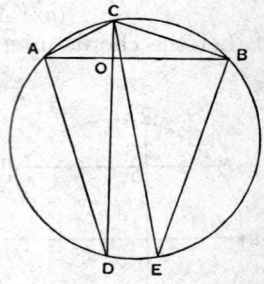

## Proposition 12

*If $AB$ be the diameter of a semicircle, and $TP$, $TQ$ the tangents to it from any point $T$, and if $AQ$, $BP$ be joined meeting in $R$, then $TR$ is perpendicular to $AB$.*

Let $TR$ produced meet $AB$ in $M$, and join $PA$, $QB$.

Since the angle $APB$ is right,
$$\angle PAB + \angle PBA = \text{(a right angle)}$$
$$= \angle AQB.$$

Add to each side the angle $RBQ$, and
$$\angle PAB + \angle QBA = \text{(exterior)} \angle PRQ.$$

But
$\angle TPR = \angle PAB$, and $\angle TQR = \angle QBA$, in the alternate segments;
therefore $\quad \angle TPR + \angle TQR = \angle PRQ.$

It follows from this that
$$TP = TQ = TR.$$

[For, if $PT$ be produced to $O$ so that $TO = TQ$, we have
$$\angle TOQ = \angle TQO.$$
And, by hypothesis, $\quad \angle PRQ = \angle TPR + TQR.$
By addition, $\quad \angle POQ + \angle PRQ = \angle TPR + OQR.$

It follows that, in the quadrilateral $OPRQ$, the opposite angles are together equal to two right angles. Therefore a circle will go round $OPQR$, and $T$ is its centre, because $TP = TO = TQ$. Therefore $TR = TP$.]

Thus $\quad \angle TRP = \angle TPR = \angle PAM.$

Adding to each the angle $PRM$,
$$\angle PAM + \angle PRM = \angle TRP + \angle PRM$$
$$= \text{(two right angles)}.$$

Therefore $\quad \angle APR + \angle AMR = \text{(two right angles)},$
whence $\quad \angle AMR = \text{(a right angle)}.$

## Proposition 13

*If a diameter $AB$ of a circle meet any chord $CD$, not a diameter, in $E$, and if $AM$, $BN$ be drawn perpendicular to $CD$, then*
$$CN = DM.$$

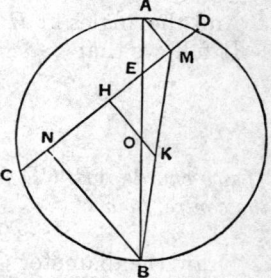

Let $O$ be the centre of the circle, and $OH$ perpendicular to $CD$. Join $BM$, and produce $HO$ to meet $BM$ in $K$.

Then $\quad CH = HD.$

And, by parallels, since $\quad BO = OA$,
$$BK = KM.$$
Therefore $\quad NH = HM.$
Accordingly $\quad CN = DM.$

## Proposition 14

Let $ACB$ be a semicircle on $AB$ as diameter, and let $AD$, $BE$ be equal lengths measured along $AB$ from $A$, $B$ respectively. On $AD$, $BE$ as diameters describe semicircles on the side towards $C$, and on $DE$ as diameter a semicircle on the opposite side. Let the perpendicular to $AB$ through $O$, the centre of the first semicircle, meet the opposite semicircles in $C$, $F$ respectively.

Then shall the area of the figure bounded by the circumferences of all the semicircles be equal to the area of the circle on $CF$ as diameter.

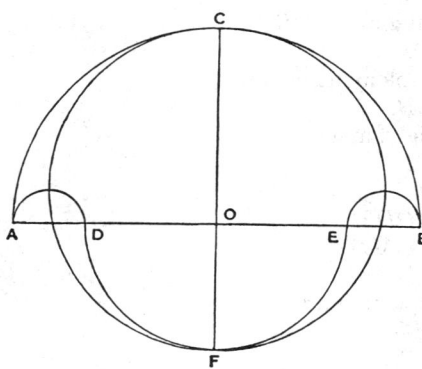

By Eucl. II. 10, since $ED$ is bisected at $O$ and produced to $A$,
$$EA^2 + AD^2 = 2(EO^2 + OA^2),$$
and $\quad CF = OA + OE = EA.$
Therefore
$$AB^2 + DE^2 = 4(EO^2 + OA^2) = 2(CF^2 + AD^2).$$

But circles (and therefore semicircles) are to one another as the squares on their radii (or diameters). Therefore
(sum of semicircles on $AB$, $DE$)
$=$ (circle on $CF$) + (sum of semicircles on $AD$, $BE$).

Therefore
(area of "salinon") = (area of circle on $CF$ as diam.).

## Proposition 15

Let $AB$ be the diameter of a circle, $AC$ a side of an inscribed regular pentagon, $D$ the middle point of the arc $AC$. Join $CD$ and produce it to meet $BA$ produced in $E$; join $AC$, $DB$ meeting in $F$, and draw $FM$ perpendicular to $AB$. Then
$$EM = (\text{radius of circle}).$$
Let $O$ be the centre of the circle, and join $DA$, $DM$, $DO$, $CB$.

Now $\quad \angle ABC = \frac{2}{5}(\text{right angle}),$
and $\quad \angle ABD = \angle DBC = \frac{1}{5}(\text{right angle}),$
whence $\quad \angle AOD = \frac{2}{5}(\text{right angle}).$

Further, the triangles $FCB$, $FMB$ are equal in all respects.

Therefore, in the triangles $DCB$, $DMB$, the sides $CB$, $MB$ being equal and $BD$ common, while the angles $CBD$, $MBD$ are equal,
$$\angle BCD = \angle BMD = \tfrac{6}{5}(\text{right angle}).$$
But $\quad \angle BCD + \angle BAD = (\text{two right angles})$
$$= \angle BAD + \angle DAE$$
$$= \angle BMD + \angle DMA,$$
so that $\quad \angle DAE = \angle BCD,$
and $\quad \angle BAD = \angle AMD.$
Therefore $\quad AD = MD.$

Now, in the triangle $DMO$,
$$\angle MOD = \tfrac{2}{5}(\text{right angle}),$$
$$\angle DMO = \tfrac{6}{5}(\text{right angle}).$$

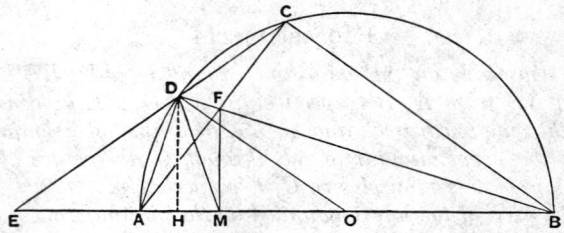

Therefore $\qquad \angle ODM = \tfrac{2}{5}(\text{right angle}) = AOD;$
whence $\qquad\qquad OM = MD.$
Again $\qquad\qquad \angle EDA = (\text{supplement of } ADC)$
$\qquad\qquad\qquad\qquad = \angle CBA$
$\qquad\qquad\qquad\qquad = \tfrac{2}{5}(\text{right angle})$
$\qquad\qquad\qquad\qquad = \angle ODM.$

Therefore, in the triangles $EDA$, $ODM$,
$$\angle EDA = \angle ODM,$$
$$\angle EAD = \angle OMD,$$
and the sides $AD$, $MD$ are equal.

Hence the triangles are equal in all respects, and
$$EA = MO.$$
Therefore $\qquad\qquad EM = AO.$

Moreover $DE = DO$; and it follows that, since $DE$ is equal to the side of an inscribed hexagon, and $DC$ is the side of an inscribed decagon, $EC$ is divided at $D$ in extreme and mean ratio [i.e. $EC : ED = ED : DC$]; "and this is proved in the book of the *Elements*." [Eucl. XIII. 9: "If the side of the hexagon and the side of the decagon inscribed in the same circle be put together, the whole straight line is divided in extreme and mean ratio, and the greater segment is the side of the hexagon."]

# THE METHOD TREATING OF MECHANICAL PROBLEMS

"Archimedes to Eratosthenes greeting.

"I sent you on a former occasion some of the theorems discovered by me, merely writing out the enunciations and inviting you to discover the proofs, which at the moment I did not give. The enunciations of the theorems which I sent were as follows:

1. "If in a right prism with a parallelogrammic base a cylinder be inscribed which has its bases in the opposite parallelograms,[1] and its sides [i.e. four generators] on the remaining planes (faces) of the prism, and if through the centre of the circle which is the base of the cylinder and (through) one side of the square in the plane opposite to it a plane be drawn, the plane so drawn will cut off from the cylinder a segment which is bounded by two planes and the surface of the cylinder, one of the two planes being the plane which has been drawn and the other the plane in which the base of the cylinder is, and the surface being that which is between the said planes; and the segment cut off from the cylinder is one sixth part of the whole prism.

2. "If in a cube a cylinder be inscribed which has its bases in the opposite parallelograms[2] and touches with its surface the remaining four planes (faces), and if there also be inscribed in the same cube another cylinder which has its bases in other parallelograms and touches with its surface the remaining four planes (faces), then the figure bounded by the surfaces of the cylinders, which is within both cylinders, is two-thirds of the whole cube.

"Now these theorems differ in character from those communicated before; for we compared the figures then in question, conoids and spheroids and segments of them, in respect to size, with figures of cones and cylinders: but none of those figures have yet been found to be equal to a solid figure bounded by planes; whereas each of the present figures bounded by two planes and surfaces of cylinders is found to be equal to one of the solid figures which are bounded by planes. The proofs then of these theorems I have written in this book and now send to you. Seeing moreover in you, as I say, an earnest student, a man of considerable eminence in philosophy, and an admirer [of mathematical inquiry], I thought fit to write out for you and explain in detail in the same book the peculiarity of a certain method, by which it will be possible for you to get a start to enable you to investigate some of the problems in mathematics by means of mechanics. This procedure is, I am persuaded, no less useful even for the proof of the theorems themselves; for certain things first became clear to me by a mechanical method, although they had to be demonstrated by geom-

[1]The parallelograms are apparently *squares*.
[2]i.e. squares.

etry afterwards because their investigation by the said method did not furnish an actual demonstration. But it is of course easier, when we have previously acquired, by the method, some knowledge of the questions, to supply the proof than it is to find it without any previous knowledge. This is a reason why, in the case of the theorems the proof of which Eudoxus was the first to discover, namely that the cone is a third part of the cylinder, and the pyramid of the prism, having the same base and equal height, we should give no small share of the credit to Democritus who was the first to make the assertion with regard to the said figure though he did not prove it. I am myself in the position of having first made the discovery of the theorem now to be published [by the method indicated], and I deem it necessary to expound the method partly because I have already spoken of it and I do not want to be thought to have uttered vain words, but equally because I am persuaded that it will be of no little service to mathematics; for I apprehend that some, either of my contemporaries or of my successors, will, by means of the method when once established, be able to discover other theorems in addition, which have not yet occurred to me.

"First then I will set out the very first theorem which became known to me by means of mechanics, namely that

"*Any segment of a section of a right-angled cone (i.e. a parabola) is four-thirds of the triangle which has the same base and equal height,*
and after this I will give each of the other theorems investigated by the same method. Then, at the end of the book, I will give the geometrical" [proofs of the propositions]...

[I premise the following propositions which I shall use in the course of the work.]

1. "If from [one magnitude another magnitude be subtracted which has not the same centre of gravity, the centre of gravity of the remainder is found by] producing [the straight line joining the centres of gravity of the whole magnitude and of the subtracted part in the direction of the centre of gravity of the whole] and cutting off from it a length which has to the distance between the said centres of gravity the ratio which the weight of the subtracted magnitude has to the weight of the remainder." [*On the Equilibrium of Planes*, I. 8]

2. "If the centres of gravity of any number of magnitudes whatever be on the same straight line, the centre of gravity of the magnitude made up of all of them will be on the same straight line." [Cf. *Ibid*. I. 5]

3. "The centre of gravity of any straight line is the point of bisection of the straight line." [Cf. *Ibid*. I. 4]

4. "The centre of gravity of any triangle is the point in which the straight lines drawn from the angular points of the triangle to the middle points of the (opposite) sides cut one another." [*Ibid*. I. 13, 14]

5. "The centre of gravity of any parallelogram is the point in which the diagonals meet." [*Ibid*. I. 10]

6. "The centre of gravity of a circle is the point which is also the centre [of the circle]."

7. "The centre of gravity of any cylinder is the point of bisection of the axis."

8. "The centre of gravity of any cone is [the point which divides its axis so that] the portion [adjacent to the vertex is] triple [of the portion adjacent to the base]."

[All these propositions have already been] proved.[1] [Besides these I require also the following proposition, which is easily proved:

If in two series of magnitudes those of the first series are, in order, proportional to those of the second series and further], "the magnitudes [of the first series], either all or some of them, are in any ratio whatever [to those of a third series], and if the magnitudes of the second series are in the same ratio to the corresponding magnitudes [of a fourth series], then the sum of the magnitudes of the first series has to the sum of the selected magnitudes of the third series the same ratio which the sum of the magnitudes of the second series has to the sum of the (correspondingly) selected magnitudes of the fourth series." [*On Conoids and Spheroids*, Prop. 1.]

## PROPOSITION 1

Let $ABC$ be a segment of a parabola bounded by the straight line $AC$ and the parabola $ABC$, and let $D$ be the middle point of $AC$. Draw the straight line $DBE$ parallel to the axis of the parabola and join $AB$, $BC$.

Then shall the segment $ABC$ be $\frac{4}{3}$ of the triangle $ABC$.

From $A$ draw $AKF$ parallel to $DE$, and let the tangent to the parabola at $C$ meet $DBE$ in $E$ and $AKF$ in $F$. Produce $CB$ to meet $AF$ in $K$, and again produce $CK$ to $H$, making $KH$ equal to $CK$.

Consider $CH$ as the bar of a balance, $K$ being its middle point.

Let $MO$ be any straight line parallel to $ED$, and let it meet $CF$, $CK$, $AC$ in $M$, $N$, $O$ and the curve in $P$.

Now, since $CE$ is a tangent to the parabola and $CD$ the semi-ordinate,
$$EB = BD;$$
"for this is proved in the Elements [of Conics]."[2]

Since $FA$, $MO$ are parallel to $ED$, it follows that
$$FK = KA, \quad MN = NO.$$

Now, by the property of the parabola, "proved in a lemma,"
$$MO : OP = CA : AO \text{ [Cf. } Quadrature\ of\ Parabola\text{, Prop. 5]}$$
$$= CK : KN$$
[Eucl. VI. 2]
$$= HK : KN.$$

Take a straight line $TG$ equal to $OP$, and place it with its centre of gravity at $H$, so that $TH = HG$; then, since $N$ is the centre of gravity of the straight line $MO$, and
$$MO : TG = HK : KN,$$
it follows that $TG$ at $H$ and $MO$ at $N$ will be in equilibrium about $K$. [*On the Equilibrium of Planes*, I. 6, 7]

---

[1] The problem of finding the centre of gravity of a cone is not solved in any extant work of Archimedes.

[2] i.e. the works on conics by Aristaeus and Euclid.

Similarly, for all other straight lines parallel to $DE$ and meeting the arc of the parabola, (1) the portion intercepted between $FC$, $AC$ with its middle point on $KC$ and (2) a length equal to the intercept between the curve and $AC$ placed with its centre of gravity at $H$ will be in equilibrium about $K$.

Therefore $K$ is the centre of gravity of the whole system consisting (1) of all the straight lines as $MO$ intercepted between $FC$, $AC$ and placed as they actually are in the figure and (2) of all the straight lines placed at $H$ equal to the straight lines as $PO$ intercepted between the curve and $AC$.

And, since the triangle $CFA$ is made up of all the parallel lines like $MO$, and the segment $CBA$ is made up of all the straight lines like $PO$ within the curve,

it follows that the triangle, placed where it is in the figure, is in equilibrium about $K$ with the segment $CBA$ placed with its centre of gravity at $H$.

Divide $KC$ at $W$ so that $CK = 3KW$;
then $W$ is the centre of gravity of the triangle $ACF$; "for this is proved in the books on equilibrium" (ἐν τοῖς ἰσορροπικοῖς).

[Cf. *On the Equilibrium of Planes* I. 15]

Therefore $\triangle ACF :$ (segment $ABC$) $= HK : KW$
$= 3 : 1$.
Therefore segment $ABC = \frac{1}{3} \triangle ACF$.
But $\triangle ACF = 4 \triangle ABC$.
Therefore segment $ABC = \frac{4}{3} \triangle ABC$.

"Now the fact here stated is not actually demonstrated by the argument used; but that argument has given a sort of indication that the conclusion is true. Seeing then that the theorem is not demonstrated, but at the same time suspecting that the conclusion is true, we shall have recourse to the geometrical demonstration which I myself discovered and have already published."

## Proposition 2

We can investigate by the same method the propositions that

(1) *Any sphere is (in respect of solid content) four times the cone with base equal to a great circle of the sphere and height equal to its radius; and*

(2) *the cylinder with base equal to a great circle of the sphere and height equal to the diameter is $1\frac{1}{2}$ times the sphere.*

(1) Let $ABCD$ be a great circle of a sphere, and $AC$, $BD$ diameters at right angles to one another.

Let a circle be drawn about $BD$ as diameter and in a plane perpendicular to $AC$, and on this circle as base let a cone be described with $A$ as vertex. Let the surface of this cone be produced and then cut by a plane through $C$ parallel to its base; the section will be a circle on $EF$ as diameter. On this circle as base let a cylinder be erected with height and axis $AC$, and produce $CA$ to $H$, making $AH$ equal to $CA$.

Let $CH$ be regarded as the bar of a balance, $A$ being its middle point.

Draw any straight line $MN$ in the plane of the circle $ABCD$ and parallel to $BD$. Let $MN$ meet the circle in $O$, $P$, the diameter $AC$ in $S$, and the straight lines $AE$, $AF$ in $Q$, $R$ respectively. Join $AO$.

Through $MN$ draw a plane at right angles to $AC$;

THE METHOD TREATING OF MECHANICAL PROBLEMS   573

this plane will cut the cylinder in a circle with diameter $MN$, the sphere in a circle with diameter $OP$, and the cone in a circle with diameter $QR$.

Now, since $MS = AC$, and $QS = AS$,
$$MS \cdot SQ = CA \cdot AS$$
$$= AO^2$$
$$= OS^2 + SQ^2.$$

And, since $HA = AC$,
$$HA : AS = CA : AS$$
$$= MS : SQ$$
$$= MS^2 : MS \cdot SQ$$
$$= MS^2 : (OS^2 + SQ^2),$$
from above,
$$= MN^2 : (OP^2 + QR^2)$$
$$= (\text{circle, diam. } MN) : (\text{circle, diam. } OP$$
$$+ \text{circle, diam. } QR).$$

That is,
$HA : AS = $ (circle in cylinder) : (circle in sphere + circle in cone).

Therefore the circle in the cylinder, placed where it is, is in equilibrium, about $A$, with the circle in the sphere together with the circle in the cone, if both the latter circles are placed with their centres of gravity at $H$.

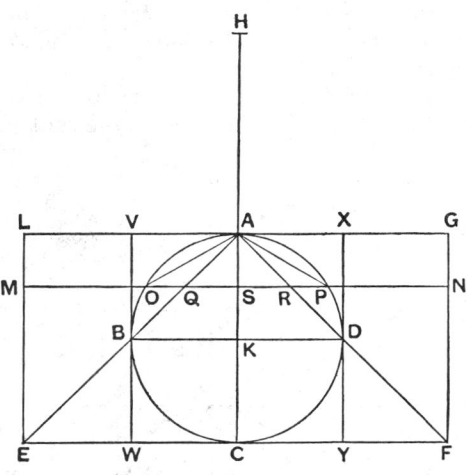

Similarly for the three corresponding sections made by a plane perpendicular to $AC$ and passing through any other straight line in the parallelogram $LF$ parallel to $EF$.

If we deal in the same way with all the sets of three circles in which planes perpendicular to $AC$ cut the cylinder, the sphere and the cone, and which make up those solids respectively, it follows that the cylinder, in the place where it is, will be in equilibrium about $A$ with the sphere and the cone together, when both are placed with their centres of gravity at $H$.

Therefore, since $K$ is the centre of gravity of the cylinder,
$$HA : AK = (\text{cylinder}) : (\text{sphere} + \text{cone } AEF).$$

But $HA = 2AK$;
therefore        cylinder $= 2$(sphere + cone $AEF$).

Now              cylinder $= 3$(cone $AEF$);        [Eucl. xii. 10]
therefore        cone $AEF = 2$(sphere).

But, since $EF = 2BD$,
$$\text{cone } AEF = 8(\text{cone } ABD);$$
therefore        sphere $= 4$(cone $ABD$).

(2) Through $B$, $D$ draw $VBW$, $XDY$ parallel to $AC$; and imagine a cylinder which has $AC$ for axis and the circles on $VX$, $WY$ as diameters for bases.

Then
$$\text{cylinder } VY = 2(\text{cylinder } VD)$$
$$= 6(\text{cone } ABD) \quad\quad \text{[Eucl. xii. 10]}$$
$$= \tfrac{3}{2}(\text{sphere}), \text{ from above.}$$

Q.E.D.

"From this theorem, to the effect that a sphere is four times as great as the cone with a great circle of the sphere as base and with height equal to the radius of the sphere, I conceived the notion that the surface of any sphere is four times as great as a great circle in it; for, judging from the fact that any circle is equal to a triangle with base equal to the circumference and height equal to the radius of the circle, I apprehended that, in like manner, any sphere is equal to a cone with base equal to the surface of the sphere and height equal to the radius."

## Proposition 3

By this method we can also investigate the theorem that

*A cylinder with base equal to the greatest circle in a spheroid and height equal to the axis of the spheroid is $1\tfrac{1}{2}$ times the spheroid;*

and, when this is established, it is plain that

*If any spheroid be cut by a plane through the centre and at right angles to the axis, the half of the spheroid is double of the cone which has the same base and the same axis as the segment (i.e. the half of the spheroid).*

Let a plane through the axis of a spheroid cut its surface in the ellipse $ABCD$, the diameters (i.e. axes) of which are $AC$, $BD$; and let $K$ be the centre.

Draw a circle about $BD$ as diameter and in a plane perpendicular to $AC$; imagine a cone with this circle as base and $A$ as vertex produced and cut by a plane through $C$ parallel to its base; the section will be a circle in a plane at right angles to $AC$ and about $EF$ as diameter.

Imagine a cylinder with the latter circle as base and axis $AC$; produce $CA$ to $H$, making $AH$ equal to $CA$.

Let $HC$ be regarded as the bar of a balance, $A$ being its middle point.

In the parallelogram $LF$ draw any straight line $MN$ parallel to $EF$ meeting the ellipse in $O$, $P$ and $AE$, $AF$, $AC$ in $Q$, $R$, $S$ respectively.

If now a plane be drawn through $MN$ at right angles to $AC$, it will cut the cylinder in a circle with diameter $MN$, the spheroid in a circle with diameter $OP$, and the cone in a circle with diameter $QR$.

Since $HA = AC$,
$$HA : AS = CA : AS$$
$$= EA : AQ$$
$$= MS : SQ.$$
Therefore
$$HA : AS = MS^2 : MS \cdot SQ.$$
But, by the property of the ellipse,
$$AS \cdot SC : SO^2 = AK^2 : KB^2$$
$$= AS^2 : SQ^2;$$
therefore
$$SQ^2 : SO^2 = AS^2 : AS \cdot SC$$
$$= SQ^2 : SQ \cdot QM,$$
and accordingly
$$SO^2 = SQ \cdot QM.$$
Add $SQ^2$ to each side, and we have
$$SO^2 + SQ^2 = SQ \cdot SM.$$
Therefore, from above, we have
$$HA : AS = MS^2 : (SO^2 + SQ^2)$$
$$= MN^2 : (OP^2 + QR^2)$$
$$= \text{(circle, diam. } MN\text{)} : \text{(circle, diam. } OP + \text{circle, diam. } QR\text{)}.$$
That is,
$$HA : AS = \text{(circle in cylinder)} : \text{(circle in spheroid} + \text{circle in cone)}.$$
Therefore the circle in the cylinder, in the place where it is, is in equilibrium, about $A$, with the circle in the spheroid and the circle in the cone together, if both the latter circles are placed with their centres of gravity at $H$.

Similarly for the three corresponding sections made by a plane perpendicular to $AC$ and passing through any other straight line in the parallelogram $LF$ parallel to $EF$.

If we deal in the same way with all the sets of three circles in which planes perpendicular to $AC$ cut the cylinder, the spheroid and the cone, and which make up those figures respectively, it follows that the cylinder, in the place where it is, will be in equilibrium about $A$ with the spheroid and the cone together, when both are placed with their centres of gravity at $H$.

Therefore, since $K$ is the centre of gravity of the cylinder,
$$HA : AK = \text{(cylinder)} : \text{(spheroid} + \text{cone } AEF\text{)}.$$
But $HA = 2AK$;
therefore $\qquad$ cylinder $= 2(\text{spheroid} + \text{cone } AEF)$.
And $\qquad$ cylinder $= 3(\text{cone } AEF)$; $\qquad$ [Eucl. XII. 10]
therefore $\qquad$ cone $AEF = 2(\text{spheroid})$.
But, since $EF = 2BD$,
$$\text{cone } AEF = 8(\text{cone } ABD);$$
therefore $\qquad$ spheroid $= 4(\text{cone } ABD)$,
and $\qquad$ half the spheroid $= 2(\text{cone } ABD)$.

Through $B$, $D$ draw $VBW$, $XDY$ parallel to $AC$; and imagine a cylinder which has $AC$ for axis and the circles on $VX$, $WY$ as diameters for bases.

Then $\qquad$ cylinder $VY = 2(\text{cylinder } VD)$
$$= 6(\text{cone } ABD)$$
$$= \tfrac{3}{2}(\text{spheroid}), \text{ from above.} \qquad \text{Q.E.D.}$$

## Proposition 4

*Any segment of a right-angled conoid (i.e. a paraboloid of revolution) cut off by a plane at right angles to the axis is $1\frac{1}{2}$ times the cone which has the same base and the same axis as the segment.*

This can be investigated by our method, as follows.

Let a paraboloid of revolution be cut by a plane through the axis in the parabola $BAC$;

and let it also be cut by another plane at right angles to the axis and intersecting the former plane in $BC$. Produce $DA$, the axis of the segment, to $H$, making $HA$ equal to $AD$.

Imagine that $HD$ is the bar of a balance, $A$ being its middle point.

The base of the segment being the circle on $BC$ as diameter and in a plane perpendicular to $AD$,
imagine (1) a cone drawn with the latter circle as base and $A$ as vertex, and (2) a cylinder with the same circle as base and $AD$ as axis.

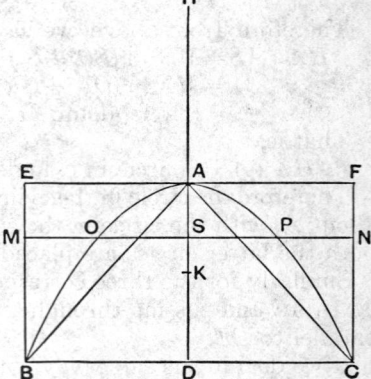

In the parallelogram $EC$ let any straight line $MN$ be drawn parallel to $BC$, and through $MN$ let a plane be drawn at right angles to $AD$; this plane will cut the cylinder in a circle with diameter $MN$ and the paraboloid in a circle with diameter $OP$.

Now, $BAC$ being a parabola and $BD$, $OS$ ordinates,
$$DA : AS = BD^2 : OS^2,$$
or $$HA : AS = MS^2 : SO^2.$$
Therefore
$$HA : AS = (\text{circle, rad. } MS) : (\text{circle, rad. } OS)$$
$$= (\text{circle in cylinder}) : (\text{circle in paraboloid}).$$

Therefore the circle in the cylinder, in the place where it is, will be in equilibrium about $A$ with the circle in the paraboloid, if the latter is placed with its centre of gravity at $H$.

Similarly for the two corresponding circular sections made by a plane perpendicular to $AD$ and passing through any other straight line in the parallelogram which is parallel to $BC$.

Therefore, as usual, if we take all the circles making up the whole cylinder and the whole segment and treat them in the same way, we find that the cylinder, in the place where it is, is in equilibrium about $A$ with the segment placed with its centre of gravity at $H$.

If $K$ is the middle point of $AD$, $K$ is the centre of gravity of the cylinder; therefore $\qquad HA : AK = (\text{cylinder}) : (\text{segment})$.

Therefore $\qquad$ cylinder $= 2(\text{segment})$.

And $\qquad$ cylinder $= 3(\text{cone } ABC)$; [Eucl. xii. 10]
therefore $\qquad$ segment $= \frac{3}{2}(\text{cone } ABC)$.

## Proposition 5

*The centre of gravity of a segment of a right-angled conoid (i.e. a paraboloid of revolution) cut off by a plane at right angles to the axis is on the straight line which is the axis of the segment, and divides the said straight line in such a way that the portion of it adjacent to the vertex is double of the remaining portion.*

This can be investigated by the method, as follows.

Let a paraboloid of revolution be cut by a plane through the axis in the parabola $BAC$; and let it also be cut by another plane at right angles to the axis and intersecting the former plane in $BC$.

Produce $DA$, the axis of the segment, to $H$, making $HA$ equal to $AD$; and imagine $DH$ to be the bar of a balance, its middle point being $A$.

The base of the segment being the circle on $BC$ as diameter and in a plane perpendicular to $AD$, imagine a cone with this circle as base and $A$ as vertex, so that $AB$, $AC$ are generators of the cone.

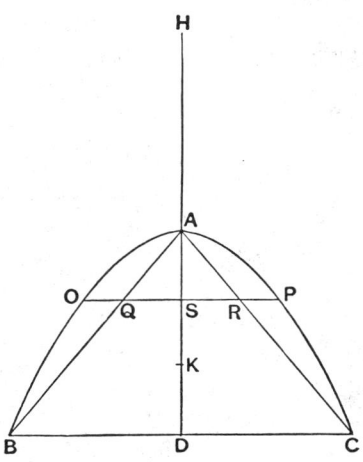

In the parabola let any double ordinate $OP$ be drawn meeting $AB$, $AD$, $AC$ in $Q$, $S$, $R$ respectively.

Now, from the property of the parabola,
$$BD^2 : OS^2 = DA : AS$$
$$= BD : QS$$
$$= BD^2 : BD \cdot QS.$$
Therefore $OS^2 = BD \cdot QS$,
or $BD : OS = OS : QS$,
whence $BD : QS = OS^2 : QS^2$.
But $BD : QS = AD : AS$
$$= HA : AS.$$
Therefore $HA : AS = OS^2 : QS^2$
$$= OP^2 : QR^2.$$

If now through $OP$ a plane be drawn at right angles to $AD$, this plane cuts the paraboloid in a circle with diameter $OP$ and the cone in a circle with diameter $QR$.

We see therefore that $HA : AS =$ (circle, diam. $OP$) : (circle, diam. $QR$)
$$= \text{(circle in paraboloid)} : \text{(circle in cone)};$$
and the circle in the paraboloid, in the place where it is, is in equilibrium about $A$ with the circle in the cone placed with its centre of gravity at $H$.

Similarly for the two corresponding circular sections made by a plane perpendicular to $AD$ and passing through any other ordinate of the parabola.

Dealing therefore in the same way with all the circular sections which make up the whole of the segment of the paraboloid and the cone respectively, we see that the segment of the paraboloid, in the place where it is, is in equilibrium about $A$ with the cone placed with its centre of gravity at $H$.

Now, since $A$ is the centre of gravity of the whole system as placed, and the centre of gravity of part of it, namely the cone, as placed, is at $H$, the centre of gravity of the rest, namely the segment, is at a point $K$ on $HA$ produced such that
$$HA : AK = \text{(segment)} : \text{(cone)}.$$
But segment $= \tfrac{3}{2}$(cone). [Prop. 4]

Therefore $HA = \frac{3}{2}AK$;
that is, $K$ divides $AD$ in such a way that $AK = 2KD$.

## Proposition 6

*The centre of gravity of any hemisphere [is on the straight line which] is its axis, and divides the said straight line in such a way that the portion of it adjacent to the surface of the hemisphere has to the remaining portion the ratio which 5 has to 3.*

Let a sphere be cut by a plane through its centre in the circle $ABCD$; let $AC$, $BD$ be perpendicular diameters of this circle, and through $BD$ let a plane be drawn at right angles to $AC$.

The latter plane will cut the sphere in a circle on $BD$ as diameter.

Imagine a cone with the latter circle as base and $A$ as vertex.

Produce $CA$ to $H$, making $AH$ equal to $CA$, and let $HC$ be regarded as the bar of a balance, $A$ being its middle point.

In the semicircle $BAD$, let any straight line $OP$ be drawn parallel to $BD$ and cutting $AC$ in $E$ and the two generators, $AB$, $AD$ of the cone in $Q$, $R$ respectively. Join $AO$.

Through $OP$ let a plane be drawn at right angles to $AC$;
this plane will cut the hemisphere in a circle with diameter $OP$ and the cone in a circle with diameter $QR$.

Now
$$HA : AE = AC : AE$$
$$= AO^2 : AE^2$$
$$= (OE^2 + AE^2) : AE^2$$
$$= (OE^2 + QE^2) : QE^2$$
$$= (\text{circle, diam. } OP + \text{circle, diam. } QR) : (\text{circle, diam. } QR).$$

Therefore the circles with diameters $OP$, $QR$, in the places where they are, are in equilibrium about $A$ with the circle with diameter $QR$ if the latter is placed with its centre of gravity at $H$.

And, since the centre of gravity of the two circles with diameters $OP$, $QR$ taken together, in the place where they are, is . . .

[There is a lacuna here; but the proof can easily be completed on the lines of the corresponding but more difficult case in Prop. 8.

We proceed thus from the point where the circles with diameters $OP$, $QR$, in the place where they are, balance, about $A$, the circle with diameter $QR$ placed with its centre of gravity at $H$.

A similar relation holds for all the other sets of circular sections made by other planes passing through points on $AG$ and at right angles to $AG$.

Taking then all the circles which fill up the hemisphere $BAD$ and the cone $ABD$ respectively, we find that
the hemisphere $BAD$ and the cone $ABD$, in the places where they are, together balance, about $A$, a cone equal to $ABD$ placed with its centre of gravity at $H$.

Let the cylinder $M+N$ be equal to the cone $ABD$.

Then, since the cylinder $M+N$ placed with its centre of gravity at $H$ balances the hemisphere $BAD$ and the cone $ABD$ in the places where they are, suppose that the portion $M$ of the cylinder, placed with its centre of gravity at

THE METHOD TREATING OF MECHANICAL PROBLEMS    579

$H$, balances the cone $ABD$ (alone) in the place where it is; therefore the portion $N$ of the cylinder placed with its centre of gravity at $H$ balances the hemisphere (alone) in the place where it is.

Now the centre of gravity of the cone is at a point $V$ such that $AG = 4GV$; therefore, since $M$ at $H$ is in equilibrium with the cone,
$$M : (\text{cone}) = \tfrac{3}{4}AG : HA = \tfrac{3}{8}AC : AC,$$
whence $\qquad\qquad M = \tfrac{3}{8}(\text{cone}).$

But $M+N = (\text{cone})$; therefore $N = \tfrac{5}{8}(\text{cone}).$

Now let the centre of gravity of the hemisphere be at $W$, which is somewhere on $AG$.

Then, since $N$ at $H$ balances the hemisphere alone,
$$(\text{hemisphere}) : N = HA : AW.$$
But the hemisphere $BAD = $ twice the cone $ABD$;

[*On the Sphere and Cylinder* i. 34 and Prop. 2 above]

and $N = \tfrac{5}{8}(\text{cone})$, from above.

Therefore $\qquad\qquad 2 : \tfrac{5}{8} = HA : AW$
$$= 2AG : AW,$$
whence $AW = \tfrac{5}{8}AG$, so that $W$ divides $AG$ in such a way that
$$AW : WG = 5 : 3.]$$

PROPOSITION 7

We can also investigate by the same method the theorem that

[*Any segment of a sphere has*] *to the cone* [*with the same base and height the ratio which the sum of the radius of the sphere and the height of the complementary segment has to the height of the complementary segment.*]

[There is a lacuna here; but all that is missing is the construction, and the construction is easily understood by means of the figure. $BAD$ is of course the segment of the sphere the volume of which is to be compared with the volume of a cone with the same base and height.]

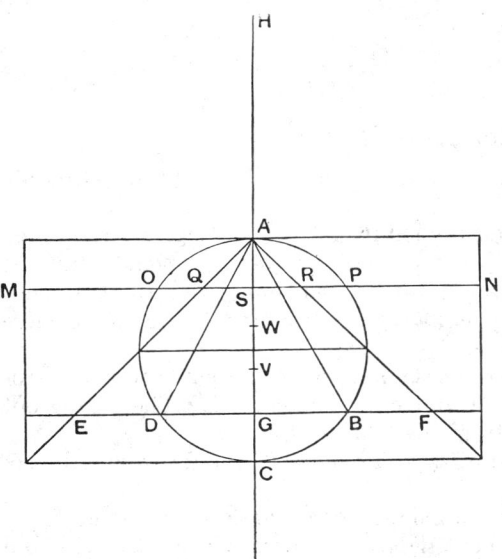

The plane drawn through $MN$ and at right angles to $AC$ will cut the cylinder in a circle with diameter $MN$, the segment of the sphere in a circle with diameter $OP$, and the cone on the base $EF$ in a circle with diameter $QR$.

In the same way as before [cf. Prop. 2] we can prove that the circle with diameter $MN$, in the place where it is, is in equilibrium about $A$ with the two circles with diameters $OP$, $QR$ if these circles are both moved and placed with their centres of gravity at $H$.

The same thing can be proved of all sets of three circles in which the cylinder, the segment of the sphere, and the cone with the common height $AG$ are all cut by any plane perpendicular to $AC$.

Since then the sets of circles make up the whole cylinder, the whole segment of the sphere and the whole cone respectively, it follows that the cylinder, in the place where it is, is in equilibrium about $A$ with the sum of the segment of the sphere and the cone if both are placed with their centres of gravity at $H$.

Divide $AG$ at $W$, $V$ in such a way that
$$AW = WG,\ AV = 3VG.$$

Therefore $W$ will be the centre of gravity of the cylinder, and $V$ will be the centre of gravity of the cone.

Since, now, the bodies are in equilibrium as described,
(cylinder) : (cone $AEF$ + segment $BAD$ of sphere) = $HA : AW$.

. . . . . . . . . . . . . . . . . . . . . . . . . . . . . . . . . . . . . . . . . . . . . . . . . . . . . . . . . . . . . . . . . . . . . . .

[The rest of the proof is lost; but it can easily be supplied thus:
We have
$$\text{(cone } AEF + \text{segmt. } BAD) : \text{(cylinder)} = AW : AC$$
$$= AW \cdot AC : AC^2.$$
But $\quad$ (cylinder) : (cone $AEF$) = $AC^2 : \tfrac{1}{3}EG^2$
$$= AC^2 : \tfrac{1}{3}AG^2.$$
Therefore, *ex aequali*,
$$\text{(cone } AEF + \text{segmt. } BAD) : \text{(cone } AEF) = AW \cdot AC : \tfrac{1}{3}AG^2$$
$$= \tfrac{1}{2}AC : \tfrac{1}{3}AG,$$
whence $\quad$ (segmt. $BAD$) : (cone $AEF$) = $(\tfrac{1}{2}AC - \tfrac{1}{3}AG) : \tfrac{1}{3}AG$.
Again $\quad$ (cone $AEF$) : (cone $ABD$) = $EG^2 : DG^2$
$$= AG^2 : AG \cdot GC$$
$$= AG : GC$$
$$= \tfrac{1}{3}AG : \tfrac{1}{3}GC.$$
Therefore, *ex aequali*,
(segment $BAD$) : (cone $ABD$) = $(\tfrac{1}{2}AC - \tfrac{1}{3}AG) : \tfrac{1}{3}GC$
$$= (\tfrac{3}{2}AC - AG) : GC$$
$$= (\tfrac{1}{2}AC + GC) : GC. \qquad \text{Q.E.D.}]$$

## Proposition 8

[The enunciation, the setting-out, and a few words of the construction are missing.

The enunciation however can be supplied from that of Prop. 9, with which it must be identical except that it cannot refer to "*any* segment," and the presumption therefore is that the proposition was enunciated with reference to one kind of segment only, i.e. either a segment greater than a hemisphere or a segment less than a hemisphere.

Heiberg's figure corresponds to the case of a segment greater than a hemisphere. The segment investigated is of course the segment $BAD$. The setting-out and construction are self-evident from the figure.]

Produce $AC$ to $H$, $O$, making $HA$ equal to $AC$ and $CO$ equal to the radius of the sphere;
and let $HC$ be regarded as the bar of a balance, the middle point being $A$.

In the plane cutting off the segment describe a circle with $G$ as centre and radius ($GE$) equal to $AG$; and on this circle as base, and with $A$ as vertex, let a cone be described. $AE$, $AF$ are generators of this cone.

THE METHOD TREATING OF MECHANICAL PROBLEMS 581

Draw $KL$, through any point $Q$ on $AG$, parallel to $EF$ and cutting the segment in $K, L$, and $AE, AF$ in $R, P$ respectively. Join $AK$.

Now
$$HA : AQ = CA : AQ$$
$$= AK^2 : AQ^2$$
$$= (KQ^2 + QA^2) : QA^2$$
$$= (KQ^2 + PQ^2) : PQ^2$$
$$= (\text{circle, diam. } KL + \text{circle, diam. } PR) : (\text{circle, diam. } PR).$$

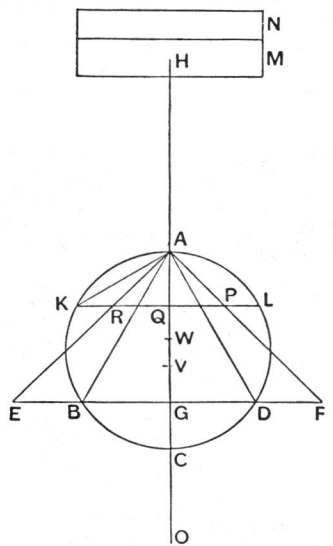

Imagine a circle equal to the circle with diameter $PR$ placed with its centre of gravity at $H$; therefore the circles on diameters $KL, PR$, in the places where they are, are in equilibrium about $A$ with the circle with diameter $PR$ placed with its centre of gravity at $H$.

Similarly for the corresponding circular sections made by any other plane perpendicular to $AG$.

Therefore, taking all the circular sections which make up the segment $ABD$ of the sphere and the cone $AEF$ respectively, we find that the segment $ABD$ of the sphere and the cone $AEF$, in the places where they are, are in equilibrium with the cone $AEF$ assumed to be placed with its centre of gravity at $H$.

Let the cylinder $M+N$ be equal to the cone $AEF$ which has $A$ for vertex and the circle on $EF$ as diameter for base.

Divide $AG$ at $V$ so that
$$AG = 4VG;$$
therefore $V$ is the centre of gravity of the cone $AEF$; "for this has been proved before."

Let the cylinder $M+N$ be cut by a plane perpendicular to the axis in such a way that the cylinder $M$ (alone), placed with its centre of gravity at $H$, is in equilibrium with the cone $AEF$.

Since $M+N$ suspended at $H$ is in equilibrium with the segment $ABD$ of the sphere and the cone $AEF$ in the places where they are,
while $M$, also at $H$, is in equilibrium with the cone $AEF$ in the place where it is, it follows that

$N$ at $H$ is in equilibrium with the segment $ABD$ of the sphere in the place where it is.

Now (segment $ABD$ of sphere) : (cone $ABD$) = $OG : GC$;
"for this is already proved" [Cf. *On the Sphere and Cylinder* II. 2 Cor. as well as Prop. 7 *ante*].

And (cone $ABD$) : (cone $AEF$)
$$= (\text{circle, diam. } BD) : (\text{circle, diam. } EF)$$
$$= BD^2 : EF^2$$
$$= BG^2 : GE^2$$
$$= CG \cdot GA : GA^2$$
$$= CG : GA.$$

Therefore, *ex aequali*,
$$\text{(segment } ABD \text{ of sphere)} : \text{(cone } AEF) = OG : GA.$$
Take a point $W$ on $AG$ such that
$$AW : WG = (GA + 4GC) : (GA + 2GC).$$
We have then, inversely,
$$GW : WA = (2GC + GA) : (4GC + GA),$$
and, *componendo*,
$$GA : AW = (6GC + 2GA) : (4GC + GA).$$
But $\quad GO = \tfrac{1}{4}(6GC + 2GA)$, $\quad\quad$ [for $GO - GC = \tfrac{1}{2}(CG + GA)$]
and $\quad\quad CV = \tfrac{1}{4}(4GC + GA)$;
therefore $\quad\quad GA : AW = OG : CV,$
and, alternately and inversely,
$$OG : GA = CV : WA.$$
It follows, from above, that
$$\text{(segment } ABD \text{ of sphere)} : \text{(cone } AEF) = CV : WA.$$
Now, since the cylinder $M$ with its centre of gravity at $H$ is in equilibrium about $A$ with the cone $AEF$ with its centre of gravity at $V$,
$$\text{(cone } AEF) : \text{(cylinder } M) = HA : AV$$
$$= CA : AV;$$
and, since the cone $AEF$ = the cylinder $M + N$, we have, *dividendo* and *invertendo*,
$$\text{(cylinder } M) : \text{(cylinder } N) = AV : CV.$$
Hence, *componendo*,
$$\text{(cone } AEF) : \text{(cylinder } N) = CA : CV$$
$$= HA : CV.$$
But it was proved that
$$\text{(segment } ABD \text{ of sphere)} : \text{(cone } AEF) = CV : WA;$$
therefore, *ex aequali*,
$$\text{(segment } ABD \text{ of sphere)} : \text{(cylinder } N) = HA : AW.$$
And it was above proved that the cylinder $N$ at $H$ is in equilibrium about $A$ with the segment $ABD$, in the place where it is;
therefore, since $H$ is the centre of gravity of the cylinder $N$, $W$ is the centre of gravity of the segment $ABD$ of the sphere.

## Proposition 9

In the same way we can investigate the theorem that

*The centre of gravity of any segment of a sphere is on the straight line which is the axis of the segment, and divides this straight line in such a way that the part of it adjacent to the vertex of the segment has to the remaining part the ratio which the sum of the axis of the segment and four times the axis of the complementary segment has to the sum of the axis of the segment and double the axis of the complementary segment.*

[As this theorem relates to "*any* segment" but states the same result as that proved in the preceding proposition, it follows that Prop. 8 must have related to one kind of segment, either a segment greater than a semicircle (as in Heiberg's figure of Prop. 8) or a segment less than a semicircle; and the present proposition completed the proof for both kinds of segments. It would only require a slight change in the figure, in any case.]

THE METHOD TREATING OF MECHANICAL PROBLEMS   583

Proposition 10

By this method too we can investigate the theorem that

[*A segment of an obtuse-angled conoid (i.e. a hyperboloid of revolution) has to the cone which has*] *the same base* [*as the segment and equal height the same ratio as the sum of the axis of the segment and three times*] *the "annex to the axis"* (*i.e. half the transverse axis of the hyperbolic section through the axis of the hyperboloid, or, in other words, the distance between the vertex of the segment and the vertex of the enveloping cone*) *has to the sum of the axis of the segment and double of the "annex"* [this is the theorem proved in On Conoids and Spheroids, Prop. 25], "and also many other theorems, which, as the method has been made clear by means of the foregoing examples, I will omit, in order that I may now proceed to compass the proofs of the theorems mentioned above."

Proposition 11

*If in a right prism with square bases a cylinder be inscribed having its bases in opposite square faces and touching with its surface the remaining four parallelogrammic faces, and if through the centre of the circle which is the base of the cylinder and one side of the opposite square face a plane be drawn, the figure cut off by the plane so drawn is one sixth part of the whole prism.*

"This can be investigated by the method, and, when it is set out, I will go back to the proof of it by geometrical considerations."

[The investigation by the mechanical method is contained in the two Propositions, 11, 12. Prop. 13 gives another solution which, although it contains no mechanics, is still of the character which Archimedes regards as inconclusive, since it assumes that the solid is actually *made up* of parallel plane sections and that an auxiliary parabola is actually *made up* of parallel straight lines in it. Prop. 14 added the conclusive geometrical proof.]

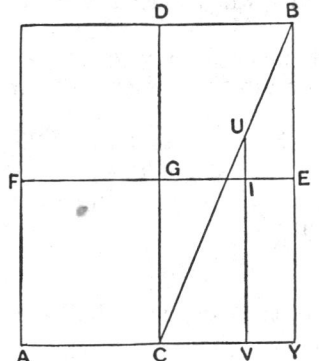

Let there be a right prism with a cylinder inscribed as stated.

Let the prism be cut through the axis of the prism and cylinder by a plane perpendicular to the plane which cuts off the portion of the cylinder; let this plane make, as section, the parallelogram $AB$, and let it cut the plane cutting off the portion of the cylinder (which plane is perpendicular to $AB$) in the straight line $BC$.

Let $CD$ be the axis of the prism and cylinder, let $EF$ bisect it at right angles, and through $EF$ let a plane be drawn at right angles to $CD$; this plane will cut the prism in a square and the cylinder in a circle.

Let $MN$ be the square and $OPQR$ the circle, and let the circle touch the sides of the square in $O$, $P$, $Q$, $R$ [$F$, $E$ in the first figure are identical with $O$, $Q$ respectively]. Let $H$ be the centre of the circle.

Let $KL$ be the intersection of the plane through $EF$ perpendicular to the axis of the cylinder and the plane cutting off the portion of the cylinder; $KL$ is bisected by $OHQ$ [and passes through the middle point of $HQ$].

Let any chord of the circle, as $ST$, be drawn perpendicular to $HQ$, meeting $HQ$ in $W$;
and through $ST$ let a plane be drawn at right angles to $OQ$ and produced on both sides of the plane of the circle $OPQR$.

The plane so drawn will cut the half cylinder having the semicircle $PQR$ for section and the axis of the prism for height in a parallelogram, one side of which is equal to $ST$ and another is a generator of the cylinder; and it will also cut the portion of the cylinder cut off in a parallelogram, one side of which is equal to $ST$ and the other is equal and parallel to $UV$ (in the first figure).

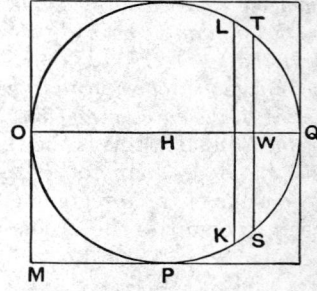

$UV$ will be parallel to $BY$ and will cut off, along $EG$ in the parallelogram $DE$, the segment $EI$ equal to $QW$.

Now, since $EC$ is a parallelogram, and $VI$ is parallel to $GC$,
$$EG : GI = YC : CV$$
$$= BY : UV$$
$$= (\square \text{ in half cyl.}) : (\square \text{ in portion of cyl.}).$$
And $EG = HQ$, $GI = HW$, $QH = OH$;
therefore $OH : HW = (\square \text{ in half cyl.}) : (\square \text{ in portion})$.

Imagine that the parallelogram in the portion of the cylinder is moved and placed at $O$ so that $O$ is the centre of gravity, and that $OQ$ is the bar of a balance, $H$ being its middle point.

Then, since $W$ is the centre of gravity of the parallelogram in the half cylinder, it follows from the above that the parallelogram in the half cylinder, in the place where it is, with its centre of gravity at $W$, is in equilibrium about $H$ with the parallelogram in the portion of the cylinder when placed with its centre of gravity at $O$.

Similarly for the other parallelogrammic sections made by any plane perpendicular to $OQ$ and passing through any other chord in the semicircle $PQR$ perpendicular to $OQ$.

If then we take all the parallelograms making up the half cylinder and the portion of the cylinder respectively, it follows that the half cylinder, in the place where it is, is in equilibrium about $H$ with the portion of the cylinder cut off when the latter is placed with its centre of gravity at $O$.

## Proposition 12

Let the parallelogram (square) $MN$ perpendicular to the axis, with the circle $OPQR$ and its diameters $OQ$, $PR$, be drawn separately.

Join $HG$, $HM$, and through them draw planes at right angles to the plane of the circle, producing them on both sides of that plane.

This produces a prism with triangular section $GHM$ and height equal to the axis of the cylinder; this prism is $\frac{1}{4}$ of the original prism circumscribing the cylinder.

Let $LK$, $UT$ be drawn parallel to $OQ$ and equidistant from it, cutting the circle in $K$, $T$, $RP$ in $S$, $F$, and $GH$, $HM$ in $W$, $V$ respectively.

Through $LK$, $UT$ draw planes at right angles to $PR$, producing them on both sides of the plane of the circle;

THE METHOD TREATING OF MECHANICAL PROBLEMS    585

these planes produce as sections in the half cylinder $PQR$ and in the prism $GHM$ four parallelograms in which the heights are equal to the axis of the cylinder, and the other sides are equal to $KS$, $TF$, $LW$, $UV$ respectively ·····
. . . . . . . . . . . . . . . . . . . . . . . . . . . . .

[The rest of the proof is missing, but, as Zeuthen says, the result obtained and the method of arriving at it are plainly indicated by the above.

Archimedes wishes to prove that the half cylinder $PQR$, in the place where it is, balances the prism $GHM$, in the place where it is, about $H$ as fixed point.

He has first to prove that the elements (1) the parallelogram with side = $KS$ and (2) the parallelogram with side = $LW$, in the places where they are, balance about $S$, or, in other words that the straight lines $SK$, $LW$, in the places where they are, balance about $S$.

Now (radius of circle $OPQR)^2 = SK^2 + SH^2$,
or $SL^2 = SK^2 + SW^2$.
Therefore $LS^2 - SW^2 = SK^2$,
and accordingly $(LS + SW) \cdot LW = SK^2$,
whence $\frac{1}{2}(LS + SW) : \frac{1}{2}SK = SK : LW$.

And $\frac{1}{2}(LS+SW)$ is the distance of the centre of gravity of $LW$ from $S$, while $\frac{1}{2}SK$ is the distance of the centre of gravity of $SK$ from $S$.

Therefore $SK$ and $LW$, in the places where they are, balance about $S$.

Similarly for the corresponding parallelograms.

Taking *all* the parallelogrammic elements in the half cylinder and prism respectively, we find that
the half cylinder $PQR$ and the prism $GHM$, in the places where they are respectively, balance about $H$.

From this result and that of Prop. 11 we can at once deduce the volume of the portion cut off from the cylinder. For in Prop. 11 the portion of the cylinder, placed with its centre of gravity at $O$, is shown to balance (about $H$) the half-cylinder in the place where it is. By Prop. 12 we may substitute for the half-cylinder in the place where it is the prism $GHM$ of that proposition turned the opposite way relatively to $RP$. The centre of gravity of the prism as thus placed is at a point (say $Z$) on $HQ$ such that $HZ = \frac{2}{3}HQ$.

Therefore, assuming the prism to be applied at its centre of gravity, we have
(portion of cylinder) : (prism) = $\frac{2}{3}HQ : OH$
= 2 : 3;
therefore (portion of cylinder) = $\frac{2}{3}$(prism $GHM$)
= $\frac{1}{6}$(original prism).

PROPOSITION 13

Let there be a right prism with square bases, one of which is $ABCD$; in the prism let a cylinder be inscribed, the base of which is the circle $EFGH$ touching the sides of the square $ABCD$ in $E$, $F$, $G$, $H$.

Through the centre and through the side corresponding to $CD$ in the square face *opposite* to $ABCD$ let a plane be drawn; this will cut off a prism equal to $\frac{1}{4}$ of the original prism and formed by three parallelograms and two triangles, the triangles forming opposite faces.

In the semicircle $EFG$ describe the parabola which has $FK$ for axis and passes through $E, G$; draw $MN$ parallel to $KF$ meeting $GE$ in $M$, the parabola in $L$, the semicircle in $O$ and $CD$ in $N$.

Then $$MN \cdot NL = NF^2;$$
"for this is clear." [Cf. Apollonius, *Conics* I. 11]
[The parameter is of course equal to $GK$ or $KF$.]
Therefore $$MN : NL = GK^2 : LS^2.$$

Through $MN$ draw a plane at right angles to $EG$;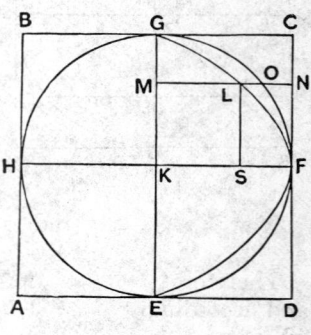
this will produce as sections (1) in the prism cut off from the whole prism a right-angled triangle, the base of which is $MN$, while the perpendicular is perpendicular at $N$ to the plane $ABCD$ and equal to the axis of the cylinder, and the hypotenuse is in the plane cutting the cylinder, and (2) in the portion of the cylinder cut off a right-angled triangle the base of which is $MO$, while the perpendicular is the generator of the cylinder perpendicular at $O$ to the plane $KN$, and the hypotenuse is ·····
. . . . . . . . . . . . . . . . . . . . . . . . . . . . .

[There is a lacuna here, to be supplied as follows.
Since $$MN : NL = GK^2 : LS^2$$
$$= MN^2 : LS^2,$$
it follows that $$MN : ML = MN^2 : (MN^2 - LS^2)$$
$$= MN^2 : (MN^2 - MK^2)$$
$$= MN^2 : MO^2.$$

But the triangle (1) in the prism is to the triangle (2) in the portion of the cylinder in the ratio of $MN^2 : MO^2$.

Therefore ($\triangle$ in prism) : ($\triangle$ in portion of cylinder)
$= MN : ML$
= (straight line in rect. $DG$) : (straight line in parabola).

We now take all the corresponding elements in the prism, the portion of the cylinder, the rectangle $DG$ and the parabola $EFG$ respectively];
and it will follow that

(all the $\triangle$s in prism) : (all the $\triangle$s in portion of cylinder)
= (all the str. lines in $\square DG$) : (all the straight lines between parabola and $EG$).

But the prism is made up of the triangles in the prism, [the portion of the cylinder is made up of the triangles in it], the parallelogram $DG$ of the straight lines in it parallel to $KF$, and the parabolic segment of the straight lines parallel to $KF$ intercepted between its circumference and $EG$;
therefore (prism) : (portion of cylinder)
$= (\square GD)$ : (parabolic segment $EFG$).
But $\square GD = \frac{3}{2}$(parabolic segment $EFG$);
"for this is proved in my earlier treatise." [*Quadrature of Parabola*]
Therefore prism $= \frac{3}{2}$(portion of cylinder).

If then we denote the portion of the cylinder by 2, the prism is 3, and the original prism circumscribing the cylinder is 12 (being 4 times the other prism); therefore the portion of the cylinder = $\frac{1}{6}$(original prism).  Q.E.D.

[The above proposition and the next are peculiarly interesting for the fact that the parabola is an auxiliary curve introduced for the sole purpose of analytically reducing the required cubature to the known quadrature of the parabola.]

### PROPOSITION 14

Let there be a right prism with square bases [and a cylinder inscribed therein having its base in the square $ABCD$ and touching its sides at $E$, $F$, $G$, $H$; let the cylinder be cut by a plane through $EG$ and the side corresponding to $CD$ in the square face opposite to $ABCD$.]

This plane cuts off from the prism a prism, and from the cylinder a portion of it.

It can be proved that the portion of the cylinder cut off by the plane is $\frac{1}{6}$ of the whole prism.

But we will first prove that it is possible to inscribe in the portion cut off from the cylinder, and to circumscribe about it, solid figures made up of prisms which have equal height and similar triangular bases, in such a way that the circumscribed figure exceeds the inscribed by less than any assigned magnitude.....

. . . . . . . . . . . . .

But it was proved that
(prism cut off by oblique plane) $<\frac{3}{2}$(figure inscribed in portion of cylinder).
  Now     (prism cut off) : (inscribed figure)
      = $\square DG$ : ($\square$s inscribed in parabolic segment);
therefore     $\square DG < \frac{3}{2}$($\square$s in parabolic segment):
which is impossible, since "it has been proved elsewhere" that the parallelogram $DG$ is $\frac{3}{2}$ of the parabolic segment.

  Consequently....................
............................................not greater.

. . . . . . . . . . .
  And    (all the prisms in prism cut off)
         : (all prisms in circumscr. figure)
= (all $\square$s in $\square DG$) : (all $\square$s in fig. circumscr. about parabolic segmt.);
therefore
    (prism cut off) : (figure circumscr. about portion of cylinder)
    = ($\square DG$) : (figure circumscr. about parabolic segment).
But the prism cut off by the oblique plane is $>\frac{3}{2}$ of the solid figure circumscribed about the portion of the cylinder.....

. . . . . . . . . . .

[There are large gaps in the exposition of this geometrical proof, but the way in which the method of exhaustion was applied, and the parallelism between this and other applications of it, are clear. The first fragment shows that solid figures made up of prisms were circumscribed and inscribed to the portion of the cylinder. The parallel triangular faces of these prisms were perpendicular to $GE$ in the figure of Prop. 13; they divided $GE$ into equal portions of the requisite smallness; each section of the portion of the cylinder by such a plane was a triangular face common to an inscribed and a circumscribed right prism. The planes also produced prisms in the prism cut off by the same oblique plane as cuts off the portion of the cylinder and standing on $GD$ as base.

The number of parts into which the parallel planes divided $GE$ was made great enough to secure that the circumscribed figure exceeded the inscribed figure by less than a small assigned magnitude.

The second part of the proof began with the assumption that the portion of the cylinder is $>\frac{2}{3}$ of the prism cut off; and this was proved to be impossible, by means of the use of the auxiliary parabola and the proportion
$$MN:ML=MN^2:MO^2$$
which are employed in Prop. 13.

We may supply the missing proof as follows.

In the accompanying figure are represented (1) the first element-prism circumscribed to the portion of the cylinder, (2) two element-prisms adjacent to the ordinate $OM$, of which that on the left is circumscribed and that on the right (equal to the other) inscribed, (3) the corresponding element-prisms forming part of the prism cut off ($CC'GEDD'$) which is $\frac{1}{4}$ of the original prism.

In the second figure are shown element-rectangles circumscribed and inscribed to the auxiliary parabola, which rectangles correspond exactly to the circumscribed and inscribed element-prisms represented in the first figure (the length of $GM$ is the same in both figures, and the breadths of the element-rectangles are the same as the heights of the element-prisms); the corresponding element-rectangles forming part of the rectangle $GD$ are similarly shown.

For convenience we suppose that $GE$ is divided into an even number of equal parts, so that $GK$ contains an integral number of these parts.

THE METHOD TREATING OF MECHANICAL PROBLEMS 589

For the sake of brevity we will call each of the two element-prisms of which $OM$ is an edge "el. prism $(O)$" and each of the element-prisms of which $MNN'$ is a common face "el. prism $(N)$." Similarly we will use the corresponding abbreviations "el. rect. $(L)$" and "el. rect. $(N)$" for the corresponding elements in relation to the auxiliary parabola as shown in the second figure.

Now it is easy to see that the figure made up of all the inscribed prisms is less than the figure made up of the circumscribed prisms by twice the final circumscribed prism adjacent to $FK$, i.e. by twice "el. prism $(N)$"; and, as the height of this prism may be made as small as we please by dividing $GK$ into sufficiently small parts, it follows that inscribed and circumscribed solid figures made up of element-prisms can be drawn differing by less than any assigned solid figure.

(1) Suppose, if possible, that
$$(\text{portion of cylinder}) > \tfrac{2}{3}(\text{prism cut off}),$$
or
$$(\text{prism cut off}) < \tfrac{3}{2}(\text{portion of cylinder}).$$
Let $(\text{prism cut off}) = \tfrac{3}{2}(\text{portion of cylinder} - X)$, say.

Construct circumscribed and inscribed figures made up of element-prisms, such that
$$(\text{circumscr. fig.}) - (\text{inscr. fig.}) < X.$$
Therefore $(\text{inscr. fig.}) > (\text{circumscr. fig.} - X),$
and *a fortiori* $> (\text{portion of cyl.} - X).$

It follows that
$$(\text{prism cut off}) < \tfrac{3}{2}(\text{inscribed figure}).$$

Considering now the element-prisms in the prism cut off and those in the inscribed figure respectively, we have

$$\text{el. prism } (N) : \text{el. prism } (O) = MN^2 : MO^2$$
$$= MN : ML \quad \text{[as in Prop. 13]}$$
$$= \text{el. rect. } (N) : \text{el. rect. } (L).$$

It follows that
$$\Sigma\{\text{el. prism } (N)\} : \Sigma\{\text{el. prism } (O)\} = \Sigma\{\text{el. rect. } (N)\} : \Sigma\{\text{el. rect. } (L)\}.$$

(There are really two more prisms and rectangles in the first and third than there are in the second and fourth terms respectively; but this makes no difference because the first and third terms may be multiplied by a common factor as $n/(n-2)$ without affecting the truth of the proportion. Cf. the proposition from *On Conoids and Spheroids* quoted on p. 571 above.)

Therefore
$$(\text{prism cut off}) : (\text{figure inscr. in portion of cyl.})$$
$$= (\text{rect. } GD) : (\text{fig. inscr. in parabola}).$$

But it was proved above that
$$(\text{prism cut off}) < \tfrac{3}{2}(\text{fig. inscr. in portion of cyl.});$$
therefore $(\text{rect. } GD) < \tfrac{3}{2}(\text{fig. inscr. in parabola}),$
and, a *fortiori* $(\text{rect. } GD) < \tfrac{3}{2}(\text{parabolic segmt.})$:
which is impossible, since
$$(\text{rect. } GD) = \tfrac{3}{2}(\text{parabolic segmt.}).$$

Therefore (portion of cyl.) is *not* greater than $\tfrac{2}{3}$(prism cut off).

(2) In the second lacuna must have come the beginning of the next *reductio ad absurdum* demolishing the other possible assumption that the portion of the cylinder is $< \tfrac{2}{3}$ of the prism cut off.

In this case our assumption is that

(prism cut off) $> \frac{3}{2}$(portion of cylinder);
and we circumscribe and inscribe figures made up of element-prisms, such that
(prism cut off) $> \frac{3}{2}$(fig. circumscr. about portion of cyl.).

We now consider the element-prisms in the prism cut off and in the circumscribed figure respectively, and the same argument as above gives
(prism cut off) : (fig. circumscr. about portion of cyl.)
= (rect. $GD$) : (fig. circumscr. about parabola),
whence it follows that
(rect. $GD$) $> \frac{3}{2}$(fig. circumscribed about parabola),
and, *a fortiori*,
(rect. $GD$) $> \frac{3}{2}$(parabolic segment):
which is impossible, since
(rect. $GD$) $= \frac{3}{2}$(parabolic segmt.).

Therefore
(portion of cyl.) is *not* less than $\frac{2}{3}$(prism cut off).
But it was also proved that neither is it greater;
therefore (portion of cyl.) $= \frac{2}{3}$(prism cut off)
$= \frac{1}{6}$(original prism).]

[PROPOSITION 15]

[This proposition, which is lost, would be the mechanical investigation of the second of the two special problems mentioned in the preface to the treatise, namely that of the cubature of the figure included between two cylinders, each of which is inscribed in one and the same cube so that its opposite bases are in two opposite faces of the cube and its surface touches the other four faces.

Zeuthen has shown how the mechanical method can be applied to this case.

In the accompanying figure $VWYX$ is a section of the cube by a plane (that of the paper) passing through the axis $BD$ of one of the cylinders inscribed in the cube and parallel to two opposite faces.

The same plane gives the circle $ABCD$ as the section of the other inscribed cylinder with axis perpendicular to the plane of the paper and extending on each side of the plane to a distance equal to the radius of the circle or half the side of the cube.

$AC$ is the diameter of the circle which is perpendicular to $BD$.

Join $AB, AD$ and produce them to meet the tangent at $C$ to the circle in $E, F$.

Then $EC = CF = CA$.

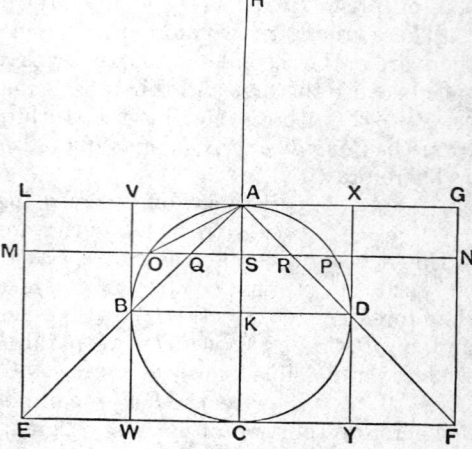

Let $LG$ be the tangent at $A$, and complete the rectangle $EFGL$.

Draw straight lines from $A$ to the four corners of the section in which the plane through $BD$ perpendicular to $AK$ cuts the cube. These straight lines, if produced, will meet the plane of the face of the cube opposite to $A$ in four points forming the four corners of a square in that plane with sides equal to $EF$ or double of the side of the cube, and we thus have a pyramid with $A$ for vertex and the latter square for base.

Complete the prism (parallelepiped) with the same base and height as the pyramid.

Draw in the parallelogram $LF$ any straight line $MN$ parallel to $EF$, and through $MN$ draw a plane at right angles to $AC$.

This plane cuts—
(1) the solid included by the two cylinders in a square with side equal to $OP$,
(2) the prism in a square with side equal to $MN$, and
(3) the pyramid in a square with side equal to $QR$.

Produce $CA$ to $H$, making $HA$ equal to $AC$, and imagine $HC$ to be the bar of a balance.

Now, as in Prop. 2, since $MS = AC$, $QS = AS$,
$$MS \cdot SQ = CA \cdot AS$$
$$= AO^2$$
$$= OS^2 + SQ^2.$$

Also $HA : AS = CA : AS$
$$= MS : SQ$$
$$= MS^2 : MS \cdot SQ$$
$$= MS^2 : (OS^2 + SQ^2), \text{ from above,}$$
$$= MN^2 : (OP^2 + QR^2)$$
$$= (\text{square, side } MN) : (\text{sq., side } OP + \text{sq., side } QR).$$

Therefore the square with side equal to $MN$, in the place where it is, is in equilibrium about $A$ with the squares with sides equal to $OP$, $QR$ respectively placed with their centres of gravity at $H$.

Proceeding in the same way with the square sections produced by other planes perpendicular to $AC$, we finally prove that the prism, in the place where it is, is in equilibrium about $A$ with the solid included by the two cylinders and the pyramid, both placed with their centres of gravity at $H$.

Now the centre of gravity of the prism is at $K$.

Therefore $\qquad HA : AK = (\text{prism}) : (\text{solid} + \text{pyramid})$
or $\qquad\qquad 2 : 1 = (\text{prism}) : (\text{solid} + \tfrac{1}{3} \text{prism})$.
Therefore $\qquad 2 \,(\text{solid}) + \tfrac{2}{3}(\text{prism}) = (\text{prism})$.
It follows that
$$(\text{solid included by cylinders}) = \tfrac{1}{6}(\text{prism})$$
$$= \tfrac{2}{3}(\text{cube}). \qquad \text{Q.E.D.}$$

There is no doubt that Archimedes proceeded to, and completed, the rigorous geometrical proof by the method of exhaustion.

As observed by Prof. C. Juel (Zeuthen *l.c.*), the solid in the present proposition is made up of 8 pieces of cylinders of the type of that treated in the preceding proposition. As however the two propositions are separately stated, there is no doubt that Archimedes' proofs of them were distinct.

In this case $AC$ would be divided into a very large number of equal parts and planes would be drawn through the points of division perpendicular to $AC$. These planes cut the solid, and also the cube $VY$, in square sections. Thus we can inscribe and circumscribe to the solid the requisite solid figures made up of element-prisms and differing by less than any assigned solid magnitude; the prisms have square bases and their heights are the small segments of $AC$. The element-prism in the inscribed and circumscribed figures which has the square equal to $OP^2$ for base corresponds to an element-prism in the cube which has for base a square with side equal to that of the cube; and as the ratio of the element-prisms is the ratio $OS^2 : BK^2$, we can use the same auxiliary parabola, and work out the proof in exactly the same way, as in Prop. 14.]

# THE INTRODUCTION TO ARITHMETIC
OF NICOMACHUS

# BIOGRAPHICAL NOTE
## NICOMACHUS, *fl. c.* A.D. 100

NICOMACHUS OF GERASA flourished around the end of the first century of our era. In one of his surviving books, the *Introduction to Harmonics*, he mentions a certain Thrasyllus, presumably Thrasyllus of Mendes, a writer on music, who lived in the reign of Tiberius. Another book by Nicomachus, the *Introduction to Arithmetic*, was translated into Latin by Apuleius under the Antonines. This places the life of Nicomachus somewhere between the middle of the first century and the middle of the second century. Perhaps the fact that Ptolemy, whose recorded astronomical observations were made between A.D. 127 and 151, is not mentioned in the *Introduction to Harmonics* makes it probable that he was not yet famous at the time Nicomachus was writing.

The manuscripts of Nicomachus' books and the scholia call him "of Gerasa." The best known city of that name was in Palestine and was primarily Greek. However, it can hardly be supposed that Nicomachus received all of his philosophical and mathematical education at Gerasa. He probably studied at Alexandria, at this time the center of mathematical studies and of Neo-Pythagoreanism. Jamblichus says of Nicomachus: "The man is great in mathematics, and had as instructors those that were most skilled in the subject."

Nothing is known of the personal life of Nicomachus except what is said or implied in the dedication of the *Introduction to Harmonics* to an unknown lady: "But I must spur on all my zeal, most noble and august lady, since it is you that bid me. . . . And, if the gods are willing, just as soon as I shall have leisure and a rest from my journeyings, I will compile for you a better and more detailed *Introduction* dealing with this very subject . . . and, so that you may the more easily follow the argument, I will take my beginning, say, from the same point as that at which I began your instruction when I was expounding the subject to you."

Nicomachus appears to have been an important member of the Neo-Pythagorean group, though his extant writings would seem to indicate that he was a popularizer and a compiler of manuals and not the head of a school. Besides the *Introduction to Arithmetic* and the *Introduction to Harmonics*, he also wrote a book on the mystical doctrine of number called *Theologoumena Arithmeticae*, which is one of the best sources on Neo-Pythagoreanism; extracts and paraphrases of this work survive in a later anonymous work of the same name and in the *Bibliotheca*, a collection of extracts from ancient works made in the ninth century by Photius, patriarch of Constantinople. Nicomachus also wrote an *Introduction to Geometry* and a *Life of Pythagoras*, which have not survived, and a larger work on music, possibly that promised in the dedication to the *Introduction to Harmonics*, of which we have only fragments. He may have written a book on the interpretation of Plato, though the evidence for it is slight, and also an *Introduction to Astronomy*, thereby completing the quadrivial series.

The success of the *Introduction to Arithmetic* must have been immediate. It was used as a text book throughout later antiquity and, in the Latin paraphrase of Boethius, throughout the Middle Ages. It had a host of commentators. In the *Philopatris*, attributed to Lucian, a character says: "You reckon like Nicomachus." This remark lends itself to more than one interpretation, but in any case it is evidence of his fame. Nicomachus also appears to have been considered one of the "golden chain," or succession, of true philosophers; for Proclus, the fifth century Neo-Platonist, who belonged to that "chain," claimed, on the basis of a dream, that he had within him the soul of Nicomachus.

# CONTENTS

BIOGRAPHICAL NOTE p. 595
BOOK I, p. 599     BOOK II, p. 617

# BOOK ONE

## CHAPTER I

*[1]* The ancients, who under the leadership of Pythagoras first made science systematic, defined philosophy as the love of wisdom. Indeed the name itself means this, and before Pythagoras all who had knowledge were called "wise" indiscriminately—a carpenter, for example, a cobbler, a helmsman, and in a word anyone who was versed in any art or handicraft. Pythagoras, however, restricting the title so as to apply to the knowledge and comprehension of reality, and calling the knowledge of the truth in this the only wisdom, naturally designated the desire and pursuit of this knowledge philosophy, as being desire for wisdom.

*[2]* He is more worthy of credence than those who have given other definitions, since he makes clear the sense of the term and the thing defined. This "wisdom" he defined as the knowledge, or science, of the truth in real things, conceiving "science" to be a steadfast and firm apprehension of the underlying substance, and "real things" to be those which continue uniformly and the same in the universe and never depart even briefly from their existence; these real things would be things immaterial, by sharing in the substance of which everything else that exists under the same name and is so called is said to be "this particular thing," and exists.

*[3]* For bodily, material things are, to be sure, forever involved in continuous flow and change—in imitation of the nature and peculiar quality of that eternal matter and substance which has been from the beginning, and which was all changeable and variable throughout. The bodiless things, however, of which we conceive in connection with or together with matter, such as qualities, quantities, configurations, largeness, smallness, equality, relations, actualities, dispositions, places, times, all those things, in a word, whereby the qualities found in each body are comprehended—all these are of themselves immovable and unchangeable, but accidentally they share in and partake of the affections of the body to which they belong.

*[4]* Now it is with such things that "wisdom" is particularly concerned, but accidentally also with things that share in them, that is, bodies.

## CHAPTER II

*[1]* Those things, however, are immaterial, eternal, without end, and it is their nature to persist ever the same and unchanging, abiding by their own essential being, and each one of them is called real in the proper sense. But what are involved in birth and destruction, growth and diminution, all kinds of change and participation, are seen to vary continually, and while they are called real things, by the same term as the former, so far as they partake of them, they are not actually real by their own nature; for they do not abide for even the shortest moment in the same condition, but are always passing over in all sorts of changes. *[2]* To quote the words of Timaeus, in Plato,[1] "What is that which always is, and has no birth, and what is that which is always becoming but never is? The one is apprehended by the mental processes, with reasoning, and is ever the same; the other can be guessed at by opinion in company with unreasoning sense, a thing which becomes and passes away, but never really is."

*[3]* Therefore, if we crave for the goal that is worthy and fitting for man, namely, happiness of life[2]—and this is accomplished by philosophy alone and by nothing else, and philosophy, as I said, means for us desire for wisdom, and wisdom the science of the truth in things, and of things some are properly so called, others merely share the name—it is reasonable and most necessary to distinguish and systematize the accidental qualities of things.

*[4]* Things, then, both those properly so called and those that simply have the name, are some of them unified and continuous, for example, an animal, the universe, a tree, and

---

[1] *Timaeus*, 27.
[2] The word used by Nicomachus, εὐζωΐα, is once employed by Aristotle in the *Ethics*, I. 8. 1098$^b$ 20 ff.

the like, which are properly and peculiarly called "magnitudes"; others are discontinuous, in a side-by-side arrangement, and, as it were, in heaps, which are called "multitudes," a flock, for instance, a people, a heap, a chorus, and the like.

*[5]* Wisdom, then, must be considered to be the knowledge of these two forms. Since, however, all multitude and magnitude are by their own nature of necessity infinite—for multitude starts from a definite root and never ceases increasing; and magnitude, when division beginning with a limited whole is carried on, cannot bring the dividing process to an end, but proceeds therefore to infinity—and since sciences are always sciences of limited things, and never of infinites, it is accordingly evident that a science dealing either with magnitude, per se, or with multitude, per se, could never be formulated, for each of them is limitless in itself, multitude in the direction of the more, and magnitude in the direction of the less. A science, however, would arise to deal with something separated from each of them, with quantity, set off from multitude, and size, set off from magnitude.

## CHAPTER III

*[1]* Again, to start afresh, since of quantity one kind is viewed by itself, having no relation to anything else, as "even," "odd," "perfect," and the like, and the other is relative to something else and is conceived of together with its relationship to another thing, like "double," "greater," "smaller," "half," "one and one-half times," "one and one-third times," and so forth, it is clear that two scientific methods will lay hold of and deal with the whole investigation of quantity; arithmetic, absolute quantity, and music, relative quantity.[1]

*[2]* And once more, inasmuch as part of "size" is in a state of rest and stability, and another part in motion and revolution, two other sciences in the same way will accurately treat of "size," geometry the part that abides and is at rest, astronomy that which moves and revolves.

*[3]* Without the aid of these, then, it is not possible to deal accurately with the forms of being nor to discover the truth in things, knowledge of which is wisdom, and evidently not even to philosophize properly, for "just as painting contributes to the menial arts toward correctness of theory, so in truth lines, numbers, harmonic intervals, and the revolutions of circles bear aid to the learning of the doctrines of wisdom," says the Pythagorean Androcydes. *[4]* Likewise Archytas of Tarentum, at the beginning of his treatise *On Harmony*, says the same thing, in about these words: "It seems to me that they do well to study mathematics, and it is not at all strange that they have correct knowledge about each thing, what it is. For if they knew rightly the nature of the whole, they were also likely to see well what is the nature of the parts. About geometry, indeed, and arithmetic and astronomy, they have handed down to us a clear understanding, and not least also about music. For these seem to be sister sciences; for they deal with sister subjects, the first two forms of being."

*[5]* Plato, too, at the end of the thirteenth book of the *Laws*, to which some give the title *The Philosopher*, because he investigates and defines in it what sort of man the real philosopher should be, in the course of his summary of what had previously been fully set forth and established, adds: "Every diagram, system of numbers, every scheme of harmony, and every law of the movement of the stars, ought to appear one to him who studies rightly; and what we say will properly appear if one studies all things looking to one principle, for there will be seen to be one bond for all these things, and if any one attempts philosophy in any other way he must call on Fortune to assist him. For there is never a path without these; this is the way, these the studies, be they hard or easy; by this course must one go, and not neglect it. The one who has attained all these things in the way I describe, him I for my part call wisest, and this I maintain through thick and thin." *[6]* For it is clear that these studies are like ladders and bridges that carry our minds from things apprehended by sense and opinion to those comprehended by the mind and understanding, and from those material, physical things, our foster-brethren known to us from childhood, to the things with which we are unacquainted, foreign to our senses, but in their immateriality and eternity more akin to our souls, and above all to the reason which is in our souls.

*[7]* And likewise in Plato's *Republic*, when the interlocutor of Socrates appears to bring certain plausible reasons to bear upon the mathematical sciences, to show that they are useful to human life; arithmetic for reckoning, distributions, contributions, exchanges, and partnerships, geometry for sieges, the founding of cities and sanctuaries, and the partition

---

[1] Cf. Aristotle, *Met.*, IV. 15. 1020$^b$ 26.

of land, music for festivals, entertainment, and the worship of the gods, and the doctrine of the spheres, or astronomy, for farming, navigation and other undertakings, revealing beforehand the proper procedure and suitable season, Socrates, reproaching him, says: "You amuse me, because you seem to fear that these are useless studies that I recommend; but that is very difficult, nay, impossible. For the eye of the soul, blinded and buried by other pursuits, is rekindled and aroused again by these and these alone, and it is better that this be saved than thousands of bodily eyes, for by it alone is the truth of the universe beheld."[1]

## CHAPTER IV

[1] Which then of these four methods must we first learn? Evidently, the one which naturally exists before them all, is superior and takes the place of origin and root and, as it were, of mother to the others. [2] And this is arithmetic,[2] not solely because we said that it existed before all the others in the mind of the creating God like some universal and exemplary plan, relying upon which as a design and archetypal example the creator of the universe sets in order his material creations and makes them attain to their proper ends; but also because it is naturally prior in birth, inasmuch as it abolishes other sciences with itself,[3] but is not abolished together with them. For example, "animal" is naturally antecedent to "man," for abolish "animal" and "man" is abolished; but if "man" be abolished, it no longer follows that "animal" is abolished at the same time. And again, "man" is antecedent to "schoolteacher"; for if "man" does not exist, neither does "schoolteacher," but if "schoolteacher" is nonexistent, it is still possible for "man" to be. Thus since it has the property of abolishing the other ideas with itself, it is likewise the older.

[3] Conversely, that is called younger and posterior which implies the other thing with itself,[4] but is not implied by it, like "musician," for this always implies "man." Again, take "horse"; "animal" is always implied along with "horse," but not the reverse; for if "animal" exists, it is not necessary that "horse" should exist, nor if "man" exists, must "musician" also be implied.

[4] So it is with the foregoing sciences; if geometry exists, arithmetic must also needs be implied, for it is with the help of this latter that we can speak of triangle, quadrilateral, octahedron, icosahedron, double, eightfold, or one and one-half times, or anything else of the sort which is used as a term by geometry, and such things cannot be conceived of without the numbers that are implied with each one. For how can "triple" exist, or be spoken of, unless the number 3 exists beforehand, or "eightfold" without 8? But on the contrary 3, 4, and the rest might be without the figures existing to which they give names. [5] Hence arithmetic abolishes geometry along with itself, but is not abolished by it, and while it is implied by geometry, it does not itself imply geometry.

## CHAPTER V

[1] And once more is this true in the case of music; not only because the absolute is prior to the relative, as "great" to "greater" and "rich" to "richer" and "man" to "father," but also because the musical harmonies, diatessaron, diapente, and diapason, are named for numbers; similarly all of their harmonic ratios are arithmetical ones, for the diatessaron is the ratio of 4:3, the diapente that of 3:2, and the diapason the double ratio; and the most perfect, the didiapason, is the quadruple ratio.

[2] More evidently still astronomy attains through arithmetic the investigations that pertain to it, not alone because it is later than geometry[5] in origin—for motion naturally comes after rest—nor because the motions of the stars have a perfectly melodious harmony, but also because risings, settings, progressions, retrogressions, increases, and all sorts of phases are governed by numerical cycles and quantities.

[3] So then we have rightly undertaken first the systematic treatment of this, as the science naturally prior, more honorable, and more venerable, and, as it were, mother and nurse of the rest; and here we will take our start for the sake of clearness.

## CHAPTER VI

[1] All that has by nature with systematic method been arranged in the universe seems both in part and as a whole to have been determined and ordered in accordance with number, by the forethought and the mind of him that

---

[1]*Republic*, 527 ff.
[2]Plato, *Rep.*, 522.
[3]Cf. below II. 22. 3. Cf. Aristotle, *Met.*, 1019$^a$ 1 ff.
[4]Cf. Aristotle, e. g., *Top.*, VI. 6. 144$^b$ 17: also *Top.*, II. 4. 111$^a$ 25 ff.

[5]Cf. Plato, *Rep.*, 528.

created all things; for the pattern was fixed, like a preliminary sketch, by the domination of number preëxistent in the mind of the world-creating God, number conceptual only and immaterial in every way, but at the same time the true and the eternal essence, so that with reference to it, as to an artistic plan, should be created all these things, time, motion, the heavens, the stars, all sorts of revolutions.

[2] It must needs be, then, that scientific number, being set over such things as these, should be harmoniously constituted, in accordance with itself; not by any other but by itself.

[3] Everything that is harmoniously constituted is knit together out of opposites and, of course, out of real things; for neither can non-existent things be set in harmony, nor can things that exist, but are like one another, nor yet things that are different, but have no relation one to another. It remains, accordingly, that those things out of which a harmony is made are both real, different, and things with some relation to one another.

[4] Of such things, therefore, scientific number consists; for the most fundamental species in it are two, embracing the essence of quantity, different from one another and not of a wholly different genus, odd and even, and they are reciprocally woven into harmony with each other, inseparably and uniformly, by a wonderful and divine Nature, as straightway we shall see.

## CHAPTER VII

[1] Number is limited multitude or a combination of units or a flow of quantity made up of units; and the first division of number is even and odd.

[2] The even[1] is that which can be divided into two equal parts without a unit intervening in the middle; and the odd is that which cannot be divided into two equal parts because of the aforesaid intervention of a unit.

[3] Now this is the definition after the ordinary conception; by the Pythagorean doctrine, however, the even number is that which admits of division into the greatest and the smallest parts at the same operation, greatest in size and smallest in quantity, in accordance with the natural contrariety of these two genera; and the odd is that which does not allow this to be done to it, but is divided into two unequal parts.

[4] In still another way, by the ancient definition, the even is that which can be divided alike into two equal and two unequal parts, except that the dyad, which is its elementary form, admits but one division, that into equal parts; and in any division whatsoever it brings to light only one species of number, however it may be divided, independent of the other. The odd is a number which in any division whatsoever, which necessarily is a division into unequal parts, shows both the two species of number together, never without intermixture one with another, but always in one another's company.

[5] By the definition in terms of each other, the odd is that which differs by a unit from the even in either direction, that is, toward the greater or the less, and the even is that which differs by a unit in either direction from the odd, that is, is greater by a unit or less by a unit.

## CHAPTER VIII

[1] Every number is at once half the sum of the two on either side of itself, and similarly half the sum of those next but one in either direction, and of those next beyond them, and so on as far as it is possible to go. [2] Unity alone, because it does not have two numbers on either side of it, is half merely of the adjoining number; hence unity is the natural starting point of all number.

[3] By subdivision of the even, there are the even-times even, the odd-times even, and the even-times odd. The even-times even and the even-times odd are opposite to one another, like extremes, and the odd-times even is common to them both like a mean term.

[4] Now the even-times even[2] is a number which is itself capable of being divided into two equal parts, in accordance with the properties of its genus, and with each of its parts similarly capable of division, and again in the same way each of their parts divisible into two equals until the division of the successive subdivisions reaches the naturally indivisible unit. [5] Take for example 64; one half of this is 32, and of this 16, and of this the half is 8, and of this 4, and of this 2, and then finally unity is half of the latter, and this is naturally indivisible and will not admit of a half.

[6] It is a property of the even-times even that, whatever part of it be taken, it is always

---

[1]Cf. Euclid, VII, Def. 6.

[2]Euclid's definition is: "The even-times even number is that which is measured by an even number an even number of times" *Elements*, VII, Def. 8.

even-times even in designation, and at the same time, by the quantity of the units in it, even-times even in value; and that neither of these two things will ever share in the other class.

*[7]* Doubtless it is because of this that it is called even-times even, because it is itself even and always has its parts, and the parts of its parts down to unity, even both in name and in value; in other words, every part that it has is even-times even in name and even-times even in value.

*[8]* There is a method of producing the even-times even, so that none will escape, but all successively fall under it, if you do as follows: *[9]* As you proceed from unity, as from a root, by the double ratio to infinity, as many terms as there are will all be even-times even, and it is impossible to find others besides these; for instance, 1, 2, 4, 8, 16, 32, 64, 128, 256, 512. . . .

*[10]* Now each of the numbers set forth was produced by the double ratio, beginning with unity, and is in every respect even-times even, and every part that it may be found to have is always named from some one of the numbers before it in the series, and the sum of units in this part is the same as one of the numbers before it, by a system of mutual correspondence, indeed, and interchange. If there is an even number of terms of the double ratio from unity, not one mean term can be found, but always two, from which the correspondence and interchange of factors and values, values and factors, will proceed in order, going first to the two on either side of the means, then to the next on either side, until it comes to the extreme terms, so that the whole will correspond in value to unity and unity to the whole. For example, if we set down 128 as the largest term, the number of terms will be even, for there are eight in all up to this number; and they will not have one mean term, for this is impossible with an even number, but of necessity two, 8 and 16. These will correspond to each other as factors; for of the whole, 128, 16 is one eighth and conversely 8 is one sixteenth. Thence proceeding in either direction, we find that 32 is one fourth, and 4 one thirty-second, and again 64 is one half, and 2 one sixty-fourth, and finally at the extremes unity is one one-hundred-twenty-eighth, and conversely 128 is the whole, to correspond with unity.

*[11]* If, however, the series consists of an odd number of terms, seven for example, and we deal with 64, there will be of necessity one mean term in accordance with the nature of the odd; the mean term will correspond to itself because it has no partner; and those on either side of it in turn will correspond to one another until this correspondence ends in the extremes. Unity, for example, will be one sixty-fourth, and 64 the whole, corresponding to unity; 32 is one half, and 2 one thirty-second; 16 is one fourth, and 4 one sixteenth; and 8 is the eighth part, with nothing else to correspond to it.

*[12]* It is the property of all these terms when they are added together successively to be equal to the next in the series, lacking one unit, so that of necessity their summation in any way whatsoever will be an odd number, for that which fails by a unit of being equal to an even number is odd. *[13]* This observation will be of use to us very shortly in the construction of perfect numbers.[1] But to take an example, the terms from unity preceding 256 in the series, when added together, are within 1 of equaling 256, and all the terms before 128, the term immediately preceding, are similarly equal to 128 save for one unit; and to the next terms the sums of those below them are similarly related. Thus unity itself[2] is within one unit of equaling the next term, which is 2, and these two together fail by 1 of equaling the next, and the three together are within 1 of the next in order, and you will find that this goes on without interruption to infinity.

*[14]* This too it is very needful to recall: If the number of terms of the even-times even series dealt with is even, the product of the extremes will always be equal to the product of the means; if there is an odd number of terms, the product of the extremes will be equal to the square of the mean. For, in the case of an even number of terms, 1 times 128 is equal to 8 times 16 and further to 2 times 64 and again to 4 times 32, and this is so in every case; and with an odd number of terms, 1 times 64 equals 2 times 32, and this equals 4 times 16, and this again equals 8 times 8, the mean term alone multiplied by itself.

## CHAPTER IX

*[1]* The even-times odd number is one which is by its genus itself even, but is specifically opposed to the aforesaid even-times even. It is a number of which, though it admits of the division into two equal halves, after the fashion of the genus common to it and the even-times even, the halves are not immediately divisible

---

[1]See Chapter 16.
[2]Cf. on I. 8. 7.

into two equals, for example, 6, 10, 14, 18, 22, 26, and the like; for after these have been divided their halves are found to be indivisible.

*[2]* It is the property of the even-times odd that whatever factor it may be discovered to have is opposite in name to its value, and that the quantity of every part is opposite in value to its name, and that the numerical value of its part never by any means is of the same genus as its name. To take a single example, the number 18, its half, with an even name, is 9, odd in value; its third part, again, with an odd designation, is 6, even in value; conversely, the sixth part is 3 and the ninth part 2; and in other numbers the same peculiarity will be found.

*[3]* It is possibly for this reason that it received such a name, that is, because, although it is even, its halves are at once odd.

*[4]* This number is produced from the series beginning with unity, with a difference of 2, namely, the odd numbers, set forth in proper order as far as you like and then multiplied by 2. The numbers produced would be, in order, these: 6, 10, 14, 18, 22, 26, 30, and so on, as far as you care to proceed. The greater terms always differ by 4 from the next smaller ones, the reason for which is that their original basic forms, the odd numbers, exceed one another by 2 and were multiplied by 2 to make this series, and 2 times 2 makes 4.

*[5]* Accordingly, in the natural series of numbers the even-times odd numbers will be found fifth from one another, exceeding one another by a difference of 4, passing over three terms, and produced by the multiplication of the odd numbers by 2.

*[6]* They are said to be opposite in properties to the even-times even, because of these the greatest extreme term alone is divisible, while of these former the smallest only proved to be indivisible; and in particular because in the former case the reciprocal arrangement of parts[1] from extremes to mean term or terms makes the product of the former equal to the square or product of the latter; but in this case by the same correspondence and comparison the mean term is one half the sum of the extremes, or if there should be two means, their sum equals that of the two extremes.

## CHAPTER X

*[1]* The odd-times even number is the one which displays the third form of the even, belonging in common to both the previously mentioned species like a single mean between two extremes, for in one respect it resembles the even-times even, and in another the even-times odd, and that property wherein it varies from the one it shares with the other, and by that property which it shares with the one it differs from the other.

*[2]* The odd-times even number is an even number which can be divided into two equal parts, whose parts also can so be divided, and sometimes even the parts of its parts, but it cannot carry the division of its parts as far as unity. Such numbers are 24, 28, 40; for each of these has its own half and indeed the half of its half, and sometimes one is found among them that will allow the halving to be carried even farther among its parts. There is none, however, that will have its parts divisible into halves as far as the naturally indivisible unit.

*[3]* Now in admitting more than one division, the odd-times even is like the even-times even and unlike the even-times odd; but in that its subdivision never ends with unity, it is like the even-times odd and unlike the even-times even.

*[4]* It alone has at once the proper qualities of each of the former two,[2] and then again properties which belong to neither of them; for of them one had only the highest term divisible, and the other only the smallest indivisible, but this neither; for it is observed to have more divisions than one in the greater term, and more than one indivisible in the lesser.

*[5]* Furthermore, there are in it certain parts whose names are not opposed to their values nor of the opposite genus,[3] after the fashion of the even-times even; and there are also always other parts of a name opposite and contrary in kind to their values, after the fashion of the even-times odd. For example, in 24, there are parts not opposed in name to their values, the fourth part, 6, the half, 12, the sixth, 4, and the twelfth, 2; but the third part, 8, the eighth, 3, and the twenty-fourth, 1, are opposed; and so it is with the rest.

*[6]* This number is produced by a somewhat complicated method, and shows, after a fashion, even in its manner of production, that it is a mixture of both other kinds. For whereas the even-times even is made from even numbers, the doubles from unity to infinity, and the even-times odd from the odd numbers from 3, progressing to infinity, this must be woven

---

[1] Cf. I. 8. 10.

[2] Cf. I. 9. 6.
[3] Cf. I. 8. 7; 9. 2.

together out of both classes, as being common to both. *[7]* Let us then set forth the odd numbers from 3 by themselves in due order in one series:

3, 5, 7, 9, 11, 13, 15, 17, 19, ...

and the even-times even, beginning with 4, again one after another in a second series after their own order:

4, 8, 16, 32, 64, 128, 256, ...

as far as you please. *[8]* Now multiply by the first number of either series—it makes no difference which—from the beginning and in order all those in the remaining series and note down the resulting numbers; then again multiply by the second number of the same series the same numbers once more, as far as you can, and write down the results; then with the third number again multiply the same terms anew, and however far you go you will get nothing but the odd-times even numbers.

*[9]* For the sake of illustration let us use the first term of the series of odd numbers and multiply by it all the terms in the second series in order, thus: $3 \times 4, 3 \times 8, 3 \times 16, 3 \times 32$, and so on to infinity. The results will be 12, 24, 48, 96, which we must note down in one line. Then taking a new start do the same thing with the second number, $5 \times 4, 5 \times 8, 5 \times 16, 5 \times 32$. The results will be 20, 40, 80, 160. Then do the same thing once more with 7, the third number, $7 \times 4, 7 \times 8, 7 \times 16, 7 \times 32$. The results are 28, 56, 112, 224; and in the same way as far as you care to go, you will get similar results.

*[10]* Now when you arrange the products of multiplication by each term in its proper line, making the lines parallel, in marvelous fashion there will appear along the breadth of the table the peculiar property of the even-times odd, that the mean term is always half the sum of the extremes, if there should be one mean, and the sum of the means equals the sum of the extremes if two. But along the length of the table the property of the even-times even will appear; for the product of the extremes is equal to the square of the mean, should there be one mean term, or their product, should there be two. Thus this one species has the peculiar properties of them both, because it is a natural mixture of them both.

## CHAPTER XI

*[1]* Again, while the odd is distinguished over against the even in classification and has nothing in common with it, since the latter is divisible into equal halves and the former is not thus divisible, nevertheless there are found three species of the odd,[1] differing from one another, of which the first is called the prime and incomposite,[2] that which is opposed to it the secondary and composite, and that which is midway between both of these and is viewed as a mean among extremes, namely, the variety which, in itself, is secondary and composite, but relatively is prime and incomposite.

*[2]* Now the first species, the prime and incomposite, is found whenever an odd number admits of no other factor save the one with the number itself as denominator, which is always unity; for example, 3, 5, 7, 11, 13, 17, 19, 23, 29, 31. None of these numbers will by any chance be found to have a fractional part with a denominator different from the number itself, but only the one with this as denominator, and this part will be unity in each case; for 3 has only a third part, which has the same denominator as the number and is of course unity, 5 a fifth, 7 a seventh, and 11 only an eleventh part, and in all of them these parts are unity.

*[3]* It has received this name because it can be measured only by the number which is first and common to all, unity, and by no other; moreover, because it is produced by no other number combined with itself save unity alone; for 5 is $5 \times 1$, and 7 is $7 \times 1$, and the others in accordance with their own quantity. To be sure, when they are combined with themselves, other

[1]Cf. Euclid, *Elem.*, VII, Deff., 11-14.
[2]Cf. Euclid, *Elem.*, VII, Def. 11; Aristotle, *Top.*, VIII. 2. 157ᵃ 39.

| Odd numbers | | 3 | 5 | 7 | 9 | 11 | 13 | 15 |
|---|---|---|---|---|---|---|---|---|
| Even-times even | | 4 | 8 | 16 | 32 | 64 | 128 | 256 |
| Odd-times even numbers, | *Breadth* | 12 | 24 | 48 | 96 | 192 | 384 | 768 |
| | | 20 | 40 | 80 | 160 | 320 | 640 | 1280 |
| | | 28 | 56 | 112 | 224 | 448 | 896 | 1792 |
| | | 36 | 72 | 144 | 288 | 576 | 1152 | 2304 |
| | | 44 | 88 | 176 | 352 | 704 | 1408 | 2816 |

*Length*

numbers might be produced, originating from them as from a fountain and a root, wherefore they are called "prime," because they exist beforehand as the beginnings of the others. For every origin is elementary and incomposite, into which everything is resolved and out of which everything is made, but the origin itself cannot be resolved into anything or constituted out of anything.

## CHAPTER XII

[1] The secondary, composite number[1] is an odd number, indeed, because it is distinguished as a member of this same class, but it has no elementary quality, for it gets its origin by the combination of something else. For this reason it is characteristic of the secondary number to have, in addition to the fractional part with the number itself as denominator, yet another part or parts with different denominators, the former always, as in all cases, unity, the latter never unity, but always either that number or those numbers by the combination of which it was produced. For example, 9, 15, 21, 25, 27, 33, 35, 39; each one of these is measured by unity, as other numbers are, and like them has a fractional part with the same denominator as the number itself, by the nature of the class common to them all; but by exception and more peculiarly they also employ a part, or parts, with a different denominator; 9, in addition to the ninth part, has a third part besides; 15 a third and a fifth besides a fifteenth; 21 a seventh and a third besides a twenty-first, and 25, in addition to the twenty-fifth, which has as a denominator 25 itself, also a fifth, with a different denominator.

[2] It is called secondary, then, because it can employ yet another measure along with unity, and because it is not elementary, but is produced by some other number combined with itself or with something else; in the case of 9, 3; in the case of 15, 5 or, by Zeus, 3; and those following in the same fashion. And it is called composite for this, or some such, reason: that it may be resolved into those numbers out of which it was made, since it can also be measured by them. For nothing that can be broken down is incomposite, but by all means composite.

## CHAPTER XIII

[1] Now while these two species of the odd are opposed to each other a third one[2] is con-

[1] Cf. Euclid, *Elements*. VII, Def. 14.
[2] Cf. Euclid, *Elements*, VII, Def. 13.

ceived of between them, deriving, as it were, its specific form from them both, namely the number which is in itself secondary and composite, but relatively to another number is prime and incomposite. This exists when a number, in addition to the common measure, unity, is measured by some other number and is therefore able to admit of a fractional part, or parts, with denominator other than the number itself, as well as the one with itself as denominator. When this is compared with another number of similar properties, it is found that it cannot be measured by a measure common to the other, nor does it have a fractional part with the same denominator as those in the other. As an illustration, let 9 be compared with 25. Each in itself is secondary and composite, but relatively to each other they have only unity as a common measure, and no factors in them have the same denominator, for the third part in the former does not exist in the latter nor is the fifth part in the latter found in the former.

[2] The production of these numbers is called by Eratosthenes the "sieve," because we take the odd numbers mingled together and indiscriminate and out of them by this method of production separate, as by a kind of instrument or sieve, the prime and incomposite by themselves, and the secondary and composite by themselves, and find the mixed class by themselves.

[3] The method of the "sieve" is as follows. I set forth all the odd numbers in order, beginning with 3, in as long a series as possible, and then starting with the first I observe what ones it can measure, and I find that it can measure the terms two places apart, as far as we care to proceed. And I find that it measures not as it chances and at random, but that it will measure the first one, that is, the one two places removed, by the quantity of the one that stands first in the series, that is, by its own quantity, for it measures it 3 times; and the one two places from this by the quantity of the second in order, for this it will measure 5 times; and again the one two places farther on by the quantity of the third in order, or 7 times, and the one two places still farther on by the quantity of the fourth in order, or 9 times, and so *ad infinitum* in the same way.

[4] Then taking a fresh start I come to the second number and observe what it can measure, and find that it measures all the terms four places apart, the first by the quantity of the first in order, or 3 times; the second by that of the second, or 5 times; the third by that of

the third, or 7 times; and in this order *ad infinitum*.

[5] Again, as before, the third term 7, taking over the measuring function, will measure terms six places apart, and the first by the quantity of 3, the first of the series, the second by that of 5, for this is the second number, and the third by that of 7, for this has the third position in the series.

[6] And analogously throughout, this process will go on without interruption, so that the numbers will succeed to the measuring function in accordance with their fixed position in the series; the interval separating terms measured is determined by the orderly progress of the even numbers from 2 to infinity, or by the doubling of the position in the series occupied by the measuring term, and the number of times a term is measured is fixed by the orderly advance of the odd numbers in series from 3.

[7] Now if you mark the numbers with certain signs, you will find that the terms which succeed one another in the measuring function neither measure all the same number—and sometimes not even two will measure the same one—nor do absolutely all of the numbers set forth submit themselves to a measure, but some entirely avoid being measured by any number whatsoever, some are measured by one only, and some by two or even more. [8] Now these that are not measured at all, but avoid it, are primes and incomposites, sifted out as it were by a sieve; those measured by only one measure in accordance with its own quantity will have but one fractional part with denominator different from the number itself, in addition to the part with the same denominator; and those which are measured by one measure only, but in accordance with the quantity of some other number than the measure and not its own, or are measured by two measures at the same time, will have several fractional parts with other denominators besides the one with the same as the number itself; these will be secondary and composite.

[9] The third division, the one common to both the former, which is in itself secondary and composite but primary and incomposite in relation to another, will consist of the numbers produced when some prime and incomposite number measures them in accordance with its own quantity, if one thus produced be compared to another of similar origin. For example, if 9, which was produced by 3 measuring by its own quantity, for it is 3 times 3, be compared with 25, which was produced from 5 measuring by its own quantity, for it is 5 times 5, these numbers have no common measure except unity.

[10] We shall now investigate how we may have a method[1] of discerning whether numbers are prime and incomposite, or secondary and composite, relatively to each other, since of the former unity is the common measure, but of the latter some other number also besides unity; and what this number is.

[11] Suppose there be given us two odd numbers and some one sets the problem and directs us to determine whether they are prime and incomposite relatively to each other or secondary and composite, and if they are secondary and composite, what number is their common measure. We must compare the given numbers and subtract the smaller from the larger as many times as possible; then after this subtraction, subtract in turn from the other as many times as possible; for this changing about and subtraction from one and the other in turn will necessarily end either in unity or in some one and the same number, which will necessarily be odd. [12] Now when the subtractions terminate in unity they show that the numbers are prime and incomposite relatively to each other; and when they end in some other number, odd in quantity and twice produced, then say that they are secondary and composite relatively to each other, and that their common measure is that very number which twice appears.

For example, if the given numbers were 23 and 45, subtract 23 from 45, and 22 will be the remainder; subtracting this from 23, the remainder is 1, subtracting this from 22 as many times as possible you will end with unity. Hence they are prime and incomposite to one another, and unity, which is the remainder, is their common measure.

[13] But if one should propose other numbers, 21 and 49, I subtract the smaller from the larger and 28 is the remainder. Then again I subtract the same 21 from this, for it can be done, and the remainder is 7. This I subtract in turn from 21 and 14 remains; from which I subtract 7 again, for it is possible, and 7 will remain. But it is not possible to subtract 7 from 7; hence the termination of the process with a repeated 7 has been brought about, and you may declare the original numbers 21 and 49 secondary and composite relatively to each

---

[1]This mode of determining common factors is found in Euclid (VII. 1; X. 2) and is commonly termed the Euclidean method of finding the greatest common divisor of numbers.

other, and 7 their common measure in addition to the universal unit.

## CHAPTER XIV

[1] To make again a fresh start, of the simple even numbers, some are superabundant, some deficient, like extremes set over against each other, and some are intermediary between them and are called perfect. [2] Those which are said to be opposites to one another, the superabundant and deficient, are distinguished from one another in the relation of inequality[1] in the directions of the greater and the less; for apart from these no other form of inequality could be conceived, nor could evil,[2] disease, disproportion, unseemliness, nor any such thing, save in terms of excess or deficiency. For in the realm of the greater[3] there arise excesses, overreaching, and superabundance, and in the less need, deficiency, privation, and lack; but in that which lies between the greater and the less, namely, the equal, are virtues, wealth, moderation, propriety, beauty, and the like, to which the aforesaid form of number, the perfect, is most akin.

[3] Now the superabundant number is one which has, over and above the factors which belong to it and fall to its share, others in addition, just as if an animal should be created with too many parts or limbs, with ten tongues, as the poet says,[4] and ten mouths, or with nine lips, or three rows of teeth, or a hundred hands, or too many fingers on one hand. Similarly if, when all the factors in a number are examined and added together in one sum, it proves upon investigation that the number's own factors exceed the number itself, this is called a superabundant number, for it oversteps the symmetry which exists between the perfect and its own parts. Such are 12, 24, and certain others, for 12 has a half, 6, a third, 4, a fourth, 3, a sixth, 2, and a twelfth, 1, which added together make 16, which is more than the original 12; its parts, therefore, are greater than the whole itself. [4] And 24 has a half, a third, fourth, sixth, eighth, twelfth, and twenty-fourth, which are 12, 8, 6, 4, 3, 2, 1. Added together they make 36, which, compared to the original number, 24, is found to be greater than it, although made up solely of its factors. Hence in this case also the parts are in excess of the whole.

[1]Cf. I. 17. 2, 4, 6; also I. 23. 4.
[2]Cf. Arist., *Ethics*, II. 6. 1106$^b$ 33.
[3]Cf. Arist., *Ethics*, II. 6. 1106$^b$ 24, 33.
[4]Homer, *Odyssey*, XII. 85 ff.

## CHAPTER XV

[1] The deficient number is one which has qualities the opposite of those pointed out, and whose factors added together are less in comparison than the number itself. It is as if some animal should fall short of the natural number of limbs or parts, or as if a man should have but one eye, as in the poem, "And one round orb was fixed in his brow"; or as though one should be one-handed, or have fewer than five fingers on one hand, or lack a tongue, or some such member. Such a one would be called deficient and so to speak maimed, after the peculiar fashion of the number whose factors are less than itself, such as 8 or 14. For 8 has the factors half, fourth, and eighth, which are 4, 2, and 1, and added together they make 7, and less than the original number. The parts, therefore, fall short of making up the whole. [2] Again, 14 has a half, a seventh, a fourteenth, 7, 2, and 1, respectively; and all together they make 10, less than the original number. So this number also is deficient in its parts, with respect to making up the whole out of them.

## CHAPTER XVI

[1] While these two varieties are opposed after the manner of extremes, the so-called perfect number[5] appears as a mean, which is discovered to be in the realm of equality, and neither makes its parts greater than itself, added together, nor shows itself greater than its parts, but is always equal to its own parts. For the equal is always conceived of as in the midground between greater and less, and is, as it were, moderation between excess and deficiency, and that which is in tune, between pitches too high and too low.

[2] Now when a number, comparing with itself the sum and combination of all the factors whose presence it will admit, neither exceeds them in multitude nor is exceeded by them, then such a number is properly said to be perfect, as one which is equal to its own parts. Such numbers are 6 and 28; for 6 has the factors half, third, and sixth, 3, 2, and 1, respectively, and these added together make 6 and are equal to the original number, and neither more nor less. Twenty-eight has the factors half, fourth, seventh, fourteenth, and twenty-eighth, which are 14, 7, 4, 2 and 1; these added together make 28, and so neither are the

[5]Euclid's definition, *Elem.*, VII. 22, is: "A perfect number is one that is equal to its own parts."

parts greater than the whole nor the whole greater than the parts, but their comparison is in equality, which is the peculiar quality of the perfect number.

*[3]* It comes about that even as fair and excellent things are few and easily enumerated, while ugly and evil ones are widespread, so also the superabundant and deficient numbers are found in great multitude and irregularly placed —for the method of their discovery is irregular—but the perfect numbers are easily enumerated and arranged with suitable order; for only one is found among the units, 6, only one other among the tens, 28, and a third in the rank of the hundreds, 496 alone, and a fourth within the limits of the thousands, that is, below ten thousand, 8,128. And it is their accompanying characteristic to end alternately in 6 or 8, and always to be even.

*[4]* There is a method of producing them,[1] neat and unfailing, which neither passes by any of the perfect numbers nor fails to differentiate any of those that are not such, which is carried out in the following way.

You must set forth the even-times even numbers from unity, advancing in order in one line, as far as you please: 1, 2, 4, 8, 16, 32, 64, 128, 256, 512, 1,024, 2,048, 4,096.... Then you must add them together, one at a time, and each time you make a summation observe the result to see what it is. If you find that it is a prime, incomposite number, multiply it by the quantity of the last number added, and the result will always be a perfect number. If, however, the result is secondary and composite, do not multiply, but add the next and observe again what the resulting number is; if it is secondary and composite, again pass it by and do not multiply; but add the next; but if it is prime and incomposite, multiply it by the last term added, and the result will be a perfect number; and so on to infinity. In similar fashion you will produce all the perfect numbers in succession, overlooking none.

For example, to 1 I add 2, and observe the sum, and find that it is 3, a prime and incomposite number in accordance with our previous demonstrations; for it has no factor with denominator different from the number itself, but only that with denominator agreeing. Therefore I multiply it by the last number to be taken into the sum, that is, 2; I get 6, and this I declare to be the first perfect number in actuality, and to have those parts which are beheld in the numbers of which it is composed. For it will have unity as the factor with denominator the same as itself, that is, its sixth part; and 3 as the half, which is seen in 2, and conversely 2 as its third part.

*[5]* Twenty-eight likewise is produced by the same method when another number, 4, is added to the previous ones. For the sum of the three, 1, 2, and 4, is 7, and is found to be prime and incomposite, for it admits only the factor with denominator like itself, the seventh part. Therefore I multiply it by the quantity of the term last taken into the summation, and my result is 28, equal to its own parts, and having its factors derived from the numbers already adduced, a half corresponding to 2; a fourth, to 7; a seventh, to 4; a fourteenth to offset the half; and a twenty-eighth, in accordance with its own nomenclature, which is 1 in all numbers.

*[6]* When these have been discovered, 6 among the units and 28 in the tens, you must do the same to fashion the next. *[7]* Again add the next number, 8, and the sum is 15. Observing this, I find that we no longer have a prime and incomposite number, but in addition to the factor with denominator like the number itself, it has also a fifth and a third, with unlike denominators. Hence I do not multiply it by 8, but add the next number, 16, and 31 results. As this is a prime, incomposite number, of necessity it will be multiplied, in accordance with the general rule of the process, by the last number added, 16, and the result is 496, in the hundreds; and then comes 8,128 in the thousands, and so on, as far as it is convenient for one to follow.

*[8]* Now unity is potentially a perfect number, but not actually; for taking it from the series as the very first I observe what sort it is, according to the rule, and find it prime and incomposite; for it is so in very truth, not by participation like the rest, but it is the primary number of all, and alone incomposite. *[9]* I multiply it, therefore, by the last term taken into the summation, that is, by itself, and my result is 1; for 1 times 1 equals 1. *[10]* Thus unity is perfect potentially; for it is potentially equal to its own parts, the others actually.

## CHAPTER XVII

*[1]* Now that we have given a preliminary systematic account of absolute quantity we come in turn to relative quantity.

*[2]* Of relative quantity, then, the highest generic divisions are two, equality and inequal-

---

[1] Cf. Euclid (IX. 36).

ity; for everything viewed in comparison with another thing is either equal or unequal, and there is no third thing besides these.

*[3]* Now the equal is seen, when of the things compared one neither exceeds nor falls short in comparison with the other, for example, 100 compared with 100, 10 with 10, 2 with 2, a mina with a mina, a talent with a talent, a cubit with a cubit, and the like, either in bulk, length, weight, or any kind of quantity. *[4]* And as a peculiar characteristic, also this relation is of itself not to be divided or separated, as being most elementary, for it admits of no difference. For there is no such thing as this kind of equality and that kind, but the equal exists in one and the same manner. *[5]* And that which corresponds to an equal thing, to be sure, does not have a different name from it, but the same; like "friend," "neighbor," "comrade," so also "equal"; for it is equal to an equal.

*[6]* The unequal, on the other hand, is split up by subdivisions, and one part of it is the greater, the other the less, which have opposite names and are antithetical to one another in their quantity and relation. For the greater is greater than some other thing, and the less again is less than another thing in comparison, and their names are not the same, but they each have different ones, for example, "father" and "son," "striker" and "struck," "teacher" and "pupil," and the like.

*[7]* Moreover, of the greater, separated by a second subdivision into five species, one kind is the multiple, another the superparticular, another the superpartient, another the multiple superparticular, and another the multiple superpartient. *[8]* And of its opposite, the less, there arise similarly by subdivision five species, opposed to the foregoing five varieties of the greater, the submultiple, subsuperparticular, subsuperpartient, submultiple-superparticular, and submultiple-superpartient; for as whole answers to whole, smaller to greater, so also the varieties correspond, each to each, in the aforesaid order, with the prefix sub-.

## CHAPTER XVIII

*[1]* Once more, then; the multiple is the species of the greater first and most original by nature, as straightway we shall see, and it is a number which, when it is observed in comparison with another, contains the whole of that number more than once. For example, compared with unity, all the successive numbers beginning with 2 generate in their proper order the regular forms of the multiple; for 2, in the first place, is and is called the double, 3 triple, 4 quadruple, and so on; for "more than once" means twice, or three times, and so on in succession as far as you like.

*[2]* Answering to this is the submultiple, which is itself primary in the smaller division of inequality. It is the number which, when it is compared with a larger, is able to measure it completely more than once, and "more than once" starts with twice and goes on to infinity. *[3]* If then it measures the larger number that is being compared twice only, it is properly called the subdouble, as 1 is of 2; if thrice, subtriple, as 1 of 3; if four times, subquadruple, as 1 of 4, and so on in succession.

*[4]* While each of these, the multiple and the submultiple, is generically infinite, the varieties by subdivision and the species also are observed naturally to make an infinite series. For the double, beginning with 2, goes on through all the even numbers, as we select alternate numbers out of the natural series; and these will be called doubles in comparison with the even and odd numbers successively placed beginning with unity. *[5]* All the numbers from the beginning two places apart, and third in order, are triples, for example, 3, 6, 9, 12, 15, 18, 21, 24. It is their property to be alternately odd and even, and they themselves in the regular series from unity are triples of all the numbers in succession as far as one wishes to go on with the process.

*[6]* The quadruples are those in the fourth places, three apart, for instance, 4, 8, 12, 16, 20, 24, 28, 32, and so on. These are the quadruples of the regular series of numbers from unity going on as far as one finds it convenient to follow. It belongs to them all to be even; for one needs only to take the alternate terms out of the even numbers already selected. Thus necessarily it is true that the even numbers, with no further designation, are all doubles, the alternate ones quadruples, those two places apart sextuples and those three places apart octuples, and this series will go on, on this same analogy, indefinitely.

*[7]* The quintuples will be seen to be those four places apart, placed fifth from one another, and themselves the quintuples of the successive numbers beginning with unity. Alternately they are odd and even, like the triples.

## CHAPTER XIX

*[1]* The superparticular, the second species of the greater both naturally and in order, is a

number that contains within itself the whole of the number compared with it, and some one factor of it besides.

*[2]* If this factor is a half, the greater of the terms compared is called specifically sesquialter, and the smaller subsesquialter; if it is a third, sesquitertian and subsesquitertian; and as you go on throughout it will always thus agree, so that these species also will progress to infinity, even though they are species of an unlimited genus.

For it comes about that the first species, the sesquialter ratio, has as its consequents the even numbers in succession from 2, and no other at all, and as antecedents the triples in succession from 3, and no other. *[3]* These must be joined together regularly, first to first, second to second, third to third—3:2, 6:4, 9:6, 12:8—and the analogous numbers to the ones corresponding to them in position.

*[4]* If we care to investigate the second species of the superparticular, the sesquitertian (for the fraction naturally following after the half is the third), we shall have this definition of it—a number which contains the whole of the number compared, and a third of it in addition to the whole. We may have examples of it, in the proper order, in the successive quadruples beginning with 4 joined to the triples from 3, each term with the one in the corresponding position in the series, for example, 4:3, 8:6, 12:9, and so on to infinity. *[5]* It is plain that that which corresponds to the sesquitertian but is called with the prefix sub-, subsesquitertian, is the number, the whole of which is contained and a third part in addition, for example, 3:4, 6:8, 9:12, and the similar pairs of numbers in the same position in the series.

*[6]* And we must observe the never-failing corollary of all this, that the first forms in each series, the so-called root numbers, are next to one another in the natural series; the next after the root-forms show an interval of only one number; the third two; the fourth three; the fifth four; and so on, as far as you like. *[7]* Furthermore, that the fraction after which each of the superparticulars is named is seen in the lesser of the root numbers, never in the greater.

*[8]* That by nature and by no disposition of ours the multiple is a more elementary and an older form than the superparticular we shall shortly learn, through a somewhat intricate process. And here, for a simple demonstration, we must prepare in regular and parallel lines the multiples specified above, according to their varieties, first the double in one line, then in a second the triple, then the quadruple in a third, and so on as far as the tenfold multiples, so that we may detect their order and variety, their regulated progress, and which of them is naturally prior, and indeed other corollaries delightful in their exactness. Let the diagram be as follows: *[9]*

| 1 | 2 | 3 | 4 | 5 | 6 | 7 | 8 | 9 | 10 |
|---|---|---|---|---|---|---|---|---|---|
| 2 | 4 | 6 | 8 | 10 | 12 | 14 | 16 | 18 | 20 |
| 3 | 6 | 9 | 12 | 15 | 18 | 21 | 24 | 27 | 30 |
| 4 | 8 | 12 | 16 | 20 | 24 | 28 | 32 | 36 | 40 |
| 5 | 10 | 15 | 20 | 25 | 30 | 35 | 40 | 45 | 50 |
| 6 | 12 | 18 | 24 | 30 | 36 | 42 | 48 | 54 | 60 |
| 7 | 14 | 21 | 28 | 35 | 42 | 49 | 56 | 63 | 70 |
| 8 | 16 | 24 | 32 | 40 | 48 | 56 | 64 | 72 | 80 |
| 9 | 18 | 27 | 36 | 45 | 54 | 63 | 72 | 81 | 90 |
| 10 | 20 | 30 | 40 | 50 | 60 | 70 | 80 | 90 | 100 |

*[10]* Let there be set forth in the first row the natural series from unity, and then in order those species of the multiple which we were bidden to insert.

*[11]* Now then in comparison with the first rows beginning with unity, if we read both across and up and down in the form of the letter gamma, the next rows both ways, themselves in the form of a gamma, beginning with 4, are multiples according to the first form of the multiple, for they are doubles. The first differs by unity from the first, the second from the second by 2, the third from the third by 3, the next by 4, those following by 5, and you will find that this follows throughout.

The third rows in both directions from 9, their common origin, will be the triples of the terms in that same first row according to the second form of the multiple; the cross-lines like the letter chi, ending in the term 3 in either direction, are to be taken into consideration. *[12]* The difference, for these numbers, will progress after the series of the even numbers, being 2 for the first, 4 for the next, 6 for the third; and this difference Nature has of her own accord interpolated for us between these rows that are being examined, as is evident in the diagram.

*[13]* The fourth row, whose common origin in both directions is 16, and whose cross-lines end with the terms 4, exhibits the third species of multiple, the quadruple, when it is compared with that same first row according to corresponding positions, first term with first, second with second, third with third, and so on. Again, the differences of these numbers are 3, 6, then 9, then 12, and the quantities that progress by steps of 3. These numbers are detected in the

structure of the diagram in places just above the quadruples, and in the subsequent forms of the multiple the analogy will hold throughout.

*[14]* In comparison with the second line reading either way, which begins with the common origin 4 and runs over in cross-lines to the term 2 in each row, the lines which are next in order beneath display the first species of the superparticular, that is, the sesquialter, between terms occupying corresponding places. Thus by divine nature, not by our convention or agreement, the superparticulars are of later origin than the multiples. For illustration, 3 is the sesquialter of 2, 6 of 4, 9 of 6, 12 of 8, 15 of 10, and throughout thus. They have as a difference the successive numbers from unity, like those before them.

*[15]* The sesquitertians, the second species of superparticular, proceed with a regular, even advance from 4:3, 8:6, 12:9, 16:12, and so on; having also a regular increase of their differences. *[16]* And in the other multiple and superparticular relations you will see that the results are in harmony and not by any means inconsistent as you go on to infinity.

*[17]* The following feature of the diagram, moreover, is of no less exactness. The terms at the corners are units; the one at the beginning a simple unit, that at the end the unit of the third course, and the other two units of the second course appearing twice; so that the product (of the first two) is equal to the square (of the last). *[18]* Furthermore, in reading either way there is an even progress from unity to the tens, and again on the opposite sides two other progressions from 10 to 100.

*[19]* The terms on the diagonal from 1 to 100 are all square numbers, the products of equals by equals, and those flanking them on either side are all heteromecic, unequal, and the products of sides of which one is greater than the other by unity; and so the sum of two successive squares and twice the heteromecic numbers between them is always a square, and conversely a square is always produced from the two heteromecic numbers on the sides and twice the square between them.

*[20]* An ambitious person might find many other pleasing things displayed in this diagram, upon which it is not now the time to dwell, for we have not yet gained recognition of them from our *Introduction*, and so we must turn to the next subject. For after these two generic relations of the multiple and the superparticular and the other two, opposite to them, with the prefix sub-, the submultiple and the subsuperparticular, there are in the greater division of inequality the superpartient, and in the less its opposite, the subsuperpartient.

## CHAPTER XX

*[1]* It is the superpartient relation when a number contains within itself the whole of the number compared and in addition more than one part of it; and "more than one" starts with 2 and goes on to all the numbers in succession. Thus the root-form of the superpartient is naturally the one which has in addition to the whole two parts of the number compared, and as a species will be called superbipartient; after this the one with three parts besides the whole will be called supertripartient as a species; then comes the superquadripartient, the superquintipartient, and so forth.

*[2]* The parts have their root and origin with the third, for it is impossible in this case to begin with the half. For if we assume that any number contains two halves of the compared number, besides the whole of it, we shall inadvertently be setting up a multiple instead of a superpartient, because each whole, plus two halves of it, added together makes double the original number. Thus it is most necessary to start with two thirds, then two fifths, two sevenths, and after these two ninths, following the advance of the odd numbers; for two quarters, for example, again are a half, two sixths a third, and thus again superparticulars will be produced instead of superpartients, which is not the problem laid before us nor in accord with the systematic construction of our science.

*[3]* After the superpartient the subsuperpartient immediately is produced, whenever a number is completely contained in the one compared with it, and in addition several parts of it, 2, 3, 4, or 5, and so on.

## CHAPTER XXI

*[1]* The regular arrangement and orderly production of both species are discovered when we set forth the successive even and odd numbers, beginning with 3, and compare with them simple series of odd numbers only, from 5 in succession, first to first—that is, 5 to 3,—second to second—that is, 7 to 4,—third to third—that is, 9 to 5,—fourth to fourth—that is, 11 to 6,— and so on in the same order as far as you like. In this way the forms of the superpartient and the subsuperpartient, in due order, will be disclosed through the root-forms of each species, the superbipartient first, then the supertripartient, superquadripartient, and super-

# INTRODUCTION TO ARITHMETIC I.

quintipartient, and further in succession in similar manner; for after the root-forms of each species the ones which follow them will be produced by doubling, or tripling, both the terms, and in general by multiplying after the regular forms of the multiple.

nerically, it will have in its subdivisions according to species a sort of diversification and change of names proper both to the first part of the name and to the second. For instance, in the first part, that is, the multiple, it will have double, triple, quadruple, quintuple, and

### Table of the Superpartients

| Root-forms | 5 | 3 | 7 | 4 | 9 | 5 | 11 | 6 | 13 | 7 |
|---|---|---|---|---|---|---|---|---|---|---|
| | 10 | 6 | 14 | 8 | 18 | 10 | 22 | 12 | 26 | 14 |
| | 15 | 9 | 21 | 12 | 27 | 15 | 33 | 18 | 39 | 21 |
| | 20 | 12 | 28 | 16 | 36 | 20 | 44 | 24 | 52 | 28 |
| | 25 | 15 | 35 | 20 | 45 | 25 | 55 | 30 | 65 | 35 |
| | 30 | 18 | 42 | 24 | 54 | 30 | 66 | 36 | 78 | 42 |
| | 35 | 21 | 49 | 28 | 63 | 35 | 77 | 42 | 91 | 49 |
| | 40 | 24 | 56 | 32 | 72 | 40 | 88 | 48 | 104 | 56 |
| | 45 | 27 | 63 | 36 | 81 | 45 | 99 | 54 | 117 | 63 |

[2] It must be observed that from the two parts in addition to the whole which are contained in the greater term, we are to understand "third," in the case of three parts, "fourth," with four parts, "fifth," with five, "sixth," and so on, so that the order of nomenclature is something like this: superbipartient, supertripartient, superquadripartient, then superquintipartient, and similarly with the rest.

[3] Now the simple, uncompounded relations of relative quantity are these which have been enumerated. Those which are compounded of them and as it were woven out of two into one are the following, of which the antecedents are the multiple superparticular and multiple superpartient, and the consequents the ones that immediately arise in connection with each of the former, named with the prefix sub-; together with the multiple superparticular the submultiple superparticular, and with the multiple superpartient the submultiple superpartient. In the subdivision of the genera the species of the one will correspond to those of the other, these also having names with the prefix sub-.

## CHAPTER XXII

[1] Now the multiple superparticular is a relation in which the greater of the compared terms contains within itself the lesser term more than once and in addition some one part of it, whatever this may be.

[2] As a compound, such a number is doubly diversified after the peculiarities of nomenclature of its components on either side; for inasmuch as the multiple superparticular is composed of the multiple and superparticular ge-

so forth, and in the second part, generically from the superparticular, its specific forms in due order, the sesquialter, sesquitertian, sesquiquartan, sesquiquintan, and so on, so that the combination will proceed in somewhat this order:

Double sesquialter, double sesquitertian, double sesquiquartan, double sesquiquintan, double sesquisextan, and analogously.

Beginning once more: triple sesquialter, triple sesquitertian, triple sesquiquartan, triple sesquiquintan.

Again: quadruple sesquialter, quadruple sesquitertian, quadruple sesquiquartan, quadruple sesquiquintan.

Again: quintuple sesquialter, quintuple sesquitertian, quintuple sesquiquartan, quintuple sesquiquintan, and the forms analogous to these *ad infinitum*. Whatever number of times the greater contains the whole of the smaller, by this quantity the first part of the ratio of the terms joined together in the multiple superparticular is named; and whatever may be the factor, in addition to the whole several times contained, that is, in the greater term, from this is named the second kind of ratio of which the multiple superparticular is compounded.

[3] Examples of it are these: 5 is the double sesquialter of 2; 7 the double sesquitertian of 3; 9 the double sesquiquartan of 4; 11 the double sesquiquintan of 5. You will furthermore always produce them in regular order, in this fashion, by comparing with the successive even and odd numbers from 2 the odd numbers, exclusively, from 5, first with first, second with second, third with third, and the others each with the one in the same position in the series.

The successive terms beginning with 5 and differing by 5 will be without exception double sesquialters of all the successive even numbers from 2 on, when terms in the same position in the series are compared; and beginning with 3, if all those with a difference of 3 be set forth, as 3, 6, 9, 12, 15, 18, 21, and in another series there be set forth those that differ by 7, to infinity, as 7, 14, 21, 28, 35, 42, 49, and the greater be compared with the smaller, first to first, second to second, third to third, fourth to fourth, and so on, the second species will appear, the double sesquitertian, disposed in its proper order.

[4] Then again, to take a fresh start, if the simple series of quadruples be set forth, 4, 8, 12, 16, 20, 24, 28, 32, and then there be placed beside it in another series the successive numbers beginning with 9, and increasing by 9, as 9, 18, 27, 36, 45, 54, we shall have revealed once more the multiple superparticular in a specific form, that is, the double sesquiquartan in its proper order; and any one who desires can contrive this to an unlimited extent.

[5] The second kind begins with the triple sesquialter, such as 7:2, 14:4, and in general the numbers that advance by steps of 7 compared with the even numbers in order from 2.

[6] Then once more, 10:3 is the first triple sesquitertian, 20:6 the second, and, in a word, the multiples of 10 in succession, compared with the successive triples. This indeed we can observe with greater exactitude and clearness in the table studied above, for in comparison with the first row the succeeding rows in order,[1] compared as whole rows, display the forms of the multiple in regular order up to infinity when they are all compared in each case to the same first row; and when each row is compared to all those above it, in succession, the second row being taken as our starting point, all the forms of the superparticular are produced in their proper order; and if we start with the third row, all of those beginning with the fifth that are odd in the series when they are compared with this same third row, and those following it, will show all the forms of the superpartient in proper order. In the case of the multiple superparticular, the comparisons will have a natural order of their own if we start with the second row and compare the terms from the fifth, first to first, second to second, third to third, and so on, and then the terms of the seventh row to the third, those of the ninth to the fourth, and follow the corresponding order as far as we are able to go. [7] It is plain that here too the smaller terms have names corresponding to the larger ones, with the prefix sub-, according to the nomenclature given them all.

## CHAPTER XXIII

[1] The multiple superpartient is the remaining relation of number. This, and the relation called by a corresponding name with the prefix sub-, exist when a number contains the whole of the number compared more than once (that is, twice, thrice, or any number of times) and certain parts of it, more than one, either two, three, or four, and so on, besides. [2] These parts[2] are not halves, for the reasons mentioned above, but either thirds, fourths, or fifths, and so on.

[3] From what has already been said it is not hard to conceive of the varieties of this relation, for they are differentiated in the same way as, and consistently with, those that precede, double superbipartient, double supertripartient, double superquadripartient, and so on. For example, 8 is the double superbipartient of 3, 16 of 6, and in general the numbers beginning with 8 and differing by 8 are double superbipartients of those beginning with 3 and differing by 3, when those in corresponding places in the series are compared, and in the case of the other varieties one could ascertain their proper sequence by following out what has already been said. In this case, too, we must conceive that the nomenclature of the number compared goes along and suffers corresponding changes, with the addition of the prefix sub-.

[4] Thus we come to the end of our speculation upon the ten arithmetical relations for a first *Introduction*. There is, however, a method very exact and necessary for all discussion of the nature of the universe which very clearly and indisputably presents to us the fact that that which is fair and limited, and which subjects itself to knowledge,[3] is naturally prior to the unlimited, incomprehensible, and ugly, and furthermore that the parts and varieties of the infinite and unlimited are given shape and boundaries by the former, and through it attain to their fitting order and sequence, and like objects brought beneath some seal or measure, all gain a share of likeness to it and similarity of name when they fall under its influence. For thus it is reasonable that the rational

---

[1] Referring to the table in Chapter 19.
[2] See 20. 2 above.
[3] Cf. I. 2. 5.

part of the soul will be the agent which puts in order the irrational part, and passion and appetite, which find their places in the two forms of inequality, will be regulated by the reasoning faculty as though by a kind of equality and sameness. *[5]* And from this equalizing process there will properly result for us the so-called ethical virtues, sobriety,¹ courage, gentleness, self-control, fortitude, and the like.

*[6]* Let us then consider the nature of the principle that pertains to these universal matters. It is capable of proving that all the complex species of inequality and the varieties of these species are produced out of equality, first and alone, as from a mother and root.

*[7]* Let there be given us equal numbers in three terms, first, units, then two's in another group of three, then three's, next four's, five's, and so on as far as you like. For them, as the setting forth of these terms has come about by a divine, and not human, contrivance, nay, by Nature herself, multiples will first be produced, and among these the double will lead the way, the triple after the double, the quadruple next, and then the quintuple, and, following the order we have previously recognized, *ad infinitum;* second, the superparticular, and here again the first form, the sesquialter, will lead, and the next after it, the sesquitertian, will follow, and after them the next in order, the sesquiquartan, the sesquiquintan, the sesquisextan, and so on *ad infinitum;* third, the superpartient, which once more the superbipartient will lead, the supertripartient will follow immediately upon it, and then will come the superquadripartient, the superquintipartient, and according to the foregoing as far as one may proceed.

*[8]* Now you must have certain rules, like invariable and inviolable natural laws, following which the whole aforesaid advance and progress from equality may go on without failure. These are the directions: Make the first equal to the first, the second equal to the sum of the first and second, and the third to the sum of the first, twice the second, and the third. For if you fashion according to these rules you would get first all the forms of the multiple in order out of the three given terms of the equality, as it were, sprouting and growing without your paying any heed or offering any aid. From equality you will first get the double; from the double the triple, from the triple successively the quadruple, and from this the quintuple in due order, and so on. *[9]* From these same multiples in their regular order, reversed, there are immediately produced by a sort of natural necessity through the agency of the same three rules the superparticulars, and these not as it chances and irregularly but in their proper sequence; for from the first, the double, reversed, comes the first, the sesquialter, and from the second, the triple, the second in this class, the sesquitertian; then the sesquiquartan from the quadruple, and in general each one from the one of similar name. *[10]* And with a fresh start, if the superparticulars are set forth in the order of their production, but with terms reversed, the superpartients, which naturally follow them, are brought to light, the superbipartient from the sesquialter, the supertripartient from the sesquitertian, the superquadripartient from the sesquiquartan, and so on *ad infinitum.* *[11]* If, however, the superparticulars are set forth with terms not in reverse but in direct order, there are produced through the three rules the multiple superparticulars, the double sesquialter out of the first, the sesquialter; the double sesquitertian from the second, the sesquitertian, the double sesquiquartan from the third, the sesquiquartan, and so on. *[12]* From those produced by the reversal of the superparticular, that is, the superpartients, and from those produced without such reversal, the multiple superparticulars, there are once more produced, in the same way and by the same rules, both when the terms are in direct or reverse order, the numbers that show the remaining numerical relations.

*[13]* The following must suffice as illustrations of all that has been said hitherto, the production of these numbers and their sequence, and the use of direct and of reverse order. *[14]* From the relation and proportion in terms of the sesquialter, reversed so as to begin with the largest term, there arises a relation in superpartient ratios, the superbipartient; and from it in direct order, beginning with the smallest term, a multiple superparticular relation, the double sesquialter. For example, from 9, 6, 4, we get either 9, 15, 25 or 4, 10, 25. From the relation in terms of sesquitertians, beginning with the greatest term, is derived a superpartient, the supertripartient; beginning with the smallest term, a double sesquitertian. For example, from 16, 12, 9 comes either 16, 28, 49 or 9, 21, 49. And from the relation in terms of sesquiquartans, when it is arranged to begin with the largest term, is derived a superpar-

---

¹Cf. Aristotle, *Ethics*, 1107ᵇ 4 ff. See *ibid.*, 1108ᵃ 4 ff.; 1145ᵇ 8 ff.

tient, the superquadripartient; when it starts with the smallest term, a multiple superparticular, the double sesquiquintan; for instance, from 25, 20, 16 comes either 25, 45, 81 or 16, 36, 81.

[15] In the case of all these relations that are thus differentiated, and of the one from which both of the differentiated ones are derived, the last term is always the same and a square; the first term becomes the smallest, and invariably the extremes are squares.

[16] Moreover the multiple superpartients and superpartients of other kinds are made to appear in yet another way out of the superpartients; for example, from the superbipartient relation arranged so as to begin with the smallest term comes the double superbipartient, but, arranged so as to start with the greatest, the superpartient ratio of 8:5. Thus from 9, 15, 25 comes either 9, 24, 64 or 25, 40, 64. From the supertripartient, beginning with the smallest term, we have the double supertripartient, and, beginning with the largest, the ratio of 11:7. Thus, from 16, 28, 49 comes either 16, 44, 121 or 49, 77, 121. [17] Again, from the superquintipartient, as, for example, 25, 45, 81, beginning with the lesser term we derive the double superquintipartient in the terms 25, 70, 196, but beginning with the greater a superpartient again, the ratio of 14:9, in the terms 81, 126, 196. And you will find the results analogous and in agreement with the foregoing in all successive cases to infinity.

# BOOK TWO

## CHAPTER I

*[1]* An element is said to be, and is, the smallest thing which enters into the composition of an object and the least thing into which it can be analyzed. Letters, for example, are called the elements of literate speech, for out of them all articulate speech is composed and into them finally it is resolved. Sounds are the elements of all melody; for they are the beginning of its composition and into them it is resolved. The so-called four elements of the universe in general are simple bodies, fire, water, air, and earth; for out of them in the first instance we account for the constitution of the universe, and into them finally we conceive of it as being resolved.

We wish also to prove that equality is the elementary principle[1] of relative number; for of absolute number, number per se, unity and the dyad are the most primitive elements, the least things out of which it is constructed, even to infinity, by which it has its growth, and with which its analysis into smaller terms comes to an end. *[2]* We have, however, demonstrated that in the realm of inequality advance and increase have their origin in equality and go on to absolutely all the relations with a certain regularity through the operation of the three rules.[2] It remains, then, in order to make it an element in very truth, to prove that analyses also finally come to an end in equality. Let this then be considered our procedure.

## CHAPTER II

*[1]* Suppose then you are given three terms, in any relation whatsoever and in any ratio, whether multiple, superparticular, superpartient, or a compound of these, multiple superparticular or multiple superpartient, provided only that the mean term is seen to be in the same ratio to the lesser as the greater to the mean, and vice versa. Subtract always from the mean the lesser term, whether it be first or last in order, and set down the lesser term itself as the first term of your new series; then put as your second term what remains from the second after the subtraction; then after having subtracted the sum of the new first term and twice the new second term from the remaining number—that is, the greater of the numbers originally given you—make the remainder your third term, and the resulting numbers will be in some other ratio, naturally more primitive. *[2]* And if again in the same way you subtract the remainder from these same terms, it will be found that your three terms have passed back into three others more primitive, and you will find that this always takes place as a consequence, until they are reduced to equality, whence by every necessity it appears evident that equality is the elementary principle of relative quantity.

*[3]* There follows upon this speculation a most elegant principle, extremely useful in its application to the Platonic psychogony[3] and the problem of all harmonic intervals; for in the Platonic passage we are frequently bidden, for the sake of the argument, to set up series of intervals of two, three, four, five, or an infinite number of sesquialter ratios, or two sesquitertians, sesquiquartans, sesquioctaves, or superparticulars of any kind whatsoever, and in each case three, four, or five of them, or as many as may be directed. *[4]* It is reasonable that we should do this not in an unscientific, unintelligent fashion, it may be even blunderingly, but artistically, surely, and quickly, by the following procedure.

## CHAPTER III

*[1]* Every multiple will stand at the head[4] of as many superparticular ratios corresponding in name with itself as it itself chances to be removed from unity, and no more nor less under any circumstances.

---

[1] See on I. 23. 4.
[2] See on I. 23. 8.
[3] See Plato, *Timaeus*, 35 ff.
[4] Refers to the table in Chapter 4.

*[2]* The doubles, then, will produce[1] sesquialters, the first one, the second two, the third three, the fourth four, the fifth five, the sixth six, and neither more nor less, but by every necessity when the superparticulars that are generated attain the proper number, that is, when their number agrees with the multiples that have generated them, at that point by a divine device, as it were, there is found the number which terminates them all because it naturally is not divisible by that factor whereby the progression of the superparticular ratios went on.

Sixteen, the fourth double, will stand at the head of four sesquialters, 24, 36, 54, and finally 81, so that they may of necessity be equal in number to what generated them; for 81 by its nature is not divisible by 2. And this, as you go on, you will find holds true in similar fashion to infinity.

*[4]* For the sake of illustration let there be set down the table of the doubles, thus:

| The double ratio in the breadth of the table | | | | | | | |
|---|---|---|---|---|---|---|---|
| | 1 | 2 | 4 | 8 | 16 | 32 | 64 |
| | | 3 | 6 | 12 | 24 | 48 | 96 |
| The triple ratio along | | | 9 | 18 | 36 | 72 | 144 | The sesquialter ratio in the depth |
| the hypotenuse | | | | 27 | 54 | 108 | 216 |
| | | | | | 81 | 162 | 324 |
| | | | | | | 243 | 486 |
| | | | | | | | 729 |

## CHAPTER IV

*[1]* We must make a similar table in illustration of the triple:

| The triple ratio in the breadth | | | | | | | |
|---|---|---|---|---|---|---|---|
| | 1 | 3 | 9 | 27 | 81 | 243 | 729 |
| | | 4 | 12 | 36 | 108 | 324 | 972 |
| The quadruple ratio | | | 16 | 48 | 144 | 432 | 1296 | The sesquitertian ratio in the depth |
| on the hypotenuse | | | | 64 | 192 | 576 | 1728 |
| | | | | | 256 | 768 | 2304 |
| | | | | | | 1024 | 3072 |
| | | | | | | | 4096 |

From the triples all the sesquitertians will proceed, likewise equal in number to the number of the generating terms, and coming to an end, after the independence of their advance is lost, in numbers not divisible by 3. Similarly the sesquiquartans come from the quadruples, reaching a culmination after their independent progression in a number that is not divisible by 4.

*[3]* As an example, since doubles generate sesquialters corresponding to them in number, the first row of multiples will be 1, 2, 4, 8, 16, 32, 64. Now since 2 is the first after unity, this will be the origin of one sesquialter only, 3, which number is not divisible by 2, so that another sesquialter might arise out of it. The first double, therefore, is productive of but one sesquialter, and the second, 4, of two. For it produces its own sesquialter, 6, and that of 6, 9, but there is none for 9 because it has no half. Eight, which is the third double, is father to three sesquialters; one its own, 12; the second, 18, the sesquialter of 12; and third, 27, that of 18; there is no fourth one, however, because of the general rule, for 27 is not divisible by 2.

[1] See I. 19. 2.

In the foregoing table we shall observe that in the same way the first triple, 3, stands at the head of but one sesquitertian ratio, 4, its own sesquitertian, which immediately shuts off the development of another like it; for 4 is not divisible by 3, and hence will not have a sesquitertian. The second triple is 9, and hence will begin a series of only two sesquitertian ratios, 12, its own, and 16, that of 12; but 16 cuts off further progress, for it is not divisible by 3 and hence will not have a sesquitertian. *[2]* Next in order is the triple 27, three times removed from 1, for the triples progress thus: 1, 3, 9, 27. Therefore this number will stand at the head of three sesquitertian ratios and no more. The first is its own, 36; the second the sesquitertian of 36, 48; the third that of the last, 64, and this no longer has a third part and therefore will not admit of a sesquitertian. The fourth leads a series of four sesquitertians and the fifth, of course, five.

*[3]* Such, then, is the illustration; and for the other multiples let the manner of your tables be the same. Observe that likewise here as we found to be true in our previous discus'

sion, Nature shows us that the doubles are more nearly original than the triples, the triples than the quadruples, these latter than the quintuples, and so on throughout. For the highest rows of figures, across the breadth of the tables, if they are doubles, will have doubles lying parallel to them, and the numbers lying diagonally, on the hypotenuse, will be of the next succeeding variety, greater by 1, that is, triples, seen also in a series of parallel lines. If, however, there are triples across the breadth, the diagonals will by all means be quadruples; if the former are quadruples, then the latter are quintuples, and so forth.

## CHAPTER V

*[1]* It remains, after we have explained what other ratios are produced by combination of ratios, to pass on to the succeeding topics of the *Introduction*.

*[2]* Now the first two ratios of the superparticular, combined, produce the first ratio of the multiple, namely, the double; for every double is a combination of sesquialter and sesquitertian, and every sesquialter and sesquitertian combined will invariably produce a double.

For example, since 3 is the sesquialter of 2, and 4 the sesquitertian of 3, 4 will be the double of 2, and is a combination of sesquialter and sesquitertian. Again, as 6 is the double of 3, we shall find between them some number that will of necessity preserve the sesquitertian ratio to the one and the sesquialter to the other; and indeed 4, lying between 6 and 3, gives the sesquitertian ratio to 3 and the sesquialter to 6.

*[3]* It was rightly said, then, that the double, when resolved, is resolved into the sesquialter and the sesquitertian, and that when sesquialter and sesquitertian are combined there arises the double, and that the first two forms of the superparticular combined make the first form of the multiple.

*[4]* But again, to take another start, this first form of the multiple which has thus been produced, together with the first form of the superparticular, will produce the next form of the same class, that is, the second multiple, the triple; for from every multiple and sesquialter combined a triple of necessity arises. For example, as the double of 6 is 12, and the sesquialter of this is 18, then immediately 18 is the triple of 6; and to take another method, if I do not care to make 12 the mean term, but rather 9, the sesquialter of 6, the same result will come about, without deviation and harmoniously; for while 18 is the double of 9 it will preserve the triple ratio to 6. Hence from the sesquialter and the double, the first forms of the superparticular and the multiple, there arises by combination the second form of the multiple, the triple, and into them it is always resolved. *[5]* For look you; 6, which is the triple of 2, will have a mean term 3, which will exhibit two ratios, the sesquialter with regard to 2, and the double ratio of 6 to itself.

But if this triple ratio, likewise, the second form of the multiple, is combined with the sesquitertian, which is the second form of the superparticular, there would be produced from them the next form of the multiple, namely, the quadruple, and this also will of necessity be resolved into them after the same fashion as the cases previously set forth; and the quadruple, taking into combination the sesquiquartan, will make the quintuple, and, once more, the latter with the sesquiquintan will make the sextuple, and so on to the end. Thus the multiples in regular order from the beginning with the superparticulars in regular order from the beginning will be found to produce the next larger multiples. For the double with the sesquialter makes the triple, the triple with the sesquitertian the quadruple, the quadruple with the sesquiquartan the quintuple, and as far as you wish to proceed no contrary result will appear.

## CHAPTER VI

*[1]* Up to this point then we have sufficiently discussed relative number, by a process of selection measuring out what is easily comprehended and appropriate to the nature of the matters thus far introduced. Whatever remains to be said on this topic will be filled in after we have put it aside and have first discussed certain subjects which involve a more serviceable inquiry, having to do with the properties of absolute number, not relative. For mathematical speculations are always to be interlocked and to be explained one by means of another. The subjects which we must first survey and observe are concerned with linear, plane, and solid numbers, cubical and spherical, equilateral and scalene, "bricks," "beams," "wedges," and the like, the tradition concerning which, to be sure, since they are more closely related to magnitude, is properly given in the *Geometrical Introduction*. Yet the germs of these ideas are taken over into arithmetic, as the science which is the mother of geometry and more elementary than it. For we recall that a short time ago we saw that arithmetic abolishes the other sciences

with itself, but is not abolished by them, and conversely is of necessity implied by them but does not itself imply them.

[2] First, however, we must recognize that each letter by which we indicate a number, such as iota, the sign for 10, kappa for 20, and omega for 800, designates that number by man's convention and agreement, not by nature. On the other hand, the natural, unartificial, and therefore simplest indication of numbers would be the setting forth one beside the other of the units contained in each. For example, the writing of one unit by means of one alpha will be the sign for 1; two units side by side, that is, a series of two alphas, will be the sign for 2; when three are put in a line it will be the character for 3, four in a line for 4, five for 5, and so on. For by means of such a notation and indication alone could the schematic arrangement of the plane and solid numbers mentioned be made clear and evident, thus:

The number 1,   a
The number 2,   a a
The number 3,   a a a
The number 4,   a a a a
The number 5,   a a a a a

and further in similar fashion.

[3] Unity, then, occupying the place and character of a point, will be the beginning of intervals and of numbers, but not itself an interval or a number, just as the point is the beginning of a line, or an interval, but is not itself line or interval. Indeed, when a point is added to a point, it makes no increase, for when an non-dimensional thing is added to another non-dimensional thing, it will not thereby have dimension; just as if one should examine the sum of nothing added to nothing, which makes nothing. We saw[1] a similar thing also in the case of equality among the relatives; for a proportion is preserved—as the first is to the second, so the second is to the third—but no interval is generated in the relation of the extremes to each other, as there is in all the other relations with the exception of equality. In exactly the same way unity alone out of all number, when it multiplies itself, produces nothing greater than itself.

Unity, therefore, is non-dimensional and elementary, and dimension first is found and seen in 2, then in 3, then in 4, and in succession in the following numbers; for "dimension" is that which is conceived of as between two limits.

[4] The first dimension is called "line," for "line" is that which is extended in one direction. Two dimensions are called "surface," for a "surface" is that which is extended in two directions. Three dimensions are called "solid," for a "solid" is that which is extended in three directions, and it is by no means possible to conceive of a solid which has more than three dimensions, depth, breadth, and length. By these are defined the six directions which are said to exist in connection with every body and by which motions in space are distinguished, forward, backward,[2] up, down, right and left; for of necessity two directions opposite to each other follow upon each dimension, up and down upon one, forward and backward upon the second, and right and left upon the third.

[5] The statement, also, as it happens, can be made conversely thus: If a thing is solid, it has by all means three dimensions, length, depth and breadth; and conversely, if it has the three dimensions, it is always a solid, and nothing else.

[6] That which has but two dimensions, therefore, will not be a solid, but a surface, for the latter admits of but two dimensions. Here too it is possible similarly to reverse the statement; directly stated, a surface is that which has two dimensions, and conversely, that which has two dimensions is always a surface.

[7] The surface, then, is exceeded by the solid by one dimension, and the line is exceeded by the surface by one, for the line is that which is extended in but one direction and has only one dimension, and it falls short of the solid by two dimensions. The point falls short of the latter by one dimension, and hence it has already been stated that it is non-dimensional, since it falls short of the solid by three dimensions, of the surface by two, and of the line by one.

## CHAPTER VII

[1] The point, then, is the beginning of dimension, but not itself a dimension, and likewise the beginning of a line, but not itself a line; the line is the beginning of surface, but not surface; and the beginning of the two-dimensional, but not itself extended in two directions. [2] Naturally, too, surface is the beginning of body, but not itself body, and likewise the beginning of the three-dimensional, but not itself extended in three directions.

---

[1] I. 23. 7 ff.

[2] Cf. Plato, *Timaeus*, 43.

## INTRODUCTION TO ARITHMETIC II.

*[3]* Exactly the same in numbers, unity is the beginning of all number that advances unit by unit in one direction; linear number is the beginning of plane number, which spreads out like a plane in one more dimension; and plane number is the beginning of solid number, which possesses a depth[1] in the third dimension, besides the original ones. To illustrate and classify, linear numbers are all those which begin with 2 and advance by the addition of 1 in one and the same dimension; and plane numbers are those[2] that begin with 3 as their most elementary root and proceed through the next succeeding numbers. They receive their names also in the same order; for there are first the triangles, then the squares, the pentagons after these, then the hexagons, the heptagons, and so on indefinitely, and, as we said, they are named after the successive numbers beginning with 3.

*[4]* The triangle, therefore, is found to be the most original and elementary form of the plane number. This we can see from the fact that, among plane figures,[3] graphically represented, if lines are drawn from the angles to the centers each rectilinear figure will by all means be resolved into as many triangles as it has sides; but the triangle itself, if treated like the rest, will not change into anything else but itself. Hence the triangle is elementary among these figures; for everything else is resolved into it, but it into nothing else. From it the others likewise would be constituted, but it from no other. It is therefore the element of the others, and has itself no element. *[5]* Likewise, as the argument proceeds in the realm of numerical forms, it will confirm this statement.

## CHAPTER VIII

*[1]* Now a triangular number is one which, when it is analyzed into units, shapes into triangular form the equilateral placement of its parts in a plane. 3, 6, 10, 15, 21, 28, and so on, are examples of it; for their regular formations, expressed graphically, will be at once triangular and equilateral. As you advance you will find that such a numerical series as far as you like takes the triangular form, if you put as the most elementary form the one that arises from unity, so that unity may appear to be potentially a triangle, and 3 the first actually.

*[2]* Their sides will increase by the successive numbers, for the side of the one potentially first is unity; that of the one actually first, that is, 3, is 2; that of 6, which is actually second, 3; that of the third, 4; the fourth, 5; the fifth, 6; and so on.

*[3]* The triangular number is produced from the natural series of number set forth in a line, and by the continued addition of successive terms, one by one, from the beginning; for by the successive combinations and additions of another term to the sum, the triangular numbers in regular order are completed. For example, from this natural series, 1, 2, 3, 4, 5, 6, 7, 8, 9, 10, 11, 12, 13, 14, 15, I take the first term and have the triangular number which is potentially first, 1,  ; then adding the next term I get the triangle actually first, for 2 plus 1 equals 3. In its graphic representation it is thus made up: Two units, side by side, are set beneath one unit, and the number three is made a triangle:

Then when next after these the following number, 3, is added, simplified into units, and joined to the former, it gives 6, the second triangle in actuality, and furthermore, it graphically represents this number:

Again, the number that naturally follows, 4, added in and set down below the former, reduced to units, gives the one in order next after the aforesaid, 10, and takes a triangular form:

5, after this, then 6, then 7, and all the numbers in order, are added, so that regularly the sides of each triangle will consist of as many

---

[1] Cf. Plato, *Timaeus*, 53.
[2] But cf. Euclid, in *Elements*, VII, Def. 17.
[3] Cf. Plato, *Timaeus*, 53 ff.

numbers as have been added from the natural series to produce it:

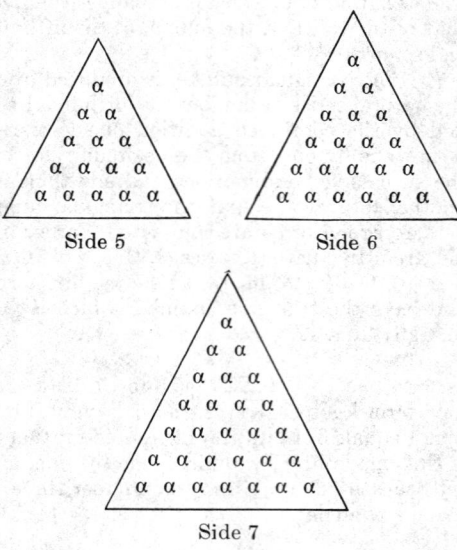

## CHAPTER IX

*[1]* The square is the next number after this, which shows us no longer 3, like the former, but 4 angles in its graphic representation, but is none the less equilateral. Take, for example, 1, 4, 9, 16, 25, 36, 49, 64, 81, 100; for the representations of these numbers are equilateral, square figures, as here shown; and it will be similar as far as you wish to go:

*[2]* It is true of these numbers, as it was also of the preceding, that the advance in their sides progresses with the natural series. The side of the square potentially first, 1, is 1; that of 4, the first in actuality, 2; that of 9, actually the second, 3; that of 16, the next, actually the third, 4; that of the fourth, 5; of the fifth, 6, and so on in general with all that follow.

*[3]* This number also is produced if the natural series is extended in a line, increasing by 1, and no longer the successive numbers are added to the numbers in order, as was shown before, but rather all those in alternate places, that is, the odd numbers. For the first, 1, is potentially the first square; the second, 1 plus 3, is the first in actuality; the third, 1 plus 3 plus 5, is the second in actuality; the fourth, 1 plus 3 plus 5 plus 7, is the third in actuality; the next is produced by adding 9 to the former numbers, the next by the addition of 11, and so on.

*[4]* In these cases, also, it is a fact that the side of each consists of as many units as there are numbers taken into the sum to produce it.

## CHAPTER X

*[1]* The pentagonal number is one which likewise upon its resolution into units and depiction as a plane figure assumes the form of an equilateral pentagon. 1, 5, 12, 22, 35, 51, 70, and analogous numbers are examples. *[2]* Each side of the first actual pentagon, 5, is 2, for 1 is the side of the pentagon potentially first, 1; 3 is the side of 12, the second of those listed; 4, that of the next, 22; 5, that of the next in order, 35, and 6 of the succeeding one, 51, and so on. In general the side contains as many units as are the numbers that have been added together to produce the pentagon, chosen out of the natural arithmetical series set forth in a row. For in a like and similar manner, there are added together to produce the pentagonal numbers the terms beginning with 1 to any extent whatever that are two places apart, that is, those that have a difference of 3.

Unity is the first pentagon, potentially, and is thus depicted:

5, made up of 1 plus 4, is the second, similarly represented:

12, the third, is made up out of the two former numbers with 7 added to them, so that it may have 3 as a side, as three numbers have been added to make it. Similarly the preceding pentagon, 5, was the combination of two numbers and had 2 as its side. The graphic representation of 12 is this:

The other pentagonal numbers will be produced by adding together one after another in due order the terms after 7 that have the difference 3, as, for example, 10, 13, 16, 19, 22, 25, and so on. The pentagons will be 22, 35, 51, 70, 92, 117, and so forth.

## CHAPTER XI

*[1]* The hexagonal, heptagonal, and succeeding numbers will be set forth in their series by following the same process, if from the natural series of number there be set forth series with their differences increasing by 1. For as the triangular number was produced by admitting into the summation the terms that differ by 1 and do not pass over any in the series; as the square was made by adding the terms that differ by 2 and are one place apart, and the pentagon similarly by adding terms with a difference of 3 and two places apart (and we have demonstrated these, by setting forth examples both of them and of the polygonal numbers made from them), so likewise the hexagons will have as their root-numbers those which differ by 4 and are three places apart in the series, which added together in succession will produce the hexagons. For example, 1, 5, 9, 13, 17, 21, and so on; so that the hexagonal numbers produced will be 1, 6, 15, 28, 45, 66, and so on, as far as one wishes to go.

*[2]* The heptagonals, which follow these, have as their root-numbers terms differing by 5 and four places apart in the series, like 1, 6, 11, 16, 21, 26, 31, 36, and so on. The heptagons that thus arise are 1, 7, 18, 34, 55, 81, 112, 148 and so forth.

*[3]* The octagonals increase after the same fashion, with a difference of 6 in their root-numbers and corresponding variation in their total constitution.

*[4]* In order that, as you survey all cases, you may have a rule generally applicable, note that the root-numbers of any polygonal differ by 2 less than the number of the angles shown by the name of the polygonal—that is, by 1 in the triangle, 2 in the square, 3 in the pentagon, 4 in the hexagon, 5 in the heptagon, and so on, with similar increase.

## CHAPTER XII

*[1]* Concerning the nature of plane polygonals this is sufficient for a first *Introduction*. That, however, the doctrine of these numbers is to the highest degree in accord with their geometrical representation, and not out of harmony with it, would be evident, not only from the graphic representation in each case, but also from the following: Every square figure diagonally divided is resolved into two triangles and every square number is resolved into two consecutive triangular numbers, and hence is made up of two successive triangular numbers. For example, 1, 3, 6, 10, 15, 21, 28, 36, 45, 55, and so on, are triangular numbers and 1, 4, 9, 16, 25, 36, 49, 64, 81, 100, squares. *[2]* If you add any two consecutive triangles that you please, you will always make a square, and hence, whatever square you resolve, you will be able to make two triangles of it.

Again, any triangle joined to any square figure makes a pentagon, for example, the triangle 1 joined with the square 4 makes the pentagon 5; the next triangle, 3 of course, with 9, the next square, makes the pentagon 12; the next, 6, with the next square, 16, gives the next pentagon, 22; 10 and 25 give 35; and so on

*[3]* Similarly, if the triangles are added to the pentagons, following the same order, they will produce the hexagonals in due order, and again the same triangles with the latter will make the heptagonals in order, the octagonals after the heptagonals, and so on to infinity.

*[4]* To remind us, let us set forth rows of the polygonals, written in parallel lines, as follows: The first row, triangles, the next squares, after them pentagonals, then hexagonals, then heptagonals, then if one wishes, the succeeding polygonals.

| Triangles   | 1 | 3 | 6  | 10 | 15 | 21 | 28  | 36  | 45  | 55  |
| Squares     | 1 | 4 | 9  | 16 | 25 | 36 | 49  | 64  | 81  | 100 |
| Pentagonals | 1 | 5 | 12 | 22 | 35 | 51 | 70  | 92  | 117 | 145 |
| Hexagonals  | 1 | 6 | 15 | 28 | 45 | 66 | 91  | 120 | 153 | 190 |
| Heptagonals | 1 | 7 | 18 | 34 | 55 | 81 | 112 | 148 | 189 | 235 |

You can also set forth the succeeding polygonals in similar parallel lines.

*[5]* In general, you will find that the squares are the sum of the triangles above those that occupy the same place in the series, plus the numbers of that same class in the next place back; for example, 4 equals 3 plus 1, 9 equals 6 plus 3, 16 equals 10 plus 6, 25 equals 15 plus 10, 36 equals 21 plus 15, and so on.

The pentagons are the sum of the squares above them in the same place in the series, plus the elementary triangles that are one place further back in the series; for example, 5 equals 4 plus 1, 12 equals 9 plus 3, 22 equals 16 plus 6, 35 equals 25 plus 10, and so on.

*[6]* Again, the hexagonals are similarly the sums of the pentagons above them in the same place in the series plus the triangles one place back; for instance, 6 equals 5 plus 1, 15 equals 12 plus 3, 28 equals 22 plus 6, 45 equals 35 plus 10, and as far as you like.

*[7]* The same applies to the heptagonals, for 7 is the sum of 6 and 1, 18 equals 15 plus 3, 34 equals 28 plus 6, and so on. Thus each polygonal number is the sum of the polygonal in the same place in the series with one less angle, plus the triangle, in the highest row, one place back in the series.

*[8]* Naturally, then, the triangle is the element of the polygon both in figures and in numbers, and we say this because in the table, reading either up and down or across, the successive numbers in the rows are discovered to have as differences the triangles in regular order.

## CHAPTER XIII

*[1]* From this it is easy to see what the solid number is and how its series advances with equal sides; for the number which, in addition to the two dimensions contemplated in graphic representation in a plane, length, and breadth, has a third dimension, which some call depth, others thickness, and some height, that number would be a solid number, extended in three directions and having length, depth, and breadth.

*[2]* This first makes its appearance in the so-called pyramids. These are produced from rather wide bases narrowing to a sharp apex, first after the triangular form from a triangular base, second after the form of the square from a square base, and succeeding these after the pentagonal form from a pentagonal base, then similarly from the hexagon, heptagon, octagon, and so on indefinitely.

*[3]* Exactly so among the geometrical solid figures; if one imagines three lines from the three angles of an equilateral triangle, equal in length to the sides of the triangle, converging in the dimension height to one and the same point, a pyramid would be produced, bounded by four triangles, equilateral and equal one to the other, one the original triangle, and the other three bounded by the aforesaid three lines. *[4]* And again, if one conceives of four lines starting from a square, equal in length to the sides of the square, each to each, and again converging in the dimension height to one and the same point, a pyramid would be completed with a square base and diminishing in square form, bounded by four equilateral triangles and one square, the original one. *[5]* And starting from a pentagon, hexagon, heptagon, and however far you care to go, lines equal in number to the angles, erected in the same fashion from the angles and converging to one and the same point, will complete a pyramid named from its pentagonal, hexagonal, or heptagonal base, or similarly.

*[6]* So likewise among numbers, each linear number increases from unity, as from a point, as for example, 1, 2, 3, 4, 5, and successive numbers to infinity; and from these same numbers, which are linear and extended in one direction, combined in no random manner, the polygonal and plane numbers are fashioned—the triangles by the combination of root-numbers immediately adjacent, the square by adding every other term, the pentagons every third term, and so on. *[7]* In exactly the same way, if the plane polygonal numbers are piled one upon the other and as it were built up, the pyramids that are akin to each of them are produced, the triangular pyramid from the triangles, the square pyramid from the squares, the pentagonal from the pentagons, the hexagonal from the hexagons, and so on throughout.

*[8]* The pyramids with a triangular base, then, in their proper order, are these: 1, 4, 10, 20, 35, 56, 84, and so on; and their origin is the piling up of the triangular numbers one upon the other, first 1, then 1, 3, then 1, 3, 6, then 10 in addition to these, and next 15 together with the foregoing, then 21 besides these, next 28, and so on to infinity.

*[9]* It is clear that the greatest number is conceived of as being lowest, for it is discovered to be the base; the next succeeding one is on top of it, and the next on top of that; until unity appears at the apex and, so to speak, tapers off the completed pyramid into a point.

## CHAPTER XIV

*[1]* The next pyramids in order are those with a square base which rise in this shape to one and the same point. These are formed in the same way as the triangular pyramids of which we have just spoken. For if I extend in series the square numbers in order beginning with unity, thus, 1, 4, 9, 16, 25, 36, 49, 64, 81, 100, and again set the successive terms, as in a pile, one upon the other in the dimension height, when I put 1 on top of 4, the first actual pyramid with square base, 5 is produced, for here again unity is potentially the first. *[2]* Once more, I put this same pyramid entire, composed of 5 units, just as it is, upon the square 9, and there is made up for me the pyramid 14, with square base and side 3—for the former pyramid had the side 2, and the one potentially first 1 as a side. For here too each side of any pyramid whatsoever must consist of as many units as there are polygonal numbers piled together to create it.

*[3]* Again, I place the whole pyramid 14, with the square 9 as its base, upon the square 16 and I have 30, the third actual pyramid of those that have a square base, and by the same order and procedure from a pentagonal, hexagonal, or heptagonal base, and even going on farther, we shall produce pyramids by piling upon one another the corresponding polygonal numbers, starting with unity as the smallest and going on to infinity in each case.

*[4]* From this too it becomes evident that triangles are the most elementary; for absolutely all of the pyramids that are exhibited and shown, with the various polygonal bases, are bounded by triangles up to the apex.

*[5]* But lest we be heedless of truncated, bi-truncated, and tri-truncated pyramids, the names of which we are sure to encounter in scientific writings, you may know that if a pyramid with any sort of polygon as its base, triangle, square, pentagon, or any of the succeeding polygons of the kind, when it increases by this process of piling up does not taper off into unity, it is called simply truncated when it is left without the natural apex that belongs to all pyramids; for it does not terminate in the potential polygon, unity, as in some one point, but in another polygon, and an actual one, and unity is not its apex, but its upper boundary becomes a plane figure with the same number of angles as the base. If, however, in addition to the failure to terminate in unity it does not even terminate in the polygon next to unity and the first in actuality, such a pyramid is called bi-truncated, and if, still further, it does not have the second actual polygon at its upper limit, but only the one next beneath, it will be called tri-truncated, yes, even four times truncated, if it does not have the next one as its limit, or five times truncated at the next step, and so on as far as you care to carry the nomenclature.

## CHAPTER XV

*[1]* While the origin, advance, increase, and nature of the equilateral solid numbers of pyramidal appearance is the foregoing, with its seed and root in the polygonal numbers and the piling up of them in their regular order, there is another series of solid numbers of a different kind, consisting of the so-called cubes, "beams," "bricks," "wedges," spheres and parallelepipedons, which has the order of its progress somewhat as follows:

*[2]* The foregoing squares 1, 4, 9, 16, 25, 36, 49, 64, and so on, which are extended in two directions and in their graphic representation in a plane have only length and breadth, will take on yet a third dimension and be solids and extended in three directions if each is multiplied by its own side; 4, which is 2 times 2, is again multiplied by 2, to make 8; 9, which is 3 times 3, is again increased by 3 in another dimension and gives 27; 16, which is 4 times 4, is multiplied by its own side, 4, and 64 results; and so on with the succeeding squares throughout.

*[3]* Here, too, the sides will be composed of as many units as were in the sides of the squares from which they arose, in each case; the sides of 8 will be 2, like those of 4; those of 27, 3, like those of 9; those of 64, 4, like those of 16; and so on, so that likewise the side of unity, the potential cube, will be 1, which is the side of the potential square, 1.

In general, each square is a single plane, and has four angles and four sides, while each several cube, having increased out of some one square multiplied by its own side, will have always six plane surfaces, each equal to the original square, and twelve edges, each equal to and containing exactly the same number of units as each side of the original square, and eight solid angles, each of which is bounded by three edges like in each case to the sides of the original square.

## CHAPTER XVI

*[1]* Now since the cube is a solid figure with equal sides in all dimensions, in length, depth,

and breadth, and is equally extended in all the six so-called directions,[1] it follows that there is opposed to it that which has its dimensions in no case equal to one another, but its depth unequal to its breadth and its length unequal to either of these, for example 2 times 3 times 4, or 2 times 4 times 8, or 3 times 5 times 12, or a figure which follows some other scheme of inequality.

[2] Such solid figures, in which the dimensions are everywhere unequal one to another, are called scalene in general. Some, however, using other names, call them "wedges," for carpenters', house-builders' and blacksmiths' wedges and those used in other crafts, having unequal sides in every direction, are fashioned so as to penetrate; they begin with a sharp end and continually broaden out unequally in all the dimensions. Some also call them *sphekiskoi*, "wasps," because wasps' bodies also are very like them, compressed in the middle and showing the resemblance mentioned. From this also the *sphekoma*, "point of the helmet," must derive its name, for where it is compressed it imitates the waist of the wasp. Others call the same numbers "altars," using their own metaphor, for the altars of ancient style, particularly the Ionic, do not have the breadth equal to the depth, nor either of these equal to the length, nor the base equal to the top, but are of varied dimensions everywhere.

[3] Now whereas the two kinds of numbers, cube and scalene, are extremes, the one equally extended in every dimension, the other unequally, the so-called parallelepipedons are solid numbers like means between them. The plane surfaces of these are heteromecic numbers,[2] just as in the case of the cubes the faces were squares, as has been shown.

## CHAPTER XVII

[1] Again, then, to take a fresh start, a number is called heteromecic if its representation, when graphically described in a plane, is quadrilateral and quadrangular, to be sure, but the sides are not equal one to another, nor is the length equal to the breadth, but they differ by 1. Examples are 2, 6, 12, 20, 30, 42, and so on, for if one represents them graphically he will always construct them thus: 1 times 2 equals 2, 2 times 3 equals 6, 3 times 4 equals 12, and the succeeding ones similarly, 4 times 5, 5 times 6, 6 times 7, 7 times 8, and thus indefinitely,

provided only that one side is greater than the other by 1 and by no other number. If, however, the sides differ otherwise than by 1, for instance, by 2, 3, 4 or succeeding numbers, as in 2 times 4, 3 times 6, 4 times 8, or however else they may differ, then no longer will such a number be properly called a heteromecic, but an oblong number. For the ancients of the school of Pythagoras and his successors saw "the other"[3] and "otherness" primarily in 2, and "the same" and "sameness" in 1, as the two beginnings of all things, and these two are found to differ from each other only by 1. Thus "the other" is fundamentally "other" by 1, and by no other number, and for this reason customarily "other" is used, among those who speak correctly, of two things and not of more than two.

[2] Moreover, it was shown that all odd number is given its specific form[4] by unity, and all even number by 2. Hence we shall naturally say that the odd partakes of the nature of "the same," and the even of that of "the other"; for indeed there are produced by the successive additions of each of these—naturally, and not by our decree—by the addition of the odd numbers from 1 to infinity the class of the squares, and by the addition of the evens from 2 to infinity, that of the heteromecic numbers.[5]

[3] There is, accordingly, every reason to think that the square once more shares in the nature of the same; for its sides display the same ratio, alike, unchanging and firmly fixed in equality, to themselves; while the heteromecic number partakes of the nature of the other; for just as 1 is differentiated from 2, differing by 1 alone, thus also the sides of every heteromecic number differ from one another, one differing from the other by 1 alone.

To illustrate, if I have set out before me the successive numbers in series beginning with 1, and select and arrange by themselves the odd numbers in the line and the even by themselves in another, there are obtained these two series:

1, 3, 5, 7, 9, 11, 13, 15, 17, 19, 21, 23, 25, 27
2, 4, 6, 8, 10, 12, 14, 16, 18, 20, 22, 24, 26, 28

[4] Now, then, the beginning of the odd series is unity, which is of the same class as the series and possesses the nature of "the same," and so whether it multiplies itself in two dimensions

---

[1] Cf. II. 6. 4.
[2] See the following chapter.
[3] Cf. Plato, *Timaeus*, 35 ff.
[4] Cf. I. 7. 2.
[5] Cf. II. 18. 2 and 20. 3.

or in three it is not made different, nor yet does it make any other number depart from what it was originally,[1] but keeps it just as it was. Such a property it is impossible to find in any other number. [5] Of the other series the beginning is 2, which is similar in kind to this series and imitates "otherness"; for whether it multiplies itself or another number, it causes a change,[2] for example, 2 times 2, 2 times 3.

[6] But in cases like 8 times 8 times 2, or 8 times 8 times 3, such solid forms are called "bricks," the product of a number by itself and then by a smaller number; if, however, a greater height is joined to the square, as in 3 times 3 times 7, 3 times 3 times 8, or 3 times 3 times 9, or however many times the square be taken, provided only it be a greater number of times than the square itself, then the number is a "beam," the product of a number by itself and then by a larger number. The "wedges," to be sure, were the products of three unequal numbers, and cubes of three equal ones.

[7] Among the cubes, some of them, in addition to being the product of three equal numbers, have the further property of ending at every multiplication in the same number as that from which they began; these are called spherical, and also recurrent. Such indeed are those with sides 5 or 6; for however many times I increase each one of these, it will by all means end each time in the same figure, the derivative of 6 in 6 and that of 5 in 5. For example, the product of 5 times 5 will end in 5, and so will 5 times this product and if necessary, 5 times this again, and to infinity no other concluding term will be found except 5. From 6, too, in the same fashion 6 and no other will be the concluding term; and so 1 likewise is potentially spherical and recurrent, for as is reasonable it has the same property as the spheres and circles. For each one of them, circling and turning around, ends where it begins. And so these numbers aforesaid are the only ones of the products of equal factors to return to the same starting point from which they began, in the course of all their increases. If they increase in the manner of planes, in two dimensions, they are called circular, like 1, 25, and 36, derived from 1 times 1, 5 times 5, and 6 times 6; but if they have three dimensions, or are multiplied still further than this, they are called spherical solid numbers, for example 1, 125, 216, or, again, 1, 625, 1,296.

## CHAPTER XVIII

[1] Regarding the solid numbers this is for the present sufficient. The physical philosophers, however, and those that take their start with mathematics, call "the same" and "the other" the principles of the universe, and it has been shown that "the same" inheres in unity and the odd numbers, to which unity gives specific form, and to an even greater degree in the squares, made by the continued addition of odd numbers, because in their sides they share in equality; while "the other" inheres in 2 and the whole even series, which is given specific form by 2, and particularly in the heteromecic numbers, which are made by the continued addition of the even numbers, because of the share of the original inequality[3] and "otherness" which they have in the difference between their sides. Therefore it is most necessary further to demonstrate how in these two, as in origins and seeds, there are potentially existent all the peculiar properties of number, of its forms and subdivisions, of all its relations, of polygonals, and the like.

[2] First, however, we must make the distinction whereby the oblong (promecic) number differs from the heteromecic. The heteromecic is, as was stated above,[4] the product of a number multiplied by another larger than the first by 1, for example, 6, which is 2 times 3, or 12, which is 3 times 4. But the oblong is similarly the product of two differing numbers, differing, however, not by 1 but by some larger number, as 2 times 4, 3 times 6, 4 times 8, and similar numbers, which in a way exceed in length and overstep the difference of 1.

[3] Therefore, since squares are produced from the multiplication of numbers by their own length, and have their length the same as their breadth, properly speaking they would be called "idiomecic" or "tautomecic"; for example, 2 times 2, 3 times 3, 4 times 4, and the rest. And if this is true, they will admit in every way of sameness and equality, and for this reason are limited and come to an end; for "the equal" and "the same" are so in one definite way. But since the heteromecic numbers are produced by the multiplication of a number by not its own, but another number's length, they are therefore called "heteromecic," and admit of infinity and boundlessness.

[4] In this way, then, all numbers and the

---

[1] Cf. II. 6. 3.
[2] Cf. Aristotle, *On the Soul*, 406[b] 13.
[3] Cf. II. 17. 2.
[4] Cf. II. 17. 1.

objects in the universe which have been created with reference to them are divided and classified and are seen to be opposite one to another, and well do the ancients at the very beginning of their account of Nature make the first subdivision in their cosmogony on this principle. Thus Plato[1] mentions the distinction between the natures of "the same" and "the other," and again, that between the essence which is indivisible and always the same and the one which is divided; and Philolaus says that existent things must all be either limitless or limited, or limited and limitless at the same time, by which it is generally agreed that he means that the universe is made up out of limited and limitless things at the same time, obviously after the image of number, for all number is composed of unity and the dyad, even and odd, and these in truth display equality and inequality, sameness and otherness, the bounded and the boundless, the defined and the undefined.

## CHAPTER XIX

[1] That we may be clearly persuaded of what is being said, namely, that things are made up of warring and opposite elements[2] and have in all likelihood taken on harmony—and harmony always arises from opposites; for harmony is the unification of the diverse and the reconciliation of the contrary-minded—let us set forth in two parallel lines no longer, as just previously, the even numbers from 2 by themselves and the odd numbers from 1, but the numbers that are produced from these by adding them successively together, the squares from the odd numbers, and the heteromecic from the even. For if we give careful attention to their setting forth, we shall admire their mutual friendship and their coöperation to produce and perfect the remaining forms, to the end that we may with probability conceive that also in the nature of the universe from some such source as this a similar thing was brought about by universal providence.

[2] Let the two series then be as follows: That of the squares, from unity, 1, 4, 9, 16, 25, 36, 49, 64, 81, 100, 121, 144, 169, 196, 225, and that of the heteromecic numbers, beginning with 2 and proceeding thus, 2, 6, 12, 20, 30, 42, 56, 72, 90, 110, 132, 156, 182, 210, 240.

[3] In the first place, then, the first square is the fundamental multiple of the first heteromecic number; the second, compared to the second, is its sesquialter; the third, sesquitertian of the third; the fourth, sesquiquartan of the fourth; then sesquiquintan, sesquisextan, and so on similarly *ad infinitum*. Their differences, too, will increase according to the successive numbers from 1; the difference of the first terms is 1, of the second 2, of the third 3, and so on. Next, if first the second term of the squares be compared with the first heteromecic number, the third with the second, the fourth with the third, and the rest similarly, they will keep unchanged the same ratios as before, but their differences will begin to progress no longer from 1, but from 2, remaining the same as before, and according to the advance observed in the former comparison, the first to the first will be the first, or root-form, multiple, the second to the second the second sesquialter from the root-form, the third to the third the third sesquitertian from the root-form, and the succeeding terms will go on in similar fashion.

[4] Furthermore, the squares among themselves will have only the odd numbers as differences, the heteromecic, even numbers. And if we put the first heteromecic number as a mean term between the first two squares, the second between the next two, the third between the two following, and the fourth between the two next succeeding, therein will be seen still more regularly the numerical relations in groups of three terms. For as 4 is to 2, so is 2 to 1; and as 9 is sesquialter to 6, so is 6 to 4; and as 16 to 12, so is 12 to 9, and so on, with both numbers and ratios regularly advancing. As the greater is to the mean, so will the mean be to the lesser, and not in the same ratio, but always a different one, by an increase. In all the groupings, too, the product of the extremes is equal to the square of the mean; and the extremes, plus twice the mean, by exchange will always give a square. What is neatest of all, from the addition of both there comes about the production of the triangles in due order, showing that the nature of these is more ancient[3] than the origin of all things, thus: 1 plus 2, 2 plus 4, 4 plus 6, 6 plus 9, 9 plus 12, 12 plus 16, 16 plus 20, and by this process the triangles, which give rise to the polygons, come forth in order.

## CHAPTER XX

[1] Still further, every square plus its own side becomes heteromecic, or by Zeus, if its side is subtracted from it. Thus, "the other" is con-

---

[1]Cf. Plato, *Timaeus*, 35.
[2]Plato, *Timaeus*, 30.
[3]Cf. II. 17. 3; 18. 1 and II. 7. 4; cf. 12. 8

ceived of as being both greater and smaller than "the same," since it is produced, both by addition and by subtraction, in the same way that the two kinds of inequality[1] also, the greater and the less, have their origin from the application of addition or subtraction to equality. *[2]* This also is sufficient evidence that the two forms partake of sameness and otherness, of otherness in an indefinite fashion, but of sameness definitely, 1 and 2 generically, but the odd of sameness after the manner of a subordinate species because it belongs to the same class as 1, and the even of otherness because it is homogeneous with 2.

*[3]* There is also a still clearer reason why the square, since it is the product of the addition of odd numbers, is akin to sameness, and the heteromecic numbers to otherness because it is made up by adding even numbers; for as though they were friends of one another, these two forms share in their two rows the same differences when they do not have the same ratios, and conversely the same ratios when they do not have the same differences. For the difference between 4 and 2 in the double ratio is found between 6 and 4 as a superparticular; and again the difference between 9 and 6, as a sesquialter, is found between 12 and 9 as a sesquitertian, and so on. What is the same in quality is different in quantity, and just the opposite, what is the same in quantity is different in quality. *[4]* Again, it is clear that in all their relations the same difference between two terms will necessarily be called fractions with names that differ by 1, and be the half of one and the third of the other, or the third of one and the quarter of the other, or the fourth of one and the fifth of the other, and so on.

*[5]* But what will most of all confirm the fact that the odd, and never the even, is preëminently the cause of sameness, is to be demonstrated in every series beginning with 1 following some ratio, for example, the double ratio, 1, 2, 4, 8, 16, 32, 64, 128, 256, or the triple, 1, 3, 9, 27, 81, 243, 729, 2,187, and as far as you like. You will find that of necessity all the terms in the odd places in the series are squares, and no others by any device whatsoever, and that no square is to be found in an even place.

But all the products of a number multiplied twice into itself, that is, the cubes, which are extended in three dimensions and seen to share in sameness to an even greater extent, are the product of the odd numbers, not the even, 1,

8, 27, 64, 125, and 216, and those that go on analogously, in a simple, unvaried progression as well. For when the successive odd numbers are set forth indefinitely beginning with 1, observe this: The first one makes the potential cube; the next two, added together, the second; the next three, the third; the four next following, the fourth; the succeeding five, the fifth; the next six, the sixth; and so on.

## CHAPTER XXI

*[1]* After this it would be the proper time to incorporate the nature of proportions, a thing most essential for speculation about the nature of the universe and for the propositions of music, astronomy, and geometry, and not least for the study of the works of the ancients, and thus to bring the *Introduction to Arithmetic* to the end that is at once suitable and fitting.

*[2]* A proportion, then, is in the proper sense, the combination of two or more *ratios*, but by the more general definition the combination of two or more *relations*, even if they are not brought under the same ratio, but rather a difference, or something else.

*[3]* Now a ratio[2] is the relation of two terms to one another, and the combination of such is a proportion, so that three is the smallest number of terms of which the latter is composed, although it can be a series of more, subject to the same ratio or the same difference. For example, 1:2 is one ratio, where there are two terms; but 2:4 is another similar ratio; hence 1, 2, 4 is a proportion, for it is a combination of ratios, or of three terms which are observed to be in the same ratio to one another. *[4]* The same thing may be observed also in greater numbers and longer series of terms; for let a fourth term, 8, be joined to the former after 4, again in a similar relation, the double, and then 16 after 8 and so on.

*[5]* Now if the same term, one and unchanging, is compared to those on either side of it, to the greater as consequent and to the lesser as antecedent, such a proportion is called continued; for example, 1, 2, 4 is a continued proportion as regards quality[3], for 4:2 equals 2:1, and conversely 1:2 equals 2:4. In quantity, 1, 2, 3, for example, is a continued proportion, for as 3 exceeds 2, so 2 exceeds 1, and conversely, as 1 is less than 2, by so much 2 is less than 3.

*[6]* If, however, one term answers to the lesser term, and becomes its antecedent and a

---

[1]Cf. I. 17. 6.
[2]Cf. Euclid, *Elements, V, init.*
[3]Cf. II. 22. 2; 23. 4 below.

greater term, and another, not the same, takes the place of consequent and lesser term with reference to the greater, such a mean and such a proportion is called no longer continued, but disjunct; for example, as regards quality, 1, 2, 4, 8, for 2:1 equals 8:4, and conversely 1:2 equals 4:8, and again 1:4 equals 2:8 or 4:1 equals 8:2; and in quantity, 1, 2, 3, 4, for as 1 is exceeded by 2, by so much 3 is exceeded by 4, or as 4 exceeds 3, so 2 exceeds 1, and by interchange, as 3 exceeds 1, so 4 exceeds 2, or as 1 is exceeded by 3, by so much 2 is exceeded by 4.

## CHAPTER XXII

*[1]* The first three proportions, then, which are acknowledged by all the ancients, Pythagoras, Plato, and Aristotle, are the arithmetic, geometric, and harmonic; and there are three others subcontrary to them, which do not have names of their own, but are called in more general terms the fourth, fifth, and sixth forms of mean; after which the moderns discover four others as well, making up the number ten, which, according to the Pythagorean view, is the most perfect possible. It was in accordance with this number indeed that not long ago the ten relations were observed to take their proper number, the so-called ten categories, the divisions and forms of the extremities of our hands and feet, and countless other things which we shall notice in the proper place.

*[2]* Now, however, we must treat from the beginning, first, that form of proportion which by quantity reconciles and binds together the comparison of the terms, which is a quantitative equality as regards the difference of the several terms to one another. This would be the arithmetic proportion, for it was previously reported that quantity is its peculiar belonging. *[3]* What, then, is the reason that we shall treat of this first, and not another? Is it not clear that Nature shows it forth before the rest? For in the natural series of simple numbers, beginning with 1, with no term passed over or omitted, the definition of this proportion alone is preserved; moreover, in our previous statements,[1] we demonstrated that the *Arithmetical Introduction* itself is antecedent to all the others, because it abolishes them together with itself, but is not abolished together with them, and because it is implied by them, but does not imply them. Thus it is natural that the mean which shares the name of arithmetic will not unreasonably take precedence of the means which are named for the other sciences, the geometric and harmonic; for it is plain that all the more will it take precedence over the subcontraries, over which the first three hold the leadership. *[4]* As the first and original, therefore, since it is most deserving of the honor, let the arithmetic proportion have its discussion at our hands before the others.

## CHAPTER XXIII

*[1]* It is an arithmetic proportion, then, whenever three or more terms are set forth in succession, or are so conceived, and the same quantitative difference is found to exist between the successive numbers, but not the same ratio among the terms, one to another. For example, 1, 2, 3, 4, 5, 6, 7, 8, 9, 10, 11, 12, 13; for in this natural series of numbers, examined consecutively and without any omissions, every term whatsoever is discovered to be placed between two and to preserve the arithmetic proportion to them. For its differences as compared with those ranged on either side of it are equal; the same ratio, however, is not preserved among them.

*[2]* And we understand that in such a series there comes about both a continued and a disjunct proportion; for if the same middle term answers to those on either side as both antecedent and consequent, it would be a continued proportion, but if there is another mean along with it, a disjunct proportion comes about.

*[3]* Now if we separate out of this series any three consecutive terms whatsoever, after the form of the continued proportion, or four or more terms after the disjunct form, and consider them, the difference of them all would be 1, but their ratios would be different throughout. If, however, again we select three or more terms, not adjacent, but separated, separated nevertheless by a constant interval, if one term was omitted in setting down each term, the difference in every case will be 2; and once more with three terms it will be a continued proportion; with more, disjunct. If two terms are omitted, the difference will always be 3 in all of them, continued or disjunct; if three, 4; if four, 5; and so on.

*[4]* Such a proportion, therefore, partakes in equal quantity in its differences, but of unequal quality; for this reason it is arithmetic. If on the contrary it partook of similar quality, but not quantity, it would be geometric instead of arithmetic.

*[5]* A thing is peculiar to this proportion

---
[1] Cf. I. 4. 2 ff.

that does not belong to any other, namely, the mean is either half of, or equal to, the sum of the extremes, whether the proportion be viewed as continuous or disjunct or by alternation; for either the mean term with itself, or the mean terms with one another, are equal to the sum of the extremes.

*[6]* It has still another peculiarity; what ratio each term has to itself, this the differences have to the differences; that is, they are equal.

Again, the thing which is most exact, and which has escaped the notice of the majority, the product of the extremes when compared to the square of the mean is found to be smaller than it by the product of the differences, whether they be 1, 2, 3, 4, or any number whatever.

In the fourth place, a thing which all previous writers also have noted, the ratios between the smaller terms are larger, as compared to those between the greater terms. It will be shown that in the harmonic proportion, on the contrary, the ratios between the greater terms are greater than those between the smaller; for this reason the harmonic proportion is subcontrary to the arithmetic, and the geometric is midway between them, as it were, between extremes, for this proportion has the ratios between the greater terms and those between the smaller equal, and we have seen that the equal is in the middle ground between the greater and the less. So much, then, about the arithmetic proportion.

## CHAPTER XXIV

*[1]* The next proportion[1] after this one, the geometric, is the only one in the strict sense of the word to be called a proportion, because its terms are seen to be in the same ratio. It exists whenever, of three or more terms, as the greatest is to the next greatest, so the latter is to the one following, and if there are more terms, as this again is to the one following it, but they do not, however, differ from one another by the same quantity, but rather by the same quality of ratio, the opposite of what was seen to be the case with the arithmetic proportion.

*[2]* For an example, set forth the numbers beginning with 1 that advance by the double ratio, 1, 2, 4, 8, 16, 32, 64, and so on, or by the triple ratio, 1, 3, 9, 27, 81, 243, and so on, or by the quadruple, or in some similar way. In each one of these series three adjacent terms, or four, or any number whatever that may be taken, will give the geometric proportion to one another; as the first is to the next smaller, so is that to the next smaller, and again that to the next smaller, and so on as far as you care to go, and also by alternation. For instance, 2, 4, 8; the ratio which 8 bears to 4, that 4 bears to 2, and conversely; they do not, however, have the same quantitative difference. Again, 2, 4, 8, 16; for not only does 16 have the same ratio to 8 as before, though not the same difference, but also by alternation it preserves a similar relation—as 16 is to 4, so 8 is to 2, and conversely, as 2 is to 8, so 4 is to 16; and disjunctly, as 2 is to 4, so 8 is to 16; and conversely and in disjunct form, as 16 is to 8 so 4 is to 2; for it has the double ratio.

*[3]* The geometric proportion has a peculiar property shared by none of the rest, that the differences of the terms are in the same ratio to each other as the terms to those adjacent to them, the greater to the less, and vice versa. Still another property is that the greater terms have as a difference, with respect to the lesser, the lesser terms themselves, and similarly difference differs from difference, by the smaller difference itself, if the terms are set forth in the double ratio; in the triple ratio both terms and differences will have as a difference twice the next smaller, in the quadruple ratio thrice, in the quintuple four times, and so on.

*[4]* Geometric proportions come about not only among the multiples, but also among all the superparticular, superpartient, and mixed forms, and the peculiar property of this proportion in all cases is preserved, that in the continued proportions the product of the extremes is equal to the square of the mean, but in disjunct proportions, or those with a greater number of terms, even if they are not continued, but with an even number of terms, that the product of the extremes equals that of the means.

*[5]* As an illustration of the fact that in all the relations, all kinds of multiples, superparticulars, superpartients, and mixed ratios the peculiar property of this proportion is preserved, let that suffice[2] and be sufficient for us wherein we fashioned, beginning with equality, by the three rules all the kinds of inequality out of one another, when they were in both direct and reverse order; for each act of fashioning and each series set forth is a geometric proportion with all the aforesaid properties as well as a fourth, namely, that they keep the

---

[1] Cf. Euclid, *Elements*, VII, Def. 21.     [2] Cf. I. 23. 7 ff.

same ratio in both the greater and the smaller terms. Moreover, if we set forth the series shared by both heteromecic and square numbers, one by one, containing the terms in both series, and then selecting the terms by groups of three beginning with 1, examine them, in each case setting down the last of the former group as the starting point of the next, we shall find that from the multiple relation—that is, the double—all the kinds of superparticulars appear one after the other, the sesquialter, sesquitertian, sesquiquartan, and so on.

*[6]* It would be most seasonable, now that we have reached this point, to mention a corollary that is of use to us for a certain Platonic theorem:[1] for plane numbers are bound together always by a single mean, solids by two, in the form of a proportion. For with two consecutive squares[2] only one mean term is discovered which preserves the geometric proportion, as antecedent to the smaller and consequent to the greater term, and never more than one. Hence we conceive of two intervals between the mean term and each extreme, in the relation of similar ratios. *[7]* Again, with two consecutive cubes[3] only two middle terms in proper ratio are found, in accordance with the geometric proportion, never more; hence there are three intervals, one, that between the mean terms compared to one another, and two between the extremes and the means on either side. *[8]* Thus the solid forms are called three-dimensional and the plane ones two-dimensional; for example, 1 and 4 are planes, and 2 a middle term in proportion, or again 4 and 9, two squares, and their middle term 6, held by the greater and holding the lesser term in the same ratio as that in which one difference holds the other. *[9]* The reason for this is that the sides of the two squares, one belonging peculiarly to each, both together produced this very number 6. In cubes, however, for example 8 and 27, no longer one but two mean terms are found, 12 and 18, which put themselves and the terms in the same ratio as that which the differences bear to one another; and the reason of this is that the two mean terms are the products of the sides of the cubes commingled, 2 times 2 times 3 and 3 times 3 times 2.

*[10]* In general, then, if a square takes a square, that is, multiplies it, it always makes a square; but if a square multiplies a heteromecic number, or vice versa, it never makes a square; and if cube multiplies cube, a cube will always result, but if a heteromecic number multiplies a cube, or vice versa, never is the result a cube. In precisely the same way if an even number multiplies an even number, the product is always even and if odd multiplies odd always odd; but if odd multiplies even or even odd, the result will always be even and never odd. *[11]* These matters will receive their proper elucidation in the commentary on Plato, with reference to the passage on the so-called marriage number in the *Republic*[4] introduced in the person of the Muses. So then let us pass over to the third proportion, the so-called harmonic, and analyze it.

## CHAPTER XXV

*[1]* The proportion that is placed in the third order is one called the harmonic, which exists whenever among three terms the mean on examination is observed to be neither in the same ratio to the extremes, antecedent of one and consequent of the other, as in the geometric proportion, nor with equal intervals, but an inequality of ratios, as in the arithmetic, but on the contrary, as the greatest term is to the smallest, so the difference between greatest and mean terms is to the difference between mean and smallest term. For example, take 3, 4, 6, or 2, 3, 6. For 6 exceeds 4 by one third of itself, since 2 is one third of 6, and 3 falls short of 4 by one third of itself, for 1 is one third of 3. In the first example, the extremes are in double ratio and their differences with the mean term are again in the same double ratio to one another; but in the second they are each in the triple ratio.

*[2]* It has a peculiar property, opposite, as we have said,[5] to that of the arithmetic proportion; for in the latter the ratios were greater among the smaller terms, and smaller among the greater terms. Here, however, on the contrary, those among the greater terms are greater and those among the smaller terms smaller, so that in the geometric proportion, like a mean between them, there may be observed the equality of ratios on either side, a midground between greater and smaller.

*[3]* Furthermore, in the arithmetic proportion the mean term is seen to be greater and smaller than those on either side by the same fraction of itself, but by different fractions of

---

[1] *Timaeus*, 32.
[2] Cf. Euclid, *Elements*, VIII, 11.
[3] Cf. Euclid, *Elements*, VIII, 12.

[4] *Republic*, 546 ff.
[5] Cf. II. 23. 6.

the terms that flank it; in the harmonic, however, it is the opposite, for the middle term is greater and less than the terms on either side by different fractions of itself, but always the same fraction of those terms at its sides, a half of them or a third; but the geometric, as if in the midground between them, shows this property neither in the mean term exclusively nor in the extremes, but in both mean and extreme.

[4] Once more, the harmonic proportion has as a peculiar property the fact that when the extremes are added together and multiplied by the mean, it makes twice the product of themselves multiplied by one another.

[5] The harmonic proportion was so called because the arithmetic proportion was distinguished by quantity, showing an equality in this respect with the intervals from one term to another, and the geometric by quality, giving similar qualitative relations between one term and another, but this form, with reference to relativity, appears now in one form, now in another, neither in its terms exclusively nor in its differences exclusively, but partly in the terms and partly in the differences; for as the greatest term is to the smallest, so also is the difference between the greatest and the next greatest, or middle, term to the difference between the least term and the middle term, and vice versa.

## CHAPTER XXVI

[1] In the classification of Being previously set forth we recognized the relative [1]as a thing peculiar to harmonic theory; but the musical ratios of the harmonic intervals are also rather to be found in this proportion. The most elementary is the diatessaron, in the sesquitertian ratio, 4:3, which is the ratio of term to term[2] in the example in the double ratio, or of difference to difference in that which follows, the triple, for these differences are of 6 to 2 or again of 6 to 3. Immediately following is the diapente, which is the sesquialter, 3:2 or again, 6:4, the ratio of term to term. Then the combination[3] of both of these, sesquialter and sesquitertian, the diapason, which comes next, is in the double ratio, 6:3 in both of the examples, the ratio of term to term. The following interval, that of the diapason and diapente together, which preserves the triple ratio of the two of them together, since it is the combination of double

[1]See I. 3. 1.
[2]The examples referred to are the harmonic proportions cited in II. 25. 1.
[3]Cf. II. 5. 2.

and sesquialter, is as 6:2, the ratio of term to term in the example in the triple ratio, and likewise of difference to difference in the same, and in the proportion with double ratio it is the ratio of the greatest term to the difference between that term and the mean term, or of the difference between the extremes to the difference between the smaller terms. The last and greatest interval, the so-called di-diapason, as it were twice the double, which is in the quadruple ratio, is as the middle term in the proportion in the double ratio to the difference between the lesser terms, or as the difference between the extremes, in the example in the triple ratio, to the difference between the lesser terms.

[2] Some, however, agreeing with Philolaus, believe that the proportion is called harmonic because it attends upon all geometric harmony, and they say that "geometric harmony" is the cube because it is harmonized in all three dimensions, being the product of a number thrice multiplied together. For in every cube this proportion is mirrored; there are in every cube 12 sides, 8 angles and 6 faces; hence 8, the mean between 6 and 12, is according to harmonic proportion, for as the extremes are to each other, so is the difference between greatest and middle term to that between the middle and smallest terms, and, again, the middle term is greater than the smallest by one fraction of itself and by another is less than the greater term, but is greater and smaller by one and the same fraction of the extremes. And again, the sum of the extremes multiplied by the mean makes double the product of the extremes multiplied together. The diatessaron is found in the ratio 8:6, which is sesquitertian, the diapente in 12:8, which is sesquialter; the diapason, the combination of these two, in 12:6, the double ratio; the diapason and diapente combined, which is triple, in the ratio of the difference of the extremes to that of the smaller terms, and the di-diapason is the ratio of the middle term to the difference between itself and the lesser term. Most properly, then, has it been called harmonic.

## CHAPTER XXVII

[1] Just as in the division of the musical canon, when a single string is stretched or one length of a pipe is used, with immovable ends, and the mid-point shifts in the pipe by means of the finger-holes, in the string by means of the bridge, and as in one way after another the aforesaid proportions, arithmetic, geometric,

and harmonic, can be produced, so that the fact becomes apparent that they are logically and very properly named, since they are brought about through changing and shifting the middle term in different ways, so too it is both reasonable and possible to insert the mean term that fits each of the three proportions between two arithmetic terms, which stay fixed and do not change, whether they are both even or odd. In the arithmetic proportion this mean term is one that exceeds and is exceeded by an equal amount; in the geometric proportion it is differentiated from the extremes by the same ratio, and in the harmonic it is greater and smaller than the extremes by the same fraction of those same extremes.

*[2]* Let there be given then, first, two even terms, between which we must find how the three means would be inserted, and what they are. Let them be 10 and 40.

*[3]* First, then, I fit to them the arithmetic mean. It is 25, and the attendant properties of the arithmetic proportion are all preserved; for as each term is to itself, so also is difference to difference; they are in equality, therefore. And as much as the greater exceeds the means by so much the latter exceeds the lesser term; the sum of the extremes is twice the mean; the ratio of the lesser terms is greater than that of the greater; the product of the extremes is less than the square of the mean by the amount of the square of the differences; and the middle term is greater and less than the extremes by the same fraction of itself, but by different fractions regarded as parts of the extremes.

*[4]* If, however, I insert 20 as a mean between the given even terms, the properties of the geometrical proportion come into view and those of the arithmetic are done away with. For as the greater term is to the middle term, so is the middle term to the lesser; the product of the extremes is equal to the square of the mean; the differences are observed to be in the same ratio to one another as that of the terms; neither in the extremes alone nor in the middle term alone does there reside the sameness of the fraction concerned in the relative excess and deficiency of the terms, but in the middle term and one of the extremes by turns; and both between greater and smaller terms there is the same ratio.

*[5]* But if I select 16 as the mean, again the properties of the two former proportions disappear and those of the harmonic are seen to remain fixed, with respect to the two even terms. For as the greatest term is to the least, so is the difference of the greater terms to that of the lesser; by what fractions, seen as fractions of the greater term, the mean is smaller than the greater term, by these the same mean term is greater than the smallest term when they are looked upon as fractions of the smallest term; the ratio between the greater terms is greater, and that of the smaller terms, smaller, a thing which is not true of any other proportion; and the sum of the extremes multiplied by the mean is double the product of the extremes.

*[6]* If, however, the two terms that are given are not even but odd, like 5, 45, the same number, 25, will make the arithmetic proportion; and the reason for this is that the terms on either side overpass it and fail to come up to it by an equal number, keeping the same quantitative difference with respect to it. 15 substituted makes the geometric proportion, as it is the triple and subtriple of each respectively; and if 9 takes over the function of mean term it gives the harmonic; for by those parts of the smaller term by which it exceeds, namely, four fifths of the smaller, it is also less than the greater, if they be regarded as parts of the greater term, for this too is four fifths, and if you try all the previously mentioned properties of the harmonic ratio you will find that they will fit.

*[7]* And let this be your method whereby you might scientifically fashion the mean terms that are illustrated in the three proportions. For the two terms given you, whether odd or even, you will find the arithmetic mean by adding the extremes and putting down half of them as the mean, or if you divide by 2 the excess of the greater over the smaller, and add this to the smaller, you will have the mean. As for the geometric mean, if you find the square root of the product of the extremes, you will produce it, or, observing the ratio of the terms to one another, divide this by 2 and make the mean, for example, the double, in the case of a quadruple ratio. For the harmonic mean, you must multiply the difference of the extremes by the lesser term and divide the product by the sum of the extremes, then add the quotient to the lesser term, and the result will be the harmonic mean.

## CHAPTER XXVIII

*[1]* So much, then, concerning the three proportions celebrated by the ancients, which we have discussed the more clearly and at length for just this reason, that they are to be met

with frequently and in various forms in the writings of those authors. The succeeding forms, however, we must only epitomize, since they do not occur frequently in the ancient writings, but are included merely for the sake of our own acquaintance with them and, so to speak, for the completeness of our reckoning. *[2]* They are set forth by us in an order based on their opposition to the three archetypes already described, since they are fashioned out of them and have the same order.

*[3]* The fourth, and the one called subcontrary, because it is opposite to, and has opposite properties to, the harmonic proportion, exists when, in three terms, as the greatest is to the smallest, so the difference of the smaller terms is to that of the greater, for example 3, 5, 6. For the terms compared are seen to be in the double ratio, and it is plain wherein it is opposite to the harmonic proportion; for whereas they both have the same extreme terms, and in double ratio, in the former the difference of the greater terms as compared to that of the lesser preserved the same ratio as that of the extremes, but in this proportion just the reverse, the difference of the smaller compared with that of the greater. You must know that its peculiar property is this. The product of the greater and the mean terms is twice the product of the mean and the smaller; for 6 times 5 is twice 5 times 3.

*[4]* The two proportions, fifth and sixth, were both fashioned after the geometrical, and they differ from each other thus.

The fifth form exists, whenever, among three terms, as the middle term is to the lesser, so their difference is to the difference between the greater and the mean, as in 2, 4, 5, for 4 is the middle term, the double of 2, the lesser, and 2 is the double of 1—the difference of the smallest terms as compared with that of the largest. That which makes it contrary to the geometric proportion is that in the former,[1] as the middle term is to the lesser, so the excess of the greater over the mean is to the excess of the mean over the lesser term, whereas in this proportion, on the contrary, it is the difference of the lesser compared to that of the greater. Nevertheless it is peculiar to this proportion that the product of the greatest by the middle term is double that of the greatest by the smallest, for 5 times 4 is twice 5 times 2.

*[5]* The sixth form[2] comes about when, in a group of three terms, as the greatest is to the mean, so the excess of the mean over the lesser is to the excess of the greater over the mean, for example 1, 4, 6, for both are in the sesquialter ratio. There is in this case also a reasonable cause for its opposition to the geometrical; for here, too, the likeness of the ratios reverses, as in the fifth form.

*[6]* These are the six proportions commonly spoken of among previous writers, the three prototypes having lasted from the times of Pythagoras down to Aristotle and Plato, and the three others, opposites of the former, coming into use among the commentators and sectarians who succeeded these men. But certain men have devised in addition, by shifting the terms and differences of the former, four more which do not much appear in the writings of the ancients, but have been sparingly touched upon as an over-nice detail. These, however, we must run over in the following fashion, lest we seem ignorant.

*[7]* The first of them, and the seventh in the list of them all, exists when, as the greatest term is to the least, so their difference is to the difference of the lesser terms, as 6, 8, 9, for on comparison the ratio of each is seen to be the sesquialter.

*[8]* The eighth proportion, which is the second of this group, comes about when, as the greatest is to the least term, so the difference of the extremes is to the difference of the greater terms, as 6, 7, 9; for this also has sesquialters for the two ratios.

*[9]* The ninth in the complete list, and third in the number of those subsequently invented, exists when there are three terms and whatever ratio the mean bears to the least, that also the difference of the extremes has in comparison with that of the smallest terms, as 4, 6, 7.

*[10]* The tenth, in the full list, which concludes them all, and the fourth in the series presented by the moderns, is seen when, among three terms, as the mean is to the lesser, so the difference of the extremes is to the difference of the greater terms, as 3, 5, 8, for it is the superbipartient ratio in each pair.

*[11]* To sum up, then, let the terms of the ten proportions be set forth in one illustration, for the sake of easy comprehension:

First: 1, 2, 3     Sixth: 1, 4, 6
Second: 1, 2, 4   Seventh: 6, 8, 9
Third: 3, 4, 6    Eighth: 6, 7, 9
Fourth: 3, 5, 6   Ninth: 4, 6, 7
Fifth: 2, 4, 5    Tenth: 3, 5, 8

---

[1] Cf. II. 24.
[2] Cf. Euclid, *Elem.*, V., Def. 16.

## CHAPTER XXIX

*[1]* It remains for me to discuss briefly the most perfect proportion, that which is three-dimensional and embraces them all, and which is most useful for all progress in music and in the theory of the nature of the universe. This alone would properly and truly be called harmony[1] rather than the others, since it is not a plane, nor bound together by only one mean term, but with two, so as thus to be extended in three dimensions,[2] just as a while ago it was explained that the cube is harmony.

*[2]* When, therefore, there are two extreme terms, both of three dimensions, either numbers multiplied thrice by themselves so as to be a cube, or numbers multiplied twice by themselves and once by another number so as to be either "beams" or "bricks," or the products of three unequal numbers, so as to be scalene, and between them there are found two other terms which preserve the same ratios to the extremes alternately and together, in such a manner that, while one of them preserves the harmonic proportion, the other completes the arithmetic, it is necessary that in such a disposition of the four the geometric proportion appear, on examination, commingled with both mean terms—as the greatest is to the third removed from it, so is the second from it to the fourth; for such a situation makes the product of the means equal to the product of the extremes. And again, if the greatest term be shown to differ from the one next beneath it by the amount whereby this latter differs from the least term, such an array becomes an arithmetic proportion and the sum of the extremes is twice the mean. But if the third term from the greatest exceeds and is exceeded by the same fraction of the extremes, it is harmonic and the product of the mean by the sum of the extremes is double the product of the extremes.

*[3]* Let this be an example of this proportion, 6, 8, 9, 12. 6 is a scalene number, derived from 1 times 2 times 3, and 12 comes from the successive multiplication of 2 times 2 times 3; of the mean terms the lesser is from 1 times 2 times 4, and the greater from 1 times 3 times 3. The extremes are both solid and three-dimensional, and the means are of the same class. According to the geometric proportion, as 12 is to 8, so 9 is to 6; according to the arithmetic, as 12 exceeds 9, by so much does 9 exceed 6; and by the harmonic, by the fraction by which 8 exceeds 6, viewed as a fraction of 6, 8 is also exceeded by 12, viewed as a fraction of 12.

*[4]* Moreover 8:6 or 12:9 is the diatessaron, in sesquitertian ratio; 9:6 or 12:8 is the diapente in the sesquialter; 12:6 is the diapason in the double. Finally, 9:8 is the interval of a tone, in the superoctave ratio, which is the common measure of all the ratios in music, since it is also the more familiar, because it is likewise the difference between the first and most elementary intervals.

*[5]* And let this be sufficient concerning the phenomena and properties of number, for a first *Introduction*.

---

[1] Cf. II. 26. 2.
[2] Cf. II. 24. 6.

# THE NINETEENTH AND TWENTIETH CENTURIES

1790　1800　1810　1820　1830　1840　1850　1860　1870　1880

HEGEL
AUSTEN
FARADAY
BALZAC

*Beethoven's Ninth Symphony*

TOCQUEVILLE
J. S. MILL
DARWIN
DICKENS
KIERKEGAARD

*First successful steam locomotive*

MARX
MELVILLE
GEORGE ELIOT
ENGELS
DOSTOEVSKY
IBSEN
TOLSTOY

*Napoleon defeated at Waterloo*

TWAIN
WILLIAM JAMES
HENRY JAMES
NIETZSCHE

*Discovery of magnetic North Pole*

FRAZER
POINCARÉ
FREUD
SHAW
CONRAD
VEBLEN
PLANCK
BERGSON
DEWEY
CHEKHOV
WHITEHEAD
WEBER
PIRANDELLO

PROUST
RUSSELL
HUIZINGA
CATHER
MANN
G. H. HARDY
EINSTEIN
TAWNEY
WOOLF
JOYCE
EDDING[TON]
KEYNES
KAFKA
LAW[RENCE]
BOH[R]
BA[RTH]
SC[HRÖDINGER]

*Inventions: telephone automobile,*

## GREAT BOOKS OF THE WESTERN WORLD

*A Chronology of the Great Authors*